Instructor's Resource Guide and Solutions Manual

Finite Mathematics

Ninth Edition

Margaret L. Lial
American River College

Raymond N. Greenwell
Hofstra University

Nathan P. Ritchey
Youngstown State University

Boston San Francisco New York
London Toronto Sydney Tokyo Singapore Madrid
Mexico City Munich Paris Cape Town Hong Kong Montreal

Reproduced by Pearson Addison-Wesley from QuarkXPress® files.

Publishing as Pearson Addison-Wesley, 75 Arlington Street, Boston, MA 02116.

ISBN-13: 978-0-321-44881-1
ISBN-10: 0-321-44881-2

1 2 3 4 5 6 OPM 10 09 08 07

CONTENTS

CHAPTER 2 SYSTEMS OF LINEAR EQUATIONS AND MATRICES

CHAPTER 3 LINEAR PROGRAMMING: THE GRAPHICAL METHOD

CHAPTER 4 LINEAR PROGRAMMING: THE SIMPLEX METHOD

CHAPTER 5 MATHEMATICS OF FINANCE

CHAPTER 6 LOGIC

CHAPTER 7 SETS AND PROBABILITY

CHAPTER 8 COUNTING PRINCIPLES; FURTHER PROBABILITY TOPICS

CHAPTER 9 STATISTICS

CHAPTER 10 MARKOV CHAINS

CHAPTER 11 GAME THEORY

PREFACE

This book provides several resources for instructors using *Finite Mathematics,* Ninth Edition, by Margaret L. Lial, Raymond N. Greenwell, and Nathan P. Ritchey.

- Hints for teaching *Finite Mathematics and Calculus with Applications* are provided as a resource for faculty.
- One open-response form and one multiple-choice form of a pretest are provided. These tests are an aid to instructors in identifying students who may need assistance.
- One open-response form and one multiple-choice form of a final examination are provided.
- Solutions for nearly all of the exercises in the textbook are included. Solutions are usually not provided for exercises with open-response answers.

The following people have made valuable contributions to the production of this *Instructor's Resource Guide and Solutions Manual:* LaurelTech Integrated Publishing Services, editors; Judy Martinez and Sheri Minkner, typists; and Joe Vetere, Senior Author Support/Technology Specialist.

HINTS FOR TEACHING FINITE MATHEMATICS

HINTS FOR TEACHING FINITE MATHEMATICS

Algebra Reference

This chapter is not as important for finite mathematics as it is for calculus. Nevertheless, we have included it in both books for those instructors who wish to cover this material. Some instructors get best results by going through this chapter carefully at the beginning of the semester. Others find it better to refer to it as needed throughout the course. Use whichever method works best for your students. We refer to the chapter as a "Reference" rather than a "Review," and the regular page numbers don't begin until Chapter 1. We hope this will make your students less anxious if you don't cover this material.

Section 1.1

This section and the next may seem fairly basic to students who covered linear functions in high school. Some students have difficulty finding the equation of a line from two points. Emphasize that there is no point-point form.

Perpendicular lines are not used in future chapters and could be skipped if you're in a hurry.

Section 1.2

Linear functions are the only functions students learn about in this section, giving them a gentle introduction to functions. Review graphing lines using intercepts, especially lines through the origin.

Supply and demand provides the students' first experience with a mathematical model. Spend time developing both the economics and the mathematics involved.

Stress that for cost, revenue, and profit functions, x represents the number of units. For supply and demand functions, we use the economists' notation of q to represent the number of units.

Emphasize the difference between the profit earned on 100 units sold as opposed to the number of units that must be sold to produce a profit of $100.

Section 1.3

The statistical functions on a calculator can greatly simplify these calculations, allowing more time for discussion and further examples. As in previous editions, we use "parallel presentation" to allow instructor choice on the extent technology is used. This section may be skipped if you are in a hurry, but your students can benefit from the realistic model and the additional work with equations of lines.

Chapter 2

The echelon method and the Gauss-Jordan method presented in the text are improved variations of the traditional methods. The "leading ones" are postponed until the last step, so as to avoid fractions and decimals. You may want to practice a few examples before presenting this method in class. We also present the traditional Gauss-Jordan method but only recommend it for use with a graphing calculator, for which keeping track of the fractions presents no difficulty.

Section 2.1

We have found it useful to spend less time on the echelon method and save the larger examples for the Gauss-Jordan method in the next section. Consequently, most of the exercises in this section involve only two equations. Use this section to introduce the concept of solving a system of linear equations and to show how a system can have one solution, no solutions, or an infinite number of solutions. Also use this section to show students how to solve applied exercises. Notice the application exercises in which a dependent system only has a finite number of solutions because the solution is restricted to nonnegative integers.

Emphasize the row notation as a way to keep track of and to check the problem solving process.

Stress the guidelines, found before Example 5, for solving an application problem.

Section 2.2

In this edition we present the traditional Gauss-Jordan method as Method 1 in Example 1, and the improved version as Method 2. Our experience is that students are much more successful in carrying out the improved version, so we present it as the first method in Example 2 and the only method in later examples. As we suggest in Example 2, the traditional method is appropriate when technology is available.

Shown below is a comparison between the improved version and the traditional Gauss-Jordan method. Note the absence of tedious fractions in the improved version.

Solve:

$$\begin{aligned} 4x - 2y - 3z &= -23 \\ -4x + 3y + \ z &= 11 \\ 8x + 5y + 4z &= 6 \end{aligned}$$

New Method

$$\left[\begin{array}{rrr|r} 4 & -2 & -3 & -23 \\ -4 & 3 & 1 & 11 \\ 8 & -5 & 4 & 6 \end{array}\right]$$

$$\begin{array}{r} \\ R_1 + R_2 \to R_2 \\ -2R_1 + R_3 \to R_3 \end{array} \left[\begin{array}{rrr|r} 4 & -2 & -3 & -23 \\ 0 & 1 & -2 & -12 \\ 0 & -1 & 10 & 52 \end{array}\right]$$

$$\begin{array}{r} R_1 + 2R_2 \to R_1 \\ \\ R_2 + R_3 \to R_3 \end{array} \left[\begin{array}{rrr|r} 4 & 0 & -7 & -47 \\ 0 & 1 & -2 & -12 \\ 0 & 0 & 8 & 40 \end{array}\right]$$

$$\begin{array}{r} 7R_3 + 8R_1 \to R_1 \\ R_3 + 4R_2 \to R_2 \\ \\ \end{array} \left[\begin{array}{rrr|r} 32 & 0 & 0 & -96 \\ 0 & 4 & 0 & -8 \\ 0 & 0 & 8 & 40 \end{array}\right]$$

$$\begin{array}{r} \frac{1}{32}R_1 \to R_1 \\ \frac{1}{4}R_2 \to R_2 \\ \frac{1}{8}R_3 \to R_3 \end{array} \left[\begin{array}{rrr|r} 1 & 0 & 0 & -3 \\ 0 & 1 & 0 & -2 \\ 0 & 0 & 1 & 5 \end{array}\right]$$

$(-3, -2, 5)$ is the solution.

Traditional Method

$$\left[\begin{array}{rrr|r} 4 & -2 & -3 & -23 \\ -4 & 3 & 1 & 11 \\ 8 & -5 & 4 & 6 \end{array}\right]$$

$$\frac{1}{4}R_1 \to R_1 \quad \left[\begin{array}{rrr|r} 1 & -\frac{1}{2} & -\frac{3}{4} & -\frac{23}{4} \\ -4 & 3 & 1 & 11 \\ 8 & -5 & 4 & 6 \end{array}\right]$$

$$\begin{array}{r} \\ 4R_1 + R_2 \to R_2 \\ -8R_1 + R_3 \to R_3 \end{array} \left[\begin{array}{rrr|r} 1 & -\frac{1}{2} & -\frac{3}{4} & -\frac{23}{4} \\ 0 & 1 & -2 & -12 \\ 0 & -1 & 10 & 52 \end{array}\right]$$

$$\begin{array}{r} \frac{1}{2}R_2 + R_1 \to R_1 \\ \\ R_2 + R_3 \to R_3 \end{array} \left[\begin{array}{rrr|r} 1 & 0 & -\frac{7}{4} & -\frac{47}{4} \\ 0 & 1 & -2 & -12 \\ 0 & 0 & 1 & 5 \end{array}\right]$$

$$\begin{array}{r} \\ \\ \frac{1}{8}R_3 \to R_3 \end{array} \left[\begin{array}{rrr|r} 1 & 0 & -\frac{7}{4} & -\frac{47}{4} \\ 0 & 1 & -2 & -12 \\ 0 & 0 & 8 & 40 \end{array}\right]$$

$$\begin{array}{r} \frac{7}{4}R_3 + R_1 \to R_1 \\ 2R_3 + R_2 \to R_2 \\ \\ \end{array} \left[\begin{array}{rrr|r} 1 & 0 & 0 & -3 \\ 0 & 1 & 0 & -2 \\ 0 & 0 & 1 & 5 \end{array}\right]$$

$(-3, -2, 5)$ is the solution.

By reworking a problem from Section 2.1 using the Gauss-Jordan method, students will see how closely this method parallels the echelon method given there.

Remind students to operate on the entire row. A common error is to forget the entry to the right of the vertical bar.

Section 2.3

Mention that, as in algebra, only like things can be added or subtracted. In this case, the like things are matrices having the same dimensions.

Section 2.4

Using the visual approach to matrix multiplication given after Example 2, students will have no trouble multiplying matrices. Most will eventually no longer need this tool.

Section 2.5

Explain that the technique used in finding the multiplicative inverse of a matrix is still the Gauss-Jordan method, now with more than one entry per row to the right of the vertical bar.

Students may be resistant to learning another method for solving a system of equations. Stress the advantage of using the inverse method to solve systems having the same matrix of coefficients. See Example 4. Point out that these systems can be found in many different fields of application. See Exercise 60.

Section 2.6

Discuss how the entries of A, the input-output matrix, could be determined. Stress the economic significance of the matrices A, D, X, and AX.

Section 3.1

Emphasize that the test point can be *any* point *not* on the boundary. Choose several points on either side of the boundary and on the boundary itself to illustrate this concept.

Students may fall into the habit of always choosing $(0, 0)$ as the test point. Do a couple of problems where $(0, 0)$ is not available for use as a test point.

Using a different color to shade each half plane for a system of inequalities will make their overlap easier to recognize.

Section 3.2

Use diagrams like Figures 11 and 12 to convince students of the believability of the corner point theorem. Emphasize that a corner point *must* be a point in the feasible region. Also, stress that not all corner points can be found by inspection. Some require solving a system of two linear equations. Have students note the equation of the boundary line next to its graph, so they will know which equations to solve as a system.

Section 3.3

Review the guidelines for setting up an applied problem (Section 2.1) to determine the objective function and all necessary constraints.

Students find those constraints comparing two unknown quantities the most difficult. See Exercise 12 for an example of this type of constraint.

Section 4.1

The simplex method in this chapter is modified from the traditional method along the lines of the Gauss-Jordan method in Chapter 2, eliminating tedious fractions until the last step. The notation of s instead of x for slack and surplus variables will help students remember which variables are the originals and which are slack or surplus variables.

Note the horizontal line in the simplex tableau to separate the constraints from the objective function.

Students may need several examples to be able to pick out the basic variables and to find the basic feasible solution from a matrix.

Section 4.2

Vocabulary is extremely important in this section. An understanding of the terms basic variables, basic feasible solution, indicators, and pivots is a necessity.

Remind students that the simplex method stated before Example 1 works only for problems in standard maximum form.

Example 1 is extremely important because it connects the two methods of solving a linear programming problem. You may want to do a similar example in class. Emphasize the advantages of the simplex method, especially for larger problems.

Section 4.3

If you are in a hurry, either Section 4.3 or 4.4 can be skipped. Section 4.3 is needed if you wish to cover Section 11.3 on game theory and linear programming. If you choose to cover this section and skip Section 4.4, your students will only know how to solve standard minimization and maximization problems, but they at least they will see the profound and amazing theorem of duality. Notice in Exercises 18 and 19 that for maximization problems, shadow costs become shadow profits.

Provide numerous examples for reading the optimal solution from the last row of the final tableau of the dual problem.

Section 4.4

The usual method for solving nonstandard problems (those with mixed constraints) is the two-phase method, which is somewhat complicated for students at this level. We use a modification of this method which students should find simpler.

Stress that slack variables are used for $\leq$ constraints, while surplus variables are used for $\geq$ constraints. Artificial variables only need to be covered if you want to solve constraints with an $=$. Even then, they can be avoided by replacing each $=$ constraint with two inequalities, one with $\leq$ and one with $\geq$.

Emphasize that to use the simplex method to find the optimal feasible solution, one must start with a feasible solution.

In Step 5 of the box "Solving a Nonstandard Problem," our choice of the positive entry that is farthest to the left is arbitrary. If your students choose a different column, they may still come up with the correct answer, and it might even require fewer steps.

Remind students to convert from z to w as the last step in solving a minimization problem.

Chapter 5

The chapter on mathematics of finance does not depend on earlier chapters and may be covered at any time.

Students may feel overwhelmed by the number of formulas presented in Chapter 5. Guidelines for choosing the appropriate formula can be found at the end of the chapter. This summary may be referred to throughout Chapter 5.

Chapter 5 requires numerous financial calculations. Make sure students are familiar with their calculators. The financial features of the TI-83/84 Plus make calculations easy.

Section 5.1

Interest is the key concept in Chapter 5. It is important that students understand that interest is the cost of borrowing money (or the reward for lending money). Both simple and compound interest are covered in the first section.

Point out that as the frequency of compounding increases, so does the amount of interest earned. Also note, however, that this increase in interest gets smaller and smaller as the interest is compounded more frequently. See Exercises 63 and 64.

The effective rate of interest is a topic that students find most useful and interesting. Bring in advertisements for loans that hide the effective rate (the APR) in the fine print.

Chapter 5 is full of symbols and formulas. It is imperative that students become familiar with the notation and know which formula is appropriate for a given problem. A summarization of the formulas in Section 5.1 is found at the end of the section.

Section 5.2

This section starts with an introduction to geometric sequences, which lays the groundwork for developing the future value formula as the sum of a geometric sequence.

Section 5.3

Make sure students understand that the present value formula presented here is for an ordinary annuity only.

Many students have had experience with amortization. Illustrate this topic using examples with present day interest rates. Students may bring in personal examples that may be used in class.

Chapter 6

This chapter leads students toward the construction of proofs in Section 5, with quantifiers briefly introduced in Section 6. Proofs are more difficult than truth tables, but they are also far more important. Throughout the chapter we use meaningful variables, such as d for "Django is a good dog," rather than generic variables such as p and q. We find (and our students do too) that this makes it easier to keep track of which variables stands for each statement.

This is a nice chapter to cover before sets (Chapter 7), because many of the same ideas appear in both contexts. You should point out the parallels to the students whenever possible.

Section 6.1

The chapter starts with fairly easy material, but the statement "Neither p nor q" can cause trouble. Notice that we introduce the basic truth tables, except for the conditional and biconditional. Material on the quantifiers "For all" and "There exists" appears in Section 6.

Section 6.2

Students usually find truth tables fun. The alternative method presented in Example 5 helps alleviate any tedium.

Sections 6.3 and 6.4

The conditional is probably the most challenging logical operator, perhaps because its usage in mathematical language is just different enough from that of common language to cause confusion. We have found that even after students have studied logic, they still give erroneous answers to tests of reason such as those in Exercises 52 and 53 of Section 6.4. The common translations of $p \to q$ given before Example 1 of Section 6.4 are particularly troublesome. Don't assume your students have mastered this material until you have firm evidence.

Section 6.5

This section is the culmination of the first four sections. The two most important skills are showing an argument is invalid by counterexample, and showing an argument is valid by proof. Look carefully at Examples 1 through 8. This is the most difficult material in the chapter, so students need a lot of practice to master these ideas. The payoff is worth it when students learn to create a proof. The puzzles by Lewis Carroll in Example 6 and Exercises 38-43 are fun.

Section 6.6

Some students won't believe Euler is pronounced "oiler." The material on quantifiers appears here. This is just an introduction; we do not try to teach proofs using quantifiers except by Euler diagrams.

Chapter 7

The material on probability is arranged so that if you are in a hurry to get to Markov chains, you can skip Section 7.6 and all of Chapters 8 and 9.

Section 7.1

Manipulatives are quite useful in this chapter, especially a deck of cards. Further, set brackets may be modeled as a box and the elements of the set as objects inside the box.

Stress the key word for each set operation: "not" for complement, "and" for intersection, "or" for union.

Section 7.2

Mention the order of set operations: If parentheses are present, simplify within them in the following order:

1) Take all complements.

2) Take the unions or intersections in the order they occur from left to right.

If no parentheses are present, start with 1).

To solve a survey problem, students must first be able to identify what type of object belongs to a certain region before they can determine how many objects belong to that region.

Have students explore the union rule for sets by determining the number of cards that are red or a king in their decks. Compare this problem with the problem of determining how many cards are fives or sevens (disjoint sets).

Section 7.3

Students need to be able to identify the experiment, the number of trials, the sample space, and the event in each probability problem.

Illustrate the basic probability principle using numerous examples utilizing the manipulatives.

Section 7.4

Redo the examples used to explore the union rule for sets to explore the related union rule for probability.

The complement rule is most useful for problems that contain statements of the form greater than, less than, etc.

Section 7.5

Sometimes independent events can be thought of as events that have the same sample space. For example, when two cards are drawn one at a time with replacement, both draws have a sample space consisting of all 52 cards. If these cards are drawn, instead, without replacement, the sample space for the second card has been reduced to 51 cards. Emphasize that the notation $P(A|B)$ reminds us how the sample space was reduced.

Section 7.6

Point out that trying to calculate $P(F|E)$ directly is sometimes impossible, too expensive, or too inconvenient. Thus, there is a need for Bayes' theorem which allows for the indirect calculation of $P(F|E)$ using $P(E|F)$. If a tree diagram is employed, then Bayes' theorem can be stated as

$$P(F|E) = \frac{\text{the probability of the branch through } F \text{ and } E}{\text{the sum of the probabilities of all branches ending in } E}$$

Point out that the branch in the numerator will also be one of the branches in the denominator.

Section 8.1

To use the multiplication principle, break down the problem (the task) into parts. Draw a blank for each part. Fill in each blank with the number of ways that part of the task can be completed. Finally, multiply these numbers to obtain the solution.

Permutations are a special case of the multiplication principle that does not allow for repetition.

Section 8.2

An additional way to determine whether to use combinations or permutations is as follows:

1) Give a label to each of the n objects.
2) Pick r objects from the n objects.
3) Rearrange the r objects.
4) If this rearrangement can be considered the same as the original arrangement, use combinations. If it is different, use permutations.

Section 8.3

This section combines the counting techniques of the previous two sections with the basic probability principle. Notice in Example 4 (d) that we have provided an alternative method for solving probabilities with poker hands.

Section 8.4

Students often have difficulty dealing with the phrases "at least," "at most," "no more than," etc. Have the students work numerous examples that include these phrases.

Section 8.5

In this section, we complete the discussion of binomial probability from the previous section by giving the formula $E(x) = np$ for the expected value in binomial probability. Having students work out expected value in a binomial probability exercise by the definition and by this formula will increase their confidence in both.

Section 9.1

Warn students that the term "average" is ambiguous. Illustrate this concept using the average salary example following Example 6. Have students find the modal salary. Discuss the problems this ambiguity may cause.

Section 9.2

The square of the standard deviation is the variance, while the square root of the variance is the standard deviation. Students often get these confused.

Section 9.3

Note that the standard normal table used in this text is different from the table that is found in many statistics books. Call this to the attention of students. Some may be familiar with the other table.

Students may find it helpful to draw the nonstandard normal curve with x-values first, then convert to z-scores and draw the standard normal curve.

If your students have graphing calculators that give normal probability, they will have no need for the standard normal table in the back of the book. Their answers to exercises and examples, however, may be slightly different from ours, which were found using the table.

Section 9.4

When using the normal approximation to the binomial, students often have difficulty choosing the appropriate x-value(s) on the normal curve. Provide numerous examples to practice this technique.

Chapter 10

Chapter 10 requires a knowledge of the Gauss-Jordan method, matrix multiplication, and matrix inverses, along with probability.

Section 10.2

Remind students that since the equilibrium vector, $V = [v_1 \quad v_2 \quad \ldots \quad v_n]$, is a probability vector, we have the additional equation $v_1 + v_2 + \ldots + v_n = 1$. This equation will always be part of the system of linear equations that is solved to determine V.

Section 10.3

Illustrate the construction of G, the transition matrix for an absorbing Markov chain, very carefully. Make sure the students can identify I_m, Q, R, O, and the number of absorbing states.

Chapter 11

Chapter 11 utilizes matrices (Chapter 2), probability (Chapter 7), and expected value (Chapter 8).

Section 11.1

Begin developing the concept of strategy that is central to the entire chapter. Contrast strategies with states of nature.

There is a lot of specialized vocabulary in this section, which can be quite confusing for students. They need to have an understanding of the following terms: game, two-person game, zero-sum game, strictly determined game, fair game, strategy, dominated strategy, optimum strategy, and value of the game.

In Example 3 of this edition, we show an alternative method of finding the saddle point for a strictly determined game.

Section 11.2

Emphasize that the optimum strategy in a non-strictly determined game occurs when $E_1 = E_2$. Notice Exercises 27 and 28, in which we show how the method of this section can be extended to matrices with two rows and more than two columns. Of course, the method can also be extended to matrices with two columns and more than two rows. This forces students to think through the process of Example 3, rather than to just memorize the formulas in the box "Optimum Strategies in a Non-Strictly-Determined Game."

Section 11.3

Section 11.3 requires an understanding of solving linear programming problems by the simplex method (Chapter 4), including Section 4.3 on duality. Point out that the technique presented in this section is used to solve games that don't have a saddle point and in which each player has an arbitrary number of choices.

PRETESTS

AND

ANSWERS

FINITE MATHEMATICS

Name:

Pretest, Form A

Find the value of each of the following expressions.

1. $(0.5)^3 \cdot (0.2)^2$ **1.** ________

2. $\sqrt{27\left(\frac{1}{3}\right)\left(1+\frac{1}{3}\right)}$ **2.** ________

3. $2000\left(1-\frac{1}{2}\right)^4$ **3.** ________

4. $\frac{8 \cdot 7 \cdot 6 \cdot 5 \cdot 4 \cdot 3 \cdot 2 \cdot 1}{4 \cdot 3 \cdot 2 \cdot 1}$ **4.** ________

5. $\frac{0.5\,(0.7)}{0.5\,(0.7)+2\,(0.35)}$ **5.** ________

6. Find the value of $\frac{3(a+2b-1)}{a(b+1)}$ if $a = 6$ and $b = -2$. **6.** ________

Solve each of the following equations.

7. $18 - \frac{2}{3}y = \frac{5}{6}y$ **7.** ________

8. $3x - (4x + 8) = 25$ **8.** ________

9. $4\,(2z - 3) + 5 = -2\,(z + 6)$ **9.** ________

10. $0.03x + 0.05\,(200 - x) = 9$ **10.** ________

11. Solve the equation $q = \frac{3}{4}p - 8$ for p. **11.** ________

12. Solve the equation $4x - 5y = 8$ for y. **12.** ________

13. Find the coordinates of the point where the graph of $6x - 5y = 10$ crosses the x-axis. **13.** ________

14. Suppose $C = 35x - 250$. Find x when C is 450. **14.** ________

15. A coat that sells for \$125 is put on sale for \$80. Find the percent of markdown. **15.** ________

16. 66 is 120% of what number? **16.** ________

17. Margaret can travel 216 miles on 9 gallons of gas. How many gallons will she need to travel 336 miles?

17. ______________________

18. Solve the inequality $3(2-x)-4(x+6)<-2(x-1)$.

18. ______________________

19. Graph the equation $5x-2y=10$.

19.

20. Find the slope of the line through the points with coordinates $(4,7)$ and $(-3,5)$.

20. ______________________

21. Write an equation in the form $ax+by=c$ for the line through the points with coordinates $(2,-3)$ and $(5,6)$.

21. ______________________

22. Solve the following system of equations.

$$\begin{aligned} 3x + 4y &= 14 \\ -2x + 5y &= 29 \end{aligned}$$

22. ______________________

23. Which of the following describes the graph of the equation $x=-4$?

(a) A line with slope -4 (b) A line with slope 4

(c) A horizontal line (d) A vertical line

23. ______________________

24. Find the slope of the line with equation $4x-5y=10$.

24. ______________________

25. Graph the inequality $3x+5y\geq 15$.

25.

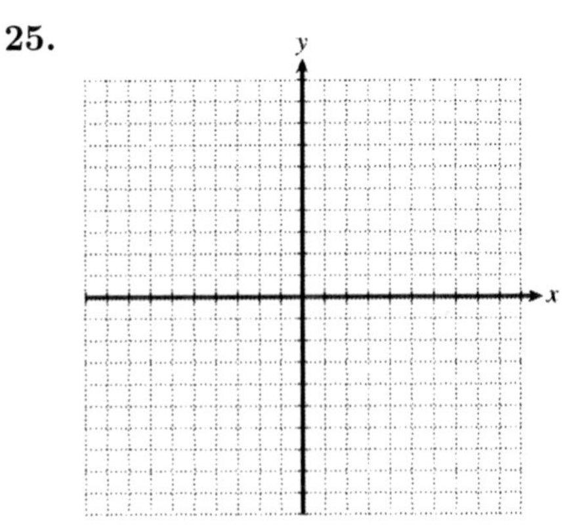

FINITE MATHEMATICS

Name:

Pretest, Form B

Choose the best answer.

Find the value of each of the following expressions.

1. $(0.3)^2 \cdot (0.7)^1$ **1.** ________

(a) 2.1 (b) 0.63 (c) 0.21 (d) 0.063

2. $\sqrt{16\left(\frac{1}{2}\right)\left(1-\frac{1}{2}\right)}$ **2.** ________

(a) 8 (b) 4 (c) 2 (d) $4\sqrt{2}$

3. $4000\left(1+\dfrac{1}{2}\right)^3$ **3.** ________

(a) 13,500 (b) 9000 (c) 6000 (d) 3000

4. $\dfrac{9 \cdot 8 \cdot 7 \cdot 6 \cdot 5 \cdot 4 \cdot 3 \cdot 2 \cdot 1}{5 \cdot 4 \cdot 3 \cdot 2 \cdot 1}$ **4.** ________

(a) 9876 (b) 6789 (c) 3024 (d) 120

5. $\dfrac{0.6\,(0.3)}{0.6\,(0.3)+0.4\,(0.9)}$ **5.** ________

(a) 2 (b) $\frac{1}{2}$ (c) $\frac{1}{3}$ (d) 0.54

6. Find the value of $\frac{2(a+1-b)}{a(a+1)}$ if $a = 10$ and $b = 5$. **6.** ________

(a) 1 (b) $\frac{6}{55}$ (c) $\frac{1}{11}$ (d) $-\frac{4}{15}$

Solve each of the following equations.

7. $12 - \dfrac{3}{4}r = \dfrac{5}{8}r + 23$ **7.** ________

(a) -8 (b) 8 (c) -1 (d) 4

8. $2x - (3x + 7) = 18$ **8.** ________

(a) 11 (b) -11 (c) 25 (d) -25

9. $-2(k-1)+8=-2(k+3)$ **9.** ________

(a) 4 (b) 10 (c) -6 (d) No solution

10. $0.04x+0.07(900-x)=51$ **10.** ________

(a) 4000 (b) 400 (c) 317 (d) 2083

11. Solve the equation $q=-\frac{2}{7}p-3$ for p. **11.** ________

(a) $p=\frac{7}{2}q+\frac{21}{2}$ (b) $p=-\frac{7}{2}q-\frac{21}{2}$
(c) $p=\frac{7}{2}q-\frac{21}{2}$ (d) $p=7q+\frac{3}{2}$

12. Solve the equation $3x+6y=7$ for y. **12.** ________

(a) $y=-\frac{1}{2}x+7$ (b) $y=\frac{1}{2}x+\frac{7}{6}$
(c) $y=-2x+\frac{7}{3}$ (d) $y=-\frac{1}{2}x+\frac{7}{6}$

13. Find the coordinates of the point where the graph of $7x-4y=8$ crosses the y-axis. **13.** ________

(a) $(0,7)$ (b) $(0,4)$ (c) $(-2,0)$ (d) $(0,-2)$

14. Suppose $C=20x+500$. Find x when C is 650. **14.** ________

(a) 13,500 (b) 1150 (c) 7.5 (d) 3

15. A boat that sells for \$5000 is marked up to \$8000. What is the percent increase? **15.** ________

(a) 80% (b) 60% (c) 62.5% (d) 37.5%

16. 68 is 85% of what number? **16.** ________

(a) 125 (b) 80 (c) 57.8 (d) 54.4

17. Bob can travel 160 miles on 8 gallons of gas. How many gallons will he need to travel 400 miles? **17.** ________

(a) 80 (b) 30 (c) 20 (d) 16

18. Solve the inequality $4(5-2x)-2(x+7)\leq -2-(x-80)$. **18.** ________

(a) $x\geq -8$ (b) $x\leq -8$ (c) $x\geq 8$ (d) $x\leq 8$

19. Graph the equation $4x - 3y = 12$.

19. 

(a)
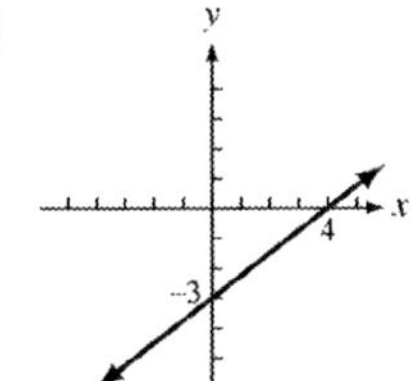

(b)
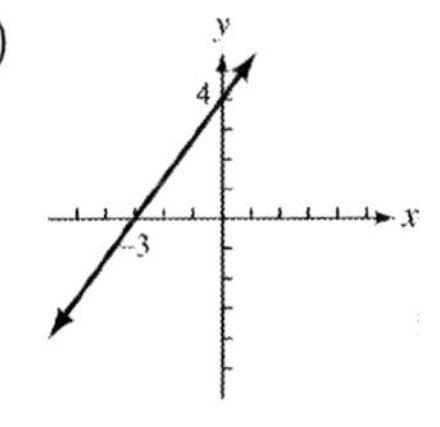

(c)
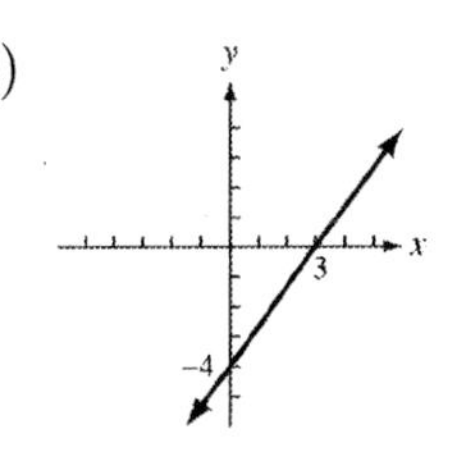

(d)
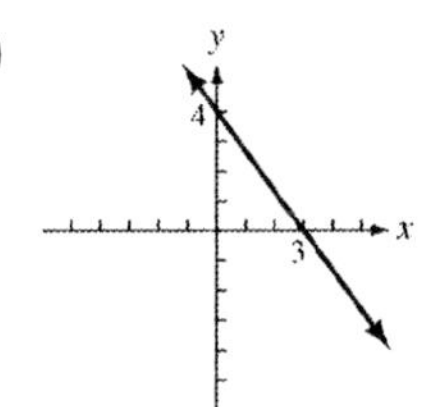

20. Find the slope of the line through the points with coordinates $(3, 8)$ and $(-2, 4)$.

20. ________

(a) 6 (b) $\frac{5}{4}$ (c) $\frac{4}{5}$ (d) $-\frac{4}{5}$

21. Write an equation in the form $ax + by = c$ for the line through the points with coordinates $(5, 8)$ and $(6, 4)$.

21. ________

(a) $4x - y = 12$ (b) $4x + y = 12$
(c) $x + 4y = 37$ (d) $4x + y = 28$

22. Solve the following system of equations.

$$x + 2y = 5$$
$$x - 20 = 3y$$

22. ________

(a) $(-50, 25)$ (b) $(11, -3)$ (c) $(-5, 5)$ (d) $(5, -5)$

23. Which of the following describes the graph of the equation $x = 7$?

23. ________

(a) A vertical line (b) A parabola
(c) A line with slope 7 (d) A horizontal line

24. Which of the following lines does *not* have slope 4?

24. 

(a) $y = 4x - 8$ (b) $2y - 8x = 7$
(c) $x = 4$ (d) $4x - y = 19$

25. Graph the inequality $6x + 4y > 12$.

25. 

(a)
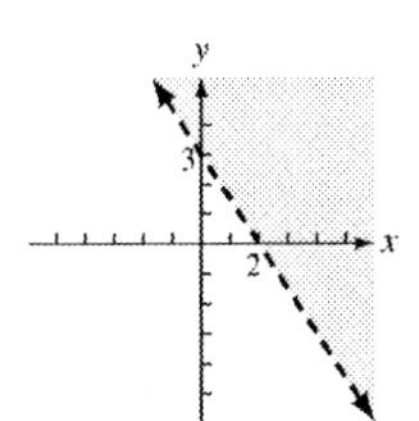

(b)
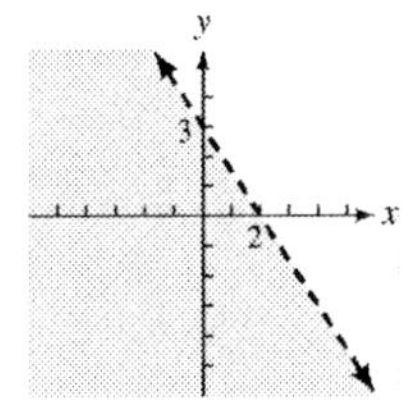

(c)
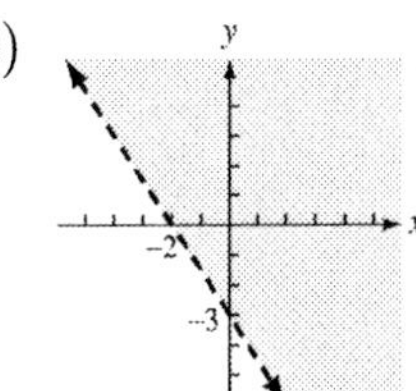

(d)
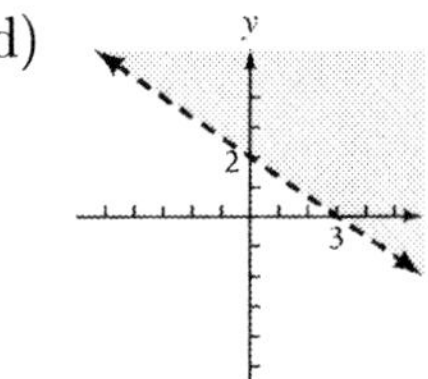

ANSWERS TO PRETESTS

PRETEST, FORM A

1. 0.005

2. $2\sqrt{3}$

3. 125

4. 1680

5. $\frac{1}{3}$

6. $-\frac{1}{2}$

7. 12

8. -33

9. $-\frac{1}{2}$

10. 50

11. $p = \frac{4}{3}q + \frac{32}{3}$

12. $y = \frac{4}{5}x - \frac{8}{5}$

13. $\left(\frac{5}{3}, 0\right)$

14. 20

15. 36%

16. 55

17. 14

18. $x > -4$

19.

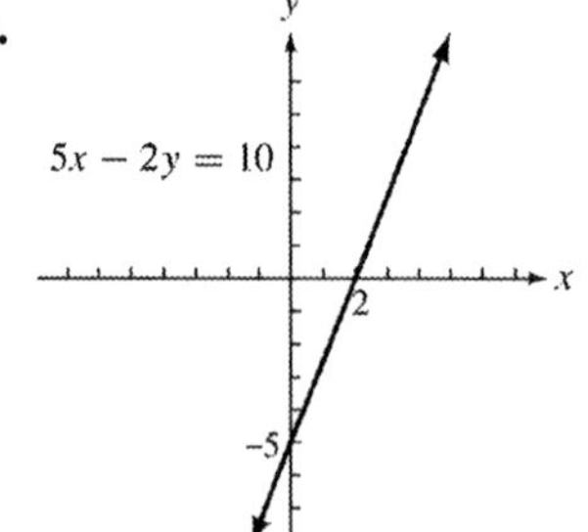

20. $\frac{2}{7}$

21. $3x - y = 9$

22. $(-2, 5)$

23. (d)

24. $\frac{4}{5}$

25.

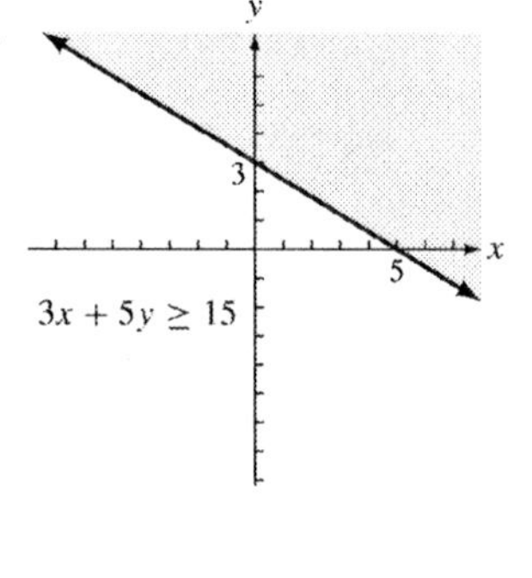

PRETEST, FORM B

1. (d)

2. (c)

3. (a)

4. (c)

5. (c)

6. (b)

7. (a)

8. (d)

9. (d)

10. (b)

11. (b)

12. (d)

13. (d)

14. (c)

15. (b)

16. (b)

17. (c)

18. (a)

19. (c)

20. (c)

21. (d)

22. (b)

23. (a)

24. (c)

25. (a)

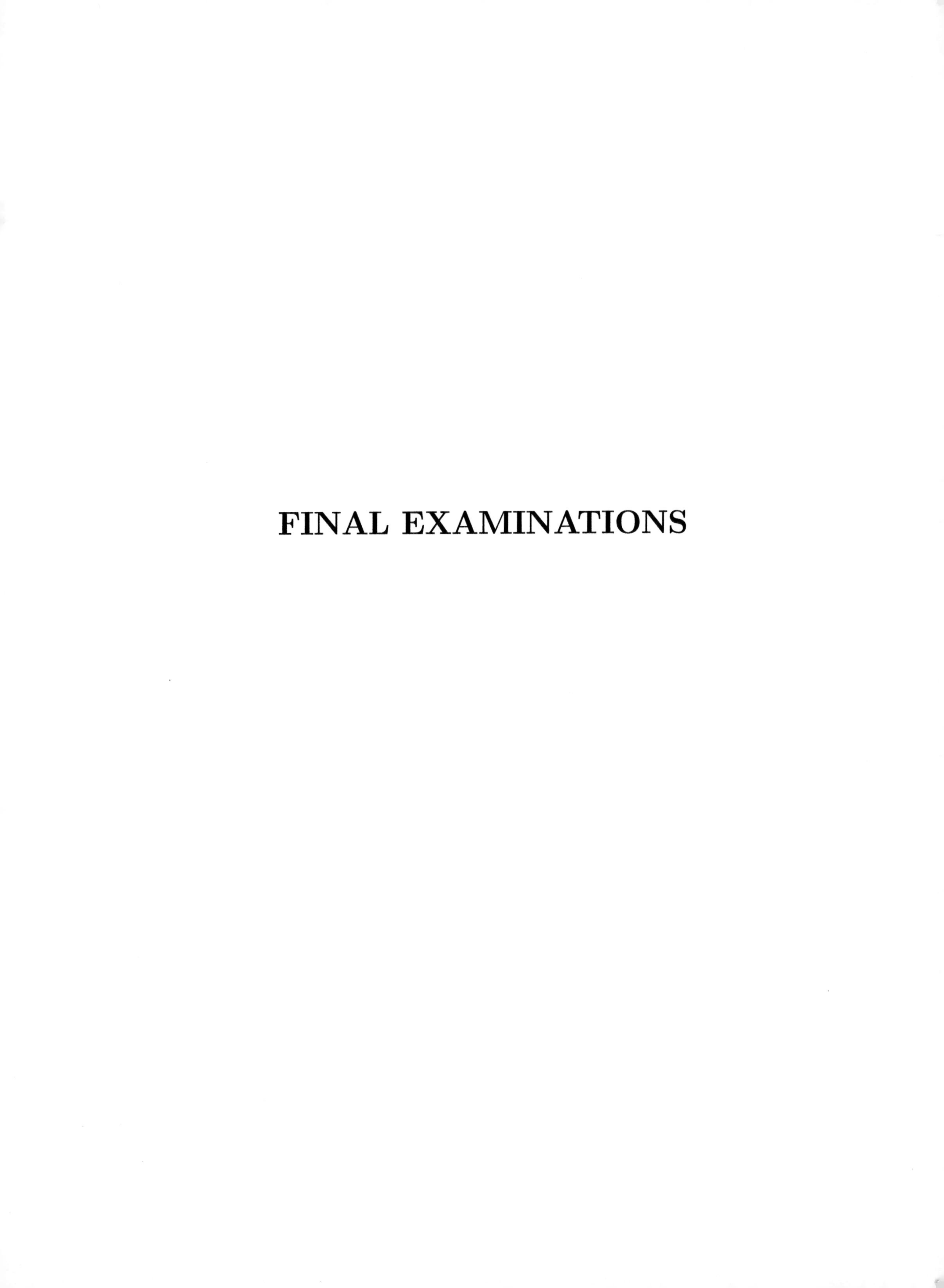

FINAL EXAMINATIONS

FINITE MATHEMATICS

Name:

Final Examination, Form A

1. The supply and demand functions for chocolate ice cream are given by

$$p = S(x) = \frac{1}{6}x \text{ and } p = D(x) = 9 - \frac{1}{3}x,$$

where p represents the price in dollars. Find the equilibrium price.

1. ______________

2. Suppose that a linear cost function for an item is given by $C(x) = 50x + 300$. The items sell for \$75 each. Find the break-even quantity.

2. ______________

3. If 6 items cost \$900 to produce and 13 items cost \$1600 to produce, find the linear cost function.

3. ______________

4. The cost in dollars for producing x units of a particular item is given by $C(x) = 0.37x + 682$. How many units could be produced for a cost of \$978?

4. ______________

5. Use the echelon method to solve the following system of equations.

$$\begin{aligned} 9x - 8y &= 12 \\ 6x + 4y &= 1 \end{aligned}$$

5. ______________

6. Use the Gauss-Jordan method to solve the following system of equations.

$$\begin{aligned} 2x + y - z &= -1 \\ x - 2y + 2z &= 7 \\ 3x + y + z &= 4 \end{aligned}$$

6. ______________

7. Let $A = \begin{bmatrix} 3 & 2 \\ -4 & -1 \end{bmatrix}$ and $B = \begin{bmatrix} 1 & 0 & -3 \\ 4 & -2 & 5 \end{bmatrix}$.

Find the products AB and BA, if these products exist.

7. ______________

8. Find the inverse of the following matrix, if the inverse exists.

$$A = \begin{bmatrix} 2 & 1 & 0 \\ 0 & 3 & 1 \\ 1 & 0 & -1 \end{bmatrix}$$

8. ______________

9. Graph the feasible region for the following system of inequalities.

$$-3 < x < 2$$
$$0 \leq y \leq 3$$
$$x + 2y < 6$$

9.

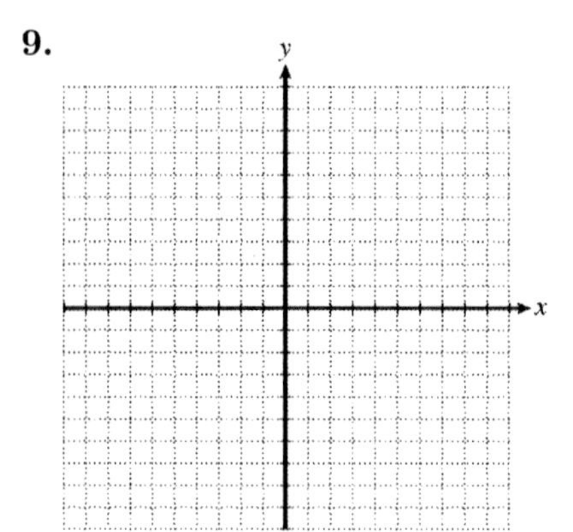

10. Give the coordinates of the corner points of the feasible region for the following system.

$$x \leq 7$$
$$y \leq x$$
$$y \geq 3$$

10. ____________________

11. For the system given in Problem 10, find the maximum value of the objective function $z = 6x - 3y$.

11. ____________________

12. Use the graphical method to solve the following linear programming problem.

$$\begin{aligned} \text{Maximize} \quad & z = 5x + 2y \\ \text{subject to:} \quad & 3x + 2y \leq 6 \\ & x + y \leq 2 \\ & x \geq 0 \\ & y \geq 0. \end{aligned}$$

12. ____________________

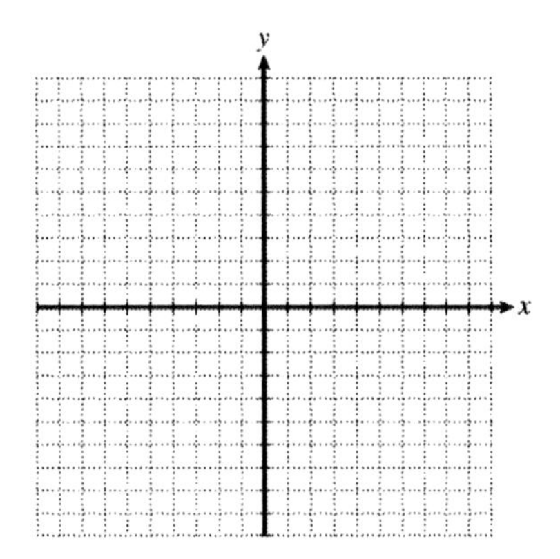

13. To pour a concrete sidewalk takes 2 hours of preparation and 3 hours of finishing. To pour a concrete patio takes 4 hours of preparation and 3 hours of finishing. There are 8 hours available for preparation and 21 hours available for finishing. ABC Concrete Company makes a profit of \$450 on a sidewalk and \$700 on a patio. How many sidewalks and patios should the company construct to maximize its profit?

Set up a system of inequalities for this problem, identify all variables used, and give the objective function, but do not solve.

13. ____________________

14. Write the initial simplex tableau for the linear programming problem given in Problem 13.

14. ____________________

15. Use the simplex method to solve the linear programming problem given in Problem 13.

15. ____________________

16. Read the solution from the following simplex tableau.

$$\begin{array}{cccccc} x_1 & x_2 & x_3 & s_1 & s_2 & z \\ \end{array}$$
$$\left[\begin{array}{cccccc|c} 0 & 2 & 4 & 1 & 6 & 0 & 200 \\ 1 & 3 & 6 & 0 & 9 & 0 & 350 \\ \hline 0 & -8 & 16 & 0 & 24 & 1 & 0 \end{array}\right]$$

16. ____________________

17. Find the maximum value of z in Problem 16.

17. ____________________

18. State the dual of the following linear programming problem.

Minimize $w = 6y_1 + 8y_2$

subject to:
$$2y_1 + 5y_2 \geq 9$$
$$2y_1 + 3y_2 \geq 11$$
$$7y_1 + 2y_2 \geq 5$$

with $y_1 \geq 0,\ y_2 \geq 0.$

18. ____________________

19. Find the compound amount if \$750 is invested at 8% compounded quarterly for 3 years.

19. ____________________

20. Jerry Herst wants to have \$2400 available for a vacation 2 years from now. How much must he invest today, at 6% compounded monthly, so that he will have the required amount?

20. ____________________

21. Find the tenth term of the geometric sequence with $a = 5$ and $r = 2$.

21. ____________________

22. Find the payment necessary to amortize a loan of \$10,000 if the interest rate is 8% compounded quarterly and there are 20 quarterly payments.

22. ____________________

23. Write the negation of

"Some pennies are made of silver."

23. ____________________

24. If p is false and q is true, find the truth value of

$$(q \vee \sim p) \longleftrightarrow (p \rightarrow q).$$

24. ____________________

25. Determine the truth value of the statement

"If it is raining, then if it is not raining it is pouring."

25. ____________________

26. Determine whether the following argument is *valid* or *invalid:*

$$\begin{array}{l} \sim p \longleftrightarrow q \\ \sim q \\ \hline p \end{array}$$

26. ____________________

27. Write "p is a necessary condition for q" symbolically.

27. ____________________

28. Let $U = \{a, b, c, d, e, f, g\}$, $M = \{b, e, f\}$, $N = \{c, f, g\}$, and $P = \{a, b, c, d\}$. List the members of each of the following sets, using set braces.

(a) $(M \cap P) \cup N$

(b) $M' \cap (N \cup P)$

28. (a) ____________________

(b) ____________________

29. Let A, B, and C be three sets. Draw a Venn diagram and use shading to show the set $A \cap (B' \cap C')$.

29.

30. In a survey, 28 people drank coffee with breakfast and 22 drank milk. 8 people drank both, and 5 people drank neither coffee nor milk.

Use a Venn diagram to determine how many people were surveyed.

30. ____________________

31. A die is rolled and then a coin is tossed.

(a) Write the sample space for this experiment.

(b) What is the probability that an even number is rolled and a head is tossed?

31. (a) ____________

(b) ____________

32. A phone number consists of seven digits. How many such numbers have the prefix (first three digits) 487?

32. ____________

33. A bag contains 4 red, 3 white, and 5 blue marbles. How many samples of 4 marbles can be drawn in which 2 marbles are red and 2 marbles are blue?

33. ____________

34. In the experiment described in Problem 33, what is the probability that a sample of 4 marbles contains 2 red and 2 white marbles?

34. ____________

35. Cass is taking a 5-question multiple-choice quiz in which each question has three choices. He guesses on all of the questions.

(a) What is the probability that Cass answers all of the questions correctly?

(b) What is the probability that he answers exactly three questions correctly?

35. (a) ____________

(b) ____________

36. A raffle has a first prize of \$400, two second prizes of \$75 each, and ten third prizes of \$20 each. One thousand tickets are sold at \$1 apiece. Find the expected winnings of a person buying 1 ticket.

36. ____________

37. Consider the following list of test scores:

98, 70, 32, 48, 71, 80, 85, 50, 46, 71.

For this data, find each of the following. Round to the nearest tenth when necessary.

(a) The mean

(b) The median

(c) The mode

(d) The range

37. (a) ____________

(b) ____________

(c) ____________

(d) ____________

38. Find the mean for the following data. Round to the nearest hundredth.

Value	Frequency
1	5
3	8
5	10
7	3
9	4

38. ____________

39. Find the standard deviation for the following set of numbers. Round to the nearest hundredth.

14, 5, 9, 3, 11, 12

39. ____________________

40. In a certain distribution of numbers, the mean is 70 with a standard deviation of 7. Use Chebyshev's theorem to tell what percent of the numbers are between 49 and 91.

40. ____________________

41. The probability that a certain basketball team will win a given game is 0.62. If the team plays 50 games, find the expected number of wins and the standard deviation. (Round to the nearest hundredth if necessary.

41. ____________________

42. Name three things that must be true of a transition matrix.

42. ____________________

____

____

43. Find the long-range distribution for the following transition matrix.

$$\begin{bmatrix} 0.8 & 0.2 \\ 0.6 & 0.4 \end{bmatrix}$$

43. ____________________

44. Identify all absorbing states for the following matrix.

$$\begin{bmatrix} 0.40 & 0.30 & 0.30 \\ 0 & 1 & 0 \\ 0 & 0 & 1 \end{bmatrix}$$

44. ____________________

45. Is the matrix in Problem 44 a transition matrix for an absorbing Markov chain? Why or why not?

45. ____________________

46. Maria Perez has $10,000 to invest. She can invest in a stock fund or a money market fund. There are two states of nature: the market goes up or the market goes down. The following payoff matrix shows the amounts she will have after 2 years under the various circumstances.

$$\begin{array}{r} \\ \text{Buy Stocks} \\ \text{Buy Money Market} \end{array} \begin{array}{c} \begin{array}{cc} \text{Market Up} & \text{Market Down} \end{array} \\ \begin{bmatrix} \$12,050 & \$7800 \\ \$11,025 & \$11,025 \end{bmatrix} \end{array}$$

Which investment should Maria make if she is

(a) an optimist;

(b) a pessimist?

46. (a) ______________

(b) ______________

47. In the following game, decide on the payoff when the given strategies are used.

$$\begin{array}{cc} & \begin{array}{ccc} & B & \\ 1 & 2 & 3 \end{array} \\ A \begin{array}{c} 1 \\ 2 \\ 3 \end{array} & \begin{bmatrix} 3 & -4 & 0 \\ 5 & 0 & 2 \\ 2 & -5 & -4 \end{bmatrix} \end{array}$$

(a) $(2, 3)$

(b) $(3, 2)$

47. (a) ______________

(b) ______________

48. Remove any dominated strategies in the following game.

$$\begin{bmatrix} -6 & 3 & 1 & -4 \\ 7 & -2 & 1 & -8 \end{bmatrix}$$

48. ______________

49. For the following game, find any saddle points and the value of the game.

$$\begin{bmatrix} 3 & 4 & -5 \\ 0 & 5 & -1 \\ 1 & 0 & -2 \end{bmatrix}$$

49. ______________

50. Suppose a game has the payoff matrix

$$M = \begin{bmatrix} 4 & -2 \\ -5 & 6 \end{bmatrix}.$$

Find the expected value of the game for the following strategies for the players A and B.

$$A = \begin{bmatrix} 0.6 & 0.4 \end{bmatrix}; B = \begin{bmatrix} 0.2 \\ 0.8 \end{bmatrix}$$

50. ______________

FINITE MATHEMATICS

Name:

Final Examination, Form B

Choose the best answer.

1. Suppose that the variable cost of producing an item is \$300 and the fixed cost is \$200. Find a linear cost function for production of this item. **1.** ________

(a) $C(x) = 200x + 300$ (b) $C(x) = 300x + 200$
(c) $C(x) = 500x + 200$ (d) $C(x) = 300x$

2. The supply and demand functions for a particular commodity are given by

$$p = S(x) = \tfrac{2}{7}x \text{ and } p = D(x) = 22 - \tfrac{1}{2}x,$$

where p represents the price in dollars. Find the equilibrium price. **2.** ________

(a) \$28 (b) \$14 (c) \$8 (d) \$6

3. An item which sells for \$37 has a linear cost function given by $C(x) = 13x + 4800$. Find the break-even quantity. **3.** ________

(a) 366 (b) 200 (c) 7400 (d) 300

4. The cost in dollars for producing x units of a particular item is given by $C(x) = 0.78x + 576$. How many units could be produced for a cost of \$849? **4.** ________

(a) 273 (b) 1088 (c) 350 (d) 1238

5. Give the solution of the system with the following augmented matrix. **5.** ________

$$\left[\begin{array}{cc|c} 1 & 0 & -2 \\ 0 & 6 & 18 \end{array}\right]$$

(a) $(-2, 6)$ (b) $(-2, 3)$ (c) $(-2, 18)$ (d) $(-2, 9)$

6. Use the Gauss–Jordan method to solve the following system of equations. Give only the x–value of the solution. **6.** ________

$$\begin{aligned} -4x + y &= -12 \\ 3y + 2z &= -18 \\ 2x - 3z &= 13 \end{aligned}$$

(a) 2 (b) -2 (c) 3 (d) No solution

7. If $A = \begin{bmatrix} 6 & 3 \\ 8 & 2 \end{bmatrix}$ and $B = \begin{bmatrix} -1 \\ 2 \end{bmatrix}$, find AB. **7.** ________

(a) $\begin{bmatrix} 0 & -4 \end{bmatrix}$ (b) $\begin{bmatrix} 0 \\ -4 \end{bmatrix}$ (c) $\begin{bmatrix} -6 & 6 \\ -8 & 4 \end{bmatrix}$

(d) Product does not exist.

8. If $A = \begin{bmatrix} 2 & 4 \\ -3 & 5 \end{bmatrix}$, find A^{-1}. **8.** ________

(a) $\begin{bmatrix} -2 & -4 \\ 3 & 5 \end{bmatrix}$ (b) $\begin{bmatrix} -1 & -\frac{3}{4} \\ 2 & -\frac{5}{2} \end{bmatrix}$ (c) $\begin{bmatrix} \frac{5}{22} & -\frac{2}{11} \\ \frac{3}{22} & \frac{1}{11} \end{bmatrix}$

(d) A^{-1} does not exist.

9. Describe the graph of the inequality $2y + 4x < 8$.

(a) The region to the left of the dashed line $y = -2x + 4$

(b) The region to the right of the dashed line $y = -2x + 4$

(c) The region to the left of and including the solid line $y = -2x + 4$

(d) The region to the right of and including the solid line $y = -2x + 4$ **9.** ________

10. Graph the feasible region for the following system of inequalities.

$$-2 < x < 4$$
$$0 \leq y \leq 5$$
$$2x + 3y > 6$$

10. ________

(a) 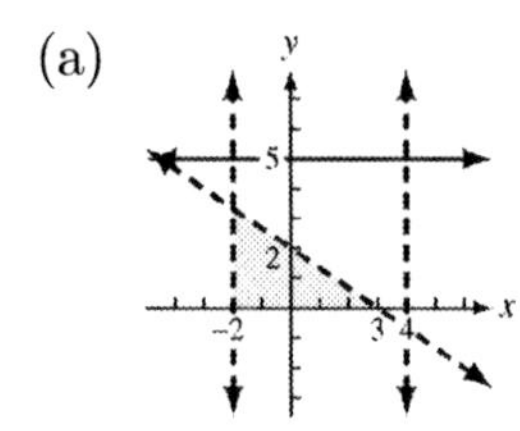

(b) 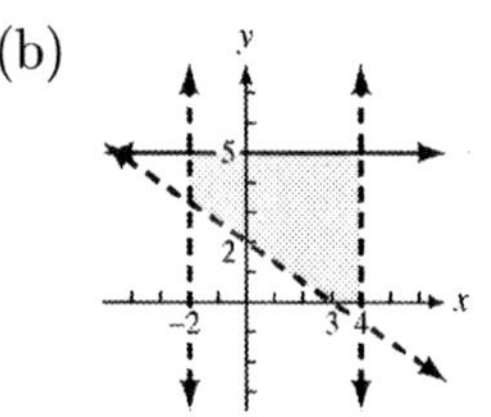

(c) 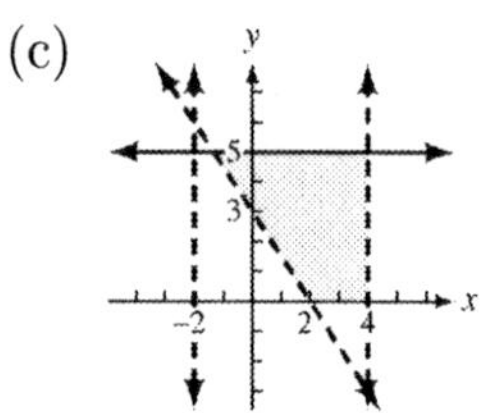

(d) 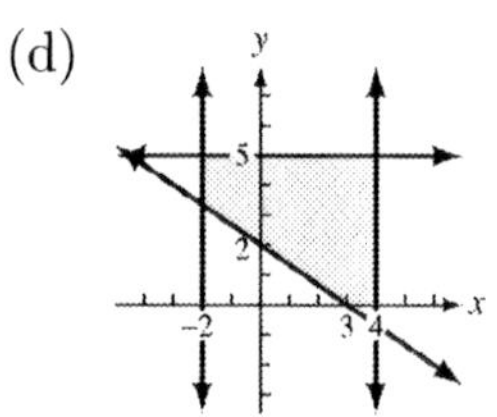

11. If the feasible region for a system has corner points $(0, 8)$, $(4, 3)$, and $(5, 0)$, find the maximum value of the objective function $z = 6x - 3y$. **11.** ________

(a) 36 (b) 32 (c) 30 (d) 24

12. Use the graphical method to solve the following linear programming problem.

12. ________

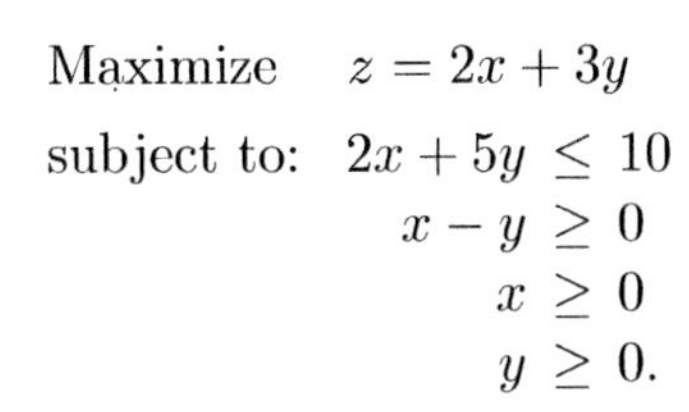

Maximize $z = 2x + 3y$

subject to:
$$2x + 5y \le 10$$
$$x - y \ge 0$$
$$x \ge 0$$
$$y \ge 0.$$

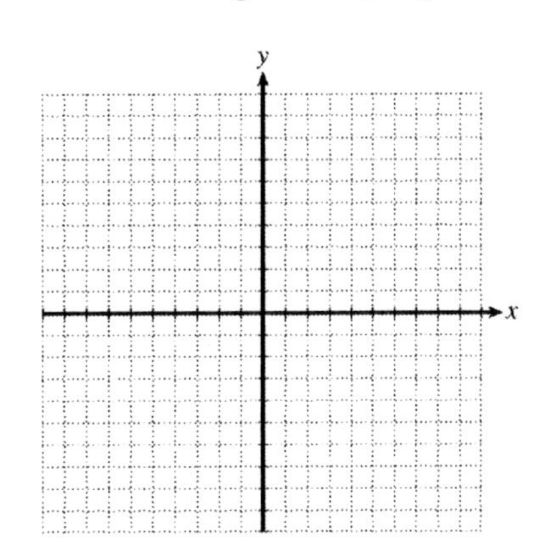

(a) 10 at $(5, 0)$ (b) $\frac{50}{7}$ at $\left(\frac{10}{7}, \frac{10}{7}\right)$ (c) 15 at $(0, 5)$ (d) No maximum value

13. It takes 3 hours to build a planter box and 2 hours to paint it. It takes 4 hours to build a step-stool and 3 hours to paint it. A man has 12 painting hours and 8 building hours available. If x is the number of planter boxes and y the number of stepstools, which of the following systems of inequalities describes this problem?

13. ________

(a) $3x + 2y \le 8$, $4x + 3y \le 12$, $x \ge 0,\ y \ge 0$

(b) $3x + 4y \le 8$, $2x + 3y \le 12$, $x \ge 0,\ y \ge 0$

(c) $3x + 8y \le 4$, $2x + 12y \le 3$, $x \ge 0,\ y \ge 0$

(d) $3x + 4y \le 12$, $2x + 3y \le 8$, $x \ge 0,\ y \ge 0$

14. Read the solution from the following simplex tableau.

14. ________

x_1	x_2	s_1	s_2	z	
3	0	3	1	0	17
4	1	5	0	0	20
−1	0	6	0	1	0

(a) $x_1 = 3,\ x_2 = 0,\ s_1 = 3,\ s_2 = 1,\ z = 17$

(b) $x_1 = -1,\ x_2 = 0,\ s_1 = 6,\ s_2 = 0,\ z = 1$

(c) $x_1 = 0,\ x_2 = 20,\ s_1 = 0,\ s_2 = 17,\ z = 0$

(d) $x_1 = 0,\ x_2 = 20,\ s_1 = 0,\ s_2 = 17,\ z = 1$

15. To solve a linear programming problem with the following initial simplex tableau, which element would be selected as the first pivot?

15. ________

x_1	x_2	s_1	s_2	z	
1	5	0	10	0	100
0	4	1	15	0	200
0	−6	0	−10	1	0

(a) 10 (b) 15 (c) 5 (d) −6

16. Find the transpose of the following matrix. **16.** ________

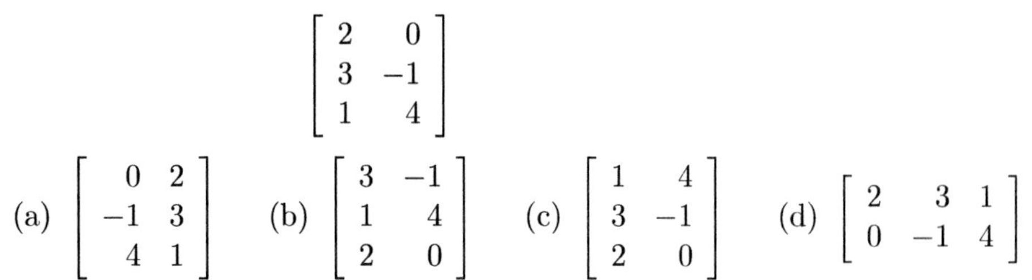

$$\begin{bmatrix} 2 & 0 \\ 3 & -1 \\ 1 & 4 \end{bmatrix}$$

(a) $\begin{bmatrix} 0 & 2 \\ -1 & 3 \\ 4 & 1 \end{bmatrix}$ (b) $\begin{bmatrix} 3 & -1 \\ 1 & 4 \\ 2 & 0 \end{bmatrix}$ (c) $\begin{bmatrix} 1 & 4 \\ 3 & -1 \\ 2 & 0 \end{bmatrix}$ (d) $\begin{bmatrix} 2 & 3 & 1 \\ 0 & -1 & 4 \end{bmatrix}$

17. Margaret Murphy opened a savings account with a deposit of \$7500. The account pays 8% interest compounded quarterly. If no further deposits and no withdrawals are made, find the balance in Margaret's account at the end of 5 years. **17.** ________

(a) \$10,500 (b) \$34,957.18 (c) \$8100 (d) \$11,144.61

18. Marc Rossoff wants to have \$25,000 available 10 years from now to buy a car. How much must he invest today, at 6% compounded monthly, so that he will have the required amount? **18.** ________

(a) \$23,584.91 (b) \$13,959.87 (c) \$13,740.82 (d) \$15,000

19. Find the sum of the first five terms of the geometric sequence with $a = 6$ and $r = -\frac{1}{2}$. **19.** ________

(a) $\frac{93}{8}$ (b) $-\frac{93}{16}$ (c) $\frac{8}{33}$ (d) $\frac{33}{8}$

20. Find the payment necessary to amortize a loan of \$20,000 if the interest rate is 10% compounded quarterly and payments are made quarterly for 10 years. **20.** ________

(a) \$296.72 (b) \$796.72 (c) \$500 (d) \$800

21. Write the negation of "Some coins are worth one dollar." **21.** ________

(a) Some coins are not worth one dollar

(b) No coins are worth one dollar.

(c) If it is a coin, it is worth one dollar.

(d) If it is not worth one dollar, it is a coin.

22. If p is true and q is false, find the true statement. **22.** ________

(a) $q \wedge p$ (b) $\sim q \vee \sim p$ (c) $q \wedge \sim p$ (d) $\sim p$

23. Find the valid argument. **23.** ________

(a) $\dfrac{p \vee q \quad p}{\sim q}$

$$\begin{array}{l} p \vee q \\ p \\ \hline \sim q \end{array}$$

(b)

$$\begin{array}{l} p \rightarrow q \\ q \rightarrow p \\ \hline p \wedge q \end{array}$$

(c)

$$\begin{array}{l} (p \rightarrow q) \wedge (q \rightarrow p) \\ p \\ \hline p \vee q \end{array}$$

(d)

$$\begin{array}{l} (\sim p \vee q) \wedge (\sim p \rightarrow q) \\ p \\ \hline \sim q \end{array}$$

24. Write "p is sufficient for q" symbolically. **24.** ________

(a) $p \rightarrow q$ (b) $q \rightarrow p$ (c) $p \longleftrightarrow q$ (d) $\sim p \rightarrow \sim q$

25. How many subsets does the set $\{a, b, c, d, e\}$ have? **25.** ________

(a) 64 (b) 32 (c) 16 (d) 30

26. Which of the following statements is false? **26.** ________

(a) $7 \in \{7, 9, 12\}$ (b) $\{a, b\} \subseteq \{a, b\}$

(c) $6 \notin \{5, 6, 7\}$ (d) $\emptyset \subseteq \{5, 6, 7\}$

27. A survey of members of a health club found that:

24 members swim;
32 members use exercise bikes;
20 members use weight machines;
8 members swim and use weight machines;
13 members use exercise bikes and weight machines;
12 members use exercise bikes only;
5 members swim, use exercise bikes, and use weight machines;
6 members do not swim and do not use either exercise bikes or weight machines

Use a Venn diagram to determine how many members were surveyed.

(a) 120 (b) 82

(c) 48 (d) 54

27. ________

28. Suppose that a single card is drawn from a standard 52-card deck. Find the probability that the card is a black seven. **28.** ________

(a) $\frac{1}{4}$ (b) $\frac{3}{14}$ (c) $\frac{1}{13}$ (d) $\frac{1}{26}$

29. If $P(A) = 0.3$, $P(B|A) = 0.6$, $P(B'|A') = 0.1$, find $P(B'|A)$. **29.** ________

(a) $\frac{2}{5}$ (b) $\frac{7}{19}$ (c) $\frac{4}{25}$ (d) .9

30. Suppose that Marco has 6 shirts, 5 pairs of pants, and 3 pairs of shoes. How many outfits can he create if an outfit consists of 1 shirt, 1 pair of pants, and 1 pair of shoes? **30.** ________

(a) 150 (b) 30 (c) 90 (d) 14

31. Find the number of distinguishable permutations of the letters in the word *moose*. **31.** ________

(a) 120 (b) 60 (c) 30 (d) 5

32. From a group of 6 boys and 3 girls, an after-school reading club of 2 boys and 2 girls is selected. How many such clubs are possible? **32.** ________

(a) 126 (b) 720 (c) 18 (d) 45

33. Georgia is taking a 5-question multiple-choice quiz in which each question has 4 choices. She guesses on all of the questions. What is the probability that she answers exactly 2 of the questions correctly? **33.** ________

(a) $\frac{1}{16}$ (b) $\frac{27}{1024}$ (c) $\frac{135}{512}$ (d) $\frac{45}{512}$

34. If 3 balls are drawn from a bag containing 4 red, 3 blue, and 2 yellow balls, what is the expected number of yellow balls in the sample? **34.** ________

(a) 2 (b) 1 (c) $\frac{2}{9}$ (d) $\frac{2}{3}$

35. Suppose that a student has test scores of 70, 78, 80, and 94. What is the student's mean score? **35.** ________

(a) 322 (b) 79 (c) 80.5 (d) 80

36. Find the median for the following set of numbers.

6, 14, 9, 13, 12, 11 **36.** ________

(a) 10.83 (b) 11.5 (c) 11 (d) No median

37. Find the mode or modes for the following set of numbers.

2, 1, 5, 2, 8, 5, 9

37. ________

(a) 2 (b) 5 (c) 2 and 5 (d) No mode

38. Find the standard deviation for the following set of numbers. Round to the nearest hundredth.

15, 13, 20, 8, 22, 12

38. ________

(a) 27.20 (b) 5.22 (c) 4.76 (d) 15.88

39. Find the mean for the following grouped data. Round to the nearest hundredth.

39. ________

Interval	Frequency
1-3	8
4-6	12
7-9	20
10-12	32

(a) 8.17 (b) 6.5 (c) 7.17 (d) 9.17

40. The probability that a certain baseball team will win a given game is 0.46. If the team plays 100 games, find the expected number of wins and the standard deviation. (Round to the nearest hundredth if necessary.)

40. 

(a) $\mu = 4.98$; $\sigma = 46$ (b) $\mu = 46$; $\sigma = 6.78$

(c) $\mu = 46$; $\sigma = 4.98$ (d) $\mu = 46$; $\sigma = 7.35$

41. Which one of the following matrices could be a probability vector?

41. 

(a) $\begin{bmatrix} 0.3 & 0.6 & 0.1 \\ 0.4 & 0.2 & 0.4 \end{bmatrix}$ (b) $\begin{bmatrix} 0.7 & 0.5 & -0.2 \end{bmatrix}$

(c) $\begin{bmatrix} 0.999 & 0.111 \end{bmatrix}$ (d) $\begin{bmatrix} 0.36 & 0.24 & 0.22 & 0.18 \end{bmatrix}$

42. Which one of the following matrices could be a transition matrix?

42. 

(a) $\begin{bmatrix} 0.6 & 0.4 & 0 \\ 0.1 & 0 & 0.9 \end{bmatrix}$ (b) $\begin{bmatrix} 0.75 & 0.35 \\ 0.25 & 0.65 \end{bmatrix}$ (c) $\begin{bmatrix} 0.32 & 0.68 \\ 0.41 & 0.59 \end{bmatrix}$ (d) $\begin{bmatrix} 2 & -1 \\ -3 & 4 \end{bmatrix}$

43. Suppose that

$$A = \begin{bmatrix} 0.2 & 0.8 \\ 0.1 & 0.9 \end{bmatrix}$$

is a transition matrix. What is the probability that state 1 changes to state 2 after two repetitions of the experiment?

43. ________

(a) 0.89 (b) 0.88 (c) 0.80 (d) 0.12

44. Which one of the following transition matrices is *not* regular?

44. ________

(a) $\begin{bmatrix} 0.1 & 0.2 & 0.7 \\ 0.3 & 0.3 & 0.4 \\ 0.1 & 0.1 & 0.8 \end{bmatrix}$ (b) $\begin{bmatrix} 0.2 & 0.4 & 0.2 \\ 0 & 0 & 1 \\ 0.1 & 0.3 & 0.3 \end{bmatrix}$ (c) $\begin{bmatrix} 0.9 & 0.1 \\ 0.3 & 0.7 \end{bmatrix}$ (d) $\begin{bmatrix} 1 & 0 \\ 0 & 1 \end{bmatrix}$

45. Find all absorbing states for the following transition matrix.

$$\begin{array}{c} \\ 1 \\ 2 \\ 3 \end{array} \begin{array}{c} \begin{array}{ccc} 1 & 2 & 3 \end{array} \\ \begin{bmatrix} 1 & 0 & 0 \\ 0.2 & 0.3 & 0.5 \\ 0 & 0 & 1 \end{bmatrix} \end{array}$$

45. ________

(a) State 1 only (b) State 2 only

(c) State 3 only (d) States 1 and 3

46. A farmer must decide whether to irrigate his fields. The payoff matrix for a given week is as follows.

	Rain	No Rain
Irrigate	−\$2500	\$8000
Don't Irrigate	\$6200	\$2100

If there is a 40% chance of rain during the week, what strategy is best?

46. ________

(a) Irrigate

(b) Don't irrigate

(c) Both strategies are equally good.

(d) The best strategy cannot be determined from the given information.

47. In the following game, decide on the payoff when the strategy $(3, 1)$ is used.

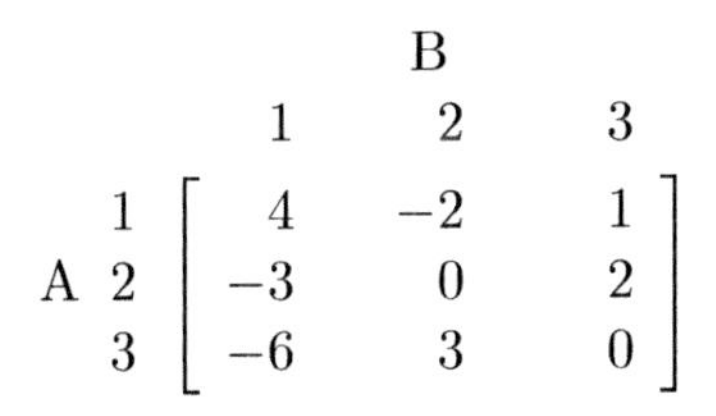

$$\begin{array}{cc} & \text{B} \\ & \begin{array}{ccc} 1 & 2 & 3 \end{array} \\ \text{A} \begin{array}{c} 1 \\ 2 \\ 3 \end{array} & \begin{bmatrix} 4 & -2 & 1 \\ -3 & 0 & 2 \\ -6 & 3 & 0 \end{bmatrix} \end{array}$$

47. ________

(a) \$1 from A to B (b) \$1 from B to A

(c) \$6 from A to B (d) \$6 from B to A

48. Remove any dominated strategies in the following game.

$$\begin{bmatrix} -3 & -2 & 5 \\ 2 & 1 & 6 \\ 4 & -2 & -3 \end{bmatrix}$$

48. ________

(a) $\begin{bmatrix} 2 & 1 & 6 \\ 4 & -2 & -3 \end{bmatrix}$ (b) $\begin{bmatrix} 1 & 6 \\ -2 & -3 \end{bmatrix}$ (c) $\begin{bmatrix} 2 & 6 \\ 4 & -3 \end{bmatrix}$

(d) No dominated strategies

49. Find any saddle points for the following game.

$$\begin{bmatrix} 2 & -1 \\ -3 & 4 \\ 6 & 5 \end{bmatrix}$$

49. ________

(a) 6 at $(3, 1)$ (b) -1 at $(2, 1)$

(c) 5 at $(3, 2)$ (d) No saddle point

50. Suppose that a game has payoff matrix

$$M = \begin{bmatrix} -2 & 3 \\ 2 & 0 \end{bmatrix}.$$

Suppose that player A chooses row 1 with probability 0.3 and player B chooses column 1 with probability 0.5. Find the expected value of the game.

50. ________

(a) \$0.90 (b) \$0.85 (c) $-$\$0.85 (d) \$1.05

ANSWERS TO FINAL EXAMINATIONS

FINAL EXAMINATION, FORM A

1. \$3

2. 12

3. $C(x) = 100x + 300$

4. 800 units

5. $\left(\frac{2}{3}, -\frac{3}{4}\right)$

6. $(1, -1, 2)$

7. $AB = \begin{bmatrix} 11 & -4 & 1 \\ -8 & 2 & 7 \end{bmatrix}$; BA does not exist.

8. $A^{-1} = \begin{bmatrix} \frac{3}{5} & -\frac{1}{5} & -\frac{1}{5} \\ -\frac{1}{5} & \frac{2}{5} & \frac{2}{5} \\ \frac{3}{5} & -\frac{1}{5} & -\frac{6}{5} \end{bmatrix}$

9.

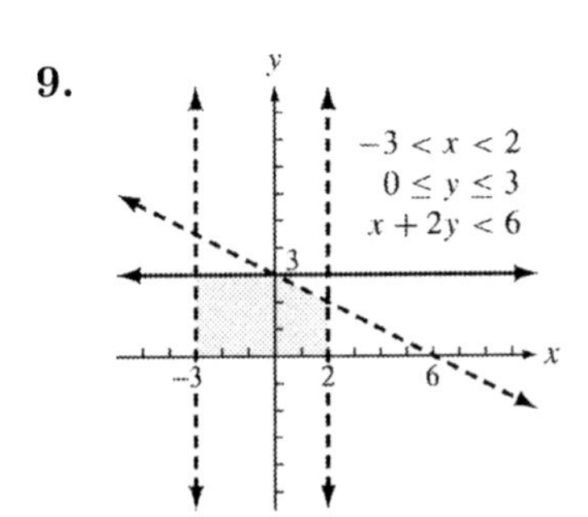

10. $(3,3)$, $(7,3)$, $(7,7)$

11. 33 at $(7,3)$

12. Maximum of 10 at $(2,0)$

13. Let x = the number of sidewalks;
y = the number of patios.

$$\begin{aligned} 2x + 4y &\le 8 \\ 3x + 3y &\le 21 \\ x &\ge 0 \\ y &\ge 0 \end{aligned}$$

Maximize $z = 450x + 700y$.

or

Let x_1 = the number of sidewalks;
x_2 = the number of patios.

$$\begin{aligned} 2x_1 + 4x_2 &\le 8 \\ 3x_1 + 3x_2 &\le 21 \\ x_1 &\ge 0 \\ x_2 &\ge 0 \end{aligned}$$

Maximize $z = 450x_1 + 700x_2$.

14.

$$\begin{array}{c} \begin{matrix} x_1 & x_2 & s_1 & s_2 & z & \end{matrix} \\ \left[\begin{array}{ccccc|c} 2 & 4 & 1 & 0 & 0 & 8 \\ 3 & 3 & 0 & 1 & 0 & 21 \\ \hline -450 & -700 & 0 & 0 & 1 & 0 \end{array}\right] \end{array}$$

15. Construct 4 sidewalks and no patios, for a profit of \$1800.

16. $x_1 = 350,\ x_2 = 0,\ x_3 = 0,\ s_1 = 200,\ s_2 = 0,\ z = 0$

17. 800

18. Maximize $z = 9x_1 + 11x_2 + 5x_3$

subject to: $2x_1 + 2x_2 + 7x_3 \le 6$
$5x_1 + 3x_2 + 2x_3 \le 8$

with $x_1 \ge 0,\ x_2 \ge 0,\ x_3 \ge 0$.

19. \$951.18

20. \$2129.25

21. 2560

22. \$611.57

23. No pennies are made of silver.

24. True

25. True

26. Valid

27. $q \rightarrow p$

28. **(a)** $\{b, c, f, g\}$ **(b)** $\{a, c, d, g\}$

29.

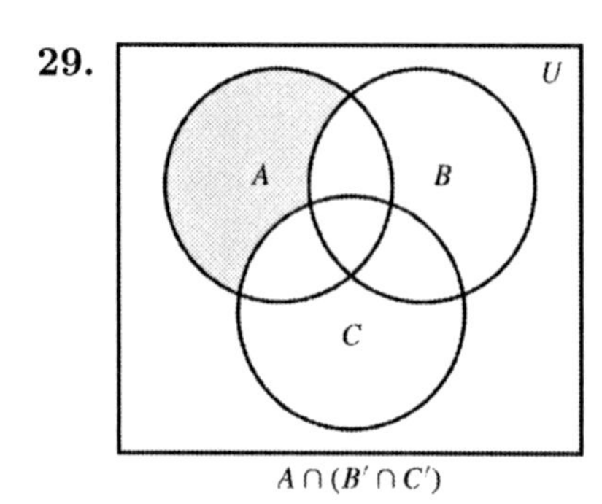

30. 47

31. **(a)** $\{1H, 2H, 3H, 4H, 5H, 6H, 1T, 2T, 3T, 4T, 5T, 6T\}$

(b) $\frac{1}{4}$

32. 10,000

33. 60

34. $\frac{2}{55}$

35. **(a)** $\frac{1}{243}$ **(b)** $\frac{40}{243}$

36. $-\$0.25$

37. **(a)** 65.1 **(b)** 70.5 **(c)** 71 **(d)** 66

38. 4.53

39. 4.24

40. At least 88.9%

41. $\mu = 31$; $\sigma = 3.43$

42.
1. It must be a square matrix.
2. All entries must be between 0 and 1, inclusive.
3. The sum of the entries in any row must be 1.

43. $\begin{bmatrix} \frac{3}{4} & \frac{1}{4} \end{bmatrix}$

44. States 2 and 3

45. Yes; it is possible to move from state 1 into state 2 or state 3.

46. **(a)** Buy stocks **(b)** Buy money market

47. **(a)** \$2 from B to A **(b)** \$5 from A to B

48. $\begin{bmatrix} -6 & -4 \\ 7 & -8 \end{bmatrix}$

49. -1 at $(2, 3)$; value -1

50. \$1.04

FINAL EXAMINATION, FORM B

1. (b)
2. (c)
3. (b)
4. (c)
5. (b)
6. (a)
7. (b)
8. (c)
9. (a)
10. (b)
11. (c)
12. (a)
13. (b)
14. (c)
15. (a)
16. (d)
17. (d)
18. (c)
19. (d)
20. (b)
21. (b)
22. (b)
23. (c)
24. (a)
25. (b)
26. (c)
27. (d)
28. (d)
29. (a)
30. (c)
31. (b)
32. (d)
33. (c)
34. (d)
35. (c)
36. (b)
37. (c)
38. (b)
39. (a)
40. (c)
41. (d)
42. (c)
43. (b)
44. (d)
45. (d)
46. (a)
47. (c)
48. (c)
49. (c)
50. (b)

SOLUTIONS TO ALL EXERCISES

Chapter R

ALGEBRA REFERENCE

R.1 Polynomials

1. $(2x^2 - 6x + 11) + (-3x^2 + 7x - 2)$
$= 2x^2 - 6x + 11 - 3x^2 + 7x - 2$
$= (2 - 3)x^2 + (7 - 6)x + (11 - 2)$
$= -x^2 + x + 9$

2. $(-4y^2 - 3y + 8) - (2y^2 - 6y - 2)$
$= (-4y^2 - 3y + 8) + (-2y^2 + 6y + 2)$
$= -4y^2 - 3y + 8 - 2y^2 + 6y + 2$
$= (-4y^2 - 2y^2) + (-3y + 6y)$
$\quad + (8 + 2)$
$= -6y^2 + 3y + 10$

3. $-6(2q^2 + 4q - 3) + 4(-q^2 + 7q - 3)$
$= (-12q^2 - 24q + 18) + (-4q^2 + 28q - 12)$
$= (-12q^2 - 4q^2) + (-24q + 28q) + (18 - 12)$
$= -16q^2 + 4q + 6$

4. $2(3r^2 + 4r + 2) - 3(-r^2 + 4r - 5)$
$= (6r^2 + 8r + 4) + (3r^2 - 12r + 15)$
$= (6r^2 + 3r^2) + (8r - 12r)$
$\quad + (4 + 15)$
$= 9r^2 - 4r + 19$

5. $(0.613x^2 - 4.215x + 0.892)$
$\quad - 0.47(2x^2 - 3x + 5)$
$= 0.613x^2 - 4.215x + 0.892$
$\quad - 0.94x^2 + 1.41x - 2.35$
$= -0.327x^2 - 2.805x - 1.458$

6. $0.5(5r^2 + 3.2r - 6) - (1.7r^2 - 2r - 1.5)$
$= (2.5r^2 + 1.6r - 3) + (-1.7r^2 + 2r + 1.5)$
$= (2.5r^2 - 1.7r^2) + (1.6r + 2r) + (-3 + 1.5)$
$= 0.8r^2 + 3.6r - 1.5$

7. $-9m(2m^2 + 3m - 1)$
$= -9m(2m^2) - 9m(3m) - 9m(-1)$
$= -18m^3 - 27m^2 + 9m$

8. $(6k - 1)(2k - 3)$
$= (6k)(2k) + (6k)(-3) + (-1)(2k)$
$\quad + (-1)(-3)$
$= 12k^2 - 18k - 2k + 3$
$= 12k^2 - 20k + 3$

9. $(3t - 2y)(3t + 5y)$
$= (3t)(3t) + (3t)(5y) + (-2y)(3t) + (-2y)(5y)$
$= 9t^2 + 15ty - 6ty - 10y^2$
$= 9t^2 + 9ty - 10y^2$

10. $(9k + q)(2k - q)$
$= (9k)(2k) + (9k)(-q) + (q)(2k)$
$\quad + (q)(-q)$
$= 18k^2 - 9kq + 2kq - q^2$
$= 18k^2 - 7kq - q^2$

11. $\left(\frac{2}{5}y + \frac{1}{8}z\right)\left(\frac{3}{5}y + \frac{1}{2}z\right)$
$= \left(\frac{2}{5}y\right)\left(\frac{3}{5}y\right) + \left(\frac{2}{5}y\right)\left(\frac{1}{2}z\right) + \left(\frac{1}{8}z\right)\left(\frac{3}{5}y\right)$
$\quad + \left(\frac{1}{8}z\right)\left(\frac{1}{2}z\right)$
$= \frac{6}{25}y^2 + \frac{1}{5}yz + \frac{3}{40}yz + \frac{1}{16}z^2$
$= \frac{6}{25}y^2 + \left(\frac{8}{40} + \frac{3}{40}\right)yz + \frac{1}{16}z^2$
$= \frac{6}{25}y^2 + \frac{11}{40}yz + \frac{1}{16}z^2$

12. $\left(\frac{3}{4}r - \frac{2}{3}s\right)\left(\frac{5}{4}r + \frac{1}{3}s\right)$
$= \left(\frac{3}{4}r\right)\left(\frac{5}{4}r\right) + \left(\frac{3}{4}r\right)\left(\frac{1}{3}s\right) + \left(-\frac{2}{3}s\right)\left(\frac{5}{4}r\right)$
$\quad + \left(-\frac{2}{3}s\right)\left(\frac{1}{3}s\right)$
$= \frac{15}{16}r^2 + \frac{1}{4}rs - \frac{5}{6}rs - \frac{2}{9}s^2$
$= \frac{15}{16}r^2 - \frac{7}{12}rs - \frac{2}{9}s^2$

13. $(2 - 3x)(2 + 3x)$
$= (2)(2) + (2)(3x) + (-3x)(2) + (-3x)(3x)$
$= 4 + 6x - 6x - 9x^2$
$= 4 - 9x^2$

14. $(6m + 5)(6m - 5)$
$= (6m)(6m) + (6m)(-5) + (5)(6m)$
$\quad + (5)(-5)$
$= 36m^2 - 30m + 30m - 25$
$= 36m^2 - 25$

15. $(3p-1)(9p^2+3p+1)$
$= (3p-1)(9p^2)+(3p-1)(3p)$
$+ (3p-1)(1)$
$= 3p(9p^2)-1(9p^2)+3p(3p)$
$- 1(3p)+3p(1)-1(1)$
$= 27p^3-9p^2+9p^2-3p+3p-1$
$= 27p^3-1$

16. $(3p+2)(5p^2+p-4)$
$= (3p)(5p^2)+(3p)(p)+(3p)(-4)$
$+ (2)(5p^2)+(2)(p)+(2)(-4)$
$= 15p^3+3p^2-12p+10p^2+2p-8$
$= 15p^3+13p^2-10p-8$

17. $(2m+1)(4m^2-2m+1)$
$= 2m(4m^2-2m+1)+1(4m^2-2m+1)$
$= 8m^3-4m^2+2m+4m^2-2m+1$
$= 8m^3+1$

18. $(k+2)(12k^3-3k^2+k+1)$
$= k(12k^3)+k(-3k^2)+k(k)+k(1)$
$+ 2(12k^3)+2(-3k^2)+2(k)+2(1)$
$= 12k^4-3k^3+k^2+k+24k^3-6k^2$
$+ 2k+2$
$= 12k^4+21k^3-5k^2+3k+2$

19. $(x+y+z)(3x-2y-z)$
$= x(3x)+x(-2y)+x(-z)+y(3x)+y(-2y)$
$+ y(-z)+z(3x)+z(-2y)+z(-z)$
$= 3x^2-2xy-xz+3xy-2y^2-yz+3xz-2yz-z^2$
$= 3x^2+xy+2xz-2y^2-3yz-z^2$

20. $(r+2s-3t)(2r-2s+t)$
$= r(2r)+r(-2s)+r(t)+2s(2r)$
$+ 2s(-2s)+2s(t)-3t(2r)-3t(-2s)-3t(t)$
$= 2r^2-2rs+rt+4rs+2st-6rt+6st-3t^2$
$+ 2rt-st+t^2$
$= 2r^2+2rs-5rt-4s^2+8st-3t^2$

21. $(x+1)(x+2)(x+3)$
$= [x(x+2)+1(x+2)](x+3)$
$= \left[x^2+2x+x+2\right](x+3)$
$= \left[x^2+3x+2\right](x+3)$
$= x^2(x+3)+3x(x+3)+2(x+3)$
$= x^3+3x^2+3x^2+9x+2x+6$
$= x^3+6x^2+11x+6$

22. $(x-1)(x+2)(x-3)$
$= [x(x+2)+(-1)(x+2)](x-3)$
$= (x^2+2x-x-2)(x-3)$
$= (x^2+x-2)(x-3)$
$= x^2(x-3)+x(x-3)+(-2)(x-3)$
$= x^3-3x^2+x^2-3x-2x+6$
$= x^3-2x^2-5x+6$

23. $(x+2)^2 = (x+2)(x+2)$
$= x(x+2)+2(x+2)$
$= x^2+2x+2x+4$
$= x^2+4x+4$

24. $(2a-4b)^2 = (2a-4b)(2a-4b)$
$= 2a(2a-4b)-4b(2a-4b)$
$= 4a^2-8ab-8ab+16b^2$
$= 4a^2-16ab+16b^2$

25. $(x-2y)^3$
$= [(x-2y)(x-2y)](x-2y)$
$= (x^2-2xy-2xy+4y^2)(x-2y)$
$= (x^2-4xy+4y^2)(x-2y)$
$= (x^2-4xy+4y^2)x+(x^2-4xy+4y^2)(-2y)$
$= x^3-4x^2y+4xy^2-2x^2y+8xy^2-8y^3$
$= x^3-6x^2y+12xy^2-8y^3$

R.2 Factoring

1. $7a^3+14a^2 = 7a^2\cdot a+7a^2\cdot 2$
$= 7a^2(a+2)$

2. $3y^3+24y^2+9y = 3y\cdot y^2+3y\cdot 8y+3y\cdot 3$
$= 3y(y^2+8y+3)$

3. $13p^4q^2-39p^3q+26p^2q^2$
$= 13p^2q\cdot p^2q-13p^2q\cdot 3p+13p^2q\cdot 2q$
$= 13p^2q(p^2q-3p+2q)$

4. $60m^4-120m^3n+50m^2n^2$
$= 10m^2\cdot 6m^2-10m^2\cdot 12mn$
$+ 10m^2\cdot 5n^2$
$= 10m^2(6m^2-12mn+5n^2)$

5. $m^2-5m-14 = (m-7)(m+2)$

since $(-7)(2) = -14$ and $-7+2 = -5$.

6. $x^2+4x-5 = (x+5)(x-1)$

since $5(-1) = -5$ and $-1+5 = 4$.

7. $z^2+9z+20 = (z+4)(z+5)$

since $4\cdot 5 = 20$ and $4+5 = 9$.

8. $b^2 - 8b + 7 = (b - 7)(b - 1)$

since $(-7)(-1) = 7$ and $-7 + (-1) = -8$.

9. $a^2 - 6ab + 5b^2 = (a - b)(a - 5b)$

since $(-b)(-5b) = 5b^2$ and $-b + (-5b) = -6b$.

10. $s^2 + 2st - 35t^2 = (s - 5t)(s + 7t)$

since $(-5t)(7t) = -35t^2$ and $7t + (-5t) = 2t$.

11. $y^2 - 4yz - 21z^2 = (y + 3z)(y - 7z)$

since $(3z)(-7z) = -21z^2$ and $3z + (-7z) = -4z$.

12. $6a^2 - 48a - 120 = 6(a^2 - 8a - 20)$
$= 6(a - 10)(a + 2)$

13. $3m^3 + 12m^2 + 9m = 3m(m^2 + 4m + 3)$
$= 3m(m + 1)(m + 3)$

14. $3x^2 + 4x - 7$

The possible factors of $3x^2$ are $3x$ and x and the possible factors of -7 are -7 and 1, or 7 and -1. Try various combinations until one works.

$$3x^2 + 4x - 7 = (3x + 7)(x - 1)$$

15. $3a^2 + 10a + 7$

The possible factors of $3a^2$ are $3a$ and a and the possible factors of 7 are 7 and 1. Try various combinations until one works.

$$3a^2 + 10a + 7 = (a + 1)(3a + 7)$$

16. $4a^2 + 10a + 6 = 2(2a^2 + 5a + 3)$
$= 2(2a + 3)(a + 1)$

17. $15y^2 + y - 2 = (5y + 2)(3y - 1)$

18. $21m^2 + 13mn + 2n^2$
$= (7m + 2n)(3m + n)$

19. $24a^4 + 10a^3b - 4a^2b^2$
$= 2a^2(12a^2 + 5ab - 2b^2)$
$= 2a^2(4a - b)(3a + 2b)$

20. $24x^4 + 36x^3y - 60x^2y^2$
$= 12x^2(2x^2 + 3xy - 5y^2)$
$= 12x^2(x - y)(2x + 5y)$

21. $x^2 - 64 = x^2 - 8^2$
$= (x + 8)(x - 8)$

22. $9m^2 - 25 = (3m)^2 - (5)^2$
$= (3m + 5)(3m - 5)$

23. $10x^2 - 160 = 10(x^2 - 16)$
$= 10(x^2 - 4^2)$
$= 10(x + 4)(x - 4)$

24. $9x^2 + 64$ is the *sum* of two perfect squares. It cannot be factored. It is prime.

25. $z^2 + 14zy + 49y^2$
$= z^2 + 2 \cdot 7zy + 7^2y^2$
$= (z + 7y)^2$

26. $s^2 - 10st + 25t^2$
$= s^2 - 2 \cdot 5st + (5t)^2$
$= (s - 5t)^2$

27. $9p^2 - 24p + 16$
$= (3p)^2 - 2 \cdot 3p \cdot 4 + 4^2$
$= (3p - 4)^2$

28. $a^3 - 216$
$= a^3 - 6^3$
$= (a - 6)[(a)^2 + (a)(6) + (6)^2]$
$= (a - 6)(a^2 + 6a + 36)$

29. $27r^3 - 64s^3$
$= (3r)^3 - (4s)^3$
$= (3r - 4s)(9r^2 + 12rs + 16s^2)$

30. $3m^3 + 375$
$= 3(m^3 + 125)$
$= 3(m^3 + 5^3)$
$= 3(m + 5)(m^2 - 5m + 25)$

31. $x^4 - y^4 = (x^2)^2 - (y^2)^2$
$= (x^2 + y^2)(x^2 - y^2)$
$= (x^2 + y^2)(x + y)(x - y)$

32. $16a^4 - 81b^4$
$= (4a^2)^2 - (9b^2)^2$
$= (4a^2 + 9b^2)(4a^2 - 9b^2)$
$= (4a^2 + 9b^2)[(2a)^2 - (3b)^2]$
$= (4a^2 + 9b^2)(2a + 3b)(2a - 3b)$

R.3 Rational Expressions

1. $\dfrac{5v^2}{35v} = \dfrac{5 \cdot v \cdot v}{5 \cdot 7 \cdot v} = \dfrac{v}{7}$

2. $\dfrac{25p^3}{10p^2} = \dfrac{5 \cdot 5 \cdot p \cdot p \cdot p}{2 \cdot 5 \cdot p \cdot p} = \dfrac{5p}{2}$

3. $\dfrac{8k + 16}{9k + 18} = \dfrac{8(k + 2)}{9(k + 2)} = \dfrac{8}{9}$

4. $\dfrac{2(t-15)}{(t-15)(t+2)} = \dfrac{2}{(t+2)}$

5. $\dfrac{4x^3 - 8x^2}{4x^2} = \dfrac{4x^2(x-2)}{4x^2}$

$= x - 2$

6. $\dfrac{36y^2 + 72y}{9y} = \dfrac{36y(y+2)}{9y}$

$= \dfrac{9 \cdot 4 \cdot y(y+2)}{9 \cdot y}$

$= 4(y+2)$

7. $\dfrac{m^2 - 4m + 4}{m^2 + m - 6} = \dfrac{(m-2)(m-2)}{(m-2)(m+3)}$

$= \dfrac{m-2}{m+3}$

8. $\dfrac{r^2 - r - 6}{r^2 + r - 12} = \dfrac{(r-3)(r+2)}{(r+4)(r-3)}$

$= \dfrac{r+2}{r+4}$

9. $\dfrac{3x^2 + 3x - 6}{x^2 - 4} = \dfrac{3(x+2)(x-1)}{(x+2)(x-2)}$

$= \dfrac{3(x-1)}{x-2}$

10. $\dfrac{z^2 - 5z + 6}{z^2 - 4} = \dfrac{(z-3)(z-2)}{(z+2)(z-2)}$

$= \dfrac{z-3}{z+2}$

11. $\dfrac{m^4 - 16}{4m^2 - 16} = \dfrac{(m^2+4)(m+2)(m-2)}{4(m+2)(m-2)}$

$= \dfrac{m^2+4}{4}$

12. $\dfrac{6y^2 + 11y + 4}{3y^2 + 7y + 4} = \dfrac{(3y+4)(2y+1)}{(3y+4)(y+1)}$

$= \dfrac{2y+1}{y+1}$

13. $\dfrac{9k^2}{25} \cdot \dfrac{5}{3k} = \dfrac{3 \cdot 3 \cdot 5k^2}{5 \cdot 5 \cdot 3k} = \dfrac{3k^2}{5k} = \dfrac{3k}{5}$

14. $\dfrac{15p^3}{9p^2} \div \dfrac{6p}{10p^2}$

$= \dfrac{15p^3}{9p^2} \cdot \dfrac{10p^2}{6p}$

$= \dfrac{150p^5}{54p^3}$

$= \dfrac{25 \cdot 6p^5}{9 \cdot 6p^3}$

$= \dfrac{25p^2}{9}$

15. $\dfrac{3a + 3b}{4c} \cdot \dfrac{12}{5(a+b)} = \dfrac{3(a+b)}{4c} \cdot \dfrac{3 \cdot 4}{5(a+b)}$

$= \dfrac{3 \cdot 3}{c \cdot 5}$

$= \dfrac{9}{5c}$

16. $\dfrac{a-3}{16} \div \dfrac{a-3}{32} = \dfrac{a-3}{16} \cdot \dfrac{32}{a-3}$

$= \dfrac{a-3}{16} \cdot \dfrac{16 \cdot 2}{a-3}$

$= \dfrac{2}{1} = 2$

17. $\dfrac{2k - 16}{6} \div \dfrac{4k - 32}{3}$

$= \dfrac{2k-16}{6} \cdot \dfrac{3}{4k-32}$

$= \dfrac{2(k-8)}{6} \cdot \dfrac{3}{4(k-8)}$

$= \dfrac{1}{4}$

18. $\dfrac{9y - 18}{6y + 12} \cdot \dfrac{3y + 6}{15y - 30}$

$= \dfrac{9(y-2)}{6(y+2)} \cdot \dfrac{3(y+2)}{15(y-2)}$

$= \dfrac{27}{90} = \dfrac{3 \cdot 3}{10 \cdot 3} = \dfrac{3}{10}$

19. $\dfrac{4a + 12}{2a - 10} \div \dfrac{a^2 - 9}{a^2 - a - 20}$

$= \dfrac{4(a+3)}{2(a-5)} \cdot \dfrac{(a-5)(a+4)}{(a-3)(a+3)}$

$= \dfrac{2(a+4)}{a-3}$

20. $\dfrac{6r-18}{9r^2+6r-24}\cdot\dfrac{12r-16}{4r-12}$

$=\dfrac{6(r-3)}{3(3r^2+2r-8)}\cdot\dfrac{4(3r-4)}{4(r-3)}$

$=\dfrac{6(r-3)}{3(3r-4)(r+2)}\cdot\dfrac{4(3r-4)}{4(r-3)}$

$=\dfrac{6}{3(r+2)}$

$=\dfrac{2}{r+2}$

21. $\dfrac{k^2+4k-12}{k^2+10k+24}\cdot\dfrac{k^2+k-12}{k^2-9}$

$=\dfrac{(k+6)(k-2)}{(k+6)(k+4)}\cdot\dfrac{(k+4)(k-3)}{(k+3)(k-3)}$

$=\dfrac{k-2}{k+3}$

22. $\dfrac{m^2+3m+2}{m^2+5m+4}\div\dfrac{m^2+5m+6}{m^2+10m+24}$

$=\dfrac{m^2+3m+2}{m^2+5m+4}\cdot\dfrac{m^2+10m+24}{m^2+5m+6}$

$=\dfrac{(m+1)(m+2)}{(m+4)(m+1)}\cdot\dfrac{(m+6)(m+4)}{(m+3)(m+2)}$

$=\dfrac{m+6}{m+3}$

23. $\dfrac{2m^2-5m-12}{m^2-10m+24}\div\dfrac{4m^2-9}{m^2-9m+18}$

$=\dfrac{2m^2-5m-12}{m^2-10m+24}\cdot\dfrac{m^2-9m+18}{4m^2-9}$

$=\dfrac{(2m+3)(m-4)(m-6)(m-3)}{(m-6)(m-4)(2m-3)(2m+3)}$

$=\dfrac{m-3}{2m-3}$

24. $\dfrac{4n^2+4n-3}{6n^2-n-15}\cdot\dfrac{8n^2+32n+30}{4n^2+16n+15}$

$=\dfrac{(2n+3)(2n-1)}{(2n+3)(3n-5)}\cdot\dfrac{2(2n+3)(2n+5)}{(2n+3)(2n+5)}$

$=\dfrac{2(2n-1)}{3n-5}$

25. $\dfrac{a+1}{2}-\dfrac{a-1}{2}$

$=\dfrac{(a+1)-(a-1)}{2}$

$=\dfrac{a+1-a+1}{2}$

$=\dfrac{2}{2}=1$

26. $\dfrac{3}{p}+\dfrac{1}{2}$

Multiply the first term by $\frac{2}{2}$ and the second by $\frac{p}{p}$.

$\dfrac{2\cdot 3}{2\cdot p}+\dfrac{p\cdot 1}{p\cdot 2}=\dfrac{6}{2p}+\dfrac{p}{2p}$

$=\dfrac{6+p}{2p}$

27. $\dfrac{6}{5y}-\dfrac{3}{2}=\dfrac{6\cdot 2}{5y\cdot 2}-\dfrac{3\cdot 5y}{2\cdot 5y}$

$=\dfrac{12-15y}{10y}$

28. $\dfrac{1}{6m}+\dfrac{2}{5m}+\dfrac{4}{m}$

$=\dfrac{5\cdot 1}{5\cdot 6m}+\dfrac{6\cdot 2}{6\cdot 5m}+\dfrac{30\cdot 4}{30\cdot m}$

$=\dfrac{5}{30m}+\dfrac{12}{30m}+\dfrac{120}{30m}$

$=\dfrac{5+12+120}{30m}$

$=\dfrac{137}{30m}$

29. $\dfrac{1}{m-1}+\dfrac{2}{m}$

$=\dfrac{m}{m}\left(\dfrac{1}{m-1}\right)+\dfrac{m-1}{m-1}\left(\dfrac{2}{m}\right)$

$=\dfrac{m+2m-2}{m(m-1)}$

$=\dfrac{3m-2}{m(m-1)}$

30. $\dfrac{5}{2r+3}-\dfrac{2}{r}$

$=\dfrac{5r}{r(2r+3)}-\dfrac{2(2r+3)}{r(2r+3)}$

$=\dfrac{5r-2(2r+3)}{r(2r+3)}$

$=\dfrac{5r-4r-6}{r(2r+3)}$

$=\dfrac{r-6}{r(2r+3)}$

31. $\dfrac{8}{3(a-1)}+\dfrac{2}{a-1}$

$=\dfrac{8}{3(a-1)}+\dfrac{3}{3}\left(\dfrac{2}{a-1}\right)$

$=\dfrac{8+6}{3(a-1)}$

$=\dfrac{14}{3(a-1)}$

32. $\frac{2}{5(k-2)} + \frac{3}{4(k-2)} = \frac{4 \cdot 2}{4 \cdot 5(k-2)} + \frac{5 \cdot 3}{5 \cdot 4(k-2)}$

$= \frac{8}{20(k-2)} + \frac{15}{20(k-2)}$

$= \frac{8+15}{20(k-2)}$

$= \frac{23}{20(k-2)}$

33. $\frac{4}{x^2+4x+3} + \frac{3}{x^2-x-2}$

$= \frac{4}{(x+3)(x+1)} + \frac{3}{(x-2)(x+1)}$

$= \frac{4(x-2)}{(x-2)(x+3)(x+1)}$

$+ \frac{3(x+3)}{(x-2)(x+3)(x+1)}$

$= \frac{4(x-2)+3(x+3)}{(x-2)(x+3)(x+1)}$

$= \frac{4x-8+3x+9}{(x-2)(x+3)(x+1)}$

$= \frac{7x+1}{(x-2)(x+3)(x+1)}$

34. $\frac{y}{y^2+2y-3} - \frac{1}{y^2+4y+3}$

$= \frac{y}{(y+3)(y-1)} - \frac{1}{(y+3)(y+1)}$

$= \frac{y(y+1)}{(y+3)(y+1)(y-1)}$

$- \frac{1(y-1)}{(y+3)(y+1)(y-1)}$

$= \frac{y(y+1)-(y-1)}{(y+3)(y+1)(y-1)}$

$= \frac{y^2+y-y+1}{(y+3)(y+1)(y-1)}$

$= \frac{y^2+1}{(y+3)(y+1)(y-1)}$

35. $\frac{3k}{2k^2+3k-2} - \frac{2k}{2k^2-7k+3}$

$= \frac{3k}{(2k-1)(k+2)} - \frac{2k}{(2k-1)(k-3)}$

$= \left(\frac{k-3}{k-3}\right) \frac{3k}{(2k-1)(k+2)}$

$- \left(\frac{k+2}{k+2}\right) \frac{2k}{(2k-1)(k-3)}$

$= \frac{(3k^2-9k)-(2k^2+4k)}{(2k-1)(k+2)(k-3)}$

$= \frac{k^2-13k}{(2k-1)(k+2)(k-3)}$

$= \frac{k(k-13)}{(2k-1)(k+2)(k-3)}$

36. $\frac{4m}{3m^2+7m-6} - \frac{m}{3m^2-14m+8}$

$= \frac{4m}{(3m-2)(m+3)} - \frac{m}{(3m-2)(m-4)}$

$= \frac{4m(m-4)}{(3m-2)(m+3)(m-4)}$

$- \frac{m(m+3)}{(3m-2)(m-4)(m+3)}$

$= \frac{4m(m-4)-m(m+3)}{(3m-2)(m-4)(m+3)}$

$= \frac{4m^2-16m-m^2-3m}{(3m-2)(m+3)(m-4)}$

$= \frac{3m^2-19m}{(3m-2)(m+3)(m-4)}$

$= \frac{m(3m-19)}{(3m-2)(m+3)(m-4)}$

37. $\frac{2}{a+2} + \frac{1}{a} + \frac{a-1}{a^2+2a}$

$= \frac{2}{a+2} + \frac{1}{a} + \frac{a-1}{a(a+2)}$

$= \left(\frac{a}{a}\right) \frac{2}{a+2} + \left(\frac{a+2}{a+2}\right) \frac{1}{a} + \frac{a-1}{a(a+2)}$

$= \frac{2a+a+2+a-1}{a(a+2)}$

$= \frac{4a+1}{a(a+2)}$

38. $\frac{5x+2}{x^2-1} + \frac{3}{x^2+x} - \frac{1}{x^2-x}$

$= \frac{5x+2}{(x+1)(x-1)} + \frac{3}{x(x+1)} - \frac{1}{x(x-1)}$

$= \left(\frac{x}{x}\right)\left(\frac{5x+2}{(x+1)(x-1)}\right) + \left(\frac{x-1}{x-1}\right)\left(\frac{3}{x(x+1)}\right)$

$- \left(\frac{x+1}{x+1}\right)\left(\frac{1}{x(x-1)}\right)$

$= \frac{x(5x+2)+(x-1)(3)-(x+1)(1)}{x(x+1)(x-1)}$

$= \frac{5x^2+2x+3x-3-x-1}{x(x+1)(x-1)}$

$= \frac{5x^2+4x-4}{x(x+1)(x-1)}$

R.4 Equations

1.
$$\begin{aligned} 0.2m - 0.5 &= 0.1m + 0.7 \\ 10(0.2m - 0.5) &= 10(0.1m + 0.7) \\ 2m - 5 &= m + 7 \\ m - 5 &= 7 \\ m &= 12 \end{aligned}$$

The solution is 12.

2. $\frac{2}{3}k - k + \frac{3}{8} = \frac{1}{2}$

Multiply both sides of the equation by 24.

$$\begin{aligned} 24\left(\frac{2}{3}k\right) - 24(k) + 24\left(\frac{3}{8}\right) &= 24\left(\frac{1}{2}\right) \\ 16k - 24k + 9 &= 12 \\ -8k + 9 &= 12 \\ -8k &= 3 \\ k &= -\frac{3}{8} \end{aligned}$$

The solution is $-\frac{3}{8}$.

3.
$$\begin{aligned} 2x + 8 &= x - 4 \\ x + 8 &= -4 \\ x &= -12 \end{aligned}$$

The solution is -12.

4.
$$\begin{aligned} 5x + 2 &= 8 - 3x \\ 8x + 2 &= 8 \\ 8x &= 6 \\ x &= \frac{3}{4} \end{aligned}$$

The solution is $\frac{3}{4}$.

5.
$$\begin{aligned} 3r + 2 - 5(r + 1) &= 6r + 4 \\ 3r + 2 - 5r - 5 &= 6r + 4 \\ -3 - 2r &= 6r + 4 \\ -3 &= 8r + 4 \\ -7 &= 8r \\ -\frac{7}{8} &= r \end{aligned}$$

The solution is $-\frac{7}{8}$.

6.
$$\begin{aligned} 5(a + 3) + 4a - 5 &= -(2a - 4) \\ 5a + 15 + 4a - 5 &= -2a + 4 \\ 9a + 10 &= -2a + 4 \\ 11a + 10 &= 4 \\ 11a &= -6 \\ a &= -\frac{6}{11} \end{aligned}$$

The solution is $-\frac{6}{11}$.

7.
$$\begin{aligned} 2[3m - 2(3 - m) - 4] &= 6m - 4 \\ 2[3m - 6 + 2m - 4] &= 6m - 4 \\ 2[5m - 10] &= 6m - 4 \\ 10m - 20 &= 6m - 4 \\ 4m - 20 &= -4 \\ 4m &= 16 \\ m &= 4 \end{aligned}$$

The solution is 4.

8.
$$\begin{aligned} 4[2p - (3 - p) + 5] &= -7p - 2 \\ 4[2p - 3 + p + 5] &= -7p - 2 \\ 4[3p + 2] &= -7p - 2 \\ 12p + 8 &= -7p - 2 \\ 19p + 8 &= -2 \\ 19p &= -10 \\ p &= -\frac{10}{19} \end{aligned}$$

The solution is $-\frac{10}{19}$.

9.
$$\begin{aligned} x^2 + 5x + 6 &= 0 \\ (x + 3)(x + 2) &= 0 \\ x + 3 = 0 \quad &\text{or} \quad x + 2 = 0 \\ x = -3 \quad &\text{or} \quad x = -2 \end{aligned}$$

The solutions are -3 and -2.

10.
$$\begin{aligned} x^2 &= 3 + 2x \\ x^2 - 2x - 3 &= 0 \\ (x - 3)(x + 1) &= 0 \\ x - 3 = 0 \quad &\text{or} \quad x + 1 = 0 \\ x = 3 \quad &\text{or} \quad x = -1 \end{aligned}$$

The solutions are 3 and -1.

11.
$$\begin{aligned} m^2 &= 14m - 49 \\ m^2 - 14m + 49 &= 0 \\ (m)^2 - 2(7m) + (7)^2 &= 0 \\ (m - 7)^2 &= 0 \\ m - 7 &= 0 \\ m &= 7 \end{aligned}$$

The solution is 7.

12.
$$\begin{aligned} 2k^2 - k &= 10 \\ 2k^2 - k - 10 &= 0 \\ (2k - 5)(k + 2) &= 0 \\ 2k - 5 = 0 \quad &\text{or} \quad k + 2 = 0 \\ k = \frac{5}{2} \quad &\text{or} \quad k = -2 \end{aligned}$$

The solutions are $\frac{5}{2}$ and -2.

13.
$$\begin{aligned} 12x^2 - 5x &= 2 \\ 12x^2 - 5x - 2 &= 0 \\ (4x+1)(3x-2) &= 0 \end{aligned}$$
$$4x + 1 = 0 \quad \text{or} \quad 3x - 2 = 0$$
$$4x = -1 \quad \text{or} \quad 3x = 2$$
$$x = -\frac{1}{4} \quad \text{or} \quad x = \frac{2}{3}$$

The solutions are $-\frac{1}{4}$ and $\frac{2}{3}$.

14.
$$\begin{aligned} m(m-7) &= -10 \\ m^2 - 7m + 10 &= 0 \\ (m-5)(m-2) &= 0 \end{aligned}$$
$$m - 5 = 0 \quad \text{or} \quad m - 2 = 0$$
$$m = 5 \quad \text{or} \quad m = 2$$

The solutions are 5 and 2.

15. $4x^2 - 36 = 0$

Divide both sides of the equation by 4.

$$\begin{aligned} x^2 - 9 &= 0 \\ (x+3)(x-3) &= 0 \end{aligned}$$
$$x + 3 = 0 \quad \text{or} \quad x - 3 = 0$$
$$x = -3 \quad \text{or} \quad x = 3$$

The solutions are -3 and 3.

16.
$$\begin{aligned} z(2z+7) &= 4 \\ 2z^2 + 7z - 4 &= 0 \\ (2z-1)(z+4) &= 0 \end{aligned}$$
$$2z - 1 = 0 \quad \text{or} \quad z + 4 = 0$$
$$z = \frac{1}{2} \quad \text{or} \quad z = -4$$

The solutions are $\frac{1}{2}$ and -4.

17.
$$\begin{aligned} 12y^2 - 48y &= 0 \\ 12y(y) - 12y(4) &= 0 \\ 12y(y-4) &= 0 \end{aligned}$$
$$12y = 0 \quad \text{or} \quad y - 4 = 0$$
$$y = 0 \quad \text{or} \quad y = 4$$

The solutions are 0 and 4.

18. $3x^2 - 5x + 1 = 0$

Use the quadratic formula.

$$x = \frac{-(-5) \pm \sqrt{(-5)^2 - 4(3)(1)}}{2(3)}$$
$$= \frac{5 \pm \sqrt{25 - 12}}{6}$$
$$x = \frac{5 + \sqrt{13}}{6} \quad \text{or} \quad x = \frac{5 - \sqrt{13}}{6}$$
$$\approx 1.4343 \qquad \approx 0.2324$$

The solutions are $\frac{5+\sqrt{13}}{6} \approx 1.4343$ and $\frac{5-\sqrt{13}}{6} \approx 0.2324$.

19.
$$\begin{aligned} 2m^2 - 4m &= 3 \\ 2m^2 - 4m - 3 &= 0 \end{aligned}$$
$$m = \frac{-(-4) \pm \sqrt{(-4)^2 - 4(2)(-3)}}{2(2)}$$
$$= \frac{4 \pm \sqrt{40}}{4} = \frac{4 \pm \sqrt{4 \cdot 10}}{4}$$
$$= \frac{4 \pm \sqrt{4}\sqrt{10}}{4}$$
$$= \frac{4 \pm 2\sqrt{10}}{4} = \frac{2 \pm \sqrt{10}}{2}$$

The solutions are $\frac{2+\sqrt{10}}{2} \approx 2.5811$ and $\frac{2-\sqrt{10}}{2} \approx -0.5811$.

20. $p^2 + p - 1 = 0$

$$p = \frac{-1 \pm \sqrt{1^2 - 4(1)(-1)}}{2(1)}$$
$$= \frac{-1 \pm \sqrt{5}}{2}$$

The solutions are $\frac{-1+\sqrt{5}}{2} \approx 0.6180$ and $\frac{-1-\sqrt{5}}{2} \approx -1.6180$.

21.
$$\begin{aligned} k^2 - 10k &= -20 \\ k^2 - 10k + 20 &= 0 \end{aligned}$$
$$k = \frac{-(-10) \pm \sqrt{(-10)^2 - 4(1)(20)}}{2(1)}$$
$$k = \frac{10 \pm \sqrt{100 - 80}}{2}$$
$$k = \frac{10 \pm \sqrt{20}}{2}$$
$$k = \frac{10 \pm \sqrt{4}\sqrt{5}}{2}$$
$$k = \frac{10 \pm 2\sqrt{5}}{2}$$
$$k = \frac{2(5 \pm \sqrt{5})}{2}$$
$$k = 5 \pm \sqrt{5}$$

The solutions are $5 + \sqrt{5} \approx 7.2361$ and $5 - \sqrt{5} \approx 2.7639$.

22. $5x^2 - 8x + 2 = 0$

$$x = \frac{-(-8) \pm \sqrt{(-8)^2 - 4(5)(2)}}{2(5)}$$
$$= \frac{8 \pm \sqrt{24}}{10} = \frac{8 \pm \sqrt{4 \cdot 6}}{10}$$
$$= \frac{8 \pm \sqrt{4}\sqrt{6}}{10} = \frac{8 \pm 2\sqrt{6}}{10}$$
$$= \frac{4 \pm \sqrt{6}}{5}$$

The solutions are $\frac{4+\sqrt{6}}{5} \approx 1.2899$ and $\frac{4-\sqrt{6}}{5} \approx 0.3101$.

23. $2r^2 - 7r + 5 = 0$

$(2r - 5)(r - 1) = 0$

$2r - 5 = 0$ or $r - 1 = 0$

$2r = 5$

$r = \frac{5}{2}$ or $r = 1$

The solutions are $\frac{5}{2}$ and 1.

24. $2x^2 - 7x + 30 = 0$

$$x = \frac{-(-7) \pm \sqrt{(-7)^2 - 4(2)(30)}}{2(2)}$$
$$x = \frac{7 \pm \sqrt{49 - 240}}{4}$$
$$x = \frac{7 \pm \sqrt{-191}}{4}$$

Since there is a negative number under the radical sign, $\sqrt{-191}$ is not a real number. Thus, there are no real number solutions.

25. $3k^2 + k = 6$

$3k^2 + k - 6 = 0$

$$k = \frac{-1 \pm \sqrt{1 - 4(3)(-6)}}{2(3)}$$
$$= \frac{-1 \pm \sqrt{73}}{6}$$

The solutions are $\frac{-1+\sqrt{73}}{6} \approx 1.2573$ and $\frac{-1-\sqrt{73}}{6} \approx -1.5907$.

26. $5m^2 + 5m = 0$

$5m(m + 1) = 0$

$5m = 0$ or $m + 1 = 0$

$m = 0$ or $m = -1$

The solutions are 0 and -1.

27. $\frac{3x - 2}{7} = \frac{x + 2}{5}$

$$35\left(\frac{3x - 2}{7}\right) = 35\left(\frac{x + 2}{5}\right)$$
$$5(3x - 2) = 7(x + 2)$$
$$15x - 10 = 7x + 14$$
$$8x = 24$$
$$x = 3$$

The solution is $x = 3$.

28. $\frac{x}{3} - 7 = 6 - \frac{3x}{4}$

Multiply both sides by 12, the least common denominator of 3 and 4.

$$12\left(\frac{x}{3} - 7\right) = 12\left(6 - \frac{3x}{4}\right)$$
$$12\left(\frac{x}{3}\right) - (12)(7) = (12)(6) - (12)\left(\frac{3x}{4}\right)$$
$$4x - 84 = 72 - 9x$$
$$13x - 84 = 72$$
$$13x = 156$$
$$x = 12$$

The solution is 12.

29. $\frac{4}{x - 3} - \frac{8}{2x + 5} + \frac{3}{x - 3} = 0$

$$\frac{4}{x - 3} + \frac{3}{x - 3} - \frac{8}{2x + 5} = 0$$
$$\frac{7}{x - 3} - \frac{8}{2x + 5} = 0$$

Multiply both sides by $(x - 3)(2x + 5)$. Note that $x \neq 3$ and $x \neq -\frac{5}{2}$.

$$(x-3)(2x+5)\left(\frac{7}{x - 3} - \frac{8}{2x + 5}\right) = (x-3)(2x+5)(0)$$
$$7(2x + 5) - 8(x - 3) = 0$$
$$14x + 35 - 8x + 24 = 0$$
$$6x + 59 = 0$$
$$6x = -59$$
$$x = -\frac{59}{6}$$

Note: It is especially important to check solutions of equations that involve rational expressions. Here, a check shows that $-\frac{59}{6}$ is a solution.

30. $$\frac{5}{p-2}-\frac{7}{p+2}=\frac{12}{p^2-4}$$
$$\frac{5}{p-2}-\frac{7}{p+2}=\frac{12}{(p-2)(p+2)}$$

Multiply both sides by $(p-2)(p+2)$. Note that $p \neq 2$ and $p \neq -2$.

$$(p-2)(p+2)\left(\frac{5}{p-2}-\frac{7}{p+2}\right)=(p-2)(p+2)\left(\frac{12}{(p-2)(p+2)}\right)$$
$$(p-2)(p+2)\left(\frac{5}{p-2}\right)-$$
$$(p-2)(p+2)\left(\frac{7}{p+2}\right)=(p-2)(p+2)\left(\frac{12}{(p-2)(p+2)}\right)$$
$$(p+2)(5)-(p-2)(7)=12$$
$$5p+10-7p+14=12$$
$$-2p+24=12$$
$$-2p=-12$$
$$p=6$$

The solution is 6.

31. $$\frac{2m}{m-2}-\frac{6}{m}=\frac{12}{m^2-2m}$$
$$\frac{2m}{m-2}-\frac{6}{m}=\frac{12}{m(m-2)}$$

Multiply both sides by $m(m-2)$.
Note that $m \neq 0$ and $m \neq 2$.

$$m(m-2)\left(\frac{2m}{m-2}-\frac{6}{m}\right)=m(m-2)\left(\frac{12}{m(m-2)}\right)$$
$$m(2m)-6(m-2)=12$$
$$2m^2-6m+12=12$$
$$2m^2-6m=0$$
$$2m(m-3)=0$$

$$2m=0 \quad \text{or} \quad m-3=0$$
$$m=0 \quad \text{or} \quad m=3$$

Since $m \neq 0$, 0 is not a solution. The solution is 3.

32. $$\frac{2y}{y-1}=\frac{5}{y}+\frac{10-8y}{y^2-y}$$
$$\frac{2y}{y-1}=\frac{5}{y}+\frac{10-8y}{y(y-1)}$$

Multiply both sides by $y(y-1)$.
Note that $y \neq 0$ and $y \neq 1$.

$$y(y-1)\left(\frac{2y}{y-1}\right)=y(y-1)\left[\frac{5}{y}+\frac{10-8y}{y(y-1)}\right]$$
$$y(y-1)\left(\frac{2y}{y-1}\right)=y(y-1)\left(\frac{5}{y}\right)$$
$$+\,y(y-1)\left[\frac{10-8y}{y(y-1)}\right]$$
$$y(2y)=(y-1)(5)+(10-8y)$$
$$2y^2=5y-5+10-8y$$
$$2y^2=5-3y$$
$$2y^2+3y-5=0$$
$$(2y+5)(y-1)=0$$
$$2y+5=0 \quad \text{or} \quad y-1=0$$
$$y=-\frac{5}{2} \quad \text{or} \quad y=1$$

Since $y \neq 1$, 1 is not a solution.
The solution is $-\frac{5}{2}$.

33. $$\frac{1}{x-2}-\frac{3x}{x-1}=\frac{2x+1}{x^2-3x+2}$$
$$\frac{1}{x-2}-\frac{3x}{x-1}=\frac{2x+1}{(x-2)(x-1)}$$

Multiply both sides by $(x-2)(x-1)$.
Note that $x \neq 2$ and $x \neq 1$.

$$(x-2)(x-1)\left(\frac{1}{x-2}-\frac{3x}{x-1}\right)=(x-2)(x-1)$$
$$\cdot\left[\frac{2x+1}{(x-2)(x-1)}\right]$$

$$(x-2)(x-1)\left(\frac{1}{x-2}\right)$$
$$-(x-2)(x-1)\cdot\left(\frac{3x}{x-1}\right)=\frac{(x-2)(x-1)(2x+1)}{(x-2)(x-1)}$$
$$(x-1)-(x-2)(3x)=2x+1$$
$$x-1-3x^2+6x=2x+1$$
$$-3x^2+7x-1=2x+1$$
$$-3x^2+5x-2=0$$
$$3x^2-5x+2=0$$
$$(3x-2)(x-1)=0$$
$$3x-2=0 \quad \text{or} \quad x-1=0$$
$$x=\frac{2}{3} \quad \text{or} \quad x=1$$

1 is not a solution since $x \neq 1$.
The solution is $\frac{2}{3}$.

34. $$\frac{5}{a}+\frac{-7}{a+1}=\frac{a^2-2a+4}{a^2+a}$$

$$a(a+1)\left(\frac{5}{a}+\frac{-7}{a+1}\right)=a(a+1)\left(\frac{a^2-2a+4}{a^2+a}\right)$$

Note that $a \neq 0$ and $a \neq -1$.

$$\begin{aligned}5(a+1)+(-7)(a)&=a^2-2a+4\\5a+5-7a&=a^2-2a+4\\5-2a&=a^2-2a+4\\5&=a^2+4\\0&=a^2-1\\0&=(a+1)(a-1)\end{aligned}$$

$$a+1=0 \quad \text{or} \quad a-1=0$$
$$a=-1 \quad \text{or} \quad a=1$$

Since -1 would make two denominators zero, 1 is the only solution.

35. $$\frac{5}{b+5}-\frac{4}{b^2+2b}=\frac{6}{b^2+7b+10}$$

$$\frac{5}{b+5}-\frac{4}{b(b+2)}=\frac{6}{(b+5)(b+2)}$$

Multiply both sides by $b(b+5)(b+2)$. Note that $b \neq 0$, $b \neq -5$, and $b \neq -2$.

$$b(b+5)(b+2)\left(\frac{5}{b+5}-\frac{4}{b(b+2)}\right)$$
$$=b(b+5)(b+2)\left(\frac{6}{(b+5)(b+2)}\right)$$

$$\begin{aligned}5b(b+2)-4(b+5)&=6b\\5b^2+10b-4b-20&=6b\\5b^2-20&=0\\b^2-4&=0\\(b+2)(b-2)&=0\end{aligned}$$

$$b+2=0 \quad \text{or} \quad b-2=0$$
$$b=-2 \quad \text{or} \quad b=2$$

Since $b \neq -2$, -2 is not a solution. The solution is 2.

36. $$\frac{2}{x^2-2x-3}+\frac{5}{x^2-x-6}=\frac{1}{x^2+3x+2}$$

$$\frac{2}{(x-3)(x+1)}+\frac{5}{(x-3)(x+2)}=\frac{1}{(x+2)(x+1)}$$

Multiply both sides by $(x-3)(x+1)(x+2)$. Note that $x \neq 3$, $x \neq -1$, and $x \neq -2$.

$$(x-3)(x+1)(x+2)\left(\frac{2}{(x-3)(x+1)}\right)$$
$$+(x-3)(x+1)(x+2)\left(\frac{5}{(x-3)(x+2)}\right)$$
$$=(x-3)(x+1)(x+2)\left(\frac{1}{(x+2)(x+1)}\right)$$

$$\begin{aligned}2(x+2)+5(x+1)&=x-3\\2x+4+5x+5&=x-3\\7x+9&=x-3\\6x+9&=-3\\6x&=-12\\x&=-2\end{aligned}$$

However, $x \neq -2$. Therefore there is no solution.

37. $$\frac{4}{2x^2+3x-9}+\frac{2}{2x^2-x-3}=\frac{3}{x^2+4x+3}$$

$$\frac{4}{(2x-3)(x+3)}+\frac{2}{(2x-3)(x+1)}=\frac{3}{(x+3)(x+1)}$$

Multiply both sides by $(2x-3)(x+3)(x+1)$. Note that $x \neq \frac{3}{2}$, $x \neq -3$, and $x \neq -1$.

$$(2x-3)(x+3)(x+1)$$
$$\cdot\left(\frac{4}{(2x-3)(x+3)}+\frac{2}{(2x-3)(x+1)}\right)$$
$$=(2x-3)(x+3)(x+1)\left(\frac{3}{(x+3)(x+1)}\right)$$

$$\begin{aligned}4(x+1)+2(x+3)&=3(2x-3)\\4x+4+2x+6&=6x-9\\6x+10&=6x-9\\10&=-9\end{aligned}$$

This is a false statement. Therefore, there is no solution.

R.5 Inequalities

1. $x < 4$

Because the inequality symbol means "less than," the endpoint at 4 is not included. This inequality is written in interval notation as $(-\infty, 4)$. To graph this interval on a number line, place an open circle at 4 and draw a heavy arrow pointing to the left.

2. $x \geq -3$

Because the inequality sign means "greater than or equal to," the endpoint at -3 is included. This inequality is written in interval notation as $[-3, \infty)$. To graph this interval on a number line, place a closed circle at -3 and draw a heavy arrow pointing to the right.

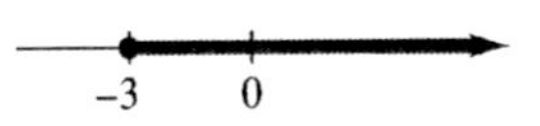

3. $1 \le x < 2$

The endpoint at 1 is included, but the endpoint at 2 is not. This inequality is written in interval notation as $[1, 2)$. To graph this interval, place a closed circle at 1 and an open circle at 2; then draw a heavy line segment between them.

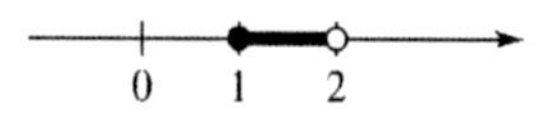

4. $-2 \le x \le 3$

The endpoints at -2 and 3 are both included. This inequality is written in interval notation as $[-2, 3]$. To graph this interval, place an open circle at -2 and another at 3 and draw a heavy line segment between them.

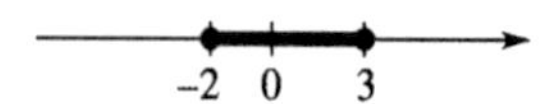

5. $-9 > x$

This inequality may be rewritten as $x < -9$, and is written in interval notation as $(-\infty, -9)$. Note that the endpoint at -9 is not included. To graph this interval, place an open circle at -9 and draw a heavy arrow pointing to the left.

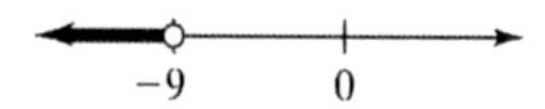

6. $6 \le x$

This inequality may be written as $x \ge 6$, and is written in interval notation as $[6, \infty)$. Note that the endpoint at 6 is included. To graph this interval, place a closed circle at 6 and draw a heavy arrow pointing to the right.

7. $[-7, -3]$

This represents all the numbers between -7 and -3, including both endpoints. This interval can be written as the inequality $-7 \le x \le -3$.

8. $[4, 10)$

This represents all the numbers between 4 and 10, including 4 but not including 10. This interval can be written as the inequality $4 \le x < 10$.

9. $(-\infty, -1]$

This represents all the numbers to the left of -1 on the number line and includes the endpoint. This interval can be written as the inequality $x \le -1$.

10. $(3, \infty)$

This represents all the numbers to the right of 3, and does not include the endpoint. This interval can be written as the inequality $x > 3$.

11. Notice that the endpoint -2 is included, but 6 is not. The interval shows in the graph can be written as the inequality $-2 \le x < 6$.

12. Notice that neither endpoint is included. The interval shown in the graph can be written as $0 < x < 8$.

13. Notice that both endpoints are included. The interval shown in the graph can be written as $x \le -4$ or $x \ge 4$.

14. Notice that the endpoint 0 is not included, but 3 is included. The interval shown in the graph can be written as $x < 0$ or $x \ge 3$.

15.
$$\begin{aligned} 6p + 7 &\le 19 \\ 6p &\le 12 \\ \left(\frac{1}{6}\right)(6p) &\le \left(\frac{1}{6}\right)(12) \\ p &\le 2 \end{aligned}$$

The solution in interval notation is $(-\infty, 2]$.

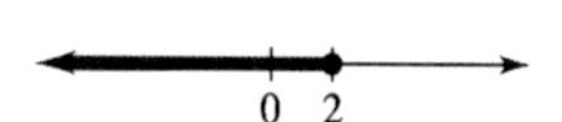

16.
$$\begin{aligned} 6k - 4 &< 3k - 1 \\ 6k &< 3k + 3 \\ 3k &< 3 \\ k &< 1 \end{aligned}$$

The solution in interval notation is $(-\infty, 1)$.

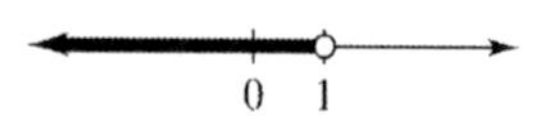

17. $m-(3m-2)+6<7m-19$

$$m-3m+2+6<7m-19$$
$$-2m+8<7m-19$$
$$-9m+8<-19$$
$$-9m<-27$$
$$-\frac{1}{9}(-9m)>-\frac{1}{9}(-27)$$
$$m>3$$

The solution is $(3,\ \infty)$.

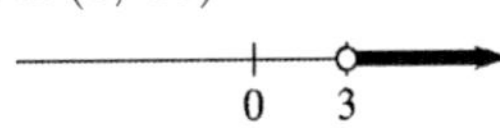

18. $-2(3y-8)\geq 5(4y-2)$

$$-6y+16\geq 20y-10$$
$$-6y+16+(-16)\geq 20y-10+(-16)$$
$$-6y\geq 20y-26$$
$$-6y+(-20y)\geq 20y+(-20y)-26$$
$$-26y\geq -26$$
$$-\frac{1}{26}(-26)y\leq -\frac{1}{26}(-26)$$
$$y\leq 1$$

The solution is $(-\infty,1]$.

19. $3p-1<6p+2(p-1)$

$$3p-1<6p+2p-2$$
$$3p-1<8p-2$$
$$-5p-1<-2$$
$$-5p<-1$$
$$-\frac{1}{5}(-5p)>-\frac{1}{5}(-1)$$
$$p>\frac{1}{5}$$

The solution is $\left(\frac{1}{5},\ \infty\right)$.

20. $x+5(x+1)>4(2-x)+x$

$$x+5x+5>8-4x+x$$
$$6x+5>8-3x$$
$$6x>3-3x$$
$$9x>3$$
$$x>\frac{1}{3}$$

The solution is $\left(\frac{1}{3},\infty\right)$.

21. $-11<y-7<-1$

$$-11+7<y-7+7<-1+7$$
$$-4<y<6$$

The solution is $(-4,6)$.

22. $8\leq 3r+1\leq 13$

$$8+(-1)\leq 3r+1+(-1)\leq 13+(-1)$$
$$7\leq 3r\leq 12$$
$$\frac{1}{3}(7)\leq\frac{1}{3}(3r)\leq\frac{1}{3}(12)$$
$$\frac{7}{3}\leq r\leq 4$$

The solution is $\left[\frac{7}{3},4\right]$.

23. $-2<\frac{1-3k}{4}\leq 4$

$$4(-2)<4\left(\frac{1-3k}{4}\right)\leq 4(4)$$
$$-8<1-3k\leq 16$$
$$-9<-3k\leq 15$$
$$-\frac{1}{3}(-9)>-\frac{1}{3}(-3k)\geq -\frac{1}{3}(15)$$

Rewrite the inequalities in the proper order.

$$-5\leq k<3$$

24. $-1\leq\frac{5y+2}{3}\leq 4$

$$3(-1)\leq 3\left(\frac{5y+2}{3}\right)\leq 3(4)$$
$$-3\leq 5y+2\leq 12$$
$$-5\leq 5y\leq 10$$
$$-1\leq y\leq 2$$

The solution is $[-1,\ 2]$.

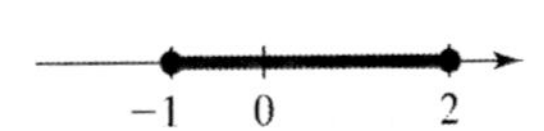

25. $\frac{3}{5}(2p+3) \geq \frac{1}{10}(5p+1)$

$$10\left(\frac{3}{5}\right)(2p+3) \geq 10\left(\frac{1}{10}\right)(5p+1)$$
$$6(2p+3) \geq 5p+1$$
$$12p+18 \geq 5p+1$$
$$7p \geq -17$$
$$p \geq -\frac{17}{7}$$

The solution is $[-\frac{17}{7}, \infty)$.

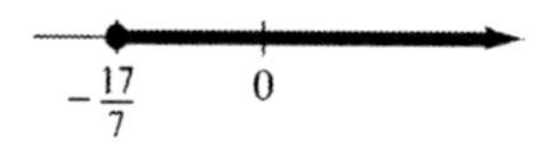

26. $\frac{8}{3}(z-4) \leq \frac{2}{9}(3z+2)$

$$(9)\frac{8}{3}(z-4) \leq (9)\frac{2}{9}(3z+2)$$
$$24(z-4) \leq 2(3z+2)$$
$$24z - 96 \leq 6z + 4$$
$$24z \leq 6z + 100$$
$$18z \leq 100$$
$$z \leq \frac{100}{18}$$
$$z \leq \frac{50}{9}$$

The solution is $(-\infty, \frac{50}{9}]$.

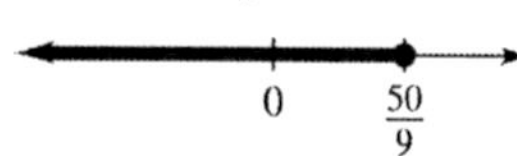

27. $(m-3)(m+5) < 0$

Solve $(m-3)(m+5) = 0$.

$$(m-3)(m+5) = 0$$
$$m = 3 \quad \text{or} \quad m = -5$$

Intervals: $(-\infty, -5)$, $(-5, 3)$, $(3, \infty)$

For $(-\infty, -5)$, choose -6 to test for m.

$$(-6-3)(-6+5) = -9(-1) = 9 \not< 0$$

For $(-5, 3)$, choose 0.

$$(0-3)(0+5) = -3(5) = -15 < 0$$

For $(3, \infty)$, choose 4.

$$(4-3)(4+5) = 1(9) = 9 \not< 0$$

The solution is $(-5, 3)$.

-5 0 3

28. $(t+6)(t-1) \geq 0$

Solve $(t+6)(t-1) = 0$.

$$(t+6)(t-1) = 0$$
$$t = -6 \quad \text{or} \quad t = 1$$

Intervals: $(-\infty, -6)$, $(-6, 1)$, $(1, \infty)$

For $(-\infty, -6)$, choose -7 to test for t.

$$(-7+6)(-7-1) = (-1)(-8) = 8 \geq 0$$

For $(-6, 1)$, choose 0.

$$(0+6)(0-1) = (6)(-1) = -6 \not\geq 0$$

For $(1, \infty)$, choose 2.

$$(2+6)(2-1) = (8)(1) = 8 \geq 0$$

Because the symbol $\geq$ is used, the endpoints -6 and 1 are included in the solution, $(-\infty, -6] \cup [1, \infty)$.

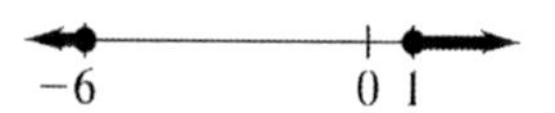

29. $y^2 - 3y + 2 < 0$

$(y-2)(y-1) < 0$

Solve $(y-2)(y-1) = 0$.

$$y = 2 \quad \text{or} \quad y = 1$$

Intervals: $(-\infty, 1)$, $(1, 2)$, $(2, \infty)$

For $(-\infty, 1)$, choose $y = 0$.

$$0^2 - 3(0) + 2 = 2 \not< 0$$

For $(1, 2)$, choose $y = \frac{3}{2}$.

$$\left(\frac{3}{2}\right)^2 - 3\left(\frac{3}{2}\right) + 2 = \frac{9}{4} - \frac{9}{2} + 2$$
$$= \frac{9 - 18 + 8}{4}$$
$$= -\frac{1}{4} < 0$$

For $(2, \infty)$, choose 3.

$$3^2 - 3(3) + 2 = 2 \not< 0$$

The solution is $(1, 2)$.

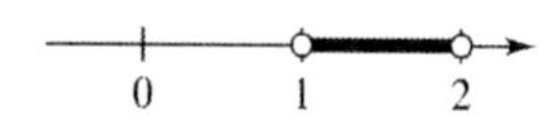

30. $2k^2 + 7k - 4 > 0$

Solve $2k^2 + 7k - 4 = 0$.

$$2k^2 + 7k - 4 = 0$$
$$(2k - 1)(k + 4) = 0$$
$$k = \frac{1}{2} \quad \text{or} \quad k = -4$$

Intervals: $(-\infty, -4), \left(-4, \frac{1}{2}\right), \left(\frac{1}{2}, \infty\right)$

For $(-\infty, -4)$, choose -5.

$$2(-5)^2 + 7(-5) - 4 = 11 > 0$$

For $\left(-4, \frac{1}{2}\right)$, choose 0.

$$2(0)^2 + 7(0) - 4 = -4 \not> 0$$

For $\left(\frac{1}{2}, \infty\right)$, choose 1.

$$2(1)^2 + 7(1) - 4 = 5 > 0$$

The solution is $(-\infty, -4) \cup \left(\frac{1}{2}, \infty\right)$.

31. $x^2 - 16 > 0$

Solve $x^2 - 16 = 0$.

$$x^2 - 16 = 0$$
$$(x + 4)(x - 4) = 0$$
$$x = -4 \quad \text{or} \quad x = 4$$

Intervals: $(-\infty, -4)$, $(-4, 4)$, $(4, \infty)$

For $(-\infty, -4)$, choose -5.

$$(-5)^2 - 16 = 9 > 0$$

For $(-4, 4)$, choose 0.

$$0^2 - 16 = -16 \not> 0$$

For $(4, \infty)$, choose 5.

$$5^2 - 16 = 9 > 0$$

The solution is $(-\infty, -4) \cup (4, \infty)$.

32. $2k^2 - 7k - 15 \le 0$

Solve $2k^2 - 7k - 15 = 0$.

$$2k^2 - 7k - 15 = 0$$
$$(2k + 3)(k - 5) = 0$$
$$k = -\frac{3}{2} \quad \text{or} \quad k = 5$$

Intervals: $\left(-\infty, -\frac{3}{2}\right), \left(-\frac{3}{2}, 5\right), (5, \infty)$

For $\left(-\infty, -\frac{3}{2}\right)$, choose -2.

$$2(-2)^2 - 7(-2) - 15 = 7 \not\le 0$$

For $\left(-\frac{3}{2}, 5\right)$, choose 0.

$$2(0)^2 - 7(0) - 15 = -15 \le 0$$

For $(5, \infty)$, choose 6.

$$2(6)^2 - 7(6) - 15 \not\le 0$$

The solution is $\left[-\frac{3}{2}, 5\right]$.

33. $x^2 - 4x \ge 5$

Solve $x^2 - 4x = 5$.

$$x^2 - 4x = 5$$
$$x^2 - 4x - 5 = 0$$
$$(x + 1)(x - 5) = 0$$
$$x + 1 = 0 \quad \text{or} \quad x - 5 = 0$$
$$x = -1 \quad \text{or} \quad x = 5$$

Intervals: $(-\infty, -1), (-1, 5), (5, \infty)$

For $(-\infty, -1)$, choose -2.

$$(-2)^2 - 4(-2) = 12 \ge 5$$

For $(-1, 5)$, choose 0.

$$0^2 - 4(0) = 0 \not\ge 5$$

For $(5, \infty)$, choose 6.

$$(6)^2 - 4(6) = 12 \ge 5$$

The solution is $(-\infty, -1] \cup [5, \infty)$.

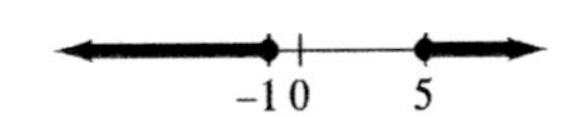

34. $10r^2 + r \le 2$

Solve $10r^2 + r = 2$.

$$\begin{aligned} 10r^2 + r &= 2 \\ 10r^2 + r - 2 &= 0 \\ (5r-2)(2r+1) &= 0 \end{aligned}$$

$$r = \frac{2}{5} \quad \text{or} \quad r = -\frac{1}{2}$$

Intervals: $\left(-\infty, -\frac{1}{2}\right), \left(-\frac{1}{2}, \frac{2}{5}\right), \left(\frac{2}{5}, \infty\right)$

For $\left(-\infty, -\frac{1}{2}\right)$, choose -1.

$$10(-1)^2 + (-1) = 9 \not\le 2$$

For $\left(-\frac{1}{2}, \frac{2}{5}\right)$, choose 0.

$$10(0)^2 + 0 = 0 \le 2$$

For $\left(\frac{2}{5}, \infty\right)$, choose 1.

$$10(1)^2 + 1 = 11 \not\le 2$$

The solution is $\left[-\frac{1}{2}, \frac{2}{5}\right]$.

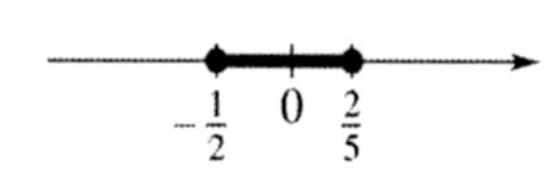

35. $3x^2 + 2x > 1$

Solve $3x^2 + 2x = 1$.

$$\begin{aligned} 3x^2 + 2x &= 1 \\ 3x^2 + 2x - 1 &= 0 \\ (3x-1)(x+1) &= 0 \\ x = \frac{1}{3} \quad &\text{or} \quad x = -1 \end{aligned}$$

Intervals: $(-\infty, -1)$, $\left(-1, \frac{1}{3}\right)$, $\left(\frac{1}{3}, \infty\right)$

For $(-\infty, -1)$, choose -2.

$$3(-2)^2 + 2(-2) = 8 > 1$$

For $\left(-1, \frac{1}{3}\right)$, choose 0.

$$3(0)^2 + 2(0) = 0 \not> 1$$

For $\left(\frac{1}{3}, \infty\right)$, choose 1.

$$3(1)^2 + 2(1) = 5 > 1$$

The solution is $(-\infty, -1) \cup \left(\frac{1}{3}, \infty\right)$

-1 0 $\frac{1}{3}$

36. $3a^2 + a > 10$

Solve $3a^2 + a = 10$.

$$\begin{aligned} 3a^2 + a &= 10 \\ 3a^2 + a - 10 &= 0 \\ (3a-5)(a+2) &= 0 \end{aligned}$$

$$a = \frac{5}{3} \quad \text{or} \quad a = -2$$

Intervals: $(-\infty, -2)$, $\left(-2, \frac{5}{3}\right), \left(\frac{5}{3}, \infty\right)$

For $(-\infty, -2)$, choose -3.

$$3(-3)^2 + (-3) = 24 > 10$$

For $\left(-2, \frac{5}{3}\right)$, choose 0.

$$3(0)^2 + 0 = 0 \not> 10$$

For $\left(\frac{5}{3}, \infty\right)$, choose 2.

$$3(2)^2 + 2 = 14 > 10$$

The solution is $(-\infty, -2) \cup \left(\frac{5}{3}, \infty\right)$.

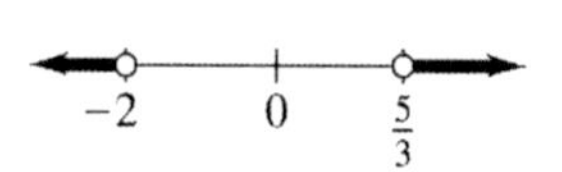

37. $9 - x^2 \le 0$

Solve $9 - x^2 = 0$.

$$\begin{aligned} 9 - x^2 &= 0 \\ (3+x)(3-x) &= 0 \\ x = -3 \quad &\text{or} \quad x = 3 \end{aligned}$$

Intervals: $(-\infty, -3)$, $(-3, 3)$, $(3, \infty)$

For $(-\infty, -3)$, choose -4.

$$9 - (-4)^2 = -7 \le 0$$

For $(-3, 3)$, choose 0.

$$9 - (0)^2 = 9 \not\le 0$$

For $(3, \infty)$, choose 4.

$$9 - (4)^2 = -7 \le 0$$

The solution is $(-\infty, -3] \cup [3, \infty)$.

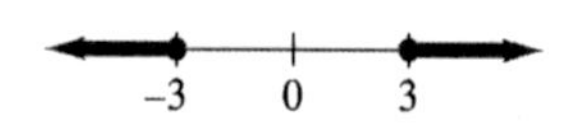

38. $p^2 - 16p > 0$

Solve $p^2 - 16p = 0$.

$$p^2 - 16p = 0$$
$$p(p-16) = 0$$
$$p = 0 \quad \text{or} \quad p = 16$$

Intervals: $(-\infty, 0)$, $(0, 16)$, $(16, \infty)$

For $(-\infty, 0)$, choose -1.

$$(-1)^2 - 16(-1) = 17 > 0$$

For $(0, 16)$, choose 1.

$$(1)^2 - 16(1) = -15 \not> 0$$

For $(16, \infty)$, choose 17.

$$(17)^2 - 16(17) = 17 > 0$$

The solution is $(-\infty, 0) \cup (16, \infty)$.

0 16

39. $\dfrac{m-3}{m+5} \le 0$

Solve $\dfrac{m-3}{m+5} = 0$.

$$(m+5)\frac{m-3}{m+5} = (m+5)(0)$$
$$m - 3 = 0$$
$$m = 3$$

Set the denominator equal to 0 and solve.

$$m + 5 = 0$$
$$m = -5$$

Intervals: $(-\infty, -5)$, $(-5, 3)$, $(3, \infty)$

For $(-\infty, -5)$, choose -6.

$$\frac{-6-3}{-6+5} = 9 \not\le 0$$

For $(-5, 3)$, choose 0.

$$\frac{0-3}{0+5} = -\frac{3}{5} \le 0$$

For $(3, \infty)$, choose 4.

$$\frac{4-3}{4+5} = \frac{1}{9} \not\le 0$$

Although the $\le$ symbol is used, including -5 in the solution would cause the denominator to be zero.
The solution is $(-5, 3]$.

40. $\dfrac{r+1}{r-1} > 0$

Solve the equation $\dfrac{r+1}{r-1} = 0$.

$$\frac{r+1}{r-1} = 0$$
$$(r-1)\frac{r+1}{r-1} = (r-1)(0)$$
$$r + 1 = 0$$
$$r = -1$$

Find the value for which the denominator equals zero.

$$r - 1 = 0$$
$$r = 1$$

Intervals: $(-\infty, -1)$, $(-1, 1)$, $(1, \infty)$

For $(-\infty, -1)$, choose -2.

$$\frac{-2+1}{-2-1} = \frac{-1}{-3} = \frac{1}{3} > 0$$

For $(-1, 1)$, choose 0.

$$\frac{0+1}{0-1} = \frac{1}{-1} = -1 \not> 0$$

For $(1, \infty)$, choose 2.

$$\frac{2+1}{2-1} = \frac{3}{1} = 3 > 0$$

The solution is $(-\infty, -1) \cup (1, \infty)$.

41. $\dfrac{k-1}{k+2} > 1$

Solve $\dfrac{k-1}{k+2} = 1$.

$$k - 1 = k + 2$$
$$-1 \ne 2$$

The equation has no solution.
Solve $k + 2 = 0$.

$$k = -2$$

Intervals: $(-\infty, -2)$, $(-2, \infty)$

For $(-\infty, -2)$, choose -3.

$$\frac{-3-1}{-3+2} = 4 > 1$$

For $(-2, \infty)$, choose 0.

$$\frac{0-1}{0+2} = -\frac{1}{2} \not> 1$$

The solution is $(-\infty, -2)$.

42. $\frac{a-5}{a+2} < -1$

Solve the equation $\frac{a-5}{a+2} = -1$.

$$\frac{a-5}{a+2} = -1$$
$$a - 5 = -1(a+2)$$
$$a - 5 = -a - 2$$
$$2a = 3$$
$$a = \frac{3}{2}$$

Set the denominator equal to zero and solve for a.

$$a + 2 = 0$$
$$a = -2$$

Intervals: $(-\infty, -2), \left(-2, \frac{3}{2}\right), \left(\frac{3}{2}, \infty\right)$

For $(-\infty, -2)$, choose -3.

$$\frac{-3-5}{-3+2} = \frac{-8}{-1} = 8 \nless -1$$

For $\left(-2, \frac{3}{2}\right)$, choose 0.

$$\frac{0-5}{0+2} = \frac{-5}{2} = -\frac{5}{2} < -1$$

For $\left(\frac{3}{2}, \infty\right)$, choose 2.

$$\frac{2-5}{2+2} = \frac{-3}{4} = -\frac{3}{4} \nless -1$$

The solution is $\left(-2, \frac{3}{2}\right)$.

43. $\frac{2y+3}{y-5} \le 1$

Solve $\frac{2y+3}{y-5} = 1$.

$$2y + 3 = y - 5$$
$$y = -8$$

Solve $y - 5 = 0$.

$$y = 5$$

Intervals: $(-\infty, -8)$, $(-8, 5)$, $(5, \infty)$

For $(-\infty, -8)$, choose $y = -10$.

$$\frac{2(-10)+3}{-10-5} = \frac{17}{15} \nleq 1$$

For $(-8, 5)$, choose $y = 0$.

$$\frac{2(0)+3}{0-5} = -\frac{3}{5} \le 1$$

For $(5, \infty)$, choose $y = 6$.

$$\frac{2(6)+3}{6-5} = \frac{15}{1} \nleq 1$$

The solution is $[-8, 5)$.

44. $\frac{a+2}{3+2a} \le 5$

For the equation $\frac{a+2}{3+2a} = 5$.

$$\frac{a+2}{3+2a} = 5$$
$$a + 2 = 5(3+2a)$$
$$a + 2 = 15 + 10a$$
$$-9a = 13$$
$$a = -\frac{13}{9}$$

Set the denominator equal to zero and solve for a.

$$3 + 2a = 0$$
$$2a = -3$$
$$a = -\frac{3}{2}$$

Intervals: $\left(-\infty, -\frac{3}{2}\right), \left(-\frac{3}{2}, -\frac{13}{9}\right), \left(-\frac{13}{9}, \infty\right)$

For $\left(-\infty, -\frac{3}{2}\right)$, choose -2.

$$\frac{-2+2}{3+2(-2)} = \frac{0}{-1} = 0 \le 5$$

For $\left(-\frac{3}{2}, -\frac{13}{9}\right)$, choose -1.46.

$$\frac{-1.46+2}{3+2(-1.46)} = \frac{0.54}{0.08} = 6.75 \nleq 5$$

For $\left(-\frac{13}{9}, \infty\right)$, choose 0.

$$\frac{0+2}{3+2(0)} = \frac{2}{3} \le 5$$

The value $-\frac{3}{2}$ cannot be included in the solution since it would make the denominator zero. The solution is $\left(-\infty, -\frac{3}{2}\right) \cup \left[-\frac{13}{9}, \infty\right)$.

45. $\frac{2k}{k-3} \le \frac{4}{k-3}$

Solve $\frac{2k}{k-3} = \frac{4}{k-3}$.

$$\begin{aligned}\frac{2k}{k-3} &= \frac{4}{k-3}\\ \frac{2k}{k-3} - \frac{4}{k-3} &= 0\\ \frac{2k-4}{k-3} &= 0\\ 2k-4 &= 0\\ k &= 2\end{aligned}$$

Set the denominator equal to 0 and solve for k.

$$\begin{aligned}k-3 &= 0\\ k &= 3\end{aligned}$$

Intervals: $(-\infty, 2)$, $(2,3)$, $(3,\infty)$

For $(-\infty, 2)$, choose 0.

$$\frac{2(0)}{0-3} = 0 \text{ and } \frac{4}{0-3} = -\frac{4}{3}, \text{ so}$$

$$\frac{2(0)}{0-3} \not\le \frac{4}{0-3}$$

For $(2,3)$, choose $\frac{5}{2}$.

$$\frac{2(\frac{5}{2})}{\frac{5}{2}-3} = \frac{5}{-\frac{1}{2}} = -10 \text{ and } \frac{4}{\frac{5}{2}-3} = \frac{4}{-\frac{1}{2}} = -8, \text{ so}$$

$$\frac{2(\frac{5}{2})}{\frac{5}{2}-3} \le \frac{4}{\frac{5}{2}-3}$$

For $(3,\infty)$, choose 4.

$$\frac{2(4)}{4-3} = 8 \text{ and } \frac{4}{4-3} = 4, \text{ so}$$

$$\frac{2(4)}{4-3} \not\le \frac{4}{4-3}$$

The solution is $[2,3)$.

46. $\frac{5}{p+1} > \frac{12}{p+1}$

Solve the equation $\frac{5}{p+1} = \frac{12}{p+1}$.

$$\begin{aligned}\frac{5}{p+1} &= \frac{12}{p+1}\\ 5 &= 12\end{aligned}$$

The equation has no solution.
Set the denominator equal to zero and solve for p.

$$\begin{aligned}p+1 &= 0\\ p &= -1\end{aligned}$$

Intervals: $(-\infty,-1)$, $(-1,\infty)$

For $(-\infty,-1)$, choose -2.

$$\frac{5}{-2+1} = -5 \text{ and } \frac{12}{-2+1} = -12, \text{ so}$$

$$\frac{5}{-2+1} > \frac{12}{-2+1}.$$

For $(-1,\infty)$, choose 0.

$$\frac{5}{0+1} = 5 \text{ and } \frac{12}{0+1} = 12, \text{ so}$$

$$\frac{5}{0+1} \not> \frac{12}{0+1}.$$

The solution is $(-\infty,-1)$.

47. $\frac{2x}{x^2-x-6} \ge 0$

Solve $\frac{2x}{x^2-x-6} = 0$.

$$\begin{aligned}\frac{2x}{x^2-x-6} &= 0\\ 2x &= 0\\ x &= 0\end{aligned}$$

Set the denominator equal to 0 and solve for x.

$$\begin{aligned}x^2-x-6 &= 0\\ (x+2)(x-3) &= 0\end{aligned}$$

$$\begin{aligned}x+2 &= 0 \quad\text{or}\quad x-3 = 0\\ x &= -2 \quad\text{or}\quad x = 3\end{aligned}$$

Intervals: $(-\infty,-2)$, $(-2,0)$, $(0,3)$, $(3,\infty)$

For $(-\infty, -2)$, choose -3.

$$\frac{2(-3)}{(-3)^2 - (-3) - 6} = -1 \not\geq 0$$

For $(-2, 0)$, choose -1.

$$\frac{2(-1)}{(-1)^2 - (-1) - 6} = \frac{1}{2} \geq 0$$

For $(0, 3)$, choose 2.

$$\frac{2(2)}{2^2 - 2 - 6} = -1 \not\geq 0$$

For $(3, \infty)$, choose 4.

$$\frac{2(4)}{4^2 - 4 - 6} = \frac{4}{3} \geq 0$$

The solution is $(-2, 0] \cup (3, \infty)$.

48. $\frac{8}{p^2 + 2p} > 1$

Solve the equation $\frac{8}{p^2 + 2p} = 1$.

$$\frac{8}{p^2 + 2p} = 1$$
$$8 = p^2 + 2p$$
$$0 = p^2 + 2p - 8$$
$$0 = (p + 4)(p - 2)$$
$$p + 4 = 0 \quad \text{or} \quad p - 2 = 0$$
$$p = -4 \quad \text{or} \quad p = 2$$

Set the denominator equal to zero and solve for p.

$$p^2 + 2p = 0$$
$$p(p + 2) = 0$$
$$p = 0 \quad \text{or} \quad p + 2 = 0$$
$$p = -2$$

Intervals: $(-\infty, -4)$, $(-4, -2)$, $(-2, 0)$, $(0, 2)$, $(2, \infty)$

For $(-\infty, -4)$, choose -5.

$$\frac{8}{(-5)^2 + 2(-5)} = \frac{8}{15} \not> 1$$

For $(-4, -2)$, choose -3.

$$\frac{8}{(-3)^2 + 2(-3)} = \frac{8}{9 - 6} = \frac{8}{3} > 1$$

For $(-2, 0)$, choose -1.

$$\frac{8}{(-1)^2 + 2(-1)} = \frac{8}{-1} = -8 \not> 1$$

For $(0, 2)$, choose 1.

$$\frac{8}{(1)^2 + 2(1)} = \frac{8}{3} > 1$$

For $(2, \infty)$, choose 3.

$$\frac{8}{(3)^2 + (2)(3)} = \frac{8}{15} \not> 1$$

The solution is $(-4, -2) \cup (0, 2)$.

49. $\frac{z^2 + z}{z^2 - 1} \geq 3$

Solve

$$\frac{z^2 + z}{z^2 - 1} = 3.$$
$$z^2 + z = 3z^2 - 3$$
$$-2z^2 + z + 3 = 0$$
$$-1(2z^2 - z - 3) = 0$$
$$-1(z + 1)(2z - 3) = 0$$
$$z = -1 \quad \text{or} \quad z = \frac{3}{2}$$

Set $z^2 - 1 = 0$.

$$z^2 = 1$$
$$z = -1 \quad \text{or} \quad z = 1$$

Intervals: $(-\infty, -1)$, $(-1, 1)$, $\left(1, \frac{3}{2}\right)$, $\left(\frac{3}{2}, \infty\right)$

For $(-\infty, -1)$, choose $x = -2$.

$$\frac{(-2)^2 + 3}{(-2)^2 - 1} = \frac{7}{3} \not\geq 3$$

For $(-1, 1)$, choose $x = 0$.

$$\frac{0^2 + 3}{0^2 - 1} = -3 \not\geq 3$$

For $\left(1, \frac{3}{2}\right)$, choose $x = \frac{3}{2}$.

$$\frac{\left(\frac{3}{2}\right)^2 + 3}{\left(\frac{3}{2}\right)^2 - 1} = \frac{21}{5} \geq 3$$

For $\left(\frac{3}{2}, \infty\right)$, choose $x = 2$.

$$\frac{2^2 + 3}{2^2 - 1} = \frac{7}{3} \not\geq 3$$

The solution is $\left(1, \frac{3}{2}\right]$.

50. $\frac{a^2+2a}{a^2-4} \le 2$

Solve the equation $\frac{a^2+2a}{a^2-4} = 2$.

$$\begin{aligned} \frac{a^2+2a}{a^2-4} &= 2 \\ a^2+2a &= 2(a^2-4) \\ a^2+2a &= 2a^2-8 \\ 0 &= a^2-2a-8 \\ 0 &= (a-4)(a+2) \\ a-4=0 \quad &\text{or} \quad a+2=0 \\ a=4 \quad &\text{or} \quad a=-2 \end{aligned}$$

But -2 is not a possible solution.
Set the denominator equal to zero and solve for a.

$$\begin{aligned} a^2-4 &= 0 \\ (a+2)(a-2) &= 0 \\ a+2=0 \quad &\text{or} \quad a-2=0 \\ a=-2 \quad &\text{or} \quad a=2 \end{aligned}$$

Intervals: $(-\infty,-2)$, $(-2,2)$, $(2,4)$, $(4,\infty)$

For $(-\infty,-2)$, choose -3.

$$\frac{(-3)^2+2(-3)}{(-3)^2-4} = \frac{9-6}{9-4} = \frac{3}{5} \le 2$$

For $(-2,2)$, choose 0.

$$\frac{(0)^2+2(0)}{0-4} = \frac{0}{-4} = 0 \le 2$$

For $(2,4)$, choose 3.

$$\frac{(3)^2+2(3)}{(3)^2-4} = \frac{9+6}{9-5} = \frac{15}{4} \not\le 2$$

For $(4,\infty)$, choose 5.

$$\frac{(5)^2+2(5)}{(5)^2-4} = \frac{25+10}{25-4} = \frac{35}{21} \le 2$$

The value 4 will satisfy the original inequality, but the values -2 and 2 will not since they make the denominator zero. The solution is $(-\infty,-2)\cup(-2,2)\cup[4,\infty)$.

R.6 Exponents

1. $8^{-2} = \frac{1}{8^2} = \frac{1}{64}$

2. $3^{-4} = \frac{1}{3^4} = \frac{1}{81}$

3. $5^0 = 1$, by definition.

4. $\left(-\frac{3}{4}\right)^0 = 1$, by definition.

5. $-(-3)^{-2} = -\frac{1}{(-3)^2} = -\frac{1}{9}$

6. $-(-3^{-2}) = -\left(-\frac{1}{3^2}\right) = -\left(-\frac{1}{9}\right) = \frac{1}{9}$

7. $\left(\frac{1}{6}\right)^{-2} = \frac{1}{\left(\frac{1}{6}\right)^2} = \frac{1}{\frac{1}{36}} = 36$

8. $\left(\frac{4}{3}\right)^{-3} = \frac{1}{\left(\frac{4}{3}\right)^3} = \frac{1}{\frac{64}{27}} = \frac{27}{64}$

9. $\frac{4^{-2}}{4} = 4^{-2-1} = 4^{-3} = \frac{1}{4^3} = \frac{1}{64}$

10. $\frac{8^9\cdot 8^{-7}}{8^{-3}} = 8^{9+(-7)-(-3)} = 8^{9-7+3} = 8^5$

11. $\frac{10^8\cdot 10^{-10}}{10^4\cdot 10^2}$

$$\begin{aligned} &= \frac{10^{8+(-10)}}{10^{4+2}} = \frac{10^{-2}}{10^6} \\ &= 10^{-2-6} = 10^{-8} \\ &= \frac{1}{10^8} \end{aligned}$$

12. $\left(\frac{7^{-12}\cdot 7^3}{7^{-8}}\right)^{-1}$

$$\begin{aligned} &= (7^{-12+3-(-8)})^{-1} \\ &= (7^{-12+3+8})^{-1} = (7^{-1})^{-1} \\ &= 7^{(-1)(-1)} = 7^1 = 7 \end{aligned}$$

13. $\frac{x^4\cdot x^3}{x^5} = \frac{x^{4+3}}{x^5} = \frac{x^7}{x^5} = x^{7-5} = x^2$

14. $\frac{y^{10}\cdot y^{-4}}{y^6} = y^{10-4-6} = y^0 = 1$

15. $\frac{(4k^{-1})^2}{2k^{-5}} = \frac{4^2k^{-2}}{2k^{-5}} = \frac{16k^{-2-(-5)}}{2}$

$$\begin{aligned} &= 8k^{-2+5} = 8k^3 \\ &= 2^3k^3 \end{aligned}$$

16. $\frac{(3z^2)^{-1}}{z^5} = \frac{3^{-1}(z^2)^{-1}}{z^5} = \frac{3^{-1}z^{2(-1)}}{z^5}$
$= \frac{3^{-1}z^{-2}}{z^5} = 3^{-1}z^{-2-5}$
$= 3^{-1}z^{-7} = \frac{1}{3} \cdot \frac{1}{z^7} = \frac{1}{3z^7}$

17. $\frac{3^{-1} \cdot x \cdot y^2}{x^{-4} \cdot y^5} = 3^{-1} \cdot x^{1-(-4)} \cdot y^{2-5}$
$= 3^{-1} \cdot x^{1+4} \cdot y^{-3}$
$= \frac{1}{3} \cdot x^5 \cdot \frac{1}{y^3}$
$= \frac{x^5}{3y^3}$

18. $\frac{5^{-2}m^2y^{-2}}{5^2m^{-1}y^{-2}} = \frac{5^{-2}}{5^2} \cdot \frac{m^2}{m^{-1}} \cdot \frac{y^{-2}}{y^{-2}}$
$= 5^{-2-2}m^{2-(-1)}y^{-2-(-2)}$
$= 5^{-2-2}m^{2+1}y^{-2+2}$
$= 5^{-4}m^3y^0 = \frac{1}{5^4} \cdot m^3 \cdot 1$
$= \frac{m^3}{5^4}$

19. $\left(\frac{a^{-1}}{b^2}\right)^{-3} = \frac{(a^{-1})^{-3}}{(b^2)^{-3}} = \frac{a^{(-1)(-3)}}{b^{2(-3)}}$
$= \frac{a^3}{b^{-6}} = a^3b^6$

20. $\left(\frac{c^3}{7d^{-1/2}}\right)^{-2} = \frac{(c^3)^{-2}}{7^{-2}(d^{-1/2})^{-2}}$
$= \frac{c^{(3)(-2)}}{7^{-2}d^{(-1/2)(-2)}} = \frac{c^{-6}}{7^{-2}d^1}$
$= \frac{7^2}{c^6d} = \frac{49}{c^6d}$

21. $\left(\frac{x^6y^{-3}}{x^{-2}y^5}\right)^{1/2} = (x^{6-(-2)}y^{-3-5})^{1/2}$
$= (x^8y^{-8})^{1/2}$
$= (x^8)^{1/2}(y^{-8})^{1/2}$
$= x^4y^{-4}$
$= \frac{x^4}{y^4}$

22. $\left(\frac{a^{-7}b^{-1}}{b^{-4}a^2}\right)^{1/3} = \left(a^{-7-2}b^{-1-(-4)}\right)^{1/3}$
$= \left(a^{-9}b^3\right)^{1/3}$
$= \left(a^{-9}\right)^{1/3}\left(b^3\right)^{1/3}$
$= a^{-3}b^1$
$= \frac{b}{a^3}$

23. $a^{-1} + b^{-1} = \frac{1}{a} + \frac{1}{b}$
$= \left(\frac{b}{b}\right)\left(\frac{1}{a}\right) + \left(\frac{a}{a}\right)\left(\frac{1}{b}\right)$
$= \frac{b}{ab} + \frac{a}{ab}$
$= \frac{b+a}{ab}$
$= \frac{a+b}{ab}$

24. $b^{-2} - a = \frac{1}{b^2} - a$
$= \frac{1}{b^2} - a\left(\frac{b^2}{b^2}\right)$
$= \frac{1}{b^2} - \frac{ab^2}{b^2}$
$= \frac{1-ab^2}{b^2}$

25. $\frac{2n^{-1} - 2m^{-1}}{m+n^2} = \frac{\frac{2}{n} - \frac{2}{m}}{m+n^2}$
$= \frac{\frac{2}{n} \cdot \frac{m}{m} - \frac{2}{m} \cdot \frac{n}{n}}{(m+n^2)}$
$= \frac{2m-2n}{mn(m+n^2)}$ or $\frac{2(m-n)}{mn(m+n^2)}$

26. $\left(\frac{m}{3}\right)^{-1} + \left(\frac{n}{2}\right)^{-2} = \left(\frac{3}{m}\right)^1 + \left(\frac{2}{n}\right)^2$
$= \frac{3}{m} + \frac{4}{n^2}$
$= \left(\frac{3}{m}\right)\left(\frac{n^2}{n^2}\right) + \left(\frac{4}{n^2}\right)\left(\frac{m}{m}\right)$
$= \frac{3n^2}{mn^2} + \frac{4m}{mn^2}$
$= \frac{3n^2+4m}{mn^2}$

27. $(x^{-1} - y^{-1})^{-1} = \frac{1}{\frac{1}{x} - \frac{1}{y}}$
$= \frac{1}{\frac{1}{x} \cdot \frac{y}{y} - \frac{1}{y} \cdot \frac{x}{x}}$
$= \frac{1}{\frac{y}{xy} - \frac{x}{xy}}$
$= \frac{1}{\frac{y-x}{xy}}$
$= \frac{xy}{y-x}$

28. $(x \cdot y^{-1} - y^{-2})^{-2} = \left(\frac{x}{y} - \frac{1}{y^2}\right)^{-2}$

$= \left[\left(\frac{x}{y}\right)\left(\frac{y}{y}\right) - \frac{1}{y^2}\right]^{-2}$

$= \left(\frac{xy}{y^2} - \frac{1}{y^2}\right)^{-2}$

$= \left(\frac{xy-1}{y^2}\right)^{-2}$

$= \left(\frac{y^2}{xy-1}\right)^{2}$

$= \frac{(y^2)^2}{(xy-1)^2}$

$= \frac{y^4}{(xy-1)^2}$

29. $121^{1/2} = (11^2)^{1/2} = 11^{2(1/2)} = 11^1 = 11$

30. $27^{1/3} = \sqrt[3]{27} = 3$

31. $32^{2/5} = (32^{1/5})^2 = 2^2 = 4$

32. $-125^{2/3} = -(125^{1/3})^2 = -5^2 = -25$

33. $\left(\frac{36}{144}\right)^{1/2} = \frac{36^{1/2}}{144^{1/2}} = \frac{6}{12} = \frac{1}{2}$

This can also be solved by reducing the fraction first.

$$\left(\frac{36}{144}\right)^{1/2} = \left(\frac{1}{4}\right)^{1/2} = \frac{1^{1/2}}{4^{1/2}} = \frac{1}{2}$$

34. $\left(\frac{64}{27}\right)^{1/3} = \frac{64^{1/3}}{27^{1/3}} = \frac{4}{3}$

35. $8^{-4/3} = (8^{1/3})^{-4} = 2^{-4} = \frac{1}{2^4} = \frac{1}{16}$

36. $625^{-1/4} = \frac{1}{625^{1/4}} = \frac{1}{5}$

37. $\left(\frac{27}{64}\right)^{-1/3} = \frac{27^{-1/3}}{64^{-1/3}} = \frac{64^{1/3}}{27^{1/3}} = \frac{4}{3}$

38. $\left(\frac{121}{100}\right)^{-3/2} = \frac{1}{\left(\frac{121}{100}\right)^{3/2}} = \frac{1}{\left[\left(\frac{121}{100}\right)^{1/2}\right]^3}$

$= \frac{1}{\left(\frac{11}{10}\right)^3} = \frac{1}{\frac{1331}{1000}} = \frac{1000}{1331}$

39. $3^{2/3} \cdot 3^{4/3} = 3^{(2/3)+(4/3)} = 3^{6/3} = 3^2 = 9$

40. $27^{2/3} \cdot 27^{-1/3} = 27^{(2/3)+(-1/3)}$

$= 27^{2/3-1/3}$

$= 27^{1/3}$

41. $\frac{4^{9/4} \cdot 4^{-7/4}}{4^{-10/4}} = 4^{9/4-7/4-(-10/4)}$

$= 4^{12/4} = 4^3 = 64$

42. $\frac{3^{-5/2} \cdot 3^{3/2}}{3^{7/2} \cdot 3^{-9/2}}$

$= 3^{(-5/2)+(3/2)-(7/2)-(-9/2)}$

$= 3^{-5/2+3/2-7/2+9/2}$

$= 3^0 = 1$

43. $\frac{7^{-1/3} \cdot 7r^{-3}}{7^{2/3} \cdot (r^{-2})^2}$

$= \frac{7^{-1/3+1}r^{-3}}{7^{2/3} \cdot r^{-4}}$

$= 7^{-1/3+3/3-2/3}r^{-3-(-4)}$

$= 7^0r^{-3+4} = 1 \cdot r^1 = r$

44. $\frac{12^{3/4} \cdot 12^{5/4} \cdot y^{-2}}{12^{-1} \cdot (y^{-3})^{-2}}$

$= \frac{12^{3/4+5/4} \cdot y^{-2}}{12^{-1} \cdot y^{(-3)(-2)}} = \frac{12^{8/4} \cdot y^{-2}}{12^{-1} \cdot y^6}$

$= \frac{12^2 \cdot y^{-2}}{12^{-1}y^6}$

$= 12^{2-(-1)} \cdot y^{-2-6} = 12^3y^{-8}$

$= \frac{12^3}{y^8}$

45. $\frac{3k^2 \cdot (4k^{-3})^{-1}}{4^{1/2} \cdot k^{7/2}}$

$= \frac{3k^2 \cdot 4^{-1}k^3}{2 \cdot k^{7/2}}$

$= 3 \cdot 2^{-1} \cdot 4^{-1}k^{2+3-(7/2)}$

$= \frac{3}{8} \cdot k^{3/2}$

$= \frac{3k^{3/2}}{8}$

46. $\frac{8p^{-3}(4p^2)^{-2}}{p^{-5}} = \frac{8p^{-3}\cdot 4^{-2}p^{(2)(-2)}}{p^{-5}}$
$= \frac{8p^{-3}4^{-2}p^{-4}}{p^{-5}}$
$= 8\cdot 4^{-2}p^{(-3)+(-4)-(-5)}$
$= 8\cdot 4^{-2}p^{-3-4+5}$
$= 8\cdot 4^{-2}p^{-2}$
$= 8\cdot \frac{1}{4^2}\cdot\frac{1}{p^2}$
$= 8\cdot \frac{1}{16}\cdot\frac{1}{p^2}$
$= \frac{8}{16p^2} = \frac{1}{2p^2}$

47. $\frac{a^{4/3}}{a^{2/3}}\cdot\frac{b^{1/2}}{b^{-3/2}} = a^{4/3-2/3}b^{1/2-(-3/2)}$
$= a^{2/3}b^2$

48. $\frac{x^{3/2}\cdot y^{4/5}\cdot z^{-3/4}}{x^{5/3}\cdot y^{-6/5}\cdot z^{1/2}}$
$= x^{3/2-(5/3)}\cdot y^{4/5-(-6/5)}\cdot z^{-3/4-(1/2)}$
$= x^{-1/6}\cdot y^2\cdot z^{-5/4}$
$= \frac{y^2}{x^{1/6}z^{5/4}}$

49. $\frac{k^{-3/5}\cdot h^{-1/3}\cdot t^{2/5}}{k^{-1/5}\cdot h^{-2/3}\cdot t^{1/5}}$
$= k^{-3/5-(-1/5)}h^{-1/3-(-2/3)}t^{2/5-1/5}$
$= k^{-3/5+1/5}h^{-1/3+2/3}t^{2/5-1/5}$
$= k^{-2/5}h^{1/3}t^{1/5}$
$= \frac{h^{1/3}t^{1/5}}{k^{2/5}}$

50. $\frac{m^{7/3}\cdot n^{-2/5}\cdot p^{3/8}}{m^{-2/3}\cdot n^{3/5}\cdot p^{-5/8}}$
$= m^{7/3-(-2/3)}n^{-2/5-(3/5)}p^{3/8-(-5/8)}$
$= m^{7/3+2/3}n^{-2/5-3/5}p^{3/8+5/8}$
$= m^{9/3}n^{-5/5}p^{8/8}$
$= m^3n^{-1}p^1$
$= \frac{m^3p}{n}$

51. $3x^3(x^2+3x)^2 - 15x(x^2+3x)^2$
$= 3x\cdot x^2(x^2+3x)^2 - 3x\cdot 5(x^2+3x)^2$
$= 3x(x^2+3x)^2(x^2-5)$

52. $6x(x^3+7)^2 - 6x^2(3x^2+5)(x^3+7)$
$= 6x(x^3+7)(x^3+7) - 6x(x)(3x^2+5)(x^3+7)$
$= 6x(x^3+7)[(x^3+7) - x(3x^2+5)]$
$= 6x(x^3+7)(x^3+7-3x^3-5x)$
$= 6x(x^3+7)(-2x^3-5x+7)$

53. $10x^3(x^2-1)^{-1/2} - 5x(x^2-1)^{1/2}$
$= 5x\cdot 2x^2(x^2-1)^{-1/2} - 5x(x^2-1)^{-1/2}(x^2-1)^1$
$= 5x(x^2-1)^{-1/2}[2x^2-(x^2-1)]$
$= 5x(x^2-1)^{-1/2}(x^2+1)$

54. $9(6x+2)^{1/2} + 3(9x-1)(6x+2)^{-1/2}$
$= 3\cdot 3(6x+2)^{-1/2}(6x+2)^1$
$+ 3(9x-1)(6x+2)^{-1/2}$
$= 3(6x+2)^{-1/2}[3(6x+2)+(9x-1)]$
$= 3(6x+2)^{-1/2}(18x+6+9x-1)$
$= 3(6x+2)^{-1/2}(27x+5)$

55. $x(2x+5)^2(x^2-4)^{-1/2} + 2(x^2-4)^{1/2}(2x+5)$
$= (2x+5)^2(x^2-4)^{-1/2}(x)$
$+ (x^2-4)^1(x^2-4)^{-1/2}(2)(2x+5)$
$= (2x+5)(x^2-4)^{-1/2}$
$\cdot [(2x+5)(x) + (x^2-4)(2)]$
$= (2x+5)(x^2-4)^{-1/2}$
$\cdot (2x^2+5x+2x^2-8)$
$= (2x+5)(x^2-4)^{-1/2}(4x^2+5x-8)$

56. $(4x^2+1)^2(2x-1)^{-1/2} + 16x(4x^2+1)(2x-1)^{1/2}$
$= (4x^2+1)(4x^2+1)(2x-1)^{-1/2}$
$+ 16x(4x^2+1)(2x-1)^{-1/2}(2x-1)$
$= (4x^2+1)(2x-1)^{-1/2}$
$\cdot [(4x^2+1) + 16x(2x-1)]$
$= (4x^2+1)(2x-1)^{-1/2}(4x^2+1+32x^2-16x)$
$= (4x^2+1)(2x-1)^{-1/2}(36x^2-16x+1)$

R.7 Radicals

1. $\sqrt[3]{125} = 5$ because $5^3 = 125$.

2. $\sqrt[4]{1296} = \sqrt[4]{6^4} = 6$

3. $\sqrt[5]{-3125} = -5$ because $(-5)^5 = -3125$.

4. $\sqrt{50} = \sqrt{25 \cdot 2} = \sqrt{25}\sqrt{2} = 5\sqrt{2}$

5. $\sqrt{2000} = \sqrt{4 \cdot 100 \cdot 5}$
$= 2 \cdot 10\sqrt{5}$
$= 20\sqrt{5}$

6. $\sqrt{32y^5} = \sqrt{(16y^4)(2y)}$
$= \sqrt{16y^4}\sqrt{2y}$
$= 4y^2\sqrt{2y}$

7. $\sqrt{27} \cdot \sqrt{3} = \sqrt{27 \cdot 3} = \sqrt{81} = 9$

8. $\sqrt{2} \cdot \sqrt{32} = \sqrt{2 \cdot 32} = \sqrt{64} = 8$

9. $7\sqrt{2} - 8\sqrt{18} + 4\sqrt{72}$
$= 7\sqrt{2} - 8\sqrt{9 \cdot 2} + 4\sqrt{36 \cdot 2}$
$= 7\sqrt{2} - 8(3)\sqrt{2} + 4(6)\sqrt{2}$
$= 7\sqrt{2} - 24\sqrt{2} + 24\sqrt{2}$
$= 7\sqrt{2}$

10. $4\sqrt{3} - 5\sqrt{12} + 3\sqrt{75}$
$= 4\sqrt{3} - 5(\sqrt{4}\sqrt{3}) + 3(\sqrt{25}\sqrt{3})$
$= 4\sqrt{3} - 5(2\sqrt{3}) + 3(5\sqrt{3})$
$= 4\sqrt{3} - 10\sqrt{3} + 15\sqrt{3}$
$= (4 - 10 + 15)\sqrt{3} = 9\sqrt{3}$

11. $4\sqrt{7} - \sqrt{28} + \sqrt{343}$
$= 4\sqrt{7} - \sqrt{4}\sqrt{7} + \sqrt{49}\sqrt{7}$
$= 4\sqrt{7} - 2\sqrt{7} + 7\sqrt{7}$
$= (4 - 2 + 7)\sqrt{7}$
$= 9\sqrt{7}$

12. $3\sqrt{28} - 4\sqrt{63} + \sqrt{112}$
$= 3(\sqrt{4}\sqrt{7}) - 4(\sqrt{9}\sqrt{7}) + (\sqrt{16}\sqrt{7})$
$= 3(2\sqrt{7}) - 4(3\sqrt{7}) + (4\sqrt{7})$
$= 6\sqrt{7} - 12\sqrt{7} + 4\sqrt{7}$
$= (6 - 12 + 4)\sqrt{7}$
$= -2\sqrt{7}$

13. $\sqrt[3]{2} - \sqrt[3]{16} + 2\sqrt[3]{54}$
$= \sqrt[3]{2} - (\sqrt[3]{8 \cdot 2}) + 2(\sqrt[3]{27 \cdot 2})$
$= \sqrt[3]{2} - \sqrt[3]{8}\sqrt[3]{2} + 2(\sqrt[3]{27}\sqrt[3]{2})$
$= \sqrt[3]{2} - 2\sqrt[3]{2} + 2(3\sqrt[3]{2})$
$= \sqrt[3]{2} - 2\sqrt[3]{2} + 6\sqrt[3]{2}$
$= 5\sqrt[3]{2}$

14. $2\sqrt[3]{5} - 4\sqrt[3]{40} + 3\sqrt[3]{135}$
$= 2\sqrt[3]{5} - 4\sqrt[3]{8 \cdot 5} + 3\sqrt[3]{27 \cdot 5}$
$= 2\sqrt[3]{5} - 4(2)\sqrt[3]{5} + 3(3)\sqrt[3]{5}$
$= 2\sqrt[3]{5} - 8\sqrt[3]{5} + 9\sqrt[3]{5}$
$= 3\sqrt[3]{5}$

15. $\sqrt{2x^3y^2z^4} = \sqrt{x^2y^2z^4 \cdot 2x}$
$= xyz^2\sqrt{2x}$

16. $\sqrt{160r^7s^9t^{12}}$
$= \sqrt{(16 \cdot 10)(r^6 \cdot r)(s^8 \cdot s)(t^{12})}$
$= \sqrt{(16r^6s^8t^{12})(10rs)}$
$= \sqrt{16r^6s^8t^{12}}\sqrt{10rs}$
$= 4r^3s^4t^6\sqrt{10rs}$

17. $\sqrt[3]{128x^3y^8z^9} = \sqrt[3]{64x^3y^6z^9 \cdot 2y^2}$
$= \sqrt[3]{64x^3y^6z^9}\sqrt[3]{2y^2}$
$= 4xy^2z^3\sqrt[3]{2y^2}$

18. $\sqrt[4]{x^8y^7z^{11}} = \sqrt[4]{(x^8)(y^4 \cdot y^3)(z^8z^3)}$
$= \sqrt[4]{(x^8y^4z^8)(y^3z^3)}$
$= \sqrt[4]{x^8y^4z^8}\sqrt[4]{y^3z^3}$
$= x^2yz^2\sqrt[4]{y^3z^3}$

19. $\sqrt{a^3b^5} - 2\sqrt{a^7b^3} + \sqrt{a^3b^9}$
$= \sqrt{a^2b^4ab} - 2\sqrt{a^6b^2ab} + \sqrt{a^2b^8ab}$
$= ab^2\sqrt{ab} - 2a^3b\sqrt{ab} + ab^4\sqrt{ab}$
$= (ab^2 - 2a^3b + ab^4)\sqrt{ab}$
$= ab\sqrt{ab}(b - 2a^2 + b^3)$

20. $\sqrt{p^7q^3} - \sqrt{p^5q^9} + \sqrt{p^9q}$
$= \sqrt{(p^6p)(q^2q)} - \sqrt{(p^4p)(q^8q)}$
$+ \sqrt{(p^8p)q}$
$= \sqrt{(p^6q^2)(pq)} - \sqrt{(p^4q^8)(pq)}$
$+ \sqrt{(p^8)(pq)}$
$= \sqrt{p^6q^2}\sqrt{pq} - \sqrt{p^4q^8}\sqrt{pq} + \sqrt{p^8}\sqrt{pq}$
$= p^3q\sqrt{pq} - p^2q^4\sqrt{pq} + p^4\sqrt{pq}$
$= p^2pq\sqrt{pq} - p^2q^4\sqrt{pq} + p^2p^2\sqrt{pq}$
$= p^2\sqrt{pq}(pq - q^4 + p^2)$

21. $\sqrt{a} \cdot \sqrt[3]{a} = a^{1/2} \cdot a^{1/3} = a^{1/2+(1/3)} = a^{5/6} = \sqrt[6]{a^5}$

22. $\sqrt{b^3} \cdot \sqrt[4]{b^3} = b^{3/2} \cdot b^{3/4}$
$= b^{3/2+(3/4)} = b^{9/4}$
$= \sqrt[4]{b^9} = \sqrt[4]{b^8 \cdot b}$
$= \sqrt[4]{b^8}\sqrt[4]{b} = b^2\sqrt[4]{b}$

23. $\dfrac{5}{\sqrt{7}} = \dfrac{5}{\sqrt{7}} \cdot \dfrac{\sqrt{7}}{\sqrt{7}} = \dfrac{5\sqrt{7}}{7}$

24. $\dfrac{5}{\sqrt{10}} = \dfrac{5}{\sqrt{10}} \cdot \dfrac{\sqrt{10}}{\sqrt{10}} = \dfrac{5\sqrt{10}}{\sqrt{100}} = \dfrac{5\sqrt{10}}{10} = \dfrac{\sqrt{10}}{2}$

25. $\frac{-3}{\sqrt{12}} = \frac{-3}{\sqrt{4 \cdot 3}}$
$= \frac{-3}{2\sqrt{3}} \cdot \frac{\sqrt{3}}{\sqrt{3}}$
$= \frac{-3\sqrt{3}}{6}$
$= -\frac{\sqrt{3}}{2}$

26. $\frac{4}{\sqrt{8}} = \frac{4}{\sqrt{8}} \cdot \frac{\sqrt{2}}{\sqrt{2}} = \frac{4\sqrt{2}}{\sqrt{16}} = \frac{4\sqrt{2}}{4} = \sqrt{2}$

27. $\frac{3}{1-\sqrt{2}} = \frac{3}{1-\sqrt{2}} \cdot \frac{1+\sqrt{2}}{1+\sqrt{2}}$
$= \frac{3(1+\sqrt{2})}{1-2}$
$= \frac{-3(1+\sqrt{2})}{4}$

28. $\frac{5}{2-\sqrt{6}} = \frac{5}{2-\sqrt{6}} \cdot \frac{2+\sqrt{6}}{2+\sqrt{6}}$
$= \frac{5(2+\sqrt{6})}{4+2\sqrt{6}-2\sqrt{6}-\sqrt{36}}$
$= \frac{5(2+\sqrt{6})}{4-\sqrt{36}}$
$= \frac{5(2+\sqrt{6})}{4-6}$
$= \frac{5(2+\sqrt{6})}{-2}$
$= -\frac{5(2+\sqrt{6})}{2}$

29. $\frac{6}{2+\sqrt{2}} = \frac{6}{2+\sqrt{2}} \cdot \frac{2-\sqrt{2}}{2-\sqrt{2}}$
$= \frac{6(2-\sqrt{2})}{4-2\sqrt{2}+2\sqrt{2}-\sqrt{4}}$
$= \frac{6(2-\sqrt{2})}{4-2}$
$= \frac{6(2-\sqrt{2})}{2}$
$= 3(2-\sqrt{2})$

30. $\frac{\sqrt{5}}{\sqrt{5}+\sqrt{2}} = \frac{\sqrt{5}}{\sqrt{5}+\sqrt{2}} \cdot \frac{\sqrt{5}-\sqrt{2}}{\sqrt{5}-\sqrt{2}}$
$= \frac{\sqrt{5}(\sqrt{5}-\sqrt{2})}{\sqrt{25}-\sqrt{10}+\sqrt{10}-\sqrt{4}}$
$= \frac{5-\sqrt{10}}{5-2}$
$= \frac{5-\sqrt{10}}{3}$

31. $\frac{1}{\sqrt{r}-\sqrt{3}} = \frac{1}{\sqrt{r}-\sqrt{3}} \cdot \frac{\sqrt{r}+\sqrt{3}}{\sqrt{r}+\sqrt{3}}$
$= \frac{\sqrt{r}+\sqrt{3}}{r-3}$

32. $\frac{5}{\sqrt{m}-\sqrt{5}} = \frac{5}{\sqrt{m}-\sqrt{5}} \cdot \frac{\sqrt{m}+\sqrt{5}}{\sqrt{m}+\sqrt{5}}$
$= \frac{5(\sqrt{m}+\sqrt{5})}{\sqrt{m^2}+\sqrt{5m}-\sqrt{5m}-\sqrt{25}}$
$= \frac{5(\sqrt{m}+\sqrt{5})}{\sqrt{m^2}-\sqrt{25}} = \frac{5(\sqrt{m}+\sqrt{5})}{m-5}$

33. $\frac{y-5}{\sqrt{y}-\sqrt{5}} = \frac{y-5}{\sqrt{y}-\sqrt{5}} \cdot \frac{\sqrt{y}+\sqrt{5}}{\sqrt{y}+\sqrt{5}}$
$= \frac{(y-5)(\sqrt{y}+\sqrt{5})}{y-5}$
$= \sqrt{y}+\sqrt{5}$

34. $\frac{\sqrt{z}-1}{\sqrt{z}-\sqrt{5}} = \frac{\sqrt{z}-1}{\sqrt{z}-\sqrt{5}} \cdot \frac{\sqrt{z}+\sqrt{5}}{\sqrt{z}+\sqrt{5}}$
$= \frac{\sqrt{z^2}+\sqrt{5z}-\sqrt{z}-\sqrt{5}}{\sqrt{z^2}+\sqrt{5z}-\sqrt{5z}-\sqrt{25}}$
$= \frac{z+\sqrt{5z}-\sqrt{z}-\sqrt{5}}{z-5}$

35. $\frac{\sqrt{x}+\sqrt{x+1}}{\sqrt{x}-\sqrt{x+1}} = \frac{\sqrt{x}+\sqrt{x+1}}{\sqrt{x}-\sqrt{x+1}} \cdot \frac{\sqrt{x}+\sqrt{x+1}}{\sqrt{x}+\sqrt{x+1}}$
$= \frac{x+2\sqrt{x(x+1)}+(x+1)}{x-(x+1)}$
$= \frac{2x+2\sqrt{x(x+1)}+1}{-1}$
$= -2x-2\sqrt{x(x+1)}-1$

36. $\frac{\sqrt{p}+\sqrt{p^2-1}}{\sqrt{p}-\sqrt{p^2-1}}$
$= \frac{\sqrt{p}+\sqrt{p^2-1}}{\sqrt{p}-\sqrt{p^2-1}} \cdot \frac{\sqrt{p}+\sqrt{p^2-1}}{\sqrt{p}+\sqrt{p^2-1}}$
$= \frac{(\sqrt{p})^2+2\sqrt{p}\sqrt{p^2-1}+(\sqrt{p^2-1}))^2}{\sqrt{p^2}+\sqrt{p}\sqrt{p^2-1}-\sqrt{p}\sqrt{p^2-1}-(\sqrt{p^2-1})^2}$
$= \frac{p+2\sqrt{p}\sqrt{p^2-1}+(p^2-1)}{p-(p^2-1)}$
$= \frac{p^2+p+2\sqrt{p(p^2-1)}-1}{-p^2+p+1}$

37. $\dfrac{1+\sqrt{2}}{2} = \dfrac{(1+\sqrt{2})(1-\sqrt{2})}{2(1-\sqrt{2})}$

$= \dfrac{1-2}{2(1-\sqrt{2})}$

$= -\dfrac{1}{2(1-\sqrt{2})}$

38. $\dfrac{3-\sqrt{3}}{6} = \dfrac{3-\sqrt{3}}{6} \cdot \dfrac{3+\sqrt{3}}{3+\sqrt{3}}$

$= \dfrac{9+3\sqrt{3}-3\sqrt{3}-\sqrt{9}}{6(3+\sqrt{3})}$

$= \dfrac{9-3}{6(3+\sqrt{3})}$

$= \dfrac{6}{6(3+\sqrt{3})}$

$= \dfrac{1}{3+\sqrt{3}}$

39. $\dfrac{\sqrt{x}+\sqrt{x+1}}{\sqrt{x}-\sqrt{x+1}}$

$= \dfrac{\sqrt{x}+\sqrt{x+1}}{\sqrt{x}-\sqrt{x+1}} \cdot \dfrac{\sqrt{x}-\sqrt{x+1}}{\sqrt{x}-\sqrt{x+1}}$

$= \dfrac{x-(x+1)}{x-2\sqrt{x}\cdot\sqrt{x+1}+(x+1)}$

$= \dfrac{-1}{2x-2\sqrt{x(x+1)}+1}$

40. $\dfrac{\sqrt{p}-\sqrt{p-2}}{\sqrt{p}} = \dfrac{\sqrt{p}-\sqrt{p-2}}{\sqrt{p}} \cdot \dfrac{\sqrt{p}+\sqrt{p-2}}{\sqrt{p}+\sqrt{p-2}}$

$= \dfrac{\sqrt{p^2}+\sqrt{p}\sqrt{p-2}-\sqrt{p}\sqrt{p-2}-\sqrt{(p-2)^2}}{\sqrt{p^2}+\sqrt{p}\sqrt{p-2}}$

$= \dfrac{p-(p-2)}{p+\sqrt{p(p-2)}}$

$= \dfrac{2}{p+\sqrt{p(p-2)}}$

41. $\sqrt{16-8x+x^2}$

$= \sqrt{(4-x)^2}$

$= |4-x|$

Since $\sqrt{}$ denotes the nonnegative root, we must have $4-x \geq 0$.

42. $\sqrt{9y^2+30y+25} = \sqrt{(3y+5)^2} = |3y+5|$

Since $\sqrt{}$ denotes the nonnegative root, we must have $3y+5 \geq 0$.

43. $\sqrt{4-25z^2} = \sqrt{(2+5z)(2-5z)}$

This factorization does not produce a perfect square, so the expression $\sqrt{4-25z^2}$ cannot be simplified.

44. $\sqrt{9k^2+h^2}$

The expression $9k^2+h^2$ is the sum of two squares and cannot be factored. Therefore, $\sqrt{9k^2+h^2}$ cannot be simplified.

Chapter 1

LINEAR FUNCTIONS

1.1 Slopes and Equations of Lines

1. Find the slope of the line through $(4, 5)$ and $(-1, 2)$.

$$m = \frac{5-2}{4-(-1)} = \frac{3}{5}$$

2. Find the slope of the line through $(5, -4)$ and $(1, 3)$.

$$m = \frac{3-(-4)}{1-5} = \frac{3+4}{-4} = -\frac{7}{4}$$

3. Find the slope of the line through $(8, 4)$ and $(8, -7)$.

$$m = \frac{4-(-7)}{8-8} = \frac{11}{0}$$

The slope is undefined; the line is vertical.

4. Find the slope of the line through $(1, 5)$ and $(-2, 5)$.

$$m = \frac{5-5}{-2-1} = \frac{0}{-3} = 0$$

5. $y = x$

Using the slope-intercept form, $y = mx + b$, we see that the slope is 1.

6. $y = 3x - 2$

This equation is in slope-intercept form, $y = mx + b$. Thus, the coefficient of the x-term, 3, is the slope.

7. $5x - 9y = 11$

Rewrite the equation in slope-intercept form.

$$9y = 5x - 11$$
$$y = \frac{5}{9}x - \frac{11}{9}$$

The slope is $\frac{5}{9}$.

8. $4x + 7y = 1$

Rewrite the equation in slope-intercept form.

$$7y = 1 - 4x$$
$$\frac{1}{7}(7y) = \frac{1}{7}(1) - \frac{1}{7}(4x)$$
$$y = \frac{1}{7} - \frac{4}{7}x$$
$$y = -\frac{4}{7}x + \frac{1}{7}$$

The slope is $-\frac{4}{7}$.

9. $x = 5$

This is a vertical line. The slope is undefined.

10. The x-axis is the horizontal line $y = 0$. Horizontal lines have a slope of 0.

11. $y = 8$

This is a horizontal line, which has a slope of 0.

12. $y = -6$

By rewriting this equation in the slope-intercept form, $y = mx + b$, we get $y = 0x - 6$, with the slope, m, being 0.

13. Find the slope of a line parallel to $6x - 3y = 12$.

Rewrite the equation in slope-intercept form.

$$-3y = -6x + 12$$
$$y = 2x - 4$$

The slope is 2, so a parallel line will also have slope 2.

14. Find the slope of a line perpendicular to $8x = 2y - 5$.
First, rewrite the given equation in slope-intercept form.

$$8x = 2y - 5$$
$$8x + 5 = 2y$$
$$4x + \frac{5}{2} = y$$
$$\text{or} \quad y = 4x + \frac{5}{2}$$

Let m be the slope of any line perpendicular to the given line. Then

$$4 \cdot m = -1$$
$$m = -\frac{1}{4}.$$

15. The line goes through $(1, 3)$, with slope $m = -2$. Use point-slope form.

$$y - 3 = -2(x - 1)$$
$$y = -2x + 2 + 3$$
$$y = -2x + 5$$

16. The line goes through $(2, 4)$, with slope $m = -1$. Use point-slope form.

$$y - 4 = -1(x - 2)$$
$$y - 4 = -x + 2$$
$$y = -x + 6$$

17. The line goes through $(-5, -7)$ with slope $m = 0$. Use point-slope form.

$$y - (-7) = 0[x - (-5)]$$
$$y + 7 = 0$$
$$y = -7$$

18. The line goes through $(-8, 1)$, with undefined slope. Since the slope is undefined, the line is vertical. The equation of the vertical line passing through $(-8, 1)$ is $x = -8$.

19. The line goes through $(4, 2)$ and $(1, 3)$.
Find the slope, then use point-slope form with either of the two given points.

$$m = \frac{3 - 2}{1 - 4}$$
$$= -\frac{1}{3}$$

$$y - 3 = -\frac{1}{3}(x - 1)$$
$$y = -\frac{1}{3}x + \frac{1}{3} + 3$$
$$y = -\frac{1}{3}x + \frac{10}{3}$$

20. The line goes through $(8, -1)$ and $(4, 3)$.
Find the slope, then use point-slope form with either of the two given points.

$$m = \frac{3 - (-1)}{4 - 8}$$
$$= \frac{3 + 1}{-4}$$
$$= \frac{4}{-4} = -1$$

$$y - (-1) = -1(x - 8)$$
$$y + 1 = -x + 8$$
$$y = -x + 7$$

21. The line goes through $\left(\frac{2}{3}, \frac{1}{2}\right)$ and $\left(\frac{1}{4}, -2\right)$.

$$m = \frac{-2 - \frac{1}{2}}{\frac{1}{4} - \frac{2}{3}} = \frac{-\frac{4}{2} - \frac{1}{2}}{\frac{3}{12} - \frac{8}{12}}$$
$$m = \frac{-\frac{5}{2}}{-\frac{5}{12}} = \frac{60}{10} = 6$$

$$y - (-2) = 6\left(x - \frac{1}{4}\right)$$
$$y + 2 = 6x - \frac{3}{2}$$
$$y = 6x - \frac{3}{2} - 2$$
$$y = 6x - \frac{3}{2} - \frac{4}{2}$$
$$y = 6x - \frac{7}{2}$$

22. The line goes through $\left(-2, \frac{3}{4}\right)$ and $\left(\frac{2}{3}, \frac{5}{2}\right)$.

$$\begin{aligned} m &= \frac{\frac{5}{2} - \frac{3}{4}}{\frac{2}{3} - (-2)} = \frac{\frac{10}{4} - \frac{3}{4}}{\frac{2}{3} + \frac{6}{3}} \\ &= \frac{\frac{7}{4}}{\frac{8}{3}} = \frac{21}{32} \end{aligned}$$

$$\begin{aligned} y - \frac{3}{4} &= \frac{21}{32}[x - (-2)] \\ y - \frac{3}{4} &= \frac{21}{32}x + \frac{42}{32} \\ y &= \frac{21}{32}x + \frac{42}{32} + \frac{3}{4} \\ y &= \frac{21}{32}x + \frac{21}{16} + \frac{12}{16} \\ y &= \frac{21}{32}x + \frac{33}{16} \end{aligned}$$

23. The line goes through $(-8, 4)$ and $(-8, 6)$.

$$m = \frac{4 - 6}{-8 - (-8)} = \frac{-2}{0};$$

which is undefined.
This is a vertical line; the value of x is always -8.
The equation of this line is $x = -8$.

24. The line goes through $(-1, 3)$ and $(0, 3)$.

$$m = \frac{3 - 3}{-1 - 0} = \frac{0}{-1} = 0$$

This is a horizontal line; the value of y is always 3. The equation of this line is $y = 3$.

25. The line has x-intercept -6 and y-intercept -3. Two points on the line are $(-6, 0)$ and $(0, -3)$. Find the slope; then use slope-intercept form.

$$\begin{aligned} m &= \frac{-3 - 0}{0 - (-6)} = \frac{-3}{6} = -\frac{1}{2} \\ b &= -3 \\ y &= -\frac{1}{2}x - 3 \end{aligned}$$

26. The line has x-intercept -2 and y-intercept 4. Two points on the line are $(-2, 0)$ and $(0, 4)$. Find the slope; then use slope-intercept form.

$$\begin{aligned} m &= \frac{4 - 0}{0 - (-2)} = \frac{4}{2} = 2 \\ y &= mx + b \\ y &= 2x + 4 \end{aligned}$$

27. The vertical line through $(-6, 5)$ goes through the point $(-6, 0)$, so the equation is $x = -6$.

28. The line is horizontal, through $(8, 7)$.
The line has an equation of the form $y = k$ where k is the y-coordinate of the point. In this case, $k = 7$, so the equation is $y = 7$.

29. Write an equation of the line through $(-4, 6)$, parallel to $3x + 2y = 13$.
Rewrite the equation of the given line in slope-intercept form.

$$\begin{aligned} 3x + 2y &= 13 \\ 2y &= -3x + 13 \\ y &= -\frac{3}{2}x + \frac{13}{2} \end{aligned}$$

The slope is $-\frac{3}{2}$.
Use $m = -\frac{3}{2}$ and the point $(-4, 6)$ in the point-slope form.

$$\begin{aligned} y - 6 &= -\frac{3}{2}[x - (-4)] \\ y &= -\frac{3}{2}(x + 4) + 6 \\ y &= -\frac{3}{2}x - 6 + 6 \\ y &= -\frac{3}{2}x \end{aligned}$$

30. Write the equation of the line through $(2, -5)$, parallel to $y - 4 = 2x$. Rewrite the equation in slope-intercept form.

$$\begin{aligned} y - 4 &= 2x \\ y &= 2x + 4 \end{aligned}$$

The slope of this line is 2.
Use $m = 2$ and the point $(2, -5)$ in the point-slope form.

$$\begin{aligned} y - (-5) &= 2(x - 2) \\ y + 5 &= 2x - 4 \\ y &= 2x - 9 \end{aligned}$$

31. Write an equation of the line through $(3, -4)$, perpendicular to $x + y = 4$.
Rewrite the equation of the given line as

$$y = -x + 4.$$

The slope of this line is -1. To find the slope of a perpendicular line, solve

$$\begin{aligned} -1m &= -1. \\ m &= 1 \end{aligned}$$

Use $m = 1$ and $(3, -4)$ in the point-slope form.

$$\begin{aligned} y - (-4) &= 1(x - 3) \\ y &= x - 3 - 4 \\ y &= x - 7 \end{aligned}$$

32. Write the equation of the line through $(-2, 6)$, perpendicular to $2x - 3y = 5$.
Rewrite the equation in slope-intercept form.

$$\begin{aligned} 2x - 3y &= 5 \\ -3y &= -2x + 5 \\ y &= \frac{2}{3}x - \frac{5}{3} \end{aligned}$$

The slope of this line is $\frac{2}{3}$. To find the slope of a perpendicular line, solve

$$\begin{aligned} \frac{2}{3}m &= -1. \\ m &= -\frac{3}{2} \end{aligned}$$

Use $m = -\frac{3}{2}$ and $(-2, 6)$ in the point-slope form.

$$\begin{aligned} y - 6 &= -\frac{3}{2}[x - (-2)] \\ y - 6 &= -\frac{3}{2}(x + 2) \\ y - 6 &= -\frac{3}{2}x - 3 \\ y &= -\frac{3}{2}x + 3 \end{aligned}$$

33. Write an equation of the line with y-intercept 4, perpendicular to $x + 5y = 7$.
Find the slope of the given line.

$$\begin{aligned} x + 5y &= 7 \\ 5y &= -x + 7 \\ y &= -\frac{1}{5}x + \frac{7}{5} \end{aligned}$$

The slope is $-\frac{1}{5}$, so the slope of the perpendicular line will be 5. If the y-intercept is 4, then using the slope-intercept form we have

$$\begin{aligned} y &= mx + b \\ y &= 5x + 4. \end{aligned}$$

34. Write the equation of the line with x-intercept $-\frac{2}{3}$, perpendicular to $2x - y = 4$.
Find the slope of the given line.

$$\begin{aligned} 2x - y &= 4 \\ 2x - 4 &= y \end{aligned}$$

The slope of this line is 2. Since the lines are perpendicular, the slope of the needed line is $-\frac{1}{2}$. The line also has an x-intercept of $-\frac{2}{3}$. Thus, it passes through the point $\left(-\frac{2}{3}, 0\right)$.
Using the point-slope form, we have

$$\begin{aligned} y - 0 &= -\frac{1}{2}\left[x - \left(-\frac{2}{3}\right)\right] \\ y &= -\frac{1}{2}\left(x + \frac{2}{3}\right) \\ y &= -\frac{1}{2}x - \frac{1}{3} \end{aligned}$$

35. Do the points $(4, 3), (2, 0)$, and $(-18, -12)$ lie on the same line?
Find the slope between $(4, 3)$ and $(2, 0)$.

$$m = \frac{0 - 3}{2 - 4} = \frac{-3}{-2} = \frac{3}{2}$$

Find the slope between $(4, 3)$ and $(-18, -12)$.

$$m = \frac{-12 - 3}{-18 - 4} = \frac{-15}{-22} = \frac{15}{22}$$

Since these slopes are not the same, the points do not lie on the same line.

36. **(a)** Write the given line in slope-intercept form.

$$\begin{aligned} 2x + 3y &= 6 \\ 3y &= -2x + 6 \\ y &= -\frac{2}{3}x + 2 \end{aligned}$$

This line has a slope of $-\frac{2}{3}$. The desired line has a slope of $-\frac{2}{3}$ since it is parallel to the given line. Use the definition of slope.

$$\begin{aligned} m &= \frac{y_2 - y_1}{x_2 - x_1} \\ -\frac{2}{3} &= \frac{2 - (-1)}{k - 4} \\ -\frac{2}{3} &= \frac{3}{k - 4} \\ -2(k - 4) &= (3)(3) \\ -2k + 8 &= 9 \\ -2k &= 1 \\ k &= -\frac{1}{2} \end{aligned}$$

(b) Write the given line in slope-intercept form.

$$\begin{aligned} 5x - 2y &= -1 \\ 2y &= 5x + 1 \\ y &= \frac{5}{2}x + \frac{1}{2} \end{aligned}$$

This line has a slope of $\frac{5}{2}$. The desired line has a slope of $-\frac{2}{5}$ since it is perpendicular to the given line. Use the definition of slope.

$$\begin{aligned} m &= \frac{y_2 - y_1}{x_2 - x_1} \\ &= \frac{2-(-1)}{k-4} \\ -\frac{2}{5} &= \frac{2+1}{k-4} \\ \frac{-2}{5} &= \frac{3}{k-4} \\ -2(k-4) &= (3)(5) \\ -2k+8 &= 15 \\ -2k &= 7 \\ k &= -\frac{7}{2} \end{aligned}$$

37. A parallelogram has 4 sides, with opposite sides parallel. The slope of the line through $(1, 3)$ and $(2, 1)$ is

$$m = \frac{3-1}{1-2} = \frac{2}{-1} = -2.$$

The slope of the line through $(-\frac{5}{2}, 2)$ and $(-\frac{7}{2}, 4)$ is

$$m = \frac{2-4}{-\frac{5}{2}-(-\frac{7}{2})} = \frac{-2}{1} = -2.$$

Since these slopes are equal, these two sides are parallel.
The slope of the line through $(-\frac{7}{2}, 4)$ and $(1, 3)$ is

$$m = \frac{4-3}{-\frac{7}{2}-1} = \frac{1}{-\frac{9}{2}} = -\frac{2}{9}.$$

Slope of the line through $(-\frac{5}{2}, 2)$ and $(2, 1)$ is

$$m = \frac{2-1}{-\frac{5}{2}-2} = \frac{1}{-\frac{9}{2}} = -\frac{2}{9}.$$

Since these slopes are equal, these two sides are parallel.
Since both pairs of opposite sides are parallel, the quadrilateral is a parallelogram.

38. Two lines are perpendicular if the product of their slopes is -1.
The slope of the diagonal containing $(4, 5)$ and $(-2, -1)$ is

$$m = \frac{5-(-1)}{4-(-2)} = \frac{6}{6} = 1.$$

The slope of the diagonal containing $(-2, 5)$ and $(4, -1)$ is

$$m = \frac{5-(-1)}{-2-4} = \frac{6}{-6} = -1.$$

The product of the slopes is $(1)(-1) = -1$, so the diagonals are perpendicular.

39. The line goes through $(0, 2)$ and $(-2, 0)$

$$m = \frac{2-0}{0-(-2)} = \frac{2}{2} = 1$$

The correct choice is (a).

40. The line goes through $(1, 3)$ and $(2, 0)$.

$$m = \frac{3-0}{1-2} = \frac{3}{-1} = -3$$

The correct choice is (f).

41. The line appears to go through $(0, 0)$ and $(-1, 4)$.

$$m = \frac{4-0}{-1-0} = \frac{4}{-1} = -4$$

42. The line goes through $(-2, 0)$ and $(0, 1)$.

$$m = \frac{1-0}{0-(-2)} = \frac{1}{2}$$

43. **(a)** See the figure in the textbook.
Segment MN is drawn perpendicular to segment PQ. Recall that MQ is the length of segment MQ.

$$m_1 = \frac{\Delta y}{\Delta x} = \frac{MQ}{PQ}$$

From the diagram, we know that $PQ = 1$. Thus, $m_1 = \frac{MQ}{1}$, so MQ has length m_1.

(b) $m_2 = \frac{\Delta y}{\Delta x} = \frac{-QN}{PQ} = \frac{-QN}{1}$

$QN = -m_2$

(c) Triangles MPQ, PNQ, and MNP are right triangles by construction. In triangles MPQ and MNP,

$$\text{angle } M = \text{angle } M,$$

and in the right triangles PNQ and MNP,

$$\text{angle } N = \text{angle } N.$$

Since all right angles are equal, and since triangles with two equal angles are similar, triangle MPQ is similar to triangle MNP and triangle PNQ is similar to triangle MNP.

Therefore, triangles MPQ and PNQ are similar to each other.

(d) Since corresponding sides in similar triangles are proportional,

$$MQ = k \cdot PQ \quad \text{and} \quad PQ = k \cdot QN.$$

$$\frac{MQ}{PQ} = \frac{k \cdot PQ}{k \cdot QN}$$

$$\frac{MQ}{PQ} = \frac{PQ}{QN}$$

From the diagram, we know that $PQ = 1$.

$$MQ = \frac{1}{QN}$$

From (a) and (b), $m_1 = MQ$ and $-m_2 = QN$.

Substituting, we get

$$m_1 = \frac{1}{-m_2}.$$

Multiplying both sides by m_2, we have

$$m_1 m_2 = -1.$$

44. $y = x - 1$

Three ordered pairs that satisfy this equation are $(0, -1)$, $(1, 0)$, and $(4, 3)$. Plot these points and draw a line through them.

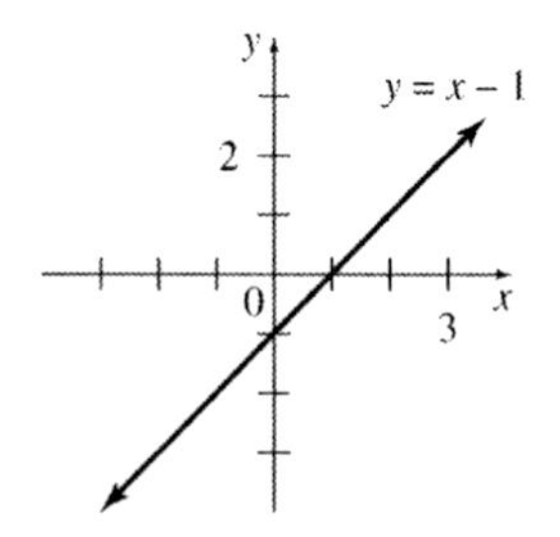

45. $y = 4x + 5$

Three ordered pairs that satisfy this equation are $(-2, -3)$, $(-1, 1)$, and $(0, 5)$. Plot these points and draw a line through them.

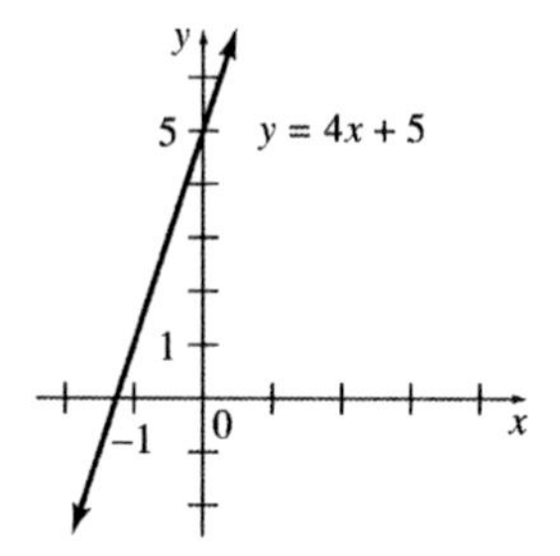

46. $y = -4x + 9$

Three ordered pairs that satisfy this equation are $(0, 9)$, $(1, 5)$, and $(2, 1)$. Plot these points and draw a line through them.

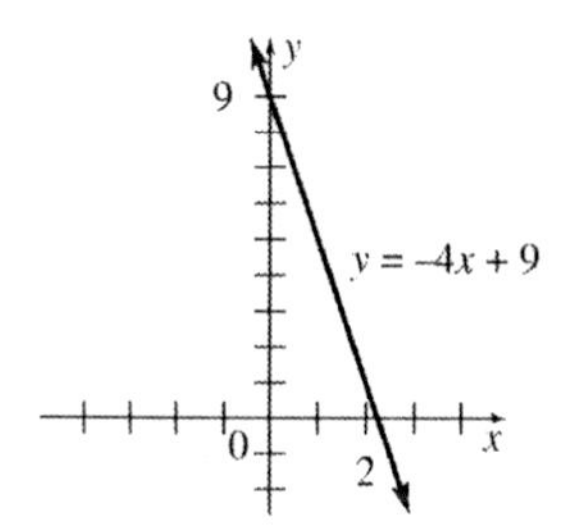

47. $y = -6x + 12$

Three ordered pairs that satisfy this equation are $(0, 12)$, $(1, 6)$, and $(2, 0)$. Plot these points and draw a line through them.

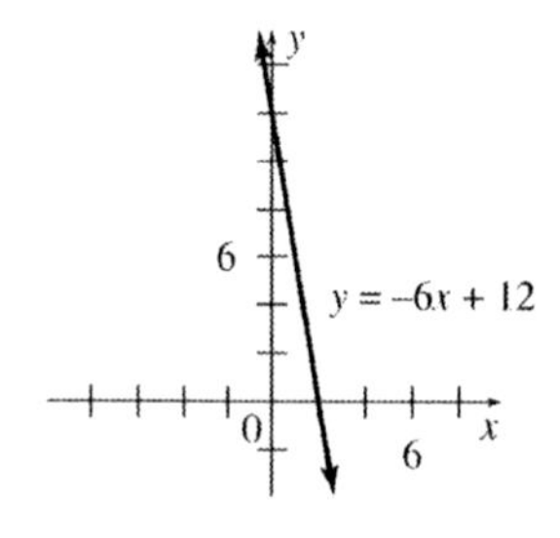

48. $2x - 3y = 12$

Find the intercepts.
If $y = 0$, then

$$\begin{aligned} 2x - 3(0) &= 12 \\ 2x &= 12 \\ x &= 6 \end{aligned}$$

so the x-intercept is 6.
If $x = 0$, then

$$\begin{aligned} 2(0) - 3y &= 12 \\ -3y &= 12 \\ y &= -4 \end{aligned}$$

so the y-intercept is -4.
Plot the ordered pairs $(6, 0)$ and $(0, -4)$ and draw a line through these points. (A third point may be used as a check.)

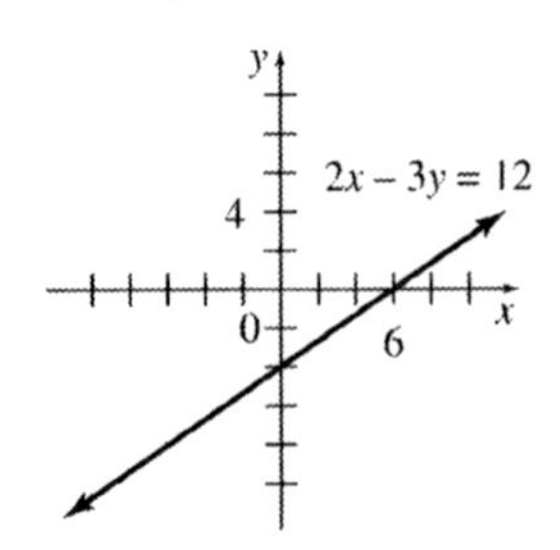

49. $3x - y = -9$

Find the intercepts.
If $y = 0$, then

$$\begin{aligned} 3x - 0 &= -9 \\ 3x &= -9 \\ x &= -3 \end{aligned}$$

If $x = 0$, then

$$\begin{aligned} 3(0) - y &= -9 \\ -y &= -9 \\ y &= 9 \end{aligned}$$

so the y-intercept is 9.
Plot the ordered pairs $(-3, 0)$ and $(0, 9)$ and draw a line through these points. (A third point may be used as a check.)

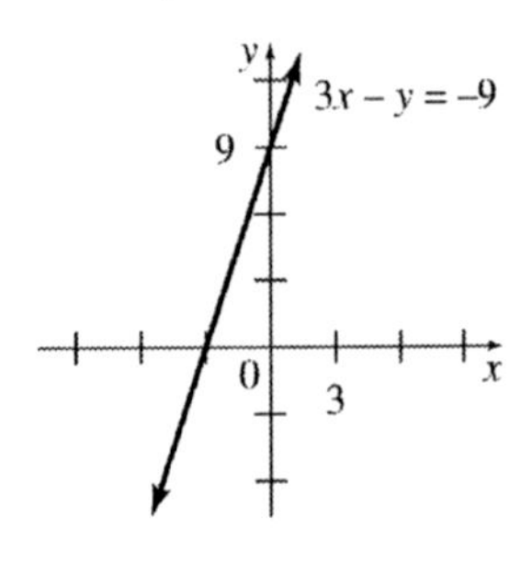

50. $3y - 7x = -21$

Find the intercepts.
If $y = 0$, then

$$\begin{aligned} 3(0) + 7x &= -21 \\ -7x &= -21 \\ x &= 3 \end{aligned}$$

so the x-intercept is 3.
If $x = 0$, then

$$\begin{aligned} 3y - 7(0) &= -21 \\ 3y &= -21 \\ y &= -7 \end{aligned}$$

so the y-intercept is -7.
Plot the ordered pairs $(3, 0)$ and $(0, -7)$ and draw a line through these points. (A third point may be used as a check.)

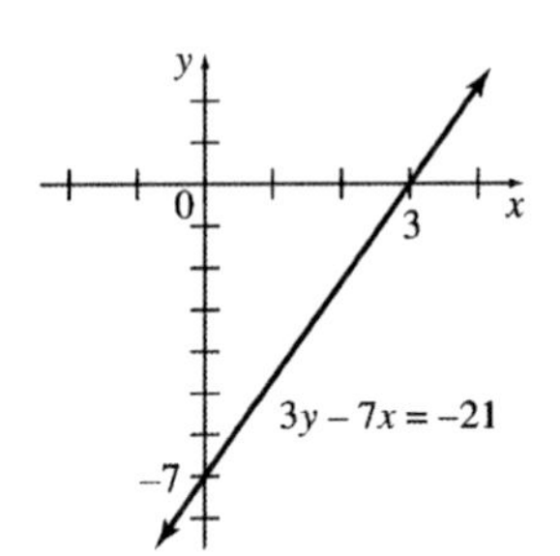

51. $5y + 6x = 11$

Find the intercepts.
If $y = 0$, then

$$\begin{aligned} 5(0) + 6x &= 11 \\ 6x &= 11 \\ x &= \frac{11}{6} \end{aligned}$$

so the x-intercept is $\frac{11}{6}$.
If $x = 0$, then

$$\begin{aligned} 5y + 6(0) &= 11 \\ 5y &= 11 \\ y &= \frac{11}{5} \end{aligned}$$

so the y-intercept is $\frac{11}{5}$.

Plot the ordered pairs $\left(\frac{11}{6}, 0\right)$ and $\left(0, \frac{11}{5}\right)$ and draw a line through these points. (A third point may be used as a check.)

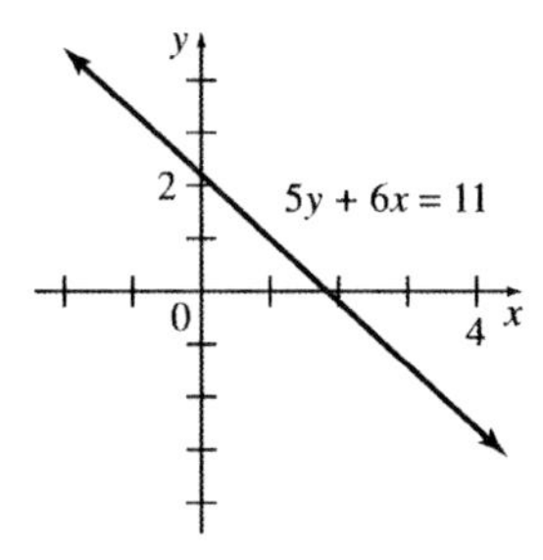

52. $y = -2$

5The equation $y = -2$, or, equivalently, $y = 0x - 2$, always gives the same y-value, -2, for any value of x. The graph of this equation is the horizontal line with y-intercept -2.

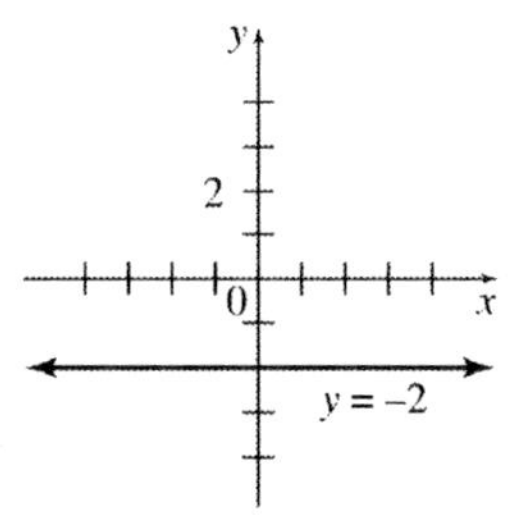

53. $x = 4$

For any value of y, the x-value is 4. Because all ordered pairs that satisfy this equation have the same first number, this equation does not represent a function. The graph is the vertical line with x-intercept 4.

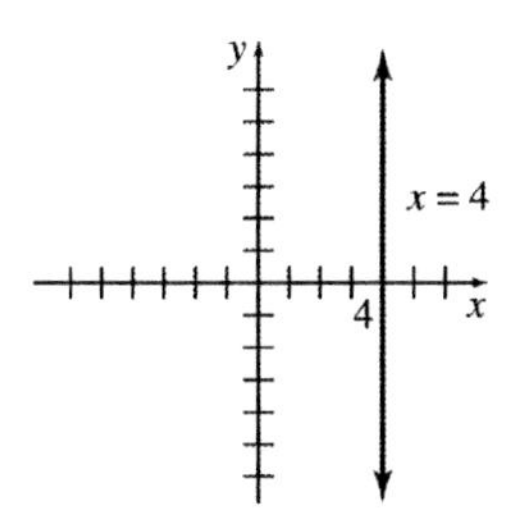

54. $x + 5 = 0$

This equation may be rewritten as $x = -5$. For any value of y, the x-value is -5. Because all ordered pairs that satisfy this equation have the same first number, this equation does not represent a function. The graph is the vertical line with x-intercept -5.

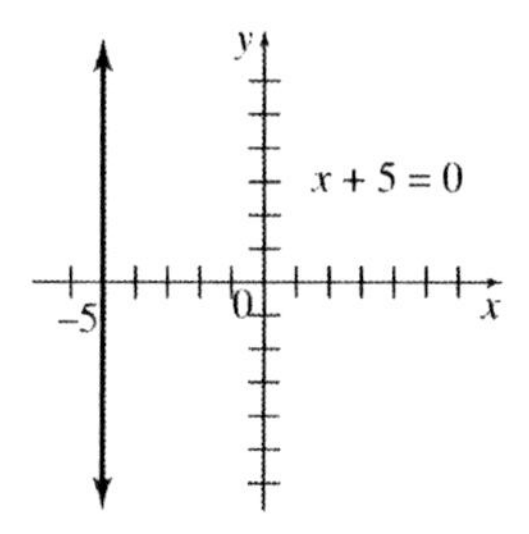

55. $y + 8 = 0$

This equation may be rewritten as $y = -8$, or, equivalently, $y = 0x + -8$. The y-value is -8 for any value of x. The graph is the horizontal line with y-intercept -8.

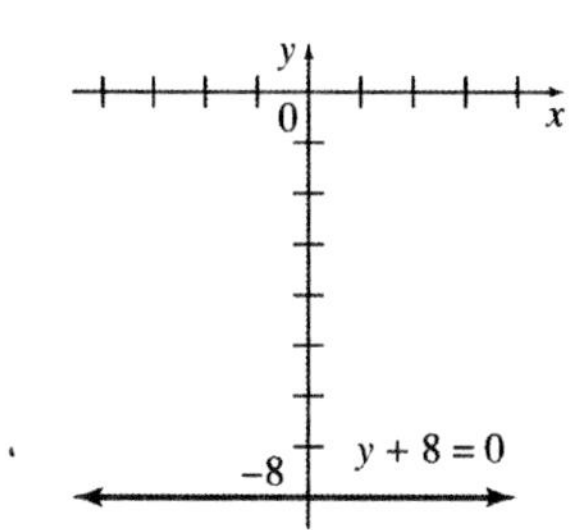

56. $y = 2x$

Three ordered pairs that satisfy this equation are $(0, 0)$, $(-2, -4)$, and $(2, 4)$. Use these points to draw the graph.

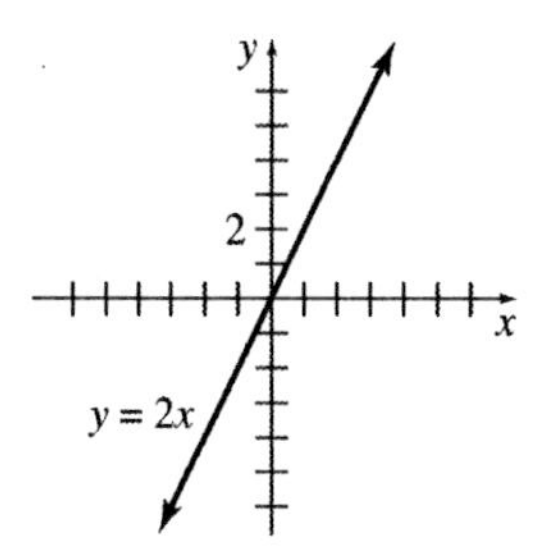

57. $y = -5x$

Three ordered pairs that satisfy this equation are $(0,0)$, $(-1,5)$, and $(1,-5)$. Use these points to draw the graph.

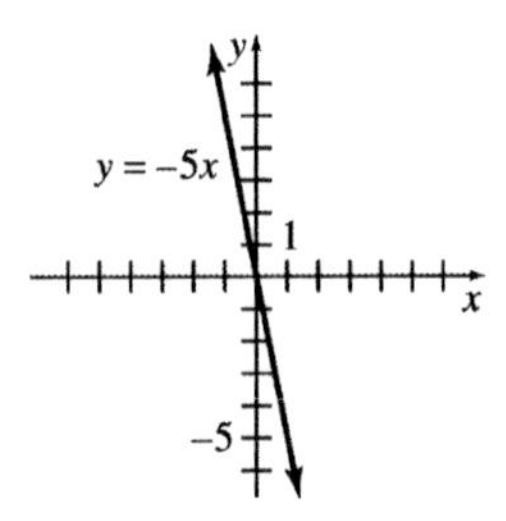

58. $x + 4y = 0$

If $y = 0$, then $x = 0$, so the x-intercept is 0. If $x = 0$, then $y = 0$, so the y-intercept is 0. Both intercepts give the same ordered pair, $(0,0)$.
To get a second point, choose some other value of x (or y). For example if $x = 4$, then

$$\begin{aligned} x + 4y &= 0 \\ 4 + 4y &= 0 \\ 4y &= -4 \\ y &= -1, \end{aligned}$$

giving the ordered pair $(4,-1)$. Graph the line through $(0,0)$ and $(4,-1)$.

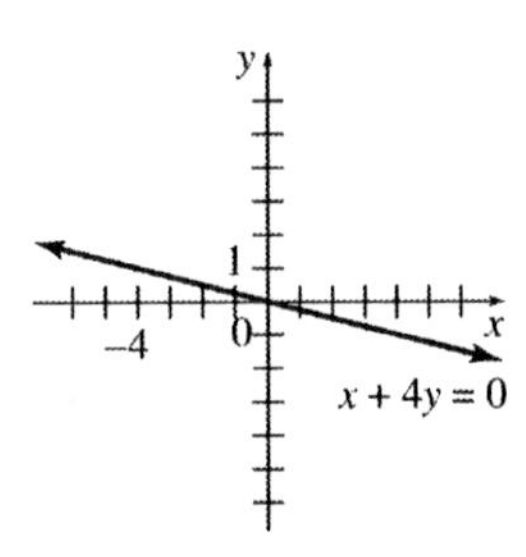

59. $3x - 5y = 0$

If $y = 0$, then $x = 0$, so the x-intercept is 0. If $x = 0$, then $y = 0$, so the y-intercept is 0. Both intercepts give the same ordered pair $(0,0)$.
To get a second point, choose some other value of x (or y). For example, if $x = 5$, then

$$\begin{aligned} 3x - 5y &= 0 \\ 3(5) - 5y &= 0 \\ 15 - 5y &= 0 \\ -5y &= -15 \\ y &= 3 \end{aligned}$$

giving the ordered pair $(5,3)$. Graph the line through $(0,0)$ and $(5,3)$.

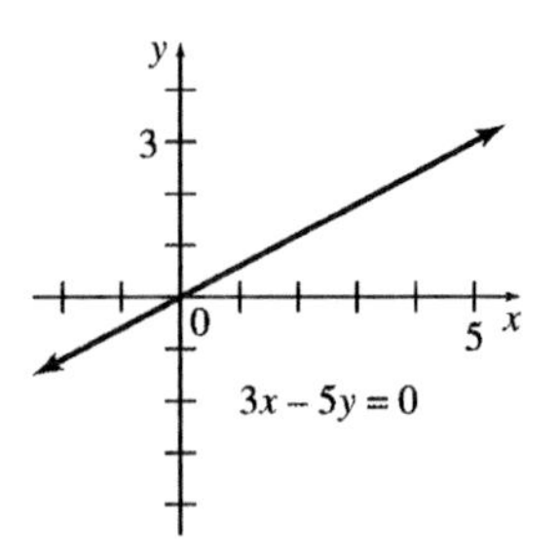

60. **(a)** The line goes through (2, 27,000) and (5, 63,000).

$$m = \frac{63{,}000 - 27{,}000}{5 - 2} = 12{,}000$$

$$\begin{aligned} y - 27{,}000 &= 12{,}000(x - 2) \\ y - 27{,}000 &= 12{,}000x - 24{,}000 \\ y &= 12{,}000x + 3000 \end{aligned}$$

(b) Let y =100,000; find x.

$$\begin{aligned} 100{,}000 &= 12{,}000x + 3000 \\ 97{,}000 &= 12{,}000x \\ 8.08 &= x \end{aligned}$$

Sales would surpass $100,000 after 8 years, 1 month.

61. **(a)**

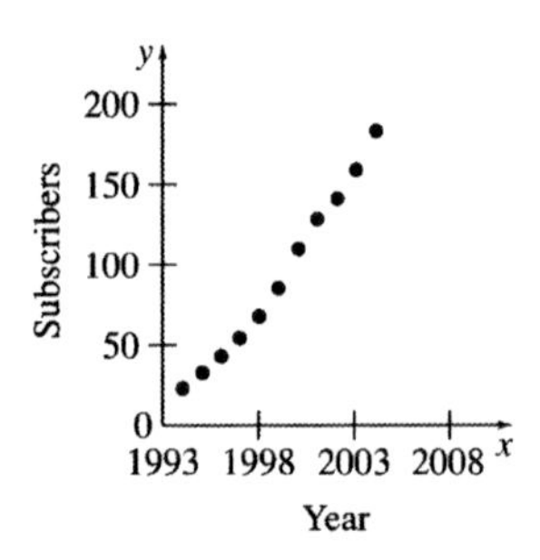

The number of subscribers is increasing and the data appear to be nearly linear.

(b) Find the slope using $(3, 44.04)$ and $(11, 182.14)$.

(c)
$$m = \frac{182.14 - 44.04}{11 - 3} = \frac{138.1}{8} = 17.2625$$

$$\begin{aligned} y - 182.14 &= 17.2625(x - 11) \\ y - 182.14 &= 17.2625x - 189.89 \\ y &= 17.2625x - 7.75 \end{aligned}$$

Rounding the slope to the nearest hundredth, the equation is $y = 17.26x - 7.75$.
The year 2005 corresponds to $x = 2005 - 1993 = 12$.

$$\begin{aligned} y &= 17.26(12) - 7.75 \\ y &= 199.37 \end{aligned}$$

The approximation using the equation is less than the actual number of subscribers.

62. (a) The line goes through $(0, 8)$ and $(5, 50)$.

$$m = \frac{50 - 8}{5 - 0} = 8.4$$

$$n - 8 = 8.4(t - 0)$$
$$n = 8.4t + 8$$

(b) Let $n = 75$; solve for t.

$$75 = 8.4t + 8$$
$$67 = 8.4t$$
$$8 \approx t$$

8 years after 2006, or in the year 2014, the number of models should exceed 75.

(c) The year 2025 is too far in the future; too many other factors may affect the demand for hybrid vehicles over that span of years.

63. (a) The line goes through $(0, 100)$ and $(24, 201.6)$.

$$m = \frac{201.6 - 100}{24 - 0} \approx 4.23$$

$$b = 100$$
$$y = 4.23x + 100$$

(b) The year 2000 corresponds to $x = 18$.

$$y = 4.23(18) + 100$$
$$y = 176.14$$

The estimate is more than, but close to, the actual CPI.

(c) It is increasing at a rate of 4.23 per year.

64. (a) The line goes through $(4, 0.17)$ and $(7, 0.33)$.

$$m = \frac{0.33 - 0.17}{7 - 4} = \frac{0.16}{3} \approx 0.053$$

$$y - 0.33 = \frac{0.16}{3}(x - 7)$$

$$y - 0.33 = 0.053x - 0.373$$
$$y \approx 0.053x - 0.043$$

(b) Let $y = 0.5$; solve for x.

$$0.5 = 0.053x - 0.043$$
$$0.543 = 0.053x$$
$$10.2 = x$$

In about 10.2 years, half of these patients will have AIDS.

65. (a) Let $x =$ age.

$$u = 0.85(220 - x) = 187 - 0.85x$$
$$l = 0.7(220 - x) = 154 - 0.7x$$

(b) $u = 187 - 0.85(20) = 170$
$l = 154 - 0.7(20) = 140$

The target heart rate zone is 140 to 170 beats per minute.

(c) $u = 187 - 0.85(40) = 153$
$l = 154 - 0.7(40) = 126$

The target heart rate zone is 126 to 153 beats per minute.

(d)

$$154 - 0.7x = 187 - 0.85(x + 36)$$
$$154 - 0.7x = 187 - 0.85x - 30.6$$
$$154 - 0.7x = 156.4 - 0.85x$$
$$0.15x = 2.4$$
$$x = 16$$

The younger woman is 16; the older woman is $16 + 36 = 52$. $l = 0.7(220 - 16) \approx 143$ beats per minute.

66. Let x represent the force and y represent the speed. The linear function contains the points $(0.75, 2)$ and $(0.93, 3)$.

$$m = \frac{3 - 2}{0.93 - 0.75} = \frac{1}{0.18} = \frac{1}{\frac{18}{100}} = \frac{100}{18} = \frac{50}{9}$$

Use point-slope form to write the equation.

$$y - 2 = \frac{50}{9}(x - 0.75)$$
$$y - 2 = \frac{50}{9}x - \frac{50}{9}(0.75)$$
$$y = \frac{50}{9}x - \frac{75}{18} + 2$$
$$y = \frac{50}{9}x - \frac{13}{6}$$

Now determine y, the speed, when x, the force, is 1.16.

$$y = \frac{50}{9}(1.16) - \frac{13}{6}$$
$$= \frac{58}{9} - \frac{13}{6}$$
$$= \frac{77}{18} \approx 4.3$$

The pony switches from a trot to a gallop at approximately 4.3 meters per second.

67. Let $x = 0$ correspond to 1900. Then the "life expectancy from birth" line contains the points $(0, 46)$ and $(104, 77.8)$.

$$m = \frac{77.8 - 46}{104 - 0} = \frac{31.3}{102} = 0.306$$

Since $(0, 46)$ is one of the points, the line is given by the equation

$$y = 0.306x + 46.$$

The "life expectancy from age 65" line contains the points $(0, 76)$ and $(104, 83.7)$.

$$m = \frac{83.7 - 76}{104 - 0} = \frac{7.7}{104} \approx 0.074$$

Since $(0, 76)$ is one of the points, the line is given by the equation

$$y = 0.074x + 76.$$

Set the two equations equal to determine where the lines intersect. At this point, life expectancy should increase no further.

$$\begin{aligned} 0.306x + 46 &= 0.074x + 76 \\ 0.232x &= 30 \\ x &\approx 129 \end{aligned}$$

Determine the y-value when $x = 129$. Use the first equation.

$$\begin{aligned} y &= 0.306(129) + 46 \\ &= 39.474 + 46 \\ &= 85.474 \end{aligned}$$

Thus, the maximum life expectancy for humans is about 86 years.

68. $y = 34x + 230$

Let $y = 1000$.

$$\begin{aligned} 1000 &= 34x + 230 \\ 770 &= 34x \\ x &\approx 22.6 \end{aligned}$$

According to this formula, approximately 23 acorns per square meter would result in 1000 deer tick larvae per 400 square meters.

69. **(a)**
$$m = \frac{27.4 - 22.8}{45 - 5} = \frac{4.6}{40} = 0.115$$

$$\begin{aligned} y - 22.8 &= 0.115(x - 5) \\ y - 22.8 &= 0.115x - 0.575 \\ y &= 0.115x + 22.2 \end{aligned}$$

(b)
$$m = \frac{25.8 - 20.6}{45 - 5} = \frac{5.2}{40} = 0.13$$

$$\begin{aligned} y - 20.6 &= 0.13(x - 5) \\ y - 20.6 &= 0.13x - 0.65 \\ y &= 0.13x + 19.95 \end{aligned}$$

(c) Since $0.13 > 0.115$, women have the faster increase.

(d) Let $y = 30$ and use the equation from part (a) to solve for x.

$$\begin{aligned} 30 &= 0.115x + 22.2 \\ 7.8 &= 0.115x \\ 68 &\approx x \end{aligned}$$

68 years after 1960, or in the year 2028, men's median age at first marriage will reach 30.

(e) Let $x = 68$ and use the equation from part (b) to find y.

$$\begin{aligned} y &= 0.13(68) + 19.95 \\ y &= 8.84 + 19.95 \\ y &= 28.79 \end{aligned}$$

The median age for women at first marriage will be about 28.8 years.

70. **(a)** The line goes through the points $(0, 86{,}821)$ and $(30, 252{,}920)$.

$$\begin{aligned} m &= \frac{252{,}920 - 86{,}821}{30 - 0} \\ &= \frac{166{,}099}{30} \\ &\approx 5536.63 \end{aligned}$$

Since one of the points is $(0, 86{,}821)$, the line is given by the equation

$$y = 5536.63x + 86{,}821.$$

(b) The year 2010 corresponds to $x = 40$.

$$\begin{aligned} y &= 5536.63(40) + 86{,}821 \\ y &\approx 308{,}286. \end{aligned}$$

We predict that the number of immigrants to California in 2010 will be about 308,286.

71. (a) The line goes through $(0, 1.59)$ and $(24, 5.08)$.

$$m = \frac{5.08 - 1.59}{24 - 0} = \frac{3.49}{24} \approx 0.145$$
$$b = 1.59$$
$$y = 0.145x + 1.59$$

(b) The year 2014 corresponds to $x = 30$.

$$y = 0.145(30) + 1.59$$
$$y = 5.94$$

In 2010, the number of cohabitating adults will be about 5.94 million.

72. (a) If the temperature rises 0.3C° per decade, it rises 0.03C° per year.

$$m = 0.03$$
$$b = 15, \text{ since a point is } (0, 15).$$

$$T = 0.03t + 15$$

(b) Let $T = 19$; find t.

$$19 = 0.03t + 15$$
$$4 = 0.03t$$
$$133.3 = t$$
$$133 \approx t$$
$$1970 + 133 = 2103$$

The temperature will rise to 19°C in about the year 2103.

73. (a) Plot the points $(15, 1600)$, $(200, 15{,}000)$, $(290, 24{,}000)$, and $(520, 40{,}000)$.

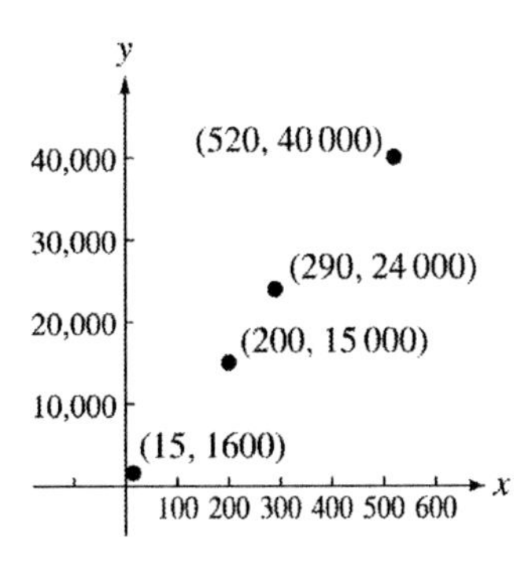

The points lie approximately on a line, so there appears to be a linear relationship between distance and time.

(b) The graph of any equation of the form $y = mx$ goes through the origin, so the line goes through $(520, 40{,}000)$ and $(0, 0)$.

$$m = \frac{40{,}000 - 0}{520 - 0} \approx 76.9$$
$$b = 0$$
$$y = 76.9x + 0$$
$$y = 76.9x$$

(c) Let $y = 60{,}000$; solve for x.

$$60{,}000 = 76.9x$$
$$780.23 \approx x$$

Hydra is about 780 megaparsecs from earth.

(d) $A = \dfrac{9.5 \times 10^{11}}{m}, m = 76.9$

$$A = \frac{9.5 \times 10^{11}}{76.9}$$
$$= 12.4 \text{ billion years}$$

74. (a) $m = \dfrac{13{,}660 - 10{,}770}{15 - 0} = \dfrac{2890}{15} \approx 192.7$

This means that each year there is an increase of about 193 stations.

(b) $b = 10{,}770$
$$y = 192.7x + 10{,}770$$

(c) Let $y = 15{,}000$ and solve the equation for x.

$$15{,}000 = 192.7x + 10{,}770$$
$$4230 = 192.7x$$
$$22 \approx x$$

The estimated year when it is expected that the number of stations will first exceed 15,000 is 2012.

75. (a)

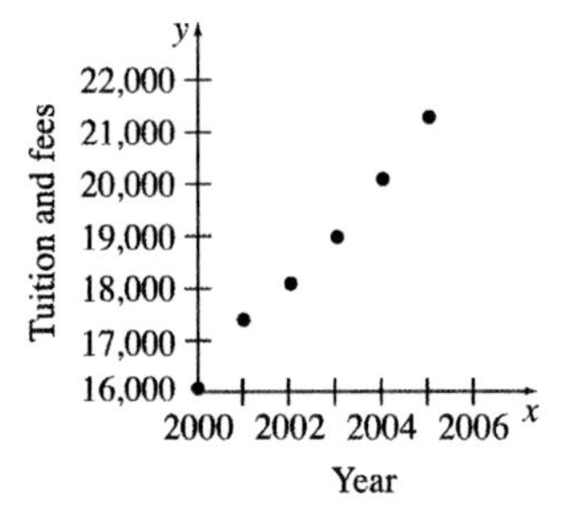

Yes, the data appear to lie roughly along a straight line.

(b) $m = \dfrac{21{,}235 - 16{,}072}{5 - 0} = \dfrac{5163}{5} = 1032.6$

$$b = 16{,}072$$
$$y = 1032.6x + 16{,}072$$

The slope 1032.6 indicates that tuition and fees have increased approximately \$1033 per year.

(c) The year 2025 is too far in the future to rely on this equation to predict costs; too many other factors may influence these costs by then.

1.2 Linear Functions and Applications

1. $f(2) = 7 - 5(2) = 7 - 10 = -3$

2. $f(4) = 7 - 5(4) = 7 - 20 = -13$

3. $f(-3) = 7 - 5(-3) = 7 + 15 = 22$

4. $f(-1) = 7 - 5(-1) = 7 + 5 = 12$

5. $g(1.5) = 2(1.5) - 3 = 3 - 3 = 0$

6. $g(2.5) = (2.5) - 3 = 5 - 3 = 2$

7. $g\left(-\frac{1}{2}\right) = 2\left(-\frac{1}{2}\right) - 3 = -1 - 3 = -4$

8. $g\left(-\frac{3}{4}\right) = 2\left(-\frac{3}{4}\right) - 3 = -\frac{3}{2} - 3 = -\frac{9}{2}$

9. $f(t) = 7 - 5(t) = 7 - 5t$

10. $g(k^2) = 2(k^2) - 3 = 2k^2 - 3$

11. This statement is true.
When we solve $y = f(x) = 0$, we are finding the value of x when $y = 0$, which is the x-intercept. When we evaluate $f(0)$, we are finding the value of y when $x = 0$, which is the y-intercept.

12. This statement is false.

The graph of $f(x) = -5$ is a horizontal line.

13. This statement is true.
Only a vertical line has an undefined slope, but a vertical line is not the graph of a function. Therefore, the slope of a linear function cannot be defined.

14. This statement is true.

For any value of a,

$$f(0) = a \cdot 0 = 0,$$

so the point $(0, 0)$, which is the origin, lies on the line.

15. The fixed cost is constant for a particular product and does not change as more items are made. The marginal cost is the rate of change of cost at a specific level of production and is equal to the slope of the cost function at that specific value; it approximates the cost of producing one additional item.

19. \$10 is the fixed cost and \$2.25 is the cost per hour.

Let $x =$ number of hours;
$R(x) =$ cost of renting a snowboard for x hours.

Thus,

$$\begin{aligned} R(x) &= \text{fixed cost} + (\text{cost per hour}) \\ &\quad \cdot (\text{number of hours}) \\ R(x) &= 10 + (2.25)(x) \\ &= 2.25x + 10 \end{aligned}$$

20. \$10 is the fixed cost and \$0.99 is the cost per downloaded song—the marginal cost.

Let $x =$ the number of downloaded songs and
$C(x) =$ cost of downloading x songs

Then,

$$\begin{aligned} C(x) &= (\text{marginal cost}) \\ &\quad \cdot (\text{number of downloaded songs}) \\ &\quad + \text{fixed cost} \\ C(x) &= 0.99x + 10. \end{aligned}$$

21. 50¢ is the fixed cost and 35¢ is the cost per half-hour.

Let $x =$ the number of half-hours;
$C(x) =$ the cost of parking a car for x half-hours.

Thus,

$$\begin{aligned} C(x) &= 50 + 35x \\ &= 35x + 50. \end{aligned}$$

22. \$44 is the fixed cost and \$0.28 is the cost per mile.

Let $x =$ the number of miles;
$R(x) =$ the cost of renting for x miles.

Thus,

$$\begin{aligned} R(x) &= \text{fixed cost} + (\text{cost per mile}) \\ &\quad \cdot (\text{number of miles}) \\ R(x) &= 44 + 0.28x. \end{aligned}$$

23. Fixed cost, \$100; 50 items cost \$1600 to produce.

Let $C(x) =$ cost of producing x items.
$C(x) = mx + b$, where b is the fixed cost.

$$C(x) = mx + 100$$

Now,

$C(x) = 1600$ when $x = 50$, so

$$1600 = m(50) + 100$$
$$1500 = 50m$$
$$30 = m.$$

Thus, $C(x) = 30x + 100$.

24. Fixed cost: \$35; 8 items cost \$395.

Let $C(x) =$ cost of x items
$C(x) = mx + b$, where b is the fixed cost
$C(x) = mx + 35$

Now, $C(x) = 395$ when $x = 8$, so

$$395 = m(8) + 35$$
$$360 = 8m$$
$$45 = m.$$

Thus, $C(x) = 45x + 35$.

25. Marginal cost: \$75; 50 items cost \$4300.

$$C(x) = 75x + b$$

Now, $C(x) = 4300$ when $x = 50$.

$$4300 = 75(50) + b$$
$$4300 = 3750 + b$$
$$550 = b$$

Thus, $C(x) = 75x + 550$.

26. Marginal cost, \$120; 700 items cost \$96,500 to produce.

$$C(x) = 120x + b$$

Now, $C(x) = 96{,}500$ when $x = 700$.

$$96{,}500 = 120(700) + b$$
$$96{,}500 = 84{,}000 + b$$
$$12{,}500 = b$$

Thus, $C(x) = 120x + 12{,}500$.

27. $D(q) = 16 - 1.25q$

(a) $D(0) = 16 - 1.25(0) = 16 - 0 = 16$

When 0 watches are demanded, the price is \$16.

(b) $D(4) = 16 - 1.25(4) = 16 - 5 = 11$

When 400 watches are demanded, the price is \$11.

(c) $D(8) = 16 - 1.25(8) = 16 - 10 = 6$

When 800 watches are demanded, the price is \$6.

(d) Let $D(q) = 8$. Find q.

$$8 = 16 - 1.25q$$
$$\frac{5}{4}q = 8$$
$$q = 6.4$$

When the price is \$8, 640 watches are demanded.

(e) Let $D(q) = 10$. Find q.

$$10 = 16 - 1.25q$$
$$\frac{5}{4}q = 6$$
$$q = 4.8$$

When the price is \$10, 480 watches are demanded.

(f) Let $D(q) = 12$. Find q.

$$12 = 16 - 1.25q$$
$$\frac{5}{4}q = 4$$
$$q = 3.2$$

When the price is \$12, 320 watches are demanded.

(g)

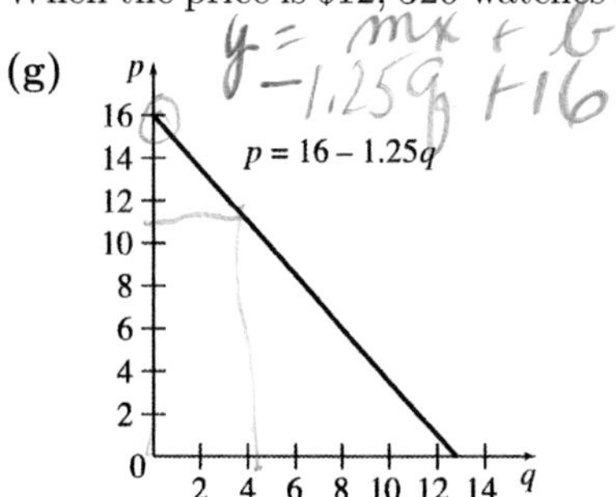

(h) $S(q) = 0.75q$

Let $S(q) = 0$. Find q.

$$0 = 0.75q$$
$$0 = q$$

When the price is \$0, 0 watches are supplied.

(i) Let $S(q) = 10$. Find q.

$$10 = 0.75q$$
$$\frac{40}{3} = q$$
$$q = 13.\overline{3}$$

When the price is \$10, about 1333 watches are supplied.

(j) Let $S(q) = 20$. Find q.

$$20 = 0.75q$$
$$\frac{80}{3} = q$$
$$q = 26.\overline{6}$$

When the price is \$20, about 2667 watches are demanded.

(k)

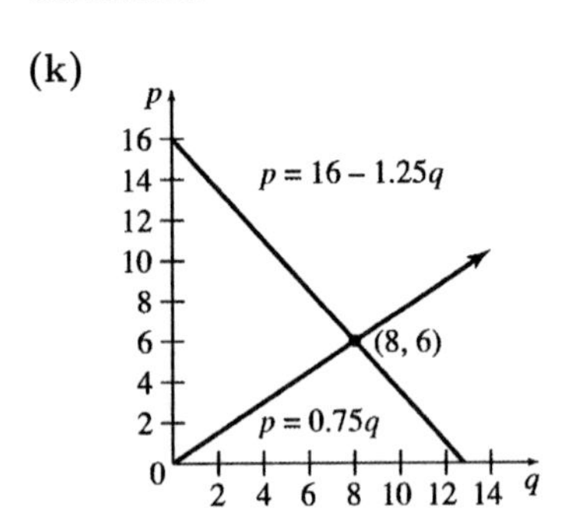

(l)

$$D(q) = S(q)$$
$$16 - 1.25q = 0.75q$$
$$16 = 2q$$
$$8 = q$$
$$S(8) = 0.75(8) = 6$$

The equilibrium quantity is 800 watches, and the equilibrium price is \$6.

28. $D(q) = 5 - 0.25q$

(a) $D(0) = 5 - 0.25(0) = 5 - 0 = 5$

When 0 quarts are demanded, the price is \$5.

(b) $D(4) = 5 - 0.25(4) = 5 - 1 = 4$

When 400 quarts are demanded, the price is \$4.

(c) $D(8.4) = 5 - 0.25(8.4) = 5 - 2.1 = 2.9$

When 840 quarts are demanded, the price is \$2.90.

(d) Let $D(q) = 4.5$. Find q.

$$4.5 = 5 - 0.25q$$
$$0.25q = 0.5$$
$$q = 2$$

When the price is \$4.50, 200 quarts are demanded.

(e) Let $D(q) = 3.25$. Find q.

$$3.25 = 5 - 0.25q$$
$$0.25q = 1.75$$
$$q = 7$$

When the price is \$3.25, 700 quarts are demanded.

(f) Let $D(q) = 2.4$. Find q.

$$2.4 = 5 - 0.25q$$
$$0.25q = 2.6$$
$$q = 10.4$$

When the price is \$2.40, 1040 quarts are demanded.

(g)

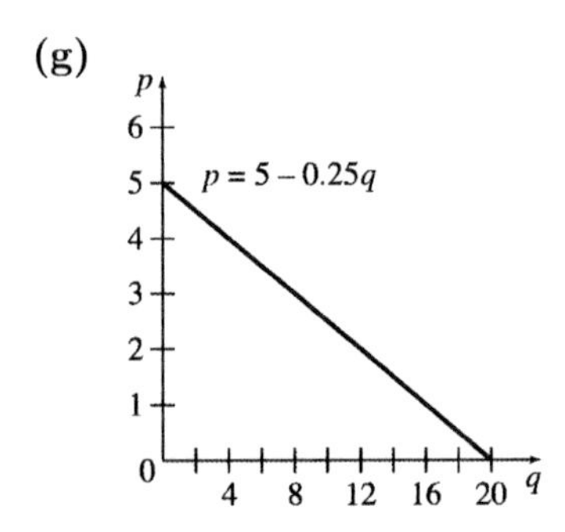

(h) $S(q) = 0.25q$

Let $S(q) = 0$. Find q.

$$0 = 0.25q$$
$$q = 0$$

When the price is \$0, 0 quarts are supplied.

(i) Let $S(q) = 2$. Find q.

$$2 = 0.25q$$
$$q = 8$$

When the price is \$2, 800 quarts are supplied.

(j) Let $S(q) = 4.5$. Find q.

$$4.5 = 0.25q$$
$$q = 18$$

When the price is \$4.50, 1800 quarts are supplied.

(k)

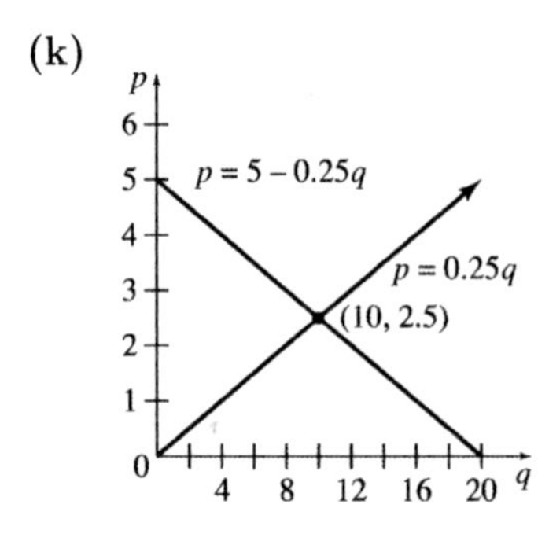

(l)
$$\begin{aligned} D(q) &= S(q) \\ 5 - 0.25q &= 0.25q \\ 5 &= 0.5q \\ 10 &= q \\ S(10) &= 0.25(10) = 2.5 \end{aligned}$$

The equilibrium quantity is 1000 quarts and the equilibrium price is \$2.50.

29. $p = S(q) = \frac{2}{5}q$; $p = D(q) = 100 - \frac{2}{5}q$

(a)

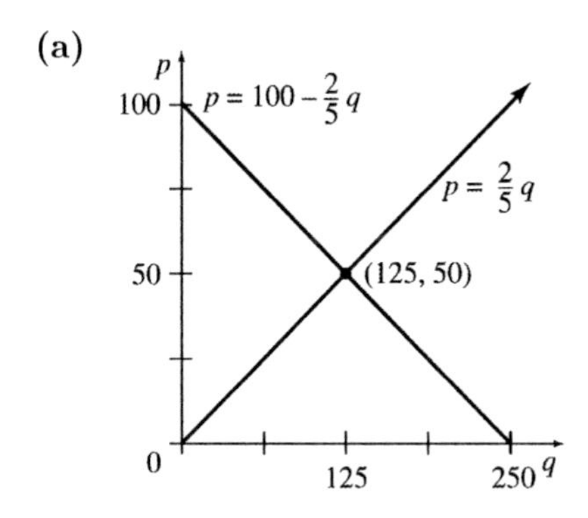

(b)
$$\begin{aligned} S(q) &= D(q) \\ \frac{2}{5}q &= 100 - \frac{2}{5}q \\ \frac{4}{5}q &= 100 \\ q &= 125 \\ S(125) &= \frac{2}{5}(125) = 50 \end{aligned}$$

The equilibrium quantity is 125, the equilibrium price is \$50

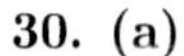

30. (a)

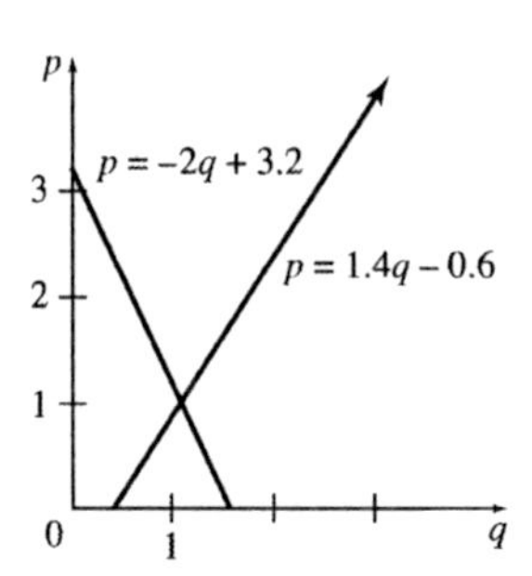

(b) $S(q) = p = 1.4q - 0.6$
$D(q) = p = -2q + 3.2$

Set supply equal to demand and solve for q.

$$\begin{aligned} 1.4q - 0.6 &= -2q + 3.2 \\ 1.4q + 2q &= 0.6 + 3.2 \\ 3.4q &= 3.8 \\ q &= \frac{3.8}{3.4} \\ q &\approx 1.12 \end{aligned}$$

$$\begin{aligned} S(1.12) &= 1.4(1.12) - .6 \\ &= 0.968 \end{aligned}$$

The equilibrium quantity is about 1120 pounds; the equilibrium price is about \$0.96

31. (a) $C(x) = mx + b$; $m = 3.50$; $C(60) = 300$

$$C(x) = 3.50x + b$$

Find b.

$$\begin{aligned} 300 &= 3.50(60) + b \\ 300 &= 210 + b \\ 90 &= b \\ C(x) &= 3.50x + 90 \end{aligned}$$

(b) $R(x) = 9x$
$C(x) = R(x)$

$$\begin{aligned} 3.50x + 90 &= 9x \\ 90 &= 5.5x \\ 16.36 &= x \end{aligned}$$

Joanne must produce and sell 17 shirts.

(c) $P(x) = R(x) - C(x)$; $P(x) = 500$

$$\begin{aligned} 500 &= 9x - (3.50x + 90) \\ 500 &= 5.5x - 90 \\ 590 &= 5.5x \\ 107.27 &= x \end{aligned}$$

To make a profit of \$500, Joanne must produce and sell 108 shirts.

32. **(a)** $C(x) = mx + b$
$C(1000) = 2675;\ b = 525$

Find m.

$$\begin{aligned} 2675 &= m(1000) + 525 \\ 2150 &= 1000m \\ 2.15 &= m \\ C(x) &= 2.15x + 525 \end{aligned}$$

(b) $R(x) = 4.95x$
$C(x) = R(x)$

$$\begin{aligned} 2.15x + 525 &= 4.95x \\ 525 &= 2.80x \\ 187.5 &= x \end{aligned}$$

In order to break even, he must produce and sell 188 books.

(c) $P(x) = R(x) - C(x);\ P(x) = 1000$

$$\begin{aligned} 1000 &= 4.95x - (2.15x + 525) \\ 1000 &= 4.95x - 2.15x - 525 \\ 1000 &= 2.80x - 525 \\ 1525 &= 2.80x \\ 544.6 &= x \end{aligned}$$

In order to make a profit of \$1000, he must produce and sell 545 books.

33. **(a)** Using the points $(100, 11.02)$ and $(400, 40.12)$,

$$m = \frac{40.12 - 11.02}{400 - 100} = \frac{29.1}{300} = 0.097.$$

$$\begin{aligned} y - 11.02 &= 0.097(x - 100) \\ y - 11.02 &= 0.097x - 9.7 \\ y &= 0.097x + 1.32 \\ C(x) &= 0.097x + 1.32 \end{aligned}$$

(b) The fixed cost is given by the constant in $C(x)$. It is \$1.32.

(c) $C(1000) = 0.097(1000) + 1.32 = 97 + 1.32$
$= 98.32$

The total cost of producing 1000 cups is \$98.32.

(d) $C(1001) = 0.097(1001) + 1.32 = 97.097 + 1.32$
$= 98.417$

The total cost of producing 1001 cups is \$98.417.

(e) Marginal cost $= 98.417 - 98.32$
$= \$0.097$ or $9.7¢$

(f) The marginal cost for *any* cup is the slope, \$0.097 or 9.7¢. This means the cost of producing one additional cup of coffee would be 9.7¢.

34. $C(10{,}000) = 547{,}500;\ C(50{,}000) = 737{,}500$

(a) $C(x) = mx + b$

$$\begin{aligned} m &= \frac{737{,}500 - 547{,}500}{50{,}000 - 10{,}000} \\ &= \frac{190{,}000}{40{,}000} = 4.75 \end{aligned}$$

$$\begin{aligned} y - 547{,}500 &= 4.75(x - 10{,}000) \\ y - 547{,}500 &= 4.75x - 47{,}500 \\ y &= 4.75x + 500{,}000 \\ C(x) &= 4.75x + 500{,}000 \end{aligned}$$

(b) The fixed cost is \$500,000.

(c) $C(100{,}000) = 4.75(100{,}000) + 500{,}000$
$= 475{,}000 + 500{,}000$
$= 975{,}000$

The total cost to produce 100,000 items is \$975,000.

(d) Since the slope of the cost function is 4.75, the marginal cost is \$4.75. This means that the cost of producing one additional item at this production level is \$4.75.

35. **(a)** $(100{,}000)(50) = 5{,}000{,}000$

Sales in 1996 would be $100{,}000 + 5{,}000{,}000 = 5{,}100{,}000$.

(b) The ordered pairs are (1, 100,000) and (6, 5,100,000).

$$m = \frac{5{,}100{,}000 - 100{,}000}{6 - 1} = \frac{5{,}000{,}000}{5} = 1{,}000{,}000$$

$$\begin{aligned} y - 100{,}000 &= 1{,}000{,}000(x - 1) \\ y - 100{,}000 &= 1{,}000{,}000x - 1{,}000{,}000 \\ y &= 1{,}000{,}000x - 900{,}000 \\ S(x) &= 1{,}000{,}000x - 900{,}000 \end{aligned}$$

(c) Let $S(x) = 1{,}000{,}000{,}000$. Find x.

$$\begin{aligned} 1{,}000{,}000{,}000 &= 1{,}000{,}000x - 900{,}000 \\ 1{,}000{,}900{,}000 &= 1{,}000{,}000x \\ x &= 1000.9 \end{aligned}$$

Sales would reach \$1 billion in about $1991 + 1000.9 = 2991.9$, or during the year 2991.
Sales would have to grow much faster than linearly to reach \$1 billion by 2003.

(d) Use ordered pairs (13, 356,000,000) and (14, 479,000,000).

$$m = \frac{479{,}000{,}000 - 356{,}000{,}000}{14 - 13} = 123{,}000{,}000$$

$$\begin{aligned} S(x) - 356{,}000{,}000 &= 123{,}000{,}000(x - 13) \\ S(x) - 356{,}000{,}000 &= 123{,}000{,}000x - 1{,}599{,}000000 \\ S(x) &= 123{,}000{,}000x - 1{,}243{,}000{,}000 \end{aligned}$$

(e) The year 2005 corresponds to $x = 2005 - 1990 = 15$.

$$\begin{aligned} S(15) &= 123{,}000{,}000(15) - 1{,}243{,}000{,}000 \\ S(15) &= 602{,}000{,}000 \end{aligned}$$

The estimated sales are \$602,000,000, which is less than the actual sales.

(f) Let $S(x) = 1{,}000{,}000{,}000$. Find x.

$$\begin{aligned} 1,000,000,000 &= 123{,}000{,}000x - 1{,}243{,}000{,}000 \\ 2{,}243{,}000{,}000 &= 123{,}000{,}000x \\ x &\approx 18.2 \end{aligned}$$

Sales would reach \$1 billion in about 1990 + 18.2 = 2008.2, or during the year 2009.

36. $C(x) = 5x + 20$; $R(x) = 15x$

(a)
$$\begin{aligned} C(x) &= R(x) \\ 5x + 20 &= 15x \\ 20 &= 10x \\ 2 &= x \end{aligned}$$

The break-even quantity is 2 units.

(b)
$$\begin{aligned} P(x) &= R(x) - C(x) \\ P(x) &= 15x - (5x + 20) \\ P(100) &= 15(100) - (5 \cdot 100 + 20) \\ &= 1500 - 520 = 980 \end{aligned}$$

The profit from 100 units is \$980.

(c)
$$\begin{aligned} P(x) &= 500 \\ 15x - (5x + 20) &= 500 \\ 10x - 20 &= 500 \\ 10x &= 520 \\ x &= 52 \end{aligned}$$

For a profit of \$500, 52 units must be produced.

37. $C(x) = 12x + 39$; $R(x) = 25x$

(a)
$$\begin{aligned} C(x) &= R(x) \\ 12x + 39 &= 25x \\ 39 &= 13x \\ 3 &= x \end{aligned}$$

The break-even quantity is 3 units.

(b)
$$\begin{aligned} P(x) &= R(x) - C(x) \\ P(x) &= 25x - (12x + 39) \\ P(x) &= 13x - 39 \\ P(250) &= 13(250) - 39 \\ &= 3250 - 39 \\ &= 3211 \end{aligned}$$

The profit from 250 units is \$3211.

(c) $P(x) = \$130$; find x.

$$\begin{aligned} 130 &= 13x - 39 \\ 169 &= 13x \\ 13 &= x \end{aligned}$$

For a profit of \$130, 13 units must be produced.

38. $C(x) = 85x + 900$
$R(x) = 105x$

Set $C(x) = R(x)$ to find the break-even quantity.

$$\begin{aligned} 85x + 900 &= 105x \\ 900 &= 20x \\ 45 &= x \end{aligned}$$

The break-even quantity is 45 units. You should decide not to produce since no more than 38 units can be sold.

$$\begin{aligned} P(x) &= R(x) - C(x) = 105x - (85x + 900) \\ &= 20x - 900 \end{aligned}$$

The profit function is $P(x) = 20x - 900$.

39. $C(x) = 105x + 6000$
$R(x) = 250x$

Set $C(x) = R(x)$ to find the break-even quantity.

$$\begin{aligned} 105x + 6000 &= 250x \\ 6000 &= 145x \\ 41.38 &\approx x \end{aligned}$$

The break-even quantity is about 41 units, so you should decide to produce.

$$\begin{aligned} P(x) &= R(x) - C(x) \\ &= 250x - (105x + 6000) \\ &= 145x - 6000 \end{aligned}$$

The profit function is $P(x) = 145x - 6000$.

40. $C(x) = 70x + 500$
$R(x) = 60x$

$$\begin{aligned} 70x + 500 &= 60x \\ 10x &= -500 \\ x &= -50 \end{aligned}$$

This represents a break-even quantity of -50 units. It is impossible to make a profit when the break-even quantity is negative. Cost will always be greater than revenue.

$$\begin{aligned} P(x) = R(x) - C(x) &= 60x - (70x + 500) \\ &= -10x - 500 \end{aligned}$$

The profit function is $P(x) = -10x - 500$.

41. $C(x) = 1000x + 5000$
$R(x) = 900x$

$$\begin{aligned} 900x &= 1000x + 5000 \\ -5000 &= 100x \\ -50 &= x \end{aligned}$$

It is impossible to make a profit when the break-even quantity is negative. Cost will always be greater than revenue.

$$\begin{aligned} P(x) &= R(x) - C(x) \\ &= 900x - (1000x + 5000) \\ &= -100x - 5000 \end{aligned}$$

The profit function is $P(x) = -100x - 5000$ (always a loss).

42. Use the formulas derived in Example 7 in this section of the textbook.

$$F = \frac{9}{5}C + 32$$

$$C = \frac{5}{9}(F - 32)$$

(a) $F = 58$; find C.

$$C = \frac{5}{9}(58 - 32)$$

$$C = \frac{5}{9}(26)$$

$$C = 14.4$$

The temperature is 14.4°C.

(b) $F = -20$; find C.

$$C = \frac{5}{9}(F - 32)$$

$$C = \frac{5}{9}(-20 - 32)$$

$$C = \frac{5}{9}(-52)$$

$$C = -28.9$$

The tempereature is -28.9°C.

(c) $C = 50$; find F.

$$F = \frac{9}{5}C + 32$$

$$F = \frac{9}{5}(50) + 32$$

$$F = 90 + 32$$
$$F = 122$$

The temperature is 122°F.

43. Use the formula derived in Example 7 in this section of the textbook.

$$F = \frac{9}{5}C + 32$$

$$C = \frac{5}{9}(F - 32)$$

(a) $C = 37$; find F.

$$F = \frac{9}{5}(37) + 32$$

$$F = \frac{333}{5} + 32$$

$$F = 98.6$$

The Fahrenheit equivalent of 37°C is 98.6°F.

(b) $C = 36.5$; find F.

$$F = \frac{9}{5}(36.5) + 32$$

$$F = 65.7 + 32$$
$$F = 97.7$$

$C = 37.5$; find F.

$$\begin{aligned} F &= \frac{9}{5}(37.5) + 32 \\ &= 67.5 + 32 = 99.5 \end{aligned}$$

The range is between 97.7°F and 99.5°F.

44. If the temperatures are numerically equal, then $F = C$.

$$F = \frac{9}{5}C + 32$$
$$C = \frac{9}{5}C + 32$$
$$-\frac{4}{5}C = 32$$
$$C = -40$$

The Celsius and Fahrenheit temperatures are numerically equal at $-40°$.

1.3 The Least Squares Line

2. For the set of points $(1, 4)$, $(2, 5)$, and $(3, 6)$, $Y = x + 3$. For the set $(4, 1)$, $(5, 2)$, and $(6, 3)$, $Y = x - 3$.

3. (a)

(b)

x	y	xy	x^2	y^2
1	0	0	1	0
2	0.5	1	4	0.25
3	1	3	9	1
4	2	8	16	4
5	2.5	12.5	25	6.25
6	3	18	36	9
7	3	21	49	9
8	4	32	64	16
9	4.5	40.5	81	20.25
10	5	50	100	25
55	25.5	186	385	90.75

$$r = \frac{n(\sum xy) - (\sum x)(\sum y)}{\sqrt{n(\sum x^2) - (\sum x)^2} \cdot \sqrt{n(\sum y^2) - (\sum y)^2}}$$
$$= \frac{10(186) - (55)(25.5)}{\sqrt{10(385) - (55)^2}\sqrt{10(90.75) - (25.5)^2}}$$
$$\approx 0.993$$

(c) The least squares line is of the form $Y = mx + b$. First solve for m.

$$m = \frac{n(\sum xy) - (\sum x)(\sum y)}{n(\sum x^2) - (\sum x)^2}$$
$$= \frac{10(186) - (55)(25.5)}{10(385) - (55)^2}$$
$$= 0.5545454545 \approx 0.55$$

Now find b.

$$b = \frac{\sum y - m(\sum x)}{n}$$
$$= \frac{25.5 - 0.5545454545(55)}{10}$$
$$= -0.5$$

Thus, $Y = 0.55x - 0.5$.

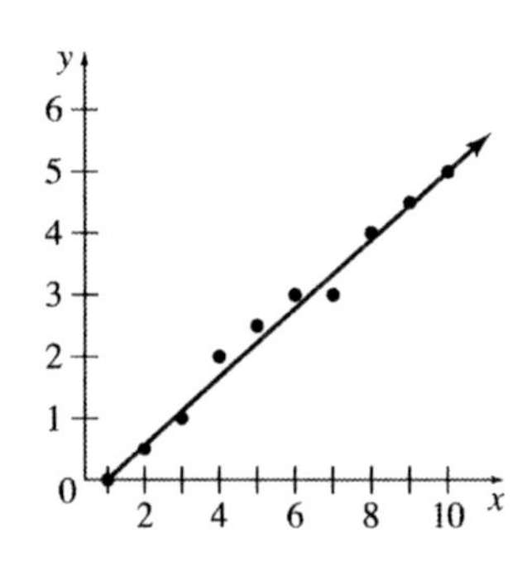

(d) Let $x = 11$. Find Y.

$$Y = 0.55(11) - 0.5 = 5.55$$

4.

x	y	xy	x^2	y^2
6.8	0.8	5.44	46.24	0.64
7.0	1.2	8.4	49.0	1.44
7.1	0.9	6.39	50.41	0.81
7.2	0.9	6.48	51.84	0.81
7.4	1.5	11.1	54.76	2.25
35.5	5.3	37.81	252.25	5.95

$$r = \frac{5(37.81) - (35.5)(5.3)}{\sqrt{5(252.25) - (35.5)^2} \cdot \sqrt{5(5.95) - (5.3)^2}} \approx 0.6985$$

$$r^2 = (0.6985)^2 \approx 0.5$$

The answer is choice (c).

5.

$$\begin{aligned}
nb + (\sum x)m &= \sum y \\
(\sum x)b + (\sum x^2)m &= \sum xy \\
nb + (\sum x)m &= \sum y \\
nb &= (\sum y) - (\sum x)m \\
b &= \frac{\sum y - m(\sum x)}{n} \\
(\sum x)\left(\frac{\sum y - m(\sum x)}{n}\right) + (\sum x^2)m &= \sum xy \\
(\sum x)[(\sum y) - m(\sum x)] + nm(\sum x^2) &= n(\sum xy) \\
(\sum x)(\sum y) - m(\sum x)^2 + nm(\sum x^2) &= n(\sum xy) \\
nm(\sum x^2) - m(\sum x)^2 &= n(\sum xy) - (\sum x)(\sum y) \\
m\left[n(\sum x^2) - (\sum x)^2\right] &= n(\sum xy) - (\sum x)(\sum y) \\
m &= \frac{n(\sum xy) - (\sum x)(\sum y)}{n(\sum x^2) - (\sum x)^2}
\end{aligned}$$

6. (a) $m = \dfrac{n(\sum xy) - (\sum x)(\sum y)}{n(\sum x^2) - (\sum x)^2}$

$$m = \frac{7(223{,}963.8) - (707)(2212)}{7(71{,}435) - 707^2}$$

$$m = 19.70714286 \approx 19.71$$

$$b = \frac{\sum y - m(\sum x)}{n}$$

$$b = \frac{2212 - (19.70714286)(707)}{7} \approx -1674.42$$

$$Y = 19.71x - 1674.42$$

(b) The year 2010 corresponds to $x = 110$.

$$Y = 19.71(110) - 1674.42 = 493.68$$

The expenditures in 2010 will reach about \$493.68 billion.

(c) Let $Y = 750$ and find x.

$$\begin{aligned}
750 &= 19.71x - 1674.42 \\
2424.42 &= 19.71x \\
x &\approx 123
\end{aligned}$$

The expenditures will reach \$750 billion in about the year 2023.

(d) $r = \dfrac{7(223{,}963.8) - (707)(2212)}{\sqrt{7(71{,}435) - 707^2} \cdot \sqrt{7(709{,}879.52) - 2212^2}}$

≈ 0.999

This indicates that the line fits the data points very well.

7. (a)
$$m = \frac{n(\sum xy) - (\sum x)(\sum y)}{n(\sum x^2) - (\sum y)}$$
$$m = \frac{10(8501.39) - (995)(85.65)}{10(99{,}085) - 995^2}$$
$$m = -0.2519393939 \approx -0.2519$$
$$b = \frac{\sum y - m(\sum x)}{n}$$
$$b = \frac{85.65 - (-0.2519393939)(995)}{10} \approx 33.6330$$
$$Y = -0.2519x + 33.6330$$

(b) The year 2010 corresponds to $x = 110$.

$$Y = -0.2519(110) + 33.6330 \approx 5.924 \text{ (in thousands)}$$

If the trend continues, there will be about 5924 banks in 2010.

(c) $$r = \frac{10(8501.39) - (995)(85.65)}{\sqrt{10(99{,}085) - 995^2} \cdot \sqrt{10(739.08) - 85.65^2}} \approx -0.977$$

This means that the least squares line fits the data points very well. The negative sign indicates that the number of banks is decreasing as the years increase.

8. (a)

Yes, the data points lie in a linear pattern.

(b)

x	y	xy	x^2	y^2
206	95	19,570	42,436	9025
802	138	110,676	643,204	19,044
1771	228	403.788	3,136,441	51,984
1198	209	250,382	1,435,204	43,681
1238	269	333,022	1,532,644	72,361
2786	309	860,874	1,761,796	95,481
1207	202	243,814	1,456,849	40,804
892	217	193,564	795,664	47,089
2411	109	262,799	5,812,921	11,881
2885	434	1,252,090	8,323,225	188,356
2705	399	1,079,295	7,317,025	159,201
948	206	195,288	898,704	42,436
2762	239	660,118	7,628,644	57,121
2815	329	926,135	7,924,225	108,241
24,626	3383	6,791,415	54,708,982	946,705

$$r = \frac{14(6{,}791{,}415) - (24{,}626)(3383)}{\sqrt{14(54{,}708{,}892) - 24{,}626^2} \cdot \sqrt{14(946{,}705) - 3383^2}} \approx 0.693$$

There is a positive correlation between the price and the distance.

(c) $m = \dfrac{n(\sum xy) - (\sum x)(\sum y)}{n(\sum x^2) - (\sum x)^2}$

$m = \dfrac{14(6{,}791{,}415) - (24{,}626)(3383)}{14(54{,}708{,}982) - 24{,}626^2}$

$m = 0.0737999664 \approx 0.0738$

$b = \dfrac{\sum y - m(\sum x)}{n}$

$b = \dfrac{3383 - (0.0737999664)(24{,}626)}{14} \approx 111.83$

$Y = 0.0738x + 111.83$

The marginal cost is about 7.38 cents per mile.

(d) In 2000, the marginal cost was 2.43 cents per mile. It increased to 7.38 cents per mile by 2006.

(e) Phoenix is the outlier.

9.

x	y	xy	x^2	y^2
97	6247	605,959	9409	39,025,009
98	6618	648,565	9604	43,797,924
99	7031	696,069	9801	49,434,961
100	7842	784,200	10,000	61,496,964
101	8234	831,634	10,201	67,798,756
102	8940	911,880	10,404	79,923,600
103	9205	948,115	10,609	84,732,025
104	9312	968,448	10,816	86,713,344
804	63,429	6,394,869	80,844	512,922,583

(a)

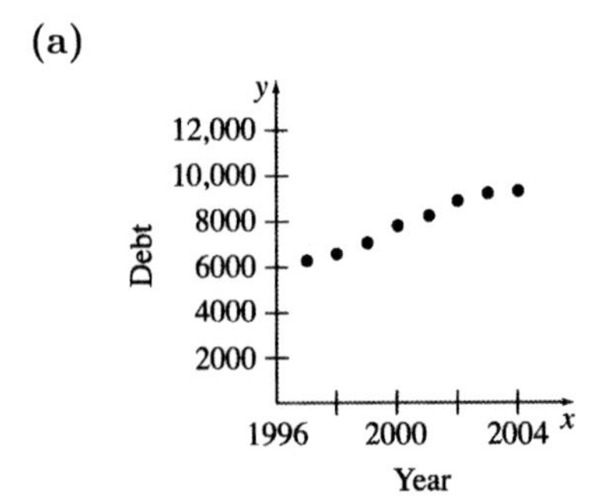

Yes, the pattern is linear.

(b) $m = \dfrac{n(\sum xy) - (\sum x)(\sum y)}{n(\sum x^2) - (\sum x)^2}$

$m = \dfrac{8(6{,}394{,}869) - (804)(63{,}429)}{8(80{,}844) - 804^2}$

$m = 482.25$

$$b = \frac{\sum y - m(\sum x)}{n}$$

$$b = \frac{63{,}429 - 482.25(804)}{8} = -40{,}537.5$$

$$Y = 482.25x - 40{,}537.5$$

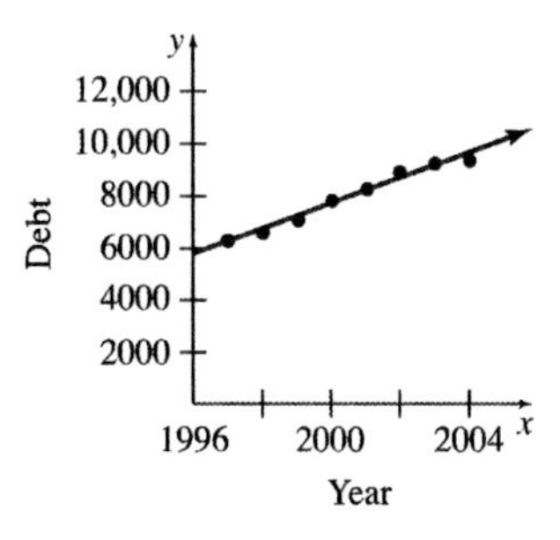

The least squares line seems to be a good fit.

(c) $r = \dfrac{8(6{,}394{,}869) - (804)(63{,}429)}{\sqrt{8(80{,}844) - 804^2} \cdot \sqrt{8(512{,}922{,}583) - 63{,}429^2}} \approx 0.987$

This confirms the least squares line is a good fit.

(d) Let $Y = 12{,}000$ and solve for x.

$$12{,}000 = 482.25x - 40{,}537.5$$
$$52{,}537.5 = 482.25x$$
$$x \approx 109$$

If the trend continues, credit card debt will reach \$12,000 in 1900 + 109, or the year 2009.

10.

x	y	xy	x^2	y^2
92	12.8	1177.6	8464	163.84
93	13.9	1292.7	8649	193.21
94	15.0	1410.0	8836	225.00
95	14.7	1396.5	9025	216.09
96	15.1	1449.6	9216	228.01
97	15.1	1464.7	9409	228.01
98	15.9	1558.2	9604	252.81
99	16.9	1673.1	9801	285.61
100	17.4	1740.0	10,000	302.76
101	17.1	1727.1	10,201	292.41
102	16.8	1713.6	10,404	282.24
103	16.6	1709.8	10,609	275.56
104	16.9	1757.6	10,816	285.61
1274	204.2	20,070.5	125,034	3231.16

(a) $m = \dfrac{n(\sum xy) - (\sum x)(\sum y)}{\sqrt{n(\sum x^2) - (\sum x)^2}}$

$m = \dfrac{13(20{,}070.5) - (1274)(204.2)}{13(125{,}034) - 1274^2}$

$m = 0.3236263736 \approx 0.324$

$b = \dfrac{\sum y - m(\sum x)}{n}$

$b = \dfrac{204.2 - 0.3236263736(1274)}{13}$

≈ -16.01

$Y = 0.324x - 16.01$

$r = \dfrac{13(20{,}070.5) - (1274)(204.2)}{\sqrt{13(125{,}034) - 1274^2} \cdot \sqrt{13(3231.16) - 204.2^2}}$

≈ 0.898

(b)

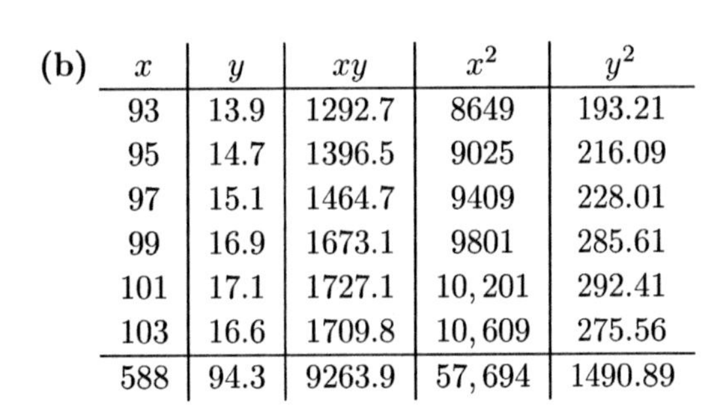

x	y	xy	x^2	y^2
93	13.9	1292.7	8649	193.21
95	14.7	1396.5	9025	216.09
97	15.1	1464.7	9409	228.01
99	16.9	1673.1	9801	285.61
101	17.1	1727.1	10,201	292.41
103	16.6	1709.8	10,609	275.56
588	94.3	9263.9	57,694	1490.89

$m = \dfrac{n(\sum xy) - (\sum x)(\sum y)}{n(\sum x^2) - (\sum x)^2}$

$m = \dfrac{6(9263.9) - (588)(94.3)}{6(57{,}694) - 588^2}$

$m = 0.3214285714 \approx 0.321$

$b = \dfrac{\sum y - m(\sum x)}{n}$

$b = \dfrac{94.3 - 0.3214285714(588)}{6} \approx -15.78$

$Y = 0.321x - 15.78$

$r = \dfrac{6(9263.9) - (588)(94.3)}{\sqrt{6(57{,}694) - 588^2} \cdot \sqrt{6(1490.89) - 94.3^2}}$

≈ 0.906

11. (a)

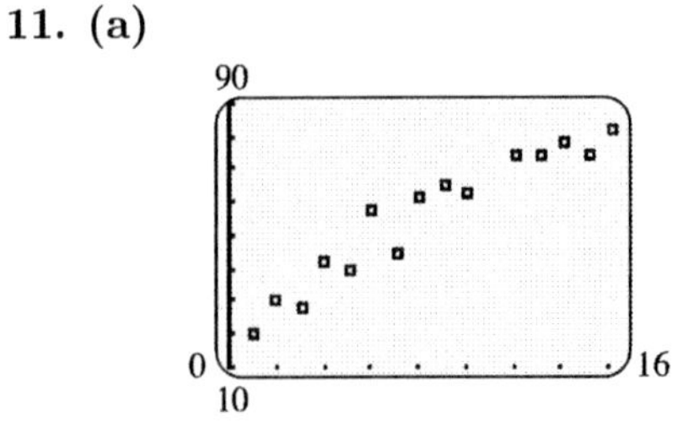

Yes, the points lie in a linear pattern.

(b) Using a calculator's STAT feature, the correlation coefficient is found to be $r \approx 0.959$. This indicates that the percentage of successful hunts does trend to increase with the size of the hunting party.

(c) $Y = 3.98x + 22.7$

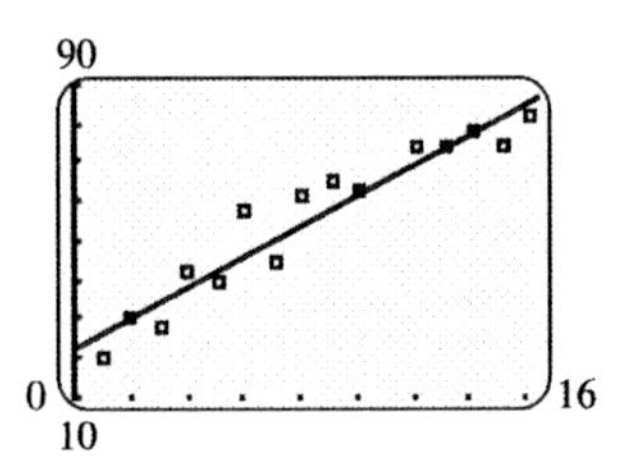

12. (a)

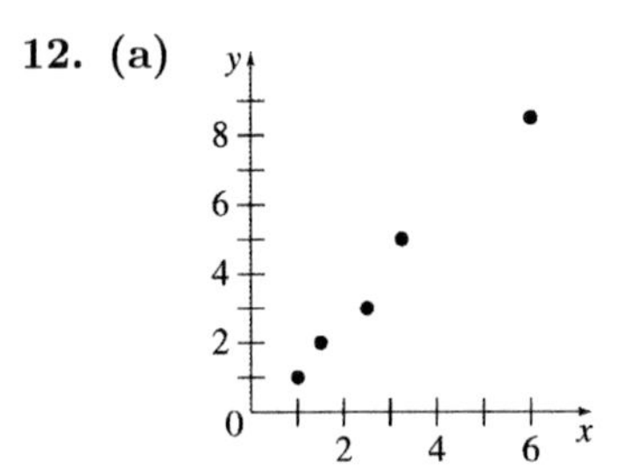

Yes, the data appear to be linear.

(b)

x	y	xy	x^2	y^2
5.8	8.6	49.88	33.64	73.96
1.5	1.9	2.85	2.25	3.61
2.3	3.1	7.13	5.29	9.61
1.0	1.0	1.0	1.0	1.0
3.3	5.0	16.5	10.89	25.0
13.9	19.6	77.36	53.07	113.18

$$m = \frac{n(\sum xy) - (\sum x)(\sum y)}{n(\sum x^2) - (\sum x)^2}$$
$$= \frac{5(77.36) - (13.9)(19.6)}{5(53.07) - 13.9^2}$$
$$= 1.585250901 \approx 1.585$$

$$b = \frac{\sum y - m(\sum x)}{n}$$
$$= \frac{19.6 - 1.585250901(13.9)}{5}$$
$$\approx -0.487$$
$$Y = 1.585x - 0.487$$

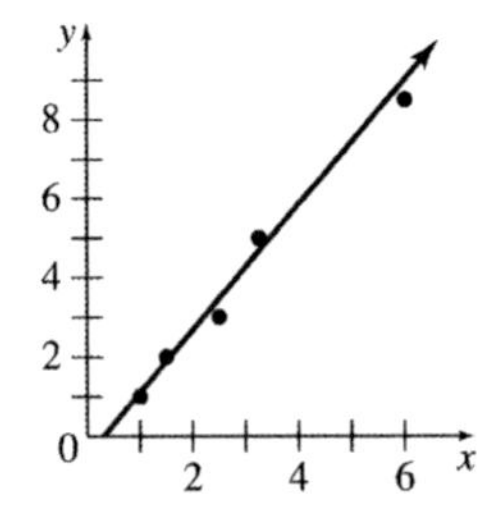

(c) No, it gives negative values for small widths.

(d) $r = \dfrac{5(77.36) - (13.9)(19.6)}{\sqrt{5(53.07) - 13.9^2} \cdot \sqrt{5(113.18) - 19.6^2}}$

≈ 0.999

13. (a)

x	y	xy	x^2	y^2
88.6	20.0	1772	7849.96	400.0
71.6	16.0	1145.6	5126.56	256.0
93.3	19.8	1847.34	8704.89	392.04
84.3	18.4	1551.12	7106.49	338.56
80.6	17.1	1378.26	6496.36	292.41
75.2	15.5	1165.6	5655.04	240.25
69.7	14.7	1024.59	4858.09	216.09
82.0	17.1	1402.2	6724	292.41
69.4	15.4	1068.76	4816.36	237.16
83.3	16.2	1349.46	6938.89	262.44
79.6	15.0	1194	6336.16	225
82.6	17.2	1420.72	6822.76	295.84
80.6	16.0	1289.6	6496.36	256.0
83.5	17.0	1419.5	6972.25	289.0
76.3	14.4	1098.72	5821.69	207.36
1200.6	249.8	20,127.47	96,725.86	4200.56

$$m = \frac{n(\sum xy) - (\sum x)(\sum y)}{n(\sum x^2) - (\sum x)^2}$$
$$= \frac{15(20{,}127.47) - (1200.6)(249.8)}{15(96{,}725.86) - 1200.6^2}$$
$$= 0.211925009 \approx 0.212$$
$$b = \frac{\sum y - m(\sum x)}{n}$$
$$= \frac{249.8 - 0.212(1200.6)}{15}$$
$$\approx -0.315$$
$$Y = 0.212x - 0.315$$

(b) Let $x = 73$; find Y.
$Y = 0.212(73) - 0.315$
≈ 15.2
If the temperature were 73°F, you would expect to hear 15.2 chirps per second.

(c) Let $Y = 18$; find x.
$18 = 0.212x - 0.315$
$18.315 = 0.212x$
$86.4 \approx x$
When the crickets are chirping 18 times per second, the temperature is 86.4°F.

(d)

$$r = \frac{15(20{,}127) - (1200.6)(249.8)}{\sqrt{15(96{,}725.86) - (1200.6)^2} \cdot \sqrt{15(4200.56) - (249.8)^2}}$$
$$= 0.835$$

14. (a)

x	y	xy	x^2	y^2
5	26.9	134.5	25	723.61
10	25.8	258.0	100	665.64
15	24.7	370.5	225	610.09
20	22.3	446.0	400	497.29
30	18.7	561.0	900	349.69
35	17.9	626.5	1225	320.41
40	17.2	688.0	1600	295.84
45	17.3	778.5	2025	299.29
50	16.0	800.0	2500	256.00
55	15.5	852.5	3025	240.25
305	202.3	5515.5	12,025	4258.11

$$m = \frac{n(\sum xy) - (\sum x)(\sum y)}{n(\sum x^2) - (\sum x)^2}$$

$$m = \frac{10(5515.5) - (305)(202.3)}{10(12{,}025) - 305^2}$$

$$m = -0.240459137 \approx -0.240$$

$$b = \frac{\sum y - m(\sum x)}{n}$$

$$b = \frac{202.9 - (-0.2428317077)(302)}{10}$$

$$\approx 27.6$$

$$Y = -0.240x + 27.6$$

(b) The year 2010 corresponds to $x = 60$. Let $x = 60$. Solve for Y.

$$Y = -0.243(60) + 27.6 \approx 13$$

The ratio in 2010 should be about 13.

(c) $$r = \frac{10(5500.2) - (302)(202.9)}{\sqrt{10(11{,}704) - 302^2} \cdot \sqrt{10(4277.07) - 202.9^2}}$$

$$\approx -0.975$$

The value indicates a strong negative linear correlation.

15. (a)

Yes, the data appear to lie along a straight line.

$$r = \frac{8(2159.635) - (140)(95.364)}{\sqrt{8(3500) - 140^2} \cdot \sqrt{8(1366.748) - 95.364^2}}$$

$$\approx 0.999$$

Yes, there is a strong positive linear correlation between the income and the year.

(c) $$m = \frac{n(\sum xy) - (\sum x)(\sum y)}{n(\sum x^2) - (\sum x)^2}$$

$$m = \frac{8(2159.635) - (140)(95.364)}{8(3500) - 140^2}$$

$$m = 0.4673952381 \approx 0.467$$

$$b = \frac{\sum y - m(\sum x)}{n}$$

$$b = \frac{95.364 - 0.4673952381(140)}{8}$$

$$\approx 3.74$$

$$Y = 0.467x + 3.74$$

(d) The year 2020 corresponds to $x = 50$.

$$Y = 0.467(50) + 3.74 = 27.09$$

The predicted poverty level in the year 2020 is $27,090.

16. (a)

x	y	xy	x^2	y^2
540	20	10,800	291,600	400
510	16	8160	260,100	256
490	10	4900	240,100	100
560	8	4480	313,600	64
470	12	5640	220,900	144
600	11	6600	360,000	121
540	10	5400	291,600	100
580	8	4640	336,400	64
680	15	10,200	462,400	225
560	8	4480	313,600	64
560	13	7280	313,600	169
500	14	7000	250,000	196
470	10	4700	220,900	100
440	10	4400	193,600	100
520	11	5720	270,400	121
620	11	6820	384,400	121
680	8	5440	462,400	64
550	8	4400	302,500	64
620	7	4340	384,400	49
10,490	210	115,400	5,872,500	2522

$$m = \frac{n(\sum xy) - (\sum x)(\sum y)}{n(\sum x^2) - (\sum x)^2}$$

$$m = \frac{19(115{,}400) - (10{,}490)(210)}{19(5{,}872{,}500) - 10{,}490^2}$$

$$m = -0.0066996227 \approx -0.0067$$

$$b = \frac{\sum y - m(\sum x)}{n}$$

$$b = \frac{210 - (-0.0066996227)(10{,}490)}{19}$$

$$\approx 14.75$$

$$Y = -0.0067x + 14.75$$

(b) Let $x = 420$; find Y.

$$Y = -0.0067(420) + 14.75 = 11.936 \approx 12$$

(c) Let $x = 620$; find Y.

$$Y = -0.0067(620) + 14.75 = 10.596 \approx 11$$

(d)

$$r = \frac{19(115{,}400) - (10{,}490)(210)}{\sqrt{19(5{,}872{,}500) - (10{,}490)^2} \cdot \sqrt{19(2522) - 210^2}}$$

$$\approx -0.13$$

(e) There is no linear relationship between a student's math SAT and mathematics placement test scores.

17. (a)

x	y	xy	x^2	y^2
150	5000	750,000	22,500	25,000,000
175	5500	962,500	30,625	30,250,000
215	6000	1,290,000	46,225	36,000,000
250	6500	1,625,000	62,500	42,250,000
280	7000	1,960,000	78,400	49,000,000
310	7500	2,325,000	96,100	56,250,000
350	8000	2,800,000	122,500	64,000,000
370	8500	3,145,000	136,900	72,250,000
420	9000	3,780,000	176,400	81,000,000
450	9500	4,275,000	202,500	90,250,000
2970	72,500	22,912,500	974,650	546,250,000

$$m = \frac{n(\sum xy) - (\sum x)(\sum y)}{n(\sum x^2) - (\sum x)^2}$$

$$m = \frac{10(22{,}912{,}500) - (2970)(72{,}500)}{10(974{,}650) - 2970^2}$$

$$m = 14.90924806 \approx 14.9$$

$$b = \frac{\sum y - m(\sum x)}{n}$$

$$b = \frac{72{,}500 - 14.9(2970)}{10}$$

$$\approx 2820$$

$$Y = 14.9x + 2820$$

(b) Let $x = 150$; find Y.

$$Y = 14.9(150) + 2820$$
$$Y \approx 5060, \text{ compared to actual } 5000$$

Let $x = 280$; find Y.

$$Y = 14.9(280) + 2820$$
$$\approx 6990, \text{ compared to actual } 7000$$

Let $x = 420$; find Y.

$$Y = 14.9(420) + 2820$$
$$\approx 9080, \text{ compared to actual } 9000$$

(c) Let $x = 230$; find Y.

$$Y = 14.9(230) + 2820$$
$$\approx 6250$$

Adam would need to buy a 6500 BTU air conditioner.

18. (a)

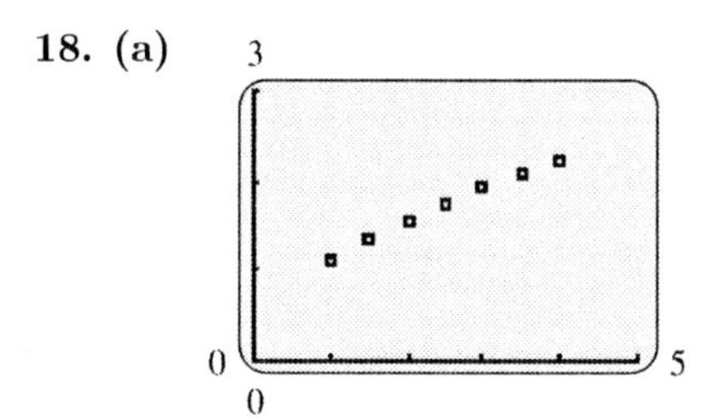

(b)

L	T	LT	L^2	T^2
1.0	1.11	1.11	1	1.2321
1.5	1.36	2.04	2.25	1.8496
2.0	1.57	3.14	4	2.4649
2.5	1.76	4.4	6.25	3.0976
3.0	1.92	5.76	9	3.6864
3.5	2.08	7.28	12.25	4.3264
4.0	2.22	8.88	16	4.9284
17.5	12.02	32.61	50.75	21.5854

$$m = \frac{n(\sum xy) - (\sum x)(\sum y)}{n(\sum x^2) - (\sum x)^2}$$

$$m = \frac{7(32.61) - (17.5)(12.02)}{7(50.75) - 17.5^2}$$

$$m = 0.3657142857 \approx 0.366$$

$$b = \frac{\sum T - m(\sum L)}{n}$$

$$b = \frac{12.02 - 0.3657142857(17.5)}{7}$$

$$\approx 0.803$$

$$Y = 0.366x + 0.803$$

The line seems to fit the data.

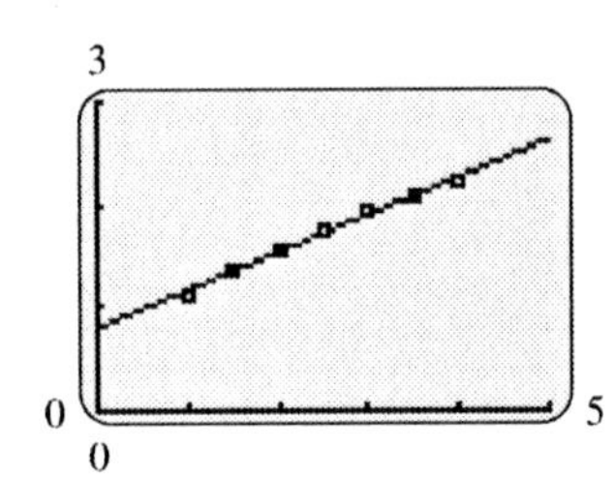

(c) $r = \dfrac{7(32.61) - (17.5)(12.02)}{\sqrt{7(50.75) - 17.5^2} \cdot \sqrt{7(21.5854) - 12.02^2}}$

$= 0.995$, which indicates a good fit and confirms the conclusion in part (b).

19. (a) Use a calculator's statistical features to obtain the least squares line.

$$y = -0.1358x + 113.94$$

(b) $y = -0.3913x + 148.98$

(c) Set the two equations equal and solve for x.

$$-0.1358x + 113.94 = -0.3913x + 148.98$$
$$0.2555x = 35.04$$
$$x \approx 137$$

The women's record will catch up with the men's record in 1900 + 137, or in the year 2037.

(d) $r_{men} \approx -0.9823$
$r_{women} \approx -0.9487$

Both sets of data points closely fit a line with negative slope.

(e)

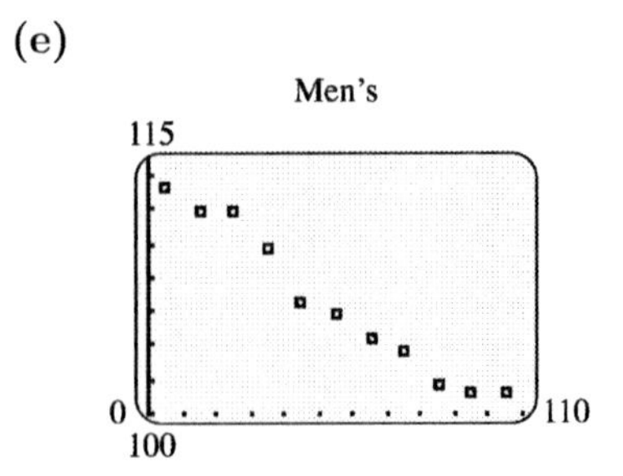

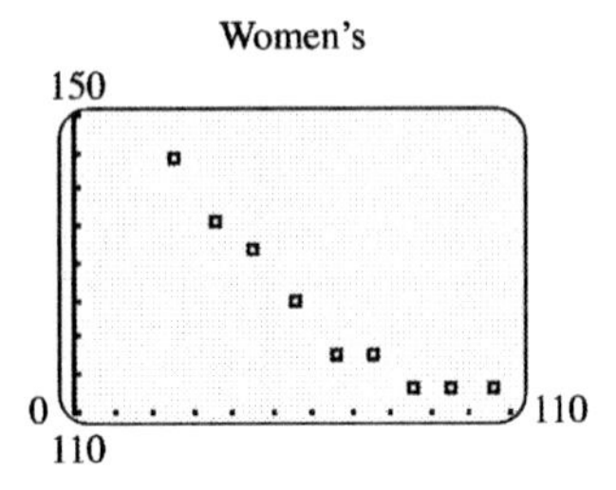

20. (a)

$$r = \frac{10(399.16) - (500)(20.668)}{\sqrt{10(33{,}250) - 500^2} \cdot \sqrt{10(91.927042) - (20.668)^2}}$$

$$= -0.995$$

Yes, there does appear to be a linear correlation.

(b) $m = \dfrac{n(\sum xy) - (\sum x)(\sum y)}{n(\sum x^2) - (\sum x)^2}$

$$m = \frac{10(399.16) - (500)(20.668)}{10(33{,}250) - 500^2}$$

$$m = -0.0768775758 \approx -0.0769$$

$$b = \frac{\sum y - m(\sum x)}{n}$$

$$b = \frac{20.668 - (-0.0768775758)(500)}{10}$$

$$\approx 5.91$$

$$Y = -0.0769x + 5.91$$

(c) Let $x = 50$

$$Y = -.0769(50) + 5.91 \approx 2.07$$

The predicted number of points expected when a team is at the 50 yard line is 2.07 points.

21. **(a)**
$$m = \frac{n(\sum xy) - (\sum x)(\sum y)}{n(\sum x^2) - (\sum x)^2}$$
$$m = \frac{10(5496) - (110)(466)}{10(1540) - 110^2}$$
$$m = 1.121212121 \approx 1.12$$
$$b = \frac{\sum y - m(\sum x)}{n}$$
$$b = \frac{466 - 1.121212121(110)}{10}$$
$$\approx 34.27$$
$$Y = 1.12x + 34.27$$

(b)
$$= \frac{10(5496) - (110)(466)}{\sqrt{10(1540) - 110^2} \cdot \sqrt{10(22{,}232) - 466^2}}$$
$$\approx 0.8963$$

Yes, the value indicates a good fit of the least squares line to the data.

(c) The year 2005 corresponds to $x = 25$.

$$Y = 1.12(25) + 34.27 = 62.27 \approx 62$$

The predicted length of a game in 2005 is 2 hours + 62 minutes, or 3:02.

22. **(a)** Convert the time from hours and minutes into hours.

$$\text{average speed} = \frac{101.7}{29.583} \approx 3.44$$

Apt's average speed was about 3.44 miles per hour.

(b)

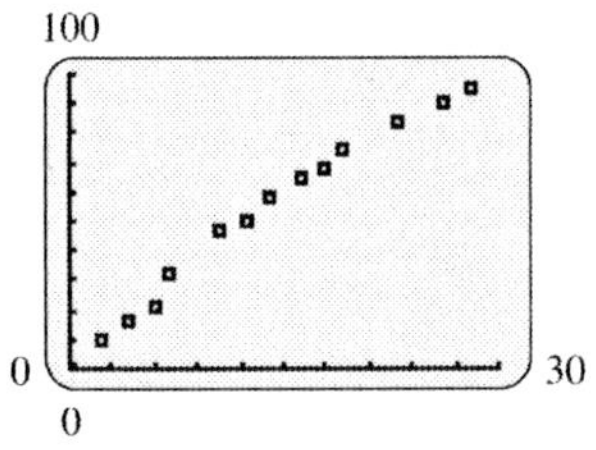

Yes, the data appear to lie approximately on a straight line.

(c)

x	y
0	0
2.233	9.6
4.133	16.5
6.167	21.6
7.167	31.6
10.85	42.4
12.7	49.8
14.333	58
16.5	65.2
18.033	68.4
19.417	73.7
23.117	83.1
26.15	89.6
28.3	95.8
29.583	101.7
218.683	807

Using a graphing calculator,

$$Y = 3.39x + 4.32.$$

(d) Using a graphing calculator,

$$r = 0.994$$

Yes, this value indicates a good fit of the least squares line to the data.

(e) A good value for Apt's average speed would be

$$m = 3.39 \text{ miles per hour.}$$

This value is slower than the average speed found in part (a).

Chapter 1 Review Exercises

2. To complete the coefficient of correlation, you need to compute the following quantities: $\sum x$, $\sum y$, $\sum xy$, $\sum x^2$, $\sum y^2$, and n.

3. Through $(-3, 7)$ and $(2, 12)$

$$m = \frac{12 - 7}{2 - (-3)} = \frac{5}{5} = 1$$

4. Through $(4, -1)$ and $(3, -3)$.

$$m = \frac{-3 - (-1)}{3 - 4}$$
$$= \frac{-3 + 1}{-1}$$
$$= \frac{-2}{-1} = 2$$

5. Through the origin and $(11, -2)$

$$m = \frac{-2-0}{11-0} = -\frac{2}{11}$$

6. Through the origin and $(0, 7)$

$$m = \frac{7-0}{0-0} = \frac{7}{0}$$

The slope of the line is undefined.

7. $4x + 3y = 6$

$$3y = -4x + 6$$

$$y = -\frac{4}{3}x + 2$$

Therefore, the slope is $m = -\frac{4}{3}$.

8. $4x - y = 7$

$$-y = -4x + 7$$
$$y = 4x - 7$$
$$m = 4$$

9. $y + 4 = 9$

$$y = 5$$
$$y = 0x + 5$$
$$m = 0$$

10. $3y - 1 = 14$

$$3y = 14 + 1$$
$$3y = 15$$
$$y = 5$$

This is a horizontal line. The slope of a horizontal line is 0.

11. $y = 5x + 4$

$$m = 5$$

12. $x = 5y$

$$\frac{1}{5}x = y$$

$$m = \frac{1}{5}$$

13. Through $(5, -1)$; slope $\frac{2}{3}$

Use point-slope form.

$$y - (-1) = \frac{2}{3}(x - 5)$$

$$y + 1 = \frac{2}{3}(x - 5)$$

$$3(y + 1) = 2(x - 5)$$
$$3y + 3 = 2x - 10$$
$$3y = 2x - 13$$

$$y = \frac{2}{3}x - \frac{13}{3}$$

14. Through $(8, 0)$, with slope $-\frac{1}{4}$

Use point-slope form.

$$y - 0 = -\frac{1}{4}(x - 8)$$

$$y = -\frac{1}{4}x + 2$$

15. Through $(-6, 3)$ and $(2, -5)$

$$m = \frac{-5-3}{2-(-6)} = \frac{-8}{8} = -1$$

Use point-slope form.

$$y - 3 = -1[x - (-6)]$$
$$y - 3 = -x - 6$$
$$y = -x - 3$$

16. Through $(2, -3)$ and $(-3, 4)$

$$m = \frac{4-(-3)}{-3-2} = -\frac{7}{5}$$

Use point-slope form.

$$y - (-3) = -\frac{7}{5}(x - 2)$$

$$y + 3 = -\frac{7}{5}x + \frac{14}{5}$$

$$y = -\frac{7}{5}x + \frac{14}{5} - 3$$

$$y = -\frac{7}{5}x + \frac{14}{5} - \frac{15}{5}$$

$$y = -\frac{7}{5}x - \frac{1}{5}$$

17. Through $(-1, 4)$; undefined slope

Undefined slope means the line is vertical. The equation of the vertical line through $(-1, 4)$ is $x = -1$.

18. Through $(-2, 5)$, with slope 0

Horizontal lines have 0 slope and an equation of the form $y = k$.
The line passes through $(-2, 5)$ so $k = 5$. An equation of the line is $y = 5$.

19. Through $(3, -4)$ parallel to $4x - 2y = 9$
Solve $4x - 2y = 9$ for y.

$$-2y = -4x + 9$$

$$y = 2x - \frac{9}{2}$$

$$m = 2$$

The desired line has the same slope. Use the point-slope form.

$$\begin{aligned} y-(-4) &= 2(x-3) \\ y+4 &= 2x-6 \\ y &= 2x-10 \end{aligned}$$

20. Through $(0, 5)$, perpendicular to $8x + 5y = 3$
Find the slope of the given line first.

$$\begin{aligned} 8x + 5y &= 3 \\ 5y &= -8x + 3 \\ y &= \frac{-8}{5}x + \frac{3}{5} \\ m &= -\frac{8}{5} \end{aligned}$$

The perpendicular line has $m = \frac{5}{8}$.
Use point-slope form.

$$\begin{aligned} y-5 &= \frac{5}{8}(x-0) \\ y &= \frac{5}{8}x + 5 \end{aligned}$$

21. Through $(2, -10)$, perpendicular to a line with undefined slope
A line with undefined slope is a vertical line. A line perpendicular to a vertical line is a horizontal line with equation of the form $y = k$. The desired line passed through $(2, -10)$, so $k = -10$. Thus, an equation of the desired line is $y = -10$.

22. Through $(3, -5)$, parallel to $y = 4$

Find the slope of the given line.
$y = 0x + 4$, so $m = 0$, and the required line will also have slope 0.
Use the point-slope form.

$$\begin{aligned} y-(-5) &= 0(x-3) \\ y+5 &= 0 \\ y &= -5 \end{aligned}$$

23. Through $(-3, 5)$, perpendicular to $y = -2$
The given line, $y = -2$, is a horizontal line. A line perpendicular to a horizontal line is a vertical line with equation of the form $x = h$.
The desired line passes through $(-3, 5)$, so $h = -3$. Thus, an equation of the desired line is $x = -3$.

24. $y = 4x + 3$

Let $x = 0$.
$$\begin{aligned} y &= 4(0) + 3 \\ y &= 3 \end{aligned}$$

Let $y = 0$.
$$\begin{aligned} 0 &= 4x + 3 \\ -3 &= 4x \\ -\frac{3}{4} &= x \end{aligned}$$

Draw the line through $(0, 3)$ and $\left(-\frac{3}{4}, 0\right)$.

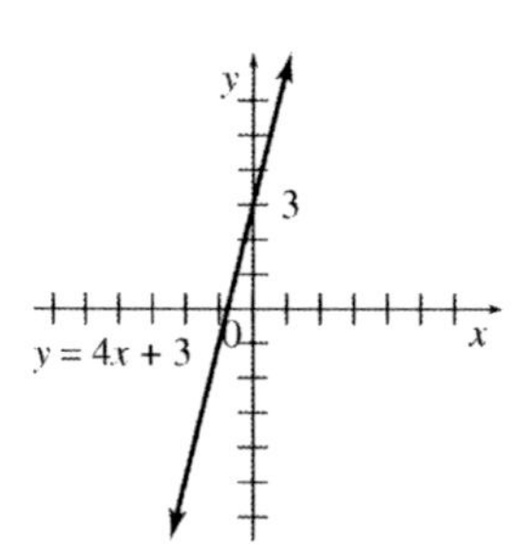

25. $y = 6 - 2x$

Find the intercepts.
Let $x = 0$.

$$y = 6 - 2(0) = 6$$

The y-intercept is 6.
Let $y = 0$.

$$\begin{aligned} 0 &= 6 - 2x \\ 2x &= 6 \\ x &= 3 \end{aligned}$$

The x-intercept is 3.
Draw the line through $(0, 6)$ and $(3, 0)$.

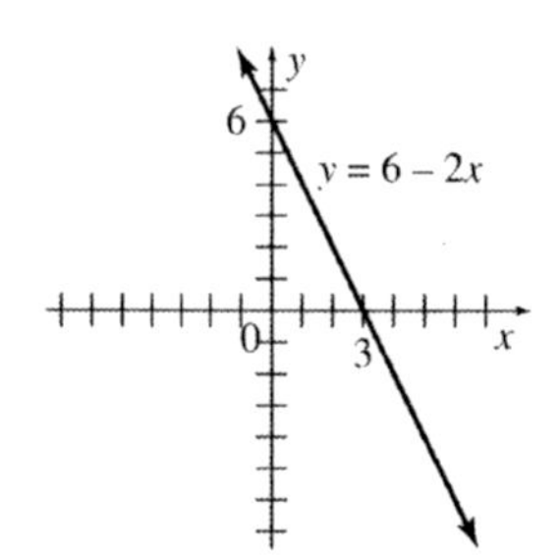

26. $3x - 5y = 15$

$$-5y = -3x + 15$$

$$y = \frac{3}{5}x - 3$$

When $x = 0$, $y = -3$.
When $y = 0$, $x = 5$.
Draw the line through $(0, -3)$ and $(5, 0)$.

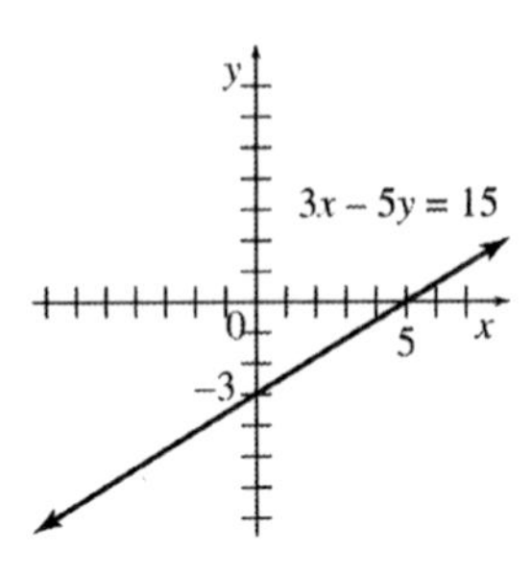

27. $4x + 6y = 12$

Find the intercepts.
When $x = 0$, $y = 2$, so the y-intercept is 2.
When $y = 0$, $x = 3$, so the x-intercept is 3.
Draw the line through $(0, 2)$ and $(3, 0)$.

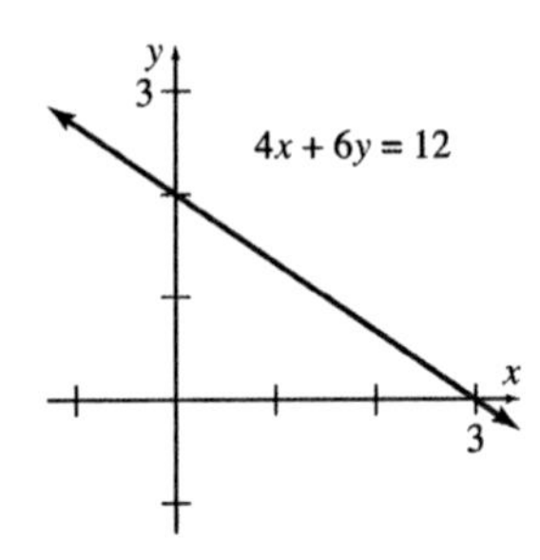

28. $x - 3 = 0$

$$x = 3$$

This is the vertical line through $(3, 0)$.

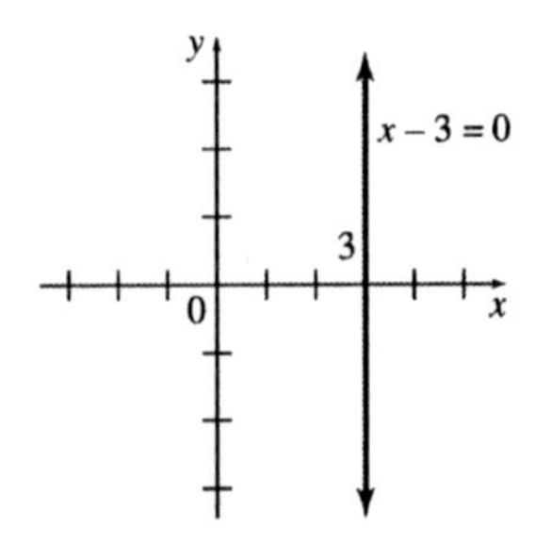

29. $y = 1$

This is the horizontal line passing through $(0, 1)$.

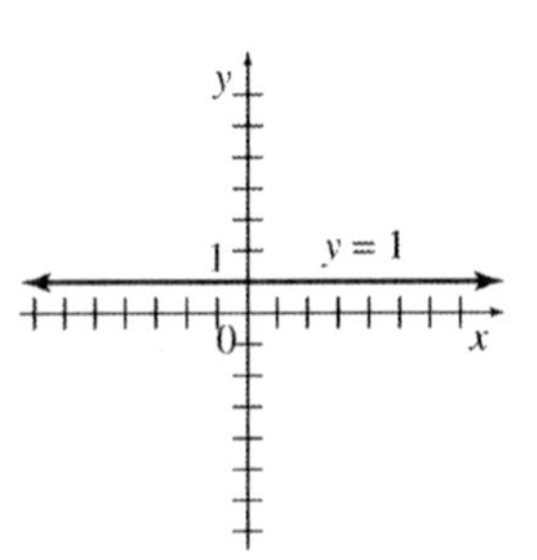

30. $y = 2x$

When $x = 0$, $y = 0$.
When $x = 1$, $y = 2$.
Draw the line through $(0, 0)$ and $(1, 2)$.

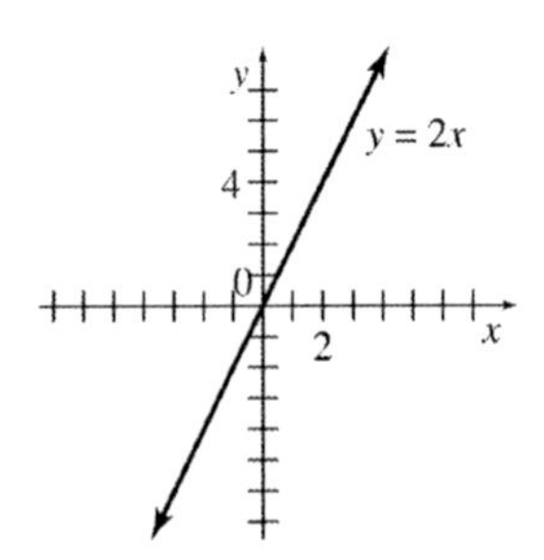

31. $x + 3y = 0$

When $x = 0$, $y = 0$.
When $x = 3$, $y = -1$.
Draw the line through $(0, 0)$ and $(3, -1)$.

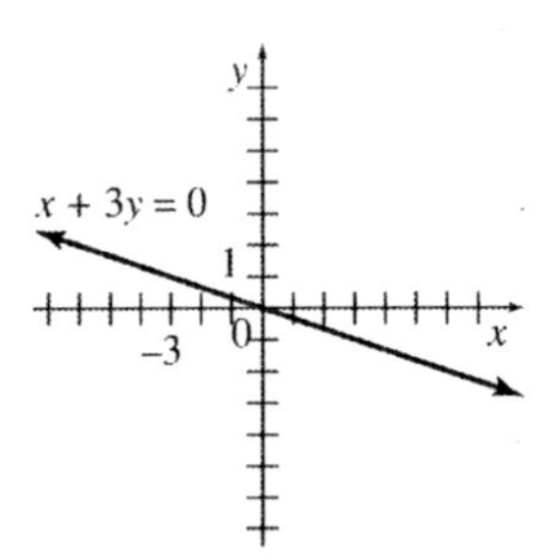

32. **(a)** $E = 352 + 42x$ (where x is in thousands)

(b) $R = 130x$ (where x is in thousands)

(c)
$$R > E$$
$$130x > 352 + 42x$$
$$88x > 352$$
$$x > 4$$

For a profit to be made, more than 4000 chips must be sold.

33. $S(q) = 6q + 3;\ D(q) = 19 - 2q$

(a) $S(q) = D(q) = 10$

$$\begin{aligned} 10 &= 6q + 3 \\ 7 &= 6q \\ \frac{7}{6} &= q \quad \text{(supply)} \end{aligned}$$

$$\begin{aligned} 10 &= 19 - 2q \\ -9 &= -2q \\ \frac{9}{2} &= q \quad \text{(demand)} \end{aligned}$$

When the price is \$10 per pound, the supply is $\frac{7}{6}$ pounds per day, and the demand is $\frac{9}{2}$ pounds per day.

(b) $S(q) = D(q) = 15$

$$\begin{aligned} 15 &= 6q + 3 \\ 12 &= 6q \\ 2 &= q \quad \text{(supply)} \end{aligned}$$

$$\begin{aligned} 15 &= 19 - 2q \\ -4 &= -2q \\ 2 &= q \quad \text{(demand)} \end{aligned}$$

When the price is \$15 per pound, the supply is 2 pounds per day, and the demand is 2 pounds per day.

(c) $S(q) = D(q) = \$18$

$$\begin{aligned} 18 &= 6q + 3 \\ 15 &= 6q \\ \frac{5}{2} &= q \quad \text{(supply)} \end{aligned}$$

$$\begin{aligned} 18 &= 19 - 2q \\ -1 &= -2q \\ \frac{1}{2} &= q \quad \text{(demand)} \end{aligned}$$

When the price is $\frac{5}{2}$ pounds per day, the demand is $\frac{1}{2}$ pound per day.

(d)

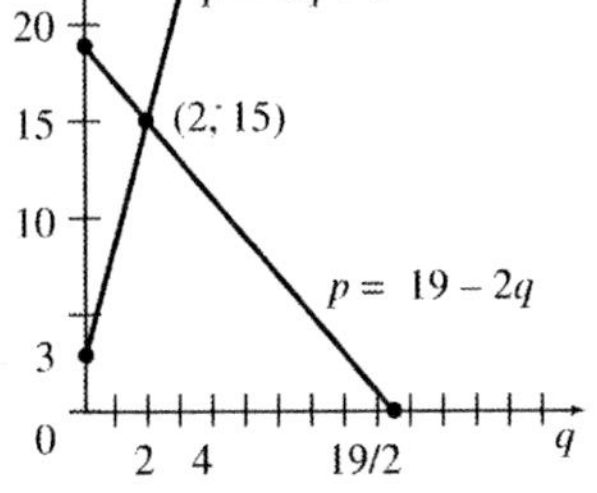

$p = 6q + 3$

$p = 19 - 2q$

(2, 15)

p: 0, 3, 10, 15, 20

q: 2, 4, 19/2

(e) The graph shows that the lines representing the supply and demand functions intersect at the point $(2, 15)$. The y-coordinate of this point gives the equilibrium price. Thus, the equilibrium price is \$15.

(f) The x-coordinate of the intersection point gives the equilibrium quantity. Thus, the equilibrium quantity is 2, representing 2 pounds of crabmeat per day.

34. Using the points $(60, 40)$ and $(100, 60)$,

$$m = \frac{60 - 40}{100 - 60} = \frac{20}{40} = 0.5.$$

$$\begin{aligned} p - 40 &= 0.5(q - 60) \\ p - 40 &= 0.5q - 30 \\ p &= 0.5q + 10 \\ S(q) &= 0.5q + 10 \end{aligned}$$

35. Using the points $(50, 47.50)$ and $(80, 32.50)$,

$$m = \frac{47.50 - 32.50}{50 - 80} = \frac{15}{-30} = \frac{-1}{2} = -0.5.$$

$$\begin{aligned} p - 47.50 &= -0.5(q - 50) \\ p - 47.50 &= -0.5q + 25 \\ p &= -0.5q + 72.50 \\ D(q) &= -0.5q + 72.50 \end{aligned}$$

36.

$$\begin{aligned} S(q) &= D(q) \\ 0.5q + 10 &= -0.5q + 72.50 \\ q &= 62.5 \\ S(62.5) &= 0.5(62.5) + 10 = 31.25 + 10 = 41.25 \end{aligned}$$

The equilibrium price is \$41.25, and the equilibrium quantity is 62.5 diet pills.

37. Eight units cost \$300; fixed cost is \$60.
The fixed cost is the cost if zero units are made.
$(8, 300)$ and $(0, 60)$ are points on the line.

$$m = \frac{60 - 300}{0 - 8} = 30$$

Use slope-intercept form.

$$y = 30x + 60$$
$$C(x) = 30x + 60$$

38. Fixed cost is \$2000; 36 units cost \$8480.
Two points on the line are $(0, 2000)$ and $(36, 8480)$, so

$$m = \frac{8480 - 2000}{36 - 0} = \frac{6480}{36} = 180.$$

Use point-slope form.

$$y = 180x + 2000$$
$$C(x) = 180x + 2000$$

39. Twelve units cost \$445; 50 units cost \$1585. Points on the line are $(12, 445)$ and $(50, 1585)$.

$$m = \frac{1585 - 445}{50 - 12} = 30$$

Use point-slope form.

$$y - 445 = 30(x - 12)$$
$$y - 445 = 30x - 360$$
$$y = 30x + 85$$
$$C(x) = 30x + 85$$

40. Thirty units cost \$1500; 120 units cost \$5640.
Two points on the line are $(30, 1500)$, $(120, 5640)$, so

$$m = \frac{5640 - 1500}{120 - 30} = \frac{4140}{90} = 46.$$

Use point-slope form.

$$y - 1500 = 46(x - 30)$$
$$y = 46x - 1380 + 1500$$
$$y = 46x + 120$$
$$C(x) = 46x + 120$$

41. $C(x) = 200x + 1000$
$R(x) = 400x$

(a) $C(x) = R(x)$

$$200x + 1000 = 400x$$
$$1000 = 200x$$
$$5 = x$$

The break-even quantity is 5 cartons.

(b) $R(5) = 400(5) = 2000$

The revenue from 5 cartons of CD's is \$2000.

42. (a) $C(x) = 3x + 160;\ R(x) = 7x$

$$C(x) = R(x)$$
$$3x + 160 = 7x$$
$$160 = 4x$$
$$40 = x$$

The break-even quantity is 40 pounds.

(b) $R(40) = 7 \cdot 40 = \$280$

The revenue for 40 pounds is \$280.

43. Let y represent imports from China in billions of dollars. Using the points $(1, 102)$ and $(5, 243)$,

$$m = \frac{243 - 102}{5 - 1} = \frac{141}{4} = 35.25$$

$$y - 102 = 35.25(x - 1)$$
$$y - 102 = 35.25x - 35.25$$
$$y = 35.25x + 66.75.$$

44. Let y represent imports to China in billions of dollars. Using the points $(1, 19)$ and $(5, 42)$,

$$m = \frac{42 - 19}{5 - 1} = \frac{23}{4} = 5.75$$

$$y - 19 = 5.75(x - 1)$$
$$y - 19 = 5.75x - 5.75$$
$$y = 5.75x + 13.25.$$

45. Using the points (97, 44,883) and (105, 46,326),

$$m = \frac{46{,}326 - 44{,}883}{105 - 97} = \frac{1443}{8} \approx 180.4$$

$$I - 44{,}883 = 180.4(x - 97)$$
$$I - 44{,}883 = 180.4x - 17{,}498.8$$
$$I(x) = 180.4x + 27{,}384.2.$$

Rounded to the nearest dollar,

$$I(x) = 180.4x + 27{,}384.$$

46. **(a)**

x	y
80	7.5
85	12
90	16
95	20.45
100	24.9
105	28.4

Using a graphing calculator, $Y = 0.8437x - 59.84$.

(b) $Y = 0.8437(110) - 59.84 = 32.967$

The average cost of a new car in the year 2010 is predicted to be about \$32,967.

(c) Using a graphing calculator, $r = 0.999$. Yes, the line is a good fit for the data.

(d)

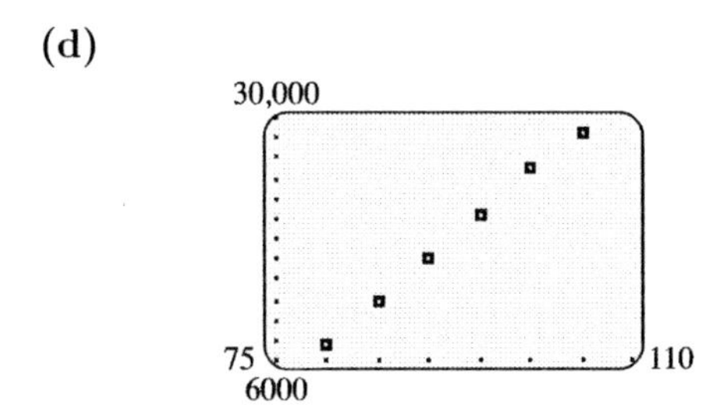

No, the scatterplot suggests that the trend is linear.

47. **(a)**

x	y
1960	43
2840	74
2060	54
3630	79
2420	63
3160	74
3220	78
2550	70
3140	80
3790	77

Using a graphing calculator, $r = 0.881$. Yes, the data seem to fit a straight line.

(b)

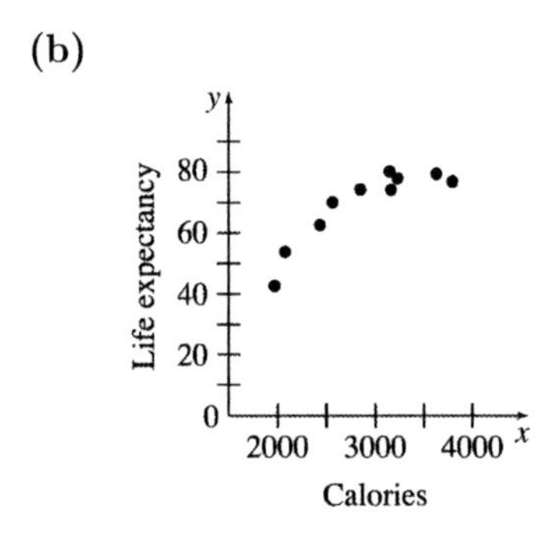

The data somewhat fit a straight line, but there is also a nonlinear trend.

(c) Using a graphing calculator, $Y = 0.0173x + 19.3$.

(d) Let $x = 3400$. Find Y.

$$Y = 0.0173(3400) + 19.3 \approx 78.1$$

The predicted life expectancy in the United Kingdom, with a daily calorie supply of 3400, is about 78.1 years. This agrees with the actual value of 78 years.

48. **(a)**

x	y	xy	x^2	y^2
130	170	22,100	16,900	28,900
138	160	22,080	19,044	25,600
142	173	24,566	20,164	29,929
159	181	28,779	25,281	32,761
165	201	33,165	27,225	40,401
200	192	38,400	40,000	36,864
210	240	50,400	44,100	57,600
250	290	72,500	62,500	84,100
1394	1607	291,990	255,214	336,155

$$m = \frac{n(\sum xy) - (\sum x)(\sum y)}{n(\sum x^2) - (\sum x)^2}$$

$$m = \frac{8(291{,}990) - (1394)(1607)}{8(225{,}214) - 1394^2}$$

$$m = 0.9724399854 \approx 0.97$$

$$b = \frac{\sum y - m(\sum x)}{n}$$

$$b = \frac{1607\text{-}0.97(1394)}{8}$$

$$\approx 31.85$$

$$Y = 0.97x + 31.85$$

(b) Let $x = 190$; find Y.

$$Y = 0.97(190) + 31.85$$
$$Y = 216.15 \approx 216$$

The cholesterol level for a person whose blood sugar level is 190 would be about 216.

(c)

$$r = \frac{8(291{,}990) - (1394)(1607)}{\sqrt{8(255{,}214) - 1394^2} \cdot \sqrt{8(336{,}155) - 1607^2}}$$

$$= 0.933814 \approx 0.93$$

49. Using the points $(74, 142.3)$ and $(104, 118.4)$,

$$m = \frac{118.4 - 142.3}{104 - 74} = \frac{-23.9}{30} = -0.797$$

$$y - 142.3 = -0.797(x - 74)$$
$$y - 142.3 = -0.797x + 59$$
$$y = -0.797x + 201.3.$$

50. Using the points $(95, 55)$ and $(105, 67)$,

$$m = \frac{67 - 55}{105 - 95} = \frac{12}{10} = 1.2$$

$$y - 55 = 1.2(x - 95)$$
$$y - 55 = 1.2x - 114$$
$$y = 1.2x - 59.0$$

51. **(a)** Using a graphing calculator, $r = 0.749$.

The data seem to fit a line but the fit is not very good.

(b)

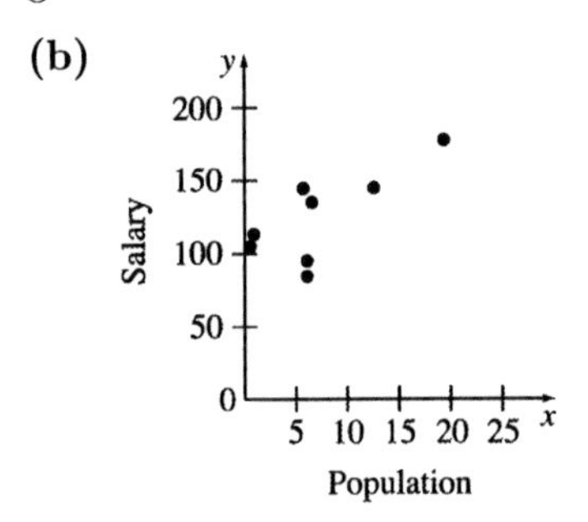

(c) Using a graphing calculator,

$Y = 3.81x + 98.24$

(d) The slope is 3.81 thousand (or 3810). On average, the governor's salary increases \$3810 for each additional million in population.

Extended Application: Using Extrapolation to Predict Life Expectancy

1.

x	y	xy	x^2	y^2
1970	74.7	147,159.0	3,880,900	5580.09
1975	76.6	151,285.0	3,900,625	5867.56
1980	77.4	153,252.0	3,920,400	5990.76
1985	78.2	155,227.0	3,940,225	6115.24
1990	78.8	156,812.0	3,960,100	6209.44
1995	78.9	157,405.5	3,980,025	6225.21
2000	79.5	159,000.0	4,000,000	6320.25
2005	80.8	162,004.0	4,020,025	6528.64
15,900	624.9	1,242,144.5	31,602,300	48,837.19

$$m = \frac{n(\sum xy) - (\sum x)(\sum y)}{n(\sum x^2) - (\sum x)^2}$$

$$m = \frac{8(1{,}242{,}144.5) - (15{,}900)(624.9)}{8(31{,}602{,}300) - 15{,}900^2}$$

$$m = 0.1483333333$$

$$b = \frac{\sum y - m(\sum x)}{n}$$

$$b = \frac{624.9 - 0.1483333333(15{,}900)}{8}$$

$$\approx -216.7$$

$$Y = 0.148x - 216.7$$

2. Let $x = 1900$. Find Y.

$$Y = 0.1483333333(1900) - 216.7 = 65.1$$

From the equation, the guess is the life expectancy of females born in 1900 is 65.1 years.

3. The poor prediction isn't surprising, since we were extrapolating far beyond the range of the original data.

4.

x	y	Predicted value	Residual
1970	74.7	75.52	−0.82
1975	76.6	76.26	0.34
1980	77.4	77.00	0.40
1985	78.2	77.74	0.46
1990	78.8	78.48	0.32
1995	78.9	79.22	−0.32
2000	79.5	79.97	−0.47
2005	80.8	80.71	0.09

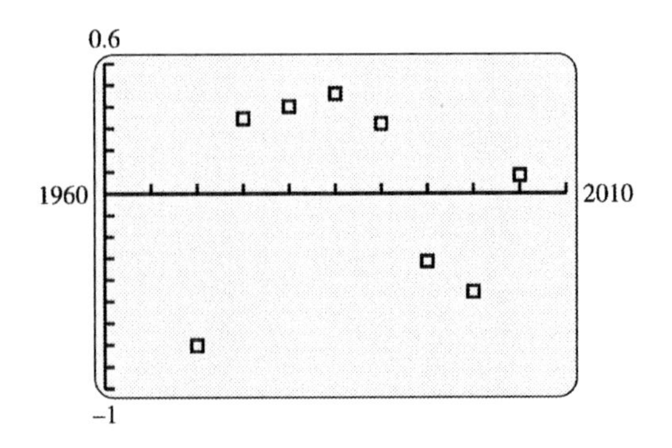

5. It's not clear that any simple smooth function will fit this data. This will make it difficult to predict the life expectancy for females born in 2015.

6. You'll get 0 slope and 0 intercept, because you've already subtracted out the linear component of the data.

7. They used a regression equation of some type to predict this value.

Chapter 2

SYSTEMS OF LINEAR EQUATIONS AND MATRICES

2.1 Solution of Linear Systems by the Echelon Method

In Exercises 1-16 and 19-28, check each solution by substituting it in the original equation of the system.

1. $x + y = 5 \quad (1)$
$2x - 2y = 2 \quad (2)$

To eliminate x in equation (2), multiply equation (1) by -2 and add the result to equation (2). The new system is

$$\begin{array}{rl} & x + y = 5 \quad (1) \\ -2R_1 + R_2 \to R_2 & -4y = -8. \quad (3) \end{array}$$

Now make the coefficient of the first term in each row equal 1. To accomplish this, multiply equation (3) by $-\frac{1}{4}$.

$$\begin{array}{rl} & x + y = 5 \quad (1) \\ -\frac{1}{4}R_2 \to R_2 & y = 2 \quad (4) \end{array}$$

Substitute 2 for y in equation (1).

$$x + 2 = 5$$
$$y = 3$$

The solution is $(3, 2)$.

2. $4x + y = 9 \quad (1)$
$3x - y = 5 \quad (2)$

First use transformation 3 to eliminate the x-term from equation (2). Multiply equation (1) by 3 and add the result to -4 times equation (2).

$$\begin{array}{rl} & 4x + y = 9 \quad (1) \\ 3R_1 + (-4)R_2 \to R_2 & 7y = 7 \quad (3) \end{array}$$

Now use transformation 2 to make the coefficient of the first term in each equation equal to 1.

$$\begin{array}{rl} \frac{1}{4}R_1 \to R_1 & x + \frac{1}{4}y = \frac{9}{4} \quad (4) \\ \frac{1}{7}R_2 \to R_2 & y = 1 \quad (5) \end{array}$$

Complete the solution by back-substitution. Substitute 1 for y in equation (4) to get

$$x + \frac{1}{4}(1) = \frac{9}{4}$$
$$x = \frac{8}{4} = 2.$$

The solution is $(2, 1)$.

3. $3x - 2y = -3 \quad (1)$
$5x - y = 2 \quad (2)$

To eliminate x in equation (2), multiply equation (1) by -5 and equation (2) by 3. Add the results. The new system is

$$\begin{array}{rl} & 3x - 2y = -3 \quad (1) \\ -5R_1 + 3R_2 \to R_2 & 7y = 21. \quad (3) \end{array}$$

Now make the coefficient of the first term in each row equal 1. To accomplish this, multiply equation (1) by $\frac{1}{3}$ and equation (3) by $\frac{1}{7}$.

$$\begin{array}{rl} \frac{1}{3}R_1 \to R_1 & x - \frac{2}{3}y = -1 \quad (4) \\ \frac{1}{7}R_2 \to R_2 & y = 3 \quad (5) \end{array}$$

Back-substitution of 3 for y in equation (4) gives

$$x - \frac{2}{3}(3) = -1$$
$$x - 2 = -1$$
$$x = 1.$$

The solution is $(1, 3)$.

4. $2x + 7y = -8 \quad (1)$
$-2x + 3y = -12 \quad (2)$

$$\begin{array}{rl} & 2x + 7y = -8 \quad (1) \\ R_1 + R_2 \to R_2 & 10y = -20 \quad (3) \end{array}$$

Make each leading coefficient equal 1.

$$\begin{array}{rl} \frac{1}{2}R_1 \to R_1 & x + \frac{7}{2}y = -4 \quad (4) \\ \frac{1}{10}R_2 \to R_2 & y = -2 \quad (5) \end{array}$$

Substitute -2 for y in equation (4).

$$x + \frac{7}{2}(-2) = -4$$
$$x - 7 = -4$$
$$x = 3$$

The solution is $(3, -2)$.

5. $3x + 2y = -6$ (*1*)
$5x - 2y = -10$ (*2*)

Eliminate x in equation (2) to get the system

$$3x + 2y = -6 \quad (1)$$
$$5R_1 + (-3)R_2 \to R_2 \qquad 16y = 0. \quad (3)$$

Make the coefficient of the first term in each equation equal 1.

$$\tfrac{1}{3}R_1 \to R_1 \quad x + \frac{2}{3}y = -2 \quad (4)$$
$$\tfrac{1}{16}R_2 \to R_2 \qquad y = 0 \quad (5)$$

Substitute 0 for y in equation (4) to get $x = -2$. The solution is $(-2, 0)$.

6. $-3x + y = 4$ (*1*)
$2x - 2y = -4$ (*2*)

Eliminate x in equation (2).

$$-3x + y = 4 \quad (1)$$
$$2R_1 + 3R_2 \to R_2 \qquad -4y = -4 \quad (3)$$

Make the coefficient of the first term in each row equal 1.

$$-\tfrac{1}{3}R_1 \to R_1 \quad x - \frac{1}{3}y = -\frac{4}{3} \quad (4)$$
$$-\tfrac{1}{4}R_2 \to R_2 \qquad y = 1 \quad (5)$$

Back-substitution of 1 for y in equation (4) gives

$$x - \frac{1}{3}(1) = -\frac{4}{3}$$
$$x - \frac{1}{3} = -\frac{4}{3}$$
$$x = -1.$$

The solution is $(-1, 1)$.

7. $6x - 2y = -4$ (*1*)
$3x + 4y = 8$ (*2*)

Eliminate x in equation (2).

$$6x - 2y = -4 \quad (1)$$
$$-1R_1 + 2R_2 \to R_2 \qquad 10y = 20 \quad (3)$$

Make the coefficient of the first term in each row equal 1.

$$\tfrac{1}{6}R_1 \to R_1 \quad x - \frac{1}{3}y = -\frac{2}{3} \quad (4)$$
$$\tfrac{1}{10}R_2 \to R_2 \qquad y = 2 \quad (5)$$

Substitute 2 for y in equation (4) to get $x = 0$. The solution is $(0, 2)$.

8. $4m + 3n = -1$
$2m + 5n = 3$

$$4m + 3n = -1$$
$$R_1 + (-2)R_2 \to R_2 \qquad -7n = -7$$

Make each leading coefficient equal 1.

$$\tfrac{1}{4}R_1 \to R_1 \quad m + \frac{3}{4}n = -\frac{1}{4}$$
$$-\tfrac{1}{7}R_2 \to R_2 \qquad n = 1$$

Back-substitution gives

$$m + \frac{3}{4}(1) = -\frac{1}{4}$$
$$m = -\frac{4}{4} = -1.$$

The solution is $(-1, 1)$.

9. $5p + 11q = -7$ (*1*)
$3p - 8q = 25$ (*2*)

Eliminate p in equation (2).

$$5p + 11q = -7 \quad (1)$$
$$-3R_1 + 5R_2 \to R_2 \qquad -73q = 146 \quad (3)$$

Make the coefficient of the first term in each row equal 1.

$$\tfrac{1}{5}R_1 \to R_1 \quad p + \frac{11}{5}q = -\frac{7}{5} \quad (4)$$
$$-\tfrac{1}{73}R_2 \to R_2 \qquad q = -1 \quad (5)$$

Substitute -2 for q in equation (4) to get $p = 3$. The solution is $(3, -2)$.

10. $12s - 5t = 9$
$3s - 8t = -18$

$$\begin{array}{rr} & 12s - 5t = 9 \\ R_1 + (-4)R_2 \to R_2 & 27t = 81 \\ \frac{1}{12}R_1 \to R_1 & s - \frac{5}{12}t = \frac{3}{4} \\ \frac{1}{27}R_2 \to R_2 & t = 3 \end{array}$$

Back substitution gives

$$s - \frac{5}{12}(3) = \frac{3}{4}$$
$$s - \frac{5}{4} = \frac{3}{4}$$
$$s = \frac{8}{4} = 2.$$

The solution is $(2, 3)$.

11. $6x + 7y = -2$ (1)
$7x - 6y = 26$ (2)

Eliminate x in equation (2).

$$\begin{array}{rrl} & 6x + 7y = -2 & (1) \\ 7R_1 + (-6)R_2 \to R_2 & 85y = -170 & (3) \end{array}$$

Make the coefficient of the first term in each equation equal 1.

$$\begin{array}{rrl} \frac{1}{6}R_1 \to R_1 & x + \frac{7}{6}y = -\frac{1}{3} & (4) \\ \frac{1}{85}R_2 \to R_2 & y = -2 & (5) \end{array}$$

Substitute -2 for y in equation (4) to get $x = 2$. The solution is $(2, -2)$.

12. $3a - 8b = 14$ (1)
$a - 2b = 2$ (2)

Eliminate a in equation (2).

$$\begin{array}{rrl} & 3a - 8b = 14 & (1) \\ R_1 + (-3)R_2 \to R_2 & -2b = 8 & (3) \end{array}$$

Make the coefficient of the first term in each row equal 1.

$$\begin{array}{rrl} \frac{1}{3}R_1 \to R_1 & a - \frac{8}{3}b = \frac{14}{3} & (4) \\ -\frac{1}{2}R_2 \to R_2 & b = -4 & (5) \end{array}$$

Back substitute -4 for b in equation (4) to get $a = -6$. The solution is $(-6, -4)$.

13. $3x + 2y = 5$ (1)
$6x + 4y = 8$ (2)

Eliminate x in equation (2).

$$\begin{array}{rrl} & 3x + 2y = 5 & (1) \\ -2R_1 + R_2 \to R_2 & 0 = -2 & (3) \end{array}$$

Equation (3) is a false statement.
The system is inconsistent and has no solution.

14. $9x - 5y = 1$
$-18x + 10y = 1$

$$\begin{array}{rr} & 9x - 5y = 1 \\ 2R_1 + R_2 \to R_2 & 0 = 3 \end{array}$$

The equation $0 = 3$ is a false statement, which indicates that the system is inconsistent and has no solution.

15. $3x - 2y = -4$ (1)
$-6x + 4y = 8$ (2)

Eliminate x in equation (2).

$$\begin{array}{rrl} & 3x - 2y = -4 & (1) \\ 2R_1 + R_2 \to R_2 & 0 = 0 & (3) \end{array}$$

The true statement in equation (3) indicates that there are an infinite number of solutions for the system. Solve equation (1) for x.

$$\begin{array}{rl} 3x - 2y = -4 & (1) \\ 3x = 2y - 4 & \\ x = \frac{2y - 4}{3} & (4) \end{array}$$

For each value of y, equation (4) indicates that $x = \frac{2y-4}{3}$, and all ordered pairs of the form $\left(\frac{2y-4}{3}, y\right)$ are solutions.

16. $3x + 5y + 2 = 0$
$9x + 15y + 6 = 0$

Begin by rewriting the equations in standard form.

$$3x + 5y = -2$$
$$9x + 15y = -6$$

$$\begin{array}{rr} & 3x + 5y = -2 \\ 3R_1 + (-1)R_2 \to R_2 & 0 = 0 \end{array}$$

The true statement, $0 = 0$, shows that the two equations have the same graph, which means that there are an infinite number of solutions for the system. All ordered pairs that satisfy the equation

$3x + 5y = -2$ are solutions. Solve this equation for x.

$$3x = -5y - 2$$
$$x = \frac{-5y-2}{3}$$

The general solution is the set of all ordered pairs of the form

$$\left(\frac{-5y-2}{3}, y\right),$$

where y is any real number.

17. An inconsistent system has *no* solutions.

18. The solution of a system with two dependent equations in two variables is *an infinite set of ordered pairs*.

19. $x - \frac{3y}{2} = \frac{5}{2}$ (1)

$\frac{4x}{3} + \frac{2y}{3} = 6$ (2)

Rewrite the equations without fractions.

$2R_1 \to R_1$ $\quad 2x - 3y = 5$ (3)

$3R_2 \to R_2$ $\quad 4x + 2y = 18$ (4)

Eliminate x in equation (4).

$2x - 3y = 5$ (3)

$-2R_1 + R_2 \to R_2$ $\quad 8y = 8$ (5)

Make the coefficient of the first term in each equation equal 1.

$\frac{1}{2}R_1 + R_1$ $\quad x - \frac{3}{2}y = \frac{5}{2}$ (6)

$\frac{1}{8}R_1 + R_2 \to R_2$ $\quad y = 1$ (7)

Substitute 1 for y in equation (6) to get $y = 4$. The solution is $(4, 1)$.

20. $\frac{x}{5} + 3y = 31$

$2x - \frac{y}{5} = 8$

Multiply each equation by 5 to eliminate fractions.

$x + 15y = 155$

$10x - y = 40$

$x + 15y = 155$

$10R_1 + (-1)R_2 \to R_2$ $\quad 151y = 1510$

$x + 15y = 155$

$\frac{1}{151}R_2 \to R_2$ $\quad y = 10$

Back-substitution gives

$$x + 15(10) = 155$$
$$x = 5.$$

The solution is $(5, 10)$.

21. $\frac{x}{2} + y = \frac{3}{2}$ (1)

$\frac{x}{3} + y = \frac{1}{3}$ (2)

Rewrite the equations without fractions.

$2R_1 \to R_1$ $\quad x + 2y = 3$ (3)

$3R_2 \to R_2$ $\quad x + 3y = 1$ (4)

Eliminate x in equation (4).

$x + 2y = 3$ (3)

$-1R_1 + R_2 \to R_2$ $\quad y = -2$ (5)

Substitute -2 for y in equation (3) to get $x = 7$. The solution is $(7, -2)$.

22. $\frac{x}{9} + \frac{y}{6} = \frac{1}{3}$ (1)

$2x + \frac{8y}{5} = \frac{2}{.5}$ (2)

Rewrite the equations without fractions.

$18R_1 \to R_1$ $\quad 2x + 3y = 6$ (3)

$5R_2 \to R_2$ $\quad 10x + 8y = 2$ (4)

Eliminate x in equation (4).

$2x + 3y = 6$ (3)

$-5R_1 + R_2 \to R_2$ $\quad -7y = -28$ (5)

Make the coefficient of the first term in each row equal 1.

$\frac{1}{2}R_1 \to R_1$ $\quad x + \frac{3}{2}y = 3$ (6)

$-\frac{1}{7}R_2 \to R_2$ $\quad y = 4$ (7)

Substitute 4 for y in equation (6) to get $x = -3$. The solution is $(-3, 4)$.

23. $x + y + z = 2$ (1)

$2x + y - z = 5$ (2)

$x - y + z = -2$ (3)

Eliminate x in equations (2) and (3).

$x + y + z = 2$ (1)

$-2R_1 + R_2 \to R_2$ $\quad -y - 3z = 1$ (4)

$-1R_1 + R_3 \to R_3$ $\quad -2y = -4$ (5)

Eliminate y in equation (5).

$$\begin{aligned} x + y + z &= 2 \quad (1) \\ -y - 3z &= 1 \quad (4) \\ -2R_2 + R_3 \to R_3 \qquad 6z &= -6 \quad (6) \end{aligned}$$

Make the coefficient of the first term in each equation equal 1.

$$\begin{aligned} x + y + z &= 2 \quad (1) \\ -1R_2 \to R_2 \qquad y + 3z &= -1 \quad (7) \\ \tfrac{1}{6}R_3 \to R_3 \qquad z &= -1 \quad (8) \end{aligned}$$

Substitute -1 for z in equation (7) to get $y = 2$. Finally, substitute -1 for z and 2 for y in equation (1) to get $x = 1$. The solution is $(1, 2, -1)$.

24. $2x + y + z = 9 \quad (1)$
$-x - y + z = 1 \quad (2)$
$3x - y + z = 9 \quad (3)$

First, eliminate the x-terms from equations (2) and (3).

$$\begin{aligned} 2x + y + z &= 9 \quad (1) \\ R_1 + 2R_2 \to R_2 \qquad -y + 3z &= 11 \quad (4) \\ 3R_1 + (-2)R_3 \to R_3 \qquad 5y + z &= 9 \quad (5) \end{aligned}$$

Next, eliminate the y-term from equation (5).

$$\begin{aligned} 2x + y + z &= 9 \quad (1) \\ -y + 3z &= 11 \quad (4) \\ 5R_2 + R_3 \to R_3 \qquad 16z &= 64 \quad (6) \end{aligned}$$

Now make the coefficient of the first term in each equation equal to 1.

$$\begin{aligned} \tfrac{1}{2}R_1 \to R_1 \qquad x + \frac{1}{2}y + \frac{1}{2}z &= \frac{9}{2} \quad (7) \\ -1R_2 \to R_2 \qquad y - 3z &= -11 \quad (8) \\ \tfrac{1}{16}R_3 \to R_3 \qquad z &= 4 \quad (9) \end{aligned}$$

Complete the solution by back-substitution. Substitute 4 for z in equation (8) to find y.

$$\begin{aligned} y - 3(4) &= -11 \\ y - 12 &= -11 \\ y &= 1 \end{aligned}$$

Finally, substitute 1 for y and 4 for z in equation (7) to find x.

$$\begin{aligned} x + \frac{1}{2}(1) + \frac{1}{2}(4) &= \frac{9}{2} \\ x + \frac{5}{2} &= \frac{9}{2} \\ x &= \frac{4}{2} = 2 \end{aligned}$$

The solution is $(2, 1, 4)$.

25. $x + 3y + 4z = 14 \quad (1)$
$2x - 3y + 2z = 10 \quad (2)$
$3x - y + z = 9 \quad (3)$

Eliminate x in equations (2) and (3).

$$\begin{aligned} x + 3y + 4z &= 14 \quad (1) \\ -2R_1 + R_2 \to R_2 \qquad -9y - 6z &= -18 \quad (4) \\ -3R_1 + R_3 \to R_3 \qquad -10y - 11z &= -33 \quad (5) \end{aligned}$$

Eliminate y in equation (5).

$$\begin{aligned} x + 3y + 4z &= 14 \quad (1) \\ -9y - 6z &= -18 \quad (4) \\ 10R_2 + (-9)R_3 \to R_3 \qquad 39z &= 117 \quad (6) \end{aligned}$$

Make the coefficient of the first term in each equation equal 1.

$$\begin{aligned} x + 3y + 4z &= 14 \quad (1) \\ -\tfrac{1}{9}R_2 \to R_2 \qquad y + \frac{2}{3}z &= 2 \quad (7) \\ \tfrac{1}{39}R_3 \to R_3 \qquad z &= 3 \quad (8) \end{aligned}$$

Substitute 3 for z in equation (2) to get $y = 0$. Finally, substitute 3 for z and 0 for y in equation (1) to get $x = 2$. The solution is $(2, 0, 3)$.

26. $4x - y + 3z = -2 \quad (1)$
$3x + 5y - z = 15 \quad (2)$
$-2x + y + 4z = 14 \quad (3)$

First, eliminate the x-terms from equations (2) and (3).

$$\begin{aligned} 4x - y + 3z &= -2 \quad (1) \\ -3R_1 + 4R_2 \to R_2 \qquad 23y - 13z &= 66 \quad (4) \\ R_1 + 2R_3 \to R_3 \qquad y + 11z &= 26 \quad (5) \end{aligned}$$

Next, eliminate the y-term from equation (5).

$$\begin{aligned} 4x - y + 3z &= -2 \quad (1) \\ 23y - 13z &= 66 \quad (4) \\ R_2 + (-23)R_3 \to R_3 \qquad -266z &= -532 \quad (6) \end{aligned}$$

Now make the coefficient of the first term in each equation equal to 1.

$$\begin{aligned} \tfrac{1}{4}R_1 \to R_1 \qquad x - \frac{1}{4}y + \frac{3}{4}z &= -\frac{1}{2} \quad (7) \\ \tfrac{1}{23}R_2 \to R_2 \qquad y - \frac{13}{23}z &= \frac{66}{23} \quad (8) \\ -\tfrac{1}{266}R_3 \to R_3 \qquad z &= 2 \quad (9) \end{aligned}$$

Complete the solution by back-substitution. Substitute 2 for z in equation (8) to find y.

$$y - \frac{13}{23}(2) = \frac{66}{23}$$
$$y - \frac{26}{23} = \frac{66}{23}$$
$$y = \frac{92}{23} = 4$$

Finally, substitute 4 for y and 2 for z in equation (7) to find x.

$$x - \frac{1}{4}(4) + \frac{3}{4}(2) = -\frac{1}{2}$$
$$x + \frac{1}{2} = -\frac{1}{2}$$
$$x = -1$$

The solution is $(-1, 4, 2)$.

27.
$$\begin{aligned} 2x + 5y + 4z &= 10 \quad (1)\\ 8x + 2y + 3z &= 27 \quad (2)\\ 4x + y + z &= 13 \quad (3)\end{aligned}$$

Eliminate x in equations (2) and (3).

$$\begin{array}{ll} & 2x + 5y + 4z = 10 \quad (1)\\ -4R_1 + R_2 \to R_2 & -18y - 13z = -13 \quad (4)\\ -2R_1 + R_3 \to R_3 & -9y - 7z = -7 \quad (5)\end{array}$$

Eliminate y in equation (5).

$$\begin{array}{ll} & 2x + 5y + 4z = 10 \quad (1)\\ & -18y - 13z = -13 \quad (4)\\ R_2 + (-2)R_3 \to R_3 & z = 1 \quad (6)\end{array}$$

Make the coefficient of the first term in each row equal 1.

$$\begin{array}{ll} \frac{1}{2}R_1 \to R_1 & x + \frac{5}{2}y + 2z = 5 \quad (7)\\ -\frac{1}{18}R_2 \to R_2 & y + \frac{13}{18}z = \frac{13}{18} \quad (8)\\ & z = 1 \quad (6)\end{array}$$

Substitute 1 for z in equation (8) to get $y = 0$. Finally, substitute 1 for z and 0 for y in equation (7) to get $x = 3$. The solution is $(3, 0, 1)$.

28.
$$\begin{aligned} 2x + y + 4z &= 5 \quad (1)\\ -3x + y + 3z &= 14 \quad (2)\\ 4x + 2y + z &= 3 \quad (3)\end{aligned}$$

Eliminate x in equations (2) and (3).

$$\begin{array}{ll} & 2x + y + 4z = 5 \quad (1)\\ 3R_1 + 2R_2 \to R_2 & 5y + 18z = 43 \quad (4)\\ -2R_1 + R_3 \to R_3 & -7z = -7 \quad (5)\end{array}$$

Make the coefficient of the first term in each row equal 1.

$$\begin{array}{ll} \frac{1}{2}R_1 \to R_1 & x + \frac{1}{2}y + 2z = \frac{5}{2} \quad (6)\\ \frac{1}{5}R_2 \to R_2 & y + \frac{18}{5}z = \frac{43}{5} \quad (7)\\ -\frac{1}{7}R_3 \to R_3 & z = 1 \quad (8)\end{array}$$

Substitute 1 for z in equation (7) to get $y = 5$. Finally, substitute 1 for z and 5 for y in equation (6) to get $x = -2$. The solution is $(-2, 5, 1)$.

30.
$$\begin{aligned} 2x + 3y - z &= 1 \quad (1)\\ 3x + 5y + z &= 3 \quad (2)\end{aligned}$$

Eliminate x in equation (2).

$$\begin{array}{ll} & 2x + 3y - z = 1 \quad (1)\\ -3R_1 + 2R_2 \to R_2 & y + 5z = 3 \quad (3)\end{array}$$

Since there are only two equations, it is not possible to continue with the echelon method as in the previous exercises involving systems with three equations and three variables. To complete the solution, make the coefficient of the first term in the each equation equal 1.

$$\begin{array}{ll} \frac{1}{2}R_1 \to R_1 & x + \frac{3}{2}y + \frac{1}{2}z = \frac{1}{2} \quad (4)\\ & y + 5z = 3 \quad (3)\end{array}$$

Solve equation (3) for y in terms of the parameter z.

$$y + 5z = 3$$
$$y = 3 - 5z$$

Substitute this expression for y in equation (4) to solve for x in terms of the parameter z.

$$x + \frac{3}{2}(3 - 5z) - \frac{1}{2}z = \frac{1}{2}$$
$$x + \frac{9}{2} - \frac{15}{2}z - \frac{1}{2}z = \frac{1}{2}$$
$$x - 8z = -4$$
$$x = 8z - 4$$

The solution is $(8z - 4, 3 - 5z, z)$.

31. $3x + y - z = 0 \quad (1)$
$2x - y + 3z = -7 \quad (2)$

Eliminate x in equation (2).

$$\begin{array}{ll} & 3x + y - z = 0 \quad (1) \\ 2R_1 + (-3)R_2 \rightarrow R_2 & 5y - 11z = 21 \quad (3) \end{array}$$

Make the coefficient of the first term in each equation equal 1.

$$\begin{array}{ll} \frac{1}{3}R_1 \rightarrow R_1 & x + \frac{1}{3}y - \frac{1}{3}z = 0 \quad (4) \\ \frac{1}{5}R_2 \rightarrow R_2 & y - \frac{11}{5}z = \frac{21}{5} \quad (5) \end{array}$$

Solve equation (5) for y in terms of z.

$$y = \frac{11}{5}z + \frac{21}{5}$$

Substitute this expression for y in equation (4), and solve the equation for x.

$$x + \frac{1}{3}\left(\frac{11}{5}z + \frac{21}{5}\right) - \frac{1}{3}z = 0$$
$$x + \frac{11}{15}z + \frac{7}{5} - \frac{1}{3}z = 0$$
$$x + \frac{2}{5}z = -\frac{7}{5}$$
$$x = -\frac{2}{5}z - \frac{7}{5}$$

The solution is

$$\left(-\frac{2}{5}z - \frac{7}{5}, \frac{11}{5}z + \frac{21}{5}, z\right) \text{ or}$$
$$\left(\frac{-2z - 7}{5}, \frac{11z + 21}{5}, z\right).$$

32. $x + 2y + 3z = 11 \quad (1)$
$2x - y + z = 2 \quad (2)$

$$\begin{array}{ll} & x + 2y + 3z = 11 \quad (1) \\ -2R_1 + R_2 \rightarrow R_2 & -5y - 5z = -20 \quad (3) \end{array}$$

$$\begin{array}{ll} & x + 2y + 3z = 11 \quad (1) \\ -\frac{1}{5}R_2 \rightarrow R_2 & y + z = 4 \quad (4) \end{array}$$

Since there are only two equations, it is not possible to continue with the echelon method. To complete the solution, solve equation (4) for y in terms of the parameter z.

$$y = 4 - z$$

Now substitute $4 - z$ for y in equation (1) and solve for x in terms of z.

$$x + 2(4 - z) + 3z = 11$$
$$x + 8 - 2z + 3z = 11$$
$$x = 3 - z$$

The solution is $(3 - z, 4 - z, z)$.

33. $-x + y - z = -7 \quad (1)$
$2x + 3y + z = 7 \quad (2)$

Eliminate x in equation (2).

$$\begin{array}{ll} & -x + y - z = -7 \quad (1) \\ 2R_1 + R_2 \rightarrow R_2 & 5y - z = -7 \quad (3) \end{array}$$

Make the coefficient of the first term in each equation equal 1.

$$\begin{array}{ll} -1R_1 \rightarrow R_1 & x - y + z = 7 \quad (4) \\ \frac{1}{5}R_2 \rightarrow R_2 & y - \frac{1}{5}z = -\frac{7}{5} \quad (5) \end{array}$$

Solve equation (5) for y in terms of z.

$$y = \frac{1}{5}z - \frac{7}{5}$$

Substitute this expression for y in equation (4), and solve the equation for x.

$$x - \left(\frac{1}{5}z - \frac{7}{5}\right) + z = 7$$
$$x - \frac{1}{5}z + \frac{7}{5} + z = 7$$
$$x + \frac{4}{5}z = \frac{28}{5}$$
$$x = -\frac{4}{5}z + \frac{28}{5}$$

The solution of the system is

$$\left(-\frac{4}{5}z + \frac{28}{5}, \frac{1}{5}z - \frac{7}{5}, z\right) \text{ or}$$
$$\left(\frac{-4z + 28}{5}, \frac{z - 7}{5}, z\right).$$

34.
$$\begin{aligned} nb + (\sum x)m &= \sum y \quad (1) \\ (\sum x)b + (\sum x^2)m &= \sum xy \quad (2) \end{aligned}$$

Multiply equation (1) by $\frac{1}{n}$.

$$b + \frac{\sum x}{n}m = \frac{\sum y}{n} \quad (3)$$
$$(\sum x)b + (\sum x^2)m = \sum xy \quad (2)$$

Eliminate b from equation (2).

$$b + \frac{\sum x}{n}m = \frac{\sum y}{n} \quad (3)$$

$(-\sum x)R_1 + R_2 \rightarrow R_2$
$$\left[-\frac{(\sum x)^2}{n} + \sum x^2\right] m = \frac{-(\sum x)(\sum y)}{n} + \sum xy \quad (4)$$

Multiply equation (4) by $\dfrac{1}{-\frac{(\sum x)^2}{n} + \sum x^2}$.

$$b + \frac{\sum x}{n}m = \frac{\sum y}{n} \quad (3)$$

$$m = \left[\frac{-(\sum x)(\sum y)}{n} + \sum xy\right]\left[\frac{1}{-\frac{(\sum x)^2}{n} + \sum x^2}\right] \quad (5)$$

Simplify the right side of equation (5).

$$m = \left[\frac{-(\sum x)(\sum y) + n\sum xy}{n}\right]\left[\frac{n}{-(\sum x)^2 + n(\sum x^2)}\right]$$
$$m = \frac{n\sum xy - (\sum x)(\sum y)}{n(\sum x^2) - (\sum x)^2}$$

From equation (3) we have

$$b = \frac{\sum y}{n} - \frac{\sum x}{n}m$$
$$b = \frac{\sum y - m(\sum x)}{n}.$$

36. Let $x =$ the cost per pound of rice, and
$y =$ the cost per pound of potatoes.

The system to be solved is

$$\begin{aligned} 20x + 10y &= 16.20 \quad (1) \\ 30x + 12y &= 23.04. \quad (2) \end{aligned}$$

Multiply equation (1) by $\frac{1}{20}$.

$$\begin{aligned} \tfrac{1}{20}R_1 \rightarrow R_1 \qquad x + 0.5y &= 0.81 \quad (3) \\ 30x + 12y &= 23.04 \quad (2) \end{aligned}$$

Eliminate x in equation (2).

$$\begin{aligned} x + 0.5y &= 0.81 \quad (3) \\ -30R_1 + R_2 \rightarrow R_2 \qquad -3y &= -1.26 \quad (4) \end{aligned}$$

Multiply equation (4) by $-\frac{1}{3}$.

$$\begin{aligned} x + 0.5y &= 0.81 \quad (3) \\ -\tfrac{1}{3}R_2 \rightarrow R_2 \qquad y &= 0.42 \quad (5) \end{aligned}$$

Substitute 0.42 for y in equation (3).

$$\begin{aligned} x + 0.5(0.42) &= 0.81 \\ x + 0.21 &= 0.81 \\ x &= 0.60 \end{aligned}$$

The cost of 10 pounds of rice and 50 pounds of potatoes is

$$10(0.60) + 50(0.42) = 27,$$

that is, $27.

37. Let $x =$ the number of skirts originally in the store, and
$y =$ the number of blouses originally in the store.

The system to be solved is

$$45x + 35y = 51{,}750 \quad (1)$$
$$45\left(\frac{1}{2}x\right) + 35\left(\frac{2}{3}y\right) = 30{,}600. \quad (2)$$

Simplify each equation. Multiply equation (1) by $\frac{1}{5}$ and equation (2) by $\frac{6}{5}$.

$$\begin{aligned} 9x + 7y &= 10{,}350 \quad (3) \\ 27x + 28y &= 36{,}720 \quad (4) \end{aligned}$$

Eliminate x from equation (4).

$$\begin{aligned} 9x + 7y &= 10{,}350 \quad (3) \\ -3R_1 + R_2 \rightarrow R_2 \qquad 7y &= 5670 \quad (5) \end{aligned}$$

Make each leading coefficient equal 1.

$$\tfrac{1}{9}R_1 \rightarrow R_1 \qquad x + \frac{7}{9}y = 1150 \quad (6)$$

$$\tfrac{1}{7}R_2 \rightarrow R_2 \qquad y = 810 \quad (7)$$

Substitute 810 for y in equation (6).

$$x + \frac{7}{9}(810) = 1150$$
$$\begin{aligned} x + 630 &= 1150 \\ x &= 520 \end{aligned}$$

Half of the skirts are sold, leaving half in the store, so

$$\frac{1}{2}x = \frac{1}{2}(520) = 260.$$

Two-thirds of the blouses are sold, leaving one-third in the store, so

$$\frac{1}{3}y = \frac{1}{3}(810) = 270.$$

There are 260 skirts and 270 blouses left in the store.

38. Let $x =$ the number of seats on the main floor, and
$y =$ the number of seats in the balcony.

The system to be solved is

$$\begin{aligned} 8x \qquad + 5y &= 4200 \quad (1) \\ 0.25(8x) + 0.40(5y) &= 1200. \quad (2) \end{aligned}$$

Make the coefficient of the first term in equation(1) equal 1.

$$\begin{aligned} \tfrac{1}{8}R_1 \to R_1 \qquad x + \frac{5}{8}y &= 525 \quad (3) \\ 2x + 2y &= 1200 \quad (2) \end{aligned}$$

Eliminate x in equation (2).

$$\begin{aligned} x + \frac{5}{8}y &= 525 \quad (3) \\ -2R_1 + R_2 \to R_2 \qquad \frac{6}{8}y &= 150 \quad (4) \end{aligned}$$

Make the coefficient of the first term in equation (4) equal 1.

$$\begin{aligned} x + \frac{5}{8}y &= 525 \quad (3) \\ \tfrac{8}{6}R_2 \to R_2 \qquad y &= 200 \quad (5) \end{aligned}$$

Substitute 200 for y in equation (3).

$$\begin{aligned} x + \frac{5}{8}(200) &= 525 \\ x + 125 &= 525 \\ x &= 400 \end{aligned}$$

There are 400 main floor seats and 200 balcony seats.

39. Let $x =$ the number of shares of Disney stock, and
$y =$ the number of shares of Intel stock.

$$\begin{aligned} 30x + 70y &= 16{,}000 \quad (1) \\ 45x + 105y &= 25{,}500 \quad (2) \end{aligned}$$

Simplify each equation. Multiply equation (1) by $\frac{1}{10}$ and equation (2) by $\frac{1}{15}$.

$$\begin{aligned} 3x + 7y &= 1600 \quad (3) \\ 3x + 7y &= 1700 \quad (4) \end{aligned}$$

Since $3x+7y$ cannot equal both 1600 and 1700 for one point (x, y), we have an inconsistent system. Therefore, this situation is not possible.

40. Let $x =$ the number of model 201 to make each day, and
$y =$ the number of model 301 to make each day.

The system to be solved is

$$\begin{aligned} 2x + 3y &= 34 \quad (1) \\ 18x + 27y &= 335. \quad (2) \end{aligned}$$

Make the coefficient of the first term in equation (1) equal 1.

$$\begin{aligned} \tfrac{1}{2}R_1 \to R_1 \qquad x + \frac{3}{2}y &= 17 \quad (3) \\ 18x + 27y &= 335 \quad (2) \end{aligned}$$

Eliminate x in equation (2).

$$\begin{aligned} x + \frac{3}{2}y &= 17 \quad (3) \\ -18R_1 + R_2 \to R_2 \qquad 0 &= 29 \quad (4) \end{aligned}$$

Since equation (4) is false, the system is inconsistent. Therefore, this situation is impossible.

41. Let $x =$ the number of fives,
$y =$ the number of tens, and
$z =$ the number of twenties.

Since the number of fives is three times the number of tens, $x = 3y$.

The system to be solved is

$$\begin{aligned} x + y + z &= 70 \quad (1) \\ x - 3y &= 0 \quad (2) \\ 5x + 10y + 20z &= 960. \quad (3) \end{aligned}$$

Eliminate x in equations (2) and (3).

$$\begin{aligned} x + y + z &= 70 \quad (1) \\ R_1 + (-1)R_2 \to R_2 \qquad 4y + z &= 70 \quad (4) \\ -5R_1 + R_3 \to R_3 \qquad 5y + 15z &= 610 \quad (5) \end{aligned}$$

Eliminate y in equation (5).

$$\begin{aligned} x + y + z &= 70 \quad (1) \\ 4y + z &= 70 \quad (4) \\ -5R_2 + 4R_3 \to R_3 \qquad 55z &= 2090 \quad (6) \end{aligned}$$

Make each leading coefficient equal 1.

$$\begin{aligned} x + y + z &= 70 \quad (1) \\ \tfrac{1}{4}R_2 \to R_2 \qquad y + \frac{1}{4}z &= \frac{35}{2} \quad (7) \\ \tfrac{1}{55}R_3 \to R_3 \qquad z &= 38 \quad (8) \end{aligned}$$

Substitute 38 for z in equation (7) to get $y = 8$. Finally, substitute 38 for z and 8 for y in equation (1) to get $x = 24$.

There are 24 fives, 8 tens, and 38 twenties.

42. Let $x =$ amount invested in U.S. savings bonds,
$y =$ amount invested in mutual funds, and
$z =$ amount invested in a money market account.

Since the total amount invested was \$10,000, $x + y + z = 10{,}000$.
Katherine invested twice as much in mutual funds as in savings bonds, so $y = 2x$.
The total return on her investments was \$470, so $0.025x + 0.06y + 0.045z = 470$.
The system to be solved is

$$\begin{aligned} x + y + z &= 10{,}000 \quad (1)\\ 2x - y &= 0 \quad (2)\\ 0.025x + 0.06y + 0.045z &= 470 \quad (3). \end{aligned}$$

Simplify the system by multiplying equation (3) by 1000.

$$\begin{aligned} x + y + z &= 10{,}000 \quad (1)\\ 2x - y &= 0 \quad (2)\\ 1000R_3 \to R_3 \quad 25x + 60y + 45z &= 470{,}000 \quad (4) \end{aligned}$$

Eliminate x in equations (2) and (4).

$$\begin{aligned} x + y + z &= 10{,}000 \quad (1)\\ -2R_1 + R_2 \to R_2 \quad -3y - 2z &= -20{,}000 \quad (5)\\ -25R_1 + R_3 \to R_3 \quad 35y + 20z &= 220{,}000 \quad (6) \end{aligned}$$

Eliminate y in equation (6).

$$\begin{aligned} x + y + z &= 10{,}000 \quad (1)\\ -3y - 2z &= -20{,}000 \quad (5)\\ 35R_2 + 3R_3 \to R_3 \quad -10z &= -40{,}000 \quad (7) \end{aligned}$$

Make each leading coefficient equal 1.

$$\begin{aligned} x + y + z &= 10{,}000 \quad (1)\\ -\tfrac{1}{3}R_2 \to R_2 \quad y + \frac{2}{3}z &= \frac{20{,}000}{3} \quad (8)\\ -\tfrac{1}{10}R_3 \to R_3 \quad z &= 4000 \quad (9) \end{aligned}$$

Substitute 4000 for z in equation (8) to get $y = 4000$. Finally, substitute 4000 for z and 4000 for y in equation (1) to get $x = 2000$. Ms. Chong invested \$2000 in U.S. savings bonds, \$4000 in mutual funds, and \$4000 in a money market account.

43. Let $x =$ the number of buffets produced each week,
$y =$ the number of chairs produced each week, and
$z =$ the number of tables produced each week.

Make a table.

	Buffet	Chair	Table	Totals
Construction	30	10	10	350
Finishing	10	10	30	150

The system to be solved is

$$\begin{aligned} 30x + 10y + 10z &= 350 \quad (1)\\ 10x + 10y + 30z &= 150. \quad (2) \end{aligned}$$

Make the coefficient of the first term in equation (1) equal 1.

$$\begin{aligned} \tfrac{1}{30}R_1 \to R_1 \quad x + \frac{1}{3}y + \frac{1}{3}z &= \frac{35}{3} \quad (3)\\ 10x + 10y + 30z &= 150 \quad (2) \end{aligned}$$

Eliminate x from equation (2).

$$\begin{aligned} x + \frac{1}{3}y + \frac{1}{3}z &= \frac{35}{3} \quad (3)\\ -10R_1 + R_2 \to R_2 \quad \frac{20}{3}y + \frac{80}{3}z &= \frac{100}{3} \quad (4) \end{aligned}$$

Solve equation (4) for y. Multiply by 3.

$$\begin{aligned} 20y + 80z &= 100\\ y + 4z &= 5\\ y &= 5 - 4z \end{aligned}$$

Substitute $5 - 4z$ for y in equation (1) and solve for x.

$$\begin{aligned} 30x + 10(5 - 4z) + 10z &= 350\\ 30x + 50 - 40z + 10z &= 350\\ 30x &= 300 + 30z\\ x &= 10 + z \end{aligned}$$

The solution is $(10 + z, 5 - 4z, z)$. All variables must be nonnegative integers. Therefore,

$$\begin{aligned} 5 - 4z &\geq 0\\ 5 &\geq 4z\\ z &\leq \frac{5}{4}, \end{aligned}$$

so $z = 0$ or $z = 1$. (Any larger value of z would cause y to be negative, which would make no sense in the problem.) If $z = 0$, then the solution is $(10, 5, 0)$. If $z = 1$, then the solution is $(11, 1, 1)$.

Therefore, the company should make either 10 buffets, 5 chairs, and no tables or 11 buffets, 1 chair, and 1 table each week.

44. Let $x =$ the number of EZ models,
$y =$ the number of compact models, and
$z =$ the number of commercial models.

Make a table.

	EZ	Compact	Commercial	Totals
Weight	10	20	60	440
Space	10	8	28	248

$$10x + 20y + 60z = 440 \quad (1)$$
$$10x + 8y + 28z = 248 \quad (2)$$

Eliminate x from equation (2).

$$10x + 20y + 60z = 440 \quad (1)$$
$$R_1 + (-1)R_2 \rightarrow R_2 \qquad 12y + 32z = 192 \quad (3)$$

Make the leading coefficients equal 1.

$$\tfrac{1}{10}R_1 \rightarrow R_1 \quad x + 2y + 6z = 44 \quad (4)$$
$$\tfrac{1}{12}R_2 \rightarrow R_2 \quad y + \frac{8}{3}z = 16 \quad (5)$$

Solve equation (5) for y.

$$y = 16 - \frac{8}{3}z$$
$$y = \frac{48 - 8z}{3}$$
$$y = \frac{8(6 - z)}{3}$$

Substitute this expression for y into equation (4) and solve for x.

$$x + 2\left[\frac{8(6 - z)}{3}\right] + 6z = 44$$
$$x = 44 - 6z - \frac{16(6 - z)}{3}$$
$$x = \frac{132 - 18z - 96 + 16z}{3}$$
$$x = \frac{36 - 2z}{3}$$
$$x = \frac{2(18 - z)}{3}$$

The solution of the system is

$$\left(\frac{2(18 - z)}{3}, \frac{8(6 - z)}{3}, z\right).$$

The solutions must be nonnegative integers. Therefore, $0 \le z \le 6$. (Any larger values of z would cause y to be negative, which would make no sense in the problem.)

Values of z	Solutions
0	$(12, 16, 0)$
1	$(\frac{34}{3}, \frac{40}{3}, 1)$
2	$(\frac{32}{3}, \frac{32}{3}, 2)$
3	$(10, 8, 3)$
4	$(\frac{28}{3}, \frac{16}{3}, 4)$
5	$(\frac{26}{3}, \frac{8}{3}, 5)$
6	$(8, 0, 6)$

Ignore solutions containing values that are not integers. There are three possible solutions:

1. 12 EZ models, 16 compact models, and 0 commercial models;
2. 10 EZ models, 8 compact models, and 3 commercial models; or
3. 8 EZ models, 0 compact models, and 6 commercial models.

45. Let $x =$ the number of long-sleeve blouses,
$y =$ the number of short-sleeve blouses, and
$z =$ the number of sleeveless blouses.

Make a table.

	Long Sleeve	Short Sleeve	Sleeve-less	Totals
Cutting	1.5	1	0.5	380
Sewing	1.2	0.9	0.6	330

The system to be solved is

$$1.5x + y + 0.5z = 380 \quad (1)$$
$$1.2x + 0.9y + 0.6z = 330. \quad (2)$$

Simplify the equations. Multiply equation (1) by 2 and equation (2) by $\frac{10}{3}$.

$$3x + 2y + z = 760 \quad (3)$$
$$4x + 3y + 2z = 1100 \quad (4)$$

Make the leading coefficient of equation (3) equal 1.

$$\tfrac{1}{3}R_1 \rightarrow R_1 \quad x + \frac{2}{3}y + \frac{1}{3}z = \frac{760}{3} \quad (5)$$
$$4x + 3y + 2z = 1100 \quad (4)$$

Eliminate x from equation (4).

$$\begin{aligned} x + \frac{2}{3}y + \frac{1}{3}z &= \frac{760}{3} \quad (5) \\ -4R_1 + R_2 \rightarrow R_2 \qquad \frac{1}{3}y + \frac{2}{3}z &= \frac{260}{3} \quad (6) \end{aligned}$$

Make the leading coefficient of equation (6) equal 1.

$$\begin{aligned} x + \frac{2}{3}y + \frac{1}{3}z &= \frac{760}{3} \quad (5) \\ 3R_2 \rightarrow R_2 \qquad y + 2z &= 260 \quad (7) \end{aligned}$$

From equation (7), $y = 260 - 2z$. Substitute this into equation (5).

$$\begin{aligned} x + \frac{2}{3}(260 - 2z) + \frac{1}{3}z &= \frac{760}{3} \\ x + \frac{520}{3} - \frac{4}{3}z + \frac{1}{3}z &= \frac{760}{3} \\ x - z &= \frac{240}{3} \\ x &= z + 80 \end{aligned}$$

The solution is $(z + 80, 260 - 2z, z)$. In this problem $x, y,$ and z must be nonnegative, so

$$\begin{aligned} 260 - 2z &\geq 0 \\ -2z &\geq -260 \\ z &\leq 130. \end{aligned}$$

Therefore, the plant should make $z + 80$ long-sleeve blouses, $260 - 2z$ short-sleeve blouses, and z sleeveless blouses with $0 \leq z \leq 130$.

46. **(a)** The system to be solved is

$$\begin{aligned} 43{,}500x - y &= 1{,}295{,}000 \quad (1) \\ 27{,}000x - y &= 440{,}000 \quad (2) \end{aligned}$$

Eliminate x in equation (2).

$$\begin{aligned} 43{,}500x - y &= 1{,}295{,}000 \quad (1) \\ -\tfrac{27{,}000}{43{,}500}R_1 + R_2 \rightarrow R_2 \qquad -\frac{11}{29}y &= -\frac{10{,}550{,}000}{29} \quad (3) \end{aligned}$$

Make the coefficient of the first term in equation (3) equal 1.

$$\begin{aligned} 43{,}500x - y &= 1{,}295{,}000 \quad (1) \\ -\tfrac{29}{11}R_2 \rightarrow R_2 \qquad y &= \frac{10{,}550{,}000}{11} \quad (4) \end{aligned}$$

Substitute $\frac{10{,}550{,}000}{11}$ for y in equation (1).

$$\begin{aligned} 43{,}500x - \frac{10{,}550{,}000}{11} &= 1{,}295{,}000 \\ 43{,}500x &= \frac{24{,}795{,}000}{11} \\ x &= \frac{570}{11} \end{aligned}$$

The solution is $\left(\frac{570}{11}, \frac{10{,}550{,}000}{11}\right)$.

The profit/loss will be equal after $\frac{570}{11}$ weeks or about 51.8 weeks. At that point, the profit will be $\frac{10{,}550{,}000}{11}$ or about \$959,091.

(b) If the show lasts longer than 51.8 weeks, Broadway is a more profitable venue. If it lasts less than 51.8 weeks, off Broadway is a more profitable venue.

47. **(a)** For the first equation, the first sighting in 2000 was on day $y = 759 - 0.338(2000) = 83$, or during the eighty-third day of the year. Since 2000 was a leap year, the eighty-third day fell on March 23.

For the second equation, the first sighting in 2000 was on day $y = 1637 - 0.779(2000) = 79$, or during the seventy-ninth day of the year. Since 2000 was a leap year, the seventh-ninth day fell on March 19.

(b)
$$\begin{aligned} y &= 759 - 0.338x \quad (1) \\ y &= 1637 - 0.779x \quad (2) \end{aligned}$$

Rewrite equations so that variables are on the left side and constant term is on the right side.

$$\begin{aligned} 0.338x + y &= 759 \quad (3) \\ 0.779x + y &= 1637 \quad (4) \end{aligned}$$

Eliminate y from equation (4).

$$\begin{aligned} 0.338x + y &= 759 \quad (3) \\ -1R_1 + R_2 \rightarrow R_2 \qquad 0.441x &= 878 \quad (5) \end{aligned}$$

Make leading coefficient for equation (5) equal 1.

$$\begin{aligned} 0.338x + y &= 759 \quad (3) \\ \tfrac{1}{0.441}R_2 \rightarrow R_2 \qquad x &= \frac{878}{0.441} \quad (6) \end{aligned}$$

The two estimates agree in the year closest to $x = \frac{878}{0.441} \approx 1990.93$, so they agree in 1991. The estimated number of days into the year when a robin can be expected is

$$\begin{aligned} 0.338\left(\frac{878}{0.441}\right) + y &= 759 \\ y &\approx 86. \end{aligned}$$

48. **(a)** We are given the equation

$$y = ax^2 + bx + c.$$

Since a car traveling at 0 mph has a stopping distance of 0 feet, then $y = 0$ when $x = 0$. Substituting these values into $y = ax^2 + bx + c$ yields

$$\begin{aligned} 0 &= a(0)^2 + b(0) + c, \text{ so} \\ c &= 0. \end{aligned}$$

Therefore, we have

$$y = ax^2 + bx.$$

After substituting the given values for the stopping distances (y) and speeds (x) in mph, the system to be solved is

$$\begin{aligned} 61.7 &= a(25)^2 + b(25) \quad (1) \\ 106 &= a(35)^2 + b(35). \quad (2) \end{aligned}$$

These equations can be written as

$$\begin{aligned} 625a + 25b &= 61.7 \quad (1) \\ 1225a + 35b &= 106. \quad (2) \end{aligned}$$

Multiply equation (1) by $\frac{1}{625}$; also eliminate the decimal in 61.7 by multiplying the numerator and denominator of the fraction by 10.

$$\begin{aligned} \tfrac{1}{625}R_1 \to R_1 \qquad a + \frac{1}{25}b &= \frac{617}{6250} \quad (3) \\ 1225a + 35b &= 106 \quad (2) \end{aligned}$$

Eliminate a in equation (2).

$$\begin{aligned} a + \frac{1}{25}b &= \frac{617}{6250} \quad (3) \\ -1225R_1 + R_2 \to R_2 \qquad -14b &= -\frac{3733}{250} \quad (4) \end{aligned}$$

Multiply equation (4) by $-\frac{1}{14}$.

$$\begin{aligned} a + \frac{1}{25}b &= \frac{617}{6250} \quad (3) \\ -\tfrac{1}{14}R_2 \to R_2 \qquad b &= \frac{3733}{3500} \quad (5) \end{aligned}$$

Substitute $\frac{3733}{3500}$ for b in equation (3).

$$\begin{aligned} a + \frac{1}{25}\left(\frac{3733}{3500}\right) &= \frac{617}{6250} \\ a &= \frac{4905}{87{,}500} \end{aligned}$$

Therefore,

$$a = \frac{4905}{87{,}500} \approx 0.056057,$$

$$\text{and} \quad b = \frac{3733}{3500} \approx 1.06657.$$

(b) Substitute the values from part (a) for a and b and 55 for x in the equation $y = ax^2 + bx$. Solve for y.

$$\begin{aligned} y &= 0.056057(55)^2 + 1.06657(55) \\ y &\approx 228 \end{aligned}$$

The stopping distance of a car traveling 55 mph is approximately 228 ft.

49. Let $x =$ number of free throws, and
$y =$ number of foul shots.

Then

$$\begin{aligned} x + y &= 64 \quad (1) \\ 2x + y &= 100 \quad (2). \end{aligned}$$

Eliminate x in equation (2).

$$\begin{aligned} x + y &= 64 \quad (1) \\ -2R_1 + R_2 \to R_2 \qquad -y &= -28 \quad (3) \end{aligned}$$

Make the coefficients of the first term of each equation equal 1.

$$\begin{aligned} x + y &= 64 \quad (1) \\ -1R_2 \to R_2 \qquad y &= 28 \quad (4) \end{aligned}$$

Substitute 28 for y in equation (1) to get $x = 36$. Wilt Chamberlain made 36 free throws and 28 foul shots.

50. Let $x =$ number of foul shots,
$y =$ number of free throws, and
$z =$ number of three pointers.

Since Bryant made a total of 46 baskets,

$$x + y + z = 46.$$

Since the number of free throw shots is equal to three times the number of three points, $y = 3z$, or

$$y - 3z = 0.$$

And since the total number of points was 81,

$$x + 2y + 3z = 81.$$

The system to be solved is

$$\begin{aligned} x + y + z &= 46 \quad (1) \\ y - 3z &= 0 \quad (2) \\ x + 2y + 3z &= 81 \quad (3). \end{aligned}$$

Eliminate x in equation (3).

$$\begin{aligned} x + y + z &= 46 \quad (1) \\ y - 3z &= 0 \quad (2) \\ -1R_1 + R_3 \to R_3 \qquad y + 2z &= 35 \quad (4) \end{aligned}$$

Eliminate y in equation (4).

$$\begin{array}{lrl} & x+y+\ \ z=46 & (1) \\ & y-3z=\ \ 0 & (2) \\ (-1)R_2+R_3 \rightarrow R_3 & 5z=35 & (5) \end{array}$$

Make each leading coefficient equal 1.

$$\begin{array}{lrl} & x+y+\ \ z=46 & (1) \\ & y-3z=\ \ 0 & (2) \\ \frac{1}{5}R_3 \rightarrow R_3 & z=\ \ 7 & (6) \end{array}$$

Substitute 7 for z in equation (2) to get $y = 21$. Finally, substitute 7 for z and 21 for y in equation (1) to get $x = 18$. Bryant made 18 foul shots, 21 free throws, and 7 three pointers.

51. **(a)** Since 8 and 9 must be two of the four numbers combined using addition, subtraction, multiplication, and/or division to get 24, begin by finding two numbers to use with 8 and 9. One possibility is 8 and 3 since $(9-8)\cdot 8\cdot 3 = 24$. If we can find values of x and y such that either $x+y=8$ and $3x+2y=3$, or $x+y=3$ and $3x+2y=8$, we will have found a solution. Solving the first system gives $x=-13$ and $y=21$. This, however, does not satisfy the condition that x and y be single-digit positive integers. Solving the second system gives $x=2$ and $y=1$. Since both of these values are single-digit positive integers, we have one possible system. Thus, one system is

$$\begin{cases} x+y=3 \\ 3x+2y=8 \end{cases}.$$

Its solution is $(2,1)$. These values of x and y give the numbers 8, 9, 8, and 3 on the game card. These numbers can be combined as $(9-8)\cdot 8\cdot 3$ to make 24.

2.2 Solution of Linear Systems by the Gauss-Jordan Method

1. $3x + y = 6$
$2x + 5y = 15$

The equations are already in proper form. The augmented matrix obtained from the coefficients and the constants is

$$\left[\begin{array}{cc|c} 3 & 1 & 6 \\ 2 & 5 & 15 \end{array}\right].$$

2. $4x - 2y = 8$
$-7y = -12$

The equations are already in proper form. The augmented matrix obtained from the coefficients and the constants is

$$\left[\begin{array}{cc|c} 4 & -2 & 8 \\ 0 & -7 & -12 \end{array}\right].$$

3. $2x + y + z = 3$
$3x - 4y + 2z = -7$
$x + y + z = 2$

leads to the augmented matrix

$$\left[\begin{array}{ccc|c} 2 & 1 & 1 & 3 \\ 3 & -4 & 2 & -7 \\ 1 & 1 & 1 & 2 \end{array}\right].$$

4. $2x - 5y + 3z = 4$
$-4x + 2y - 7z = -5$
$3x - y = 8$

The equations are already in proper form. The augmented matrix obtained from the coefficients and the constants is

$$\left[\begin{array}{ccc|c} 2 & -5 & 3 & 4 \\ -4 & 2 & -7 & -5 \\ 3 & -1 & 0 & 8 \end{array}\right].$$

5. We are given the augmented matrix

$$\left[\begin{array}{cc|c} 1 & 0 & 2 \\ 0 & 1 & 3 \end{array}\right].$$

This is equivalent to the system of equations

$$\begin{aligned} x \quad &= 2 \\ y &= 3, \end{aligned}$$

or $x = 2$, $y = 3$.

6. $\left[\begin{array}{cc|c} 1 & 0 & 5 \\ 0 & 1 & -3 \end{array}\right]$

is equivalent to the system

$$\begin{aligned} x &= 5 \\ y &= -3. \end{aligned}$$

7. $\left[\begin{array}{ccc|c} 1 & 0 & 0 & 4 \\ 0 & 1 & 0 & -5 \\ 0 & 0 & 1 & 1 \end{array}\right]$

The system associated with this matrix is

$$\begin{aligned} x \qquad &= 4 \\ y \quad &= -5 \\ z &= 1, \end{aligned}$$

or $x = 4,\ y = -5,\ z = 1$.

8. $\left[\begin{array}{ccc|c} 1 & 0 & 0 & 4 \\ 0 & 1 & 0 & 2 \\ 0 & 0 & 1 & 3 \end{array}\right]$

is equivalent to the system

$$\begin{aligned} x &= 4 \\ y &= 2 \\ z &= 3. \end{aligned}$$

9. *Row operations* on a matrix correspond to transformations of a system of equations.

11. $\left[\begin{array}{ccc|c} 3 & 7 & 4 & 10 \\ 1 & 2 & 3 & 6 \\ 0 & 4 & 5 & 11 \end{array}\right]$

Find $R_1 + (-3)R_2$.

In row 2, column 1,

$$3 + (-3)1 = 0.$$

In row 2, column 2,

$$7 + (-3)2 = 1.$$

In row 2, column 3,

$$4 + (-3)3 = -5.$$

In row 2, column 4,

$$10 + (-3)6 = -8.$$

Replace R_2 with these values. The new matrix is

$$\left[\begin{array}{ccc|c} 3 & 7 & 4 & 10 \\ 0 & 1 & -5 & -8 \\ 0 & 4 & 5 & 11 \end{array}\right].$$

12. Replace R_3 by $-1R_1 + 3R_3$.
The original matrix is

$$\left[\begin{array}{ccc|c} 3 & 2 & 6 & 18 \\ 2 & -2 & 5 & 7 \\ 1 & 0 & 5 & 20 \end{array}\right].$$

The resulting matrix is

$$\left[\begin{array}{ccc|c} 3 & 2 & 6 & 18 \\ 2 & -2 & 5 & 7 \\ 0 & -2 & 9 & 42 \end{array}\right].$$

13. $\left[\begin{array}{ccc|c} 1 & 6 & 4 & 7 \\ 0 & 3 & 2 & 5 \\ 0 & 5 & 3 & 7 \end{array}\right]$

Find $(-2)R_2 + R_1 \rightarrow R_1$

$$\left[\begin{array}{ccc|c} (-2)0+1 & (-2)3+6 & (-2)2+4 & (-2)5+7 \\ 0 & 3 & 2 & 5 \\ 0 & 5 & 3 & 7 \end{array}\right]$$

$$= \left[\begin{array}{ccc|c} 1 & 0 & 0 & -3 \\ 0 & 3 & 2 & 5 \\ 0 & 5 & 3 & 7 \end{array}\right]$$

14. Replace R_1 by $R_3 + (-3)R_1$.

The original matrix is

$$\left[\begin{array}{ccc|c} 1 & 0 & 4 & 21 \\ 0 & 6 & 5 & 30 \\ 0 & 0 & 12 & 15 \end{array}\right].$$

The resulting matrix is

$$\left[\begin{array}{ccc|c} -3 & 0 & 0 & -48 \\ 0 & 6 & 5 & 30 \\ 0 & 0 & 12 & 15 \end{array}\right].$$

15. $\left[\begin{array}{ccc|c} 3 & 0 & 0 & 18 \\ 0 & 5 & 0 & 9 \\ 0 & 0 & 4 & 8 \end{array}\right]$

$\frac{1}{3}R_1 \rightarrow R_1$

$$\left[\begin{array}{ccc|c} \frac{1}{3}(3) & \frac{1}{3}(0) & \frac{1}{3}(0) & \frac{1}{3}(18) \\ 0 & 5 & 0 & 9 \\ 0 & 0 & 4 & 8 \end{array}\right] = \left[\begin{array}{ccc|c} 1 & 0 & 0 & 6 \\ 0 & 5 & 0 & 9 \\ 0 & 0 & 4 & 8 \end{array}\right]$$

16. Replace R_3 by $\frac{1}{6}R_3$.

$$\left[\begin{array}{ccc|c} 1 & 0 & 0 & 30 \\ 0 & 1 & 0 & 17 \\ 0 & 0 & 6 & 162 \end{array}\right].$$

The resulting matrix is

$$\left[\begin{array}{ccc|c} 1 & 0 & 0 & 30 \\ 0 & 1 & 0 & 17 \\ 0 & 0 & 1 & 27 \end{array}\right].$$

17. $x + y = 5$
$3x + 2y = 12$

Write the augmented matrix and use row operations.

$$\left[\begin{array}{cc|c} 1 & 1 & 5 \\ 3 & 2 & 12 \end{array}\right]$$

$$-3R_1 + R_2 \rightarrow R_2 \quad \left[\begin{array}{cc|c} 1 & 1 & 5 \\ 0 & -1 & -3 \end{array}\right]$$

$$-1R_2 \rightarrow R_2 \quad \left[\begin{array}{cc|c} 1 & 1 & 5 \\ 0 & 1 & 3 \end{array}\right]$$

$$-1R_2 + R_1 \rightarrow R_1 \quad \left[\begin{array}{cc|c} 1 & 0 & 2 \\ 0 & 1 & 3 \end{array}\right]$$

The solution is $(2, 3)$.

18. $x + 2y = 5$
$2x + y = -2$

To begin, write the augmented matrix for the given system.

$$\left[\begin{array}{cc|c} 1 & 2 & 5 \\ 2 & 1 & -2 \end{array}\right]$$

The third row operation is used to change the 2 in row 2 to 0.

$$-2R_1 + R_2 \rightarrow R_2 \quad \left[\begin{array}{cc|c} 1 & 2 & 5 \\ 0 & -3 & -12 \end{array}\right]$$

Next, change the 2 in row 1 to 0.

$$2R_2 + 3R_1 \rightarrow R_1 \quad \left[\begin{array}{cc|c} 3 & 0 & -9 \\ 0 & -3 & -12 \end{array}\right]$$

Finally, change the first nonzero number in each row to 1.

$$\begin{array}{l} \frac{1}{3}R_1 \rightarrow R_1 \\ -\frac{1}{3}R_2 \rightarrow R_2 \end{array} \quad \left[\begin{array}{cc|c} 1 & 0 & -3 \\ 0 & 1 & 4 \end{array}\right]$$

The final matrix is equivalent to the system

$$\begin{aligned} x &= -3 \\ y &= 4, \end{aligned}$$

so the solution of the original system is $(-3, 4)$.

19. $x + y = 7$
$4x + 3y = 22$

Write the augmented matrix and use row operations.

$$\left[\begin{array}{cc|c} 1 & 1 & 7 \\ 4 & 3 & 22 \end{array}\right]$$

$$-4R_1 + R_2 \rightarrow R_2 \quad \left[\begin{array}{cc|c} 1 & 1 & 7 \\ 0 & -1 & -6 \end{array}\right]$$

$$-1R_2 \rightarrow R_2 \quad \left[\begin{array}{cc|c} 1 & 1 & 7 \\ 0 & 1 & 6 \end{array}\right]$$

$$-1R_2 + R_1 \rightarrow R_1 \quad \left[\begin{array}{cc|c} 1 & 0 & 1 \\ 0 & 1 & 6 \end{array}\right]$$

The solution is $(1, 6)$.

20. $4x - 2y = 3$
$-2x + 3y = 1$

The augmented matrix for the system is

$$\left[\begin{array}{cc|c} 4 & -2 & 3 \\ -2 & 3 & 1 \end{array}\right].$$

$$R_1 + 2R_2 \rightarrow R_2 \quad \left[\begin{array}{cc|c} 4 & -2 & 3 \\ 0 & 4 & 5 \end{array}\right]$$

$$R_2 + 2R_1 \rightarrow R_1 \quad \left[\begin{array}{cc|c} 8 & 0 & 11 \\ 0 & 4 & 5 \end{array}\right]$$

$$\begin{array}{l} \frac{1}{8}R_1 \rightarrow R_1 \\ \frac{1}{4}R_2 \rightarrow R_2 \end{array} \quad \left[\begin{array}{cc|c} 1 & 0 & \frac{11}{8} \\ 0 & 1 & \frac{5}{4} \end{array}\right]$$

The solution is $\left(\frac{11}{8}, \frac{5}{4}\right)$.

21. $2x - 3y = 2$
$4x - 6y = 1$

Write the augmented matrix and use row operations.

$$\left[\begin{array}{cc|c} 2 & -3 & 2 \\ 4 & -6 & 1 \end{array}\right]$$

$$-2R_1 + R_2 \rightarrow R_2 \quad \left[\begin{array}{cc|c} 2 & -3 & 2 \\ 0 & 0 & -3 \end{array}\right]$$

The system associated with the last matrix is

$$\begin{aligned} 2x - 3y &= 2 \\ 0x + 0y &= -3. \end{aligned}$$

Since the second equation, $0 = -3$, is false, the system is inconsistent and therefore has no solution.

22. $2x + 3y = 9$
$4x + 6y = 7$

Write the augmented matrix and use row operations.

$$\left[\begin{array}{cc|c} 2 & 3 & 9 \\ 4 & 6 & 7 \end{array}\right]$$

$$-2R_1 + R_2 \to R_2 \quad \left[\begin{array}{cc|c} 2 & 3 & 9 \\ 0 & 0 & -11 \end{array}\right]$$

The system associated with the last matrix is

$$\begin{aligned} 2x + 3y &= 9 \\ 0x + 0y &= -11. \end{aligned}$$

Since the second equation $0 = -11$, is false, the system is inconsistent and therefore has no solution.

23. $6x - 3y = 1$
$-12x + 6y = -2$

Write the augmented matrix of the system and use row operations.

$$\left[\begin{array}{cc|c} 6 & -3 & 1 \\ -12 & 6 & -2 \end{array}\right]$$

$$2R_1 + R_2 \to R_2 \quad \left[\begin{array}{cc|c} 6 & -3 & 1 \\ 0 & 0 & 0 \end{array}\right]$$

$$\tfrac{1}{6}R_1 \to R_1 \quad \left[\begin{array}{cc|c} 1 & -\frac{1}{2} & \frac{1}{6} \\ 0 & 0 & 0 \end{array}\right]$$

This is as far as we can go with the Gauss-Jordan method. To complete the solution, write the equation that corresponds to the first row of the matrix.

$$x - \frac{1}{2}y = \frac{1}{6}$$

Solve this equation for x in terms of y.

$$x = \frac{1}{2}y + \frac{1}{6} = \frac{3y+1}{6}$$

The solution is $\left(\frac{3y+1}{6}, y\right)$, where y is any real number.

24. $x - y = 1$
$-x + y = -1$

The augmented matrix is

$$\left[\begin{array}{cc|c} 1 & -1 & 1 \\ -1 & 1 & -1 \end{array}\right].$$

$$R_1 + R_2 \to R_2 \quad \left[\begin{array}{cc|c} 1 & -1 & 1 \\ 0 & 0 & 0 \end{array}\right]$$

The row of zeros indicates dependent equations. (Both equations have the same line as their graph.) The remaining equation is $x - y = 1$. Solving for x gives $x = y + 1$. There are an infinite number of solutions, each of the form $(y + 1, y)$, for any real number y.

25. $y = x - 3$
$y = 1 + z$
$z = 4 - x$

First write the system in proper form.

$$\begin{aligned} -x + y \quad\quad &= -3 \\ y - z &= 1 \\ x \quad\quad + z &= 4 \end{aligned}$$

Write the augmented matrix and use row operations.

$$\left[\begin{array}{ccc|c} -1 & 1 & 0 & -3 \\ 0 & 1 & -1 & 1 \\ 1 & 0 & 1 & 4 \end{array}\right]$$

$$-1R_1 \to R_1 \quad \left[\begin{array}{ccc|c} 1 & -1 & 0 & 3 \\ 0 & 1 & -1 & 1 \\ 1 & 0 & 1 & 4 \end{array}\right]$$

$$-1R_1 + R_3 \to R_3 \quad \left[\begin{array}{ccc|c} 1 & -1 & 0 & 3 \\ 0 & 1 & -1 & 1 \\ 0 & 1 & 1 & 1 \end{array}\right]$$

$$\begin{array}{c} R_2 + R_1 \to R_1 \\ \\ -1R_2 + R_3 \to R_3 \end{array} \quad \left[\begin{array}{ccc|c} 1 & 0 & -1 & 4 \\ 0 & 1 & -1 & 1 \\ 0 & 0 & 2 & 0 \end{array}\right]$$

$$\begin{array}{c} R_3 + 2R_1 \to R_1 \\ R_3 + 2R_2 \to R_2 \end{array} \quad \left[\begin{array}{ccc|c} 2 & 0 & 0 & 8 \\ 0 & 2 & 0 & 2 \\ 0 & 0 & 2 & 0 \end{array}\right]$$

$$\begin{array}{c} \frac{1}{2}R_1 \to R_1 \\ \frac{1}{2}R_2 \to R_2 \\ \frac{1}{2}R_3 \to R_3 \end{array} \quad \left[\begin{array}{ccc|c} 1 & 0 & 0 & 4 \\ 0 & 1 & 0 & 1 \\ 0 & 0 & 1 & 0 \end{array}\right]$$

The solution is $(4, 1, 0)$.

26. $x = 1 - y$
$2x = z$
$2z = -2 - y$

Put the equations in proper form to obtain the system

$$\begin{aligned} x + y &= 1 \\ 2x - z &= 0 \\ y + 2z &= -2. \end{aligned}$$

The augmented matrix is

$$\left[\begin{array}{rrr|r} 1 & 1 & 0 & 1 \\ 2 & 0 & -1 & 0 \\ 0 & 1 & 2 & -2 \end{array}\right].$$

$$-2R_1 + R_2 \to R_2 \quad \left[\begin{array}{rrr|r} 1 & 1 & 0 & 1 \\ 0 & -2 & -1 & -2 \\ 0 & 1 & 2 & -2 \end{array}\right]$$

$$\begin{array}{l} R_2 + 2R_1 \to R_1 \\ \\ R_2 + 2R_3 \to R_3 \end{array} \quad \left[\begin{array}{rrr|r} 2 & 0 & -1 & 0 \\ 0 & -2 & -1 & -2 \\ 0 & 0 & 3 & -6 \end{array}\right]$$

$$\begin{array}{l} R_3 + 3R_1 \to R_1 \\ R_3 + 3R_2 \to R_2 \end{array} \quad \left[\begin{array}{rrr|r} 6 & 0 & 0 & -6 \\ 0 & -6 & 0 & -12 \\ 0 & 0 & 3 & -6 \end{array}\right]$$

$$\begin{array}{r} \frac{1}{6}R_1 \to R_1 \\ -\frac{1}{6}R_2 \to R_2 \\ \frac{1}{3}R_3 \to R_3 \end{array} \quad \left[\begin{array}{rrr|r} 1 & 0 & 0 & -1 \\ 0 & 1 & 0 & 2 \\ 0 & 0 & 1 & -2 \end{array}\right]$$

The solution is $(-1, 2, -2)$.

27. $2x - 2y = -5$
$2y + z = 0$
$2x + z = -7$

Write the augmented matrix and use row operations.

$$\left[\begin{array}{rrr|r} 2 & -2 & 0 & -5 \\ 0 & 2 & 1 & 0 \\ 2 & 0 & 1 & -7 \end{array}\right]$$

$$-1R_1 + R_3 \to R_3 \quad \left[\begin{array}{rrr|r} 2 & -2 & 0 & -5 \\ 0 & 2 & 1 & 0 \\ 0 & 2 & 1 & -2 \end{array}\right]$$

$$\begin{array}{l} R_2 + R_1 \to R_1 \\ \\ -1R_2 + R_3 \to R_3 \end{array} \quad \left[\begin{array}{rrr|r} 2 & 0 & 1 & -5 \\ 0 & 2 & 1 & 0 \\ 0 & 0 & 0 & -2 \end{array}\right]$$

This matrix corresponds to the system of equations

$$\begin{aligned} 2x + z &= -5 \\ 2y + z &= 0 \\ 0 &= -2. \end{aligned}$$

This false statement $0 = -2$ indicates that the system is inconsistent and therefore has no solution.

28. $x \quad - z = -3$
$y + z = 9$
$-2x + 3y + 5z = 33$

Write the augmented matrix and use row operations.

$$\left[\begin{array}{rrr|r} 1 & 0 & -1 & -3 \\ 0 & 1 & 1 & 9 \\ -2 & 3 & 5 & 33 \end{array}\right]$$

$$2R_1 + R_3 \to R_3 \quad \left[\begin{array}{rrr|r} 1 & 0 & -1 & -3 \\ 0 & 1 & 1 & 9 \\ 0 & 3 & 3 & 27 \end{array}\right]$$

$$-3R_2 + R_3 \to R_3 \quad \left[\begin{array}{rrr|r} 1 & 0 & -1 & -3 \\ 0 & 1 & 1 & 9 \\ 0 & 0 & 0 & 0 \end{array}\right]$$

The last row indicates an infinite number of solutions. The remaining equations are

$$x - z = -3 \quad \text{and} \quad y + z = 9.$$

Solve these for x and y, the solutions are

$$(z - 3, -z + 9, z)$$

for any real number z.

29. $4x + 4y - 4z = 24$
$2x - y + z = -9$
$x - 2y + 3z = 1$

Write the augmented matrix and use row operations.

$$\left[\begin{array}{rrr|r} 4 & 4 & -4 & 24 \\ 2 & -1 & 1 & -9 \\ 1 & -2 & 3 & 1 \end{array}\right]$$

$$\begin{array}{l} R_1 + (-2)R_2 \to R_2 \\ R_1 + (-4)R_3 \to R_3 \end{array} \quad \left[\begin{array}{rrr|r} 4 & 4 & -4 & 24 \\ 0 & 6 & -6 & 42 \\ 0 & 12 & -16 & 20 \end{array}\right]$$

$$\begin{array}{r} 2R_2 + (-3)R_1 \to R_1 \\ \\ -2R_2 + R_3 \to R_3 \end{array} \quad \left[\begin{array}{rrr|r} -12 & 0 & 0 & 12 \\ 0 & 6 & -6 & 42 \\ 0 & 0 & -4 & -64 \end{array}\right]$$

$$-3R_3 + 2R_2 \to R_2 \quad \left[\begin{array}{rrr|r} -12 & 0 & 0 & 12 \\ 0 & 12 & 0 & 276 \\ 0 & 0 & -4 & -64 \end{array}\right]$$

$$\begin{array}{r} -\frac{1}{12}R_1 \to R_1 \\ -\frac{1}{12}R_2 \to R_2 \\ -\frac{1}{4}R_3 \to R_3 \end{array} \quad \left[\begin{array}{rrr|r} 1 & 0 & 0 & -1 \\ 0 & 1 & 0 & 23 \\ 0 & 0 & 1 & 16 \end{array}\right]$$

The solution is $(-1, 23, 16)$.

30.
$$\begin{aligned} x + 2y - 7z &= -2 \\ -2x - 5y + 2z &= 1 \\ 3x + 5y + 4z &= -9 \end{aligned}$$

Write the augmented matrix and use row operations.

$$\left[\begin{array}{rrr|r} 1 & 2 & -7 & -2 \\ -2 & -5 & 2 & 1 \\ 3 & 5 & 4 & -9 \end{array}\right]$$

$$\begin{array}{r} \\ 2R_1 + R_2 \to R_2 \\ -3R_1 + R_3 \to R_3 \end{array} \left[\begin{array}{rrr|r} 1 & 2 & -7 & -2 \\ 0 & -1 & -12 & -3 \\ 0 & -1 & 25 & -3 \end{array}\right]$$

$$\begin{array}{r} 2R_2 + R_1 \to R_1 \\ \\ -1R_2 + R_3 \to R_3 \end{array} \left[\begin{array}{rrr|r} 1 & 0 & -31 & -8 \\ 0 & -1 & -12 & -3 \\ 0 & 0 & 37 & 0 \end{array}\right]$$

$$\begin{array}{r} 31R_3 + 37R_1 \to R_1 \\ 12R_3 + 37R_2 \to R_2 \\ \\ \end{array} \left[\begin{array}{rrr|r} 37 & 0 & 0 & -296 \\ 0 & -37 & 0 & -111 \\ 0 & 0 & 37 & 0 \end{array}\right]$$

$$\begin{array}{r} \frac{1}{37}R_1 \to R_1 \\ -\frac{1}{37}R_2 \to R_2 \\ \frac{1}{37}R_3 \to R_3 \end{array} \left[\begin{array}{rrr|r} 1 & 0 & 0 & -8 \\ 0 & 1 & 0 & 3 \\ 0 & 0 & 1 & 0 \end{array}\right]$$

The solution is $(-8, 3, 0)$.

31.
$$\begin{aligned} 3x + 5y - z &= 0 \\ 4x - y + 2z &= 1 \\ 7x + 4y + z &= 1 \end{aligned}$$

Write the augmented matrix and use row operations.

$$\left[\begin{array}{rrr|r} 3 & 5 & -1 & 0 \\ 4 & -1 & 2 & 1 \\ 7 & 4 & 1 & 1 \end{array}\right]$$

$$\begin{array}{r} \\ 4R_1 + (-3)R_2 \to R_2 \\ 7R_1 + (-3)R_3 \to R_3 \end{array} \left[\begin{array}{rrr|r} 3 & 5 & -1 & 0 \\ 0 & 23 & -10 & -3 \\ 0 & 23 & -10 & -3 \end{array}\right]$$

$$\begin{array}{r} 23R_1 + (-5)R_2 \to R_1 \\ \\ R_2 + (-1)R_3 \to R_3 \end{array} \left[\begin{array}{rrr|r} 69 & 0 & 27 & 15 \\ 0 & 23 & -10 & -3 \\ 0 & 0 & 0 & 0 \end{array}\right]$$

$$\begin{array}{r} \frac{1}{69}R_1 \to R_1 \\ \frac{1}{23}R_2 \to R_2 \\ \\ \end{array} \left[\begin{array}{rrr|r} 1 & 0 & \frac{9}{23} & \frac{5}{23} \\ 0 & 1 & -\frac{10}{23} & -\frac{3}{23} \\ 0 & 0 & 0 & 0 \end{array}\right]$$

The row of zeros indicates dependent equations. Solve the first two equations respectively for x and y in terms of z to obtain

$$x = -\frac{9}{23}z + \frac{5}{23} = \frac{-9z + 5}{23}$$

and

$$y = \frac{10}{23}z - \frac{3}{23} = \frac{10x - 3}{23}.$$

The solution is $\left(\frac{-9z+5}{23}, \frac{10z-3}{23}, z\right)$.

32.
$$\begin{aligned} 3x - 6y + 3z &= 11 \\ 2x + y - z &= 2 \\ 5x - 5y + 2z &= 6 \end{aligned}$$

Write the augmented matrix and use row operations.

$$\left[\begin{array}{rrr|r} 3 & -6 & 3 & 11 \\ 2 & 1 & -1 & 2 \\ 5 & -5 & 2 & 6 \end{array}\right].$$

$$\begin{array}{r} \\ -2R_1 + 3R_2 \to R_2 \\ -5R_1 + 3R_3 \to R_3 \end{array} \left[\begin{array}{rrr|r} 3 & -6 & 3 & 11 \\ 0 & 15 & -9 & -16 \\ 0 & 15 & -9 & -37 \end{array}\right]$$

$$\begin{array}{r} 2R_2 + 5R_1 \to R_1 \\ \\ -R_2 + R_3 \to R_3 \end{array} \left[\begin{array}{rrr|r} 15 & 0 & -3 & 23 \\ 0 & 15 & -9 & -16 \\ 0 & 0 & 0 & -21 \end{array}\right]$$

The last row indicates inconsistent equations. There is no solution to the system.

33.
$$\begin{aligned} 5x - 4y + 2z &= 6 \\ 5x + 3y - z &= 11 \\ 15x - 5y + 3z &= 23 \end{aligned}$$

Write the augmented matrix and use row operations.

$$\left[\begin{array}{rrr|r} 5 & -4 & 2 & 6 \\ 5 & 3 & -1 & 11 \\ 15 & -5 & 3 & 23 \end{array}\right]$$

$$\begin{array}{r} \\ -1R_1 + R_2 \to R_2 \\ -3R_1 + R_3 \to R_3 \end{array} \left[\begin{array}{rrr|r} 5 & -4 & 2 & 6 \\ 0 & 7 & -3 & 5 \\ 0 & 7 & -3 & 5 \end{array}\right]$$

$$\begin{array}{r} 4R_2 + 7R_1 \to R_1 \\ \\ -1R_2 + R_3 \to R_3 \end{array} \left[\begin{array}{rrr|r} 35 & 0 & 2 & 62 \\ 0 & 7 & -3 & 5 \\ 0 & 0 & 0 & 0 \end{array}\right]$$

$$\begin{array}{r} \frac{1}{35}R_1 \to R_1 \\ \frac{1}{7}R_2 \to R_2 \\ \\ \end{array} \left[\begin{array}{rrr|r} 1 & 0 & \frac{2}{35} & \frac{62}{35} \\ 0 & 1 & -\frac{3}{7} & \frac{5}{7} \\ 0 & 0 & 0 & 0 \end{array}\right]$$

The row of zeros indicates dependent equations. Solve the first two equations respectively for x and y in terms of z to obtain

$$x = -\frac{2}{35}z + \frac{62}{35} = \frac{-2z+62}{35}$$

and

$$y = \frac{3}{7}z + \frac{5}{7} = \frac{3z+5}{7}.$$

The solution is $\left(\frac{-2z+62}{35}, \frac{3z+5}{7}, z\right)$.

34. $3x + 2y - z = -16$
$6x - 4y + 3z = 12$
$5x - 2y + 2z = 4$

Write the augmented matrix and use row operations.

$$\left[\begin{array}{ccc|c} 3 & 2 & -1 & -16 \\ 6 & -4 & 3 & 12 \\ 5 & -2 & 2 & 4 \end{array}\right]$$

$$\begin{array}{l} \\ -2R_1 + R_2 \to R_2 \\ -5R_1 + 3R_3 \to R_3 \end{array} \left[\begin{array}{ccc|c} 3 & 2 & -1 & -16 \\ 0 & -8 & 5 & 44 \\ 0 & -16 & 11 & 92 \end{array}\right]$$

$$\begin{array}{l} R_2 + 4R_1 \to R_1 \\ \\ -2R_2 + R_3 \to R_3 \end{array} \left[\begin{array}{ccc|c} 12 & 0 & 1 & -20 \\ 0 & -8 & 5 & 44 \\ 0 & 0 & 1 & 4 \end{array}\right]$$

$$\begin{array}{l} -1R_3 + R_1 \to R_1 \\ -5R_3 + R_2 \to R_2 \end{array} \left[\begin{array}{ccc|c} 12 & 0 & 0 & -24 \\ 0 & -8 & 0 & 24 \\ 0 & 0 & 1 & 4 \end{array}\right]$$

$$\begin{array}{l} \frac{1}{12}R_1 \to R_1 \\ -\frac{1}{8}R_2 \to R_2 \end{array} \left[\begin{array}{ccc|c} 1 & 0 & 0 & -2 \\ 0 & 1 & 0 & -3 \\ 0 & 0 & 1 & 4 \end{array}\right]$$

Read the solution from the last column of the matrix. The solution is $(-2, -3, 4)$.

35. $2x + 3y + z = 9$
$4x + 6y + 2z = 18$
$-\frac{1}{2}x - \frac{3}{4}y - \frac{1}{4}z = -\frac{9}{4}$

Write the augmented matrix and use row operations.

$$\left[\begin{array}{ccc|c} 2 & 3 & 1 & 9 \\ 4 & 6 & 2 & 18 \\ -\frac{1}{2} & -\frac{3}{4} & -\frac{1}{4} & -\frac{9}{4} \end{array}\right]$$

$$\begin{array}{l} -2R_1 + R_2 \to R_2 \\ \frac{1}{4}R_1 + R_3 \to R_3 \end{array} \left[\begin{array}{ccc|c} 2 & 3 & 1 & 9 \\ 0 & 0 & 0 & 0 \\ 0 & 0 & 0 & 0 \end{array}\right]$$

The rows of zeros indicate dependent equations. Since the equation involves x, y, and z, let y and z be parameters. Solve the equation for x to obtain $x = \frac{9-3y-z}{2}$.

The solution is $\left(\frac{9-3y-z}{2}, y, z\right)$, where y and z are any real numbers.

36. $3x - 5y - 2z = -9$
$-4x + 3y + z = 11$
$8x - 5y + 4z = 6$

Write the augmented matrix and use row operations.

$$\left[\begin{array}{ccc|c} 3 & -5 & -2 & -9 \\ -4 & 3 & 1 & 11 \\ 8 & -5 & 4 & 6 \end{array}\right]$$

$$\begin{array}{l} \\ 4R_1 + 3R_2 \to R_2 \\ -8R_1 + 3R_3 \to R_3 \end{array} \left[\begin{array}{ccc|c} 3 & -5 & -2 & -9 \\ 0 & -11 & -5 & -3 \\ 0 & 25 & 28 & 90 \end{array}\right]$$

$$\begin{array}{l} -5R_2 + 11R_1 \to R_1 \\ \\ 25R_2 + 11R_3 \to R_3 \end{array} \left[\begin{array}{ccc|c} 33 & 0 & 3 & -84 \\ 0 & -11 & -5 & -3 \\ 0 & 0 & 183 & 915 \end{array}\right]$$

$$\begin{array}{l} -R_3 + 61R_1 \to R_1 \\ 5R_3 + 183R_2 \to R_2 \end{array} \left[\begin{array}{ccc|c} 2013 & 0 & 0 & -6039 \\ 0 & -2013 & 0 & 4026 \\ 0 & 0 & 183 & 915 \end{array}\right]$$

$$\begin{array}{l} \frac{1}{2013}R_1 \to R_1 \\ -\frac{1}{2013}R_2 \to R_2 \\ \frac{1}{183}R_3 \to R_3 \end{array} \left[\begin{array}{ccc|c} 1 & 0 & 0 & -3 \\ 0 & 1 & 0 & -2 \\ 0 & 0 & 1 & 5 \end{array}\right]$$

Read the solution from the last column of the matrix. The solution is $(-3, -2, 5)$.

37.
$$\begin{aligned} x + 2y \qquad\quad - w &= 3 \\ 2x \qquad + 4z + 2w &= -6 \\ x + 2y - z \qquad\quad &= 6 \\ 2x - y + z + w &= -3 \end{aligned}$$

38.
$$\begin{aligned} x + 3y - 2z - w &= 9 \\ 2x + 4y \qquad + 2w &= 10 \\ -3x - 5y + 2z - w &= -15 \\ x - y - 3z + 2w &= 6 \end{aligned}$$

Write the augmented matrix and use row operations.

37.

$$\left[\begin{array}{rrrr|r} 1 & 2 & 0 & -1 & 3 \\ 2 & 0 & 4 & 2 & -6 \\ 1 & 2 & -1 & 0 & 6 \\ 2 & -1 & 1 & 1 & -3 \end{array}\right]$$

$$\begin{array}{r} \\ -2R_1+R_2 \to R_2 \\ -1R_1+R_3 \to R_3 \\ -2R_1+R_4 \to R_4 \end{array} \quad \left[\begin{array}{rrrr|r} 1 & 2 & 0 & -1 & 3 \\ 0 & -4 & 4 & 4 & -12 \\ 0 & 0 & -1 & 1 & 3 \\ 0 & -5 & 1 & 3 & -9 \end{array}\right]$$

$$\begin{array}{r} R_2 + 2R_1 \to R_1 \\ \\ \\ -5R_2 + 4R_4 \to R_4 \end{array} \quad \left[\begin{array}{rrrr|r} 2 & 0 & 4 & 2 & -6 \\ 0 & -4 & 4 & 4 & -12 \\ 0 & 0 & -1 & 1 & 3 \\ 0 & 0 & -16 & -8 & 24 \end{array}\right]$$

$$\begin{array}{r} 4R_3 + R_1 \to R_1 \\ 4R_3 + R_2 \to R_2 \\ \\ 16R_3 + (-1)R_4 \to R_4 \end{array} \quad \left[\begin{array}{rrrr|r} 2 & 0 & 0 & 6 & 6 \\ 0 & -4 & 0 & 8 & 0 \\ 0 & 0 & -1 & 1 & 3 \\ 0 & 0 & 0 & 24 & 24 \end{array}\right]$$

$$\begin{array}{r} R_4 + (-4R_1) \to R_1 \\ R_4 + (-3R_2) \to R_2 \\ R_4 + (-24R_3) \to R_3 \\ \\ \end{array} \quad \left[\begin{array}{rrrr|r} -8 & 0 & 0 & 0 & 0 \\ 0 & 12 & 0 & 0 & 24 \\ 0 & 0 & 24 & 0 & -48 \\ 0 & 0 & 0 & 24 & 24 \end{array}\right]$$

$$\begin{array}{r} -\frac{1}{8}R_1 \to R_1 \\ \frac{1}{12}R_2 \to R_2 \\ \frac{1}{24}R_3 \to R_3 \\ \frac{1}{24}R_4 \to R_4 \end{array} \quad \left[\begin{array}{rrrr|r} 1 & 0 & 0 & 0 & 0 \\ 0 & 1 & 0 & 0 & 2 \\ 0 & 0 & 1 & 0 & -2 \\ 0 & 0 & 0 & 1 & 1 \end{array}\right]$$

The solution is $x = 0,\ y = 2,\ z = -2,\ w = 1$, or $(0, 2, -2, 1)$.

38.

$$\left[\begin{array}{rrrr|r} 1 & 3 & -2 & -1 & 9 \\ 2 & 4 & 0 & 2 & 10 \\ -3 & -5 & 2 & -1 & -15 \\ 1 & -1 & -3 & 2 & 6 \end{array}\right]$$

$$\begin{array}{r} \\ -2R_1 + R_2 \to R_2 \\ 3R_1 + R_3 \to R_3 \\ -1R_1 + R_4 \to R_4 \end{array} \quad \left[\begin{array}{rrrr|r} 1 & 3 & -2 & -1 & 9 \\ 0 & -2 & 4 & 4 & -8 \\ 0 & 4 & -4 & -4 & 12 \\ 0 & -4 & -1 & 3 & -3 \end{array}\right]$$

$$\begin{array}{r} 3R_2 + 2R_1 \to R_1 \\ \\ 2R_2 + R_3 \to R_3 \\ -2R_2 + R_4 \to R_4 \end{array} \quad \left[\begin{array}{rrrr|r} 2 & 0 & 8 & 10 & -6 \\ 0 & -2 & 4 & 4 & -8 \\ 0 & 0 & 4 & 4 & -4 \\ 0 & 0 & -9 & -5 & 13 \end{array}\right]$$

$$\begin{array}{r} -2R_3 + R_1 \to R_1 \\ -1R_3 + R_2 \to R_2 \\ \\ 9R_3 + 4R_4 \to R_4 \end{array} \quad \left[\begin{array}{rrrr|r} 2 & 0 & 0 & 2 & 2 \\ 0 & -2 & 0 & 0 & -4 \\ 0 & 0 & 4 & 4 & -4 \\ 0 & 0 & 0 & 16 & 16 \end{array}\right]$$

$$\begin{array}{r} R_4 + (-8)R_1 \to R_1 \\ \\ R_4 + (-4)R_3 \to R_3 \\ \\ \end{array} \quad \left[\begin{array}{rrrr|r} -16 & 0 & 0 & 0 & 0 \\ 0 & -2 & 0 & 0 & -4 \\ 0 & 0 & -16 & 0 & 32 \\ 0 & 0 & 0 & 16 & 16 \end{array}\right]$$

$$\begin{array}{r} -\frac{1}{16}R_1 \to R_1 \\ -\frac{1}{2}R_2 \to R_2 \\ -\frac{1}{16}R_3 \to R_3 \\ \frac{1}{16}R_4 \to R_4 \end{array} \quad \left[\begin{array}{rrrr|r} 1 & 0 & 0 & 0 & 0 \\ 0 & 1 & 0 & 0 & 2 \\ 0 & 0 & 1 & 0 & -2 \\ 0 & 0 & 0 & 1 & 1 \end{array}\right]$$

The solution is $(0, 2, -2, 1)$.

39. $x + y - z + 2w = -20$
$2x - y + z + w = 11$
$3x - 2y + z - 2w = 27$

$$\left[\begin{array}{rrrr|r} 1 & 1 & -1 & 2 & -20 \\ 2 & -1 & 1 & 1 & 11 \\ 3 & -2 & 1 & -2 & 27 \end{array}\right]$$

$$\begin{array}{l} -2R_1 + R_2 \to R_2 \\ -3R_1 + R_3 \to R_3 \end{array} \left[\begin{array}{rrrr|r} 1 & 1 & -1 & 2 & -20 \\ 0 & -3 & 3 & -3 & 51 \\ 0 & -5 & 4 & -8 & 87 \end{array}\right]$$

$$-\tfrac{1}{3}R_2 \to R_2 \left[\begin{array}{rrrr|r} 1 & 1 & -1 & 2 & -20 \\ 0 & 1 & -1 & 1 & -17 \\ 0 & -5 & 4 & -8 & 87 \end{array}\right]$$

$$\begin{array}{l} -1R_2 + R_1 \to R_1 \\ \\ 5R_2 + R_3 \to R_3 \end{array} \left[\begin{array}{rrrr|r} 1 & 0 & 0 & 1 & -3 \\ 0 & 1 & -1 & 1 & -17 \\ 0 & 0 & -1 & -3 & 2 \end{array}\right]$$

$$-1R_3 \to R_3 \left[\begin{array}{rrrr|r} 1 & 0 & 0 & 1 & -3 \\ 0 & 1 & -1 & 1 & -17 \\ 0 & 0 & 1 & 3 & -2 \end{array}\right]$$

$$R_3 + R_2 \to R_2 \left[\begin{array}{rrrr|r} 1 & 0 & 0 & 1 & -3 \\ 0 & 1 & 0 & 4 & -19 \\ 0 & 0 & 1 & 3 & -2 \end{array}\right]$$

This is as far as we can go using row operations. To complete the solution, write the equations that correspond to the matrix.

$$\begin{aligned} x + w &= -3 \\ y + 4w &= -19 \\ z + 3w &= -2 \end{aligned}$$

Let w be the parameter and express x, y, and z in terms of w. From the equations above, $x = -w - 3$, $y = -4w - 19$, and $z = -3w - 2$. The solution is $(-w - 3, -4w - 19, -3w - 2, w)$, where w is any real number.

40. $4x - 3y + z + w = 21$
$-2x - y + 2z + 7w = 2$
$10x - 5z - 20w = 15$

$$\left[\begin{array}{rrrr|r} 4 & -3 & 1 & 1 & 21 \\ -2 & -1 & 2 & 7 & 2 \\ 10 & 0 & -5 & -20 & 15 \end{array}\right]$$

Interchange rows 1 and 2.

$$\left[\begin{array}{rrrr|r} -2 & -1 & 2 & 7 & 2 \\ 4 & -3 & 1 & 1 & 21 \\ 10 & 0 & -5 & -20 & 15 \end{array}\right]$$

$$\begin{array}{l} 2R_1 + R_2 \to R_2 \\ 5R_1 + R_3 \to R_3 \end{array} \left[\begin{array}{rrrr|r} -2 & -1 & 2 & 7 & 2 \\ 0 & -5 & 5 & 15 & 25 \\ 0 & -5 & 5 & 15 & 25 \end{array}\right]$$

$$\begin{array}{l} -\tfrac{1}{5}R_2 \to R_2 \\ \tfrac{1}{5}R_3 \to R_3 \end{array} \left[\begin{array}{rrrr|r} -2 & -1 & 2 & 7 & 2 \\ 0 & 1 & -1 & -3 & -5 \\ 0 & -1 & 1 & 3 & 5 \end{array}\right]$$

$$\begin{array}{l} R_2 + R_1 \to R_1 \\ \\ R_2 + R_3 \to R_3 \end{array} \left[\begin{array}{rrrr|r} -2 & 0 & 1 & 4 & -3 \\ 0 & 1 & -1 & -3 & -5 \\ 0 & 0 & 0 & 0 & 0 \end{array}\right]$$

The last row indicates that there are an infinite number of solutions. The remaining equations are

$-2x + z + 4w = -3$ and $y - z - 3w = -5$

Solve these for x and y to obtain

$$x = \frac{z + 4w + 3}{2} \quad \text{and} \quad y = z + 3w - 5.$$

There are an infinite number of solutions, each of the form

$$\left(\frac{z + 4w + 3}{2}, z + 3w - 5, z, w\right),$$

or

$$(1.5 + 0.5z + 2w, -5 + z + 3w, z, w),$$

for any real numbers z and w.

41. $10.47x + 3.52y + 2.58z - 6.42w = 218.65$
$8.62x - 4.93y - 1.75z + 2.83w = 157.03$
$4.92x + 6.83y - 2.97z + 2.65w = 462.3$
$2.86x + 19.10y - 6.24z - 8.73w = 398.4$

Write the augmented matrix of the system.

$$\left[\begin{array}{rrrr|r} 10.47 & 3.52 & 2.58 & -6.42 & 218.65 \\ 8.62 & -4.93 & -1.75 & 2.83 & 157.03 \\ 4.92 & 6.83 & -2.97 & 2.65 & 462.3 \\ 2.86 & 19.10 & -6.24 & -8.73 & 398.4 \end{array}\right]$$

This exercise should be solved by graphing calculator or computer methods. The solution, which may vary slightly, is $x \approx 28.9436$, $y \approx 36.6326$, $z \approx 9.6390$, and $w \approx 37.1036$, or

$$(28.9436, 36.6326, 9.6390, 37.1036).$$

42. $28.6x + 94.5y + 16.0z - 2.94w = 198.3$
$16.7x + 44.3y - 27.3z + 8.9w = 254.7$
$12.5x - 38.7y + 92.5z + 22.4w = 562.7$
$40.1x - 28.3y + 17.5z - 10.2w = 375.4$

This exercise should be solved by graphing calculator or computer methods. The solution, which may vary slightly, is

$$(11.844, -1.153, 0.609, 14.004).$$

43. Insert the given values, introduce variables, and the table is as follows.

$\frac{3}{8}$	a	b
c	d	$\frac{1}{4}$
e	f	g

From this, we obtain the following system of equations.

$$\begin{array}{llllllll} a+b & & & & & & +\frac{3}{8} & =1 \\ & c+d & & & & & +\frac{1}{4} & =1 \\ & & & e & +f & +g & & =1 \\ & c & & +e & & & +\frac{3}{8} & =1 \\ a & & +d & & +f & & & =1 \\ b & & & & & +g & +\frac{1}{4} & =1 \\ & & d & & & +g & +\frac{3}{8} & =1 \\ b & & +d & +e & & & & =1 \end{array}$$

The augmented matrix and the final form after row operations are as follows.

$$\left[\begin{array}{ccccccc|c} 1 & 1 & 0 & 0 & 0 & 0 & 0 & \frac{5}{8} \\ 0 & 0 & 1 & 1 & 0 & 0 & 0 & \frac{3}{4} \\ 0 & 0 & 0 & 0 & 1 & 1 & 1 & 1 \\ 0 & 0 & 1 & 0 & 1 & 0 & 0 & \frac{5}{8} \\ 1 & 0 & 0 & 1 & 0 & 1 & 0 & 1 \\ 0 & 1 & 0 & 0 & 0 & 0 & 1 & \frac{3}{4} \\ 0 & 0 & 0 & 1 & 0 & 0 & 1 & \frac{5}{8} \\ 0 & 1 & 0 & 1 & 1 & 0 & 0 & 1 \end{array}\right] \rightarrow \left[\begin{array}{ccccccc|c} 1 & 0 & 0 & 0 & 0 & 0 & 0 & \frac{1}{6} \\ 0 & 1 & 0 & 0 & 0 & 0 & 0 & \frac{11}{24} \\ 0 & 0 & 1 & 0 & 0 & 0 & 0 & \frac{5}{12} \\ 0 & 0 & 0 & 1 & 0 & 0 & 0 & \frac{1}{3} \\ 0 & 0 & 0 & 0 & 1 & 0 & 0 & \frac{5}{24} \\ 0 & 0 & 0 & 0 & 0 & 1 & 0 & \frac{1}{2} \\ 0 & 0 & 0 & 0 & 0 & 0 & 1 & \frac{7}{12} \\ 0 & 0 & 0 & 0 & 0 & 0 & 0 & 0 \end{array}\right]$$

The solution to the system is read from the last column.

$$a = \frac{1}{6}, b = \frac{11}{24}, c = \frac{5}{12}, d = \frac{1}{3}, e = \frac{5}{24}, f = \frac{1}{2}, \text{ and } g = \frac{7}{24}$$

So the magic square is:

$\frac{3}{8}$	$\frac{1}{6}$	$\frac{11}{24}$
$\frac{5}{12}$	$\frac{1}{3}$	$\frac{1}{4}$
$\frac{5}{24}$	$\frac{1}{2}$	$\frac{7}{24}$

44. Let $x =$ the number of hours to hire the Garcia firm, and
$y =$ the number of hours to hire the Wong firm.

The system to be solved is

$$\begin{aligned} 10x + 20y &= 500 \quad (1) \\ 30x + 10y &= 750 \quad (2) \\ 5x + 10y &= 250. \quad (3) \end{aligned}$$

Write the augmented matrix of the system.

$$\left[\begin{array}{cc|c} 10 & 20 & 500 \\ 30 & 10 & 750 \\ 5 & 10 & 250 \end{array}\right]$$

$$\begin{array}{l} \frac{1}{10}R_1 \to R_1 \\ \frac{1}{10}R_2 \to R_2 \\ \frac{1}{5}R_3 \to R_3 \end{array} \left[\begin{array}{cc|c} 1 & 2 & 50 \\ 3 & 1 & 75 \\ 1 & 2 & 50 \end{array}\right]$$

$$\begin{array}{l} -3R_1 + R_2 \to R_2 \\ -1R_1 + R_3 \to R_3 \end{array} \left[\begin{array}{cc|c} 1 & 2 & 50 \\ 0 & -5 & -75 \\ 0 & 0 & 0 \end{array}\right]$$

$$-\frac{1}{5}R_2 \to R_2 \left[\begin{array}{cc|c} 1 & 2 & 50 \\ 0 & 1 & 15 \\ 0 & 0 & 0 \end{array}\right]$$

$$-2R_2 + R_1 \to R_1 \left[\begin{array}{cc|c} 1 & 0 & 20 \\ 0 & 1 & 15 \\ 0 & 0 & 0 \end{array}\right]$$

The solution is $(20, 15)$. Hire the Garcia firm for 20 hr and the Wong firm for 15 hr.

45. Let $x =$ the number of units ordered from Toronto,
$y =$ the number of units ordered from Montreal, and
$z =$ the number of units ordered from Ottawa.

The system to be solved is

$$\begin{aligned} x + y + z &= 100 \quad (1) \\ 80x + 50y + 65z &= 5990 \quad (2) \\ x &= z. \quad (3) \end{aligned}$$

Write the augmented matrix of the system.

$$\left[\begin{array}{ccc|c} 1 & 1 & 1 & 100 \\ 80 & 50 & 65 & 5990 \\ 1 & 0 & -1 & 0 \end{array}\right]$$

$$\begin{array}{l} -80R_1 + R_2 \to R_2 \\ -1R_1 + R_3 \to R_3 \end{array} \left[\begin{array}{ccc|c} 1 & 1 & 1 & 100 \\ 0 & -30 & -15 & -2010 \\ 0 & -1 & -2 & -100 \end{array}\right]$$

$$-\frac{1}{30}R_2 \to R_2 \left[\begin{array}{ccc|c} 1 & 1 & 1 & 100 \\ 0 & 1 & \frac{1}{2} & 67 \\ 0 & -1 & -2 & -100 \end{array}\right]$$

$$\begin{array}{l} -1R_2 + R_1 \to R_1 \\ R_2 + R_3 \to R_3 \end{array} \left[\begin{array}{ccc|c} 1 & 0 & \frac{1}{2} & 33 \\ 0 & 1 & \frac{1}{2} & 67 \\ 0 & 0 & -\frac{3}{2} & -33 \end{array}\right]$$

$$-\frac{2}{3}R_3 \to R_3 \left[\begin{array}{ccc|c} 1 & 0 & \frac{1}{2} & 33 \\ 0 & 1 & \frac{1}{2} & 67 \\ 0 & 0 & 1 & 22 \end{array}\right]$$

$$\begin{array}{l} -\frac{1}{2}R_3 + R_1 \to R_1 \\ -\frac{1}{2}R_3 + R_2 \to R_2 \end{array} \left[\begin{array}{ccc|c} 1 & 0 & 0 & 22 \\ 0 & 1 & 0 & 56 \\ 0 & 0 & 1 & 22 \end{array}\right]$$

The solution is $(22, 56, 22)$. There were 22 units ordered from Toronto, 56 units ordered from Montreal, and 22 units ordered from Ottawa.

46. Let $x =$ the number of chairs produced each week,
$y =$ the number of cabinets produced each week, and
$z =$ the number of buffets produced each week.

Make a table to organize the information.

	Chair	Cabinet	Buffet	Totals
Cutting	0.2	0.5	0.3	1950
Assembly	0.3	0.4	0.1	1490
Finishing	0.1	0.6	0.4	2160

The system to be solved is

$$\begin{aligned} 0.2x + 0.5y + 0.3z &= 1950 \\ 0.3x + 0.4y + 0.1z &= 1490 \\ 0.1x + 0.6y + 0.4z &= 2160. \end{aligned}$$

Write the augmented matrix of the system.

$$\left[\begin{array}{ccc|c} 0.2 & 0.5 & 0.3 & 1950 \\ 0.3 & 0.4 & 0.1 & 1490 \\ 0.1 & 0.6 & 0.4 & 2160 \end{array}\right]$$

$$\begin{array}{l} 10R_1 \to R_1 \\ 10R_2 \to R_2 \\ 10R_3 \to R_3 \end{array} \left[\begin{array}{ccc|c} 2 & 5 & 3 & 19{,}500 \\ 3 & 4 & 1 & 14{,}900 \\ 1 & 6 & 4 & 21{,}600 \end{array}\right]$$

Interchange rows 1 and 3.

$$\left[\begin{array}{ccc|c} 1 & 6 & 4 & 21{,}600 \\ 3 & 4 & 1 & 14{,}900 \\ 2 & 5 & 3 & 19{,}500 \end{array}\right]$$

$$\begin{array}{l} \\ -3R_1 + R_2 \to R_2 \\ -2R_1 + R_3 \to R_3 \end{array} \left[\begin{array}{ccc|c} 1 & 6 & 4 & 21{,}600 \\ 0 & -14 & -11 & -49{,}900 \\ 0 & -7 & -5 & -23{,}700 \end{array}\right]$$

$$-\tfrac{1}{14}R_2 \to R_2 \quad \left[\begin{array}{ccc|c} 1 & 6 & 4 & 21{,}600 \\ 0 & 1 & \frac{11}{14} & \frac{24{,}950}{7} \\ 0 & -7 & -5 & -23{,}700 \end{array}\right]$$

$$\begin{array}{l} -6R_2 + R_1 \to R_1 \\ \\ 7R_2 + R_3 \to R_3 \end{array} \left[\begin{array}{ccc|c} 1 & 0 & -\frac{5}{7} & \frac{1500}{7} \\ 0 & 1 & \frac{11}{14} & \frac{24{,}950}{7} \\ 0 & 0 & \frac{1}{2} & 1250 \end{array}\right]$$

$$2R_3 \to R_3 \quad \left[\begin{array}{ccc|c} 1 & 0 & -\frac{5}{7} & \frac{1500}{7} \\ 0 & 1 & \frac{11}{14} & \frac{24{,}950}{7} \\ 0 & 0 & 1 & 2500 \end{array}\right]$$

$$\begin{array}{l} \frac{5}{7}R_3 + R_1 \to R_1 \\ -\frac{11}{14}R_3 + R_2 \to R_2 \end{array} \left[\begin{array}{ccc|c} 1 & 0 & 0 & 2000 \\ 0 & 1 & 0 & 1600 \\ 0 & 0 & 1 & 2500 \end{array}\right]$$

The solution is $(2000, 1600, 2500)$. Therefore, 2000 chairs, 1600 cabinets, and 2500 buffets should be produced.

47. (a) Let $x =$ the number of deluxe models,
$y =$ the number of super-deluxe models, and
$z =$ the number of ultra models.

Make a table to organize the information.

	Deluxe	Super-Deluxe	Ultra	Totals
Electronic	2	1	3	100
Assembly	2	3	2	100
Finishing	1	1	2	65

The system to be solved is

$$\begin{aligned} 2x + y + 3z &= 100 \quad (1) \\ 2x + 3y + 2z &= 100 \quad (2) \\ x + y + 2z &= 65. \quad (3) \end{aligned}$$

Write the augmented matrix of the system.

$$\left[\begin{array}{ccc|c} 2 & 1 & 3 & 100 \\ 2 & 3 & 2 & 100 \\ 1 & 1 & 2 & 65 \end{array}\right]$$

Interchange rows 1 and 3.

$$\left[\begin{array}{ccc|c} 1 & 1 & 2 & 65 \\ 2 & 3 & 2 & 100 \\ 2 & 1 & 3 & 100 \end{array}\right]$$

$$\begin{array}{l} \\ -2R_1 + R_2 \to R_2 \\ -2R_1 + R_3 \to R_3 \end{array} \left[\begin{array}{ccc|c} 1 & 1 & 2 & 65 \\ 0 & 1 & -2 & -30 \\ 0 & -1 & -1 & -30 \end{array}\right]$$

$$\begin{array}{l} -1R_2 + R_1 \to R_1 \\ \\ R_2 + R_3 \to R_3 \end{array} \left[\begin{array}{ccc|c} 1 & 0 & 4 & 95 \\ 0 & 1 & -2 & -30 \\ 0 & 0 & -3 & -60 \end{array}\right]$$

$$-\tfrac{1}{3}R_3 \to R_3 \quad \left[\begin{array}{ccc|c} 1 & 0 & 4 & 95 \\ 0 & 1 & -2 & -30 \\ 0 & 0 & 1 & 20 \end{array}\right]$$

$$\begin{array}{l} -4R_3 + R_1 \to R_1 \\ 2R_3 + R_2 \to R_2 \end{array} \left[\begin{array}{ccc|c} 1 & 0 & 0 & 15 \\ 0 & 1 & 0 & 10 \\ 0 & 0 & 1 & 20 \end{array}\right]$$

The solution is $(15, 10, 20)$. Each week 15 deluxe models, 10 super-deluxe models, and 20 ultra models should be produced.

(b) The system to be solved is

$$\begin{aligned} 2x + y + 6z &= 100 \\ 2x + 3y + 2z &= 100 \\ x + y + 2z &= 65 \end{aligned}$$

Write the augmented matrix of the system.

$$\left[\begin{array}{ccc|c} 2 & 1 & 6 & 100 \\ 2 & 3 & 2 & 100 \\ 1 & 1 & 2 & 65 \end{array}\right]$$

Interchange rows 1 and 3.

$$\left[\begin{array}{ccc|c} 1 & 1 & 2 & 65 \\ 2 & 3 & 2 & 100 \\ 2 & 1 & 6 & 100 \end{array}\right]$$

$$\begin{array}{l} \\ -2R_1 + R_2 \rightarrow R_2 \\ -2R_1 + R_3 \rightarrow R_3 \end{array} \left[\begin{array}{ccc|c} 1 & 1 & 2 & 65 \\ 0 & 1 & -2 & -30 \\ 0 & -1 & 2 & -30 \end{array}\right]$$

$$\begin{array}{l} -1R_2 + R_1 \rightarrow R_1 \\ \\ R_2 + R_3 \rightarrow R_3 \end{array} \left[\begin{array}{ccc|c} 1 & 0 & 4 & 95 \\ 0 & 1 & -2 & -30 \\ 0 & 0 & 0 & -60 \end{array}\right]$$

The last row indicates there is no solution to the system.

(c) The system to be solved is

$$\begin{aligned} 2x + y + 6z &= 160 \\ 2x + 3y + 2z &= 100 \\ x + y + 2z &= 65 \end{aligned}$$

Write the augmented matrix of the system.

$$\left[\begin{array}{ccc|c} 2 & 1 & 6 & 160 \\ 2 & 3 & 2 & 100 \\ 1 & 1 & 2 & 65 \end{array}\right]$$

Interchange rows 1 and 3.

$$\left[\begin{array}{ccc|c} 1 & 1 & 2 & 65 \\ 2 & 3 & 2 & 100 \\ 2 & 1 & 6 & 160 \end{array}\right]$$

$$\begin{array}{l} \\ -2R_1 + R_2 \rightarrow R_2 \\ -2R_1 + R_3 \rightarrow R_3 \end{array} \left[\begin{array}{ccc|c} 1 & 1 & 2 & 65 \\ 0 & 1 & -2 & -30 \\ 0 & -1 & 2 & -30 \end{array}\right]$$

$$\begin{array}{l} -1R_2 + R_1 \rightarrow R_1 \\ \\ R_2 + R_3 \rightarrow R_3 \end{array} \left[\begin{array}{ccc|c} 1 & 0 & 4 & 95 \\ 0 & 1 & -2 & -30 \\ 0 & 0 & 0 & 0 \end{array}\right]$$

The system is dependent. Let z be the parameter and solve the first two equations for x and y, yielding

$$x = 95 - 4z \quad \text{and} \quad y = 2z - 30.$$

Since $x, y,$ and z must be nonnegative integers, $95 - 4z \geq 0$ and $2z - 30 \geq 0$.

$$\begin{aligned} 95 - 4z &\geq 0 \\ -4z &\geq -95 \\ z &\leq 23.75 \\ 2z - 30 &\geq 0 \\ 2z &\geq 30 \\ z &\geq 15 \end{aligned}$$

Thus, z in an integer such that $15 \geq z \leq 23.75$. There are 9 solutions.

48. (a) Let x be the number of trucks used, y be the number of vans, and z be the number of station wagons. We first obtain the equations given here.

$$\begin{aligned} 2x + 3y + 3z &= 25 \\ 2x + 4y + 5z &= 33 \\ 3x + 2y + z &= 22 \end{aligned}$$

Write the augmented matrix and use row operations.

$$\left[\begin{array}{ccc|c} 2 & 3 & 3 & 25 \\ 2 & 4 & 5 & 33 \\ 3 & 2 & 1 & 22 \end{array}\right]$$

$$\begin{array}{l} \\ -1R_1 + R_2 \rightarrow R_2 \\ -3R_1 + 2R_3 \rightarrow R_3 \end{array} \left[\begin{array}{ccc|c} 2 & 3 & 3 & 25 \\ 0 & 1 & 2 & 8 \\ 0 & -5 & -7 & -31 \end{array}\right]$$

$$\begin{array}{l} -3R_2 + R_1 \rightarrow R_1 \\ \\ 5R_2 + R_3 \rightarrow R_3 \end{array} \left[\begin{array}{ccc|c} 2 & 0 & -3 & 1 \\ 0 & 1 & 2 & 8 \\ 0 & 0 & 3 & 9 \end{array}\right]$$

$$\begin{array}{l} R_3 + R_1 \rightarrow R_1 \\ -2R_3 + 3R_2 \rightarrow R_2 \end{array} \left[\begin{array}{ccc|c} 2 & 0 & 0 & 10 \\ 0 & 3 & 0 & 6 \\ 0 & 0 & 3 & 9 \end{array}\right]$$

$$\begin{array}{l} \frac{1}{2}R_1 \rightarrow R_1 \\ \frac{1}{3}R_2 \rightarrow R_2 \\ \frac{1}{3}R_3 \rightarrow R_3 \end{array} \left[\begin{array}{ccc|c} 1 & 0 & 0 & 5 \\ 0 & 1 & 0 & 2 \\ 0 & 0 & 1 & 3 \end{array}\right]$$

Read the solution from the last column of the matrix. The solution is 5 trucks, 2 vans, and 3 station wagons.

(b) The system of equations is now

$$\begin{aligned} 2x + 3y + 3z &= 25 \\ 2x + 4y + 5z &= 33. \end{aligned}$$

Write the augmented matrix and use row operations.

$$\left[\begin{array}{ccc|c} 2 & 3 & 3 & 25 \\ 2 & 4 & 5 & 33 \end{array}\right]$$

$$\begin{array}{l} \\ -R_1 + R_2 \rightarrow R_2 \end{array} \left[\begin{array}{ccc|c} 2 & 3 & 3 & 25 \\ 0 & 1 & 2 & 8 \end{array}\right]$$

$$-3R_2 + R_1 \rightarrow R_1 \quad \left[\begin{array}{ccc|c} 2 & 0 & -3 & 1 \\ 0 & 1 & 2 & 8 \end{array}\right]$$

Obtain a one in row 1, column 1.

$$\frac{1}{2}R_1 \rightarrow R_1 \quad \left[\begin{array}{ccc|c} 1 & 0 & -\frac{3}{2} & \frac{1}{2} \\ 0 & 1 & 2 & 8 \end{array}\right]$$

The last row indicates multiple solutions are possible. The remaining equations are

$$x - \frac{3}{2}z = \frac{1}{2} \text{ and } y + 2z = 8.$$

Solving these for x and y, we have

$$x = \frac{3}{2}z + \frac{1}{2} \text{ and } y = -2z + 8.$$

The form of the solution is $(\frac{3}{2}z + \frac{1}{2}, -2z + 8, z)$. Since the solutions must be whole numbers,

$$\begin{aligned} \frac{3}{2}z + \frac{1}{2} &\geq 0 \\ \frac{3}{2}z &\geq -\frac{1}{2} \\ z &\geq -\frac{1}{3} \end{aligned} \qquad \text{and} \qquad \begin{aligned} -2z + 8 &\geq 0 \\ -2z &\geq -8 \\ z &\leq 4 \end{aligned}$$

Thus, there are 4 possible solutions but each must be checked to determine if they produce whole numbers for x and y.

When $z = 0$, $\left(\frac{1}{2}, 8, 0\right)$ which is not realistic.

When $z = 1$, $(2, 6, 1)$.

When $z = 2$, $\left(\frac{7}{2}, 4, 2\right)$ which is not realistic.

When $z = 3$, $(5, 2, 3)$.

When $z = 4$, $\left(\frac{13}{2}, 0, 4\right)$ which is not realistic.

The company has 2 options. Either use 2 trucks, 6 vans, and 1 station wagon or use 5 trucks, 2 vans, and 3 station wagons.

49. Let $x =$ the number of vans to be purchased,
$y =$ the number of small trucks to be purchased, and
$z =$ the number of large trucks to be purchased.

The system to be solved is

$$\begin{aligned} x + y + z &= 200 \\ 35{,}000x + 30{,}000y + 50{,}000z &= 7{,}000{,}000 \\ x &= 2y. \end{aligned}$$

To simplify the system, divide the second equation by 1000. Write the system in proper form, obtain the augmented matrix, and use row operations to solve.

$$\left[\begin{array}{ccc|c} 1 & 1 & 1 & 200 \\ 35 & 30 & 50 & 7000 \\ 1 & -2 & 0 & 0 \end{array}\right]$$

$$\begin{array}{r} \\ -35R_1 + R_2 \to R_2 \\ -1R_1 + R_3 \to R_3 \end{array} \left[\begin{array}{ccc|c} 1 & 1 & 1 & 200 \\ 0 & -5 & 15 & 0 \\ 0 & -3 & -1 & -200 \end{array}\right]$$

$$\begin{array}{r} R_2 + 5R_1 \to R_1 \\ \\ -3R_2 + 5R_3 \to R_3 \end{array} \left[\begin{array}{ccc|c} 5 & 0 & 20 & 1000 \\ 0 & -5 & 15 & 0 \\ 0 & 0 & -50 & -1000 \end{array}\right]$$

$$\begin{array}{r} 2R_3 + 5R_1 \to R_1 \\ 3R_3 + 10R_2 \to R_2 \\ \end{array} \left[\begin{array}{ccc|c} 25 & 0 & 0 & 3000 \\ 0 & -50 & 0 & -3000 \\ 0 & 0 & -50 & -1000 \end{array}\right]$$

$$\begin{array}{r} \frac{1}{25}R_1 \to R_1 \\ -\frac{1}{50}R_2 \to R_2 \\ -\frac{1}{50}R_3 \to R_3 \end{array} \left[\begin{array}{ccc|c} 1 & 0 & 0 & 120 \\ 0 & 1 & 0 & 60 \\ 0 & 0 & 1 & 20 \end{array}\right]$$

The solution is (120, 60, 20). U-Drive Rent-A-Truck should buy 120 vans, 60 small trucks, and 20 large trucks.

50. Let $x =$ the amount borrowed at 8%,
$y =$ the amount borrowed at 9%, and
$z =$ the amount borrowed at 10%.

(a) The system to be solved is

$$\begin{aligned} x + y + z &= 25{,}000 \\ 0.08x + 0.09y + 0.10z &= 2190 \\ y &= z + 1000 \end{aligned}$$

Multiply the second equation by 100 and rewrite the equations in standard form.

$$\begin{aligned} x + \quad y + \quad z &= 25{,}000 \\ 8x + 9y + 10z &= 219{,}000 \\ y - \quad z &= 1000. \end{aligned}$$

Write the augmented matrix and use row operations to solve

$$\left[\begin{array}{ccc|c} 1 & 1 & 1 & 25{,}000 \\ 8 & 9 & 10 & 219{,}000 \\ 0 & 1 & -1 & 1000 \end{array}\right]$$

$$-8R_1 + R_2 \to R_2 \quad \left[\begin{array}{ccc|c} 1 & 1 & 1 & 25{,}000 \\ 0 & 1 & 2 & 19{,}000 \\ 0 & 1 & -1 & 1000 \end{array}\right]$$

$$\begin{array}{l} -1R_2 + R_1 \to R_1 \\ \\ -1R_2 + R_3 \to R_3 \end{array} \quad \left[\begin{array}{ccc|c} 1 & 0 & -1 & 6000 \\ 0 & 1 & 2 & 19{,}000 \\ 0 & 0 & -3 & -18{,}000 \end{array}\right]$$

$$\begin{array}{l} -1R_3 + 3R_1 \to R_1 \\ 2R_3 + 3R_2 \to R_2 \end{array} \quad \left[\begin{array}{ccc|c} 3 & 0 & 0 & 36{,}000 \\ 0 & 3 & 0 & 21{,}000 \\ 0 & 0 & -3 & -18{,}000 \end{array}\right]$$

$$\begin{array}{l} \frac{1}{3}R_1 \to R_1 \\ \frac{1}{3}R_2 \to R_2 \\ -\frac{1}{3}R_3 \to R_3 \end{array} \quad \left[\begin{array}{ccc|c} 1 & 0 & 0 & 12{,}000 \\ 0 & 1 & 0 & 7000 \\ 0 & 0 & 1 & 6000 \end{array}\right]$$

The solution is (12,000, 7000, 6000). The company borrowed $12,000 at 8%, $7000 at 9%, and $6000 at 10%.

(b) If the condition is dropped, the initial augmented matrix and solution is found as before.

$$\left[\begin{array}{ccc|c} 1 & 1 & 1 & 25{,}000 \\ 8 & 9 & 10 & 219{,}000 \end{array}\right]$$

$$-8R_1 + R_2 \to R_2 \quad \left[\begin{array}{ccc|c} 1 & 1 & 1 & 25{,}000 \\ 0 & 1 & 2 & 19{,}000 \end{array}\right]$$

$$-1R_2 + R_1 \to R_1 \quad \left[\begin{array}{ccc|c} 1 & 0 & -1 & 6000 \\ 0 & 1 & 2 & 19{,}000 \end{array}\right]$$

This gives the system of equations

$$\begin{aligned} x &= z + 6000 \\ y &= -2x + 19{,}000 \end{aligned}$$

Since all values must be nonnegative,

$$\begin{aligned} z + 6000 &\geq 0 \quad \text{and} \quad -2z + 19{,}000 \geq 0 \\ z &\geq -6000 \qquad\qquad\qquad z \leq 9500. \end{aligned}$$

The second inequality produces the condition that the amount borrowed at 10% must be less than or equal to $9500. If $5000 is borrowed at 10%, $z = 5000$, and

$$\begin{aligned} x &= 500 + 6000 = 11{,}000 \\ y &= -2(5000) + 19{,}000 = 9000. \end{aligned}$$

This means $11,000 is borrowed at 8% and $9000 is borrowed at 9%.

(c) The original conditions resulted in $12,000 borrowed at 8%. So, if the bank sets a maximum of $10,000 at the 8% rate, no solution is possible.

(d) The total interest would be

$$\begin{aligned} &0.08(10{,}000) + 0.09(8000) + 0.10(7000) \\ &= 800 + 720 + 700 \\ &= 2220 \end{aligned}$$

or $2220, which is not the $2190 interest as specified as one of the conditions of the problem.

51. Let $x_1 =$ the number of cars sent from I to A,

$x_2 =$ the number of cars sent from II to A,

$x_3 =$ the number of cars sent from I to B, and

$x_4 =$ the number of cars sent from II to B.

	A	B
I	x_1	x_3
II	x_2	x_4

Plant I has 28 cars, so

$$x_1 + x_3 = 28.$$

Plant II has 8 cars, so

$$x_2 + x_4 = 8.$$

Dealer A needs 20 cars, so

$$x_1 + x_2 = 20.$$

Dealer B needs 16 cars, so

$$x_3 + x_4 = 16.$$

The total transportation cost is $10,640, so

$$220x_1 + 400x_2 + 300x_3 + 180x_4 = 10{,}640.$$

The system to be solved is

$$\begin{array}{rcrcrcrl} x_1 & & & + & x_3 & & & = 28 \\ & & x_2 & & & + & x_4 & = 8 \\ x_1 & + & x_2 & & & & & = 20 \\ & & & & x_3 & + & x_4 & = 16 \\ 220x_1 & + & 400x_2 & + & 300x_3 & + & 180x_4 & = 10{,}640. \end{array}$$

Write the augmented matrix and use row operations.

$$\left[\begin{array}{cccc|c} 1 & 0 & 1 & 0 & 28 \\ 0 & 1 & 0 & 1 & 8 \\ 1 & 1 & 0 & 0 & 20 \\ 0 & 0 & 1 & 1 & 16 \\ 220 & 400 & 300 & 180 & 10{,}640 \end{array}\right]$$

$$\begin{array}{r} \\ \\ -1R_1 + R_3 \rightarrow R_3 \\ \\ -220R_1 + R_5 \rightarrow R_5 \end{array} \left[\begin{array}{cccc|c} 1 & 0 & 1 & 0 & 28 \\ 0 & 1 & 0 & 1 & 8 \\ 0 & 1 & -1 & 0 & -8 \\ 0 & 0 & 1 & 1 & 16 \\ 0 & 400 & 80 & 180 & 4480 \end{array}\right]$$

$$\begin{array}{r} \\ \\ -1R_2 + R_3 \rightarrow R_3 \\ \\ -400R_2 + R_5 \rightarrow R_5 \end{array} \left[\begin{array}{cccc|c} 1 & 0 & 1 & 0 & 28 \\ 0 & 1 & 0 & 1 & 8 \\ 0 & 0 & -1 & -1 & -16 \\ 0 & 0 & 1 & 1 & 16 \\ 0 & 0 & 80 & -220 & 1280 \end{array}\right]$$

$$\begin{array}{r} R_1 + R_3 \rightarrow R_1 \\ \\ \\ R_3 + R_4 \rightarrow R_4 \\ 80R_3 + R_5 \rightarrow R_5 \end{array} \left[\begin{array}{cccc|c} 1 & 0 & 0 & -1 & 12 \\ 0 & 1 & 0 & 1 & 8 \\ 0 & 0 & -1 & -1 & -16 \\ 0 & 0 & 0 & 0 & 0 \\ 0 & 0 & 0 & -300 & 0 \end{array}\right]$$

There is a 0 now in row 4, column 4, where we would like to get a 1. To proceed, interchange the fourth and fifth rows.

$$\left[\begin{array}{cccc|c} 1 & 0 & 0 & -1 & 12 \\ 0 & 1 & 0 & 1 & 8 \\ 0 & 0 & -1 & -1 & -16 \\ 0 & 0 & 0 & -300 & 0 \\ 0 & 0 & 0 & 0 & 0 \end{array}\right]$$

$$\begin{array}{r} -1R_4 + 300R_1 \rightarrow R_1 \\ R_4 + 300R_2 \rightarrow R_2 \\ -1R_4 + 300R_3 \rightarrow R_3 \\ \\ \end{array} \left[\begin{array}{cccc|c} 300 & 0 & 0 & 0 & 3600 \\ 0 & 300 & 0 & 0 & 2400 \\ 0 & 0 & -300 & 0 & -4800 \\ 0 & 0 & 0 & -300 & 0 \\ 0 & 0 & 0 & 0 & 0 \end{array}\right]$$

$$\begin{array}{r} \frac{1}{300}R_1 \rightarrow R_1 \\ \frac{1}{300}R_2 \rightarrow R_2 \\ -\frac{1}{300}R_3 \rightarrow R_3 \\ -\frac{1}{300}R_4 \rightarrow R_4 \\ \\ \end{array} \left[\begin{array}{cccc|c} 1 & 0 & 0 & 0 & 12 \\ 0 & 1 & 0 & 0 & 8 \\ 0 & 0 & 1 & 0 & 16 \\ 0 & 0 & 0 & 1 & 0 \\ 0 & 0 & 0 & 0 & 0 \end{array}\right]$$

Each of the original variables has a value, so the last row of all zeros may be ignored. The solution of the system is $x_1 = 12$, $x_2 = 8$, $x_3 = 16$, $x_4 = 0$. Therefore, 12 cars should be sent from I to A, 8 cars from II to A, 16 cars from I to B, and no cars from II to B.

52. Let $x_1 =$ the number of units from first supplier for Roseville,
$x_2 =$ the number of units from first supplier for Akron,
$x_3 =$ the number of units from second supplier for Roseville, and
$x_4 =$ the number of units from second supplier for Akron.

Roseville needs 40 units so

$$x_1 + x_3 = 40.$$

Akron needs 75 units so

$$x_2 + x_4 = 75.$$

The manufacturer orders 75 units from the first supplier so

$$x_1 + x_2 = 75.$$

The total cost is $10,750 so

$$70x_1 + 90x_2 + 80x_3 + 120x_4 = 10{,}750.$$

The system to be solve is

$$\begin{aligned} x_1 + x_3 &= 40 \\ x_2 + x_4 &= 75 \\ x_1 + x_2 &= 75 \\ 70x_1 + 90x_2 + 80x_3 + 120x_4 &= 10{,}750. \end{aligned}$$

Write augmented matrix and use row operations.

$$\left[\begin{array}{cccc|c} 1 & 0 & 1 & 0 & 40 \\ 0 & 1 & 0 & 1 & 75 \\ 1 & 1 & 0 & 0 & 75 \\ 70 & 90 & 80 & 120 & 10{,}750 \end{array}\right]$$

$$\begin{array}{r} \\ \\ -1R_1 + R_3 \rightarrow R_3 \\ -70R_1 + R_4 \rightarrow R_4 \end{array} \left[\begin{array}{cccc|c} 1 & 0 & 1 & 0 & 40 \\ 0 & 1 & 0 & 1 & 75 \\ 0 & 1 & -1 & 0 & 35 \\ 0 & 90 & 10 & 120 & 7950 \end{array}\right]$$

$$\begin{array}{r} \\ \\ -1R_2 + R_3 \rightarrow R_3 \\ -90R_2 + R_4 \rightarrow R_4 \end{array} \left[\begin{array}{cccc|c} 1 & 0 & 1 & 0 & 40 \\ 0 & 1 & 0 & 1 & 75 \\ 0 & 0 & -1 & -1 & -40 \\ 0 & 0 & 10 & 30 & 1200 \end{array}\right]$$

$$\begin{array}{r} \\ \\ -1R_3 \rightarrow R_3 \\ 10R_3 + R_4 \rightarrow R_4 \end{array} \left[\begin{array}{cccc|c} 1 & 0 & 1 & 0 & 40 \\ 0 & 1 & 0 & 1 & 75 \\ 0 & 0 & 1 & 1 & 40 \\ 0 & 0 & 0 & 20 & 800 \end{array}\right]$$

$$\begin{array}{r} \\ \\ \\ \frac{1}{20}R_4 \rightarrow R_4 \end{array} \left[\begin{array}{cccc|c} 1 & 0 & 1 & 0 & 40 \\ 0 & 1 & 0 & 1 & 75 \\ 0 & 0 & 1 & 1 & 40 \\ 0 & 0 & 0 & 1 & 40 \end{array}\right]$$

$$\begin{array}{r} \\ -1R_4 + R_2 \rightarrow R_2 \\ -1R_4 + R_3 \rightarrow R_3 \\ \\ \end{array} \left[\begin{array}{cccc|c} 1 & 0 & 1 & 0 & 40 \\ 0 & 1 & 0 & 0 & 35 \\ 0 & 0 & 1 & 0 & 0 \\ 0 & 0 & 0 & 1 & 40 \end{array}\right]$$

$$\begin{array}{r} \\ -1R_3 + R_1 \rightarrow R_1 \\ \\ \\ \end{array} \left[\begin{array}{cccc|c} 1 & 0 & 0 & 0 & 40 \\ 0 & 1 & 0 & 0 & 35 \\ 0 & 0 & 1 & 0 & 0 \\ 0 & 0 & 0 & 1 & 40 \end{array}\right]$$

The solution of the system is $x_1 = 40, x_2 = 35, x_3 = 0, x_4 = 40$, or $(40, 35, 0, 40)$. The first supplier should send 40 units to Roseville and 35 units to Akron. The second supplier should send 0 units to Roseville and 40 units to Akron.

53. Let $x =$ the number of Italian style vegetable packages,
$y =$ the number of French style vegetable packages, and
$z =$ the number of Oriental style vegetable packages.

$$\begin{aligned} 0.3x + 0.2z &= 16{,}200 \\ 0.3x + 0.6y + 0.5z &= 41{,}400 \\ 0.4x + 0.4y + 0.3z &= 29{,}400 \end{aligned}$$

Expressing the amount of each vegetable in thousands, the system becomes

$$\begin{aligned} 0.3x + 0.2z &= 16.2 \\ 0.3x + 0.6y + 0.5z &= 41.4 \\ 0.4x + 0.4y + 0.3z &= 29.4. \end{aligned}$$

Multiply each equation by 10, and write the augmented matrix.

$$\left[\begin{array}{ccc|c} 3 & 0 & 2 & 162 \\ 3 & 6 & 5 & 414 \\ 4 & 4 & 3 & 294 \end{array}\right]$$

$$\begin{array}{r} \frac{1}{3}R_1 \rightarrow R_1 \\ \\ \\ \end{array} \left[\begin{array}{ccc|c} 1 & 0 & \frac{2}{3} & 54 \\ 3 & 6 & 5 & 414 \\ 4 & 4 & 3 & 294 \end{array}\right]$$

$$\begin{array}{r} \\ -3R_1 + R_2 \rightarrow R_2 \\ -4R_1 + R_3 \rightarrow R_3 \end{array} \left[\begin{array}{ccc|c} 1 & 0 & \frac{2}{3} & 54 \\ 0 & 6 & 3 & 252 \\ 0 & 4 & \frac{1}{3} & 78 \end{array}\right]$$

$$\begin{array}{r} \\ \frac{1}{6}R_2 \rightarrow R_2 \\ \\ \end{array} \left[\begin{array}{ccc|c} 1 & 0 & \frac{2}{3} & 54 \\ 0 & 1 & \frac{1}{2} & 42 \\ 0 & 4 & \frac{1}{3} & 78 \end{array}\right]$$

$$\begin{array}{r} \\ \\ -4R_2 + R_3 \rightarrow R_3 \end{array} \left[\begin{array}{ccc|c} 1 & 0 & \frac{2}{3} & 54 \\ 0 & 1 & \frac{1}{2} & 42 \\ 0 & 0 & -\frac{5}{3} & -90 \end{array}\right]$$

$$\begin{array}{r} \\ \\ -\frac{3}{5}R_3 \rightarrow R_3 \end{array} \left[\begin{array}{ccc|c} 1 & 0 & \frac{2}{3} & 54 \\ 0 & 1 & \frac{1}{2} & 42 \\ 0 & 0 & 1 & 54 \end{array}\right]$$

$$\begin{array}{r} -\frac{2}{3}R_3 + R_1 \rightarrow R_1 \\ -\frac{1}{2}R_3 + R_2 \rightarrow R_2 \\ \\ \end{array} \left[\begin{array}{ccc|c} 1 & 0 & 0 & 18 \\ 0 & 1 & 0 & 15 \\ 0 & 0 & 1 & 54 \end{array}\right]$$

Therefore, the company should prepare 18 thousand or 18,000 packages of Italian style, 15 thousand or 15,000 of French style, and 54 thousand or 54,000 of Oriental style vegetables.

54. Let $x =$ the number of two-person tents,
$y =$ the number of four-person tents, and
$z =$ the number of six-person tents that were ordered.

(a) The problem is to solve the following system of equations.

$$\begin{aligned} 2x + 4y + 6z &= 200 \\ 40x + 64y + 88z &= 3200 \\ 129x + 179y + 229z &= 8950 \end{aligned}$$

Write the augmented matrix and use row operations to solve.

$$\left[\begin{array}{rrr|r} 2 & 4 & 6 & 200 \\ 40 & 64 & 88 & 3200 \\ 129 & 179 & 229 & 8950 \end{array}\right]$$

$$\begin{array}{r} \\ 20R_1 + (-1)R_2 \to R_2 \\ 129R_1 + (-2)R_3 \to R_3 \end{array} \left[\begin{array}{rrr|r} 2 & 4 & 6 & 200 \\ 0 & 16 & 32 & 800 \\ 0 & 158 & 316 & 7900 \end{array}\right]$$

$$\begin{array}{r} R_2 + (-4)R_1 \to R_1 \\ \\ 79R_2 + (-8)R_3 \to R_3 \end{array} \left[\begin{array}{rrr|r} -8 & 0 & 8 & 0 \\ 0 & 16 & 32 & 800 \\ 0 & 0 & 0 & 0 \end{array}\right]$$

$$\begin{array}{r} -\frac{1}{8}R_1 \to R_1 \\ \frac{1}{16}R_2 \to R_2 \\ \\ \end{array} \left[\begin{array}{rrr|r} 1 & 0 & -1 & 0 \\ 0 & 1 & 2 & 50 \\ 0 & 0 & 0 & 0 \end{array}\right]$$

Since the last row is all zeros, there is more than one solution. Let z be the parameter. The matrix gives

$$\begin{aligned} x - z &= \\ y + 2z &= 50. \end{aligned}$$

Solving these equations for x and y, the solution is $(z, -2z + 50, z)$. The numbers in the solution must be nonnegative integers. Therefore,

$$\begin{aligned} y &\geq 0 \\ -2z + 50 &\geq 0 \\ z &\leq 25. \end{aligned}$$

Thus, $z \in \{0, 1, 2, 3, \ldots, 25\}$. In other words, depending on the number of six-person tents, there are 26 solutions to this problem.

(b) The number of four-person tents is given by the value of the variable y. Since $y = -2z + 50$, the most four-person tents will result when z is as small as possible, or 0. When this occurs, $y = -2(0) + 50 = 50$. And since $x = z$, the solution with the most four-person tents is 0 two-person tents, 50 four-person tents, and 0 six-person tents.

(c) The number of two-person tents is given by the value of the variable x. Since $x = z$, the most two-person tents will result when y is as small as possible, or 0. When this occurs,

$$\begin{aligned} 2x + 4y + 6z &= 200 \\ 2(z) + 4(0) + 6(z) &= 200 \\ 8z &= 200 \\ z &= 25. \end{aligned}$$

The solution with the most two-person tents is 25 two-person tents, 0 four-person tents, and 25 six-person tents.

55. Let $x_1 =$ the number of cases of Brand A,
$x_2 =$ the number of cases of Brand B,
$x_3 =$ the number of cases of Brand C, and
$x_4 =$ the number of cases of Brand D.

$$\begin{aligned} 25x_1 + 50x_2 + 75x_3 + 100x_4 &= 1200 \\ 30x_1 + 30x_2 + 30x_3 + 60x_4 &= 600 \\ 30x_1 + 20x_2 + 20x_3 + 30x_4 &= 400 \end{aligned}$$

The augmented matrix of the system is

$$\left[\begin{array}{rrrr|r} 25 & 50 & 75 & 100 & 1200 \\ 30 & 30 & 30 & 60 & 600 \\ 30 & 20 & 20 & 30 & 400 \end{array}\right].$$

$$\begin{array}{r} \frac{1}{5}R_1 \to R_1 \\ \frac{1}{30}R_2 \to R_2 \\ \frac{1}{10}R_3 \to R_3 \end{array} \left[\begin{array}{rrrr|r} 5 & 10 & 15 & 20 & 240 \\ 1 & 1 & 1 & 2 & 20 \\ 3 & 2 & 2 & 3 & 40 \end{array}\right]$$

Interchange rows 1 and 2.

$$\left[\begin{array}{rrrr|r} 1 & 1 & 1 & 2 & 20 \\ 5 & 10 & 15 & 20 & 240 \\ 3 & 2 & 2 & 3 & 40 \end{array}\right]$$

$$\begin{array}{r} \\ -5R_1 + R_2 \to R_2 \\ -3R_1 + R_3 \to R_3 \end{array} \left[\begin{array}{rrrr|r} 1 & 1 & 1 & 2 & 20 \\ 0 & 5 & 10 & 10 & 140 \\ 0 & -1 & -1 & -3 & -20 \end{array}\right]$$

$$\begin{array}{r} \\ \frac{1}{5}R_2 \to R_2 \\ \\ \end{array} \left[\begin{array}{rrrr|r} 1 & 1 & 1 & 2 & 20 \\ 0 & 1 & 2 & 2 & 28 \\ 0 & -1 & -1 & -3 & -20 \end{array}\right]$$

$$\begin{array}{r} -1R_2 + R_1 \to R_1 \\ \\ R_2 + R_3 \to R_3 \end{array} \left[\begin{array}{rrrr|r} 1 & 0 & -1 & 0 & -8 \\ 0 & 1 & 2 & 2 & 28 \\ 0 & 0 & 1 & -1 & 8 \end{array}\right]$$

$$\begin{array}{r} R_3 + R_1 \to R_1 \\ -2R_3 + R_2 \to R_2 \\ \\ \end{array} \left[\begin{array}{rrrr|r} 1 & 0 & 0 & -1 & 0 \\ 0 & 1 & 0 & 4 & 12 \\ 0 & 0 & 1 & -1 & 8 \end{array}\right]$$

We cannot change the values in column 4 further without changing the form of the other three columns. Therefore, let x_4 be arbitrary. This matrix gives the equations

$$\begin{aligned} x_1 - x_4 &= 0 &&\text{or}\quad x_1 = x_4, \\ x_2 + 4x_4 &= 12 &&\text{or}\quad x_2 = 12 - 4x_4, \\ x_3 - x_4 &= 8 &&\text{or}\quad x_3 = 8 + x_4. \end{aligned}$$

The solution is $(x_4, 12 - 4x_4, 8 + x_4, x_4)$. Since all solutions must be nonnegative,

$$\begin{aligned} 12 - 4x_4 &\geq 0 \\ x_4 &\leq 3. \end{aligned}$$

If $x_4 = 0$, then $x_1 = 0$, $x_2 = 12$, and $x_3 = 8$.
If $x_4 = 1$, then $x_1 = 1$, $x_2 = 8$, and $x_3 = 9$.
If $x_4 = 2$, then $x_1 = 2$, $x_2 = 4$, and $x_3 = 10$.
If $x_4 = 3$, then $x_1 = 3$, $x_2 = 0$, and $x_3 = 11$.

Therefore, there are four possible solutions. The breeder should mix

1. 0 cases of A, 12 cases of B, 8 cases of C, and 0 cases of D;

2. 1 case of A, 8 cases of B, 9 cases of C, and 1 case of D;

3. 2 cases of A, 4 cases of B, 10 cases of C, and 2 cases of D; or

4. 3 cases of A, 0 cases of B, 11 cases of C, and 3 cases of D.

56. Let $x =$ the number of grams of group A,
$y =$ the number of grams of group B, and
$z =$ the number of grams of group C.

(a) The system to be solved is

$$\begin{aligned} x + y + z &= 400 \quad (1) \\ x &= \frac{1}{3}y \quad (2) \\ x \quad + z &= 2y. \quad (3) \end{aligned}$$

Rewrite equations (2) and (3) in proper form and multiply both sides of equation (2) by 3.

$$\begin{aligned} x + \ y + z &= 400 \\ 3x - \ y \quad &= 0 \\ x - 2y + z &= 0 \end{aligned}$$

Write the augmented matrix.

$$\left[\begin{array}{rrr|r} 1 & 1 & 1 & 400 \\ 3 & -1 & 0 & 0 \\ 1 & -2 & 1 & 0 \end{array}\right]$$

$$\begin{array}{r} \\ -3R_1 + R_2 \rightarrow R_2 \\ -1R_1 + R_3 \rightarrow R_3 \end{array} \left[\begin{array}{rrr|r} 1 & 1 & 1 & 400 \\ 0 & -4 & -3 & -1200 \\ 0 & -3 & 0 & -400 \end{array}\right]$$

$$\begin{array}{r} \\ \\ -\frac{1}{3}R_3 \rightarrow R_3 \end{array} \left[\begin{array}{rrr|r} 1 & 1 & 1 & 400 \\ 0 & -4 & -3 & -1200 \\ 0 & 1 & 0 & \frac{400}{3} \end{array}\right]$$

Interchange rows 2 and 3.

$$\left[\begin{array}{rrr|r} 1 & 1 & 1 & 400 \\ 0 & 1 & 0 & \frac{400}{3} \\ 0 & -4 & -3 & -1200 \end{array}\right]$$

$$\begin{array}{r} -1R_2 + R_1 \rightarrow R_1 \\ \\ 4R_2 + R_3 \rightarrow R_3 \end{array} \left[\begin{array}{rrr|r} 1 & 0 & 1 & \frac{800}{3} \\ 0 & 1 & 0 & \frac{400}{3} \\ 0 & 0 & -3 & -\frac{2000}{3} \end{array}\right]$$

$$\begin{array}{r} \\ \\ -\frac{1}{3}R_3 \rightarrow R_3 \end{array} \left[\begin{array}{rrr|r} 1 & 0 & 1 & \frac{800}{3} \\ 0 & 1 & 0 & \frac{400}{3} \\ 0 & 0 & 1 & \frac{2000}{9} \end{array}\right]$$

$$\begin{array}{r} -1R_3 + R_1 \rightarrow R_1 \\ \\ \\ \end{array} \left[\begin{array}{rrr|r} 1 & 0 & 0 & \frac{400}{9} \\ 0 & 1 & 0 & \frac{400}{3} \\ 0 & 0 & 1 & \frac{2000}{9} \end{array}\right]$$

The solution is $\left(\frac{400}{9}, \frac{400}{3}, \frac{2000}{9}\right)$. Include $\frac{400}{9}$ g of group A, $\frac{400}{3}$ g of group B, and $\frac{2000}{9}$ g of group C.

(b) If the requirement that the diet include one-third as much of A as of B is dropped, refer to the first two rows of the fifth augmented matrix in part (a).

$$\left[\begin{array}{rrr|r} 1 & 0 & 1 & \frac{800}{3} \\ 0 & 1 & 0 & \frac{400}{3} \end{array}\right]$$

This gives

$$x = \frac{800}{3} - z$$
$$y = \frac{400}{3}.$$

Therefore, for any positive number of grams of group C, there should be C grams less than $\frac{800}{3}$ g of group A and $\frac{400}{3}$ g of group B.

(c) Since there was a unique solution for the original problem, by adding an additional condition, the only possible solution would be the one from part (a). However, by substituting those values of A, B, and C for x, y, and z in the equation for the additional condition, $0.02x + 0.02y + 0.03z = 8.00$, the values do not work. Therefore, a solution is not possible.

57. Let $x =$ the number of the first species,
$y =$ the number of the second species, and
$z =$ the number of the third species.

$$\begin{aligned} 1.3x + 1.1y + 8.1z &= 16{,}000 \\ 1.3x + 2.4y + 2.9z &= 28{,}000 \\ 2.3x + 3.7y + 5.1z &= 44{,}000 \end{aligned}$$

Write the augmented matrix of the system.

$$\left[\begin{array}{ccc|c} 1.3 & 1.1 & 8.1 & 16{,}000 \\ 1.3 & 2.4 & 2.9 & 28{,}000 \\ 2.3 & 3.7 & 5.1 & 44{,}000 \end{array}\right]$$

This exercise should be solved by graphing calculator or computer methods. The solution, which may vary slightly, is 2340 of the first species, 10,128 of the second species, and 224 of the third species. (All of these are rounded to the nearest whole number.)

58. Let $x =$ the number of species A,
$y =$ the number of species B, and
$z =$ the number of species C.

Use a chart to organize the information.

		Species			
		A	B	C	Totals
Food	I	1.32	2.1	0.86	490
	II	2.9	0.95	1.52	897
	III	1.75	0.6	2.01	653

The system to be solved is

$$\begin{aligned} 1.32x + 2.1y + 0.86z &= 490 \\ 2.9x + 0.95y + 1.52z &= 897 \\ 1.75x + 0.6y + 2.01z &= 653. \end{aligned}$$

Use graphing calculator or computer methods to solve this system. The solution, which may vary slightly, is to stock about 244 fish of species A, 39 fish of species B, and 101 fish of species C.

59. Let $x =$ the number of acres for honeydews,
$y =$ the number of acres for yellow onions, and
$z =$ the number of acres for lettuce.

(a)
$$\begin{aligned} x + y + z &= 220 \\ 120x + 150y + 180z &= 29{,}100 \\ 180x + 80y + 80z &= 32{,}600 \\ 4.97x + 4.45y + 4.65z &= 480 \end{aligned}$$

Write the augmented matrix for this system.

$$\left[\begin{array}{ccc|c} 1 & 1 & 1 & 220 \\ 120 & 150 & 180 & 29{,}100 \\ 180 & 80 & 80 & 32{,}600 \\ 4.97 & 4.45 & 4.65 & 480 \end{array}\right]$$

Using graphing calculator or computer methods, we obtain

$$\left[\begin{array}{ccc|c} 1 & 0 & 0 & 150 \\ 0 & 1 & 0 & 50 \\ 0 & 0 & 1 & 20 \\ 0 & 0 & 0 & -581 \end{array}\right].$$

There is no solution to the system. Therefore, it is not possible to utilize all resources completely.

(b) If 1061 hr of labor are available, the augmented matrix becomes,

$$\left[\begin{array}{ccc|c} 1 & 1 & 1 & 220 \\ 120 & 150 & 180 & 29{,}100 \\ 180 & 80 & 80 & 32{,}600 \\ 4.97 & 4.45 & 4.65 & 1061 \end{array}\right].$$

Again, using graphing calculator or computer methods we obtain

$$\left[\begin{array}{ccc|c} 1 & 0 & 0 & 150 \\ 0 & 1 & 0 & 50 \\ 0 & 0 & 1 & 20 \\ 0 & 0 & 0 & 0 \end{array}\right].$$

The solution is $(150, 50, 20)$. Therefore, allot 150 acres for honeydews, 50 acres for onions, and 20 acres for lettuce.

60. **(a)** Bulls:

The number of white ones was one half plus one third the number of black greater than the brown.

$$\begin{aligned} X &= \left(\frac{1}{2} + \frac{1}{3}\right) Y + T \\ X &= \frac{5}{6} Y + T \\ 6X &= 5Y + 6T \\ 6X - 5Y &= 6T \end{aligned}$$

The number of the black, one quarter plus one fifth the number of the spotted greater than the brown.

$$\begin{aligned} Y &= \left(\frac{1}{4} + \frac{1}{5}\right) Z + T \\ Y &= \frac{9}{20} Z + T \\ 20Y &= 9Z + 20T \\ 20Y - 9Z &= 20T \end{aligned}$$

The number of the spotted, one sixth and one seventh the number of the white greater than the brown.

$$Z = \left(\frac{1}{6} + \frac{1}{7}\right) X + T$$
$$Z = \frac{13}{42}X + T$$
$$42Z = 13X + 42T$$
$$42Z - 13X = 42T$$

So the system of equations for the bulls is

$$\begin{aligned} 6X - 5Y &= 6T \\ 20Y - 9Z &= 20T \\ 42Z - 13X &= 42T. \end{aligned}$$

Cows:

The number of white ones was one third plus one quarter of the total black cattle.

$$x = \left(\frac{1}{3} + \frac{1}{4}\right)(Y + y)$$
$$x = \frac{7}{12}(Y + y)$$
$$12x = 7Y + 7y$$
$$12x - 7y = 7Y$$

The number of the black, one quarter plus one fifth the total of the spotted cattle.

$$y = \left(\frac{1}{4} + \frac{1}{5}\right)(Z + z)$$
$$y = \frac{9}{20}(Z + z)$$
$$20y = 9Z + 9z$$
$$20y - 9z = 9Z$$

The number of the spotted, one fifth plus one sixth the total of the brown cattle.

$$z = \left(\frac{1}{5} + \frac{1}{6}\right)(T + t)$$
$$z = \frac{11}{30}(T + t)$$
$$30z = 11T + 11t$$
$$30z - 11t = 11T$$

The number of the brown, one sixth plus one seventh the total of the white cattle.

$$t = \left(\frac{1}{6} + \frac{1}{7}\right)(X + x)$$
$$t = \frac{13}{42}(X + x)$$
$$42t = 13X + 13x$$
$$42t - 13x = 13X$$

So the system of equations for the cows is

$$\begin{aligned} 12x - 7y &= 7Y \\ 20y - 9z &= 9Z \\ 30z - 11t &= 11T \\ -13x + 42t &= 13X \end{aligned}$$

(b) For $T = 4{,}149{,}387$, the 3×3 system to be solved is

$$\begin{aligned} 6X - 5Y &= 24{,}896{,}322 \\ 20Y - 9Z &= 82{,}987{,}740 \\ -13X + 42Z &= 174{,}274{,}254 \end{aligned}$$

Write the augmented matrix of the system.

$$\left[\begin{array}{rrr|r} 6 & -5 & 0 & 24{,}896{,}322 \\ 0 & 20 & -9 & 82{,}987{,}740 \\ -13 & 0 & 42 & 174{,}274{,}254 \end{array}\right]$$

This exercise should be solved by graphing calculator or computer methods. The solution is $X = 10{,}366{,}482$ white bulls, $Y = 7{,}460{,}514$ black bulls, and $Z = 7{,}358{,}060$ spotted bulls.
For $X = 10{,}366{,}482$, $Y = 7{,}460{,}514$, and $Z = 7{,}358{,}060$, the 4×4 system to be solved is

$$\begin{aligned} 12x - 7y &= 52{,}223{,}598 \\ 20y - 9z &= 66{,}222{,}540 \\ 30z - 11t &= 45{,}643{,}257 \\ -13x + 42t &= 134{,}764{,}266 \end{aligned}$$

Write the augmented matrix of the system.

$$\left[\begin{array}{rrrr|r} 12 & -7 & 0 & 0 & 52{,}223{,}598 \\ 0 & 20 & -9 & 0 & 66{,}222{,}540 \\ 0 & 0 & 30 & -11 & 45{,}643{,}257 \\ -13 & 0 & 0 & 42 & 134{,}764{,}266 \end{array}\right]$$

This exercise should be solved by graphing calculator or computer methods. The solution is $x = 7{,}206{,}360$ white cows, $y = 4{,}893{,}246$ black cows, $z = 3{,}515{,}820$ spotted cows, and $t = 5{,}439{,}213$ brown cows.

61. **(a)** In 1980, $t = 0$ and $R = 207.9$.

$$\begin{aligned} 207.9 &= a(0)^2 + b(0) + c \\ 207.9 &= c \end{aligned}$$

In 1990, $t = 10$ and $R = 216.0$.

$$\begin{aligned} 216.0 &= a(10)^2 + b(10) + c \\ 216.0 &= 100a + 10b + c \end{aligned}$$

In 2000, $t = 20$ and $R = 199.6$.

$$\begin{aligned} 199.6 &= a(20)^2 + b(20) + c \\ 199.6 &= 400a + 20b + c \end{aligned}$$

The linear system to be solved is

$$\begin{aligned} 400a + 20b + c &= 199.6 \\ 100a + 10b + c &= 216.0 \\ c &= 207.9 \end{aligned}$$

Write the augmented matrix and use row operations to solve.

$$\left[\begin{array}{ccc|c} 400 & 20 & 1 & 199.6 \\ 100 & 10 & 1 & 216.0 \\ 0 & 0 & 1 & 207.9 \end{array}\right]$$

$$-1R_1 + 4R_2 \to R_2 \quad \left[\begin{array}{ccc|c} 400 & 20 & -2 & 199.6 \\ 0 & 20 & 3 & 664.4 \\ 0 & 0 & 1 & 207.9 \end{array}\right]$$

$$-1R_2 + R_1 \to R_1 \quad \left[\begin{array}{ccc|c} 400 & 0 & -2 & -464.8 \\ 0 & 20 & 3 & 664.4 \\ 0 & 0 & 1 & 207.9 \end{array}\right]$$

$$\begin{array}{r} 2R_3 + R_1 \to R_1 \\ -3R_3 + R_2 \to R_2 \end{array} \quad \left[\begin{array}{ccc|c} 400 & 0 & 0 & -49 \\ 0 & 20 & 0 & 40.7 \\ 0 & 0 & 1 & 207.9 \end{array}\right]$$

$$\begin{array}{r} \frac{1}{400}R_1 \to R_1 \\ \frac{1}{20}R_2 \to R_2 \end{array} \quad \left[\begin{array}{ccc|c} 1 & 0 & 0 & -0.1225 \\ 0 & 1 & 0 & 2.035 \\ 0 & 0 & 1 & 207.9 \end{array}\right]$$

The solution is $a = -0.1225, b = 2.035$, and $c = 207.9$.

(b) In 2003, $t = 23$.

$$\begin{aligned} R &= -0.1225t^2 + 2.035t + 207.9 \\ &= -0.1225(23)^2 + 2.035(23) + 207.9 \\ &\approx 189.9 \end{aligned}$$

The predicated value is close to the actual value, 194.0 deaths per 1,000,000.

(c) In 1980, $t = 0$ and $R = 207.9$.

$$\begin{aligned} 207.9 &= a(0)^3 + b(0)^2 + c(0) + d \\ 207.9 &= d \end{aligned}$$

Similarly, we obtain the remaining three equations for $t = 10, t = 20$, and $t = 23$. The linear system to be solved is

$$\begin{aligned} 12{,}167a + 529b + 23c + d &= 190.1 \\ 8000a + 400b + 20c + d &= 199.6 \\ 1000a + 100b + 10c + d &= 216.0 \\ d &= 207.9. \end{aligned}$$

The augmented matrix is

$$\left[\begin{array}{cccc|c} 12{,}167 & 529 & 23 & 1 & 190.1 \\ 8000 & 400 & 20 & 1 & 199.6 \\ 1000 & 100 & 10 & 1 & 216.0 \\ 0 & 0 & 0 & 1 & 207.9 \end{array}\right]$$

Use a graphing calculator or computer methods to obtain the solution $a = 0.0002202, b = -0.1291$, $c = 2.079$, and $d = 207.9$.

62. **(a)** The system to be solved is

$$\begin{aligned} 0 &= 200{,}000 - 0.5r - 0.3b \\ 0 &= 350{,}000 - 0.5r - 0.7b. \end{aligned}$$

First, write the system in proper form.

$$\begin{aligned} 0.5r + 0.3b &= 200{,}000 \\ 0.5r + 0.7b &= 350{,}000 \end{aligned}$$

Write the augmented matrix and use row operations.

$$\left[\begin{array}{cc|c} 0.5 & 0.3 & 200{,}000 \\ 0.5 & 0.7 & 350{,}000 \end{array}\right]$$

$$\begin{array}{r} 10R_1 \to R_1 \\ 10R_2 \to R_2 \end{array} \quad \left[\begin{array}{cc|c} 5 & 3 & 2{,}000{,}000 \\ 5 & 7 & 3{,}500{,}000 \end{array}\right]$$

$$-1R_1 + R_2 \to R_2 \quad \left[\begin{array}{cc|c} 5 & 3 & 2{,}000{,}000 \\ 0 & 4 & 1{,}500{,}000 \end{array}\right]$$

$$-\tfrac{3}{4}R_2 + R_1 \to R_1 \quad \left[\begin{array}{cc|c} 5 & 0 & 875{,}000 \\ 0 & 4 & 1{,}500{,}000 \end{array}\right]$$

$$\begin{array}{r} \frac{1}{5}R_1 \to R_1 \\ \frac{1}{4}R_2 \to R_2 \end{array} \quad \left[\begin{array}{cc|c} 1 & 0 & 175{,}000 \\ 0 & 1 & 375{,}000 \end{array}\right]$$

The solution is (175,000, 375,000). When the rate of increase for each is zero, there are 175,000 soldiers in the Red Army and 375,000 soldiers in the Blue Army.

63. (a) The other two equations are

$$x_2 + x_3 = 700$$
$$x_3 + x_4 = 600.$$

(b) The augmented matrix is

$$\left[\begin{array}{cccc|c} 1 & 0 & 0 & 1 & 1000 \\ 1 & 1 & 0 & 0 & 1100 \\ 0 & 1 & 1 & 0 & 700 \\ 0 & 0 & 1 & 1 & 600 \end{array}\right].$$

$$-1R_1 + R_2 \to R_2 \quad \left[\begin{array}{cccc|c} 1 & 0 & 0 & 1 & 1000 \\ 0 & 1 & 0 & -1 & 100 \\ 0 & 1 & 1 & 0 & 700 \\ 0 & 0 & 1 & 1 & 600 \end{array}\right]$$

$$-1R_2 + R_3 \to R_3 \quad \left[\begin{array}{cccc|c} 1 & 0 & 0 & 1 & 1000 \\ 0 & 1 & 0 & -1 & 100 \\ 0 & 0 & 1 & 1 & 600 \\ 0 & 0 & 1 & 1 & 600 \end{array}\right]$$

$$-1R_3 + R_4 \to R_4 \quad \left[\begin{array}{cccc|c} 1 & 0 & 0 & 1 & 1000 \\ 0 & 1 & 0 & -1 & 100 \\ 0 & 0 & 1 & 1 & 600 \\ 0 & 0 & 0 & 0 & 0 \end{array}\right]$$

Let x_4 be arbitrary. Solve the first three equations for x_1, x_2, and x_3.

$$x_1 = 1000 - x_4$$
$$x_2 = 100 + x_4$$
$$x_3 = 600 - x_4$$

The solution is $(1000 - x_4, 100 + x_4, 600 - x_4, x_4)$.

(c) For x_4, we see that $x_4 \geq 0$ and $x_4 \leq 600$ since $600 - x_4$ must be nonnegative. Therefore, $0 \leq x_4 \leq 600$.

(d) x_1: If $x_4 = 0$, then $x_1 = 1000$.
If $x_4 = 600$, then $x_1 = 1000 - 600 = 400$.

Therefore, $400 \leq x_1 \leq 1000$.

x_2: If $x_4 = 0$, then $x_2 = 100$.
If $x_4 = 600$, then $x_2 = 100 + 600 = 700$.

Therefore, $100 \leq x_2 \leq 700$.

x_3: If $x_4 = 0$, then $x_3 = 600$.
If $x_4 = 600$, then $x_3 = 600 - 600 = 0$.

Therefore, $0 \leq x_3 \leq 600$.

(e) If you know the number of cars entering or leaving three of the intersections, then the number entering or leaving the fourth is automatically determined because the number leaving must equal the number entering.

64. (a)
$$5.4 = a(8)^2 + b(8) + c$$
$$5.4 = 64a + 8b + c$$
$$6.3 = a(13)^2 + b(13) + c$$
$$6.3 = 169a + 13b + c$$
$$5.6 = a(18)^2 + b(18) + c$$
$$5.6 = 324a + 18b + c$$

The linear system to be solved is

$$\begin{aligned} 64a + 8b + c &= 5.4 \\ 169a + 13b + c &= 6.3 \\ 324a + 18b + c &= 5.6. \end{aligned}$$

Use a graphing calculator or computer methods to solve this system. The solution is $a = -0.032, b = 0.852$, and $c = 0.632$. Thus, the equation is

$$y = -0.032x^2 + 0.852x + 0.632.$$

(b)

```
QuadReg
 y=ax²+bx+c
 a=-.032
 b=.852
 c=.632
 R²=1
```

The answer obtained using Gauss–Jordan elimination is the same as the answer obtained using the quadratic regression feature on a graphing calculator.

65. Let $x =$ the number of balls,
$y =$ the number of dolls, and
$z =$ the number of cars.

(a) The system to be solved is

$$\begin{aligned} x + y \quad z &= 100 \\ 2x + 3y + 4z &= 295 \\ 12x + 16y + 18z &= 1542. \end{aligned}$$

Write the augmented matrix of the system.

$$\left[\begin{array}{ccc|c} 1 & 1 & 1 & 100 \\ 2 & 3 & 4 & 295 \\ 12 & 16 & 18 & 1542 \end{array}\right]$$

$$\begin{array}{l} \\ -2R_1 + R_2 \rightarrow R_2 \\ -12R_1 + R_3 \rightarrow R_3 \end{array} \left[\begin{array}{ccc|c} 1 & 1 & 1 & 100 \\ 0 & 1 & 2 & 95 \\ 0 & 4 & 6 & 342 \end{array}\right]$$

$$\begin{array}{l} -1R_2 + R_1 \rightarrow R_1 \\ \\ -4R_2 + R_3 \rightarrow R_3 \end{array} \left[\begin{array}{ccc|c} 1 & 0 & -1 & 5 \\ 0 & 1 & 2 & 95 \\ 0 & 0 & -2 & -38 \end{array}\right]$$

$$\begin{array}{l} \\ \\ -\frac{1}{2}R_3 \rightarrow R_3 \end{array} \left[\begin{array}{ccc|c} 1 & 0 & -1 & 5 \\ 0 & 1 & 2 & 95 \\ 0 & 0 & 1 & 19 \end{array}\right]$$

$$\begin{array}{l} R_3 + R_1 \rightarrow R_1 \\ -2R_3 + R_2 \rightarrow R_2 \end{array} \left[\begin{array}{ccc|c} 1 & 0 & 0 & 24 \\ 0 & 1 & 0 & 57 \\ 0 & 0 & 1 & 19 \end{array}\right]$$

The solution is $(24, 57, 19)$. There were 24 balls, 57 dolls, and 19 cars.

(b) The augmented matrix becomes

$$\left[\begin{array}{ccc|c} 1 & 1 & 1 & 100 \\ 2 & 3 & 4 & 295 \\ 11 & 15 & 19 & 1542 \end{array}\right].$$

$$\begin{array}{l} \\ -2R_1 + R_2 \rightarrow R_2 \\ -11R_1 + R_3 \rightarrow R_3 \end{array} \left[\begin{array}{ccc|c} 1 & 1 & 1 & 100 \\ 0 & 1 & 2 & 95 \\ 0 & 4 & 8 & 442 \end{array}\right]$$

$$\begin{array}{l} -1R_2 + R_1 \rightarrow R_1 \\ \\ -4R_2 + R_3 \rightarrow R_3 \end{array} \left[\begin{array}{ccc|c} 1 & 0 & -1 & 5 \\ 0 & 1 & 2 & 95 \\ 0 & 0 & 0 & 62 \end{array}\right]$$

Since row 3 yields a false statement, $0 = 62$, there is no solution.

(c) The augmented matrix becomes

$$\left[\begin{array}{ccc|c} 1 & 1 & 1 & 100 \\ 2 & 3 & 4 & 295 \\ 11 & 15 & 19 & 1480 \end{array}\right].$$

$$\begin{array}{l} \\ -2R_1 + R_2 \rightarrow R_2 \\ -11R_1 + R_3 \rightarrow R_3 \end{array} \left[\begin{array}{ccc|c} 1 & 1 & 1 & 100 \\ 0 & 1 & 2 & 95 \\ 0 & 4 & 8 & 380 \end{array}\right]$$

$$\begin{array}{l} -1R_2 + R_1 \rightarrow R_1 \\ \\ -4R_2 + R_3 \rightarrow R_3 \end{array} \left[\begin{array}{ccc|c} 1 & 0 & -1 & 5 \\ 0 & 1 & 2 & 95 \\ 0 & 0 & 0 & 0 \end{array}\right]$$

Since the last row is all zeros, there are infinitely many solutions. Let z be the parameter. The matrix gives

$$\begin{aligned} x - z &= 5 \\ y + 2z &= 95. \end{aligned}$$

Solving these equations for x and y, the solution is $(5 + z, 95 - 2z, z)$. The numbers in the solution must be nonnegative integers. Therefore,

$$\begin{aligned} 95 - 2z &\geq 0 \\ -2z &\geq -95 \\ z &\leq 47.5. \end{aligned}$$

Thus, $z \in \{0, 1, 2, 3, \ldots, 47\}$. There are 48 possible solutions.

(d) For the smallest number of cars, $z = 0$, the solution is $(5, 95, 0)$. This means 5 balls, 95 dolls, and no cars.

(e) For the largest number of cars, $z = 47$, the solution is $(52, 1, 47)$. This means 52 balls, 1 doll, and 47 cars.

66. (a)

$$\begin{aligned} x_{11} + x_{12} + x_{21} &= 1 \\ x_{11} + x_{12} + x_{22} &= 1 \\ x_{11} + x_{21} + x_{22} &= 1 \\ x_{12} + x_{21} + x_{22} &= 1 \end{aligned}$$

Write the augmented matrix of the system.

$$\left[\begin{array}{cccc|c} 1 & 1 & 1 & 0 & 1 \\ 1 & 1 & 0 & 1 & 1 \\ 1 & 0 & 1 & 1 & 1 \\ 0 & 1 & 1 & 1 & 1 \end{array}\right]$$

$$\begin{array}{l} \\ -1R_1 + R_2 \rightarrow R_2 \\ -1R_1 + R_3 \rightarrow R_3 \\ \\ \end{array} \left[\begin{array}{cccc|c} 1 & 1 & 1 & 0 & 1 \\ 0 & 0 & -1 & 1 & 0 \\ 0 & -1 & 0 & 1 & 0 \\ 0 & 1 & 1 & 1 & 1 \end{array}\right]$$

Since $-1 = 1$ modulo 2, replace -1 with 1.

$$\left[\begin{array}{cccc|c} 1 & 1 & 1 & 0 & 1 \\ 0 & 0 & 1 & 1 & 0 \\ 0 & 1 & 0 & 1 & 0 \\ 0 & 1 & 1 & 1 & 1 \end{array}\right]$$

Interchange rows 2 and 3.

$$\left[\begin{array}{cccc|c} 1 & 1 & 1 & 0 & 1 \\ 0 & 1 & 0 & 1 & 0 \\ 0 & 0 & 1 & 1 & 0 \\ 0 & 1 & 1 & 1 & 1 \end{array}\right]$$

$$\begin{array}{l} -1R_2 + R_1 \rightarrow R_1 \\ \\ \\ -R_2 + R_4 \rightarrow R_4 \end{array} \left[\begin{array}{cccc|c} 1 & 0 & 1 & -1 & 1 \\ 0 & 1 & 0 & 1 & 0 \\ 0 & 0 & 1 & 1 & 0 \\ 0 & 0 & 1 & 0 & 1 \end{array}\right]$$

Again, replace -1 with 1.

$$\left[\begin{array}{cccc|c} 1 & 0 & 1 & 1 & 1 \\ 0 & 1 & 0 & 1 & 0 \\ 0 & 0 & 1 & 1 & 0 \\ 0 & 0 & 1 & 0 & 1 \end{array}\right]$$

$$\begin{array}{l} -1R_3 + R_1 \to R_1 \\ \\ \\ -1R_3 + R_4 \to R_4 \end{array} \left[\begin{array}{cccc|c} 1 & 0 & 0 & 0 & 1 \\ 0 & 1 & 0 & 1 & 0 \\ 0 & 0 & 1 & 1 & 0 \\ 0 & 0 & 0 & -1 & 1 \end{array}\right]$$

Replace -1 with 1.

$$\left[\begin{array}{cccc|c} 1 & 0 & 0 & 0 & 1 \\ 0 & 1 & 0 & 1 & 0 \\ 0 & 0 & 1 & 1 & 0 \\ 0 & 0 & 0 & 1 & 1 \end{array}\right]$$

$$\begin{array}{l} \\ -1R_4 + R_2 \to R_2 \\ -1R_4 + R_3 \to R_3 \\ \\ \end{array} \left[\begin{array}{cccc|c} 1 & 0 & 0 & 0 & 1 \\ 0 & 1 & 0 & 0 & -1 \\ 0 & 0 & 1 & 0 & -1 \\ 0 & 0 & 0 & 1 & 1 \end{array}\right]$$

Finally, replace -1 with 1.

$$\left[\begin{array}{cccc|c} 1 & 0 & 0 & 0 & 1 \\ 0 & 1 & 0 & 0 & 1 \\ 0 & 0 & 1 & 0 & 1 \\ 0 & 0 & 0 & 1 & 1 \end{array}\right]$$

The solution $(1, 1, 1, 1)$ corresponds to $x_{11} = 1$, $x_{12} = 1, x_{21} = 1$, and $x_{22} = 1$. Since 1 indicates that a button is pushed, the strategy required to turn all the lights out is to push every button one time.

(b)

$$\begin{aligned} x_{11} + x_{12} + x_{21} &= 0 \\ x_{11} + x_{12} + x_{22} &= 1 \\ x_{11} + x_{21} + x_{22} &= 1 \\ x_{12} + x_{21} + x_{22} &= 0 \end{aligned}$$

Write the augmented matrix of the system.

$$\left[\begin{array}{cccc|c} 1 & 1 & 1 & 0 & 0 \\ 1 & 1 & 0 & 1 & 1 \\ 1 & 0 & 1 & 1 & 1 \\ 0 & 1 & 1 & 1 & 0 \end{array}\right]$$

$$\begin{array}{l} \\ -1R_1 + R_2 \to R_2 \\ -1R_1 + R_3 \to R_3 \\ \\ \end{array} \left[\begin{array}{cccc|c} 1 & 1 & 1 & 0 & 0 \\ 0 & 0 & -1 & 1 & 1 \\ 0 & -1 & 0 & 1 & 1 \\ 0 & 1 & 1 & 1 & 0 \end{array}\right]$$

Replace -1 with 1.

$$\left[\begin{array}{cccc|c} 1 & 1 & 1 & 0 & 0 \\ 0 & 0 & 1 & 1 & 1 \\ 0 & 1 & 0 & 1 & 1 \\ 0 & 1 & 1 & 1 & 0 \end{array}\right]$$

Interchange rows 2 and 3.

$$\left[\begin{array}{cccc|c} 1 & 1 & 1 & 0 & 0 \\ 0 & 1 & 0 & 1 & 1 \\ 0 & 0 & 1 & 1 & 1 \\ 0 & 1 & 1 & 1 & 0 \end{array}\right]$$

$$\begin{array}{l} -1R_2 + R_1 \to R_1 \\ \\ \\ -1R_2 + R_4 \to R_4 \end{array} \left[\begin{array}{cccc|c} 1 & 0 & 1 & -1 & -1 \\ 0 & 1 & 0 & 1 & 1 \\ 0 & 0 & 1 & 1 & 1 \\ 0 & 0 & 1 & 0 & -1 \end{array}\right]$$

Replace -1 with 1.

$$\left[\begin{array}{cccc|c} 1 & 0 & 1 & 1 & 1 \\ 0 & 1 & 0 & 1 & 1 \\ 0 & 0 & 1 & 1 & 1 \\ 0 & 0 & 1 & 0 & 1 \end{array}\right]$$

$$\begin{array}{l} -1R_3 + R_1 \to R_1 \\ \\ \\ -1R_3 + R_4 \to R_4 \end{array} \left[\begin{array}{cccc|c} 1 & 0 & 0 & 0 & 0 \\ 0 & 1 & 0 & 1 & 1 \\ 0 & 0 & 1 & 1 & 1 \\ 0 & 0 & 0 & -1 & 0 \end{array}\right]$$

Replace -1 with 1.

$$\left[\begin{array}{cccc|c} 1 & 0 & 0 & 0 & 0 \\ 0 & 1 & 0 & 1 & 1 \\ 0 & 0 & 1 & 1 & 1 \\ 0 & 0 & 0 & 1 & 0 \end{array}\right]$$

$$\begin{array}{l} \\ -1R_4 + R_2 \to R_2 \\ -1R_4 + R_3 \to R_3 \\ \\ \end{array} \left[\begin{array}{cccc|c} 1 & 0 & 0 & 0 & 0 \\ 0 & 1 & 0 & 0 & 1 \\ 0 & 0 & 1 & 0 & 1 \\ 0 & 0 & 0 & 1 & 0 \end{array}\right]$$

The solution $(0, 1, 1, 0)$ corresponds to $x_{11} = 0, x_{12} = 1, x_{21} = 1$, and $x_{22} = 0$. Since 1 indicates that a button is pushed and 0 indicates that it is not, the strategy required to turn all the lights out is to push the button in the first row, second column, and push the button in the second row first column.

67. Let $x =$ the number of singles,
$y =$ the number of doubles,
$z =$ the number of triples, and
$w =$ the number of home runs hit by Ichiro Suzuki.

The system to be solved is

$$\begin{aligned} x + y + z + w &= 262 \\ z &= w - 3 \\ y &= 3w \\ x &= 45z \end{aligned}$$

Write the equations in proper form, obtain the augmented matrix, and use row operations to solve.

$$\left[\begin{array}{cccc|c} 1 & 1 & 1 & 1 & 262 \\ 0 & 0 & 1 & -1 & -3 \\ 0 & 1 & 0 & -3 & 0 \\ 1 & 0 & -45 & 0 & 0 \end{array}\right]$$

$$-1R_1 + R_4 \rightarrow R_4 \left[\begin{array}{cccc|c} 1 & 1 & 1 & 1 & 262 \\ 0 & 0 & 1 & -1 & -3 \\ 0 & 1 & 0 & -3 & 0 \\ 0 & -1 & -46 & -1 & -262 \end{array}\right]$$

$$R_2 \longleftrightarrow R_3 \left[\begin{array}{cccc|c} 1 & 1 & 1 & 1 & 262 \\ 0 & 1 & 0 & -3 & 0 \\ 0 & 0 & 1 & -1 & -3 \\ 0 & -1 & -46 & -1 & -262 \end{array}\right]$$

$$\begin{array}{r} -1R_2 + R_1 \rightarrow R_1 \\ \\ \\ R_2 + R_4 \rightarrow R_4 \end{array} \left[\begin{array}{cccc|c} 1 & 0 & 1 & 4 & 262 \\ 0 & 1 & 0 & -3 & 0 \\ 0 & 0 & 1 & -1 & -3 \\ 0 & 0 & -46 & -4 & -262 \end{array}\right]$$

$$\begin{array}{r} -1R_3 + R_1 \rightarrow R_1 \\ \\ \\ 46R_3 + R_4 \rightarrow R_4 \end{array} \left[\begin{array}{cccc|c} 1 & 0 & 0 & 5 & 265 \\ 0 & 1 & 0 & -3 & 0 \\ 0 & 0 & 1 & -1 & -3 \\ 0 & 0 & 0 & -50 & -400 \end{array}\right]$$

$$\begin{array}{r} R_4 + 10R_1 \rightarrow R_1 \\ -3R_4 + 50R_2 \rightarrow R_2 \\ -1R_4 + 50R_3 \rightarrow R_3 \\ \\ \end{array} \left[\begin{array}{cccc|c} 10 & 0 & 0 & 0 & 2250 \\ 0 & 50 & 0 & 0 & 1200 \\ 0 & 0 & 50 & 0 & 250 \\ 0 & 0 & 0 & -50 & -400 \end{array}\right]$$

$$\begin{array}{r} \frac{1}{10}R_1 \rightarrow R_1 \\ \frac{1}{50}R_2 \rightarrow R_2 \\ \frac{1}{50}R_3 \rightarrow R_3 \\ -\frac{1}{50}R_4 \rightarrow R_4 \end{array} \left[\begin{array}{cccc|c} 1 & 0 & 0 & 0 & 225 \\ 0 & 1 & 0 & 0 & 24 \\ 0 & 0 & 1 & 0 & 5 \\ 0 & 0 & 0 & 1 & 8 \end{array}\right]$$

Ichiro Suzuki hit 225 singles, 24 doubles, 5 triples, and 8 home runs during the 2004 season.

2.3 Addition and Subtraction of Matrices

1. $\begin{bmatrix} 1 & 3 \\ 5 & 7 \end{bmatrix} = \begin{bmatrix} 1 & 5 \\ 3 & 7 \end{bmatrix}$

This statement is false, since not all corresponding elements are equal.

2. $\begin{bmatrix} 1 \\ 2 \\ 3 \end{bmatrix} = [1 \quad 2 \quad 3]$

This statement is false. For two matrices to be equal, they must be the same size, and each pair of corresponding elements must be equal. These two matrices are different sizes.

3. $\begin{bmatrix} x \\ y \end{bmatrix} = \begin{bmatrix} -2 \\ 8 \end{bmatrix}$ if $x = -2$ and $y = 8$.

This statement is true. The matrices are the same size and corresponding elements are equal.

4. $\begin{bmatrix} 3 & 5 & 2 & 8 \\ 1 & -1 & 4 & 0 \end{bmatrix}$ is a 4×2 matrix.

This statement is false. Since the matrix has 2 rows and 4 columns, it is a 2×4 matrix.

5. $\begin{bmatrix} 1 & 9 & -4 \\ 3 & 7 & 2 \\ -1 & 1 & 0 \end{bmatrix}$ is a square matrix.

This statement is true. The matrix has 3 rows and 3 columns.

6. $\begin{bmatrix} 2 & 4 & -1 \\ 3 & 7 & 5 \\ 0 & 0 & 0 \end{bmatrix} = \begin{bmatrix} 2 & 4 & -1 \\ 3 & 7 & 5 \end{bmatrix}$

This statement is false since the matrices are different sizes.

7. $\begin{bmatrix} -4 & 8 \\ 2 & 3 \end{bmatrix}$ is a 2×2 square matrix.

Its additive inverse is $\begin{bmatrix} 4 & -8 \\ -2 & -3 \end{bmatrix}$.

8. $\begin{bmatrix} 2 & -3 & 7 \\ 1 & 0 & 4 \end{bmatrix}$

This matrix has 2 rows and 3 columns, so it is a 2×3 matrix. The additive inverse is

$$\begin{bmatrix} -2 & 3 & -7 \\ -1 & 0 & -4 \end{bmatrix}.$$

9. $\begin{bmatrix} -6 & 8 & 0 & 0 \\ 4 & 1 & 9 & 2 \\ 3 & -5 & 7 & 1 \end{bmatrix}$ is a 3×4 matrix.

Its additive inverse is

$$\begin{bmatrix} 6 & -8 & 0 & 0 \\ -4 & -1 & -9 & -2 \\ -3 & 5 & -7 & -1 \end{bmatrix}.$$

10. $\begin{bmatrix} 8 & -2 & 4 & 6 & 3 \end{bmatrix}$

The matrix has 1 row and 5 columns, so it is a 1×5 matrix. It is a row matrix since it has only 1 row. The additive inverse is

$$\begin{bmatrix} -8 & 2 & -4 & -6 & -3 \end{bmatrix}.$$

11. $\begin{bmatrix} -7 \\ 5 \end{bmatrix}$ is a 2×1 column matrix.

Its additive inverse is

$$\begin{bmatrix} 7 \\ -5 \end{bmatrix}.$$

12. $[-9]$

This matrix has 1 row and 1 column, so it is a 1×1 square matrix. It is also a row matrix since it has only 1 row, and a column matrix because it has only 1 column. The additive inverse is $[9]$.

13. The sum of an $n \times m$ matrix and its additive inverse is the $n \times m$ zero matrix.

14. Since A is a 5×2 matrix, and since A and K can be added, we know that K is also a 5×2 matrix. Also, since $A + K = A$, all entries of K must be 0.

15. $\begin{bmatrix} 3 & 4 \\ -8 & 1 \end{bmatrix} = \begin{bmatrix} 3 & x \\ y & z \end{bmatrix}$

Corresponding elements must be equal for the matrices to be equal. Therefore, $x = 4, y = -8$, and $z = 1$.

16. $\begin{bmatrix} -5 \\ y \end{bmatrix} = \begin{bmatrix} -5 \\ 8 \end{bmatrix}$

Two matrices can be equal only if they are the same size and corresponding elements are equal. These matrices will be equal if $y = 8$.

17. $\begin{bmatrix} s-4 & t+2 \\ -5 & 7 \end{bmatrix} = \begin{bmatrix} 6 & 2 \\ -5 & r \end{bmatrix}$

Corresponding elements must be equal

$$\begin{aligned} s - 4 &= 6 & t + 2 &= 2 & r &= 7. \\ s &= 10 & t &= 0 \end{aligned}$$

Thus, $s = 10, t = 0$, and $r = 7$.

18. $\begin{bmatrix} 9 & 7 \\ r & 0 \end{bmatrix} = \begin{bmatrix} m-3 & n+5 \\ 8 & 0 \end{bmatrix}$

The matrices are the same size, so they will be equal if corresponding elements are equal.

$$\begin{aligned} 9 &= m - 3 & 7 &= n + 5 & r &= 8 \\ 12 &= m & 2 &= n \end{aligned}$$

Thus, $m = 12$, $n = 2$, and $r = 8$.

19. $\begin{bmatrix} a+2 & 3b & 4c \\ d & 7f & 8 \end{bmatrix} + \begin{bmatrix} -7 & 2b & 6 \\ -3d & -6 & -2 \end{bmatrix} = \begin{bmatrix} 15 & 25 & 6 \\ -8 & 1 & 6 \end{bmatrix}$

Add the two matrices on the left side to obtain

$$\begin{bmatrix} a+2 & 3b & 4c \\ d & 7f & 8 \end{bmatrix} + \begin{bmatrix} -7 & 2b & 6 \\ -3d & -6 & -2 \end{bmatrix}$$

$$= \begin{bmatrix} (a+2)+(-7) & 3b+2b & 4c+6 \\ d+(-3d) & 7f+(-6) & 8+(-2) \end{bmatrix}$$

$$= \begin{bmatrix} a-5 & 5b & 4c+6 \\ -2d & 7f-6 & 6 \end{bmatrix}$$

Corresponding elements of this matrix and the matrix on the right side of the original equation must be equal.

$$\begin{aligned} a - 5 &= 15 & 5b &= 25 & 4c + 6 &= 6 \\ a &= 20 & b &= 5 & c &= 0 \end{aligned}$$

$$\begin{aligned} -2d &= -8 & 7f - 6 &= 1 \\ d &= 4 & f &= 1 \end{aligned}$$

Thus, $a = 20, b = 5, c = 0, d = 4$, and $f = 1$.

20. $\begin{bmatrix} a+2 & 3z+1 & 5m \\ 4k & 0 & 3 \end{bmatrix} + \begin{bmatrix} 3a & 2z & 5m \\ 2k & 5 & 6 \end{bmatrix}$

$$= \begin{bmatrix} 10 & -14 & 80 \\ 10 & 5 & 9 \end{bmatrix}$$

$$\begin{bmatrix} 4a+2 & 5z+1 & 10m \\ 6k & 5 & 9 \end{bmatrix}$$

$$= \begin{bmatrix} 10 & -14 & 80 \\ 10 & 5 & 9 \end{bmatrix}$$

$$\begin{aligned} 4a + 2 &= 10 & 5z + 1 &= -14 \\ a &= 2 & z &= -3 \end{aligned}$$

$$\begin{aligned} 10m &= 80 & 6k &= 10 \\ m &= 8 & k &= \frac{5}{3} \end{aligned}$$

Thus, $a = 2$, $z = -3$, $m = 8$, and $k = \frac{5}{3}$.

21. $\begin{bmatrix} 2 & 4 & 5 & -7 \\ 6 & -3 & 12 & 0 \end{bmatrix} + \begin{bmatrix} 8 & 0 & -10 & 1 \\ -2 & 8 & -9 & 11 \end{bmatrix}$

$$= \begin{bmatrix} 2+8 & 4+0 & 5+(-10) & -7+1 \\ 6+(-2) & -3+8 & 12+(-9) & 0+11 \end{bmatrix}$$

$$= \begin{bmatrix} 10 & 4 & -5 & -6 \\ 4 & 5 & 3 & 11 \end{bmatrix}$$

22. $\begin{bmatrix} 1 & 5 \\ 2 & -3 \\ 3 & 7 \end{bmatrix} + \begin{bmatrix} 2 & 3 \\ 8 & 5 \\ -1 & 9 \end{bmatrix} = \begin{bmatrix} 1+2 & 5+3 \\ 2+8 & -3+5 \\ 3+(-1) & 7+9 \end{bmatrix}$

$$= \begin{bmatrix} 3 & 8 \\ 10 & 2 \\ 2 & 16 \end{bmatrix}$$

23. $\begin{bmatrix} 1 & 3 & -2 \\ 4 & 7 & 1 \end{bmatrix} + \begin{bmatrix} 3 & 0 \\ 6 & 4 \\ -5 & 2 \end{bmatrix}$

These matrices cannot be added since the first matrix has size 2×3, while the second has size 3×2. Only matrices that are the same size can be added.

24. $\begin{bmatrix} 8 & 0 & -3 \\ 1 & 19 & -5 \end{bmatrix} - \begin{bmatrix} 1 & -5 & 2 \\ 3 & 9 & -8 \end{bmatrix}$

$$= \begin{bmatrix} 8 & 0 & -3 \\ 1 & 19 & -5 \end{bmatrix} + \begin{bmatrix} -1 & 5 & -2 \\ -3 & -9 & 8 \end{bmatrix}$$

$$= \begin{bmatrix} 7 & 5 & -5 \\ -2 & 10 & 3 \end{bmatrix}$$

25. The matrices have the same size, so the subtraction can be done. Let A and B represent the given matrices. Using the definition of subtraction, we have

$$A - B = A + (-B)$$

$$= \begin{bmatrix} 2 & 8 & 12 & 0 \\ 7 & 4 & -1 & 5 \\ 1 & 2 & 0 & 10 \end{bmatrix} + \begin{bmatrix} -1 & -3 & -6 & -9 \\ -2 & 3 & 3 & -4 \\ -8 & 0 & 2 & -17 \end{bmatrix}$$

$$= \begin{bmatrix} 1 & 5 & 6 & -9 \\ 5 & 7 & 2 & 1 \\ -7 & 2 & 2 & -7 \end{bmatrix}.$$

26. $\begin{bmatrix} 2 & 1 \\ 5 & -3 \\ -7 & 2 \\ 9 & 0 \end{bmatrix} + \begin{bmatrix} 1 & -8 & 0 \\ 5 & 3 & 2 \\ -6 & 7 & -5 \\ 2 & -1 & 0 \end{bmatrix}$

This operation is not possible because the matrices are different sizes. Only matrices of the same size can be added.

27. $\begin{bmatrix} 2 & 3 \\ -2 & 4 \end{bmatrix} + \begin{bmatrix} 4 & 3 \\ 7 & 8 \end{bmatrix} - \begin{bmatrix} 3 & 2 \\ 1 & 4 \end{bmatrix}$

$$= \begin{bmatrix} 2+4-3 & 3+3-2 \\ -2+7-1 & 4+8-4 \end{bmatrix} = \begin{bmatrix} 3 & 4 \\ 4 & 8 \end{bmatrix}$$

28. $\begin{bmatrix} 4 & 3 \\ 1 & 2 \end{bmatrix} - \begin{bmatrix} 1 & 1 \\ 1 & 0 \end{bmatrix} + \begin{bmatrix} 1 & 1 \\ 1 & 4 \end{bmatrix}$

$$= \begin{bmatrix} 4 & 3 \\ 1 & 2 \end{bmatrix} + \begin{bmatrix} -1 & -1 \\ -1 & 0 \end{bmatrix} + \begin{bmatrix} 1 & 1 \\ 1 & 4 \end{bmatrix}$$

$$= \begin{bmatrix} 4+(-1)+1 & 3+(-1)+1 \\ 1+(-1)+1 & 2+0+4 \end{bmatrix}$$

$$= \begin{bmatrix} 4 & 3 \\ 1 & 6 \end{bmatrix}$$

29. $\begin{bmatrix} 2 & -1 \\ 0 & 13 \end{bmatrix} - \begin{bmatrix} 4 & 8 \\ -5 & 7 \end{bmatrix} + \begin{bmatrix} 12 & 7 \\ 5 & 3 \end{bmatrix}$

$$= \begin{bmatrix} 2 & -1 \\ 0 & 13 \end{bmatrix} + \begin{bmatrix} -4 & -8 \\ 5 & -7 \end{bmatrix} + \begin{bmatrix} 12 & 7 \\ 5 & 3 \end{bmatrix}$$

$$= \begin{bmatrix} 2+(-4)+12 & -1+(-8)+7 \\ 0+5+5 & 13+(-7)+3 \end{bmatrix}$$

$$= \begin{bmatrix} 10 & -2 \\ 10 & 9 \end{bmatrix}$$

30. $\begin{bmatrix} 5 & 8 \\ -3 & 1 \end{bmatrix} + \begin{bmatrix} 0 & 1 \\ -2 & -2 \end{bmatrix} + \begin{bmatrix} -5 & -8 \\ 6 & 1 \end{bmatrix}$

$$= \begin{bmatrix} 5+0+(-5) & 8+1+(-8) \\ -3+(-2)+6 & 1+(-2)+1 \end{bmatrix}$$

$$= \begin{bmatrix} 0 & 1 \\ 1 & 0 \end{bmatrix}$$

31. $\begin{bmatrix} -4x+2y & -3x+y \\ 6x-3y & 2x-5y \end{bmatrix} + \begin{bmatrix} -8x+6y & 2x \\ 3y-5x & 6x+4y \end{bmatrix}$

$$= \begin{bmatrix} (-4x+2y)+(-8x+6y) & (-3x+y)+2x \\ (6x-3y)+(3y-5x) & (2x-5y)+(6x+4y) \end{bmatrix}$$

$$= \begin{bmatrix} -12x+8y & -x+y \\ x & 8x-y \end{bmatrix}$$

32. $\begin{bmatrix} 4k-8y \\ 6z-3x \\ 2k+5a \\ -4m+2n \end{bmatrix} - \begin{bmatrix} 5k+6y \\ 2z+5x \\ 4k+6a \\ 4m-2n \end{bmatrix}$

$$= \begin{bmatrix} 4k-8y \\ 6z-3x \\ 2k+5a \\ -4m+2n \end{bmatrix} + \begin{bmatrix} -5k-6y \\ -2z-5x \\ -4k-6a \\ -4m+2n \end{bmatrix}$$

$$= \begin{bmatrix} -k-14y \\ 4z-8x \\ -2k-a \\ -8m+4n \end{bmatrix}$$

33. The additive inverse of

$$X = \begin{bmatrix} x & y \\ z & w \end{bmatrix}$$

is

$$-X = \begin{bmatrix} -x & -y \\ -z & -w \end{bmatrix}.$$

34. Verify that $X+T=T+X$.

$$X+T = \begin{bmatrix} x+r & y+s \\ z+t & w+u \end{bmatrix}$$

$$T+X = \begin{bmatrix} r+x & s+y \\ t+z & u+w \end{bmatrix}$$

Because of the commutative property for addition of real numbers, $x+r=r+x$. This also applies to the other corresponding elements, so we conclude that $T+X=X+T$.

35. Show that $X+(T+P)=(X+T)+P$.

On the left side, the sum $T+P$ is obtained first, and then

$$X+(T+P).$$

This gives the matrix

$$\begin{bmatrix} x+(r+m) & y+(s+n) \\ z+(t+p) & w+(u+q) \end{bmatrix}.$$

For the right side, first the sum $X+T$ is obtained, and then

$$(X+T)+P.$$

This gives the matrix

$$\begin{bmatrix} (x+r)+m & (y+s)+n \\ (z+t)+p & (w+u)+q \end{bmatrix}.$$

Comparing corresponding elements, we see that they are equal by the associative property of addition of real numbers. Thus,

$$X+(T+P)=(X+T)+P.$$

36. Verify that $X+(-X)=O$.

$$X+(-X) = \begin{bmatrix} x & y \\ z & w \end{bmatrix} + \begin{bmatrix} -x & -y \\ -z & -w \end{bmatrix}$$

$$= \begin{bmatrix} x+(-x) & y+(-y) \\ z+(-z) & w+(-w) \end{bmatrix}$$

$$= \begin{bmatrix} 0 & 0 \\ 0 & 0 \end{bmatrix} = O$$

37. Show that $P+O=P$.

$$P+O = \begin{bmatrix} m & n \\ p & q \end{bmatrix} + \begin{bmatrix} 0 & 0 \\ 0 & 0 \end{bmatrix}$$

$$= \begin{bmatrix} m+0 & n+0 \\ p+0 & q+0 \end{bmatrix}$$

$$= \begin{bmatrix} m & n \\ p & q \end{bmatrix}$$

$$= P$$

Thus, $P+O=P$.

38. All of these properties are valid for matrices that are not square, as long as all necessary sums exist. The sizes of all matrices in each equation must be the same.

39. (a) The production cost matrix for Chicago is

$$\begin{array}{r} \\ \text{Material} \\ \text{Labor} \end{array} \begin{array}{c} \text{Phones} \quad \text{Calculators} \\ \begin{bmatrix} 4.05 & 7.01 \\ 3.27 & 3.51 \end{bmatrix} \end{array}.$$

The production cost matrix for Seattle is

$$\begin{array}{r} \\ \text{Material} \\ \text{Labor} \end{array} \begin{array}{c} \text{Phones} \quad \text{Calculators} \\ \begin{bmatrix} 4.40 & 6.90 \\ 3.54 & 3.76 \end{bmatrix} \end{array}.$$

(b) The new production cost matrix for Chicago is

$$\begin{array}{r} \\ \text{Material} \\ \text{Labor} \end{array} \begin{array}{c} \text{Phones} \qquad \text{Calculators} \\ \begin{bmatrix} 4.05+0.37 & 7.01+0.42 \\ 3.27+0.11 & 3.51+0.11 \end{bmatrix} \end{array}$$

or

$$\begin{bmatrix} 4.42 & 7.43 \\ 3.38 & 3.62 \end{bmatrix}.$$

40. (a)

$$\begin{array}{l} \\ \text{Bread} \\ \text{Milk} \\ \text{PB} \\ \text{Cold cuts} \end{array} \begin{array}{c} \begin{array}{ccc} \text{I} & \text{II} & \text{III} \end{array} \\ \begin{bmatrix} 88 & 105 & 60 \\ 48 & 72 & 40 \\ 16 & 21 & 0 \\ 112 & 147 & 50 \end{bmatrix} \end{array}$$

(b)

$$\begin{bmatrix} 88+0.25(88) & 105+\frac{1}{3}(105) & 60+0.1(60) \\ 48+0.25(48) & 72+\frac{1}{3}(72) & 40+0.1(40) \\ 16+0.25(16) & 21+\frac{1}{3}(21) & 0+0.1(0) \\ 112+0.25(112) & 147+\frac{1}{3}(147) & 50+0.1(50) \end{bmatrix} = \begin{bmatrix} 110 & 140 & 66 \\ 60 & 96 & 44 \\ 20 & 28 & 0 \\ 140 & 196 & 55 \end{bmatrix}$$

(c) Add the final matrices from parts (a) and (b).

$$\begin{bmatrix} 88 & 105 & 60 \\ 48 & 72 & 40 \\ 16 & 21 & 0 \\ 112 & 147 & 50 \end{bmatrix} + \begin{bmatrix} 110 & 140 & 66 \\ 60 & 96 & 44 \\ 20 & 28 & 0 \\ 140 & 196 & 55 \end{bmatrix} = \begin{bmatrix} 198 & 245 & 126 \\ 108 & 168 & 84 \\ 36 & 49 & 0 \\ 252 & 343 & 105 \end{bmatrix}$$

41. (a) There are four food groups and three meals. To represent the data by a 3×4 matrix, we must use the rows to correspond to the meals, breakfast, lunch, and dinner, and the columns to correspond to the four food groups. Thus, we obtain the matrix

$$\begin{bmatrix} 2 & 1 & 2 & 1 \\ 3 & 2 & 2 & 1 \\ 4 & 3 & 2 & 1 \end{bmatrix}.$$

(b) There are four food groups. These will correspond to the four rows. There are three components in each food group: fat, carbohydrates, and protein. These will correspond to the three columns. The matrix is

$$\begin{bmatrix} 5 & 0 & 7 \\ 0 & 10 & 1 \\ 0 & 15 & 2 \\ 10 & 12 & 8 \end{bmatrix}.$$

(c) The matrix is

$$\begin{bmatrix} 8 \\ 4 \\ 5 \end{bmatrix}.$$

42. (a)

$$\begin{array}{l} \text{Length} \\ \text{Weight} \end{array} \begin{bmatrix} 5.6 & 6.4 & 6.9 & 7.6 & 6.1 \\ 144 & 138 & 149 & 152 & 146 \end{bmatrix}$$

(b)

$$\begin{array}{l} \text{Length} \\ \text{Weight} \end{array} \begin{bmatrix} 10.2 & 11.4 & 11.4 & 12.7 & 10.8 \\ 196 & 196 & 225 & 250 & 230 \end{bmatrix}$$

(c) Subtract the matrix in part (a) from the one in part (b).

$$\begin{bmatrix} 10.2 & 11.4 & 11.4 & 12.7 & 10.8 \\ 196 & 196 & 225 & 250 & 230 \end{bmatrix} - \begin{bmatrix} 5.6 & 6.4 & 6.9 & 7.6 & 6.1 \\ 144 & 138 & 149 & 152 & 146 \end{bmatrix}$$

$$= \begin{bmatrix} 4.6 & 5.0 & 4.5 & 5.1 & 4.7 \\ 52 & 58 & 76 & 98 & 84 \end{bmatrix} \begin{array}{l} \text{Change in length} \\ \text{Change in weight} \end{array}$$

(d) Add the new matrix to the one from part (b).

$$\begin{bmatrix} 10.2 & 11.4 & 11.4 & 12.7 & 10.8 \\ 196 & 196 & 225 & 250 & 230 \end{bmatrix} + \begin{bmatrix} 1.8 & 1.5 & 2.3 & 1.8 & 2.0 \\ 25 & 22 & 29 & 33 & 20 \end{bmatrix}$$

$$= \begin{bmatrix} 12.0 & 12.9 & 13.7 & 14.5 & 12.8 \\ 221 & 218 & 254 & 283 & 250 \end{bmatrix} \begin{matrix} \text{Final length} \\ \text{Final weight} \end{matrix}$$

43.

$$\begin{matrix} & \text{Obtained Pain Relief} & \\ & \text{Yes} & \text{No} \\ \text{Painfree} & \left[\begin{matrix} 22 \\ 8 \end{matrix}\right. & \left.\begin{matrix} 3 \\ 17 \end{matrix}\right] \\ \text{Placebo} & & \end{matrix}$$

(a) Of the 25 patients who took the placebo, 8 got relief.

(b) Of the 25 patients who took Painfree, 3 got no relief.

(c) $\begin{bmatrix} 22 & 3 \\ 8 & 17 \end{bmatrix} + \begin{bmatrix} 21 & 4 \\ 6 & 19 \end{bmatrix} + \begin{bmatrix} 19 & 6 \\ 10 & 15 \end{bmatrix} + \begin{bmatrix} 23 & 2 \\ 3 & 22 \end{bmatrix} = \begin{bmatrix} 85 & 15 \\ 27 & 73 \end{bmatrix}$

(d) Yes, it appears that Painfree is effective. Of the 100 patients who took the medication, 85% got relief.

44. (a) The matrix for the driving of male drivers is

$$\begin{matrix} & \text{Percentage of Males} \\ \begin{matrix} \text{Rarely or never wore seatbelts} \\ \text{Rode with drinking driver} \\ \text{Drove after drinking} \end{matrix} & \begin{bmatrix} 23.2 & 20.8 & 18.1 & 21.5 \\ 38.3 & 34.4 & 31.8 & 29.2 \\ 27.9 & 25.5 & 24.6 & 22.4 \end{bmatrix} \end{matrix}.$$

(b) The matrix for the driving habits of female drivers is

$$\begin{matrix} & \text{Percentage of Females} \\ \begin{matrix} \text{Rarely or never wore seatbelts} \\ \text{Rode with drinking driver} \\ \text{Drove after drinking} \end{matrix} & \begin{bmatrix} 14.5 & 11.9 & 10.2 & 14.6 \\ 34.5 & 31.7 & 29.6 & 31.1 \\ 16.2 & 13.3 & 14.1 & 12.3 \end{bmatrix} \end{matrix}.$$

(c) The matrix showing the difference between the driving habits of male and female drivers is

$$\begin{matrix} & \text{Percentage of Females} \\ \begin{matrix} \text{Rarely or never wore seatbelts} \\ \text{Rode with drinking driver} \\ \text{Drove after drinking} \end{matrix} & \begin{bmatrix} 8.7 & 8.9 & 7.9 & 6.9 \\ 3.8 & 2.7 & 2.2 & -1.9 \\ 11.7 & 12.2 & 10.5 & 10.1 \end{bmatrix} \end{matrix}.$$

45. (a) The matrix for the life expectancy of African Americans is

$$\begin{matrix} & \text{M} \quad\quad \text{F} \\ \begin{matrix} 1970 \\ 1980 \\ 1990 \\ 2000 \end{matrix} & \begin{bmatrix} 60.0 & 68.3 \\ 63.8 & 72.5 \\ 64.5 & 73.6 \\ 68.2 & 74.9 \end{bmatrix} \end{matrix}$$

(b) The matrix for the life expectancy of White Americans is

$$\begin{matrix} & \text{M} \quad\quad \text{F} \\ \begin{matrix} 1970 \\ 1980 \\ 1990 \\ 2000 \end{matrix} & \begin{bmatrix} 68.0 & 75.6 \\ 70.7 & 78.1 \\ 72.7 & 79.4 \\ 74.8 & 80.0 \end{bmatrix} \end{matrix}$$

(c) The matrix showing the difference between the life expectancy between the two groups is

$$\begin{bmatrix} 60.0 & 68.3 \\ 63.8 & 72.5 \\ 64.5 & 73.6 \\ 68.2 & 74.9 \end{bmatrix} - \begin{bmatrix} 68.0 & 75.6 \\ 70.7 & 78.1 \\ 72.7 & 79.4 \\ 74.8 & 80.0 \end{bmatrix}$$

$$= \begin{bmatrix} 60.0 & 68.3 \\ 63.8 & 72.5 \\ 64.5 & 73.6 \\ 68.2 & 74.9 \end{bmatrix} + \begin{bmatrix} -68.0 & -75.6 \\ -70.7 & -78.1 \\ -72.7 & -79.4 \\ -74.8 & -80.0 \end{bmatrix}$$

$$= \begin{bmatrix} -8.0 & -7.3 \\ -6.9 & -5.6 \\ -8.2 & -5.8 \\ -6.6 & -5.1 \end{bmatrix}$$

46. (a) The matrix for the educational attainment of males is

	4 Years of High School or More	4 Years of College or More
1960	39.5	9.7
1970	51.9	13.5
1980	67.3	20.1
1990	77.7	24.4
2000	84.2	27.8
2004	84.8	29.4

(b) The matrix for the educational attainment of females is

	4 Years of High School or More	4 Years of College or More
1960	42.5	5.8
1970	52.8	8.1
1980	65.8	12.8
1990	77.5	18.4
2000	84.0	23.6
2004	85.4	26.1

(c) The matrix showing how much more (or less) education males have attained than females is

$$\begin{bmatrix} 39.5 & 9.7 \\ 51.9 & 13.5 \\ 67.3 & 20.1 \\ 77.7 & 24.4 \\ 84.2 & 27.8 \\ 84.8 & 29.4 \end{bmatrix} - \begin{bmatrix} 42.5 & 5.8 \\ 52.8 & 8.1 \\ 65.8 & 12.8 \\ 77.5 & 18.4 \\ 84.0 & 23.6 \\ 85.4 & 26.1 \end{bmatrix}$$

$$= \begin{bmatrix} 39.5 & 9.7 \\ 51.9 & 13.5 \\ 67.3 & 20.1 \\ 77.7 & 24.4 \\ 84.2 & 27.8 \\ 84.8 & 29.4 \end{bmatrix} + \begin{bmatrix} -42.5 & -5.8 \\ -52.8 & -8.1 \\ -65.8 & -12.8 \\ -77.5 & -18.4 \\ -84.0 & -23.6 \\ -85.4 & -2.61 \end{bmatrix}$$

$$= \begin{bmatrix} -3.0 & 3.9 \\ -0.9 & 5.4 \\ 1.5 & 7.3 \\ 0.2 & 6.0 \\ 0.2 & 4.2 \\ -0.6 & 3.3 \end{bmatrix}$$

47. (a) The matrix for the educational attainment of African Americans is

	Four Years of High School or More	Four Years of College or More
1980	51.4	7.9
1985	59.9	11.1
1990	66.2	11.3
1995	73.8	13.3
2000	78.9	16.6
2004	80.6	17.6

(b) The matrix for the educational attainment of Hispanic Americans is

	Four Years of High School or More	Four Years of College or More
1980	44.5	7.6
1985	47.9	8.5
1990	50.8	9.2
1995	53.4	9.3
2000	57.0	10.6
2004	58.4	12.1

(c) The matrix showing the difference in the educational attainment between African and Hispanic Americans is

$$\begin{bmatrix} 51.4 & 7.9 \\ 59.9 & 11.1 \\ 66.2 & 11.3 \\ 73.8 & 13.3 \\ 78.9 & 16.6 \\ 80.6 & 17.6 \end{bmatrix} - \begin{bmatrix} 44.5 & 7.6 \\ 47.9 & 8.5 \\ 50.8 & 9.2 \\ 53.4 & 9.3 \\ 57.0 & 10.6 \\ 58.4 & 12.1 \end{bmatrix}$$

$$= \begin{bmatrix} 51.4 & 7.9 \\ 59.9 & 11.1 \\ 66.2 & 11.3 \\ 73.8 & 13.3 \\ 78.9 & 16.6 \\ 80.6 & 17.6 \end{bmatrix} + \begin{bmatrix} -44.5 & -7.6 \\ -47.9 & -8.5 \\ -50.8 & -9.2 \\ -53.4 & -9.3 \\ -57.0 & -10.6 \\ -58.4 & -12.1 \end{bmatrix}$$

$$= \begin{bmatrix} 6.9 & 0.3 \\ 12.0 & 2.6 \\ 15.4 & 2.1 \\ 20.4 & 4.0 \\ 21.9 & 6.0 \\ 22.2 & 5.5 \end{bmatrix}.$$

48. (a)

$$\begin{array}{c|cccc} & \text{M} & \text{J} & \text{Ca} & \text{Cl} \\ \hline \text{M} & 1 & 1 & 1 & 1 \\ \text{J} & 0 & 1 & 0 & 0 \\ \text{Ca} & 0 & 1 & 1 & 1 \\ \text{Cl} & 0 & 1 & 1 & 1 \end{array}$$

(b) Rows 1 and 2 will stay the same. Since the cats now like Musk, the zeros in rows 3 and 4 change to ones.

$$\begin{array}{c|cccc} & \text{M} & \text{J} & \text{Ca} & \text{Cl} \\ \hline \text{M} & 1 & 1 & 1 & 1 \\ \text{J} & 0 & 1 & 0 & 0 \\ \text{Ca} & 1 & 1 & 1 & 1 \\ \text{Cl} & 1 & 1 & 1 & 1 \end{array}$$

2.4 Multiplication of Matrices

In Exercises 1-6, let

$$A = \begin{bmatrix} -2 & 4 \\ 0 & 3 \end{bmatrix} \text{ and } B = \begin{bmatrix} -6 & 2 \\ 4 & 0 \end{bmatrix}.$$

1. $2A = 2\begin{bmatrix} -2 & 4 \\ 0 & 3 \end{bmatrix} = \begin{bmatrix} -4 & 8 \\ 0 & 6 \end{bmatrix}$

2. $-3B = -3\begin{bmatrix} -6 & 2 \\ 4 & 0 \end{bmatrix} = \begin{bmatrix} 18 & -6 \\ -12 & 0 \end{bmatrix}$

3. $-6A = -6\begin{bmatrix} -2 & 4 \\ 0 & 3 \end{bmatrix} = \begin{bmatrix} 12 & -24 \\ 0 & -18 \end{bmatrix}$

4. $5B = 5\begin{bmatrix} -6 & 2 \\ 4 & 0 \end{bmatrix} = \begin{bmatrix} -30 & 10 \\ 20 & 0 \end{bmatrix}$

5. $-4A + 5B = -4\begin{bmatrix} -2 & 4 \\ 0 & 3 \end{bmatrix} + 5\begin{bmatrix} -6 & 2 \\ 4 & 0 \end{bmatrix}$

$$= \begin{bmatrix} 8 & -16 \\ 0 & -12 \end{bmatrix} + \begin{bmatrix} -30 & 10 \\ 20 & 0 \end{bmatrix}$$

$$= \begin{bmatrix} -22 & -6 \\ 20 & -12 \end{bmatrix}$$

6. $7B - 3A = 7\begin{bmatrix} -6 & 2 \\ 4 & 0 \end{bmatrix} - 3\begin{bmatrix} -2 & 4 \\ 0 & 3 \end{bmatrix}$

$$= \begin{bmatrix} -42 & 14 \\ 28 & 0 \end{bmatrix} - \begin{bmatrix} -6 & 12 \\ 0 & 9 \end{bmatrix}$$

$$= \begin{bmatrix} -42 & 14 \\ 28 & 0 \end{bmatrix} + \begin{bmatrix} 6 & -12 \\ 0 & -9 \end{bmatrix}$$

$$= \begin{bmatrix} -36 & 2 \\ 28 & -9 \end{bmatrix}$$

7. Matrix A size $2 \times \underline{2}$ Matrix B size $\underline{2} \times 2$

The number of columns of A is the same as the number of rows of B, so the product AB exists. The size of the matrix AB is 2×2.

Matrix B size $2 \times \underline{2}$ Matrix A size $\underline{2} \times 2$

Since the number of columns of B is the same as the number of rows of A, the product BA also exists and has size 2×2.

8. A is 3×3, and B is 3×3.

The number of columns of A is the same as the number of rows of B, so the product AB exists; its size is 3×3. The number of columns of B is the same as the number of rows of A, so the product BA also exists; its size is 3×3.

9. Matrix A size Matrix B size

$3 \times \underline{\mathbf{4}}$ $\underline{\mathbf{4}} \times 4$

Since matrix A has 4 columns and matrix B has 4 rows, the product AB exists and has size 3×4.

Matrix B size Matrix A size

$4 \times \underline{\mathbf{4}}$ $\underline{\mathbf{3}} \times 4$

Since B has 4 columns and A has 3 rows, the product BA does not exist.

10. Matrix A size Matrix B size

$4 \times \underline{\mathbf{3}}$ $\underline{\mathbf{3}} \times 6$

Since the number of columns of A, 3, is the same as the number of rows of B, 3, the product AB exists. Its size is 4×6.

Matrix B size Matrix A size

$3 \times \underline{\mathbf{6}}$ $\underline{\mathbf{4}} \times 3$

The product BA does not exist since the number of columns of B, 6, is not the same as the number of rows of A, 4.

11. Matrix A size Matrix B size

$4 \times \underline{\mathbf{2}}$ $\underline{\mathbf{3}} \times 4$

The number of columns of A is not the same as the number of rows of B, so the product AB does not exist.

Matrix B size Matrix A size

$3 \times \underline{\mathbf{4}}$ $\underline{\mathbf{4}} \times 2$

The number of columns of B is the same as the number of rows of A, so the product BA exists and has size 3×2.

12. A is 3×2, and B is 1×3.

The product AB does not exist, since the number of columns of A is not the same as the number of rows of B.

The product BA exists; its size is 1×2.

13. To find the product matrix AB, the number of *columns* of A must be the same as the number of *rows* of B.

14. The product matrix AB has the same number of *rows* as A and the same number of *columns* as B.

15. Call the first matrix A and the second matrix B. The product matrix AB will have size 2×1.

Step 1: Multiply the elements of the first row of A by the corresponding elements of the column of B and add.

$$\begin{bmatrix} \mathbf{2} & \mathbf{-1} \\ 5 & 8 \end{bmatrix} \begin{bmatrix} \mathbf{3} \\ \mathbf{-2} \end{bmatrix} \qquad 2(3) + (-1)(-2) = 8$$

Therefore, 8 is the first row entry of the product matrix AB.

Step 2: Multiply the elements of the second row of A by the corresponding elements of the column of B and add.

$$\begin{bmatrix} 2 & -1 \\ \mathbf{5} & \mathbf{8} \end{bmatrix} \begin{bmatrix} \mathbf{3} \\ \mathbf{-2} \end{bmatrix} \qquad 5(3) + 8(-2) = -1$$

The second row entry of the product is -1.

Step 3: Write the product using the two entries found above.

$$AB = \begin{bmatrix} 2 & -1 \\ 5 & 8 \end{bmatrix} \begin{bmatrix} 3 \\ -2 \end{bmatrix} = \begin{bmatrix} 8 \\ -1 \end{bmatrix}$$

16. $$\begin{bmatrix} -1 & 5 \\ 7 & 0 \end{bmatrix} \begin{bmatrix} 6 \\ 2 \end{bmatrix} = \begin{bmatrix} -1 \cdot 6 + 5 \cdot 2 \\ 7 \cdot 6 + 0 \cdot 2 \end{bmatrix} = \begin{bmatrix} 4 \\ 42 \end{bmatrix}$$

17. $$\begin{bmatrix} 2 & -1 & 7 \\ -3 & 0 & -4 \end{bmatrix} \begin{bmatrix} 5 \\ 10 \\ 2 \end{bmatrix}$$

$$= \begin{bmatrix} 2 \cdot 5 + (-1) \cdot 10 + 7 \cdot 2 \\ (-3) \cdot 5 + 0 \cdot 10 + (-4) \cdot 2 \end{bmatrix}$$

$$= \begin{bmatrix} 14 \\ -23 \end{bmatrix}$$

18. $$\begin{bmatrix} 5 & 2 \\ 7 & 6 \\ 1 & 0 \end{bmatrix} \begin{bmatrix} 1 & 4 & 0 \\ 2 & -1 & 2 \end{bmatrix}$$

$$= \begin{bmatrix} 5 \cdot 1 + 2 \cdot 2 & 5 \cdot 4 + 2(-1) & 5 \cdot 0 + 2 \cdot 2 \\ 7 \cdot 1 + 6 \cdot 2 & 7 \cdot 4 + 6(-1) & 7 \cdot 0 + 6 \cdot 2 \\ 1 \cdot 1 + 0 \cdot 2 & 1 \cdot 4 + 0(-1) & 1 \cdot 0 + 0 \cdot 2 \end{bmatrix}$$

$$= \begin{bmatrix} 9 & 18 & 4 \\ 19 & 22 & 12 \\ 1 & 4 & 0 \end{bmatrix}$$

19. $\begin{bmatrix} 2 & -1 \\ 3 & 6 \end{bmatrix} \begin{bmatrix} -1 & 0 & 4 \\ 5 & -2 & 0 \end{bmatrix} = \begin{bmatrix} 2\cdot(-1)+(-1)\cdot 5 & 2\cdot 0+(-1)\cdot(-2) & 2\cdot 4+(-1)\cdot 0 \\ 3\cdot(-1)+6\cdot 5 & 3\cdot 0+6\cdot(-2) & 3\cdot 4+6\cdot 0 \end{bmatrix} = \begin{bmatrix} -7 & 2 & 8 \\ 27 & -12 & 12 \end{bmatrix}$

20. $\begin{bmatrix} 6 & 0 & -4 \\ 1 & 2 & 5 \\ 10 & -1 & 3 \end{bmatrix} \begin{bmatrix} 1 \\ 2 \\ 0 \end{bmatrix} = \begin{bmatrix} 6\cdot 1+0\cdot 2+(-4)0 \\ 1\cdot 1+2\cdot 2+5\cdot 0 \\ 10\cdot 1+(-1)2+3\cdot 0 \end{bmatrix} = \begin{bmatrix} 6 \\ 5 \\ 8 \end{bmatrix}$

21. $\begin{bmatrix} 2 & 2 & -1 \\ 3 & 0 & 1 \end{bmatrix} \begin{bmatrix} 0 & 2 \\ -1 & 4 \\ 0 & 2 \end{bmatrix} = \begin{bmatrix} 2\cdot 0+2(-1)+(-1)0 & 2\cdot 2+2\cdot 4+(-1)2 \\ 3\cdot 0+0(-1)+1(0) & 3\cdot 2+0\cdot 4+1\cdot 2 \end{bmatrix} = \begin{bmatrix} -2 & 10 \\ 0 & 8 \end{bmatrix}$

22. $\begin{bmatrix} -3 & 1 & 0 \\ 6 & 0 & 8 \end{bmatrix} \begin{bmatrix} 3 \\ -1 \\ -2 \end{bmatrix} = \begin{bmatrix} (-3)\cdot 3+1\cdot(-1)+0\cdot(-2) \\ 6\cdot 3+0\cdot(-1)+8\cdot(-2) \end{bmatrix} = \begin{bmatrix} -10 \\ 2 \end{bmatrix}$

23. $\begin{bmatrix} 1 & 2 \\ 3 & 4 \end{bmatrix} \begin{bmatrix} -1 & 5 \\ 7 & 0 \end{bmatrix} = \begin{bmatrix} 1(-1)+2\cdot 7 & 1\cdot 5+2\cdot 0 \\ 3(-1)+4\cdot 7 & 3\cdot 5+4\cdot 0 \end{bmatrix} = \begin{bmatrix} 13 & 5 \\ 25 & 15 \end{bmatrix}$

24. $\begin{bmatrix} 2 & 8 \\ -7 & 5 \end{bmatrix} \begin{bmatrix} 1 & 0 \\ 0 & 1 \end{bmatrix} = \begin{bmatrix} 2\cdot 1+8\cdot 0 & 2\cdot 0+8\cdot 1 \\ (-7)\cdot 1+5\cdot 0 & (-7)\cdot 0+5\cdot 1 \end{bmatrix} = \begin{bmatrix} 2 & 8 \\ -7 & 5 \end{bmatrix}$

25. $\begin{bmatrix} -2 & -3 & 7 \\ 1 & 5 & 6 \end{bmatrix} \begin{bmatrix} 1 \\ 2 \\ 3 \end{bmatrix} = \begin{bmatrix} -2(1)+(-3)2+7\cdot 3 \\ 1\cdot 1+5\cdot 2+6\cdot 3 \end{bmatrix} = \begin{bmatrix} 13 \\ 29 \end{bmatrix}$

26. $\begin{bmatrix} 2 \\ -9 \\ 12 \end{bmatrix} \begin{bmatrix} 1 & 0 & -1 \end{bmatrix} = \begin{bmatrix} 2\cdot 1 & 2\cdot 0 & 2\cdot(-1) \\ (-9)\cdot 1 & (-9)\cdot 0 & (-9)\cdot(-1) \\ 12\cdot 1 & 12\cdot 0 & 12\cdot(-1) \end{bmatrix} = \begin{bmatrix} 2 & 0 & -2 \\ -9 & 0 & 9 \\ 12 & 0 & -12 \end{bmatrix}$

27. $\left(\begin{bmatrix} 2 & 1 \\ -3 & -6 \\ 4 & 0 \end{bmatrix} \begin{bmatrix} 1 & -2 \\ 2 & -1 \end{bmatrix} \right) \begin{bmatrix} 3 \\ 1 \end{bmatrix} = \begin{bmatrix} 4 & -5 \\ -15 & 12 \\ 4 & -8 \end{bmatrix} \begin{bmatrix} 3 \\ 1 \end{bmatrix} = \begin{bmatrix} 7 \\ -33 \\ 4 \end{bmatrix}$

28. $\begin{bmatrix} 2 & 1 \\ -3 & -6 \\ 4 & 0 \end{bmatrix} \left(\begin{bmatrix} 1 & -2 \\ 2 & -1 \end{bmatrix} \begin{bmatrix} 3 \\ 1 \end{bmatrix} \right) = \begin{bmatrix} 2 & 1 \\ -3 & -6 \\ 4 & 0 \end{bmatrix} \begin{bmatrix} 1 \\ 5 \end{bmatrix} = \begin{bmatrix} 7 \\ -33 \\ 4 \end{bmatrix}$

29. $\begin{bmatrix} 2 & -2 \\ 1 & -1 \end{bmatrix} \left(\begin{bmatrix} 4 & 3 \\ 1 & 2 \end{bmatrix} + \begin{bmatrix} 7 & 0 \\ -1 & 5 \end{bmatrix} \right) = \begin{bmatrix} 2 & -2 \\ 1 & -1 \end{bmatrix} \begin{bmatrix} 11 & 3 \\ 0 & 7 \end{bmatrix} = \begin{bmatrix} 22 & -8 \\ 11 & -4 \end{bmatrix}$

30. $\begin{bmatrix} 2 & -2 \\ 1 & -1 \end{bmatrix} \begin{bmatrix} 4 & 3 \\ 1 & 2 \end{bmatrix} + \begin{bmatrix} 2 & -2 \\ 1 & -1 \end{bmatrix} \begin{bmatrix} 7 & 0 \\ -1 & 5 \end{bmatrix} = \begin{bmatrix} 6 & 2 \\ 3 & 1 \end{bmatrix} + \begin{bmatrix} 16 & -10 \\ 8 & -5 \end{bmatrix} = \begin{bmatrix} 22 & -8 \\ 11 & -4 \end{bmatrix}$

31. **(a)** $AB = \begin{bmatrix} -2 & 4 \\ 1 & 3 \end{bmatrix}\begin{bmatrix} -2 & 1 \\ 3 & 6 \end{bmatrix} = \begin{bmatrix} 16 & 22 \\ 7 & 19 \end{bmatrix}$

(b) $BA = \begin{bmatrix} -2 & 1 \\ 3 & 6 \end{bmatrix}\begin{bmatrix} -2 & 4 \\ 1 & 3 \end{bmatrix} = \begin{bmatrix} 5 & -5 \\ 0 & 30 \end{bmatrix}$

(c) No, AB and BA are not equal here.

(d) No, AB does not always equal BA.

32. Verify that $(PX)T = P(XT)$.

$$(PX)T = \left(\begin{bmatrix} m & n \\ p & q \end{bmatrix}\begin{bmatrix} x & y \\ z & w \end{bmatrix}\right)\begin{bmatrix} r & s \\ t & u \end{bmatrix} = \begin{bmatrix} mx+nz & my+nw \\ px+qz & py+qw \end{bmatrix}\begin{bmatrix} r & s \\ t & u \end{bmatrix}$$
$$= \begin{bmatrix} (mx+nz)r+(my+nw)t & (mx+nz)s+(my+nw)u \\ (px+qz)r+(py+qw)t & (px+qz)s+(py+qw)u \end{bmatrix}$$
$$= \begin{bmatrix} mxr+nzr+myt+nwt & mxs+nzs+myu+nwu \\ pxr+qzr+pyt+qwt & pxs+qzs+pyu+qwu \end{bmatrix}$$

$$P(XT) = \begin{bmatrix} m & n \\ p & q \end{bmatrix}\left(\begin{bmatrix} x & y \\ z & w \end{bmatrix}\begin{bmatrix} r & s \\ t & u \end{bmatrix}\right) = \begin{bmatrix} m & n \\ p & q \end{bmatrix}\begin{bmatrix} xr+yt & xs+yu \\ zr+wt & zs+wu \end{bmatrix}$$
$$= \begin{bmatrix} m(xr+yt)+n(zr+wt) & m(xs+yu)+n(zs+wu) \\ p(xr+yt)+q(zr+wt) & p(xs+yu)+q(zs+wu) \end{bmatrix}$$
$$= \begin{bmatrix} mxr+myt+nzr+nwt & mxs+myu+nzs+nwu \\ pxr+pyt+qzr+qwt & pxs+pyu+qzs+qwu \end{bmatrix}$$
$$= \begin{bmatrix} mxr+nzr+myt+nwt & mxs+nzs+myu+nwu \\ pxr+qzr+pyt+qwt & pxs+qzs+pyu+qwu \end{bmatrix}$$

Thus, $(PX)T = P(XT)$.

33. Verify that $P(X+T) = PX + PT$.
Find $P(X+T)$ and $PX+PT$ separately and compare their values to see if they are the same.

$$P(X+T) = \begin{bmatrix} m & n \\ p & q \end{bmatrix}\left(\begin{bmatrix} x & y \\ z & w \end{bmatrix}+\begin{bmatrix} r & s \\ t & u \end{bmatrix}\right) = \begin{bmatrix} m & n \\ p & q \end{bmatrix}\left(\begin{bmatrix} x+r & y+s \\ z+t & w+u \end{bmatrix}\right)$$
$$= \begin{bmatrix} m(x+r)+n(z+t) & m(y+s)+n(w+u) \\ p(x+r)+q(z+t) & p(y+s)+q(w+u) \end{bmatrix} = \begin{bmatrix} mx+mr+nz+nt & my+ms+nw+nu \\ px+pr+qz+qt & py+ps+qw+qu \end{bmatrix}$$

$$PX+PT = \begin{bmatrix} m & n \\ p & q \end{bmatrix}\begin{bmatrix} x & y \\ z & w \end{bmatrix}+\begin{bmatrix} m & n \\ p & q \end{bmatrix}\begin{bmatrix} r & s \\ t & u \end{bmatrix} = \begin{bmatrix} mx+nz & my+nw \\ px+qz & py+qw \end{bmatrix}+\begin{bmatrix} mr+nt & ms+nu \\ pr+qt & ps+qu \end{bmatrix}$$
$$= \begin{bmatrix} (mx+nz)+(mr+nt) & (my+nw)+(ms+nu) \\ (px+qz)+(pr+qt) & (py+qw)+(ps+qu) \end{bmatrix} = \begin{bmatrix} mx+nz+mr+nt & my+nw+ms+nu \\ px+qz+pr+qt & py+qw+ps+qu \end{bmatrix}$$
$$= \begin{bmatrix} mx+mr+nz+nt & my+ms+nw+nu \\ px+pr+qz+qt & py+ps+qw+qu \end{bmatrix}$$

Observe that the two results are identical. Thus, $P(X+T) = PX + PT$.

34. Prove that $k(X+T) = kX + kT$ for any real number k.

$$k(X+T) = k\left(\begin{bmatrix} x & y \\ z & w \end{bmatrix} + \begin{bmatrix} r & s \\ t & u \end{bmatrix}\right)$$
$$= k\left(\begin{bmatrix} x+r & y+s \\ z+t & w+u \end{bmatrix}\right)$$
$$= \begin{bmatrix} k(x+r) & k(y+s) \\ k(z+t) & k(w+u) \end{bmatrix}$$
$$= \begin{bmatrix} kx+kr & ky+ks \\ kz+kt & kw+ku \end{bmatrix} \quad \textit{Distributive property for real numbers}$$
$$= \begin{bmatrix} kx & ky \\ kz & kw \end{bmatrix} + \begin{bmatrix} kr & ks \\ kt & ku \end{bmatrix}$$
$$= k\begin{bmatrix} x & y \\ z & w \end{bmatrix} + k\begin{bmatrix} r & s \\ t & u \end{bmatrix} = kX + kT$$

35. Verify that $(k+h)P = kP + hP$ for any real numbers k and h.

$$(k+h)P = (k+h)\begin{bmatrix} m & n \\ p & q \end{bmatrix}$$
$$= \begin{bmatrix} (k+h)m & (k+h)n \\ (k+h)p & (k+h)q \end{bmatrix}$$
$$= \begin{bmatrix} km+hm & kn+hn \\ kp+hp & kq+hq \end{bmatrix}$$
$$= \begin{bmatrix} km & kn \\ kp & kq \end{bmatrix} + \begin{bmatrix} hm & hn \\ hp & hq \end{bmatrix}$$
$$= k\begin{bmatrix} m & n \\ p & q \end{bmatrix} + h\begin{bmatrix} m & n \\ p & q \end{bmatrix}$$
$$= kP + hP$$

Thus, $(k+h)P = kP + hP$ for any real numbers k and h.

36. (a)

$$IP = \begin{bmatrix} 1 & 0 \\ 0 & 1 \end{bmatrix}\begin{bmatrix} m & n \\ p & q \end{bmatrix} = \begin{bmatrix} m & n \\ p & q \end{bmatrix} = P$$

Thus, $IP = P$.

$$PI = \begin{bmatrix} m & n \\ p & q \end{bmatrix}\begin{bmatrix} 1 & 0 \\ 0 & 1 \end{bmatrix} = \begin{bmatrix} m & n \\ p & q \end{bmatrix} = P$$

Thus, $PI = P$.

$$IX = \begin{bmatrix} 1 & 0 \\ 0 & 1 \end{bmatrix}\begin{bmatrix} x & y \\ z & w \end{bmatrix} = \begin{bmatrix} x & y \\ z & w \end{bmatrix} = X$$

Thus, $IX = X$.

(b) $IT = T$

The matrix I is called an identity matrix because it acts like the multiplicative identity for real numbers, which is 1.

If x is a real number,

$$1 \cdot x = x \cdot 1 = x.$$

If X is a 2×2 matrix,

$$IX = XI = X.$$

(c) I is called an identity matrix, because if a matrix is multiplied by I (assuming that these matrices are 2×2), the resulting matrix is the matrix you originally started with. Hence, I maintains the identity of any 2×2 matrix under multiplication.

37. $$\begin{bmatrix} 2 & 3 & 1 \\ 1 & -4 & 5 \end{bmatrix}\begin{bmatrix} x_1 \\ x_2 \\ x_3 \end{bmatrix} = \begin{bmatrix} 2x_1 + 3x_2 + x_3 \\ x_1 - 4x_2 + 5x_3 \end{bmatrix},$$

and $$\begin{bmatrix} 2x_1 + 3x_2 + x_3 \\ x_1 - 4x_2 + 5x_3 \end{bmatrix} = \begin{bmatrix} 5 \\ 8 \end{bmatrix}.$$

This is equivalent to

$$2x_1 + 3x_2 + x_3 = 5$$
$$x_1 - 4x_2 + 5x_3 = 8$$

since corresponding elements of equal matrices must be equal. Reversing this, observe that the given system of linear equations can be written as the matrix equation

$$\begin{bmatrix} 2 & 3 & 1 \\ 1 & -4 & 5 \end{bmatrix}\begin{bmatrix} x_1 \\ x_2 \\ x_3 \end{bmatrix} = \begin{bmatrix} 5 \\ 8 \end{bmatrix}.$$

38. $A = \begin{bmatrix} 1 & 2 \\ -3 & 5 \end{bmatrix}$, $X = \begin{bmatrix} x_1 \\ x_2 \end{bmatrix}$, $B = \begin{bmatrix} -4 \\ 12 \end{bmatrix}$

If $AX = B$, then

$$\begin{bmatrix} 1 & 2 \\ -3 & 5 \end{bmatrix}\begin{bmatrix} x_1 \\ x_2 \end{bmatrix} = \begin{bmatrix} -4 \\ 12 \end{bmatrix}.$$

Using the definition of matrix multiplication,

$$\begin{bmatrix} 1x_1 + 2x_2 \\ -3x_1 + 5x_2 \end{bmatrix} = \begin{bmatrix} -4 \\ 12 \end{bmatrix}.$$

By the definition of equality of matrices, corresponding elements must be equal, so

$$x_1 + 2x_2 = -4 \quad (1)$$
$$-3x_1 + 5x_2 = 12. \quad (2)$$

This is a linear system of two equations in two variables, x_1 and x_2.
Solve this system by the elimination (addition) method. Multiply equation (1) by 3 and add the result to equation (2).

$$\begin{aligned} 3x_1 + 6x_2 &= -12 \\ -3x_1 + 5x_2 &= 12 \\ \hline 11x_2 &= 0 \\ x_2 &= 0 \end{aligned}$$

Substitute 0 for x_2 in equation (1) to find x_1.

$$\begin{aligned} x_1 + 2(0) &= -4 \\ x_1 &= -4 \end{aligned}$$

The solution of the system is $(-4, 0)$.

Substitute -4 for x_1 and 0 for x_2 in the matrix equation to check this result.

$$\begin{bmatrix} 1 & 2 \\ -3 & 5 \end{bmatrix}\begin{bmatrix} -4 \\ 0 \end{bmatrix} = \begin{bmatrix} 1(-4)+2(0) \\ -3(-4)+5(0) \end{bmatrix} = \begin{bmatrix} -4 \\ 12 \end{bmatrix}.$$

39. **(a)** Use a graphing calculator or a computer to find the product matrix. The answer is

$$AC = \begin{bmatrix} 6 & 106 & 158 & 222 & 28 \\ 120 & 139 & 64 & 75 & 115 \\ -146 & -2 & 184 & 144 & -129 \\ 106 & 94 & 24 & 116 & 110 \end{bmatrix}.$$

(b) CA does not exist.

(c) AC and CA are clearly not equal, since CA does not even exist.

40. This exercise should be solved by graphing calculator or computer methods. The answers are as follows:

(a) $CD = \begin{bmatrix} 44 & 75 & -60 & -33 & 11 \\ 20 & 169 & -164 & 18 & 105 \\ 113 & -82 & 239 & 218 & -55 \\ 119 & 83 & 7 & 82 & 106 \\ 162 & 20 & 175 & 143 & 74 \end{bmatrix};$

(b) $DC = \begin{bmatrix} 110 & 96 & 30 & 226 & 37 \\ -94 & 127 & 134 & -87 & -33 \\ -52 & 126 & 193 & 153 & 22 \\ 117 & 56 & -55 & 147 & 57 \\ 54 & 69 & 58 & 37 & 31 \end{bmatrix};$

(c) No, $CD \neq DC$.

41. Use a graphing calculator or computer to find the matrix products and sums. The answers are as follows.

(a) $C + D = \begin{bmatrix} -1 & 5 & 9 & 13 & -1 \\ 7 & 17 & 2 & -10 & 6 \\ 18 & 9 & -12 & 12 & 22 \\ 9 & 4 & 18 & 10 & -3 \\ 1 & 6 & 10 & 28 & 5 \end{bmatrix}$

(b) $(C + D)B = \begin{bmatrix} -2 & -9 & 90 & 77 \\ -42 & -63 & 127 & 62 \\ 413 & 76 & 180 & -56 \\ -29 & -44 & 198 & 85 \\ 137 & 20 & 162 & 103 \end{bmatrix}$

(c) $CB = \begin{bmatrix} -56 & -1 & 1 & 45 \\ -156 & -119 & 76 & 122 \\ 315 & 86 & 118 & -91 \\ -17 & -17 & 116 & 51 \\ 118 & 19 & 125 & 77 \end{bmatrix}$

(d) $DB = \begin{bmatrix} 54 & -8 & 89 & 32 \\ 114 & 56 & 51 & -60 \\ 98 & -10 & 62 & 35 \\ -12 & -27 & 82 & 34 \\ 19 & 1 & 37 & 26 \end{bmatrix}$

(e) $CB + DB = \begin{bmatrix} -2 & -9 & 90 & 77 \\ -42 & -63 & 127 & 62 \\ 413 & 76 & 180 & -56 \\ -29 & -44 & 198 & 85 \\ 137 & 20 & 162 & 103 \end{bmatrix}$

(f) Yes, $(C+D)B$ and $CB+DB$ are equal, as can be seen by observing that the answers to parts (b) and (e) are identical.

42. Exercise 41 illustrates the distributive property.

43. (a) $\begin{bmatrix} 10 & 4 & 3 & 5 & 6 \\ 7 & 2 & 2 & 3 & 8 \\ 4 & 5 & 1 & 0 & 10 \\ 0 & 3 & 4 & 5 & 5 \end{bmatrix} \begin{bmatrix} 2 & 3 \\ 1 & 1 \\ 4 & 3 \\ 3 & 3 \\ 1 & 2 \end{bmatrix}$

$$= \begin{matrix} \text{Dept. 1} \\ \text{Dept. 2} \\ \text{Dept. 3} \\ \text{Dept. 4} \end{matrix} \overset{\begin{matrix} \text{A} & \text{B} \end{matrix}}{\begin{bmatrix} 57 & 70 \\ 41 & 54 \\ 27 & 40 \\ 39 & 40 \end{bmatrix}}$$

(b) The total cost to buy from supplier A is $57 + 41 + 27 + 39 = \$164$, and the total cost to buy from supplier B is $70 + 54 + 40 + 40 = \$204$. The company should make the purchase from supplier A, since \$164 is a lower total cost than \$204.

44. (a) $\begin{matrix} \text{S} \\ \text{C} \end{matrix} \overset{\begin{matrix} \text{CC} & \text{MM} & \text{AD} \end{matrix}}{\begin{bmatrix} 0.5 & 0.4 & 0.3 \\ 0.2 & 0.3 & 0.3 \end{bmatrix}}$

(b) $\begin{matrix} \text{SD} \\ \text{MC} \\ \text{M} \end{matrix} \overset{\begin{matrix} \text{S} & \text{C} \end{matrix}}{\begin{bmatrix} 4 & 3 \\ 2 & 5 \\ 1 & 7 \end{bmatrix}}$

(c) $\begin{bmatrix} 4 & 3 \\ 2 & 5 \\ 1 & 7 \end{bmatrix} \begin{bmatrix} 0.5 & 0.4 & 0.3 \\ 0.2 & 0.3 & 0.3 \end{bmatrix}$

$$= \begin{matrix} \text{SD} \\ \text{MC} \\ \text{M} \end{matrix} \overset{\begin{matrix} \text{CC} & \text{MM} & \text{AD} \end{matrix}}{\begin{bmatrix} 2.6 & 2.5 & 2.1 \\ 2 & 2.3 & 2.1 \\ 1.9 & 2.5 & 2.4 \end{bmatrix}}$$

(d) Look at the entry in row 3, column 2 of the last matrix. The cost is \$2.50.

(e) $\begin{bmatrix} 2.6 & 2.5 & 2.1 \\ 2 & 2.3 & 2.1 \\ 1.9 & 2.5 & 2.4 \end{bmatrix} \begin{bmatrix} 100 \\ 200 \\ 500 \end{bmatrix} = \begin{bmatrix} 1810 \\ 1710 \\ 1890 \end{bmatrix}$

The total sugar and chocolate cost is \$1810 in San Diego, \$1710 in Mexico City, and \$1890 in Managua, so the order can be produced for the lowest cost in Mexico City.

45. (a) To find the average, add the matrices. Then multiply the resulting matrix by $\frac{1}{3}$. (Multiplying by $\frac{1}{3}$ is the same as dividing by 3.)

$$\frac{1}{3}\left(\begin{bmatrix} 4.27 & 6.94 \\ 3.45 & 3.65 \end{bmatrix} + \begin{bmatrix} 4.05 & 7.01 \\ 3.27 & 3.51 \end{bmatrix} + \begin{bmatrix} 4.40 & 6.90 \\ 3.54 & 3.76 \end{bmatrix}\right)$$

$$= \frac{1}{3}\begin{bmatrix} 12.72 & 20.85 \\ 10.26 & 10.92 \end{bmatrix} = \begin{bmatrix} 4.24 & 6.95 \\ 3.42 & 3.64 \end{bmatrix}$$

(b) To find the new average, add the new matrix for the Chicago plant and the matrix for the Seattle plant. Since there are only two matrices now, multiply the resulting matrix by $\frac{1}{2}$ to get the average. (Multiplying by $\frac{1}{2}$ is the same as dividing by 2.)

$$\frac{1}{2}\left(\begin{bmatrix} 4.42 & 7.43 \\ 3.38 & 3.62 \end{bmatrix} + \begin{bmatrix} 4.40 & 6.90 \\ 3.54 & 3.76 \end{bmatrix}\right)$$

$$= \frac{1}{2}\begin{bmatrix} 8.82 & 14.33 \\ 6.92 & 7.38 \end{bmatrix} = \begin{bmatrix} 4.41 & 7.17 \\ 3.46 & 3.69 \end{bmatrix}$$

46. $P = \begin{bmatrix} 0 & 30 \\ 10 & 20 \\ 20 & 20 \end{bmatrix}, \; Q = \begin{bmatrix} 10 & 2 & 0 & 2 \\ 50 & 1 & 20 & 2 \end{bmatrix},$

$R = \begin{bmatrix} 20 \\ 180 \\ 60 \\ 25 \end{bmatrix}$

(a) $QR = \begin{bmatrix} 10 & 2 & 0 & 2 \\ 50 & 1 & 20 & 2 \end{bmatrix} \begin{bmatrix} 20 \\ 180 \\ 60 \\ 25 \end{bmatrix}$

$$= \begin{bmatrix} 10(20) + 2(180) + 0(60) + 2(25) \\ 50(20) + 1(180) + 20(60) + 2(25) \end{bmatrix}$$

$$= \begin{bmatrix} 610 \\ 2430 \end{bmatrix}$$

The rows represent the cost of materials for each type of house.

(b) From part (a), $QR = \begin{bmatrix} 610 \\ 2430 \end{bmatrix}$.

$$P(QR) = \begin{bmatrix} 0 & 30 \\ 10 & 20 \\ 20 & 20 \end{bmatrix} \begin{bmatrix} 610 \\ 2430 \end{bmatrix} = \begin{bmatrix} 72{,}900 \\ 54{,}700 \\ 60{,}800 \end{bmatrix}$$

$$(PQ)R = \left(\begin{bmatrix} 0 & 30 \\ 10 & 20 \\ 20 & 20 \end{bmatrix} \begin{bmatrix} 10 & 2 & 0 & 2 \\ 50 & 1 & 20 & 2 \end{bmatrix}\right) \begin{bmatrix} 20 \\ 180 \\ 60 \\ 25 \end{bmatrix}$$

$$= \begin{bmatrix} 1500 & 30 & 600 & 60 \\ 1100 & 40 & 400 & 60 \\ 1200 & 60 & 400 & 80 \end{bmatrix} \begin{bmatrix} 20 \\ 180 \\ 60 \\ 25 \end{bmatrix}$$

$$= \begin{bmatrix} 72{,}900 \\ 54{,}700 \\ 60{,}800 \end{bmatrix}$$

Therefore, $P(QR) = (PQ)R$.

47. (a)

$$P = \begin{array}{c} \\ \text{Sal's} \\ \text{Fred's} \end{array} \begin{array}{c} \begin{array}{ccc} \text{Sh} & \text{Sa} & \text{B} \end{array} \\ \begin{bmatrix} 80 & 40 & 120 \\ 60 & 30 & 150 \end{bmatrix} \end{array}$$

(b)

$$F = \begin{array}{c} \\ \text{Sh} \\ \text{Sa} \\ \text{B} \end{array} \begin{array}{c} \begin{array}{cc} \text{CA} & \text{AR} \end{array} \\ \begin{bmatrix} \frac{1}{2} & \frac{1}{5} \\ \frac{1}{4} & \frac{1}{5} \\ \frac{1}{4} & \frac{3}{5} \end{bmatrix} \end{array}$$

(c) $$PF = \begin{bmatrix} 80 & 40 & 120 \\ 60 & 30 & 150 \end{bmatrix} \begin{bmatrix} \frac{1}{2} & \frac{1}{5} \\ \frac{1}{4} & \frac{1}{5} \\ \frac{1}{4} & \frac{3}{5} \end{bmatrix} = \begin{bmatrix} 80\left(\frac{1}{2}\right)+40\left(\frac{1}{4}\right)+120\left(\frac{1}{4}\right) & 80\left(\frac{1}{5}\right)+40\left(\frac{1}{5}\right)+120\left(\frac{3}{5}\right) \\ 60\left(\frac{1}{2}\right)+30\left(\frac{1}{4}\right)+150\left(\frac{1}{4}\right) & 60\left(\frac{1}{5}\right)+30\left(\frac{1}{5}\right)+150\left(\frac{3}{5}\right) \end{bmatrix} = \begin{bmatrix} 80 & 96 \\ 75 & 108 \end{bmatrix}$$

The rows give the average price per pair of footwear sold by each store, and the columns give the state.

48. (a) To increase by 25%, multiply by 1.25 or $\frac{5}{4}$. To increase by $\frac{1}{3}$, multiply by $1\frac{1}{3}$ or $\frac{4}{3}$. To increase by 10%, multiply by 1.10 or $\frac{11}{10}$. The matrix is

$$\begin{bmatrix} \frac{5}{4} \\ \frac{4}{3} \\ \frac{11}{10} \end{bmatrix}.$$

(b) $$\begin{bmatrix} 88 & 105 & 60 \\ 48 & 72 & 40 \\ 16 & 21 & 0 \\ 112 & 147 & 50 \end{bmatrix} \begin{bmatrix} \frac{5}{4} \\ \frac{4}{3} \\ \frac{11}{10} \end{bmatrix} = \begin{bmatrix} 316 \\ 200 \\ 48 \\ 391 \end{bmatrix}$$

49. (a) $$XY = \begin{bmatrix} 2 & 1 & 2 & 1 \\ 3 & 2 & 2 & 1 \\ 4 & 3 & 2 & 1 \end{bmatrix} \begin{bmatrix} 5 & 0 & 7 \\ 0 & 10 & 1 \\ 0 & 15 & 2 \\ 10 & 12 & 8 \end{bmatrix} = \begin{bmatrix} 20 & 52 & 27 \\ 25 & 62 & 35 \\ 30 & 72 & 43 \end{bmatrix}$$

The rows give the amounts of fat, carbohydrates, and protein, respectively, in each of the daily meals.

(b) $$YZ = \begin{bmatrix} 5 & 0 & 7 \\ 0 & 10 & 1 \\ 0 & 15 & 2 \\ 10 & 12 & 8 \end{bmatrix} \begin{bmatrix} 8 \\ 4 \\ 5 \end{bmatrix} = \begin{bmatrix} 75 \\ 45 \\ 70 \\ 168 \end{bmatrix}$$

The rows give the number of calories in one exchange of each of the food groups.

(c) Use the matrices found for XY and YZ from parts (a) and (b).

$$(XY)Z = \begin{bmatrix} 20 & 52 & 27 \\ 25 & 62 & 35 \\ 30 & 72 & 43 \end{bmatrix} \begin{bmatrix} 8 \\ 4 \\ 5 \end{bmatrix} = \begin{bmatrix} 503 \\ 623 \\ 743 \end{bmatrix}$$

$$X(YZ) = \begin{bmatrix} 2 & 1 & 2 & 1 \\ 3 & 2 & 2 & 1 \\ 4 & 3 & 2 & 1 \end{bmatrix} \begin{bmatrix} 75 \\ 45 \\ 70 \\ 168 \end{bmatrix} = \begin{bmatrix} 503 \\ 623 \\ 743 \end{bmatrix}$$

The rows give the number of calories in each meal.

50. $$\frac{1}{2}\left(\begin{bmatrix} 23.2 & 20.8 & 18.1 & 21.5 \\ 38.3 & 34.4 & 31.8 & 29.2 \\ 27.9 & 25.5 & 24.6 & 22.4 \end{bmatrix} + \begin{bmatrix} 14.5 & 11.9 & 10.2 & 14.6 \\ 34.5 & 31.7 & 29.6 & 31.1 \\ 16.2 & 13.3 & 14.1 & 12.3 \end{bmatrix}\right) = \frac{1}{2}\begin{bmatrix} 37.7 & 32.7 & 28.3 & 36.1 \\ 72.8 & 66.1 & 61.4 & 60.3 \\ 44.1 & 38.8 & 38.7 & 34.7 \end{bmatrix}$$

$$= \begin{bmatrix} 18.85 & 16.35 & 14.15 & 18.05 \\ 36.40 & 33.05 & 30.70 & 30.15 \\ 22.05 & 19.40 & 19.35 & 17.35 \end{bmatrix}$$

51. $$\frac{1}{6}\left(\begin{bmatrix} 60.0 & 68.3 \\ 63.8 & 72.5 \\ 64.5 & 73.6 \\ 68.2 & 74.9 \end{bmatrix} + 5\begin{bmatrix} 68.0 & 75.6 \\ 70.7 & 78.1 \\ 72.7 & 79.4 \\ 74.8 & 80.0 \end{bmatrix}\right) = \frac{1}{6}\left(\begin{bmatrix} 60.0 & 68.3 \\ 63.8 & 72.5 \\ 64.5 & 73.6 \\ 68.2 & 74.9 \end{bmatrix} + 5\begin{bmatrix} 68.0 & 75.6 \\ 70.7 & 78.1 \\ 72.7 & 79.4 \\ 74.8 & 80.0 \end{bmatrix}\right)$$

$$= \frac{1}{6}\left(\begin{bmatrix} 60.0 & 68.3 \\ 63.8 & 72.5 \\ 64.5 & 73.6 \\ 68.2 & 74.9 \end{bmatrix} + \begin{bmatrix} 340.0 & 378.0 \\ 353.5 & 390.5 \\ 363.5 & 397.0 \\ 374.0 & 400.0 \end{bmatrix}\right)$$

$$= \frac{1}{6}\begin{bmatrix} 400.0 & 446.3 \\ 417.3 & 463.0 \\ 428.0 & 470.6 \\ 442.2 & 474.9 \end{bmatrix}$$

$$= \begin{bmatrix} 66.7 & 74.4 \\ 69.6 & 77.2 \\ 71.3 & 78.4 \\ 73.7 & 79.2 \end{bmatrix}$$

52. (a) Let n represent the present year. Then $j_n = 900, s_n = 500, a_n = 2600$.

For the next year, $n+1$, we have

$$\begin{bmatrix} j_{n+1} \\ s_{n+1} \\ a_{n+1} \end{bmatrix} = \begin{bmatrix} 0 & 0 & 0.33 \\ 0.18 & 0 & 0 \\ 0 & 0.71 & 0.94 \end{bmatrix}\begin{bmatrix} j_n \\ s_n \\ a_n \end{bmatrix} = \begin{bmatrix} 0 & 0 & 0.33 \\ 0.18 & 0 & 0 \\ 0 & 0.71 & 0.94 \end{bmatrix}\begin{bmatrix} 900 \\ 500 \\ 2600 \end{bmatrix} = \begin{bmatrix} 858 \\ 162 \\ 2799 \end{bmatrix}.$$

For the year $n+1$, there is a total of
$858 + 162 + 2799 = 3819$ female owls.
For the next year, $n+2$, we have

$$\begin{bmatrix} j_{n+2} \\ s_{n+2} \\ a_{n+2} \end{bmatrix} = \begin{bmatrix} 0 & 0 & 0.33 \\ 0.18 & 0 & 0 \\ 0 & 0.71 & 0.94 \end{bmatrix}\begin{bmatrix} j_{n+1} \\ s_{n+1} \\ a_{n+1} \end{bmatrix} = \begin{bmatrix} 0 & 0 & 0.33 \\ 0.18 & 0 & 0 \\ 0 & 0.71 & 0.94 \end{bmatrix}\begin{bmatrix} 858 \\ 162 \\ 2799 \end{bmatrix} \approx \begin{bmatrix} 924 \\ 154 \\ 2746 \end{bmatrix}.$$

For the year $n+2$, there is a total of approximately $924 + 154 + 2746 = 3824$ female owls.
For the next year, $n+3$, we have

$$\begin{bmatrix} j_{n+3} \\ s_{n+3} \\ a_{n+3} \end{bmatrix} = \begin{bmatrix} 0 & 0 & 0.33 \\ 0.18 & 0 & 0 \\ 0 & 0.71 & 0.94 \end{bmatrix}\begin{bmatrix} j_{n+2} \\ s_{n+2} \\ a_{n+2} \end{bmatrix} = \begin{bmatrix} 0 & 0 & 0.33 \\ 0.18 & 0 & 0 \\ 0 & 0.71 & 0.94 \end{bmatrix}\begin{bmatrix} 924 \\ 154 \\ 2746 \end{bmatrix} \approx \begin{bmatrix} 906 \\ 166 \\ 2691 \end{bmatrix}.$$

For the year $n+3$, there is a total of approximately $906 + 166 + 2691 = 3763$ female owls.

For the next year, $n+4$, we have

$$\begin{bmatrix} j_{n+4} \\ s_{n+4} \\ a_{n+4} \end{bmatrix} = \begin{bmatrix} 0 & 0 & 0.33 \\ 0.18 & 0 & 0 \\ 0 & 0.71 & 0.94 \end{bmatrix} \begin{bmatrix} j_{n+3} \\ s_{n+3} \\ a_{n+3} \end{bmatrix}$$
$$= \begin{bmatrix} 0 & 0 & 0.33 \\ 0.18 & 0 & 0 \\ 0 & 0.71 & 0.94 \end{bmatrix} \begin{bmatrix} 906 \\ 166 \\ 2691 \end{bmatrix}$$
$$\approx \begin{bmatrix} 888 \\ 163 \\ 2647 \end{bmatrix}.$$

For the near $n+4$, there is a total of approximately $888 + 163 + 2647 = 3698$ female owls.
For the year $n+5$, we have

$$\begin{bmatrix} j_{n+5} \\ s_{n+5} \\ a_{n+5} \end{bmatrix} = \begin{bmatrix} 0 & 0 & 0.33 \\ 0.18 & 0 & 0 \\ 0 & 0.71 & 0.94 \end{bmatrix} \begin{bmatrix} j_{n+4} \\ s_{n+4} \\ a_{n+4} \end{bmatrix}$$
$$= \begin{bmatrix} 0 & 0 & 0.33 \\ 0.18 & 0 & 0 \\ 0 & 0.71 & 0.94 \end{bmatrix} \begin{bmatrix} 888 \\ 163 \\ 2647 \end{bmatrix}$$
$$\approx \begin{bmatrix} 874 \\ 160 \\ 2604 \end{bmatrix}.$$

For the year $n+5$, there is a total of approximately $874 + 160 + 2604 = 3638$ female owls.

(b) Each year, the population is about 98 percent of the population of the previous year. In the long run, the northern spotted owl will become extinct.

(c) Change 0.18 in the original matrix equation to 0.40.
For the next year, $n+1$, we have

$$\begin{bmatrix} j_{n+1} \\ s_{n+1} \\ a_{n+1} \end{bmatrix} = \begin{bmatrix} 0 & 0 & 0.33 \\ 0.40 & 0 & 0 \\ 0 & 0.71 & 0.94 \end{bmatrix} \begin{bmatrix} j_{n} \\ s_{n} \\ a_{n} \end{bmatrix}$$
$$= \begin{bmatrix} 0 & 0 & 0.33 \\ 0.40 & 0 & 0 \\ 0 & 0.71 & 0.94 \end{bmatrix} \begin{bmatrix} 900 \\ 500 \\ 2600 \end{bmatrix}$$
$$= \begin{bmatrix} 858 \\ 360 \\ 2799 \end{bmatrix}.$$

For the year $n+1$, there would be a total of $858 + 360 + 2799 = 4017$ female owls.

For the next year, $n+2$, we have

$$\begin{bmatrix} j_{n+2} \\ s_{n+2} \\ a_{n+2} \end{bmatrix} = \begin{bmatrix} 0 & 0 & 0.33 \\ 0.40 & 0 & 0 \\ 0 & 0.71 & 0.94 \end{bmatrix} \begin{bmatrix} j_{n+1} \\ s_{n+1} \\ a_{n+1} \end{bmatrix}$$
$$= \begin{bmatrix} 0 & 0 & 0.33 \\ 0.40 & 0 & 0 \\ 0 & 0.71 & 0.94 \end{bmatrix} \begin{bmatrix} 858 \\ 360 \\ 2799 \end{bmatrix}$$
$$\approx \begin{bmatrix} 924 \\ 343 \\ 2887 \end{bmatrix}.$$

For the year $n+2$, there would be a total of approximately $924 + 343 + 2887 = 4154$ female owls.
For the next year, $n+3$, we have

$$\begin{bmatrix} j_{n+3} \\ s_{n+3} \\ a_{n+3} \end{bmatrix} = \begin{bmatrix} 0 & 0 & 0.33 \\ 0.40 & 0 & 0 \\ 0 & 0.71 & 0.94 \end{bmatrix} \begin{bmatrix} j_{n+2} \\ s_{n+2} \\ a_{n+2} \end{bmatrix}$$
$$= \begin{bmatrix} 0 & 0 & 0.33 \\ 0.40 & 0 & 0 \\ 0 & 0.71 & 0.94 \end{bmatrix} \begin{bmatrix} 924 \\ 343 \\ 2887 \end{bmatrix}$$
$$= \begin{bmatrix} 953 \\ 370 \\ 2957 \end{bmatrix}.$$

For the year $n+3$, there would be a total of approximately $953 + 370 + 2957 = 4280$ female owls.
For the next year, $n+4$, we have

$$\begin{bmatrix} j_{n+4} \\ s_{n+4} \\ a_{n+4} \end{bmatrix} = \begin{bmatrix} 0 & 0 & 0.33 \\ 0.40 & 0 & 0 \\ 0 & 0.71 & 0.94 \end{bmatrix} \begin{bmatrix} j_{n+3} \\ s_{n+3} \\ a_{n+3} \end{bmatrix}$$
$$= \begin{bmatrix} 0 & 0 & 0.33 \\ 0.40 & 0 & 0 \\ 0 & 0.71 & 0.94 \end{bmatrix} \begin{bmatrix} 953 \\ 370 \\ 2957 \end{bmatrix}$$
$$\approx \begin{bmatrix} 976 \\ 381 \\ 3042 \end{bmatrix}.$$

For the year $n+4$, there would be a total of approximately $976 + 381 + 3042 = 4399$ female owls.

For the next year, $n+5$, we have

$$\begin{bmatrix} j_{n+5} \\ s_{n+5} \\ a_{n+5} \end{bmatrix} = \begin{bmatrix} 0 & 0 & 0.33 \\ 0.40 & 0 & 0 \\ 0 & 0.71 & 0.94 \end{bmatrix} \begin{bmatrix} j_{n+4} \\ s_{n+4} \\ a_{n+4} \end{bmatrix} = \begin{bmatrix} 0 & 0 & 0.33 \\ 0.40 & 0 & 0 \\ 0 & 0.71 & 0.94 \end{bmatrix} \begin{bmatrix} 976 \\ 381 \\ 3042 \end{bmatrix} \approx \begin{bmatrix} 1004 \\ 390 \\ 3130 \end{bmatrix}.$$

For the year $n+5$, there would be a total of approximately $1004 + 390 + 3130 = 4524$ female owls. Assuming that better habitat management could increase the survival rate of juvenile female spotted owls from 18 percent to 40 percent, the overall population would increase each year and would, therefore, not become extinct.

53. **(a)** The matrices are

$$A = \begin{bmatrix} 0.036 & 0.014 \\ 0.019 & 0.008 \\ 0.021 & 0.006 \\ 0.014 & 0.008 \\ 0.011 & 0.011 \end{bmatrix} \text{ and } B = \begin{bmatrix} 283 & 1628 & 218 & 199 & 425 \\ 361 & 2038 & 286 & 227 & 460 \\ 473 & 2494 & 362 & 252 & 484 \\ 627 & 2978 & 443 & 278 & 499 \\ 839 & 3518 & 539 & 320 & 513 \end{bmatrix}$$

(b) The total number of births and deaths each year is found by multiplying matrix B by matrix A.

$$BA = \begin{bmatrix} 283 & 1628 & 218 & 199 & 425 \\ 361 & 2038 & 286 & 227 & 460 \\ 473 & 2494 & 362 & 252 & 484 \\ 627 & 2978 & 443 & 278 & 499 \\ 839 & 3518 & 539 & 320 & 513 \end{bmatrix} \begin{bmatrix} 0.036 & 0.014 \\ 0.019 & 0.008 \\ 0.021 & 0.006 \\ 0.014 & 0.008 \\ 0.011 & 0.011 \end{bmatrix}$$

$$= \begin{array}{c} \\ 1960 \\ 1970 \\ 1980 \\ 1990 \\ 2002 \end{array} \begin{array}{c} \begin{array}{cc} \text{Births} & \text{Deaths} \end{array} \\ \begin{bmatrix} 53.159 & 24.561 \\ 65.962 & 29.950 \\ 80.868 & 36.086 \\ 97.838 & 42.973 \\ 118.488 & 51.327 \end{bmatrix} \end{array}$$

2.5 Matrix Inverses

1. $$\begin{bmatrix} 2 & 1 \\ 5 & 3 \end{bmatrix} \begin{bmatrix} 3 & -1 \\ -5 & 2 \end{bmatrix} = \begin{bmatrix} 6-5 & -2+2 \\ 15-15 & -5+6 \end{bmatrix} = \begin{bmatrix} 1 & 0 \\ 0 & 1 \end{bmatrix} = I$$

$$\begin{bmatrix} 3 & -1 \\ -5 & 2 \end{bmatrix} \begin{bmatrix} 2 & 1 \\ 5 & 3 \end{bmatrix} = \begin{bmatrix} 6-5 & 3-3 \\ -10+10 & -5+6 \end{bmatrix} = \begin{bmatrix} 1 & 0 \\ 0 & 1 \end{bmatrix} = I$$

Since the products obtained by multiplying the matrices in either order are both the 2×2 identity matrix, the given matrices are inverses of each other.

2. $\begin{bmatrix} 1 & -4 \\ 2 & -7 \end{bmatrix} \begin{bmatrix} -7 & 4 \\ -2 & 1 \end{bmatrix}$

$= \begin{bmatrix} -7+8 & 4-4 \\ -14+14 & 8-7 \end{bmatrix}$

$= \begin{bmatrix} 1 & 0 \\ 0 & 1 \end{bmatrix} = I$

$\begin{bmatrix} -7 & 4 \\ -2 & 1 \end{bmatrix} \begin{bmatrix} 1 & -4 \\ 2 & -7 \end{bmatrix}$

$= \begin{bmatrix} -7+8 & 28-28 \\ -2+2 & 8-7 \end{bmatrix}$

$= \begin{bmatrix} 1 & 0 \\ 0 & 1 \end{bmatrix} = I$

Since the products obtained by multiplying the matrices in either order are both the 2×2 identity matrix, the given matrices are inverses of each other.

3. $\begin{bmatrix} 2 & 6 \\ 2 & 4 \end{bmatrix} \begin{bmatrix} -1 & 2 \\ 2 & -4 \end{bmatrix} = \begin{bmatrix} 10 & -20 \\ 6 & -12 \end{bmatrix} \neq I$

No, the matrices are not inverses of each other since their product matrix is not I.

4. $\begin{bmatrix} -1 & 2 \\ 3 & -5 \end{bmatrix} \begin{bmatrix} -5 & -2 \\ -3 & -1 \end{bmatrix} = \begin{bmatrix} -1 & 0 \\ 0 & -1 \end{bmatrix} \neq I$

Since this product is not the 2×2 identity matrix, the given matrices are not inverses of each other.

5. $\begin{bmatrix} 2 & 0 & 1 \\ 1 & 1 & 2 \\ 0 & 1 & 0 \end{bmatrix} \begin{bmatrix} 1 & 1 & -1 \\ 0 & 1 & 0 \\ -1 & -2 & 2 \end{bmatrix}$

$= \begin{bmatrix} 2+0-1 & 2+0-2 & -2+0+2 \\ 1+0-2 & 1+1-4 & -1+0+4 \\ 0+0+0 & 0+1+0 & 0+0+0 \end{bmatrix}$

$= \begin{bmatrix} 1 & 0 & 0 \\ -1 & -2 & 3 \\ 0 & 1 & 0 \end{bmatrix} \neq I$

No, the matrices are not inverses of each other since their product matrix is not I.

6. $\begin{bmatrix} 0 & 1 & 0 \\ 0 & 0 & -2 \\ 1 & -1 & 0 \end{bmatrix} \begin{bmatrix} 1 & 0 & 1 \\ 1 & 0 & 0 \\ 0 & -1 & 0 \end{bmatrix} = \begin{bmatrix} 1 & 0 & 0 \\ 0 & 2 & 0 \\ 0 & 0 & 1 \end{bmatrix} \neq I$

Since this product is not the 3×3 identity matrix, the given matrices are not inverses of each other.

7. $\begin{bmatrix} 1 & 3 & 3 \\ 1 & 4 & 3 \\ 1 & 3 & 4 \end{bmatrix} \begin{bmatrix} 7 & -3 & -3 \\ -1 & 1 & 0 \\ -1 & 0 & 1 \end{bmatrix} = \begin{bmatrix} 1 & 0 & 0 \\ 0 & 1 & 0 \\ 0 & 0 & 1 \end{bmatrix} = I$

$\begin{bmatrix} 7 & -3 & -3 \\ -1 & 1 & 0 \\ -1 & 0 & 1 \end{bmatrix} \begin{bmatrix} 1 & 3 & 3 \\ 1 & 4 & 3 \\ 1 & 3 & 4 \end{bmatrix} = \begin{bmatrix} 1 & 0 & 0 \\ 0 & 1 & 0 \\ 0 & 0 & 1 \end{bmatrix} = I$

Yes, these matrices are inverses of each other.

8. $\begin{bmatrix} 1 & 0 & 0 \\ -1 & -2 & 3 \\ 0 & 1 & 0 \end{bmatrix} \begin{bmatrix} 1 & 0 & 0 \\ 0 & 0 & 1 \\ \frac{1}{3} & \frac{1}{3} & \frac{2}{3} \end{bmatrix}$

$= \begin{bmatrix} 1+0+0 & 0+0+0 & 0+0+0 \\ -1+0+1 & 0+0+1 & 0-2+2 \\ 0+0+0 & 0+0+0 & 0+1+0 \end{bmatrix}$

$= \begin{bmatrix} 1 & 0 & 0 \\ 0 & 1 & 0 \\ 0 & 0 & 1 \end{bmatrix} = I$

$\begin{bmatrix} 1 & 0 & 0 \\ 0 & 0 & 1 \\ \frac{1}{3} & \frac{1}{3} & \frac{2}{3} \end{bmatrix} \begin{bmatrix} 1 & 0 & 0 \\ -1 & -2 & 3 \\ 0 & 1 & 0 \end{bmatrix}$

$= \begin{bmatrix} 1+0+0 & 0+0+0 & 0+0+0 \\ 0+0+0 & 0+0+1 & 0+0+0 \\ \frac{1}{3}-\frac{1}{3}+0 & 0-\frac{2}{3}+\frac{2}{3} & 0+1+0 \end{bmatrix}$

$= \begin{bmatrix} 1 & 0 & 0 \\ 0 & 1 & 0 \\ 0 & 0 & 1 \end{bmatrix} = I$

Since the products obtained by multiplying the matrices in either order are both the 3×3 identity matrix, the given matrices are inverses of each other.

9. No, a matrix with a row of all zeros does not have an inverse; the row of all zeros makes it impossible to get all the 1's in the main diagonal of the identity matrix.

10. Since the inverse of A is A^{-1}, $(A^{-1})^{-1}$ would be the inverse of the inverse of A, which is A.

11. Let $A = \begin{bmatrix} 1 & -1 \\ 2 & 0 \end{bmatrix}$.

Form the augmented matrix $[A|I]$.

$$[A|I] = \left[\begin{array}{cc|cc} 1 & -1 & 1 & 0 \\ 2 & 0 & 0 & 1 \end{array}\right]$$

Perform row operations on $[A|I]$ to get a matrix of the form $[I|B]$.

$$\left[\begin{array}{cc|cc} 1 & -1 & 1 & 0 \\ 2 & 0 & 0 & 1 \end{array}\right]$$

$$-2R_1 + R_2 \rightarrow R_2 \quad \left[\begin{array}{cc|cc} 1 & -1 & 1 & 0 \\ 0 & 2 & -2 & 1 \end{array}\right]$$

$$2R_1 + R_2 \rightarrow R_1 \quad \left[\begin{array}{cc|cc} 2 & 0 & 0 & 1 \\ 0 & 2 & -2 & 1 \end{array}\right]$$

$$\begin{array}{l} \frac{1}{2}R_1 \rightarrow R_1 \\ \frac{1}{2}R_2 \rightarrow R_2 \end{array} \quad \left[\begin{array}{cc|cc} 1 & 0 & 0 & \frac{1}{2} \\ 0 & 1 & -1 & \frac{1}{2} \end{array}\right] = [I|B]$$

The matrix B in the last transformation is the desired multiplicative inverse.

$$A^{-1} = \begin{bmatrix} 0 & \frac{1}{2} \\ -1 & \frac{1}{2} \end{bmatrix}$$

This answer may be checked by showing that $AA^{-1} = I$ and $A^{-1}A = I$.

12. Find the inverse of $A = \begin{bmatrix} 1 & 1 \\ 2 & 3 \end{bmatrix}$, if it exists.

Write the augmented matrix $[A|I]$.

$$[A|I] = \left[\begin{array}{cc|cc} 1 & 1 & 1 & 0 \\ 2 & 3 & 0 & 1 \end{array}\right]$$

Perform row operations on $[A|I]$ to get a matrix of the form $[I|B]$.

$$-2R_1 + R_2 \rightarrow R_2 \quad \left[\begin{array}{cc|cc} 1 & 1 & 1 & 0 \\ 0 & 1 & -2 & 1 \end{array}\right]$$

$$-1R_2 + R_1 \rightarrow R_1 \quad \left[\begin{array}{cc|cc} 1 & 0 & 3 & -1 \\ 0 & 1 & -2 & 1 \end{array}\right]$$

The last augmented matrix is of the form $[I|B]$, so the desired inverse is

$$A^{-1} = \begin{bmatrix} 3 & -1 \\ -2 & 1 \end{bmatrix}.$$

13. Let $A = \begin{bmatrix} 3 & -1 \\ -5 & 2 \end{bmatrix}$.

$$[A|I] = \left[\begin{array}{cc|cc} 3 & -1 & 1 & 0 \\ -5 & 2 & 0 & 1 \end{array}\right]$$

$$5R_1 + 3R_2 \rightarrow R_2 \quad \left[\begin{array}{cc|cc} 3 & -1 & 1 & 0 \\ 0 & 1 & 5 & 3 \end{array}\right]$$

$$R_1 + R_2 \rightarrow R_1 \quad \left[\begin{array}{cc|cc} 3 & 0 & 6 & 3 \\ 0 & 1 & 5 & 3 \end{array}\right]$$

$$\tfrac{1}{3}R_1 \rightarrow R_1 \quad \left[\begin{array}{cc|cc} 1 & 0 & 2 & 1 \\ 0 & 1 & 5 & 3 \end{array}\right] = [I|B]$$

The desired inverse is

$$A^{-1} = \begin{bmatrix} 2 & 1 \\ 5 & 3 \end{bmatrix}.$$

14. Find the inverse of $A = \begin{bmatrix} -3 & -8 \\ 1 & 3 \end{bmatrix}$, if it exists.

Write the augmented matrix $[A|I]$.

$$[A|I] = \left[\begin{array}{cc|cc} -3 & -8 & 1 & 0 \\ 1 & 3 & 0 & 1 \end{array}\right]$$

Perform row operations on $[A|I]$ to get a matrix of the form $[I|B]$.

$$R_1 + 3R_2 \rightarrow R_2 \quad \left[\begin{array}{cc|cc} -3 & -8 & 1 & 0 \\ 0 & 1 & 1 & 3 \end{array}\right]$$

$$8R_2 + R_1 \rightarrow R_1 \quad \left[\begin{array}{cc|cc} -3 & 0 & 9 & 24 \\ 0 & -1 & 1 & 3 \end{array}\right]$$

$$-\tfrac{1}{3}R_1 \rightarrow R_1 \quad \left[\begin{array}{cc|cc} 1 & 0 & -3 & -8 \\ 0 & 1 & 1 & 3 \end{array}\right]$$

The last augmented matrix is of the form $[I|B]$, so the desired inverse is $A^{-1} = \begin{bmatrix} -3 & -8 \\ 1 & 3 \end{bmatrix}$.

Note that matrix A is its own inverse: $AA = I$.

15. Let $A = \begin{bmatrix} 1 & -3 \\ -2 & 6 \end{bmatrix}$.

$$[A|I] = \left[\begin{array}{cc|cc} 1 & -3 & 1 & 0 \\ -2 & 6 & 0 & 1 \end{array}\right]$$

$$2R_1 + R_2 \rightarrow R_2 \quad \left[\begin{array}{cc|cc} 1 & -3 & 1 & 0 \\ 0 & 0 & 2 & 1 \end{array}\right]$$

Because the last row has all zeros to the left of the vertical bar, there is no way to complete the desired transformation. A has no inverse.

16. Find the inverse of $A = \begin{bmatrix} 5 & 10 \\ -3 & -6 \end{bmatrix}$, if it exists.

$$[A|I] = \left[\begin{array}{cc|cc} 5 & 10 & 1 & 0 \\ -3 & -6 & 0 & 1 \end{array}\right]$$

$$3R_1 + 5R_2 \rightarrow R_2 \quad \left[\begin{array}{cc|cc} 5 & 10 & 1 & 0 \\ 0 & 0 & 3 & 5 \end{array}\right]$$

At this point, the matrix should be changed so that the first row, second column element will be 0. Since this cannot be done using row operations, the inverse of the given matrix does not exist.

17. Let $A = \begin{bmatrix} 1 & 0 & 0 \\ 0 & -1 & 0 \\ 1 & 0 & 1 \end{bmatrix}$.

$$[A|I] = \left[\begin{array}{ccc|ccc} 1 & 0 & 0 & 1 & 0 & 0 \\ 0 & -1 & 0 & 0 & 1 & 0 \\ 1 & 0 & 1 & 0 & 0 & 1 \end{array}\right]$$

$$-1R_1 + R_3 \rightarrow R_3 \quad \left[\begin{array}{ccc|ccc} 1 & 0 & 0 & 1 & 0 & 0 \\ 0 & -1 & 0 & 0 & 1 & 0 \\ 0 & 0 & 1 & -1 & 0 & 1 \end{array}\right]$$

$$-1R_2 \rightarrow R_2 \quad \left[\begin{array}{ccc|ccc} 1 & 0 & 0 & 1 & 0 & 0 \\ 0 & 1 & 0 & 0 & -1 & 0 \\ 0 & 0 & 1 & -1 & 0 & 1 \end{array}\right]$$

$$A^{-1} = \begin{bmatrix} 1 & 0 & 0 \\ 0 & -1 & 0 \\ -1 & 0 & 1 \end{bmatrix}$$

18. Find the inverse of $A = \begin{bmatrix} 1 & 3 & 0 \\ 0 & 2 & -1 \\ 1 & 0 & 2 \end{bmatrix}$, if it exists.

$$[A|I] = \left[\begin{array}{ccc|ccc} 1 & 3 & 0 & 1 & 0 & 0 \\ 0 & 2 & -1 & 0 & 1 & 0 \\ 1 & 0 & 2 & 0 & 0 & 1 \end{array}\right]$$

$$-1R_1 + R_3 \rightarrow R_3 \quad \left[\begin{array}{ccc|ccc} 1 & 3 & 0 & 1 & 0 & 0 \\ 0 & 2 & -1 & 0 & 1 & 0 \\ 0 & -3 & 2 & -1 & 0 & 1 \end{array}\right]$$

$$\begin{array}{r} -3R_2 + 2R_1 \rightarrow R_1 \\ 3R_2 + 2R_3 \rightarrow R_3 \end{array} \quad \left[\begin{array}{ccc|ccc} 2 & 0 & 3 & 2 & -3 & 0 \\ 0 & 2 & -1 & 0 & 1 & 0 \\ 0 & 0 & 1 & -2 & 3 & 2 \end{array}\right]$$

$$\begin{array}{r} -3R_3 + R_1 \rightarrow R_1 \\ R_3 + R_2 \rightarrow R_2 \end{array} \quad \left[\begin{array}{ccc|ccc} 2 & 0 & 0 & 8 & -12 & -6 \\ 0 & 2 & 0 & -2 & 4 & 2 \\ 0 & 0 & 1 & -2 & 3 & 2 \end{array}\right]$$

$$\begin{array}{r} \frac{1}{2}R_1 \rightarrow R_1 \\ \frac{1}{2}R_2 \rightarrow R_2 \end{array} \quad \left[\begin{array}{ccc|ccc} 1 & 0 & 0 & 4 & -6 & -3 \\ 0 & 1 & 0 & -1 & 2 & 1 \\ 0 & 0 & 1 & -2 & 3 & 2 \end{array}\right]$$

$$A^{-1} = \begin{bmatrix} 4 & -6 & -3 \\ -1 & 2 & 1 \\ -2 & 3 & 2 \end{bmatrix}$$

19. Let $A = \begin{bmatrix} -1 & -1 & -1 \\ 4 & 5 & 0 \\ 0 & 1 & -3 \end{bmatrix}$.

$$[A|I] = \left[\begin{array}{ccc|ccc} -1 & -1 & -1 & 1 & 0 & 0 \\ 4 & 5 & 0 & 0 & 1 & 0 \\ 0 & 1 & -3 & 0 & 0 & 1 \end{array}\right]$$

$$4R_1 + R_2 \rightarrow R_2 \quad \left[\begin{array}{ccc|ccc} -1 & -1 & -1 & 1 & 0 & 0 \\ 0 & 1 & -4 & 4 & 1 & 0 \\ 0 & 1 & -3 & 0 & 0 & 1 \end{array}\right]$$

$$\begin{array}{r} R_2 + R_1 \rightarrow R_1 \\ -1R_2 + R_3 \rightarrow R_3 \end{array} \quad \left[\begin{array}{ccc|ccc} -1 & 0 & -5 & 5 & 1 & 0 \\ 0 & 1 & -4 & 4 & 1 & 0 \\ 0 & 0 & 1 & -4 & -1 & 1 \end{array}\right]$$

$$\begin{array}{r} 5R_3 + R_1 \rightarrow R_1 \\ 4R_3 + R_2 \rightarrow R_2 \end{array} \quad \left[\begin{array}{ccc|ccc} -1 & 0 & 0 & -15 & -4 & 5 \\ 0 & 1 & 0 & -12 & -3 & 4 \\ 0 & 0 & 1 & -4 & -1 & 1 \end{array}\right]$$

$$-1R_1 \rightarrow R_1 \quad \left[\begin{array}{ccc|ccc} 1 & 0 & 0 & 15 & 4 & -5 \\ 0 & 1 & 0 & -12 & -3 & 4 \\ 0 & 0 & 1 & -4 & -1 & 1 \end{array}\right]$$

$$A^{-1} = \begin{bmatrix} 15 & 4 & -5 \\ -12 & -3 & 4 \\ -4 & -1 & 1 \end{bmatrix}$$

20. Find the inverse of $A = \begin{bmatrix} 2 & 1 & 0 \\ 0 & 3 & 1 \\ 4 & -1 & -3 \end{bmatrix}$, if it exists.

$$[A|I] = \left[\begin{array}{ccc|ccc} 2 & 1 & 0 & 1 & 0 & 0 \\ 0 & 3 & 1 & 0 & 1 & 0 \\ 4 & -1 & -3 & 0 & 0 & 1 \end{array}\right]$$

$$-2R_1 + R_3 \to R_3 \quad \left[\begin{array}{ccc|ccc} 2 & 1 & 0 & 1 & 0 & 0 \\ 0 & 3 & 1 & 0 & 1 & 0 \\ 0 & -3 & -3 & -2 & 0 & 1 \end{array}\right]$$

$$\begin{array}{l} -1R_2 + 3R_1 \to R_1 \\ \\ R_2 + R_3 \to R_3 \end{array} \quad \left[\begin{array}{ccc|ccc} 6 & 0 & -1 & 3 & -1 & 0 \\ 0 & 3 & 1 & 0 & 1 & 0 \\ 0 & 0 & -2 & -2 & 1 & 1 \end{array}\right]$$

$$\begin{array}{l} -1R_3 + 2R_1 \to R_1 \\ R_3 + 2R_2 \to R_2 \end{array} \quad \left[\begin{array}{ccc|ccc} 12 & 0 & 0 & 8 & -3 & -1 \\ 0 & 1 & 0 & -2 & 3 & 1 \\ 0 & 0 & -1 & -2 & 1 & 1 \end{array}\right]$$

$$\begin{array}{l} \frac{1}{12} R_1 \to R_1 \\ \frac{1}{6} R_2 \to R_2 \\ -\frac{1}{2} R_3 \to R_3 \end{array} \quad \left[\begin{array}{ccc|ccc} 1 & 0 & 0 & \frac{2}{3} & -\frac{1}{4} & -\frac{1}{12} \\ 0 & 1 & 0 & -\frac{1}{3} & \frac{1}{2} & \frac{1}{6} \\ 0 & 0 & 1 & 1 & -\frac{1}{2} & -\frac{1}{2} \end{array}\right]$$

$$A^{-1} = \begin{bmatrix} \frac{2}{3} & -\frac{1}{4} & -\frac{1}{12} \\ -\frac{1}{3} & \frac{1}{2} & \frac{1}{6} \\ 1 & -\frac{1}{2} & -\frac{1}{2} \end{bmatrix}$$

21. Let $A = \begin{bmatrix} 1 & 2 & 3 \\ -3 & -2 & -1 \\ -1 & 0 & 1 \end{bmatrix}$.

$$[A|I] = \left[\begin{array}{ccc|ccc} 1 & 2 & 3 & 1 & 0 & 0 \\ -3 & -2 & -1 & 0 & 1 & 0 \\ -1 & 0 & 1 & 0 & 0 & 1 \end{array}\right]$$

$$\begin{array}{l} 3R_1 + R_2 \to R_2 \\ R_1 + R_3 \to R_3 \end{array} \quad \left[\begin{array}{ccc|ccc} 1 & 2 & 3 & 1 & 0 & 0 \\ 0 & 4 & 8 & 3 & 1 & 0 \\ 0 & 2 & 4 & 1 & 0 & 1 \end{array}\right]$$

$$\begin{array}{l} R_2 + (-2R_1) \to R_1 \\ \\ R_2 + (-2R_3) \to R_3 \end{array} \quad \left[\begin{array}{ccc|ccc} -2 & 0 & 2 & 1 & 1 & 0 \\ 0 & 4 & 8 & 3 & 1 & 0 \\ 0 & 0 & 0 & 1 & 1 & -2 \end{array}\right]$$

Because the last row has all zeros to the left of the vertical bar, there is no way to complete the desired transformation. A has no inverse.

22. Find the inverse of $A = \begin{bmatrix} 2 & 0 & 4 \\ 1 & 0 & -1 \\ 0 & 0 & -2 \end{bmatrix}$, if it exists.

$$[A|I] = \left[\begin{array}{ccc|ccc} 2 & 0 & 4 & 1 & 0 & 0 \\ 1 & 0 & -1 & 0 & 1 & 0 \\ 3 & 0 & -2 & 0 & 0 & 1 \end{array}\right]$$

$$\begin{array}{l} R_1 + (-2)R_2 \to R_2 \\ 3R_1 + (-2)R_3 \to R_3 \end{array} \quad \left[\begin{array}{ccc|ccc} 2 & 0 & 4 & 1 & 0 & 0 \\ 0 & 0 & 6 & 1 & -2 & 0 \\ 0 & 0 & 16 & 3 & 0 & -2 \end{array}\right]$$

Since the second column is all zeros, it will not be possible to get a 1 in the second row, second column position. Therefore, the inverse of the given matrix does not exist

23. Find the inverse of $A = \begin{bmatrix} 1 & 3 & -2 \\ 2 & 7 & -3 \\ 3 & 8 & -5 \end{bmatrix}$, if it exists.

$$[A|I] = \left[\begin{array}{ccc|ccc} 1 & 3 & -2 & 1 & 0 & 0 \\ 2 & 7 & -3 & 0 & 1 & 0 \\ 3 & 8 & -5 & 0 & 0 & 1 \end{array}\right]$$

$$\begin{array}{l} -2R_1 + R_2 \to R_2 \\ -3R_1 + R_3 \to R_3 \end{array} \quad \left[\begin{array}{ccc|ccc} 1 & 3 & -2 & 1 & 0 & 0 \\ 0 & 1 & 1 & -2 & 1 & 0 \\ 0 & -1 & 1 & -3 & 0 & 1 \end{array}\right]$$

$$\begin{array}{l} -3R_2 + R_1 \to R_1 \\ \\ R_2 + R_3 \to R_3 \end{array} \quad \left[\begin{array}{ccc|ccc} 1 & 0 & -5 & 7 & -3 & 0 \\ 0 & 1 & 1 & -2 & 1 & 0 \\ 0 & 0 & 2 & -5 & 1 & 1 \end{array}\right]$$

$$\begin{array}{l} 5R_3 + 2R_1 \to R_1 \\ -1R_3 + 2R_2 \to R_2 \end{array} \quad \left[\begin{array}{ccc|ccc} 2 & 0 & 0 & -11 & -1 & 5 \\ 0 & 2 & 0 & 1 & 1 & -1 \\ 0 & 0 & 2 & -5 & 1 & 1 \end{array}\right]$$

$$\begin{array}{l} \frac{1}{2}R_1 \to R_1 \\ \frac{1}{2}R_2 \to R_2 \\ \frac{1}{2}R_3 \to R_3 \end{array} \quad \left[\begin{array}{ccc|ccc} 1 & 0 & 0 & -\frac{11}{2} & -\frac{1}{2} & \frac{5}{2} \\ 0 & 1 & 0 & \frac{1}{2} & \frac{1}{2} & -\frac{1}{2} \\ 0 & 0 & 1 & -\frac{5}{2} & \frac{1}{2} & \frac{1}{2} \end{array}\right]$$

$$A^{-1} = \begin{bmatrix} -\frac{11}{2} & -\frac{1}{2} & \frac{5}{2} \\ \frac{1}{2} & \frac{1}{2} & -\frac{1}{2} \\ -\frac{5}{2} & \frac{1}{2} & \frac{1}{2} \end{bmatrix}$$

24. Find the inverse of $A = \begin{bmatrix} 4 & 1 & -4 \\ 2 & 1 & -1 \\ -2 & -4 & 5 \end{bmatrix}$, if it exists.

$$[A|I] = \left[\begin{array}{rrr|rrr} 4 & 1 & -4 & 1 & 0 & 0 \\ 2 & 1 & -1 & 0 & 1 & 0 \\ -2 & -4 & 5 & 0 & 0 & 1 \end{array}\right]$$

$-R_1 + 2R_2 \to R_2$
$R_1 + 2R_3 \to R_3$
$$\left[\begin{array}{rrr|rrr} 4 & 1 & -4 & 1 & 0 & 0 \\ 0 & 1 & 2 & -1 & 2 & 0 \\ 0 & -7 & 6 & 1 & 0 & 2 \end{array}\right]$$

$-1R_2 + R_1 \to R_1$
$7R_2 + R_3 \to R_3$
$$\left[\begin{array}{rrr|rrr} 4 & 0 & -6 & 2 & -2 & 0 \\ 0 & 1 & 2 & -1 & 2 & 0 \\ 0 & 0 & 20 & -6 & 14 & 2 \end{array}\right]$$

$3R_3 + 10R_1 \to R_1$
$-1R_3 + 10R_2 \to R_2$
$$\left[\begin{array}{rrr|rrr} 40 & 0 & 0 & 2 & 22 & 6 \\ 0 & 10 & 0 & -4 & 6 & -2 \\ 0 & 0 & 20 & -6 & 12 & 2 \end{array}\right]$$

$\frac{1}{40}R_1 \to R_1$
$\frac{1}{10}R_2 \to R_2$
$\frac{1}{20}R_3 \to R_3$
$$\left[\begin{array}{rrr|rrr} 1 & 0 & 0 & \frac{1}{20} & \frac{11}{20} & \frac{3}{20} \\ 0 & 1 & 0 & -\frac{2}{5} & \frac{3}{5} & -\frac{1}{5} \\ 0 & 0 & 1 & -\frac{3}{10} & \frac{7}{10} & \frac{1}{10} \end{array}\right]$$

$$A^{-1} = \begin{bmatrix} \frac{1}{20} & \frac{11}{20} & \frac{3}{20} \\ -\frac{2}{5} & \frac{3}{5} & -\frac{1}{5} \\ -\frac{3}{10} & \frac{7}{10} & \frac{1}{10} \end{bmatrix}$$

25. Let $A = \begin{bmatrix} 1 & -2 & 3 & 0 \\ 0 & 1 & -1 & 1 \\ -2 & 2 & -2 & 4 \\ 0 & 2 & -3 & 1 \end{bmatrix}$.

$$[A|I] = \left[\begin{array}{rrrr|rrrr} 1 & -2 & 3 & 0 & 1 & 0 & 0 & 0 \\ 0 & 1 & -1 & 1 & 0 & 1 & 0 & 0 \\ -2 & 2 & -2 & 4 & 0 & 0 & 1 & 0 \\ 0 & 2 & -3 & 1 & 0 & 0 & 0 & 1 \end{array}\right]$$

$2R_1 + R_3 \to R_3$
$$\left[\begin{array}{rrrr|rrrr} 1 & -2 & 3 & 0 & 1 & 0 & 0 & 0 \\ 0 & 1 & -1 & 1 & 0 & 1 & 0 & 0 \\ 0 & -2 & 4 & 4 & 2 & 0 & 1 & 0 \\ 0 & 2 & -3 & 1 & 0 & 0 & 0 & 1 \end{array}\right]$$

$2R_2+R_1 \to R_1$
$2R_2+R_3 \to R_3$
$-2R_2+R_4 \to R_4$
$$\left[\begin{array}{rrrr|rrrr} 1 & 0 & 1 & 2 & 1 & 2 & 0 & 0 \\ 0 & 1 & -1 & 1 & 0 & 1 & 0 & 0 \\ 0 & 0 & 2 & 6 & 2 & 2 & 1 & 0 \\ 0 & 0 & -1 & -1 & 0 & -2 & 0 & 1 \end{array}\right]$$

$R_3+(-2)R_1 \to R_1$
$R_3+2R_2 \to R_2$
$R_3 + 2R_4 \to R_4$
$$\left[\begin{array}{rrrr|rrrr} -2 & 0 & 0 & 2 & 0 & -2 & 1 & 0 \\ 0 & 2 & 0 & 8 & 2 & 4 & 1 & 0 \\ 0 & 0 & 2 & 6 & 2 & 2 & 1 & 0 \\ 0 & 0 & 0 & 4 & 2 & -2 & 1 & 2 \end{array}\right]$$

$-2R_1+R_4 \to R_1$
$R_2+(-2)R_4 \to R_2$
$2R_3+(-3)R_4 \to R_3$
$$\left[\begin{array}{rrrr|rrrr} 4 & 0 & 0 & 0 & 2 & 2 & -1 & 2 \\ 0 & 2 & 0 & 0 & -2 & 8 & -1 & -4 \\ 0 & 0 & 4 & 0 & -2 & 10 & -1 & -6 \\ 0 & 0 & 0 & 4 & 2 & -2 & 1 & 2 \end{array}\right]$$

$\frac{1}{4}R_1 \to R_1$
$\frac{1}{2}R_2 \to R_2$
$\frac{1}{4}R_3 \to R_3$
$\frac{1}{4}R_4 \to R_4$
$$\left[\begin{array}{rrrr|rrrr} 1 & 0 & 0 & 0 & \frac{1}{2} & \frac{1}{2} & -\frac{1}{4} & \frac{1}{2} \\ 0 & 1 & 0 & 0 & -1 & 4 & -\frac{1}{2} & -2 \\ 0 & 0 & 1 & 0 & -\frac{1}{2} & \frac{5}{2} & -\frac{1}{4} & -\frac{3}{2} \\ 0 & 0 & 0 & 1 & \frac{1}{2} & -\frac{1}{2} & \frac{1}{4} & \frac{1}{2} \end{array}\right]$$

$$A^{-1} = \begin{bmatrix} \frac{1}{2} & \frac{1}{2} & -\frac{1}{4} & \frac{1}{2} \\ -1 & 4 & -\frac{1}{2} & -2 \\ -\frac{1}{2} & \frac{5}{2} & -\frac{1}{4} & -\frac{3}{2} \\ \frac{1}{2} & -\frac{1}{2} & \frac{1}{4} & \frac{1}{2} \end{bmatrix}$$

26. Find the inverse of $A = \begin{bmatrix} 1 & 1 & 0 & 2 \\ 2 & -1 & 1 & -1 \\ 3 & 3 & 2 & -2 \\ 1 & 2 & 1 & 0 \end{bmatrix}$, if it exists.

$$[A|I] = \left[\begin{array}{rrrr|rrrr} 1 & 1 & 0 & 2 & 1 & 0 & 0 & 0 \\ 2 & -1 & 1 & -1 & 0 & 1 & 0 & 0 \\ 3 & 3 & 2 & -2 & 0 & 0 & 1 & 0 \\ 1 & 2 & 1 & 0 & 0 & 0 & 0 & 1 \end{array}\right]$$

Carry out these row operations to get the next matrix: $-2R_1 + R_2 \to R_2$, $-3R_1 + R_3 \to R_3$, $-1R_1 + R_4 \to R_4$.

$$\left[\begin{array}{rrrr|rrrr} 1 & 1 & 0 & 2 & 1 & 0 & 0 & 0 \\ 0 & -3 & 1 & -5 & -2 & 1 & 0 & 0 \\ 0 & 0 & 2 & -8 & -3 & 0 & 1 & 0 \\ 0 & 1 & 1 & -2 & -1 & 0 & 0 & 1 \end{array}\right]$$

Carry out the row operations $R_2 + 3R_1 \to R_1$, $R_2 + 3R_4 \to R_4$

$$\left[\begin{array}{rrrr|rrrr} 3 & 0 & 1 & 1 & 1 & 1 & 0 & 0 \\ 0 & -3 & 1 & -5 & -2 & 1 & 0 & 0 \\ 0 & 0 & 2 & -8 & -3 & 0 & 1 & 0 \\ 0 & 0 & 4 & -11 & -5 & 1 & 0 & 3 \end{array}\right]$$

$R_3 + (-2)R_1 \to R_1$, $R_3 + (-2)R_2 \to R_2$, $-2R_3 + R_4 \to R_4$

$$\left[\begin{array}{rrrr|rrrr} -6 & 0 & 0 & -10 & -5 & -2 & 1 & 0 \\ 0 & 6 & 0 & 2 & 1 & -2 & 1 & 0 \\ 0 & 0 & 2 & -8 & -3 & 0 & 1 & 0 \\ 0 & 0 & 0 & 5 & 1 & 1 & -2 & 3 \end{array}\right]$$

$2R_4+R_1 \to R_1$, $-2R_4+5R_2 \to R_2$, $8R_4+5R_3 \to R_3$

$$\left[\begin{array}{rrrr|rrrr} -6 & 0 & 0 & 0 & -3 & 0 & -3 & 6 \\ 0 & 30 & 0 & 0 & 3 & -12 & 9 & -6 \\ 0 & 0 & 10 & 0 & -7 & 8 & -11 & 24 \\ 0 & 0 & 0 & 5 & 1 & 1 & -2 & 3 \end{array}\right]$$

$-\frac{1}{6}R_1 \to R_1,\ \frac{1}{30}R_2 \to R_2,\ \frac{1}{10}R_3 \to R_3,\ \frac{1}{5}R_4 \to R_4$

$$\left[\begin{array}{cccc|cccc} 1 & 0 & 0 & 0 & \frac{1}{2} & 0 & \frac{1}{2} & -1 \\ 0 & 1 & 0 & 0 & \frac{1}{10} & -\frac{2}{5} & \frac{3}{10} & -\frac{1}{5} \\ 0 & 0 & 1 & 0 & -\frac{7}{10} & \frac{4}{5} & -\frac{11}{10} & \frac{12}{5} \\ 0 & 0 & 0 & 1 & \frac{1}{5} & \frac{1}{5} & -\frac{2}{5} & \frac{3}{5} \end{array}\right]$$

$$A^{-1} = \begin{bmatrix} \frac{1}{2} & 0 & \frac{1}{2} & -1 \\ \frac{1}{10} & -\frac{2}{5} & \frac{3}{10} & -\frac{1}{5} \\ -\frac{7}{10} & \frac{4}{5} & -\frac{11}{10} & \frac{12}{5} \\ \frac{1}{5} & \frac{1}{5} & -\frac{2}{5} & \frac{3}{5} \end{bmatrix}$$

27. $2x + 5y = 15$
$x + 4y = 9$

First, write the system in matrix form.

$$\begin{bmatrix} 2 & 5 \\ 1 & 4 \end{bmatrix}\begin{bmatrix} x \\ y \end{bmatrix} = \begin{bmatrix} 15 \\ 9 \end{bmatrix}$$

Let $A = \begin{bmatrix} 2 & 5 \\ 1 & 4 \end{bmatrix}$, $X = \begin{bmatrix} x \\ y \end{bmatrix}$, and $B = \begin{bmatrix} 15 \\ 9 \end{bmatrix}$.

The system in matrix form is $AX = B$. We wish to find $X = A^{-1}AX = A^{-1}B$. Use row operations to find A^{-1}.

$$[A|I] = \left[\begin{array}{cc|cc} 2 & 5 & 1 & 0 \\ 1 & 4 & 0 & 1 \end{array}\right]$$

$$-1R_1 + 2R_2 \to R_2 \left[\begin{array}{cc|cc} 2 & 5 & 1 & 0 \\ 0 & 3 & -1 & 2 \end{array}\right]$$

$$-5R_2 + 3R_1 \to R_1 \left[\begin{array}{cc|cc} 6 & 0 & 8 & -10 \\ 0 & 3 & -1 & 2 \end{array}\right]$$

$$\begin{array}{l} \frac{1}{6}R_1 \to R_1 \\ \frac{1}{3}R_2 \to R_2 \end{array} \left[\begin{array}{cc|cc} 1 & 0 & \frac{4}{3} & -\frac{5}{3} \\ 0 & 1 & -\frac{1}{3} & \frac{2}{3} \end{array}\right]$$

$$A^{-1} = \begin{bmatrix} \frac{4}{3} & -\frac{5}{3} \\ -\frac{1}{3} & \frac{2}{3} \end{bmatrix} = \frac{1}{3}\begin{bmatrix} 4 & -5 \\ -1 & 2 \end{bmatrix}$$

Next find the product $A^{-1}B$.

$$X = A^{-1}B = \begin{bmatrix} \frac{4}{3} & -\frac{5}{3} \\ -\frac{1}{3} & \frac{2}{3} \end{bmatrix}\begin{bmatrix} 15 \\ 9 \end{bmatrix}$$

$$= \frac{1}{3}\begin{bmatrix} 4 & -5 \\ -1 & 2 \end{bmatrix}\begin{bmatrix} 15 \\ 9 \end{bmatrix}$$

$$= \frac{1}{3}\begin{bmatrix} 15 \\ 3 \end{bmatrix} = \begin{bmatrix} 5 \\ 1 \end{bmatrix}$$

Thus, the solution is $(5, 1)$.

28. $-x + 2y = 15$
$-2x - y = 20$

This system may be written as the matrix equation

$$\begin{bmatrix} -1 & 2 \\ -2 & -1 \end{bmatrix}\begin{bmatrix} x \\ y \end{bmatrix} = \begin{bmatrix} 15 \\ 20 \end{bmatrix}.$$

In Exercise 12, it was calculated that

$$\begin{bmatrix} -1 & 2 \\ -2 & -1 \end{bmatrix}^{-1} = \begin{bmatrix} -\frac{1}{5} & -\frac{2}{5} \\ \frac{2}{5} & -\frac{1}{5} \end{bmatrix},$$

and we now know that $X = A^{-1}B$ is the solution to $AX = B$.

Thus,

$$\begin{bmatrix} x \\ y \end{bmatrix} = \begin{bmatrix} -\frac{1}{5} & -\frac{2}{5} \\ \frac{2}{5} & -\frac{1}{5} \end{bmatrix}\begin{bmatrix} 15 \\ 20 \end{bmatrix} = \begin{bmatrix} -11 \\ 2 \end{bmatrix},$$

and $(-11, 2)$ is the solution of the system.

29. $2x + y = 5$
$5x + 3y = 13$

Let $A = \begin{bmatrix} 2 & 1 \\ 5 & 3 \end{bmatrix}$, $X = \begin{bmatrix} x \\ y \end{bmatrix}$, $B = \begin{bmatrix} 5 \\ 13 \end{bmatrix}$.

Use row operations to obtain

$$A^{-1} = \begin{bmatrix} 3 & -1 \\ -5 & 2 \end{bmatrix}.$$

$$X = A^{-1}B = \begin{bmatrix} 3 & -1 \\ -5 & 2 \end{bmatrix}\begin{bmatrix} 5 \\ 13 \end{bmatrix} = \begin{bmatrix} 2 \\ 1 \end{bmatrix}$$

The solution is $(2, 1)$.

30. $-x - 2y = 8$
$3x + 4y = 24$

This system may be written as the matrix equation

$$\begin{bmatrix} -1 & -2 \\ 3 & 4 \end{bmatrix}\begin{bmatrix} x \\ y \end{bmatrix} = \begin{bmatrix} 8 \\ 24 \end{bmatrix}.$$

In Exercise 14, it was calculated that

$$\begin{bmatrix} -1 & -2 \\ 3 & 4 \end{bmatrix}^{-1} = \begin{bmatrix} 2 & 1 \\ -\frac{3}{2} & -\frac{1}{2} \end{bmatrix},$$

and since $X = A^{-1}B$, we get

$$\begin{bmatrix} x \\ y \end{bmatrix} = \begin{bmatrix} 2 & 1 \\ -\frac{3}{2} & -\frac{1}{2} \end{bmatrix}\begin{bmatrix} 8 \\ 24 \end{bmatrix} = \begin{bmatrix} 40 \\ -24 \end{bmatrix}.$$

Therefore, the solution is $(40, -24)$.

31. $3x - 2y = 3$
$7x - 5y = 0$

First, write the system in matrix form.

$$\begin{bmatrix} 3 & -2 \\ 7 & -5 \end{bmatrix}\begin{bmatrix} x \\ y \end{bmatrix} = \begin{bmatrix} 3 \\ 0 \end{bmatrix}$$

Let $A = \begin{bmatrix} 3 & -2 \\ 7 & -5 \end{bmatrix}$, $X = \begin{bmatrix} x \\ y \end{bmatrix}$, and $B = \begin{bmatrix} 3 \\ 0 \end{bmatrix}$.

The system is in matrix form $AX = B$. We wish to find $X = A^{-1}AX = A^{-1}B$. Use row operations to find A^{-1}.

$$[A|I] = \left[\begin{array}{cc|cc} 3 & -2 & 1 & 0 \\ 7 & -5 & 0 & 1 \end{array}\right]$$

$$-7R_1 + 3R_2 \to R_2 \left[\begin{array}{cc|cc} 3 & -2 & 1 & 0 \\ 0 & -1 & -7 & 3 \end{array}\right]$$

$$-2R_2 + R_1 \to R_1 \left[\begin{array}{cc|cc} 3 & 0 & 15 & -6 \\ 0 & -1 & -7 & 3 \end{array}\right]$$

$$\begin{array}{r} \frac{1}{3}R_1 \to R_1 \\ -1R_2 \to R_2 \end{array} \left[\begin{array}{cc|cc} 1 & 0 & 5 & -2 \\ 0 & 1 & 7 & -3 \end{array}\right]$$

$$A^{-1} = \begin{bmatrix} 5 & -2 \\ 7 & -3 \end{bmatrix}$$

Next find the product $A^{-1}B$.

$$X = A^{-1}B = \begin{bmatrix} 5 & -2 \\ 7 & -3 \end{bmatrix} \begin{bmatrix} 3 \\ 0 \end{bmatrix} = \begin{bmatrix} 15 \\ 21 \end{bmatrix}$$

Thus, the solution is $(15, 21)$.

32. $3x - 6y = 1$
$-5x + 9y = -1$

This system may be written as the matrix equation

$$\begin{bmatrix} 3 & -6 \\ -5 & 9 \end{bmatrix} \begin{bmatrix} x \\ y \end{bmatrix} = \begin{bmatrix} 1 \\ -1 \end{bmatrix}.$$

Calculate the inverse of

$$A = \begin{bmatrix} 3 & -6 \\ -5 & 9 \end{bmatrix}.$$

$$A^{-1} = \begin{bmatrix} -3 & -2 \\ -\frac{5}{3} & -1 \end{bmatrix},$$

so

$$\begin{bmatrix} x \\ y \end{bmatrix} = \begin{bmatrix} -3 & -2 \\ -\frac{5}{3} & -1 \end{bmatrix} \begin{bmatrix} 1 \\ -1 \end{bmatrix} = \begin{bmatrix} -1 \\ -\frac{2}{3} \end{bmatrix}.$$

The solution is $\left(-1, -\frac{2}{3}\right)$.

33. $-x - 8y = 12$
$3x + 24y = -36$

Let $A = \begin{bmatrix} -1 & -8 \\ 3 & 24 \end{bmatrix}$, $X = \begin{bmatrix} x \\ y \end{bmatrix}$, $B = \begin{bmatrix} 12 \\ -36 \end{bmatrix}$.

Using row operations on $[A|I]$ leads to the matrix

$$\left[\begin{array}{cc|cc} 1 & 8 & -1 & 0 \\ 0 & 0 & 3 & 1 \end{array}\right],$$

but the zeros in the second row indicate that matrix A does not have an inverse. We cannot complete the solution by this method.

Since the second equation is a multiple of the first, the equations are dependent. Solve the first equation of the system for x.

$$\begin{aligned} -x - 8y &= 12 \\ -x &= 8y + 12 \\ x &= -8y - 12 \end{aligned}$$

The solution is $(-8y - 12, y)$, where y is any real number.

34. $2x + 7y = 14$
$3x + 4y = 8$

First, write the system in matrix form.

$$\begin{bmatrix} 2 & 7 \\ 3 & 4 \end{bmatrix} \begin{bmatrix} x \\ y \end{bmatrix} = \begin{bmatrix} 14 \\ 8 \end{bmatrix}$$

Let $A = \begin{bmatrix} 2 & 7 \\ 3 & 4 \end{bmatrix}$, $X = \begin{bmatrix} x \\ y \end{bmatrix}$, and $B = \begin{bmatrix} 14 \\ 8 \end{bmatrix}$.

The system is in matrix form $AX = B$. We wish to find $X = A^{-1}AX = A^{-1}B$. Use row operations to find A^{-1}.

$$[A|I] = \left[\begin{array}{cc|cc} 2 & 7 & 1 & 0 \\ 3 & 4 & 0 & 1 \end{array}\right]$$

$$-3R_1 + 2R_2 \to R_2 \left[\begin{array}{cc|cc} 2 & 7 & 1 & 0 \\ 0 & -13 & -3 & 2 \end{array}\right]$$

$$7R_2 + 13R_1 \to R_1 \left[\begin{array}{cc|cc} 26 & 0 & -8 & 14 \\ 0 & -13 & -3 & 2 \end{array}\right]$$

$$\begin{array}{r} \frac{1}{26}R_1 \to R_1 \\ -\frac{1}{13}R_2 \to R_2 \end{array} \left[\begin{array}{cc|cc} 1 & 0 & -\frac{4}{13} & \frac{7}{13} \\ 0 & 1 & \frac{3}{13} & -\frac{2}{13} \end{array}\right]$$

$$A^{-1} = \begin{bmatrix} -\frac{4}{13} & \frac{7}{13} \\ \frac{3}{13} & -\frac{2}{13} \end{bmatrix} = \frac{1}{13}\begin{bmatrix} -4 & 7 \\ 3 & -2 \end{bmatrix}$$

Next find the product $A^{-1}B$.

$$X = A^{-1}B = \frac{1}{13}\begin{bmatrix} -4 & 7 \\ 3 & -2 \end{bmatrix}\begin{bmatrix} 14 \\ 8 \end{bmatrix} = \frac{1}{13}\begin{bmatrix} 0 \\ 26 \end{bmatrix} =$$

$$\begin{bmatrix} 0 \\ 2 \end{bmatrix}$$

Thus, the solution $(0, 2)$.

35.
$$\begin{aligned} -x - y - z &= 1 \\ 4x + 5y \quad &= -2 \\ y - 3z &= 3 \end{aligned}$$

has coefficient matrix

$$A = \begin{bmatrix} -1 & -1 & -1 \\ 4 & 5 & 0 \\ 0 & 1 & -3 \end{bmatrix}.$$

In Exercise 19, it was found that

$$A^{-1} = \begin{bmatrix} -1 & -1 & -1 \\ 4 & 5 & 0 \\ 0 & 1 & 3 \end{bmatrix}^{-1}$$

$$= \begin{bmatrix} 15 & 4 & -5 \\ -12 & -3 & 4 \\ -4 & -1 & 1 \end{bmatrix}.$$

Since $X = A^{-1}B$,

$$\begin{bmatrix} x \\ y \\ z \end{bmatrix} = \begin{bmatrix} 15 & 4 & -5 \\ -12 & -3 & 4 \\ -4 & -1 & 1 \end{bmatrix}\begin{bmatrix} 1 \\ -2 \\ 3 \end{bmatrix} = \begin{bmatrix} -8 \\ 6 \\ 1 \end{bmatrix}.$$

The solution is $(-8, 6, 1)$.

36.
$$\begin{aligned} 2x + y \quad &= 1 \\ 3y + z &= 8 \\ 4x - y - 3z &= 8 \end{aligned}$$

has coefficient matrix

$$A = \begin{bmatrix} 2 & 1 & 0 \\ 0 & 3 & 1 \\ 4 & -1 & -3 \end{bmatrix}.$$

In Exercise 20, it was calculated that

$$A^{-1} = \begin{bmatrix} 2 & 1 & 0 \\ 0 & 3 & 1 \\ 4 & -1 & -3 \end{bmatrix}^{-1} = \begin{bmatrix} \frac{2}{3} & -\frac{1}{4} & -\frac{1}{12} \\ -\frac{1}{3} & \frac{1}{2} & \frac{1}{6} \\ 1 & -\frac{1}{2} & -\frac{1}{2} \end{bmatrix}.$$

Since $X = A^{-1}B$,

$$\begin{bmatrix} x \\ y \\ z \end{bmatrix} = \begin{bmatrix} \frac{2}{3} & -\frac{1}{4} & -\frac{1}{12} \\ -\frac{1}{3} & \frac{1}{2} & \frac{1}{6} \\ 1 & -\frac{1}{2} & -\frac{1}{2} \end{bmatrix}\begin{bmatrix} 1 \\ 8 \\ 8 \end{bmatrix} = \begin{bmatrix} -2 \\ 5 \\ -7 \end{bmatrix}.$$

Thus, the solution is $(-2, 5, -7)$.

37.
$$\begin{aligned} x + 3y - 2z &= 4 \\ 2x + 7y - 3z &= 8 \\ 3x + 8y - 5z &= -4 \end{aligned}$$

has coefficient matrix

$$A = \begin{bmatrix} 1 & 3 & -2 \\ 2 & 7 & -3 \\ 3 & 8 & -5 \end{bmatrix}.$$

In Exercise 23, it was calculated that

$$A^{-1} = \begin{bmatrix} 1 & 3 & -2 \\ 2 & 7 & -3 \\ 3 & 8 & -5 \end{bmatrix}^{-1} = \begin{bmatrix} -\frac{11}{2} & -\frac{1}{2} & \frac{5}{2} \\ \frac{1}{2} & \frac{1}{2} & -\frac{1}{2} \\ -\frac{5}{2} & \frac{1}{2} & \frac{1}{2} \end{bmatrix}$$

$$= \frac{1}{2}\begin{bmatrix} -11 & -1 & 5 \\ 1 & 1 & -1 \\ -5 & 1 & 1 \end{bmatrix}.$$

Since $X = A^{-1}B$.

$$\begin{bmatrix} x \\ y \\ z \end{bmatrix} = \frac{1}{2}\begin{bmatrix} -11 & -1 & 5 \\ 1 & 1 & -1 \\ -5 & 1 & 1 \end{bmatrix}\begin{bmatrix} 4 \\ 8 \\ -4 \end{bmatrix}$$

$$= \frac{1}{2}\begin{bmatrix} -72 \\ 16 \\ -16 \end{bmatrix} = \begin{bmatrix} -36 \\ 8 \\ -8 \end{bmatrix}$$

Thus, the solution is $(-36, 8, -8)$.

38.
$$\begin{aligned} 4x + y - 4z &= 17 \\ 2x + y - z &= 12 \\ -2x - 4y + 5z &= 17 \end{aligned}$$

has coefficient matrix

$$A = \begin{bmatrix} 4 & 1 & -4 \\ 2 & 1 & -1 \\ -2 & -4 & 5 \end{bmatrix}.$$

In Exercise 24, it was calculated that

$$A^{-1} = \begin{bmatrix} 4 & 1 & -4 \\ 2 & 1 & -1 \\ -2 & -4 & 5 \end{bmatrix} = \begin{bmatrix} \frac{1}{20} & \frac{11}{20} & \frac{3}{20} \\ -\frac{2}{5} & \frac{3}{5} & -\frac{1}{5} \\ -\frac{3}{10} & \frac{7}{10} & \frac{1}{10} \end{bmatrix}$$

$$= \frac{1}{20}\begin{bmatrix} 1 & 11 & 3 \\ -8 & 12 & -4 \\ -6 & 14 & 2 \end{bmatrix}.$$

Since $X = A^{-1}B$,

$$\begin{bmatrix} x \\ y \\ z \end{bmatrix} = \frac{1}{20}\begin{bmatrix} 1 & 11 & 3 \\ -8 & 12 & -4 \\ -6 & 14 & 2 \end{bmatrix}\begin{bmatrix} 17 \\ 12 \\ 17 \end{bmatrix}$$

$$= \frac{1}{20}\begin{bmatrix} 200 \\ -60 \\ 100 \end{bmatrix}$$

$$= \begin{bmatrix} 10 \\ -3 \\ 5 \end{bmatrix}.$$

Thus, the solution is $(10, -3, 5)$.

39.
$$\begin{aligned} 2x - 2y \quad &= 5 \\ 4y + 8z &= 7 \\ x \quad + 2z &= 1 \end{aligned}$$

has coefficient matrix

$$A = \begin{bmatrix} 2 & -2 & 0 \\ 0 & 4 & 8 \\ 1 & 0 & 2 \end{bmatrix}.$$

However, using row operations on $[A|I]$ shows that A does not have an inverse, so another method must be used.

Try the Gauss-Jordan method. The augmented matrix is

$$\left[\begin{array}{ccc|c} 2 & -2 & 0 & 5 \\ 0 & 4 & 8 & 7 \\ 1 & 0 & 2 & 1 \end{array}\right].$$

After several row operations, we obtain the matrix

$$\left[\begin{array}{ccc|c} 1 & 0 & 2 & \frac{17}{4} \\ 0 & 1 & 2 & \frac{7}{4} \\ 0 & 0 & 0 & 13 \end{array}\right].$$

The bottom row of this matrix shows that the system has no solution, since $0 = 13$ is a false statement.

40.
$$\begin{aligned} x \quad\quad + 2z &= -1 \\ y - \quad z &= 5 \\ -x - y \quad\quad &= -8 \end{aligned}$$

The system may be written as the matrix equation

$$\begin{bmatrix} 1 & 0 & 2 \\ 0 & 1 & -1 \\ -1 & -1 & 0 \end{bmatrix}\begin{bmatrix} x \\ y \\ z \end{bmatrix} = \begin{bmatrix} -1 \\ 5 \\ -8 \end{bmatrix}.$$

First calculate A^{-1} using row operations.

$$[A|I] = \left[\begin{array}{ccc|ccc} 1 & 0 & 2 & 1 & 0 & 0 \\ 0 & 1 & -1 & 0 & 1 & 0 \\ -1 & -1 & 0 & 0 & 0 & 1 \end{array}\right]$$

$$R_1 + R_3 \rightarrow R_3 \left[\begin{array}{ccc|ccc} 1 & 0 & 2 & 1 & 0 & 0 \\ 0 & 1 & -1 & 0 & 1 & 0 \\ 0 & -1 & 2 & 1 & 0 & 1 \end{array}\right]$$

$$R_2 + R_3 \rightarrow R_3 \left[\begin{array}{ccc|ccc} 1 & 0 & 2 & 1 & 0 & 0 \\ 0 & 1 & -1 & 0 & 1 & 0 \\ 0 & 0 & 1 & 1 & 1 & 1 \end{array}\right]$$

$$\begin{matrix} -2R_3 + R_1 \rightarrow R_1 \\ R_3 + R_2 \rightarrow R_2 \end{matrix} \left[\begin{array}{ccc|ccc} 1 & 0 & 0 & -1 & -2 & -2 \\ 0 & 1 & 0 & 1 & 2 & 1 \\ 0 & 0 & 1 & 1 & 1 & 1 \end{array}\right]$$

$$A^{-1} = \begin{bmatrix} -1 & -2 & -2 \\ 1 & 2 & 1 \\ 1 & 1 & 1 \end{bmatrix}$$

Now use $X = A^{-1}B$ to solve.

$$X = A^{-1}B = \begin{bmatrix} -1 & -2 & -2 \\ 1 & 2 & 1 \\ 1 & 1 & 1 \end{bmatrix}\begin{bmatrix} -1 \\ 5 \\ -8 \end{bmatrix} = \begin{bmatrix} 7 \\ 1 \\ -4 \end{bmatrix}$$

The solution is $(7, 1, -4)$.

41.
$$\begin{aligned} x - 2y + 3z \quad\quad &= 4 \\ y - \ z + \ w &= -8 \\ -2x + 2y - 2z + 4w &= 12 \\ 2y - 3z + \ w &= -4 \end{aligned}$$

has coefficient matrix

$$A = \begin{bmatrix} 1 & -2 & 3 & 0 \\ 0 & 1 & -1 & 1 \\ -2 & 2 & -2 & 4 \\ 0 & 2 & -3 & 1 \end{bmatrix}.$$

In Exercise 25, it was found that

$$A^{-1} = \begin{bmatrix} \frac{1}{2} & \frac{1}{2} & -\frac{1}{4} & \frac{1}{2} \\ -1 & 4 & -\frac{1}{2} & -2 \\ -\frac{1}{2} & \frac{5}{2} & -\frac{1}{4} & -\frac{3}{2} \\ \frac{1}{2} & -\frac{1}{2} & \frac{1}{4} & \frac{1}{2} \end{bmatrix}.$$

Since $X = A^{-1}B$,

$$\begin{bmatrix} x \\ y \\ z \\ w \end{bmatrix} = \begin{bmatrix} \frac{1}{2} & \frac{1}{2} & -\frac{1}{4} & \frac{1}{2} \\ -1 & 4 & -\frac{1}{2} & -2 \\ -\frac{1}{2} & \frac{5}{2} & -\frac{1}{4} & -\frac{3}{2} \\ \frac{1}{2} & -\frac{1}{2} & \frac{1}{4} & \frac{1}{2} \end{bmatrix}\begin{bmatrix} 4 \\ -8 \\ 12 \\ -4 \end{bmatrix} = \begin{bmatrix} -7 \\ -34 \\ -19 \\ 7 \end{bmatrix}.$$

The solution is $(-7, -34, -19, 7)$.

42. $$\begin{aligned} x + y \quad\quad + 2w &= 3 \\ 2x - y + z - w &= 3 \\ 3x + 3y + 2z - 2w &= 5 \\ x + 2y + z \quad\quad &= 3 \end{aligned}$$

This system may be written as the matrix equation

$$\begin{bmatrix} 1 & 1 & 0 & 2 \\ 2 & -1 & 1 & -1 \\ 3 & 3 & 2 & -2 \\ 1 & 2 & 1 & 0 \end{bmatrix} \begin{bmatrix} x \\ y \\ z \\ w \end{bmatrix} = \begin{bmatrix} 3 \\ 3 \\ 5 \\ 3 \end{bmatrix}.$$

The inverse of this coefficient matrix was calculated in Exercise 26. Use that result to obtain

$$\begin{bmatrix} x \\ y \\ z \\ w \end{bmatrix} = \begin{bmatrix} \frac{1}{2} & 0 & \frac{1}{2} & -1 \\ \frac{1}{10} & -\frac{2}{5} & \frac{3}{10} & -\frac{1}{5} \\ -\frac{7}{10} & \frac{4}{5} & -\frac{11}{10} & \frac{12}{5} \\ \frac{1}{5} & \frac{1}{5} & -\frac{2}{5} & \frac{3}{5} \end{bmatrix} \begin{bmatrix} 3 \\ 3 \\ 5 \\ 3 \end{bmatrix} = \begin{bmatrix} 1 \\ 0 \\ 2 \\ 1 \end{bmatrix}.$$

The solution is $(1, 0, 2, 1)$.

In Exercises 44–48, let $A = \begin{bmatrix} a & b \\ c & d \end{bmatrix}$.

43. $IA = \begin{bmatrix} 1 & 0 \\ 0 & 1 \end{bmatrix} \begin{bmatrix} a & b \\ c & d \end{bmatrix} = \begin{bmatrix} a & b \\ c & d \end{bmatrix} = A$

Thus, $IA = A$.

44. $$\begin{aligned} AI &= \begin{bmatrix} a & b \\ c & d \end{bmatrix} \begin{bmatrix} 1 & 0 \\ 0 & 1 \end{bmatrix} \\ &= \begin{bmatrix} a \cdot 1 + b \cdot 0 & a \cdot 0 + b \cdot 1 \\ c \cdot 1 + d \cdot 0 & c \cdot 0 + d \cdot 1 \end{bmatrix} \\ &= \begin{bmatrix} a & b \\ c & d \end{bmatrix} = A \end{aligned}$$

45. $A \cdot 0 = \begin{bmatrix} a & b \\ c & d \end{bmatrix} \begin{bmatrix} 0 & 0 \\ 0 & 0 \end{bmatrix} = \begin{bmatrix} 0 & 0 \\ 0 & 0 \end{bmatrix} = 0$

Thus, $A \cdot 0 = 0$.

46. $$\left[\begin{array}{cc|cc} a & b & 1 & 0 \\ c & d & 0 & 1 \end{array}\right]$$

$$-cR_1 + aR_2 \to R_2 \quad \left[\begin{array}{cc|cc} a & b & 1 & 0 \\ 0 & ad - bc & -c & a \end{array}\right]$$

$$-\frac{b}{ad-bc}R_2 + R_1 \to R_1 \quad \left[\begin{array}{cc|cc} a & 0 & \frac{ad}{ad-bc} & \frac{-ab}{ad-bc} \\ 0 & ad - bc & -c & a \end{array}\right]$$

$$\begin{array}{r} \frac{1}{a}R_1 \to R_1 \\ \frac{1}{ad-bc}R_2 \to R_2 \end{array} \quad \left[\begin{array}{cc|cc} 1 & 0 & \frac{d}{ad-bc} & \frac{-b}{ad-bc} \\ 0 & 1 & \frac{-c}{ad-bc} & \frac{a}{ad-bc} \end{array}\right]$$

Thus, $A^{-1} = \begin{bmatrix} \frac{d}{ad-bc} & \frac{-b}{ad-bc} \\ \frac{-c}{ad-bc} & \frac{a}{ad-bc} \end{bmatrix}$, if $ad - bc \neq 0$..

47. In Exercise 46, it was found that

$$A^{-1} = \frac{1}{ad - bc} \begin{bmatrix} d & -b \\ -c & a \end{bmatrix}.$$

$$\begin{aligned} A^{-1}A &= \left(\frac{1}{ad - bc} \begin{bmatrix} d & -b \\ -c & a \end{bmatrix} \right) \begin{bmatrix} a & b \\ c & d \end{bmatrix} \\ &= \frac{1}{ad - bc} \left(\begin{bmatrix} d & -b \\ -c & a \end{bmatrix} \begin{bmatrix} a & b \\ c & d \end{bmatrix} \right) \\ &= \frac{1}{ad - bc} \begin{bmatrix} ad - bc & 0 \\ 0 & ad - bc \end{bmatrix} \\ &= \begin{bmatrix} 1 & 0 \\ 0 & 1 \end{bmatrix} = I \end{aligned}$$

Thus, $A^{-1}A = I$.

48. Show that $AA^{-1} = I$.

From Exercise 46,

$$A^{-1} = \begin{bmatrix} \frac{d}{ad-bc} & \frac{-b}{ad-bc} \\ \frac{-c}{ad-bc} & \frac{a}{ad-bc} \end{bmatrix}.$$

$$\begin{aligned} AA^{-1} &= \begin{bmatrix} a & b \\ c & d \end{bmatrix} \begin{bmatrix} \frac{d}{ad-bc} & \frac{-b}{ad-bc} \\ \frac{-c}{ad-bc} & \frac{a}{ad-bc} \end{bmatrix} \\ &= \begin{bmatrix} \frac{ad-bc}{ad-bc} & \frac{-ab+ab}{ad-bc} \\ \frac{cd-cd}{ad-bc} & \frac{-bc+ad}{ad-bc} \end{bmatrix} = \begin{bmatrix} 1 & 0 \\ 0 & 1 \end{bmatrix} = I. \end{aligned}$$

49. $$\begin{aligned} AB &= O \\ A^{-1}(AB) &= A^{-1} \cdot O \\ (A^{-1}A)B &= O \\ I \cdot B &= O \\ B &= O \end{aligned}$$

Thus, if $AB = O$ and A^{-1} exists, then $B = O$.

50. Assume that matrix A has two inverses B and C. Then

$$AB = BA = I \quad (1)$$
$$\text{and} \quad AC = CA = I. \quad (2)$$

Multiply equation (1) by C.

$$C(AB) = C(BA) = CI$$

Since matrix multiplication is associative,

$$C(AB) = (CA)B.$$

Since I is an identity matrix,

$$CI = C.$$

Combining these results, we have

$$C(AB) = C$$
$$(CA)B = C.$$

From equation (2), $CA = I$, giving

$$IB = C$$
$$B = C.$$

Thus, if it exists, the inverse of a matrix is unique.

51. This exercise should be solved by graphing calculator or computer methods. The solution, which may vary slightly, is

$$C^{-1} = \begin{bmatrix} -0.0477 & -0.0230 & 0.0292 & 0.0895 & -0.0402 \\ 0.0921 & 0.0150 & 0.0321 & 0.0209 & -0.0276 \\ -0.0678 & 0.0315 & -0.0404 & 0.0326 & 0.0373 \\ 0.0171 & -0.0248 & 0.0069 & -0.0003 & 0.0246 \\ -0.0208 & 0.0740 & 0.0096 & -0.1018 & 0.0646 \end{bmatrix}.$$

(Entries are rounded to 4 places.)

52. Use a graphing calculator or a computer to perform this calculation. With entries rounded to 6 places, the answer is

$$(CD)^{-1} = \begin{bmatrix} 0.010146 & -0.011883 & 0.002772 & 0.020724 & -0.012273 \\ 0.006353 & 0.014233 & -0.001861 & -0.029146 & 0.019225 \\ -0.000638 & 0.006782 & -0.004823 & -0.022658 & 0.019344 \\ -0.005261 & 0.003781 & 0.006192 & 0.004837 & -0.006910 \\ -0.012252 & -0.001177 & -0.006126 & 0.006744 & 0.002792 \end{bmatrix}.$$

53. This exercise should be solved by graphing calculator or computer methods. The solution, which may vary slightly, is

$$D^{-1} = \begin{bmatrix} 0.0394 & 0.0880 & 0.0033 & 0.0530 & -0.1499 \\ -0.1492 & 0.0289 & 0.0187 & 0.1033 & 0.1668 \\ -0.1330 & -0.0543 & 0.0356 & 0.1768 & 0.1055 \\ 0.1407 & 0.0175 & -0.0453 & -0.1344 & 0.0655 \\ 0.0102 & -0.0653 & 0.0993 & 0.0085 & -0.0388 \end{bmatrix}.$$

(Entries are rounded to 4 places.)

54. Use a graphing calculator or a computer to determine that, no, $C^{-1}D^{-1}$ and $(CD)^{-1}$ are not equal.

55. This exercise should be solved by graphing calculator or computer methods. The solution may vary slightly. The answer is, yes, $D^{-1}C^{-1} = (CD)^{-1}$.

56. Use a graphing calculator to obtain

$$A^{-1} = \begin{bmatrix} -\frac{2}{27} & \frac{4}{27} & \frac{1}{27} \\ \frac{2}{99} & -\frac{31}{99} & \frac{8}{99} \\ \frac{53}{297} & -\frac{79}{297} & \frac{14}{297} \end{bmatrix}.$$

Use a graphing calculator again to solve the matrix equation $X = A^{-1}B$.

$$X = \begin{bmatrix} 1.18519 \\ -0.95960 \\ -1.30976 \end{bmatrix}$$

57. This exercise should be solved by graphing calculator or computer methods. The solution, which may vary slightly, is

$$\begin{bmatrix} 1.51482 \\ 0.053479 \\ -0.637242 \\ 0.462629 \end{bmatrix}.$$

58. Use a graphing calculator or a computer to obtain

$$X = \begin{bmatrix} 0.489558 \\ 1.00104 \\ 2.11853 \\ -1.20793 \\ -0.961346 \end{bmatrix}.$$

59. **(a)** The matrix is $B = \begin{bmatrix} 72 \\ 48 \\ 60 \end{bmatrix}$.

(b) The matrix equation is

$$\begin{bmatrix} 2 & 4 & 2 \\ 2 & 1 & 2 \\ 2 & 1 & 3 \end{bmatrix} \begin{bmatrix} x_1 \\ x_2 \\ x_3 \end{bmatrix} = \begin{bmatrix} 72 \\ 48 \\ 60 \end{bmatrix}.$$

(c) To solve the system, begin by using row operations to find A^{-1}.

$$[A|I] = \left[\begin{array}{ccc|ccc} 2 & 4 & 2 & 1 & 0 & 0 \\ 2 & 1 & 2 & 0 & 1 & 0 \\ 2 & 1 & 3 & 0 & 0 & 1 \end{array}\right]$$

$$\begin{array}{r} \\ R_1 - 1R_2 \to R_2 \\ R_1 - 1R_3 \to R_3 \end{array} \left[\begin{array}{ccc|ccc} 2 & 4 & 2 & 1 & 0 & 0 \\ 0 & 3 & 0 & 1 & -1 & 0 \\ 0 & 3 & -1 & 1 & 0 & -1 \end{array}\right]$$

$$\begin{array}{r} -4R_2 + 3R_1 \to R_1 \\ \\ R_2 - 1R_3 \to R_3 \end{array} \left[\begin{array}{ccc|ccc} 6 & 0 & 6 & -1 & 4 & 0 \\ 0 & 3 & 0 & 1 & -1 & 0 \\ 0 & 0 & 1 & 0 & -1 & 1 \end{array}\right]$$

$$\begin{array}{r} \\ -6R_3 + R_1 \to R_1 \\ \\ \end{array} \left[\begin{array}{ccc|ccc} 6 & 0 & 0 & -1 & 10 & -6 \\ 0 & 3 & 0 & 1 & -1 & 0 \\ 0 & 0 & 1 & 0 & -1 & 1 \end{array}\right]$$

$$\begin{array}{r} \frac{1}{6}R_1 \to R_1 \\ \frac{1}{3}R_2 \to R_2 \\ \\ \end{array} \left[\begin{array}{ccc|ccc} 1 & 0 & 0 & -\frac{1}{6} & \frac{5}{3} & -1 \\ 0 & 1 & 0 & \frac{1}{3} & -\frac{1}{3} & 0 \\ 0 & 0 & 1 & 0 & -1 & 1 \end{array}\right]$$

The inverse matrix is

$$A^{-1} = \begin{bmatrix} -\frac{1}{6} & \frac{5}{3} & -1 \\ \frac{1}{3} & -\frac{1}{3} & 0 \\ 0 & -1 & 1 \end{bmatrix}.$$

Since $X = A^{-1}B$,

$$\begin{bmatrix} x_1 \\ x_2 \\ x_3 \end{bmatrix} = \begin{bmatrix} -\frac{1}{6} & \frac{5}{3} & -1 \\ \frac{1}{3} & -\frac{1}{3} & 0 \\ 0 & -1 & 1 \end{bmatrix} \begin{bmatrix} 72 \\ 48 \\ 60 \end{bmatrix} = \begin{bmatrix} 8 \\ 8 \\ 12 \end{bmatrix}.$$

There are 8 daily orders for type I, 8 for type II, and 12 for type III.

60. Let $x =$ the number of transistors,
$y =$ the number of resistors, and
$z =$ the number of computer chips.

Solve the following system:

$$\begin{aligned} 3x + 3y + 2z &= \text{amount of copper available;} \\ x + 2y + z &= \text{amount of zinc available;} \\ 2x + y + 2z &= \text{amount of glass available.} \end{aligned}$$

First, find the inverse of the coefficient matrix

$$\begin{bmatrix} 3 & 3 & 2 \\ 1 & 2 & 1 \\ 2 & 1 & 2 \end{bmatrix}.$$

$$\left[\begin{array}{ccc|ccc} 3 & 3 & 2 & 1 & 0 & 0 \\ 1 & 2 & 1 & 0 & 1 & 0 \\ 2 & 1 & 2 & 0 & 0 & 1 \end{array}\right]$$

$$\begin{array}{r} \\ R_1 + (-3)R_2 \to R_2 \\ 2R_1 + (-3)R_3 \to R_3 \end{array} \left[\begin{array}{ccc|ccc} 3 & 3 & 2 & 1 & 0 & 0 \\ 0 & -3 & -1 & 1 & -3 & 0 \\ 0 & 3 & -2 & 2 & 0 & -3 \end{array}\right]$$

$$\begin{array}{r} R_2 + R_1 \to R_1 \\ \\ R_2 + R_3 \to R_3 \end{array} \left[\begin{array}{ccc|ccc} 3 & 0 & 1 & 2 & -3 & 0 \\ 0 & -3 & -1 & 1 & -3 & 0 \\ 0 & 0 & -3 & 3 & -3 & -3 \end{array}\right]$$

$$\begin{array}{r} R_3 + 3R_1 \to R_1 \\ R_3 + (-3)R_2 \to R_2 \\ \\ \end{array} \left[\begin{array}{ccc|ccc} 9 & 0 & 0 & 9 & -12 & -3 \\ 0 & 9 & 0 & 0 & 6 & -3 \\ 0 & 0 & -3 & 3 & -3 & -3 \end{array}\right]$$

$$\begin{array}{r} \frac{1}{9}R_1 \to R_1 \\ \frac{1}{9}R_2 \to R_2 \\ -\frac{1}{3}R_3 \to R_3 \end{array} \left[\begin{array}{ccc|ccc} 1 & 0 & 0 & 1 & -\frac{4}{3} & -\frac{1}{3} \\ 0 & 1 & 0 & 0 & \frac{2}{3} & -\frac{1}{3} \\ 0 & 0 & 1 & -1 & 1 & 1 \end{array}\right]$$

$$A^{-1} = \begin{bmatrix} 1 & -\frac{4}{3} & -\frac{1}{3} \\ 0 & \frac{2}{3} & -\frac{1}{3} \\ -1 & 1 & 1 \end{bmatrix}$$

(a) 810 units of copper, 410 units of zinc, and 490 units of glass

$$\begin{bmatrix} x \\ y \\ z \end{bmatrix} = \begin{bmatrix} 1 & -\frac{4}{3} & -\frac{1}{3} \\ 0 & \frac{2}{3} & -\frac{1}{3} \\ -1 & 1 & 1 \end{bmatrix} \begin{bmatrix} 810 \\ 410 \\ 490 \end{bmatrix} = \begin{bmatrix} 100 \\ 110 \\ 90 \end{bmatrix}$$

100 transistors, 110 resistors, and 90 computer chips can be made.

(b) 765 units of copper, 385 units of zinc, and 470 units of glass

$$\begin{bmatrix} x \\ y \\ z \end{bmatrix} = \begin{bmatrix} 1 & -\frac{4}{3} & -\frac{1}{3} \\ 0 & \frac{2}{3} & -\frac{1}{3} \\ -1 & 1 & 1 \end{bmatrix} \begin{bmatrix} 765 \\ 385 \\ 470 \end{bmatrix} = \begin{bmatrix} 95 \\ 100 \\ 90 \end{bmatrix}$$

95 transistors, 100 resistors, and 90 computer chips can be made.

(c) 1010 units of copper, 500 units of zinc, and 610 units of glass

$$\begin{bmatrix} x \\ y \\ z \end{bmatrix} = \begin{bmatrix} 1 & -\frac{4}{3} & -\frac{1}{3} \\ 0 & \frac{2}{3} & -\frac{1}{3} \\ -1 & 1 & 1 \end{bmatrix} \begin{bmatrix} 1010 \\ 500 \\ 610 \end{bmatrix} = \begin{bmatrix} 140 \\ 130 \\ 100 \end{bmatrix}$$

140 transistors, 130 resistors, and 100 computer chips can be made.

61. Let $x =$ the amount invested in AAA bonds,
$y =$ the amount invested in A bonds, and
$z =$ amount invested in B bonds.

(a) The total investment is $x + y + z = 25{,}000$.
The annual return is
$0.06x = 0.065y + 0.08z = 1650$.
Since twice as much is invested in AAA bonds as in B bonds, $x = 2z$.
The system to be solved is

$$\begin{array}{rcrcrl} x & + & y & + & z = & 25{,}000 \\ 0.06x & + & 0.065y & + & 0.08z = & 1650 \\ x & & & - & 2z = & 0 \end{array}$$

Let $A = \begin{bmatrix} 1 & 1 & 1 \\ 0.06 & 0.065 & 0.08 \\ 1 & 0 & -2 \end{bmatrix}$, $B = \begin{bmatrix} 25{,}000 \\ 1650 \\ 0 \end{bmatrix}$,

and $X = \begin{bmatrix} x \\ y \\ z \end{bmatrix}$.

Use a graphing calculator to obtain

$$A^{-1} \begin{bmatrix} -26 & 400 & 3 \\ 40 & -600 & -4 \\ -13 & 200 & 1 \end{bmatrix}.$$

Use a graphing calculator again to solve the matrix equation $X = A^{-1}B$.

$$\begin{bmatrix} x \\ y \\ z \end{bmatrix} = \begin{bmatrix} -26 & 400 & 3 \\ 40 & -600 & -4 \\ -13 & 200 & 1 \end{bmatrix} \begin{bmatrix} 25{,}000 \\ 1650 \\ 0 \end{bmatrix}$$

$$= \begin{bmatrix} 10{,}000 \\ 10{,}000 \\ 5000 \end{bmatrix}$$

\$10,000 should be invested at 6% in AAA bonds, \$10,000 at 6.5% in A bonds, and \$5000 at 8% in B bonds.

(b) The matrix of constants is changed to

$$B = \begin{bmatrix} 30{,}000 \\ 1985 \\ 0 \end{bmatrix}.$$

$$\begin{bmatrix} x \\ y \\ z \end{bmatrix} = \begin{bmatrix} -26 & 400 & 3 \\ 40 & -600 & -4 \\ -13 & 200 & 1 \end{bmatrix} \begin{bmatrix} 30{,}000 \\ 1985 \\ 0 \end{bmatrix}$$

$$= \begin{bmatrix} 14{,}000 \\ 9000 \\ 7000 \end{bmatrix}$$

\$14,000 should be invested at 6% in AAA bonds, \$9000 at 6.5% in A bonds, and \$7000 at 8% in B bonds.

(c) The matrix of constants is changed to $B = \begin{bmatrix} 40{,}000 \\ 2660 \\ 0 \end{bmatrix}$.

$$\begin{bmatrix} x \\ y \\ z \end{bmatrix} = \begin{bmatrix} -26 & 400 & 3 \\ 40 & -600 & -4 \\ -13 & 200 & 1 \end{bmatrix} \begin{bmatrix} 40{,}000 \\ 2660 \\ 0 \end{bmatrix}$$

$$= \begin{bmatrix} 24{,}000 \\ 4000 \\ 12{,}000 \end{bmatrix}$$

\$24,000 should be invested at 6% in AAA bonds, \$4000 at 6.5% in A bonds, and \$12,000 at 8% in B bonds.

62. Let $x =$ the number of pounds of pretzels,
$y =$ the number of pounds of dried fruit, and
$z =$ the number of pounds of nuts.

The total amount of trail mix is $x + y + z$.
The cost of the trail mix is $4x + 5y + 9z$.
Since twice the weight of pretzels as dried fruit is to be used, $x = 2y$.

(a) For a total of 140 pounds at \$6 per pound, a total value of $140 \times \$6 = \$840$, the system to be solved is

$$\begin{aligned} x + y + z &= 140 \\ 4x + 5y + 9z &= 840 \\ x - 2y \quad &= 0 \end{aligned}$$

Let $A = \begin{bmatrix} 1 & 1 & 1 \\ 4 & 5 & 9 \\ 1 & -2 & 0 \end{bmatrix}$, $B = \begin{bmatrix} 140 \\ 840 \\ 0 \end{bmatrix}$, and $X = \begin{bmatrix} x \\ y \\ z \end{bmatrix}$.

Use row operations to obtain the inverse of the coefficient matrix.

$$A^{-1} = \begin{bmatrix} \frac{9}{7} & -\frac{1}{7} & \frac{2}{7} \\ \frac{9}{14} & -\frac{1}{14} & -\frac{5}{14} \\ -\frac{13}{14} & \frac{3}{14} & \frac{1}{14} \end{bmatrix} = \frac{1}{14} \begin{bmatrix} 18 & -2 & 4 \\ 9 & -1 & -5 \\ -13 & 3 & 1 \end{bmatrix}$$

Since $X = A^{-1}B$,

$$\begin{bmatrix} x \\ y \\ z \end{bmatrix} = \frac{1}{14} \begin{bmatrix} 18 & -2 & 4 \\ 9 & -1 & -5 \\ -13 & 3 & 1 \end{bmatrix} \begin{bmatrix} 140 \\ 840 \\ 0 \end{bmatrix}$$

$$= \frac{1}{14} \begin{bmatrix} 840 \\ 420 \\ 700 \end{bmatrix}$$

$$= \begin{bmatrix} 60 \\ 30 \\ 50 \end{bmatrix}.$$

Use 60 pounds of pretzels, 30 pounds of dried fruits, and 50 pounds of nuts.

(b) For a total of 100 pounds at \$7.60 per pound, a total value of $100 \times \$7.60 = \$760$, the system to be solved is

$$\begin{aligned} x + y + z &= 100 \\ 4x + 5y + 9z &= 760 \\ x - 2y \quad &= 0 \end{aligned}$$

The matrix of constants is changed to $B = \begin{bmatrix} 100 \\ 760 \\ 0 \end{bmatrix}$.

Since $X = A^{-1}B$,

$$\begin{bmatrix} x \\ y \\ z \end{bmatrix} = \frac{1}{14} \begin{bmatrix} 18 & -2 & 4 \\ 9 & -1 & -5 \\ -13 & 3 & 1 \end{bmatrix} \begin{bmatrix} 100 \\ 760 \\ 0 \end{bmatrix}$$

$$= \frac{1}{14} \begin{bmatrix} 280 \\ 140 \\ 980 \end{bmatrix}$$

$$= \begin{bmatrix} 20 \\ 10 \\ 70 \end{bmatrix}.$$

Use 20 pounds of pretzels, 10 pounds of dried fruits, and 70 pounds of nuts.

(c) For a total of 125 lb at \$6.20 per pound, a total value of $125 \times \$6.20 = \$775$, the system to be solved is

$$\begin{aligned} x + y + z &= 125 \\ 4x + 5y + 9z &= 775 \\ x - 2y \quad &= 0 \end{aligned}$$

The matrix of constants is changed to $B = \begin{bmatrix} 125 \\ 775 \\ 0 \end{bmatrix}$.

Since $X = A^{-1}B$.

$$\begin{bmatrix} x \\ y \\ z \end{bmatrix} = \frac{1}{14}\begin{bmatrix} 18 & -2 & 4 \\ 9 & -1 & -5 \\ -13 & 3 & 1 \end{bmatrix}\begin{bmatrix} 125 \\ 775 \\ 0 \end{bmatrix}$$

$$= \frac{1}{14}\begin{bmatrix} 700 \\ 350 \\ 700 \end{bmatrix}$$

$$= \begin{bmatrix} 50 \\ 25 \\ 50 \end{bmatrix}.$$

Use 50 pounds of pretzels, 25 pounds of dried fruits, and 50 pounds of nuts.

63. Let $x =$ the number of Super Vim tablets,
$y =$ the number of Multitab tablets, and
$z =$ the number of Mighty Mix tablets.

The total number of vitamins is

$$x + y + z.$$

The total amount of niacin is

$$15x + 20y + 25z.$$

The total amount of Vitamin E is

$$12x + 15y + 35z.$$

(a) The system to be solved is

$$\begin{aligned} x + y + z &= 225 \\ 15x + 20y + 25z &= 4750 \\ 12x + 15y + 35z &= 5225. \end{aligned}$$

Let $A = \begin{bmatrix} 1 & 1 & 1 \\ 15 & 20 & 25 \\ 12 & 15 & 35 \end{bmatrix}$, $X = \begin{bmatrix} x \\ y \\ z \end{bmatrix}$, $B = \begin{bmatrix} 225 \\ 4750 \\ 5225 \end{bmatrix}$.

Thus, $AX = B$ and

$$\begin{bmatrix} 1 & 1 & 1 \\ 15 & 20 & 25 \\ 12 & 15 & 35 \end{bmatrix}\begin{bmatrix} x \\ y \\ z \end{bmatrix} = \begin{bmatrix} 225 \\ 4750 \\ 5225 \end{bmatrix}.$$

Use row operations to obtain the inverse of the coefficient matrix.

$$A^{-1} = \begin{bmatrix} \frac{65}{17} & -\frac{4}{17} & \frac{1}{17} \\ -\frac{45}{17} & \frac{23}{85} & -\frac{2}{17} \\ -\frac{3}{17} & -\frac{3}{85} & \frac{1}{17} \end{bmatrix}$$

Since $X = A^{-1}B$,

$$\begin{bmatrix} x \\ y \\ z \end{bmatrix} = \begin{bmatrix} \frac{65}{17} & -\frac{4}{17} & \frac{1}{17} \\ -\frac{45}{17} & \frac{23}{85} & -\frac{2}{17} \\ -\frac{3}{17} & -\frac{3}{85} & \frac{1}{17} \end{bmatrix}\begin{bmatrix} 225 \\ 4750 \\ 5225 \end{bmatrix} = \begin{bmatrix} 50 \\ 75 \\ 100 \end{bmatrix}.$$

There are 50 Super Vim tablets, 75 Multitab tablets, and 100 Mighty Mix tablets.

(b) The matrix of constants is changed to

$$B = \begin{bmatrix} 185 \\ 3625 \\ 3750 \end{bmatrix}.$$

$$\begin{bmatrix} x \\ y \\ z \end{bmatrix} = \begin{bmatrix} \frac{65}{17} & -\frac{4}{17} & \frac{1}{17} \\ -\frac{45}{17} & \frac{23}{85} & -\frac{2}{17} \\ -\frac{3}{17} & -\frac{3}{85} & \frac{1}{17} \end{bmatrix}\begin{bmatrix} 185 \\ 3625 \\ 3750 \end{bmatrix} = \begin{bmatrix} 75 \\ 50 \\ 60 \end{bmatrix}$$

There are 75 Super Vim tablets, 50 Multitab tablets, and 60 Mighty Mix tablets.

(c) The matrix of constants is changed to

$$B = \begin{bmatrix} 230 \\ 4450 \\ 4210 \end{bmatrix}.$$

$$\begin{bmatrix} x \\ y \\ z \end{bmatrix} = \begin{bmatrix} \frac{65}{17} & -\frac{4}{17} & \frac{1}{17} \\ -\frac{45}{17} & \frac{23}{85} & -\frac{2}{17} \\ -\frac{3}{17} & -\frac{3}{85} & \frac{1}{17} \end{bmatrix}\begin{bmatrix} 230 \\ 4450 \\ 4210 \end{bmatrix} = \begin{bmatrix} 80 \\ 100 \\ 50 \end{bmatrix}$$

There are 80 Super Vim tablets, 100 Multitab tablets, and 50 Mighty Mix tablets.

64. **(a)** First, divide the letters and spaces of the sentence into groups of 3, writing each group as a column vector.

$$\begin{bmatrix} A \\ l \\ l \end{bmatrix}, \begin{bmatrix} \text{(space)} \\ i \\ s \end{bmatrix}, \begin{bmatrix} \text{(space)} \\ f \\ a \end{bmatrix}, \begin{bmatrix} i \\ r \\ \text{(space)} \end{bmatrix},$$

$$\begin{bmatrix} i \\ n \\ \text{(space)} \end{bmatrix}, \begin{bmatrix} l \\ o \\ v \end{bmatrix}, \begin{bmatrix} e \\ \text{(space)} \\ a \end{bmatrix}, \begin{bmatrix} n \\ d \\ \text{(space)} \end{bmatrix}, \begin{bmatrix} w \\ a \\ r \end{bmatrix}$$

Next, convert each letter into a number, assigning 1 to A, 2 to B, and so on, with the number 27 used to represent each space between words.

$$\begin{bmatrix} 1 \\ 12 \\ 12 \end{bmatrix}, \begin{bmatrix} 27 \\ 9 \\ 19 \end{bmatrix}, \begin{bmatrix} 27 \\ 6 \\ 1 \end{bmatrix}, \begin{bmatrix} 9 \\ 18 \\ 27 \end{bmatrix}, \begin{bmatrix} 9 \\ 14 \\ 27 \end{bmatrix},$$

$$\begin{bmatrix} 12 \\ 15 \\ 22 \end{bmatrix}, \begin{bmatrix} 5 \\ 27 \\ 1 \end{bmatrix}, \begin{bmatrix} 14 \\ 4 \\ 27 \end{bmatrix}, \begin{bmatrix} 23 \\ 1 \\ 18 \end{bmatrix}$$

Now find the product of the coding matrix presented in Example 6, $A = \begin{bmatrix} 1 & 3 & 4 \\ 2 & 1 & 3 \\ 4 & 2 & 1 \end{bmatrix}$, and each column vector above. This produces a new set of vectors, which represents the coded message.

$$\begin{bmatrix} 85 \\ 50 \\ 40 \end{bmatrix}, \begin{bmatrix} 130 \\ 120 \\ 145 \end{bmatrix}, \begin{bmatrix} 49 \\ 63 \\ 121 \end{bmatrix}, \begin{bmatrix} 171 \\ 117 \\ 99 \end{bmatrix}, \begin{bmatrix} 159 \\ 113 \\ 91 \end{bmatrix}, \begin{bmatrix} 145 \\ 105 \\ 100 \end{bmatrix}, \begin{bmatrix} 90 \\ 40 \\ 75 \end{bmatrix}, \begin{bmatrix} 134 \\ 113 \\ 91 \end{bmatrix}, \begin{bmatrix} 98 \\ 101 \\ 112 \end{bmatrix}$$

The message will be transmitted as 85, 50, 40, 130, 120, 145, 49, 63, 121, 171, 117, 99, 159, 113, 91, 145, 105, 100, 90, 40, 75, 134, 113, 91, 98, 101, 112.

(b) First, divide the coded message into groups of three numbers and form each group into a column vector.

$$\begin{bmatrix} 138 \\ 81 \\ 102 \end{bmatrix}, \begin{bmatrix} 101 \\ 67 \\ 109 \end{bmatrix}, \begin{bmatrix} 162 \\ 124 \\ 173 \end{bmatrix}, \begin{bmatrix} 210 \\ 150 \\ 165 \end{bmatrix}$$

Next, find the product of the decoding matrix presented in Example 6, the inverse of matrix A in part (a) above, $A^{-1} = \begin{bmatrix} -0.2 & 0.2 & 0.2 \\ 0.4 & -0.6 & 0.2 \\ 0 & 0.4 & -0.2 \end{bmatrix}$, and each of the column vectors above. This produces a new set of vectors, which represents the decoded message.

$$\begin{bmatrix} 9 \\ 27 \\ 12 \end{bmatrix}, \begin{bmatrix} 15 \\ 22 \\ 5 \end{bmatrix}, \begin{bmatrix} 27 \\ 25 \\ 15 \end{bmatrix}, \begin{bmatrix} 21 \\ 27 \\ 27 \end{bmatrix}$$

Lastly, convert each number into a letter, assigning A to 1, B to 2, and so on, with the number 27 used to represent each space between words.
Decoded message: I love you

65. **(a)** First, divide the letters and spaces of the message into groups of three, writing each group as a column vector.

$$\begin{bmatrix} T \\ o \\ \text{(space)} \end{bmatrix}, \begin{bmatrix} b \\ e \\ \text{(space)} \end{bmatrix}, \begin{bmatrix} o \\ r \\ \text{(space)} \end{bmatrix}, \begin{bmatrix} n \\ o \\ t \end{bmatrix}, \begin{bmatrix} \text{(space)} \\ t \\ o \end{bmatrix}, \begin{bmatrix} \text{(space)} \\ b \\ e \end{bmatrix}$$

Next, convert each letter into a number, assigning 1 to A, 2 to B, and so on, with the number 27 used to represent each space between words.

$$\begin{bmatrix} 20 \\ 15 \\ 27 \end{bmatrix}, \begin{bmatrix} 2 \\ 5 \\ 27 \end{bmatrix}, \begin{bmatrix} 15 \\ 18 \\ 27 \end{bmatrix}, \begin{bmatrix} 14 \\ 15 \\ 20 \end{bmatrix}, \begin{bmatrix} 27 \\ 20 \\ 15 \end{bmatrix}, \begin{bmatrix} 27 \\ 2 \\ 5 \end{bmatrix}$$

Now, find the product of the coding matrix B and each column vector. This produces a new set of vectors, which represents the coded message.

$$\begin{bmatrix} 262 \\ -161 \\ -12 \end{bmatrix}, \begin{bmatrix} 186 \\ -103 \\ -22 \end{bmatrix}, \begin{bmatrix} 264 \\ -168 \\ -9 \end{bmatrix}, \begin{bmatrix} 208 \\ -134 \\ -5 \end{bmatrix}, \begin{bmatrix} 224 \\ -152 \\ 5 \end{bmatrix}, \begin{bmatrix} 92 \\ -50 \\ -3 \end{bmatrix}$$

This message will be transmitted as 262, −161, −12, 186, −103, −22, 264, −168, −9, 208, −134, −5, 224, −152, 5, 92, −50, −3.

(b) Use row operations or a graphing calculator to find the inverse of the coding matrix B.

$$B^{-1} = \begin{bmatrix} 1.75 & 2.5 & 3 \\ -0.25 & -0.5 & 0 \\ -0.25 & -0.5 & -1 \end{bmatrix}$$

(c) First, divide the coded message into groups of three numbers and form each group into a column vector.

$$\begin{bmatrix} 116 \\ -60 \\ -15 \end{bmatrix}, \begin{bmatrix} 294 \\ -197 \\ -2 \end{bmatrix}, \begin{bmatrix} 148 \\ -92 \\ -9 \end{bmatrix}, \begin{bmatrix} 96 \\ -64 \\ 4 \end{bmatrix}, \begin{bmatrix} 264 \\ -182 \\ -2 \end{bmatrix}$$

Next, find the product of the decoding matric B^{-1} and each of the column vectors. This produces a new set of vectors, which represents the decoded message.

$$\begin{bmatrix} 8 \\ 1 \\ 16 \end{bmatrix}, \begin{bmatrix} 16 \\ 25 \\ 27 \end{bmatrix}, \begin{bmatrix} 2 \\ 9 \\ 18 \end{bmatrix}, \begin{bmatrix} 20 \\ 8 \\ 4 \end{bmatrix}, \begin{bmatrix} 1 \\ 25 \\ 27 \end{bmatrix}$$

Last, convert each number into a letter, assigning A to 1, B to 2, and so on, with the number 27 used to represent a space between words. The decoded message is HAPPY BIRTHDAY.

66. (a) $[B|I] = \left[\begin{array}{ccc|ccc} 50 & 50 & 45 & 1 & 0 & 0 \\ 0 & 15 & 20 & 0 & 1 & 0 \\ 1 & 1 & 1 & 0 & 0 & 1 \end{array}\right]$

Interchange rows 1 and 3.

$$\left[\begin{array}{ccc|ccc} 1 & 1 & 1 & 0 & 0 & 1 \\ 0 & 15 & 20 & 0 & 1 & 0 \\ 50 & 50 & 45 & 1 & 0 & 0 \end{array}\right]$$

$$-50R_1 + R_3 \to R_3 \quad \left[\begin{array}{ccc|ccc} 1 & 1 & 1 & 0 & 0 & 1 \\ 0 & 15 & 20 & 0 & 1 & 0 \\ 0 & 0 & -5 & 1 & 0 & -50 \end{array}\right]$$

$$R_2 + (-15)R_1 \to R_1 \quad \left[\begin{array}{ccc|ccc} -15 & 0 & 5 & 0 & 1 & -15 \\ 0 & 15 & 20 & 0 & 1 & 0 \\ 0 & 0 & -5 & 1 & 0 & -50 \end{array}\right]$$

$$\begin{array}{r} R_3 + R_1 \to R_1 \\ 4R_3 + R_2 \to R_2 \end{array} \quad \left[\begin{array}{ccc|ccc} -15 & 0 & 0 & 1 & 1 & -65 \\ 0 & 15 & 0 & 4 & 1 & -200 \\ 0 & 0 & -5 & 1 & 0 & -50 \end{array}\right]$$

$$\begin{array}{r} -\frac{1}{15}R_1 \to R_1 \\ \frac{1}{15}R_2 \to R_2 \\ -\frac{1}{5}R_3 \to R_3 \end{array} \quad \left[\begin{array}{ccc|ccc} 1 & 0 & 0 & -\frac{1}{15} & -\frac{1}{15} & \frac{13}{3} \\ 0 & 1 & 0 & \frac{4}{15} & \frac{1}{15} & -\frac{40}{3} \\ 0 & 0 & 1 & -\frac{1}{5} & 0 & 10 \end{array}\right]$$

$$B^{-1} = \begin{bmatrix} -\frac{1}{15} & -\frac{1}{15} & \frac{13}{3} \\ \frac{4}{15} & \frac{1}{15} & -\frac{40}{3} \\ -\frac{1}{5} & 0 & 10 \end{bmatrix}$$

(b) $A = \begin{bmatrix} 40 & 55 & 60 \\ 10 & 10 & 15 \\ 1 & 1 & 1 \end{bmatrix} B^{-1} = \begin{bmatrix} 40 & 55 & 60 \\ 10 & 10 & 15 \\ 1 & 1 & 1 \end{bmatrix} \begin{bmatrix} -\frac{1}{15} & -\frac{1}{15} & \frac{13}{3} \\ \frac{4}{15} & \frac{1}{15} & -\frac{40}{3} \\ -\frac{1}{5} & 0 & 10 \end{bmatrix} = \begin{bmatrix} 0 & 1 & 40 \\ -1 & 0 & 60 \\ 0 & 0 & 1 \end{bmatrix}$

(c) Denoting the original positions of the band members as x_1, x_2, and so on, the original shape was

25								
20			x_1	x_2	x_3	x_4	x_5	
15					x_6			
10					x_7			
5					x_8			
0					x_9			
	30	35	40	45	50	55	60	65

We are given that band member x_9, originally positioned at $(50, 0)$, moved to $(40, 10)$; band member x_6, originally at $(50, 15)$, moved to $(55, 10)$; band member x_2, originally at $(45, 20)$, moved to $(60, 15)$.

To find the new position of x_1, originally at $(40, 20)$, multiply A by the vector $\begin{bmatrix} 40 \\ 20 \\ 1 \end{bmatrix}$.

$$A \begin{bmatrix} 40 \\ 20 \\ 1 \end{bmatrix} = \begin{bmatrix} 0 & 1 & 40 \\ -1 & 0 & 60 \\ 0 & 0 & 1 \end{bmatrix} \begin{bmatrix} 40 \\ 20 \\ 1 \end{bmatrix} = \begin{bmatrix} 60 \\ 20 \\ 1 \end{bmatrix}$$

The new position of band member x_1 is $(60, 20)$.

To find the new position of x_3, originally at $(50, 20)$, multiply A by the vector $\begin{bmatrix} 50 \\ 20 \\ 1 \end{bmatrix}$.

$$A \begin{bmatrix} 50 \\ 20 \\ 1 \end{bmatrix} = \begin{bmatrix} 0 & 1 & 40 \\ -1 & 0 & 60 \\ 0 & 0 & 1 \end{bmatrix} \begin{bmatrix} 50 \\ 20 \\ 1 \end{bmatrix} = \begin{bmatrix} 60 \\ 10 \\ 1 \end{bmatrix}$$

The new position of band member x_3 is $(60, 10)$.

To find the new position of x_4, originally at $(55, 20)$, multiply A by the vector $\begin{bmatrix} 55 \\ 20 \\ 1 \end{bmatrix}$.

$$A \begin{bmatrix} 55 \\ 20 \\ 1 \end{bmatrix} = \begin{bmatrix} 0 & 1 & 40 \\ -1 & 0 & 60 \\ 0 & 0 & 1 \end{bmatrix} \begin{bmatrix} 55 \\ 20 \\ 1 \end{bmatrix} = \begin{bmatrix} 60 \\ 5 \\ 1 \end{bmatrix}$$

The new position of band member x_4 is $(60, 5)$.

To find the new position of x_5, originally at $(60, 20)$, multiply A by the vector $\begin{bmatrix} 60 \\ 20 \\ 1 \end{bmatrix}$.

$$A\begin{bmatrix} 60 \\ 20 \\ 1 \end{bmatrix} = \begin{bmatrix} 0 & 1 & 40 \\ -1 & 0 & 60 \\ 0 & 0 & 1 \end{bmatrix}\begin{bmatrix} 60 \\ 20 \\ 1 \end{bmatrix} = \begin{bmatrix} 60 \\ 0 \\ 1 \end{bmatrix}$$

The new position of band member x_5 is $(60, 0)$.

To find the new position of x_7, originally at $(50, 10)$,

multiply A by the vector $\begin{bmatrix} 50 \\ 10 \\ 1 \end{bmatrix}$.

$$A\begin{bmatrix} 50 \\ 10 \\ 1 \end{bmatrix} = \begin{bmatrix} 0 & 1 & 40 \\ -1 & 0 & 60 \\ 0 & 0 & 1 \end{bmatrix}\begin{bmatrix} 50 \\ 10 \\ 1 \end{bmatrix} = \begin{bmatrix} 50 \\ 10 \\ 1 \end{bmatrix}$$

The new position of band member x_7 is $(50, 10)$.

To find the new position of x_8, originally at $(50, 5)$,

multiply A by the vector $\begin{bmatrix} 50 \\ 5 \\ 1 \end{bmatrix}$.

$$A\begin{bmatrix} 50 \\ 5 \\ 1 \end{bmatrix} = \begin{bmatrix} 0 & 1 & 40 \\ -1 & 0 & 60 \\ 0 & 0 & 1 \end{bmatrix}\begin{bmatrix} 50 \\ 5 \\ 1 \end{bmatrix} = \begin{bmatrix} 45 \\ 10 \\ 1 \end{bmatrix}$$

The new position of band member x_8 is $(45, 10)$.

The new position of the band is

25								
20							x_1	
15							x_2	
10			x_9	x_8	x_7	x_6	x_3	
5							x_4	
0							x_5	
	30	35	40	45	50	55	60	65

Thus, the new shape is a sideways T whose vertical and horizontal intersection is at mark $(60, 10)$.

2.6 Input-Output Models

1. $A = \begin{bmatrix} 0.8 & 0.2 \\ 0.2 & 0.7 \end{bmatrix}, D = \begin{bmatrix} 2 \\ 3 \end{bmatrix}$

To find the production matrix, first calculate $I - A$.

$$I - A = \begin{bmatrix} 1 & 0 \\ 0 & 1 \end{bmatrix} - \begin{bmatrix} 0.8 & 0.2 \\ 0.2 & 0.7 \end{bmatrix} = \begin{bmatrix} 0.2 & -0.2 \\ -0.2 & 0.3 \end{bmatrix}$$

Using row operations, find the inverse of $I - A$.

$$[I - A \mid I] = \left[\begin{array}{rr|rr} 0.2 & -0.2 & 1 & 0 \\ -0.2 & 0.3 & 0 & 1 \end{array}\right]$$

$$\begin{array}{l} 10R_1 \to R_1 \\ 10R_2 \to R_2 \end{array} \left[\begin{array}{rr|rr} 2 & -2 & 10 & 0 \\ -2 & 3 & 0 & 10 \end{array}\right]$$

$$R_1 + R_2 \to R_2 \left[\begin{array}{rr|rr} 2 & -2 & 10 & 0 \\ 0 & 1 & 10 & 10 \end{array}\right]$$

$$2R_2 + R_1 \to R_1 \left[\begin{array}{rr|rr} 2 & 0 & 30 & 20 \\ 0 & 1 & 10 & 10 \end{array}\right]$$

$$\tfrac{1}{2}R_1 \to R_1 \left[\begin{array}{rr|rr} 1 & 0 & 15 & 10 \\ 0 & 1 & 10 & 10 \end{array}\right]$$

$$(I - A)^{-1} = \begin{bmatrix} 15 & 10 \\ 10 & 10 \end{bmatrix}$$

Since $X = (I - A)^{-1}D$, the product matrix is

$$X = \begin{bmatrix} 15 & 10 \\ 10 & 10 \end{bmatrix} \begin{bmatrix} 2 \\ 3 \end{bmatrix} = \begin{bmatrix} 60 \\ 50 \end{bmatrix}.$$

2. $A = \begin{bmatrix} 0.2 & 0.04 \\ 0.6 & 0.05 \end{bmatrix}, D = \begin{bmatrix} 3 \\ 10 \end{bmatrix}$

To find the production matrix X, first calculate $I - A$.

$$I - A = \begin{bmatrix} 1 & 0 \\ 0 & 1 \end{bmatrix} - \begin{bmatrix} 0.2 & 0.04 \\ 0.6 & 0.05 \end{bmatrix} = \begin{bmatrix} 0.8 & -0.04 \\ -0.6 & 0.95 \end{bmatrix}$$

Next, use row operations to find the inverse of $I - A$.

$$(I - A)^{-1} = \begin{bmatrix} 1.29 & 0.054 \\ 0.815 & 1.087 \end{bmatrix}$$

Since $X = (I - A)^{-1}D$,

$$X = \begin{bmatrix} 1.29 & 0.054 \\ 0.815 & 1.087 \end{bmatrix} \begin{bmatrix} 3 \\ 10 \end{bmatrix} = \begin{bmatrix} 4.4 \\ 13.3 \end{bmatrix}.$$

3. $A = \begin{bmatrix} 0.1 & 0.03 \\ 0.07 & 0.6 \end{bmatrix}, D = \begin{bmatrix} 5 \\ 10 \end{bmatrix}$

First, calculate $I - A$.

$$I - A = \begin{bmatrix} 0.9 & -0.03 \\ -0.07 & 0.4 \end{bmatrix}$$

Use row operations to find the inverse of $I - A$, which is

$$(I - A)^{-1} \approx \begin{bmatrix} 1.118 & 0.084 \\ 0.196 & 2.515 \end{bmatrix}.$$

Since $X = (I - A)^{-1}D$, the production matrix is

$$X = \begin{bmatrix} 1.118 & 0.084 \\ 0.196 & 2.515 \end{bmatrix} \begin{bmatrix} 5 \\ 10 \end{bmatrix} = \begin{bmatrix} 6.43 \\ 26.12 \end{bmatrix}.$$

4. $A = \begin{bmatrix} 0.02 & 0.03 \\ 0.06 & 0.08 \end{bmatrix}, D = \begin{bmatrix} 100 \\ 200 \end{bmatrix}$

To find the production matrix, first calculate $I - A$.

$$I - A = \begin{bmatrix} 1 & 0 \\ 0 & 1 \end{bmatrix} - \begin{bmatrix} 0.02 & 0.03 \\ 0.06 & 0.08 \end{bmatrix} = \begin{bmatrix} 0.98 & -0.03 \\ -0.06 & 0.92 \end{bmatrix}$$

Using row operations, find the inverse of $I - A$.

$$[I - A \mid I] = \left[\begin{array}{rr|rr} 0.98 & -0.03 & 1 & 0 \\ -0.06 & 0.92 & 0 & 1 \end{array}\right]$$

$$\begin{array}{l} 100R_1 \to R_1 \\ 100R_2 \to R_2 \end{array} \left[\begin{array}{rr|rr} 98 & -3 & 100 & 0 \\ -6 & 92 & 0 & 100 \end{array}\right]$$

$$3R_1 + 49R_2 \to R_2 \left[\begin{array}{rr|rr} 98 & -3 & 100 & 0 \\ 0 & 4499 & 300 & 4900 \end{array}\right]$$

$$3R_2 + 4499R_1 \to R_1 \left[\begin{array}{rr|rr} 440{,}902 & 0 & 450{,}800 & 14{,}700 \\ 0 & 4499 & 300 & 4900 \end{array}\right]$$

$$\begin{array}{l} \frac{1}{440{,}902}R_1 \to R_1 \\ \frac{1}{4499}R_2 \to R_2 \end{array} \left[\begin{array}{rr|rr} 1 & 0 & 1.022449 & 0.033341 \\ 0 & 1 & 0.066681 & 1.089131 \end{array}\right]$$

$$(I - A)^{-1} = \begin{bmatrix} 1.022449 & 0.033341 \\ 0.066681 & 1.089131 \end{bmatrix}$$

Since $X = (I - A)^{-1}D$, the product matrix is

$$X = \begin{bmatrix} 1.022449 & 0.033341 \\ 0.066681 & 1.089131 \end{bmatrix} \begin{bmatrix} 100 \\ 200 \end{bmatrix} = \begin{bmatrix} 108.91 \\ 224.49 \end{bmatrix} \text{ (rounded).}$$

5. $A = \begin{bmatrix} 0.8 & 0 & 0.1 \\ 0.1 & 0.5 & 0.2 \\ 0 & 0 & 0.7 \end{bmatrix}, D = \begin{bmatrix} 1 \\ 6 \\ 3 \end{bmatrix}$

To find the production matrix, first calculate $I - A$.

$$I - A = \begin{bmatrix} 1 & 0 & 0 \\ 0 & 1 & 0 \\ 0 & 0 & 1 \end{bmatrix} - \begin{bmatrix} 0.8 & 0 & 0.1 \\ 0.1 & 0.5 & 0.2 \\ 0 & 0 & 0.7 \end{bmatrix}$$
$$= \begin{bmatrix} 0.2 & 0 & -0.1 \\ -0.1 & 0.5 & -0.2 \\ 0 & 0 & 0.3 \end{bmatrix}$$

Using row operations, find the inverse of $I - A$.

$$[I - A \mid I] = \left[\begin{array}{ccc|ccc} 0.2 & 0 & -0.1 & 1 & 0 & 0 \\ -0.1 & 0.5 & -0.2 & 0 & 1 & 0 \\ 0 & 0 & 0.3 & 0 & 0 & 1 \end{array}\right]$$

$$\begin{array}{l} 10R_1 \to R_1 \\ 10R_2 \to R_2 \\ 10R_3 \to R_3 \end{array} \left[\begin{array}{ccc|ccc} 2 & 0 & -1 & 10 & 0 & 0 \\ -1 & 5 & -2 & 0 & 10 & 0 \\ 0 & 0 & 3 & 0 & 0 & 10 \end{array}\right]$$

$$R_1 + 2R_2 \to R_2 \left[\begin{array}{ccc|ccc} 2 & 0 & -1 & 10 & 0 & 0 \\ 0 & 10 & -5 & 10 & 20 & 0 \\ 0 & 0 & 3 & 0 & 0 & 10 \end{array}\right]$$

$$\begin{array}{l} R_3 + 3R_1 \to R_1 \\ 5R_3 + 3R_2 \to R_2 \end{array} \left[\begin{array}{ccc|ccc} 6 & 0 & 0 & 30 & 0 & 10 \\ 0 & 30 & 0 & 30 & 60 & 50 \\ 0 & 0 & 3 & 0 & 0 & 10 \end{array}\right]$$

$$\begin{array}{l} \frac{1}{6} R_1 \to R_1 \\ \frac{1}{30} R_2 \to R_2 \\ \frac{1}{3} R_3 \to R_3 \end{array} \left[\begin{array}{ccc|ccc} 1 & 0 & 0 & 5 & 0 & \frac{5}{3} \\ 0 & 1 & 0 & 1 & 2 & \frac{5}{3} \\ 0 & 0 & 1 & 0 & 0 & \frac{10}{3} \end{array}\right]$$

$$(I - A)^{-1} = \begin{bmatrix} 5 & 0 & \frac{5}{3} \\ 1 & 2 & \frac{5}{3} \\ 0 & 0 & \frac{10}{3} \end{bmatrix}$$

Since $X = (I - A)^{-1}D$, the product matrix is

$$X = \begin{bmatrix} 5 & 0 & \frac{5}{3} \\ 1 & 2 & \frac{5}{3} \\ 0 & 0 & \frac{10}{3} \end{bmatrix} \begin{bmatrix} 1 \\ 6 \\ 3 \end{bmatrix} = \begin{bmatrix} 10 \\ 18 \\ 10 \end{bmatrix}.$$

6. $A = \begin{bmatrix} 0.1 & 0.5 & 0 \\ 0 & 0.3 & 0.4 \\ 0.1 & 0.2 & 0.1 \end{bmatrix}, D = \begin{bmatrix} 10 \\ 4 \\ 2 \end{bmatrix}$

$$I - A = \begin{bmatrix} 0.9 & -0.5 & 0 \\ 0 & 0.7 & -0.4 \\ -0.1 & -0.2 & 0.9 \end{bmatrix}$$

$$(I - A)^{-1} = \begin{bmatrix} 1.158 & 0.947 & 0.421 \\ 0.084 & 1.705 & 0.758 \\ 0.147 & 0.484 & 1.33 \end{bmatrix}$$

$$X = (I - A)^{-1}D = \begin{bmatrix} 1.158 & 0.947 & 0.421 \\ 0.084 & 1.705 & 0.758 \\ 0.147 & 0.484 & 1.33 \end{bmatrix} \begin{bmatrix} 10 \\ 4 \\ 2 \end{bmatrix}$$
$$= \begin{bmatrix} 16.21 \\ 9.18 \\ 6.06 \end{bmatrix}$$

7.
$$\begin{array}{c} \\ A \\ B \\ C \end{array} \begin{array}{c} \begin{array}{ccc} A & B & C \end{array} \\ \begin{bmatrix} 0.3 & 0.1 & 0.8 \\ 0.5 & 0.6 & 0.1 \\ 0.2 & 0.3 & 0.1 \end{bmatrix} \end{array} = A$$

$$I - A = \begin{bmatrix} 0.7 & -0.1 & -0.8 \\ -0.5 & 0.4 & -0.1 \\ -0.2 & -0.3 & 0.9 \end{bmatrix}$$

Set $(I - A)X = O$ to obtain the following.

$$\begin{bmatrix} 0.7 & -0.1 & -0.8 \\ -0.5 & 0.4 & -0.1 \\ -0.2 & -0.3 & 0.9 \end{bmatrix} \begin{bmatrix} x_1 \\ x_2 \\ x_3 \end{bmatrix} = \begin{bmatrix} 0 \\ 0 \\ 0 \end{bmatrix}$$

$$\begin{bmatrix} 0.7x_1 - 0.1x_2 - 0.8x_3 \\ -0.5x_1 + 0.4x_2 - 0.1x_3 \\ -0.2x_1 - 0.3x_2 + 0.9x_3 \end{bmatrix} = \begin{bmatrix} 0 \\ 0 \\ 0 \end{bmatrix}$$

Rewrite this matrix equation as a system of equations.

$$\begin{aligned} 0.7x_1 - 0.1x_2 - 0.8x_3 &= 0 \\ -0.5x_1 + 0.4x_2 - 0.1x_3 &= 0 \\ -0.2x_1 - 0.3x_2 + 0.9x_3 &= 0 \end{aligned}$$

Rewrite the equations without decimals.

$$\begin{aligned} 7x_1 - x_2 - 8x_3 &= 0 \quad (1) \\ -5x_1 + 4x_2 - x_3 &= 0 \quad (2) \\ -2x_1 - 3x_2 + 9x_3 &= 0 \quad (3) \end{aligned}$$

Use row operations to solve this system of equations. Begin by eliminating x_1 in equations (2) and (3).

$$\begin{array}{lr} & 7x_1 - x_2 - 8x_3 = 0 \quad (1) \\ 5R_1 + 7R_2 \to R_2 & 23x_2 - 47x_3 = 0 \quad (4) \\ 2R_1 + 7R_3 \to R_3 & -23x_2 + 47x_3 = 0 \quad (5) \end{array}$$

Eliminate x_2 in equations (1) and (5).

$$\begin{array}{lrrl} 23R_1 + R_2 \rightarrow R_1 & 161x_1 & -231x_3 = 0 & (6) \\ & & 23x_2 - 47x_3 = 0 & (4) \\ R_2 + R_3 \rightarrow R_3 & & 0 = 0 & (7) \end{array}$$

The true statement in equation (7) indicates that the equations are dependent. Solve equation (6) for x_1 and equation (4) for x_2, each in terms of x_3.

$$x_1 = \frac{231}{161}x_3 = \frac{33}{23}x_3$$

$$x_2 = \frac{47}{23}x_3$$

The solution of the system is

$$\left(\frac{33}{23}x_3, \frac{47}{23}x_3, x_3\right).$$

If $x_3 = 23$, then $x_1 = 33$ and $x_2 = 47$, so the production of the three commodities should be in the ratio 33:47:23.

8.

$$\begin{array}{c} \\ A \\ B \\ C \end{array} \begin{array}{c} \begin{array}{ccc} A & B & C \end{array} \\ \begin{bmatrix} 0.3 & 0.2 & 0.3 \\ 0.1 & 0.5 & 0.4 \\ 0.6 & 0.3 & 0.3 \end{bmatrix} \end{array} = A$$

Calculate $I - A$, and then set $(I - A)X = O$ to find X.

$$I - A = \begin{bmatrix} 1 & 0 & 0 \\ 0 & 1 & 0 \\ 0 & 0 & 1 \end{bmatrix} - \begin{bmatrix} 0.3 & 0.2 & 0.3 \\ 0.1 & 0.5 & 0.4 \\ 0.6 & 0.3 & 0.3 \end{bmatrix}$$

$$= \begin{bmatrix} 0.7 & -0.2 & -0.3 \\ -0.1 & 0.5 & -0.4 \\ -0.6 & -0.3 & 0.7 \end{bmatrix}$$

$$(I - A)X = \begin{bmatrix} 0.7 & -0.2 & -0.3 \\ -0.1 & 0.5 & -0.4 \\ -0.6 & -0.3 & 0.7 \end{bmatrix} \begin{bmatrix} x_1 \\ x_2 \\ x_3 \end{bmatrix}$$

$$= \begin{bmatrix} 0 \\ 0 \\ 0 \end{bmatrix}$$

$$0.7x_1 - 0.2x_2 - 0.3x_3 = 0$$
$$-0.1x_1 + 0.5x_2 - 0.4x_3 = 0$$
$$0.6x_1 - 0.3x_2 + 0.7x_3 = 0$$

Solving this system with x_3 as the parameter will give the solution

$$\left(\frac{23}{33}x_3, \frac{31}{33}x_3, x_3\right).$$

If $x_3 = 33$, then $x_1 = 23$ and $x_2 = 31$, so the production of A, B, and C should be in the ratio 23:31:33.

9. Use a graphing calculator or a computer to find the production matrix $X = (I - A)^{-1}D$. The answer is

$$X = \begin{bmatrix} 7697 \\ 4205 \\ 6345 \\ 4106 \end{bmatrix}.$$

Values have been rounded.

10. This exercise should be solved using a graphing calculator or a computer. The answer, rounded to the nearest whole number, is

$$x = \begin{bmatrix} 7022 \\ 4854 \\ 5116 \\ 4647 \end{bmatrix}.$$

11. In Example 4, it was found that

$$(I - A)^{-1} \approx \begin{bmatrix} 1.3882 & 0.1248 \\ 0.5147 & 1.1699 \end{bmatrix}.$$

Since $X = (I - A)^{-1}D$, the production matrix is

$$X = \begin{bmatrix} 1.3882 & 0.1248 \\ 0.5147 & 1.1699 \end{bmatrix} \begin{bmatrix} 925 \\ 1250 \end{bmatrix} = \begin{bmatrix} 1440.085 \\ 1938.473 \end{bmatrix}.$$

Thus, about 1440.1 metric tons of wheat and 1938.5 metric tons of oil should be produced.

12. $A = \begin{bmatrix} 0 & \frac{1}{3} \\ \frac{1}{5} & 0 \end{bmatrix}, D = \begin{bmatrix} 500 \\ 1000 \end{bmatrix}$

$$X = (I - A)^{-1}D$$

$$= \begin{bmatrix} 1 & -\frac{1}{3} \\ -\frac{1}{5} & 1 \end{bmatrix}^{-1} \begin{bmatrix} 500 \\ 1000 \end{bmatrix}$$

$$= \begin{bmatrix} \frac{15}{14} & \frac{5}{14} \\ \frac{3}{14} & \frac{15}{14} \end{bmatrix} \begin{bmatrix} 500 \\ 1000 \end{bmatrix}$$

$$= \begin{bmatrix} 892.9 \\ 1178.6 \end{bmatrix}$$

Produce about 892.9 metric tons of wheat and about 1178.6 metric tons of oil.

13. In Example 3, it was found that

$$(I-A)^{-1} \approx \begin{bmatrix} 1.40 & 0.50 & 0.59 \\ 0.84 & 1.36 & 0.62 \\ 0.56 & 0.47 & 1.30 \end{bmatrix}.$$

Since $X = (I-A)^{-1}D$, the production matrix is

$$X = \begin{bmatrix} 1.40 & 0.50 & 0.59 \\ 0.84 & 1.36 & 0.62 \\ 0.56 & 0.47 & 1.30 \end{bmatrix} \begin{bmatrix} 607 \\ 607 \\ 607 \end{bmatrix} = \begin{bmatrix} 1511.43 \\ 1711.74 \\ 1414.31 \end{bmatrix}.$$

Thus, about 1511.4 units of agriculture, 1711.7 units of manufacturing, and 1414.3 units of transportation should be produced.

14. $$A = \begin{bmatrix} 0 & 0 & \frac{1}{2} \\ \frac{1}{3} & 0 & 0 \\ 0 & \frac{1}{4} & 0 \end{bmatrix}, \quad D = \begin{bmatrix} 1000 \\ 1000 \\ 1000 \end{bmatrix}$$

$$I - A = \begin{bmatrix} 1 & 0 & -\frac{1}{2} \\ -\frac{1}{3} & 1 & 0 \\ 0 & -\frac{1}{4} & 1 \end{bmatrix}$$

$$(I-A)^{-1} = \begin{bmatrix} 1.043 & 0.130 & 0.5217 \\ 0.3478 & 1.043 & 0.1739 \\ 0.0870 & 0.2609 & 1.043 \end{bmatrix}$$

$$X = (I-A)^{-1}D = \begin{bmatrix} 1694.7 \\ 1564.7 \\ 1390.9 \end{bmatrix}$$

Produce about 1694.7 units of agriculture, about 1564.7 units of manufacturing, and about 1390.9 units of transportation.

15. From the given data, we get the input-output matrix

$$A = \begin{bmatrix} 0 & \frac{1}{2} & \frac{1}{4} \\ \frac{1}{4} & 0 & \frac{1}{4} \\ \frac{1}{2} & \frac{1}{4} & 0 \end{bmatrix}.$$

$$I - A = \begin{bmatrix} 1 & -\frac{1}{2} & -\frac{1}{4} \\ -\frac{1}{4} & 1 & -\frac{1}{4} \\ -\frac{1}{2} & -\frac{1}{4} & 1 \end{bmatrix}$$

Use row operations to find the inverse of $I - A$, which is

$$(I-A)^{-1} \approx \begin{bmatrix} 1.538 & 0.923 & 0.615 \\ 0.615 & 1.436 & 0.513 \\ 0.923 & 0.821 & 1.436 \end{bmatrix}.$$

Since $X = (I-A)^{-1}D$, the production matrix is

$$X = \begin{bmatrix} 1.538 & 0.923 & 0.615 \\ 0.615 & 1.436 & 0.513 \\ 0.923 & 0.821 & 1.436 \end{bmatrix} \begin{bmatrix} 1000 \\ 1000 \\ 1000 \end{bmatrix}$$

$$\approx \begin{bmatrix} 3077 \\ 2564 \\ 3179 \end{bmatrix}.$$

Thus, the production should be about 3077 units of agriculture, 2564 units of manufacturing, and 3179 units of transportation.

16. $$A = \begin{bmatrix} 0 & \frac{1}{2} & \frac{1}{4} \\ \frac{1}{4} & 0 & \frac{1}{4} \\ \frac{1}{2} & \frac{1}{4} & 0 \end{bmatrix}, \quad D = \begin{bmatrix} 500 \\ 500 \\ 500 \end{bmatrix}$$

$$I - A = \begin{bmatrix} 1 & -\frac{1}{2} & -\frac{1}{4} \\ -\frac{1}{4} & 1 & -\frac{1}{4} \\ -\frac{1}{2} & -\frac{1}{4} & 1 \end{bmatrix}$$

$$(I-A)^{-1} = \begin{bmatrix} 1.538 & 0.9231 & 0.6154 \\ 0.6154 & 1.436 & 0.5128 \\ 0.9231 & 0.8205 & 1.436 \end{bmatrix}$$

$$X = (I-A)^{-1}D = \begin{bmatrix} 1538.3 \\ 1282.1 \\ 1589.8 \end{bmatrix}$$

Produce about 1538.3 units of agriculture, about 1282.1 units of manufacturing, and about 1589.8 units of transportation.

17. From the given data, we get the input-output matrix

$$A = \begin{bmatrix} \frac{1}{4} & \frac{1}{6} \\ \frac{1}{2} & 0 \end{bmatrix}.$$

$$I - A = \begin{bmatrix} \frac{3}{4} & -\frac{1}{6} \\ -\frac{1}{2} & 1 \end{bmatrix}$$

Use row operations to find the inverse of $I - A$, which is

$$(I-A)^{-1} = \begin{bmatrix} \frac{3}{2} & \frac{1}{4} \\ \frac{3}{4} & \frac{9}{8} \end{bmatrix}.$$

(a) The production matrix is

$$X = (I-A)^{-1}D = \begin{bmatrix} \frac{3}{2} & \frac{1}{4} \\ \frac{3}{4} & \frac{9}{8} \end{bmatrix} \begin{bmatrix} 1 \\ 1 \end{bmatrix} = \begin{bmatrix} \frac{7}{4} \\ \frac{15}{8} \end{bmatrix}.$$

Thus, $\frac{7}{4}$ bushels of yams and $\frac{15}{8} \approx 2$ pigs should be produced.

(b) The production matrix is

$$X = (I - A)^{-1}D = \begin{bmatrix} \frac{3}{2} & \frac{1}{4} \\ \frac{3}{4} & \frac{9}{8} \end{bmatrix} \begin{bmatrix} 100 \\ 70 \end{bmatrix} = \begin{bmatrix} 167.5 \\ 153.75 \end{bmatrix}.$$

Thus, 167.5 bushels of yams and $153.75 \approx 154$ pigs should be produced.

18. For this economy,

$$A = \begin{bmatrix} 0.2 & 0.4 & 0.2 \\ 0.4 & 0.2 & 0.1 \\ 0 & 0.1 & 0.2 \end{bmatrix}.$$

Use a graphing calculator or a computer to find $(I - A)^{-1}D$ where

$$D = \begin{bmatrix} 1000 \\ 1000 \\ 1000 \end{bmatrix}.$$

The solution, which may vary slightly, is

$$\begin{bmatrix} 3179.35 \\ 3043.48 \\ 1630.43 \end{bmatrix}.$$

Produce about 3179 units of oil, 3043 units of corn, and 1630 units of coffee.

19. Use a graphing calculator or a computer to find the production matrix $X = (I - A)^{-1}D$. The answer is

$$\begin{bmatrix} 848 \\ 516 \\ 2970 \end{bmatrix}.$$

Values have been rounded.

Produce 848 units of agriculture, 516 units of manufacturing, and 2970 units of households.

20. Use a graphing calculator or a computer to find $(I-A)^{-1}D$. The solution, which may vary slightly, is

$$\begin{bmatrix} 18.2 \\ 73.2 \\ 66.7 \end{bmatrix}.$$

Values have been rounded.

Produce \$18.2 billion of agriculture, \$73.2 billion of manufacturing, and \$66.7 billion of households.

21. Use a graphing calculator or a computer to find the production matrix $X = (I - A)^{-1}D$. The answer is

$$\begin{bmatrix} 195{,}492 \\ 25{,}933 \\ 13{,}580 \end{bmatrix}.$$

Values have been rounded. Change from thousands of pounds to millions of pounds.

Produce about 195 million lb of agriculture, 26 million lb of manufacturing, and 13.6 million lb of energy.

22. (a) Use a graphing calculator or a computer to find $(I - A)^{-1}D$. The solution, which may vary slightly, is

$$\begin{bmatrix} 183{,}464 \\ 304{,}005 \\ 42{,}037 \end{bmatrix}.$$

Values have been rounded.

In 100,000 RMB, produce about 183,000 for agriculture, 304,000 for industry/construction, and 42,000 for transportation/commerce.

(b) The entries in matrix $(I-A)^{-1}$ are called multipliers, and they give the desired economic values.

$$(I - A)^{-1} \approx \begin{bmatrix} 1.24 & 0.34 & 0.04 \\ 0.30 & 1.85 & 0.14 \\ 0.03 & 0.08 & 1.02 \end{bmatrix}$$

(Each entry has been rounded to two decimal places.) Since we are interested in the result when there is a 1 RMB increase in demand for agricultural exports, we are interested in the first column of this matrix. Interpreting the multipliers shown, we find that an increase of 1 RMB in demand for agricultural exports will result in a 1.24 RMB increase in production of agricultural commodities, a 0.30 RMB increase in production of industrial/construction commodities, and a 0.03 RMB increase in production of transportation/commercial commodities.

23. Use a graphing calculator or a computer to find the production matrix $X = (I - A)^{-1}D$. The answer is

$$\begin{bmatrix} 532 \\ 481 \\ 805 \\ 1185 \end{bmatrix}.$$

Values have been rounded.

Produce about 532 units of natural resources, 481 manufacturing units, 805 trade and service units, and 1185 personal consumption units.

24. **(a)** Use a graphing calculator or a computer to find $(I - B)^{-1}C$. The solution, which may vary slightly, is

$$\begin{bmatrix} 3 \\ 60 \\ 27 \\ 42 \\ 1002 \end{bmatrix}.$$

Values have been rounded.

A $50 million increase in manufacturing demand will result in a $3 million production increase in natural resources, a $60 million production increase in manufacturing, a $27 million production increase in trade and services, a $42 million production increase in personal consumption, and 1002 new jobs.

(b) The matrix $(I - B)^{-1}$ is

$$\begin{bmatrix} 1.1 & 0.1 & 0 & 0 & 0 \\ 0.2 & 1.2 & 0.2 & 0.1 & 0 \\ 0.7 & 0.5 & 1.9 & 0.7 & 0 \\ 1.3 & 0.8 & 1.3 & 1.6 & 0 \\ 40.9 & 20.0 & 39.2 & 16.0 & 1 \end{bmatrix}$$

The bottom row of this matrix indicates the total employment requirement, per million dollars, of a sector. For example, the total employment requirement, per million dollars, of natural resource output is 40.9 employees.

25. **(a)** Use a graphing calculator or a computer to find the matrix $(I - A)^{-1}$. The answer is

$$\begin{bmatrix} 1.67 & 0.56 & 0.56 \\ 0.19 & 1.17 & 0.06 \\ 3.15 & 3.27 & 4.38 \end{bmatrix}.$$

Values have been rounded.

(b) These multipliers imply that if the demand for one community's output increases by $1 then the output in the other community will increase by the amount in the row and column of this matrix. For example, if the demand for Hermitage's output increases by $1, then output from Sharon will increase $0.56, from Farrell by $0.06, and from Hermitage by $4.38.

26. Find the value of $I - A$, then set $(I - A)X = O$.

$$(I - A)X = \left(\begin{bmatrix} 1 & 0 \\ 0 & 1 \end{bmatrix} - \begin{bmatrix} \frac{1}{4} & \frac{1}{2} \\ \frac{3}{4} & \frac{1}{2} \end{bmatrix}\right)\begin{bmatrix} x_1 \\ x_2 \end{bmatrix}$$

$$= \begin{bmatrix} \frac{3}{4} & -\frac{1}{2} \\ -\frac{3}{4} & \frac{1}{2} \end{bmatrix}\begin{bmatrix} x_1 \\ x_2 \end{bmatrix}$$

$$= \begin{bmatrix} \frac{3}{4}x_1 - \frac{1}{2}x_2 \\ -\frac{3}{4}x_1 + \frac{1}{2}x_2 \end{bmatrix} = \begin{bmatrix} 0 \\ 0 \end{bmatrix}$$

Thus,

$$\frac{3}{4}x_1 - \frac{1}{2}x_2 = 0$$

$$\frac{3}{4}x_1 = \frac{1}{2}x_2$$

$$x_1 = \frac{2}{3}x_2.$$

If $x_2 = 3$, then $x_1 = 2$. Therefore, produce 2 units of yams for every 3 units of pigs.

27. Calculate $I - A$, and then set $(I - A)X = O$ to find X.

$$(I - A)X = \left(\begin{bmatrix} 1 & 0 \\ 0 & 1 \end{bmatrix} - \begin{bmatrix} \frac{3}{4} & \frac{1}{3} \\ \frac{1}{4} & \frac{2}{3} \end{bmatrix}\right)\begin{bmatrix} x_1 \\ x_2 \end{bmatrix}$$

$$= \begin{bmatrix} \frac{1}{4} & -\frac{1}{3} \\ -\frac{1}{4} & \frac{1}{3} \end{bmatrix}\begin{bmatrix} x_1 \\ x_2 \end{bmatrix}$$

$$= \begin{bmatrix} \frac{1}{4}x_1 - \frac{1}{3}x_2 \\ -\frac{1}{4}x_1 + \frac{1}{3}x_2 \end{bmatrix} \begin{bmatrix} 0 \\ 0 \end{bmatrix}$$

Thus,

$$\frac{1}{4}x_1 - \frac{1}{3}x_2 = 0$$

$$\frac{1}{4}x_1 = \frac{1}{3}x_2$$

$$x_1 = \frac{4}{3}x_2$$

If $x_2 = 3$, $x_1 = 4$. Therefore, produce 4 units of steel for every 3 units of coal.

28. Find the value of $I - A$, then set $(I - A)X = O$.

$$(I-A)X = \left(\begin{bmatrix} 1 & 0 & 0 \\ 0 & 1 & 0 \\ 0 & 0 & 1 \end{bmatrix} - \begin{bmatrix} \frac{1}{3} & \frac{1}{2} & 0 \\ \frac{1}{3} & \frac{1}{4} & \frac{1}{4} \\ \frac{1}{3} & \frac{1}{4} & \frac{3}{4} \end{bmatrix}\right)\begin{bmatrix} x_1 \\ x_2 \\ x_3 \end{bmatrix}$$

$$= \begin{bmatrix} \frac{2}{3} & -\frac{1}{2} & 0 \\ -\frac{1}{3} & \frac{3}{4} & -\frac{1}{4} \\ -\frac{1}{3} & -\frac{1}{4} & \frac{1}{4} \end{bmatrix}\begin{bmatrix} x_1 \\ x_2 \\ x_3 \end{bmatrix}$$

$$= \begin{bmatrix} \frac{2}{3}x_1 - \frac{1}{2}x_2 \\ -\frac{1}{3}x_1 + \frac{3}{4}x_2 - \frac{1}{4}x_3 \\ -\frac{1}{3}x_1 - \frac{1}{4}x_2 + \frac{1}{4}x_3 \end{bmatrix} = \begin{bmatrix} 0 \\ 0 \\ 0 \end{bmatrix}$$

The system to be solved is

$$\begin{aligned} \frac{2}{3}x_1 - \frac{1}{2}x_2 \qquad\quad &= 0 \\ -\frac{1}{3}x_1 + \frac{3}{4}x_2 - \frac{1}{4}x_3 &= 0 \\ -\frac{1}{3}x_1 - \frac{1}{4}x_2 + \frac{1}{4}x_3 &= 0. \end{aligned}$$

Write the augmented matrix of the system.

$$\left[\begin{array}{ccc|c} \frac{2}{3} & -\frac{1}{2} & 0 & 0 \\ -\frac{1}{3} & \frac{3}{4} & -\frac{1}{4} & 0 \\ -\frac{1}{3} & -\frac{1}{4} & \frac{1}{4} & 0 \end{array}\right]$$

$$\begin{array}{l} \frac{3}{2}R_1 \to R_1 \\ 12R_2 \to R_2 \\ 12R_3 \to R_3 \end{array} \left[\begin{array}{ccc|c} 1 & -\frac{3}{4} & 0 & 0 \\ -4 & 9 & -3 & 0 \\ -4 & -3 & 3 & 0 \end{array}\right]$$

$$\begin{array}{l} 4R_1 + R_2 \to R_2 \\ 4R_1 + R_3 \to R_3 \end{array} \left[\begin{array}{ccc|c} 1 & -\frac{3}{4} & 0 & 0 \\ 0 & 6 & -3 & 0 \\ 0 & -6 & 3 & 0 \end{array}\right]$$

$$\frac{1}{6}R_2 \to R_2 \quad \left[\begin{array}{ccc|c} 1 & -\frac{3}{4} & 0 & 0 \\ 0 & 1 & -\frac{1}{2} & 0 \\ 0 & -6 & 3 & 0 \end{array}\right]$$

$$\begin{array}{l} \frac{3}{4}R_2 + R_1 \to R_1 \\ 6R_2 + R_3 \to R_3 \end{array} \left[\begin{array}{ccc|c} 1 & 0 & -\frac{3}{8} & 0 \\ 0 & 1 & -\frac{1}{2} & 0 \\ 0 & 0 & 0 & 0 \end{array}\right]$$

Use x_3 as the parameter. Therefore, $x_1 = \frac{3}{8}x_3$ and $x_2 = \frac{1}{2}x_3$, and the solution is $\left(\frac{3}{8}x_3, \frac{1}{2}x_3, x_3\right)$. If $x_3 = 8$, then $x_1 = 3$ and $x_2 = 4$.

Produce 3 units of agriculture to every 4 units of manufacturing and 8 units of transportation.

29. For this economy,

$$A = \begin{bmatrix} \frac{1}{5} & \frac{3}{5} & 0 \\ \frac{2}{5} & \frac{1}{5} & \frac{4}{5} \\ \frac{2}{5} & \frac{1}{5} & \frac{1}{5} \end{bmatrix}.$$

Find the value of $I - A$, then set $(I - A)X = O$.

$$(I-A)X = \left(\begin{bmatrix} 1 & 0 & 0 \\ 0 & 1 & 0 \\ 0 & 0 & 1 \end{bmatrix} - \begin{bmatrix} \frac{1}{5} & \frac{3}{5} & 0 \\ \frac{2}{5} & \frac{1}{5} & \frac{4}{5} \\ \frac{2}{5} & \frac{1}{5} & \frac{1}{5} \end{bmatrix}\right)\begin{bmatrix} x_1 \\ x_2 \\ x_3 \end{bmatrix}$$

$$= \begin{bmatrix} \frac{4}{5} & -\frac{3}{5} & 0 \\ -\frac{2}{5} & \frac{4}{5} & -\frac{4}{5} \\ -\frac{2}{5} & -\frac{1}{5} & \frac{4}{5} \end{bmatrix}\begin{bmatrix} x_1 \\ x_2 \\ x_3 \end{bmatrix}$$

$$= \begin{bmatrix} \frac{4}{5}x_1 - \frac{3}{5}x_2 \\ -\frac{2}{5}x_1 + \frac{4}{5}x_2 - \frac{4}{5}x_3 \\ -\frac{2}{5}x_1 - \frac{1}{5}x_2 + \frac{4}{5}x_3 \end{bmatrix} = \begin{bmatrix} 0 \\ 0 \\ 0 \end{bmatrix}$$

The system to be solved is

$$\begin{aligned} \frac{4}{5}x_1 - \frac{3}{5}x_2 \qquad\quad &= 0 \\ -\frac{2}{5}x_1 + \frac{4}{5}x_2 - \frac{4}{5}x_3 &= 0 \\ -\frac{2}{5}x_1 - \frac{1}{5}x_2 + \frac{4}{5}x_3 &= 0. \end{aligned}$$

Write the augmented matrix of the system.

$$\left[\begin{array}{ccc|c} \frac{4}{5} & -\frac{3}{5} & 0 & 0 \\ -\frac{2}{5} & \frac{4}{5} & -\frac{4}{5} & 0 \\ -\frac{2}{5} & -\frac{1}{5} & \frac{4}{5} & 0 \end{array}\right]$$

$$\begin{array}{l} \frac{5}{4}R_1 \to R_1 \\ 5R_2 \to R_2 \\ 5R_3 \to R_3 \end{array} \left[\begin{array}{ccc|c} 1 & -\frac{3}{4} & 0 & 0 \\ -2 & 4 & -4 & 0 \\ -2 & -1 & 4 & 0 \end{array}\right]$$

$$\begin{array}{l} 2R_1 + R_2 \to R_2 \\ 2R_1 + R_3 \to R_3 \end{array} \left[\begin{array}{ccc|c} 1 & -\frac{3}{4} & 0 & 0 \\ 0 & \frac{5}{2} & -4 & 0 \\ 0 & -\frac{5}{2} & 4 & 0 \end{array}\right]$$

$$\frac{2}{5}R_2 \to R_2 \quad \left[\begin{array}{ccc|c} 1 & -\frac{3}{4} & 0 & 0 \\ 0 & 1 & -\frac{8}{5} & 0 \\ 0 & -\frac{5}{2} & 4 & 0 \end{array}\right]$$

$$\begin{array}{l} \frac{3}{4}R_2 + R_1 \to R_1 \\ \frac{5}{2}R_2 + R_3 \to R_3 \end{array} \left[\begin{array}{ccc|c} 1 & 0 & -\frac{6}{5} & 0 \\ 0 & 1 & -\frac{8}{5} & 0 \\ 0 & 0 & 0 & 0 \end{array}\right]$$

Use x_3 as the parameter. Therefore, $x_1 = \frac{6}{5}x_3$ and $x_2 = \frac{8}{5}x_3$, and the solution is $\left(\frac{6}{5}x_3, \frac{8}{5}x_3, x_3\right)$. If $x_3 = 5$, then $x_1 = 6$ and $x_2 = 8$.

Produce 6 units of mining for every 8 units of manufacturing and 5 units of communication.

Chapter 2 Review Exercises

3. $2x - 3y = 14 \quad (1)$
$3x + 2y = -5 \quad (2)$

Eliminate x in equation (2).

$$\begin{array}{lrl} & 2x - 3y = 14 & (1) \\ -3R_1 + 2R_2 \to R_2 & 13y = -52 & (3) \end{array}$$

Make each leading coefficient equal 1.

$$\begin{array}{lrl} \frac{1}{2}R_1 \to R_1 & x - \frac{3}{2}y = 7 & (4) \\ \frac{1}{13}R_2 \to R_2 & y = -4 & (5) \end{array}$$

Substitute -4 for y in equation (4) to get $x = 1$. The solution is $(1, -4)$.

4. $\frac{x}{2} + \frac{y}{4} = 3$
$\frac{x}{4} - \frac{y}{2} = 4$

First, multiply both equations by 4 to clear fractions.

$$\begin{aligned} 2x + y &= 12 \\ x - 2y &= 16 \end{aligned}$$

Now proceed by the echelon method.

$$\begin{array}{lr} & 2x + y = 12 \\ R_1 + (-2)R_2 \to R_2 & 5y = -20 \\ \frac{1}{2}R_1 \to R_1 & x + \frac{1}{2}y = 6 \\ \frac{1}{5}R_2 \to R_2 & y = -4 \end{array}$$

Back-substitution gives

$$\begin{aligned} x + \frac{1}{2}(-4) &= 6 \\ x &= 8. \end{aligned}$$

The solution is $(8, -4)$.

5. $2x - 3y + z = -5 \quad (1)$
$x + 4y + 2z = 13 \quad (2)$
$5x + 5y + 3z = 14 \quad (3)$

Eliminate x in equations (2) and (3).

$$\begin{array}{lrl} & 2x - 3y + z = -5 & (1) \\ -2R_2 + R_1 \to R_2 & -11y - 3z = -31 & (4) \\ 5R_1 + (-2)R_3 \to R_3 & -25y - z = -53 & (5) \end{array}$$

Eliminate y in equation (5).

$$\begin{array}{lrl} & 2x - 3y + z = -5 & (1) \\ & -11y - 3z = -31 & (4) \\ -25R_2 + 11R_3 \to R_3 & 64z = 192 & (6) \end{array}$$

Make each leading coefficient equal 1.

$$\begin{array}{lrl} \frac{1}{2}R_1 \to R_1 & x - \frac{3}{2}y + \frac{1}{2}z = -\frac{5}{2} & (7) \\ -\frac{1}{11}R_2 \to R_2 & y + \frac{3}{11}z = \frac{31}{11} & (8) \\ \frac{1}{64}R_3 \to R_3 & z = 3 & (9) \end{array}$$

Substitute 3 for z in equation (8) to get $y = 2$. Substitute 3 for z and 2 for y in equation (7) to get $x = -1$.

The solution is $(-1, 2, 3)$.

6. $x + 2y + 3z = 9$
$x - 2y = 4$
$3x + 2z = 12$

Eliminate x in equations (2) and (3).

$$\begin{array}{lrl} & x + 2y + 3z = 9 & (1) \\ -1R_1 + R_2 \to R_2 & -4y - 3z = -5 & (4) \\ -3R_1 + R_3 \to R_3 & -6y - 7z = -15 & (5) \end{array}$$

Eliminate y in equation (5).

$$\begin{array}{lrl} & x + 2y + 3z = 9 & (1) \\ & -4y - 3z = -5 & (4) \\ 3R_2 + (-2)R_3 \to R_3 & 5z = 15 & (6) \end{array}$$

Make each leading coefficient equal 1.

$$\begin{array}{lrl} & x + 2y + 3z = 9 & (1) \\ -\frac{1}{4}R_2 \to R_2 & y + \frac{3}{4}z = \frac{5}{4} & (7) \\ \frac{1}{5}R_3 \to R_3 & z = 3 & (8) \end{array}$$

Back-substitution gives

$$\begin{aligned} y + \frac{3}{4}(3) &= \frac{5}{4} \\ y &= \frac{5}{4} - \frac{9}{4} = -1 \end{aligned}$$

and

$$\begin{aligned} x + 2(-1) + 3(3) &= 9 \\ x &= 2. \end{aligned}$$

The solution is $(2, -1, 3)$.

7. $2x + 4y = -6$
$-3x - 5y = 12$

Write the augmented matrix and use row operations.

$$\left[\begin{array}{rr|r} 2 & 4 & -6 \\ -3 & -5 & 12 \end{array}\right]$$

$$3R_1 + 2R_2 \to R_2 \quad \left[\begin{array}{rr|r} 2 & 4 & -6 \\ 0 & 2 & 6 \end{array}\right]$$

$$-2R_2 + R_1 \to R_1 \quad \left[\begin{array}{rr|r} 2 & 0 & -18 \\ 0 & 2 & 6 \end{array}\right]$$

$$\begin{array}{r} \frac{1}{2}R_1 \to R_1 \\ \frac{1}{2}R_2 \to R_2 \end{array} \quad \left[\begin{array}{rr|r} 1 & 0 & -9 \\ 0 & 1 & 3 \end{array}\right]$$

The solution is $(-9, 3)$.

8. $x - 4y = 10$
$5x + 3y = 119$

Write the system in augmented matrix form and use row operations to solve.

$$\left[\begin{array}{rr|r} 1 & -4 & 10 \\ 5 & 3 & 119 \end{array}\right]$$

$$-5R_1 + R_2 \to R_2 \quad \left[\begin{array}{rr|r} 1 & -4 & 10 \\ 0 & 23 & 69 \end{array}\right]$$

$$4R_2 + 23R_1 \to R_1 \quad \left[\begin{array}{rr|r} 23 & 0 & 506 \\ 0 & 23 & 69 \end{array}\right]$$

$$\begin{array}{r} \frac{1}{23}R_1 \to R_1 \\ \frac{1}{23}R_2 \to R_2 \end{array} \quad \left[\begin{array}{rr|r} 1 & 0 & 22 \\ 0 & 1 & 3 \end{array}\right]$$

The solution is $(22, 3)$.

9. $x - y + 3z = 13$
$4x + y + 2z = 17$
$3x + 2y + 2z = 1$

Write the augmented matrix and use row operations.

$$\left[\begin{array}{rrr|r} 1 & -1 & 3 & 13 \\ 4 & 1 & 2 & 17 \\ 3 & 2 & 2 & 1 \end{array}\right]$$

$$\begin{array}{r} -4R_1 + R_2 \to R_2 \\ -3R_1 + R_3 \to R_3 \end{array} \quad \left[\begin{array}{rrr|r} 1 & -1 & 3 & 13 \\ 0 & 5 & -10 & -35 \\ 0 & 5 & -7 & -38 \end{array}\right]$$

$$\begin{array}{r} R_2 + 5R_1 \to R_1 \\ \\ -1R_2 + R_3 \to R_3 \end{array} \quad \left[\begin{array}{rrr|r} 5 & 0 & 5 & 30 \\ 0 & 5 & -10 & -35 \\ 0 & 0 & 3 & -3 \end{array}\right]$$

$$\begin{array}{r} 5R_3 + (-3R_1) \to R_1 \\ 10R_3 + 3R_2 \to R_2 \end{array} \quad \left[\begin{array}{rrr|r} -15 & 0 & 0 & -105 \\ 0 & 15 & 0 & -135 \\ 0 & 0 & 3 & -3 \end{array}\right]$$

$$\begin{array}{r} -\frac{1}{15}R_1 \to R_1 \\ \frac{1}{15}R_2 \to R_2 \\ \frac{1}{3}R_3 \to R_3 \end{array} \quad \left[\begin{array}{rrr|r} 1 & 0 & 0 & 7 \\ 0 & 1 & 0 & -9 \\ 0 & 0 & 1 & -1 \end{array}\right]$$

The solution is $(7, -9, -1)$.

10. $x - 2z = 5$
$3x + 2y = 8$
$-x + 2z = 10$

Write the system in augmented matrix form and apply row operations.

$$\left[\begin{array}{rrr|r} 1 & 0 & -2 & 5 \\ 3 & 2 & 0 & 8 \\ -1 & 0 & 2 & 10 \end{array}\right]$$

$$\begin{array}{r} -3R_1 + R_2 \to R_2 \\ R_1 + R_3 \to R_3 \end{array} \quad \left[\begin{array}{rrr|r} 1 & 0 & -2 & 5 \\ 0 & 2 & 6 & -7 \\ 0 & 0 & 0 & 15 \end{array}\right]$$

The last row says that $0 = 15$, which is false, so the system is inconsistent and there is no solution.

11. $3x - 6y + 9z = 12$
$-x + 2y - 3z = -4$
$x + y + 2z = 7$

Write the augmented matrix and use row operations.

$$\left[\begin{array}{rrr|r} 3 & -6 & 9 & 12 \\ -1 & 2 & -3 & -4 \\ 1 & 1 & 2 & 7 \end{array}\right]$$

$$\begin{array}{r} R_1 + 3R_2 \to R_2 \\ -1R_1 + 3R_3 \to R_3 \end{array} \quad \left[\begin{array}{rrr|r} 3 & -6 & 9 & 12 \\ 0 & 0 & 0 & 0 \\ 0 & 9 & -3 & 9 \end{array}\right]$$

The zero in row 2, column 2 is an obstacle. To proceed, interchange the second and third rows.

$$\left[\begin{array}{rrr|r} 3 & -6 & 9 & 12 \\ 0 & 9 & -3 & 9 \\ 0 & 0 & 0 & 0 \end{array}\right]$$

$$3R_1 + 2R_2 \to R_1 \quad \left[\begin{array}{rrr|r} 9 & 0 & 21 & 54 \\ 0 & 9 & -3 & 9 \\ 0 & 0 & 0 & 0 \end{array}\right]$$

$$\begin{array}{r} \frac{1}{9}R_1 \to R_1 \\ \frac{1}{9}R_2 \to R_2 \end{array} \quad \left[\begin{array}{rrr|r} 1 & 0 & \frac{7}{3} & 6 \\ 0 & 1 & -\frac{1}{3} & 1 \\ 0 & 0 & 0 & 0 \end{array}\right]$$

The row of zeros indicates dependent equations.

Solve the first two equations respectively for x and y in terms of z to obtain

$$x = 6 - \frac{7}{3}z \quad \text{and} \quad y = 1 + \frac{1}{3}z.$$

The solution of the system is

$$\left(6 - \frac{7}{3}z, 1 + \frac{1}{3}z, z\right),$$

where z is any real number.

In Exercises 12 – 15, corresponding elements must be equal.

12. $\begin{bmatrix} 2 & 3 \\ 5 & q \end{bmatrix} = \begin{bmatrix} a & b \\ c & 9 \end{bmatrix}$

Size: 2×2; $a = 2$, $b = 3$, $c = 5$, $q = 9$; square matrix

13. $\begin{bmatrix} 2 & x \\ y & 6 \\ 5 & z \end{bmatrix} = \begin{bmatrix} a & -1 \\ 4 & 6 \\ p & 7 \end{bmatrix}$

The size of these matrices is 3×2. For matrices to be equal, corresponding elements must be equal, so $a = 2$, $x = -1$, $y = 4$, $p = 5$, and $z = 7$.

14. $\begin{bmatrix} 2m & 4 & 3z & -12 \end{bmatrix} = \begin{bmatrix} 12 & k+1 & -9 & r-3 \end{bmatrix}$

Size: 1×4; $m = 6$, $k = 3$, $z = -3$, $r = -9$; row matrix

15. $\begin{bmatrix} a+5 & 3b & 6 \\ 4c & 2+d & -3 \\ -1 & 4p & q-1 \end{bmatrix} = \begin{bmatrix} -7 & b+2 & 2k-3 \\ 3 & 2d-1 & 4\ell \\ m & 12 & 8 \end{bmatrix}$

These are 3×3 square matrices. Since corresponding elements must be equal,

$a + 5 = -7$, so $a = -12$;
$3b = b + 2$, so $b = 1$;

$6 = 2k - 3$, so $k = \frac{9}{2}$;

$4c = 3$, so $c = \frac{3}{4}$;

$2 + d = 2d - 1$, so $d = 3$;

$-3 = 4\ell$, so $\ell = -\frac{3}{4}$;

$m = -1$;
$4p = 12$, so $p = 3$; and
$q - 1 = 8$, so $q = 9$.

16. $A + C = \begin{bmatrix} 4 & 10 \\ -2 & -3 \\ 6 & 9 \end{bmatrix} + \begin{bmatrix} 5 & 0 \\ -1 & 3 \\ 4 & 7 \end{bmatrix}$

$$= \begin{bmatrix} 9 & 10 \\ -3 & 0 \\ 10 & 16 \end{bmatrix}$$

17. $2G - 4F = 2\begin{bmatrix} -2 & 0 \\ 1 & 5 \end{bmatrix} - 4\begin{bmatrix} -1 & 4 \\ 3 & 7 \end{bmatrix}$

$$= \begin{bmatrix} -4 & 0 \\ 2 & 10 \end{bmatrix} + \begin{bmatrix} 4 & -16 \\ -12 & -28 \end{bmatrix}$$

$$= \begin{bmatrix} 0 & -16 \\ -10 & -18 \end{bmatrix}$$

18. $3C + 2A = 3\begin{bmatrix} 5 & 0 \\ -1 & 3 \\ 4 & 7 \end{bmatrix} + 2\begin{bmatrix} 4 & 10 \\ -2 & -3 \\ 6 & 9 \end{bmatrix}$

$$= \begin{bmatrix} 15 & 0 \\ -3 & 9 \\ 12 & 21 \end{bmatrix} + \begin{bmatrix} 8 & 20 \\ -4 & -6 \\ 12 & 18 \end{bmatrix}$$

$$= \begin{bmatrix} 23 & 20 \\ -7 & 3 \\ 24 & 39 \end{bmatrix}$$

19. Since B is a 3×3 matrix, and C is a 3×2 matrix, the calculation of $B - C$ is not possible.

20. $2A - 5C = 2\begin{bmatrix} 4 & 10 \\ -2 & -3 \\ 6 & 9 \end{bmatrix} - 5\begin{bmatrix} 5 & 0 \\ -1 & 3 \\ 4 & 7 \end{bmatrix}$

$$= \begin{bmatrix} 8 & 20 \\ -4 & -6 \\ 12 & 18 \end{bmatrix} - \begin{bmatrix} 25 & 0 \\ -5 & 15 \\ 20 & 35 \end{bmatrix}$$

$$= \begin{bmatrix} -17 & 20 \\ 1 & -21 \\ -8 & -17 \end{bmatrix}$$

21. A has size 3×2 and G has 2×2, so AG will have size 3×2.

$$AG = \begin{bmatrix} 4 & 10 \\ -2 & -3 \\ 6 & 9 \end{bmatrix} \begin{bmatrix} -2 & 0 \\ 1 & 5 \end{bmatrix} = \begin{bmatrix} 2 & 50 \\ 1 & -15 \\ -3 & 45 \end{bmatrix}$$

22. A is 3×2 and C is 3×2, so finding the product AC is not possible.

$$\underset{3 \times \mathbf{2}}{A} \quad \underset{\mathbf{3} \times 2}{C}$$

(The inner 2 numbers must match.)

23. D has size 3×1 and E has size 1×3, so DE will have size 3×3.

$$DE = \begin{bmatrix} 6 \\ 1 \\ 0 \end{bmatrix} \begin{bmatrix} 1 & 3 & -4 \end{bmatrix} = \begin{bmatrix} 6 & 18 & -24 \\ 1 & 3 & -4 \\ 0 & 0 & 0 \end{bmatrix}$$

24. $ED = \begin{bmatrix} 1 & 3 & -4 \end{bmatrix} \begin{bmatrix} 6 \\ 1 \\ 0 \end{bmatrix} = [1\cdot 6 + 3\cdot 1 + (-4)0] = [9]$

25. B has size 3×3 and D has size 3×1, so BD will have size 3×1.

$$BD = \begin{bmatrix} 2 & 3 & -2 \\ 2 & 4 & 0 \\ 0 & 1 & 2 \end{bmatrix} \begin{bmatrix} 6 \\ 1 \\ 0 \end{bmatrix} = \begin{bmatrix} 15 \\ 16 \\ 1 \end{bmatrix}$$

26. $EC = \begin{bmatrix} 1 & 3 & -4 \end{bmatrix} \begin{bmatrix} 5 & 0 \\ -1 & 3 \\ 4 & 7 \end{bmatrix}$

$$= \begin{bmatrix} 1\cdot 5 + 3(-1) + (-4)\cdot 4 & 1\cdot 0 + 3\cdot 3 + (-4)\cdot 7 \end{bmatrix}$$
$$= \begin{bmatrix} -14 & -19 \end{bmatrix}$$

27.

$$F = \begin{bmatrix} -1 & 4 \\ 3 & 7 \end{bmatrix}$$

$$[F|I] = \left[\begin{array}{cc|cc} -1 & 4 & 1 & 0 \\ 3 & 7 & 0 & 1 \end{array}\right]$$

$$3R_1 + R_2 \to R_2 \quad \left[\begin{array}{cc|cc} -1 & 4 & 1 & 0 \\ 0 & 19 & 3 & 1 \end{array}\right]$$

$$4R_2 + (-19R_1) \to R_1 \quad \left[\begin{array}{cc|cc} 19 & 0 & -7 & 4 \\ 0 & 19 & 3 & 1 \end{array}\right]$$

$$\begin{array}{l} \frac{1}{19}R_1 \to R_1 \\ \frac{1}{19}R_2 \to R_2 \end{array} \quad \left[\begin{array}{cc|cc} 1 & 0 & -\frac{7}{19} & \frac{4}{19} \\ 0 & 1 & \frac{3}{19} & \frac{1}{19} \end{array}\right]$$

$$F^{-1} = \begin{bmatrix} -\frac{7}{19} & \frac{4}{19} \\ \frac{3}{19} & \frac{1}{19} \end{bmatrix}$$

28. Find the inverse of $B = \begin{bmatrix} 2 & 3 & -2 \\ 2 & 4 & 0 \\ 0 & 1 & 2 \end{bmatrix}$, if it exists.

Write the augmented matrix to obtain

$$[B|I] = \left[\begin{array}{ccc|ccc} 2 & 3 & -2 & 1 & 0 & 0 \\ 2 & 4 & 0 & 0 & 1 & 0 \\ 0 & 1 & 2 & 0 & 0 & 1 \end{array}\right].$$

$$-1R_1 + R_2 \to R_2 \quad \left[\begin{array}{ccc|ccc} 2 & 3 & -2 & 1 & 0 & 0 \\ 0 & 1 & 2 & -1 & 1 & 0 \\ 0 & 1 & 2 & 0 & 0 & 1 \end{array}\right]$$

$$\begin{array}{l} -3R_2 + R_1 \to R_1 \\ \\ -1R_2 + R_3 \to R_3 \end{array} \quad \left[\begin{array}{ccc|ccc} 2 & 0 & -8 & 4 & -3 & 0 \\ 0 & 1 & 2 & -1 & 1 & 0 \\ 0 & 0 & 0 & 1 & -1 & 1 \end{array}\right]$$

No inverse exists, since the third row is all zeros to the left of the vertical bar.

29. A and C are 3×2 matrices, so their sum $A+C$ is a 3×2 matrix. Only square matrices have inverses. Therefore, $(A+C)^{-1}$ does not exist.

30. Find the inverse of $A = \begin{bmatrix} 1 & 3 \\ 2 & 7 \end{bmatrix}$, if it exists.

Write the augmented matrix $[A|I]$.

$$[A|I] = \left[\begin{array}{cc|cc} 1 & 3 & 1 & 0 \\ 2 & 7 & 0 & 1 \end{array}\right]$$

Perform row operations on $[A|I]$ to get a matrix of the form $[I|B]$.

$$-2R_1 + R_2 \to R_2 \quad \left[\begin{array}{cc|cc} 1 & 3 & 1 & 0 \\ 0 & 1 & -2 & 1 \end{array}\right]$$

$$-3R_2 + R_1 \to R_1 \quad \left[\begin{array}{cc|cc} 1 & 0 & 7 & -3 \\ 0 & 1 & -2 & 1 \end{array}\right]$$

The last augmented matrix is of the form $[I|B]$, so the desired inverse is

$$A^{-1} = \begin{bmatrix} 7 & -3 \\ -2 & 1 \end{bmatrix}.$$

31. Let

$$A = \begin{bmatrix} -4 & 2 \\ 0 & 3 \end{bmatrix}.$$

$$[A|I] = \left[\begin{array}{cc|cc} -4 & 2 & 1 & 0 \\ 0 & 3 & 0 & 1 \end{array}\right]$$

$$2R_2 + (-3R_1) \to R_1 \quad \left[\begin{array}{cc|cc} 12 & 0 & -3 & 2 \\ 0 & 3 & 0 & 1 \end{array}\right]$$

$$\begin{array}{l} \frac{1}{12}R_1 \to R_1 \\ \frac{1}{3}R_2 \to R_2 \end{array} \quad \left[\begin{array}{cc|cc} 1 & 0 & -\frac{1}{4} & \frac{1}{6} \\ 0 & 1 & 0 & \frac{1}{3} \end{array}\right]$$

$$A^{-1} = \begin{bmatrix} -\frac{1}{4} & \frac{1}{6} \\ 0 & \frac{1}{3} \end{bmatrix}$$

32. Find the inverse of $A = \begin{bmatrix} 3 & -6 \\ -4 & 8 \end{bmatrix}$, if it exists.

Write the augmented matrix $[A|I]$.

$$[A|I] = \left[\begin{array}{cc|cc} 3 & -6 & 1 & 0 \\ -4 & 8 & 0 & 1 \end{array}\right]$$

Perform row operations on $[A|I]$ to get a matrix of the form $[I|B]$.

$$4R_1 + 3R_2 \to R_2 \quad \left[\begin{array}{cc|cc} 3 & -6 & 1 & 0 \\ 0 & 0 & 4 & 3 \end{array}\right]$$

Since the entries left of the vertical bar in the second row are zeros, no inverse exists.

33. Let

$$A = \begin{bmatrix} 6 & 4 \\ 3 & 2 \end{bmatrix}.$$

$$[A|I] = \left[\begin{array}{cc|cc} 6 & 4 & 1 & 0 \\ 3 & 2 & 0 & 1 \end{array}\right]$$

$$\text{R}_1 + (-2)\text{R}_2 \to \text{R}_2 \quad \left[\begin{array}{cc|cc} 6 & 4 & 1 & 0 \\ 0 & 0 & 1 & -2 \end{array}\right]$$

The zeros in the second row indicate that the original matrix has no inverse.

34. Find the inverse of $A = \begin{bmatrix} 2 & -1 & 0 \\ 1 & 0 & 1 \\ 1 & -2 & 0 \end{bmatrix}$, if it exists.

The augmented matrix is

$$[A|I] = \left[\begin{array}{ccc|ccc} 2 & -1 & 0 & 1 & 0 & 0 \\ 1 & 0 & 1 & 0 & 1 & 0 \\ 1 & -2 & 0 & 0 & 0 & 1 \end{array}\right].$$

$$\begin{array}{r} \\ \text{R}_1 + (-2)\text{R}_2 \to \text{R}_2 \\ \text{R}_1 + (-2)\text{R}_3 \to \text{R}_3 \end{array} \left[\begin{array}{ccc|ccc} 2 & -1 & 0 & 1 & 0 & 0 \\ 0 & -1 & -2 & 1 & -2 & 0 \\ 0 & 3 & 0 & 1 & 0 & -2 \end{array}\right]$$

$$\begin{array}{r} -1\text{R}_2 + \text{R}_1 \to \text{R}_1 \\ \\ 3\text{R}_2 + \text{R}_3 \to \text{R}_3 \end{array} \left[\begin{array}{ccc|ccc} 2 & 0 & 2 & 0 & 2 & 0 \\ 0 & -1 & -2 & 1 & -2 & 0 \\ 0 & 0 & -6 & 4 & -6 & -2 \end{array}\right]$$

$$\begin{array}{r} \text{R}_3 + 3\text{R}_1 \to \text{R}_1 \\ \text{R}_3 + (-3)\text{R}_2 \to \text{R}_2 \\ \\ \end{array} \left[\begin{array}{ccc|ccc} 6 & 0 & 0 & 4 & 0 & -2 \\ 0 & 3 & 0 & 1 & 0 & -2 \\ 0 & 0 & -6 & 4 & -6 & -2 \end{array}\right]$$

$$\begin{array}{r} \frac{1}{6}\text{R}_1 \to \text{R}_1 \\ \frac{1}{3}\text{R}_2 \to \text{R}_2 \\ -\frac{1}{6}\text{R}_3 \to \text{R}_3 \end{array} \left[\begin{array}{ccc|ccc} 1 & 0 & 0 & \frac{2}{3} & 0 & -\frac{1}{3} \\ 0 & 1 & 0 & \frac{1}{3} & 0 & -\frac{2}{3} \\ 0 & 0 & 1 & -\frac{2}{3} & 1 & \frac{1}{3} \end{array}\right]$$

$$A^{-1} = \begin{bmatrix} \frac{2}{3} & 0 & -\frac{1}{3} \\ \frac{1}{3} & 0 & -\frac{2}{3} \\ -\frac{2}{3} & 1 & \frac{1}{3} \end{bmatrix}$$

35. Let

$$A = \begin{bmatrix} 2 & 0 & 4 \\ 1 & -1 & 0 \\ 0 & 1 & -2 \end{bmatrix}.$$

$$[A|I] = \left[\begin{array}{ccc|ccc} 2 & 0 & 4 & 1 & 0 & 0 \\ 1 & -1 & 0 & 0 & 1 & 0 \\ 0 & 1 & -2 & 0 & 0 & 1 \end{array}\right]$$

$$-2\text{R}_2 + \text{R}_1 \to \text{R}_2 \quad \left[\begin{array}{ccc|ccc} 2 & 0 & 4 & 1 & 0 & 0 \\ 0 & 2 & 4 & 1 & -2 & 0 \\ 0 & 1 & -2 & 0 & 0 & 1 \end{array}\right]$$

$$-2\text{R}_3 + \text{R}_2 \to \text{R}_3 \quad \left[\begin{array}{ccc|ccc} 2 & 0 & 4 & 1 & 0 & 0 \\ 0 & 2 & 4 & 1 & -2 & 0 \\ 0 & 0 & 8 & 1 & -2 & -2 \end{array}\right]$$

$$\begin{array}{r} -1\text{R}_3 + 2\text{R}_1 \to \text{R}_1 \\ -1\text{R}_3 + 2\text{R}_2 \to \text{R}_2 \\ \\ \end{array} \left[\begin{array}{ccc|ccc} 4 & 0 & 0 & 1 & 2 & 2 \\ 0 & 4 & 0 & 1 & -2 & 2 \\ 0 & 0 & 8 & 1 & -2 & -2 \end{array}\right]$$

$$\begin{array}{r} \frac{1}{4}\text{R}_1 \to \text{R}_1 \\ \frac{1}{4}\text{R}_2 \to \text{R}_2 \\ \frac{1}{8}\text{R}_3 \to \text{R}_3 \end{array} \left[\begin{array}{ccc|ccc} 1 & 0 & 0 & \frac{1}{4} & \frac{1}{2} & \frac{1}{2} \\ 0 & 1 & 0 & \frac{1}{4} & -\frac{1}{2} & \frac{1}{2} \\ 0 & 0 & 1 & \frac{1}{8} & -\frac{1}{4} & -\frac{1}{4} \end{array}\right]$$

$$A^{-1} = \begin{bmatrix} \frac{1}{4} & \frac{1}{2} & \frac{1}{2} \\ \frac{1}{4} & -\frac{1}{2} & \frac{1}{2} \\ \frac{1}{8} & -\frac{1}{4} & -\frac{1}{4} \end{bmatrix}.$$

36. Find the inverse of $A = \begin{bmatrix} 1 & 3 & 6 \\ 4 & 0 & 9 \\ 5 & 15 & 30 \end{bmatrix}$, if it exists.

$$[A|I] = \left[\begin{array}{ccc|ccc} 1 & 3 & 6 & 1 & 0 & 0 \\ 4 & 0 & 9 & 0 & 1 & 0 \\ 5 & 15 & 30 & 0 & 0 & 1 \end{array}\right]$$

$$\begin{array}{r} \\ -4\text{R}_1 + \text{R}_2 \to \text{R}_2 \\ -5\text{R}_1 + \text{R}_3 \to \text{R}_3 \end{array} \left[\begin{array}{ccc|ccc} 1 & 3 & 6 & 1 & 0 & 0 \\ 0 & -12 & -15 & -4 & 1 & 0 \\ 0 & 0 & 0 & -5 & 0 & 1 \end{array}\right]$$

The last row is all zeros, so no inverse exists to the left of the bar line.

37. Find the inverse of $A = \begin{bmatrix} 2 & -3 & 4 \\ 1 & 5 & 7 \\ -4 & 6 & -8 \end{bmatrix}$, if it exists.

$$[A|I] = \left[\begin{array}{ccc|ccc} 2 & -3 & 4 & 1 & 0 & 0 \\ 1 & 5 & 7 & 0 & 1 & 0 \\ -4 & 6 & -8 & 0 & 0 & 1 \end{array}\right]$$

$$\begin{array}{r} \\ -1\text{R}_1 + 2\text{R}_2 \to \text{R}_2 \\ 2\text{R}_1 + \text{R}_3 \to \text{R}_3 \end{array} \left[\begin{array}{ccc|ccc} 2 & -3 & 4 & 1 & 0 & 0 \\ 0 & 13 & 10 & -1 & 2 & 0 \\ 0 & 0 & 0 & 2 & 0 & 1 \end{array}\right]$$

The zeros in the third row to the left of the vertical bar indicate that the original matrix has no inverse.

38. $A = \begin{bmatrix} 5 & 1 \\ -1 & -2 \end{bmatrix}$, $B = \begin{bmatrix} -8 \\ 24 \end{bmatrix}$

The matrix equation to be solved is $AX = B$, or

$$\begin{bmatrix} 5 & 1 \\ -1 & -2 \end{bmatrix}\begin{bmatrix} x \\ y \end{bmatrix} = \begin{bmatrix} -8 \\ 24 \end{bmatrix}.$$

Calculate the inverse of the coefficient matrix A to obtain

$$\begin{bmatrix} 5 & 1 \\ -1 & -2 \end{bmatrix}^{-1} = \begin{bmatrix} \frac{1}{4} & \frac{1}{8} \\ -\frac{1}{4} & -\frac{5}{8} \end{bmatrix}.$$

Now $X = A^{-1}B$, so

$$\begin{bmatrix} x \\ y \end{bmatrix} = \begin{bmatrix} \frac{1}{4} & \frac{1}{8} \\ -\frac{1}{4} & -\frac{5}{8} \end{bmatrix}\begin{bmatrix} -8 \\ 24 \end{bmatrix} = \begin{bmatrix} 1 \\ -13 \end{bmatrix}.$$

39. $A = \begin{bmatrix} 1 & 2 \\ 2 & 4 \end{bmatrix}$, $B = \begin{bmatrix} 5 \\ 10 \end{bmatrix}$

Row operations may be used to see that matrix A has no inverse. The matrix equation $AX = B$ may be written as the system of equations

$$\begin{aligned} x + 2y &= 5 \quad (1) \\ 2x + 4y &= 10. \quad (2) \end{aligned}$$

Use the elimination method to solve this system. Begin by eliminating x in equation (2).

$$\begin{aligned} & & x + 2y &= 5 \quad (1) \\ -2R_1 + R_2 &\to R_2 & 0 &= 0 \quad (3) \end{aligned}$$

The true statement in equation (3) indicates that the equations are dependent. Solve equation (1) for x in terms of y.

$$x = -2y + 5$$

The solution is $(-2y + 5, y)$, where y is any real number.

40. $A = \begin{bmatrix} 1 & 0 & 2 \\ -1 & 1 & 0 \\ 3 & 0 & 4 \end{bmatrix}$, $B = \begin{bmatrix} 8 \\ 4 \\ -6 \end{bmatrix}$

By the usual method, we find that the inverse of the coefficient matrix is

$$A^{-1} = \begin{bmatrix} -2 & 0 & 1 \\ -2 & 1 & 1 \\ \frac{3}{2} & 0 & -\frac{1}{2} \end{bmatrix}.$$

Since $X = A^{-1}B$,

$$X = \begin{bmatrix} -2 & 0 & 1 \\ -2 & 1 & 1 \\ \frac{3}{2} & 0 & -\frac{1}{2} \end{bmatrix}\begin{bmatrix} 8 \\ 4 \\ -6 \end{bmatrix} = \begin{bmatrix} -22 \\ -18 \\ 15 \end{bmatrix}.$$

41. $A = \begin{bmatrix} 2 & 4 & 0 \\ 1 & -2 & 0 \\ 0 & 0 & 3 \end{bmatrix}$, $B = \begin{bmatrix} 72 \\ -24 \\ 48 \end{bmatrix}$

Use row operations to find the inverse of A, which is

$$A^{-1} = \begin{bmatrix} \frac{1}{4} & \frac{1}{2} & 0 \\ \frac{1}{8} & -\frac{1}{4} & 0 \\ 0 & 0 & \frac{1}{3} \end{bmatrix}.$$

Since $X = A^{-1}B$,

$$X = \begin{bmatrix} \frac{1}{4} & \frac{1}{2} & 0 \\ \frac{1}{8} & -\frac{1}{4} & 0 \\ 0 & 0 & \frac{1}{3} \end{bmatrix}\begin{bmatrix} 72 \\ -24 \\ 48 \end{bmatrix} = \begin{bmatrix} 6 \\ 15 \\ 16 \end{bmatrix}.$$

42. $x + 2y = 4$
$2x - 3y = 1$

The coefficient matrix is

$$A = \begin{bmatrix} 1 & 2 \\ 2 & -3 \end{bmatrix}.$$

Calculate the inverse of A.

$$A^{-1} = \begin{bmatrix} \frac{3}{7} & \frac{2}{7} \\ \frac{2}{7} & -\frac{1}{7} \end{bmatrix}$$

Use $X = A^{-1}B$ to solve.

$$\begin{bmatrix} x \\ y \end{bmatrix} = \begin{bmatrix} \frac{3}{7} & \frac{2}{7} \\ \frac{2}{7} & -\frac{1}{7} \end{bmatrix}\begin{bmatrix} 4 \\ 1 \end{bmatrix} = \begin{bmatrix} 2 \\ 1 \end{bmatrix}$$

The solution is $(2, 1)$.

43. $5x + 10y = 80$
$3x - 2y = 120$

Let $A = \begin{bmatrix} 5 & 10 \\ 3 & -2 \end{bmatrix}$, $X = \begin{bmatrix} x \\ y \end{bmatrix}$, $B = \begin{bmatrix} 80 \\ 120 \end{bmatrix}$.

Use row operations to find the inverse of A, which is

$$A^{-1} = \begin{bmatrix} \frac{1}{20} & \frac{1}{4} \\ \frac{3}{40} & -\frac{1}{8} \end{bmatrix}.$$

Since $X = A^{-1}B$,

$$\begin{bmatrix} x \\ y \end{bmatrix} = \begin{bmatrix} \frac{1}{20} & \frac{1}{4} \\ \frac{3}{40} & -\frac{1}{8} \end{bmatrix} \begin{bmatrix} 80 \\ 120 \end{bmatrix} = \begin{bmatrix} 34 \\ -9 \end{bmatrix}$$

The solution is $(34, -9)$.

44. $x + y + z = 1$
$2x + y = -2$
$3y + z = 2$

The coefficient matrix is

$$A = \begin{bmatrix} 1 & 1 & 1 \\ 2 & 1 & 0 \\ 0 & 3 & 1 \end{bmatrix}.$$

Find that the inverse of A is

$$A^{-1} = \begin{bmatrix} \frac{1}{5} & \frac{2}{5} & -\frac{1}{5} \\ -\frac{2}{5} & \frac{1}{5} & \frac{2}{5} \\ \frac{6}{5} & -\frac{3}{5} & -\frac{1}{5} \end{bmatrix}.$$

Now $X = A^{-1}B$, so

$$\begin{bmatrix} x \\ y \\ z \end{bmatrix} = \begin{bmatrix} \frac{1}{5} & \frac{2}{5} & -\frac{1}{5} \\ -\frac{2}{5} & \frac{1}{5} & \frac{2}{5} \\ \frac{6}{5} & -\frac{3}{5} & -\frac{1}{5} \end{bmatrix} \begin{bmatrix} 1 \\ -2 \\ 2 \end{bmatrix}$$
$$= \begin{bmatrix} -1 \\ 0 \\ 2 \end{bmatrix}.$$

The solution is $(-1, 0, 2)$.

45. $x - 4y + 2z = -1$
$-2x + y - 3z = -9$
$3x + 5y - 2z = 7$

Let $A = \begin{bmatrix} 1 & -4 & 2 \\ -2 & 1 & -3 \\ 3 & 5 & -2 \end{bmatrix}$, $X = \begin{bmatrix} x \\ y \\ z \end{bmatrix}$,

$B = \begin{bmatrix} -1 \\ -9 \\ 7 \end{bmatrix}$.

Use row operations to find the inverse of A, which is

$$A^{-1} = \begin{bmatrix} \frac{1}{3} & \frac{2}{39} & \frac{10}{39} \\ -\frac{1}{3} & -\frac{8}{39} & -\frac{1}{39} \\ -\frac{1}{3} & -\frac{17}{39} & -\frac{7}{39} \end{bmatrix} = \frac{1}{39} \begin{bmatrix} 13 & 2 & 10 \\ -13 & -8 & -1 \\ -13 & -17 & -7 \end{bmatrix}.$$

Since $X = A^{-1}B$,

$$\begin{bmatrix} x \\ y \\ z \end{bmatrix} = \frac{1}{39} \begin{bmatrix} 13 & 2 & 10 \\ -13 & -8 & -1 \\ -13 & -17 & -7 \end{bmatrix} \begin{bmatrix} -1 \\ -9 \\ 7 \end{bmatrix}$$
$$= \frac{1}{39} \begin{bmatrix} 39 \\ 78 \\ 117 \end{bmatrix}$$
$$= \begin{bmatrix} 1 \\ 2 \\ 3 \end{bmatrix}.$$

The solution is $(1, 2, 3)$.

46. $A = \begin{bmatrix} 0.01 & 0.05 \\ 0.04 & 0.03 \end{bmatrix}$, $D = \begin{bmatrix} 200 \\ 300 \end{bmatrix}$

$X = (I - A)^{-1}D$

$$I - A = \begin{bmatrix} 1 & 0 \\ 0 & 1 \end{bmatrix} - \begin{bmatrix} 0.01 & 0.05 \\ 0.04 & 0.03 \end{bmatrix}$$
$$= \begin{bmatrix} 0.99 & -0.05 \\ -0.04 & 0.97 \end{bmatrix}$$

Use row operations to find the inverse of $I - A$, which is

$$(I - A)^{-1} = \begin{bmatrix} 1.0122 & 0.0522 \\ 0.0417 & 1.0331 \end{bmatrix}.$$

Since $X = (I - A)^{-1}D$, the production matrix is

$$X = \begin{bmatrix} 1.0122 & 0.0522 \\ 0.0417 & 1.0331 \end{bmatrix} \begin{bmatrix} 200 \\ 300 \end{bmatrix}$$
$$= \begin{bmatrix} 218.1 \\ 318.3 \end{bmatrix}.$$

47. $A = \begin{bmatrix} 0.2 & 0.1 & 0.3 \\ 0.1 & 0 & 0.2 \\ 0 & 0 & 0.4 \end{bmatrix}$, $D = \begin{bmatrix} 500 \\ 200 \\ 100 \end{bmatrix}$

$X = (I - A)^{-1}D$

$$I - A = \begin{bmatrix} 0.8 & -0.1 & -0.3 \\ -0.1 & 1 & -0.2 \\ 0 & 0 & 0.6 \end{bmatrix}$$

$$(I - A)^{-1} \approx \begin{bmatrix} 1.266 & 0.1266 & 0.6751 \\ 0.1266 & 1.0127 & 0.40084 \\ 0 & 0 & 1.6667 \end{bmatrix}$$

Since $X = (I - A)^{-1}D$,

$$X = \begin{bmatrix} 1.266 & 0.1266 & 0.6751 \\ 0.1266 & 1.0127 & 0.40084 \\ 0 & 0 & 1.6667 \end{bmatrix} \begin{bmatrix} 500 \\ 200 \\ 100 \end{bmatrix}$$

$$= \begin{bmatrix} 725.7 \\ 305.9 \\ 166.7 \end{bmatrix}.$$

48.
$$\begin{aligned} x + 2y + z &= 7 \quad (1) \\ 2x - y - z &= 2 \quad (2) \\ 3x - 3y + 2z &= -5 \quad (3) \end{aligned}$$

(a) To solve the system by the echelon method, begin by eliminating x in equations (2) and (3).

$$\begin{aligned} & x + 2y + z = 7 \quad (1) \\ -2R_1 + R_2 \rightarrow R_2 \quad & -5y - 3z = -12 \quad (4) \\ -3R_1 + R_3 \rightarrow R_3 \quad & -9y - z = -26 \quad (5) \end{aligned}$$

Eliminate y in equation (5).

$$\begin{aligned} & x + 2y + z = 7 \quad (1) \\ & -5y - 3z = -12 \quad (4) \\ -9R_2 + 5R_3 \rightarrow R_3 \quad & 22z = -22 \quad (6) \end{aligned}$$

Make each leading coefficient equal 1.

$$\begin{aligned} & x + 2y + z = 7 \quad (1) \\ -\tfrac{1}{5}R_2 \rightarrow R_2 \quad & y + \frac{3}{5}z = \frac{12}{5} \quad (7) \\ \tfrac{1}{22}R_3 \rightarrow R_3 \quad & z = -1 \quad (8) \end{aligned}$$

Substitute -1 for z in equation (7) to get $y = 3$. Substitute -1 for z and 3 for y in equation (1) to get $x = 2$.

The solution is $(2, 3, -1)$.

(b) The same system is to be solved using the Gauss-Jordan method. Write the augmented matrix and use row operations.

$$\left[\begin{array}{ccc|c} 1 & 2 & 1 & 7 \\ 2 & -1 & -1 & 2 \\ 3 & -3 & 2 & -5 \end{array}\right]$$

$$\begin{array}{l} \\ -2R_1 + R_2 \rightarrow R_2 \\ -3R_1 + R_3 \rightarrow R_3 \end{array} \left[\begin{array}{ccc|c} 1 & 2 & 1 & 7 \\ 0 & -5 & -3 & -12 \\ 0 & -9 & -1 & -26 \end{array}\right]$$

$$\begin{array}{l} 2R_2 + 5R_1 \rightarrow R_1 \\ \\ -9R_2 + 5R_3 \rightarrow R_3 \end{array} \left[\begin{array}{ccc|c} 5 & 0 & -1 & 11 \\ 0 & -5 & -3 & -12 \\ 0 & 0 & 22 & -22 \end{array}\right]$$

$$\begin{array}{l} R_3 + 22R_1 \rightarrow R_1 \\ 3R_3 + 22R_2 \rightarrow R_2 \\ \\ \end{array} \left[\begin{array}{ccc|c} 110 & 0 & 0 & 220 \\ 0 & -110 & 0 & -330 \\ 0 & 0 & 22 & -22 \end{array}\right]$$

$$\begin{array}{l} \tfrac{1}{110}R_1 + R_1 \\ -\tfrac{1}{110}R_2 \rightarrow R_2 \\ \tfrac{1}{22}R_3 \rightarrow R_3 \end{array} \left[\begin{array}{ccc|c} 1 & 0 & 0 & 2 \\ 0 & 1 & 0 & 3 \\ 0 & 0 & 1 & -1 \end{array}\right]$$

The corresponding system is

$$\begin{aligned} x &= 2 \\ y &= 3 \\ z &= -1. \end{aligned}$$

The solution is $(2, 3, -1)$

(c) The system can be written as a matrix equation $AX = B$ by writing

$$\begin{bmatrix} 1 & 2 & 1 \\ 2 & -1 & -1 \\ 3 & -3 & 2 \end{bmatrix} \begin{bmatrix} x \\ y \\ z \end{bmatrix} = \begin{bmatrix} 7 \\ 2 \\ -5 \end{bmatrix}.$$

(d) The inverse of the coefficient matrix A can be found by using row operations.

$$[A|I] = \left[\begin{array}{ccc|ccc} 1 & 2 & 1 & 1 & 0 & 0 \\ 2 & -1 & -1 & 0 & 1 & 0 \\ 3 & -3 & 2 & 0 & 0 & 1 \end{array}\right]$$

$$\begin{array}{l} \\ -2R_1 + R_2 \rightarrow R_2 \\ -3R_1 + R_3 \rightarrow R_3 \end{array} \left[\begin{array}{ccc|ccc} 1 & 2 & 1 & 1 & 0 & 0 \\ 0 & -5 & -3 & -2 & 1 & 0 \\ 0 & -9 & -1 & -3 & 0 & 1 \end{array}\right]$$

$$\begin{array}{l} 2R_2 + 5R_1 \rightarrow R_1 \\ \\ -9R_2 + 5R_3 \rightarrow R_3 \end{array} \left[\begin{array}{ccc|ccc} 5 & 0 & -1 & 1 & 2 & 0 \\ 0 & -5 & -3 & -2 & 1 & 0 \\ 0 & 0 & 22 & 3 & -9 & 5 \end{array}\right]$$

$$\begin{array}{l} R_3 + 22R_1 \rightarrow R_1 \\ 3R_3 + 22R_2 \rightarrow R_2 \\ \\ \end{array} \left[\begin{array}{ccc|ccc} 110 & 0 & 0 & 25 & 35 & 5 \\ 0 & -110 & 0 & -35 & -5 & 15 \\ 0 & 0 & 22 & 3 & -9 & 5 \end{array}\right]$$

The inverse of matrix A is

$$A^{-1} = \begin{bmatrix} \frac{5}{22} & \frac{7}{22} & \frac{1}{22} \\ \frac{7}{22} & \frac{1}{22} & -\frac{3}{22} \\ \frac{3}{22} & -\frac{9}{22} & \frac{5}{22} \end{bmatrix} \approx \begin{bmatrix} 0.23 & 0.32 & 0.05 \\ 0.32 & 0.05 & -0.14 \\ 0.14 & -0.41 & 0.23 \end{bmatrix}.$$

(e) Since $X = A^{-1}B$,

$$\begin{bmatrix} x \\ y \\ z \end{bmatrix} = \begin{bmatrix} \frac{5}{22} & \frac{7}{22} & \frac{1}{22} \\ \frac{7}{22} & \frac{1}{22} & -\frac{3}{22} \\ \frac{3}{22} & -\frac{9}{22} & \frac{5}{22} \end{bmatrix} \begin{bmatrix} 7 \\ 2 \\ -5 \end{bmatrix} = \begin{bmatrix} 2 \\ 3 \\ -1 \end{bmatrix}.$$

Once again, the solution is $(2, 3, -1)$.

49. Use a table to organize the information.

	Standard	Extra Large	Time Available
Hours Cutting	$\frac{1}{4}$	$\frac{1}{3}$	4
Hours Shaping	$\frac{1}{2}$	$\frac{1}{3}$	6

Let $x =$ the number of standard paper clips (in thousands),
and $y =$ the number of extra large paper clips (in thousands).

The given information leads to the system

$$\frac{1}{4}x + \frac{1}{3}y = 4$$
$$\frac{1}{2}x + \frac{1}{3}y = 6.$$

Solve this system by any method to get $x = 8$, $y = 6$. The manufacturer can make 8 thousand (8000) standard and 6 thousand (6000) extra large paper clips.

50. Let $x_1 =$ the number of blankets,
$x_2 =$ the number of rugs, and
$x_3 =$ the number of skirts.

The given information leads to the system

$$\begin{aligned} 24x_1 + 30x_2 + 12x_3 &= 306 \quad (1) \\ 4x_1 + 5x_2 + 3x_3 &= 59 \quad (2) \\ 15x_1 + 18x_2 + 9x_3 &= 201. \quad (3) \end{aligned}$$

Simplify equations (1) and (3).

$$\begin{aligned} \tfrac{1}{6}R_1 \to R_1 \quad 4x_1 + 5x_2 + 2x_3 &= 51 \quad (4) \\ 4x_1 + 5x_2 + 3x_3 &= 59 \quad (2) \\ \tfrac{1}{3}R_3 \to R_3 \quad 5x_1 + 6x_2 + 3x_3 &= 67 \quad (5) \end{aligned}$$

Solve this system by the Gauss-Jordan method. Write the augmented matrix and use row operations.

$$\left[\begin{array}{ccc|c} 4 & 5 & 2 & 51 \\ 4 & 5 & 3 & 59 \\ 5 & 6 & 3 & 67 \end{array}\right]$$

$$\begin{array}{r} \\ -1R_1 + R_2 \to R_2 \\ -4R_3 + 5R_1 \to R_3 \end{array} \left[\begin{array}{ccc|c} 4 & 5 & 2 & 51 \\ 0 & 0 & 1 & 8 \\ 0 & 1 & -2 & -13 \end{array}\right]$$

Interchange the second and third rows.

$$\left[\begin{array}{ccc|c} 4 & 5 & 2 & 51 \\ 0 & 1 & -2 & -13 \\ 0 & 0 & 1 & 8 \end{array}\right]$$

$$-5R_2 + R_1 \to R_1 \left[\begin{array}{ccc|c} 4 & 0 & 12 & 116 \\ 0 & 1 & -2 & -13 \\ 0 & 0 & 1 & 8 \end{array}\right]$$

$$\begin{array}{r} -12R_3 + R_1 \to R_1 \\ 2R_3 + R_2 \to R_2 \end{array} \left[\begin{array}{ccc|c} 4 & 0 & 0 & 20 \\ 0 & 1 & 0 & 3 \\ 0 & 0 & 1 & 8 \end{array}\right]$$

$$\tfrac{1}{4}R_1 \to R_1 \left[\begin{array}{ccc|c} 1 & 0 & 0 & 5 \\ 0 & 1 & 0 & 3 \\ 0 & 0 & 1 & 8 \end{array}\right]$$

The solution of the system is $x = 5$, $y = 3$, $z = 8$. 5 blankets, 3 rugs, and 8 skirts can be made.

51. Let $x =$ Tulsa's number of gallons,
$y =$ New Orleans' number of gallons, and
$z =$ Ardmore's number of gallons.

The system that may be written is

$$\begin{aligned} 0.5x + 0.4y + 0.3z &= 219{,}000 \quad \textit{Chicago} \\ 0.2x + 0.4y + 0.4z &= 192{,}000 \quad \textit{Dallas} \\ 0.3x + 0.2y + 0.3z &= 144{,}000. \quad \textit{Atlanta} \end{aligned}$$

The augmented matrix is

$$\left[\begin{array}{ccc|c} 0.5 & 0.4 & 0.3 & 219{,}000 \\ 0.2 & 0.4 & 0.4 & 192{,}000 \\ 0.3 & 0.2 & 0.3 & 144{,}000 \end{array}\right].$$

$$\begin{array}{r} \\ 2R_1+(-5)R_2 \to R_2 \\ 3R_1+(-5)R_3 \to R_3 \end{array} \left[\begin{array}{ccc|c} 0.5 & 0.4 & 0.3 & 219{,}000 \\ 0 & -1.2 & -1.4 & -522{,}000 \\ 0 & 0.2 & -0.6 & -63{,}000 \end{array}\right]$$

$$\begin{array}{r} -2R_3+R_1 \to R_1 \\ \\ R_2+6R_3 \to R_3 \end{array} \left[\begin{array}{ccc|c} 0.5 & 0 & 1.5 & 345{,}000 \\ 0 & -1.2 & -1.4 & -522{,}000 \\ 0 & 0 & -5 & -900{,}000 \end{array}\right]$$

$$\begin{array}{r} 0.3R_3+R_1 \to R_1 \\ -14R_3+50R_2 \to R_2 \\ \\ \end{array} \left[\begin{array}{ccc|c} 0.5 & 0 & 0 & 75{,}000 \\ 0 & -60 & 0 & -13{,}500{,}000 \\ 0 & 0 & -5 & -900{,}000 \end{array}\right]$$

$$\begin{array}{r} 2R_1 \to R_1 \\ -\frac{1}{60}R_2 \to R_2 \\ -\frac{1}{5}R_3 \to R_3 \end{array} \left[\begin{array}{ccc|c} 1 & 0 & 0 & 150{,}000 \\ 0 & 1 & 0 & 225{,}000 \\ 0 & 0 & 1 & 180{,}000 \end{array}\right]$$

Thus, 150,000 gal were produced at Tulsa, 225,000 gal at New Orleans, and 180,000 gal at Ardmore.

52. The 4×5 matrix of stock reports is

	div	*ratio*	*sales*	*price*	*change*
AT &T	1.33	17.6	152,000	26.75	1.88
GE	1.00	20	238,200	32.36	−1.50
SaraLee	0.79	25.4	39,110	16.51	−0.89
Disney	0.27	21.2	122,500	28.60	0.75

53. (a) $\begin{array}{l} \text{High} \\ \text{Medium} \\ \text{Coated} \end{array} \begin{bmatrix} 3170 \\ 2360 \\ 1800 \end{bmatrix}$

(b) $\begin{bmatrix} x \\ y \\ z \end{bmatrix}$

(c) $\begin{bmatrix} 10 & 5 & 8 \\ 12 & 0 & 4 \\ 0 & 10 & 5 \end{bmatrix} \begin{bmatrix} x \\ y \\ z \end{bmatrix} = \begin{bmatrix} 3170 \\ 2360 \\ 1800 \end{bmatrix}$

(d) $$\begin{bmatrix} x \\ y \\ z \end{bmatrix} = \begin{bmatrix} 10 & 5 & 8 \\ 12 & 0 & 4 \\ 0 & 10 & 5 \end{bmatrix}^{-1} \begin{bmatrix} 3170 \\ 2360 \\ 1800 \end{bmatrix}$$

$$= \begin{bmatrix} -0.154 & 0.212 & 0.0769 \\ -0.231 & 0.192 & 0.2154 \\ 0.462 & -0.385 & -0.231 \end{bmatrix} \begin{bmatrix} 3170 \\ 2360 \\ 1800 \end{bmatrix}$$

$$= \begin{bmatrix} 150 \\ 110 \\ 140 \end{bmatrix}$$

54. (a) The input-output matrix is

$$A = \begin{bmatrix} 0 & \frac{1}{2} \\ \frac{2}{3} & 0 \end{bmatrix}.$$

(b) $I - A = \begin{bmatrix} 1 & -\frac{1}{2} \\ -\frac{2}{3} & 1 \end{bmatrix}$, $D = \begin{bmatrix} 400 \\ 800 \end{bmatrix}$

Use row operations to find the inverse of $I - A$, which is

$$(I - A)^{-1} = \begin{bmatrix} \frac{3}{2} & \frac{3}{4} \\ 1 & \frac{3}{2} \end{bmatrix}.$$

Since $X = (I - A)^{-1}D$,

$$X = \begin{bmatrix} \frac{3}{2} & \frac{3}{4} \\ 1 & \frac{3}{2} \end{bmatrix} \begin{bmatrix} 400 \\ 800 \end{bmatrix} = \begin{bmatrix} 1200 \\ 1600 \end{bmatrix}.$$

The production required is 1200 units of cheese and 1600 units of goats.

55. (a) Use a graphing calculator or a computer to find $(I - A)^{-1}$. The solution, which may vary slightly, is

$$\begin{bmatrix} 1.30 & 0.045 & 0.567 & 0.012 & 0.068 & 0.020 \\ 0.204 & 1.03 & 0.183 & 0.004 & 0.022 & 0.006 \\ 0.155 & 0.038 & 1.12 & 0.020 & 0.114 & 0.034 \\ 0.018 & 0.021 & 0.028 & 1.08 & 0.016 & 0.033 \\ 0.537 & 0.525 & 0.483 & 0.279 & 1.74 & 0.419 \\ 0.573 & 0.346 & 0.497 & 0.536 & 0.087 & 1.94 \end{bmatrix}$$

Values have been rounded.

The value in row 2, column 1 of this matrix, 0.204, indicates that every \$1 of increased demand for livestock will result in an increase of production demand of \$0.204 in crops.

(b) Use a graphing calculator or computer to find $(I - A)^{-1}D$. The solution, which may vary slightly, is

$$\begin{bmatrix} 3855 \\ 1476 \\ 2726 \\ 1338 \\ 8439 \\ 10{,}256 \end{bmatrix}.$$

Values have been rounded.

In millions of dollars, produce \$3855 in livestock, \$1476 in crops, \$2726 in food products, \$1338 in mining and manufacturing, \$8439 in households, and \$10,256 in other business sectors.

56. The given information can be written as the following 4×3 matrix.

$$\begin{bmatrix} 8 & 8 & 8 \\ 10 & 5 & 9 \\ 7 & 10 & 7 \\ 8 & 9 & 7 \end{bmatrix}$$

57. (a) The X-ray passes through cells B and C, so the attenuation value for beam 3 is $b+c$.

(b) Beam 1: $a+b=0.8$
Beam 2: $a+c=0.55$
Beam 3: $b+c=0.65$

$$\begin{bmatrix} 1 & 1 & 0 \\ 1 & 0 & 1 \\ 0 & 1 & 1 \end{bmatrix}\begin{bmatrix} a \\ b \\ c \end{bmatrix}=\begin{bmatrix} 0.8 \\ 0.55 \\ 0.65 \end{bmatrix}$$

$$\begin{bmatrix} a \\ b \\ c \end{bmatrix}=\begin{bmatrix} 1 & 1 & 0 \\ 1 & 0 & 1 \\ 0 & 1 & 1 \end{bmatrix}^{-1}\begin{bmatrix} 0.8 \\ 0.55 \\ 0.65 \end{bmatrix}$$

$$=\begin{bmatrix} \frac{1}{2} & \frac{1}{2} & -\frac{1}{2} \\ \frac{1}{2} & -\frac{1}{2} & \frac{1}{2} \\ -\frac{1}{2} & \frac{1}{2} & \frac{1}{2} \end{bmatrix}\begin{bmatrix} 0.8 \\ 0.55 \\ 0.65 \end{bmatrix}$$

$$=\begin{bmatrix} 0.35 \\ 0.45 \\ 0.2 \end{bmatrix}$$

The solution is $(0.35, 0.45, 0.2)$, so A is tumorous, B is bone, and C is healthy.

(c) For patient X,

$$\begin{bmatrix} a \\ b \\ c \end{bmatrix}=\begin{bmatrix} \frac{1}{2} & \frac{1}{2} & -\frac{1}{2} \\ \frac{1}{2} & -\frac{1}{2} & \frac{1}{2} \\ -\frac{1}{2} & \frac{1}{2} & \frac{1}{2} \end{bmatrix}\begin{bmatrix} 0.54 \\ 0.40 \\ 0.52 \end{bmatrix}=\begin{bmatrix} 0.21 \\ 0.33 \\ 0.19 \end{bmatrix}.$$

A and C are healthy; B is tumorous.

For patient Y,

$$\begin{bmatrix} a \\ b \\ c \end{bmatrix}=\begin{bmatrix} \frac{1}{2} & \frac{1}{2} & -\frac{1}{2} \\ \frac{1}{2} & -\frac{1}{2} & \frac{1}{2} \\ -\frac{1}{2} & \frac{1}{2} & \frac{1}{2} \end{bmatrix}\begin{bmatrix} 0.65 \\ 0.80 \\ 0.75 \end{bmatrix}=\begin{bmatrix} 0.35 \\ 0.3 \\ 0.45 \end{bmatrix}.$$

A and B are tumorous; C is bone.

For patient Z,

$$\begin{bmatrix} a \\ b \\ c \end{bmatrix}=\begin{bmatrix} \frac{1}{2} & \frac{1}{2} & -\frac{1}{2} \\ \frac{1}{2} & -\frac{1}{2} & \frac{1}{2} \\ -\frac{1}{2} & \frac{1}{2} & \frac{1}{2} \end{bmatrix}\begin{bmatrix} 0.51 \\ 0.49 \\ 0.44 \end{bmatrix}=\begin{bmatrix} 0.28 \\ 0.23 \\ 0.21 \end{bmatrix}.$$

A could be healthy or tumorous; B and C are healthy.

58. (a)
$$\begin{aligned} a+b&=0.60 \quad (1) \\ c+d&=0.75 \quad (2) \\ a+c&=0.65 \quad (3) \\ b+d&=0.70 \quad (4) \end{aligned}$$

The augmented matrix of the system is

$$\left[\begin{array}{cccc|c} 1 & 1 & 0 & 0 & 0.60 \\ 0 & 0 & 1 & 1 & 0.75 \\ 1 & 0 & 1 & 0 & 0.65 \\ 0 & 1 & 0 & 1 & 0.70 \end{array}\right].$$

$$-1R_1+R_3 \rightarrow R_3 \quad \left[\begin{array}{cccc|c} 1 & 1 & 0 & 0 & 0.60 \\ 0 & 0 & 1 & 1 & 0.75 \\ 0 & -1 & 1 & 0 & 0.05 \\ 0 & 1 & 0 & 1 & 0.70 \end{array}\right]$$

Interchange rows 2 and 4.

$$\left[\begin{array}{cccc|c} 1 & 1 & 0 & 0 & 0.60 \\ 0 & 1 & 0 & 1 & 0.70 \\ 0 & -1 & 1 & 0 & 0.05 \\ 0 & 0 & 1 & 1 & 0.75 \end{array}\right]$$

$$\begin{array}{l} -1R_2+R_1 \rightarrow R_1 \\ \\ R_2+R_3 \rightarrow R_3 \end{array} \quad \left[\begin{array}{cccc|c} 1 & 0 & 0 & -1 & -0.10 \\ 0 & 1 & 0 & 1 & 0.70 \\ 0 & 0 & 1 & 1 & 0.75 \\ 0 & 0 & 1 & 1 & 0.75 \end{array}\right]$$

Since R_3 and R_4 are identical, there will be infinitely many solutions. We do not have enough information to determine the values of a, b, c, and d.

(b) i. If $d=0.33$, the system of equations in part (a) becomes

$$\begin{aligned} a+b&=0.60 \quad (1) \\ c+0.33&=0.75 \quad (2) \\ a+c&=0.65 \quad (3) \\ b+0.33&=0.70. \quad (4) \end{aligned}$$

Equation (2) gives $c=0.42$, and equation (4) gives $b=0.37$. Substituting $c=0.42$ into equation (3) gives $a=0.23$. Therefore, $a=0.23$, $b=0.37$, $c=0.42$, and $d=0.33$.

Thus, A is healthy, B and D are tumorous, and C is bone.

ii. If $d=0.43$, the system of equations in part (a) becomes

$$\begin{aligned} a+b&=0.60 \quad (1) \\ c+0.43&=0.75 \quad (2) \\ a+c&=0.65 \quad (3) \\ b+0.43&=0.70. \quad (4) \end{aligned}$$

Equation (2) gives $c = 0.32$, and equation (4) gives $b = 0.27$. Substituting $c = 0.32$ into equation (3) gives $a = 0.33$. Therefore, $a = 0.33$, $b = 0.27$, $c = 0.32$, and $d = 0.43$.

Thus, A and C are tumorous, B could be healthy or tumorous, and D is bone.

(c) The original system now has two additional equations.

$$\begin{aligned} a + b &= 0.60 \quad (1)\\ c + d &= 0.75 \quad (2)\\ a + c &= 0.65 \quad (3)\\ b + d &= 0.70 \quad (4)\\ b + c &= 0.85 \quad (5)\\ a + d &= 0.50 \quad (6) \end{aligned}$$

The augmented matrix of this system is

$$\left[\begin{array}{cccc|c} 1 & 1 & 0 & 0 & 0.60\\ 0 & 0 & 1 & 1 & 0.75\\ 1 & 0 & 1 & 0 & 0.65\\ 0 & 1 & 0 & 1 & 0.70\\ 0 & 1 & 1 & 0 & 0.85\\ 1 & 0 & 0 & 1 & 0.50 \end{array}\right].$$

Using the Gauss-Jordan method we obtain

$$\left[\begin{array}{cccc|c} 1 & 0 & 0 & 0 & 0.20\\ 0 & 1 & 0 & 0 & 0.40\\ 0 & 0 & 1 & 0 & 0.45\\ 0 & 0 & 0 & 1 & 0.30\\ 0 & 0 & 0 & 0 & 0\\ 0 & 0 & 0 & 0 & 0 \end{array}\right].$$

Therefore, $a = 0.20$, $b = 0.40$, $c = 0.45$, and $d = 0.30$. Thus, A is healthy, B and C are bone, and D is tumorous.

(d) As we saw in part (c), the six equations reduced to four independent equations. We need only four beams, correctly chosen, to obtain a solution. The four beams must pass through all four cells and must lead to independent equations. One such choice would be beams 1, 2, 3, and 6. Another choice would be beams 1, 2, 4, and 5.

59. The matrix representing the rates per 1000 athlete-exposures for specific injuries that caused a player wearing either shield to miss one or more events is

$$\begin{bmatrix} 3.54 & 1.41\\ 1.53 & 1.57\\ 0.34 & 0.29\\ 7.53 & 6.21 \end{bmatrix}.$$

Since an equal number of players wear each type of shield and the total number of athlete-exposures for the league in a season is 8000, each type of shield is worn by 4000 players. Since the rates are given per 1000 athletic-exposures, the matrix representing the number of 1000 athlete-exposures for each type of shield is

$$\begin{bmatrix} 4\\ 4 \end{bmatrix}.$$

The product of these matrices is

$$\begin{bmatrix} 20\\ 12\\ 3\\ 55 \end{bmatrix}.$$

Values have been rounded.

There would be about 20 head and face injuries, 12 concussions, 3 neck injuries, and 55 other injuries.

60. $$\begin{aligned} \frac{\sqrt{3}}{2}(W_1 + W_2) &= 100 \quad (1)\\ W_1 - W_2 &= 0 \quad\;\;\; (2) \end{aligned}$$

Equation (2) gives $W_1 = W_2$. Substitute W_1 for W_2 in equation (1).

$$\begin{aligned} \frac{\sqrt{3}}{2}(W_1 + W_1) &= 100\\ \frac{\sqrt{3}}{2}(2W_1) &= 100\\ \sqrt{3}W_1 &= 100\\ W_1 &= \frac{100}{\sqrt{3}} = \frac{100\sqrt{3}}{3} \approx 58 \end{aligned}$$

Therefore, $W_1 = W_2 \approx 58$ lb.

61. $\frac{1}{2}W_1 + \frac{\sqrt{2}}{2}W_2 = 150 \quad (1)$

$\frac{\sqrt{3}}{2}W_1 - \frac{\sqrt{2}}{2}W_2 = \quad 0 \quad (2)$

Adding equations (1) and (2) gives

$$\left(\frac{1}{2} + \frac{\sqrt{3}}{2}\right)W_1 = 150.$$

Multiply by 2.

$$(1+\sqrt{3})W_1 = 300$$
$$W_1 = \frac{300}{1+\sqrt{3}} \approx 110$$

From equation (2),

$$\frac{\sqrt{3}}{2}W_1 = \frac{\sqrt{2}}{2}W_2$$
$$W_2 = \frac{\sqrt{3}}{\sqrt{2}}W_1.$$

Substitute $\frac{300}{1+\sqrt{3}}$ from above for W_1.

$$W_2 = \frac{\sqrt{3}}{\sqrt{2}} \cdot \frac{300}{1+\sqrt{3}} = \frac{300\sqrt{3}}{(1+\sqrt{3})\sqrt{2}} \approx 134$$

Therefore, $W_1 \approx 110$ lb and $W_2 \approx 134$ lb.

62. $C = at^2 + by + c$

Use the values for C from the table.

(a) For 1960, $t = 0$ and $C = 317$.

$$317 = a(0)^2 + b(0) + c$$
$$317 = c$$

For 1980, $t = 20$ and $C = 339$.

$$339 = a(20)^2 + b(20) + 317$$
$$22 = 400a + 20b$$

For 2004, $t = 44$ and $C = 377$.

$$377 = a(44)^2 + b(44) + 317$$
$$60 = 1936a + 44b$$

Thus, we need to solve the system

$$\begin{bmatrix} 400 & 20 \\ 1936 & 44 \end{bmatrix} = \begin{bmatrix} 22 \\ 60 \end{bmatrix}$$

$$\begin{bmatrix} a \\ b \end{bmatrix} = \begin{bmatrix} 400 & 20 \\ 1936 & 44 \end{bmatrix} \begin{bmatrix} 22 \\ 60 \end{bmatrix}$$
$$= \begin{bmatrix} -\frac{1}{480} & \frac{1}{1056} \\ \frac{11}{120} & -\frac{5}{264} \end{bmatrix} \begin{bmatrix} 22 \\ 60 \end{bmatrix}$$
$$= \begin{bmatrix} \frac{29}{2640} \\ \frac{581}{660} \end{bmatrix} \approx \begin{bmatrix} 0.010985 \\ 0.8830 \end{bmatrix}$$

Therefore, $C = 0.010985t^2 + 0.8803t + 317$.

(b) In 1960, $C = 317$. So, double that level would be $C = 634$.

$$634 = 0.010985t^2 + 0.8803t + 317$$
$$0 = 0.010985t^2 + 0.8803t - 317$$

Multiply this equation by 2640 to clear the decimal values.

$$0 = 29t^2 + 2324t - 836{,}880$$

Use the quadratic formula with $a = 29, b = 2324$, and $c = -836{,}880$.

$$t = \frac{-2324 \pm \sqrt{2324^2 - 4(29)(-836{,}880)}}{2(29)}$$
$$= \frac{-2324 \pm \sqrt{5{,}400{,}976 - (-97{,}078{,}080)}}{2(29)}$$
$$\approx \frac{-2324 \pm 10{,}123}{58}$$
$$\approx 134.5 \text{ or } -214.6$$

Ignore the negative value. If $t = 134.5$, then $1960 + 134.5 = 2094.5$. The 1960 CO_2 level will double in the year 2095.

63. (a) $\begin{bmatrix} 1 \\ 1 \end{bmatrix} x + \begin{bmatrix} 0 \\ 2 \end{bmatrix} y = \begin{bmatrix} 1 \\ 2 \end{bmatrix}$

$$\begin{bmatrix} x \\ x \end{bmatrix} + \begin{bmatrix} 0 \\ 2y \end{bmatrix} = \begin{bmatrix} 1 \\ 2 \end{bmatrix}$$
$$\begin{bmatrix} x \\ x+2y \end{bmatrix} = \begin{bmatrix} 1 \\ 2 \end{bmatrix}$$

Since corresponding elements must be equal, $x = 1$ and $x+2y = 2$. Substituting $x = 1$ in the second equation gives $y = \frac{1}{2}$. Note that $x = 1$ and $y = \frac{1}{2}$ are the values that balance the equation.

(b) $x\text{CO}_2 + y\text{H}_2 + z\text{CO} = \text{H}_2\text{O}$

$$\begin{bmatrix} 1 \\ 0 \\ 2 \end{bmatrix} x + \begin{bmatrix} 0 \\ 2 \\ 0 \end{bmatrix} y + \begin{bmatrix} 1 \\ 0 \\ 1 \end{bmatrix} z = \begin{bmatrix} 0 \\ 2 \\ 1 \end{bmatrix}$$
$$\begin{bmatrix} x \\ 0 \\ 2x \end{bmatrix} + \begin{bmatrix} 0 \\ 2y \\ 0 \end{bmatrix} + \begin{bmatrix} z \\ 0 \\ z \end{bmatrix} = \begin{bmatrix} 0 \\ 2 \\ 1 \end{bmatrix}$$
$$\begin{bmatrix} x+z \\ 2y \\ 2x+z \end{bmatrix} = \begin{bmatrix} 0 \\ 2 \\ 1 \end{bmatrix}$$

Since corresponding elements must be equal, $x + z = 0$, $2y = 2$, and $2x+z = 1$. Solving $2y = 2$ gives $y = 1$. Solving the system $\begin{cases} x+z=0 \\ 2x+z=1 \end{cases}$ gives $x = 1$ and $z = -1$. Thus, the values that balance the equation are $x = 1$, $y = 1$, and $z = -1$.

64. Let $x =$ the number of boys and $y =$ the number of girls.

$$\begin{aligned} 0.2x + 0.3y &= 500 \quad (1) \\ 0.6x + 0.9y &= 1500 \quad (2) \end{aligned}$$

The augmented matrix is

$$\left[\begin{array}{cc|c} 0.2 & 0.3 & 500 \\ 0.6 & 0.9 & 1500 \end{array}\right].$$

$$5R_1 \to R_1 \quad \left[\begin{array}{cc|c} 1 & 1.5 & 2500 \\ 0.6 & 0.9 & 1500 \end{array}\right]$$

$$-0.6R_1 + R_2 \to R_2 \quad \left[\begin{array}{cc|c} 1 & 1.5 & 2500 \\ 0 & 0 & 0 \end{array}\right]$$

Thus,

$$\begin{aligned} x + 1.5y &= 2500 \\ x &= 2500 - 1.5y. \end{aligned}$$

There are y girls and $2500 - 1.5y$ boys, where y is any even integer between 0 and 1666 since $y \geq 0$ and

$$\begin{aligned} 2500 - 1.5y &\geq 0 \\ -1.5y &\geq -2500 \\ y &\leq 1666.\bar{6}. \end{aligned}$$

65. Let $x =$ the number of singles,
$y =$ the number of doubles,
$z =$ the number of triples, and
$w =$ the number of home runs hit by Barry Bonds.

If he had a total of 135 hits, then $x + y + z + w = 135$.
If he hit 15 times as many home runs as triples, then $w = 15z$.
If he hit 50% more home runs than doubles and triples, then $w = 1.5(y + z)$.
If he hit twice as many singles as doubles and triples, then $x = 2(y + z)$.

Write the equations in proper form, obtain the augmented matrix, and use row operations to solve.

$$\left[\begin{array}{cccc|c} 1 & 1 & 1 & 1 & 135 \\ 0 & 0 & 15 & -1 & 0 \\ 0 & 1.5 & 1.5 & -1 & 0 \\ 1 & -2 & -2 & 0 & 0 \end{array}\right]$$

$$R_2 \longleftrightarrow R_3 \quad \left[\begin{array}{cccc|c} 1 & 1 & 1 & 1 & 135 \\ 0 & 1.5 & 1.5 & -1 & 0 \\ 0 & 0 & 15 & -1 & 0 \\ 1 & -2 & -2 & 0 & 0 \end{array}\right]$$

$$-1R_1 + R_4 \to R_4 \quad \left[\begin{array}{cccc|c} 1 & 1 & 1 & 1 & 135 \\ 0 & 1.5 & 1.5 & -1 & 0 \\ 0 & 0 & 15 & -1 & 0 \\ 0 & -3 & -3 & -1 & -135 \end{array}\right]$$

$$\begin{array}{r} -10R_2 + 15R_1 \to R_1 \\ \\ \\ 2R_2 + R_4 \to R_4 \end{array} \quad \left[\begin{array}{cccc|c} 15 & 0 & 0 & 25 & 2025 \\ 0 & 1.5 & 1.5 & -1 & 0 \\ 0 & 0 & 15 & -1 & 0 \\ 0 & 0 & 0 & -3 & -135 \end{array}\right]$$

$$-1R_3 + 10R_2 \to R_2 \quad \left[\begin{array}{cccc|c} 15 & 0 & 0 & 25 & 2025 \\ 0 & 15 & 0 & -9 & 0 \\ 0 & 0 & 15 & -1 & 0 \\ 0 & 0 & 0 & -3 & -135 \end{array}\right]$$

$$\begin{array}{r} 25R_4 + 3R_1 \to R_1 \\ -3R_4 + R_2 \to R_2 \\ -1R_4 + 3R_3 \to R_3 \end{array} \quad \left[\begin{array}{cccc|c} 45 & 0 & 0 & 0 & 2700 \\ 0 & 15 & 0 & 0 & 405 \\ 0 & 0 & 45 & 0 & 135 \\ 0 & 0 & 0 & -3 & -135 \end{array}\right]$$

$$\begin{array}{r} \frac{1}{45}R_1 \to R_1 \\ \frac{1}{15}R_2 \to R_2 \\ \frac{1}{45}R_3 \to R_3 \\ -\frac{1}{3}R_4 \to R_4 \end{array} \quad \left[\begin{array}{cccc|c} 1 & 0 & 0 & 0 & 60 \\ 0 & 1 & 0 & 0 & 27 \\ 0 & 0 & 1 & 0 & 3 \\ 0 & 0 & 0 & 1 & 45 \end{array}\right]$$

Barry Bonds hit 60 singles, 27 doubles, 3 triples, and 45 home runs.

66. Let $x =$ the weight of a single chocolate wafer and
$y =$ the weight of a single layer of vanilla creme.

A serving of regular Oreo cookies is three cookies so that $3(2x + y) = 34$.

A serving of Double Stuf is two cookies so that $2(2x + 2y) = 29$.

Write the equations in proper form, obtain the augmented matrix, and use row operations to solve.

$$\left[\begin{array}{cc|c} 6 & 3 & 34 \\ 4 & 4 & 29 \end{array}\right]$$

$$-2R_1 + 3R_2 \rightarrow R_2 \quad \left[\begin{array}{cc|c} 6 & 3 & 34 \\ 0 & 6 & 19 \end{array}\right]$$

$$-1R_2 + 2R_1 \rightarrow R_1 \quad \left[\begin{array}{cc|c} 12 & 0 & 49 \\ 0 & 6 & 19 \end{array}\right]$$

$$\begin{array}{l} \frac{1}{12}R_1 \rightarrow R_1 \\ \frac{1}{6}R_2 \rightarrow R_2 \end{array} \quad \left[\begin{array}{cc|c} 1 & 0 & \frac{49}{12} \\ 0 & 1 & \frac{19}{6} \end{array}\right]$$

The solution is $\left(\frac{49}{12}, \frac{19}{6}\right)$, or about (4.08,3.17). A choclate wafer weighs 4.08 g and a single layer of vanilla creme weighs 3.17g.

Extended Application: Contagion

1. $$PQ = \begin{bmatrix} 1 & 0 & 0 & 1 & 0 \\ 0 & 0 & 1 & 1 & 0 \\ 1 & 1 & 0 & 0 & 0 \end{bmatrix} \begin{bmatrix} 1 & 1 & 0 & 1 & 1 & 1 \\ 0 & 0 & 0 & 0 & 1 & 0 \\ 0 & 0 & 0 & 0 & 0 & 0 \\ 0 & 1 & 0 & 1 & 0 & 0 \\ 1 & 0 & 0 & 0 & 1 & 0 \end{bmatrix}$$

$$= \begin{bmatrix} 1 & 2 & 0 & 2 & 1 & 1 \\ 0 & 1 & 0 & 1 & 0 & 0 \\ 1 & 1 & 0 & 1 & 2 & 1 \end{bmatrix}$$

2. In the product PQ, $a_{23} = 0$, so there were no contacts.

3. In the product PQ, column 3 has all zeros. The third person had no contacts with the first group.

4. In the product PQ, the entries in columns 2 and 4 both have a sum of 4 while the entries in column 5 have a sum of 3. In Q, columns 2, 4, and 5 have a sum of 2, 2, and 3, respectively. Therefore, the second, fourth, and fifth persons in the third group each had a total of 6 first-and second-order contacts.

Chapter 3

LINEAR PROGRAMMING: THE GRAPHICAL METHOD

3.1 Graphing Linear Inequalities

1. $x + y \leq 2$

First graph the boundary line $x + y = 2$ using the points $(2, 0)$ and $(0, 2)$. Since the points on this line satisfy $x + y \leq 2$, draw a solid line. To find the correct region to shade, choose any point not on the line. If $(0, 0)$ is used as the test point, we have

$$\begin{aligned} x + y &\leq 2 \\ 0 + 0 &\leq 2 \\ 0 &\leq 2, \end{aligned}$$

which is a true statement. Shade the half-plane containing $(0, 0)$, or all points below the line.

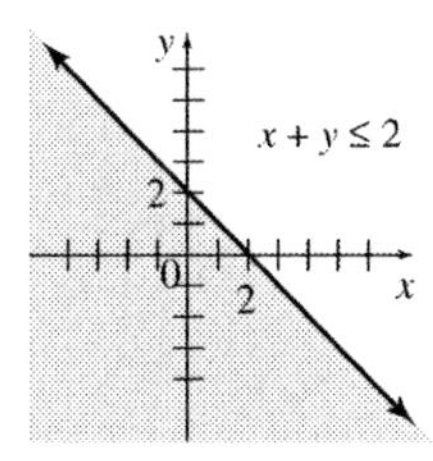

2. $y \leq x + 1$

The boundary is the line $y = x + 1$. Graph a solid line using the points $(0, 1)$ and $(-1, 0)$. Use $(0, 0)$ as a test point to get $0 \leq 1$, which is true. Shade all points below the line, or the half-plane containing $(0, 0)$.

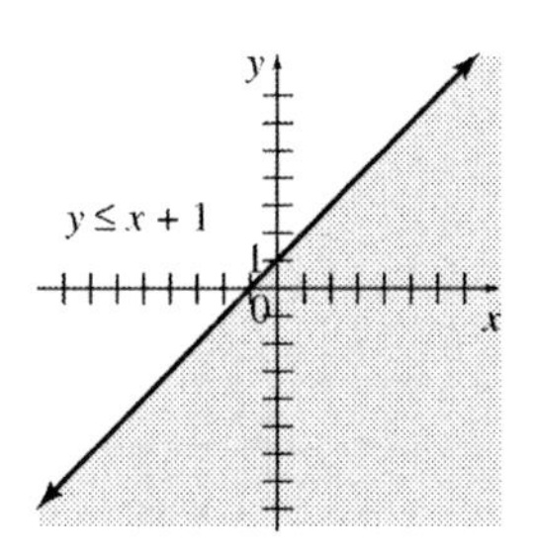

3. $x \geq 2 - y$

First graph the boundary line $x = 2 - y$ using the points $(0, 2)$ and $(2, 0)$. This will be a solid line. Choose $(0, 0)$ as a test point.

$$\begin{aligned} x &\geq 2 - y \\ 0 &\geq 2 - 0 \\ 0 &\geq 2, \end{aligned}$$

which is a false statement. Shade the half-plane that does not contain $(0, 0)$, or all points below the line.

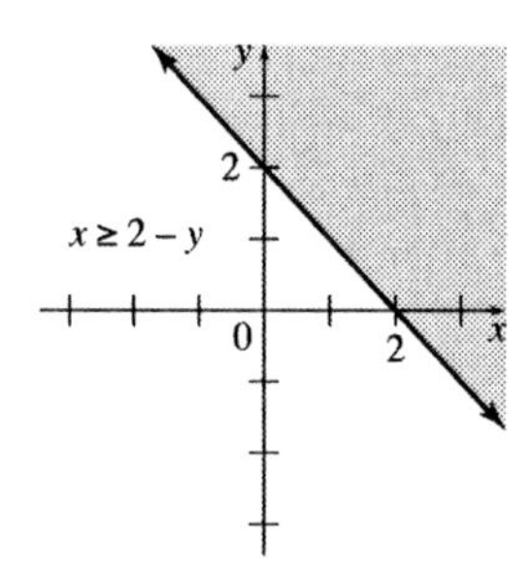

4. $y \geq x - 3$

The boundary is the line $y = x - 3$. Graph a solid line using the points $(0, -3)$ and $(3, 0)$. Use $(0, 0)$ as a test point to get $0 \geq 0 - 3$, which is true. Shade all points above the line, or the half-plane containing $(0, 0)$.

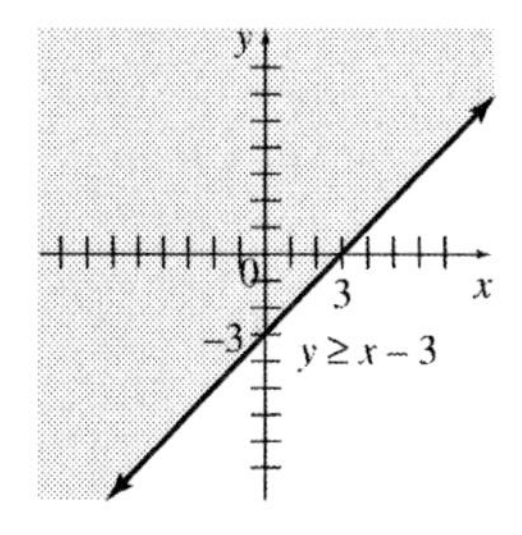

5. $4x - y < 6$

Graph $4x-y=6$ as a dashed line, since the points on the line are not part of the solution; the line passes through the points $(0,-6)$ and $\left(\frac{3}{2},0\right)$. Using the test point $(0,0)$, we have $0-0<6$ or $0<6$, a true statement. Shade the half-plane containing $(0,0)$, or all points above the line.

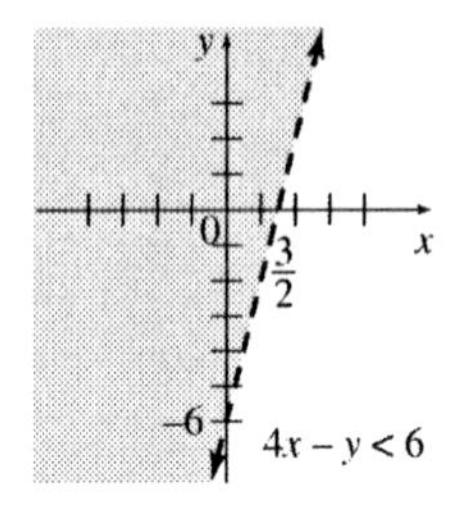

6. $4y + x > 6$

The boundary is the line $4y+x=6$. Graph a dashed line using the points $(6,0)$ and $\left(0,\frac{3}{2}\right)$. Use $(0,0)$ as a test point to get $0+0>6$, which is false. Shade the half-plane that does not contain $(0,0)$, or all points above the line.

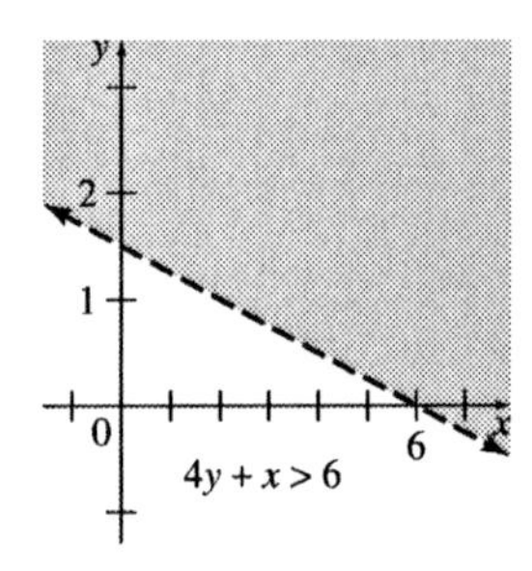

7. $4x + y < 8$

Graph $4x+y=8$ as a dashed line through $(2,0)$ and $(0,8)$. Using the test point $(0,0)$, we get $4(0)+0<8$ or $0<8$, a true statement. Shade the half-plane containing $(0,0)$, or all points below the line.

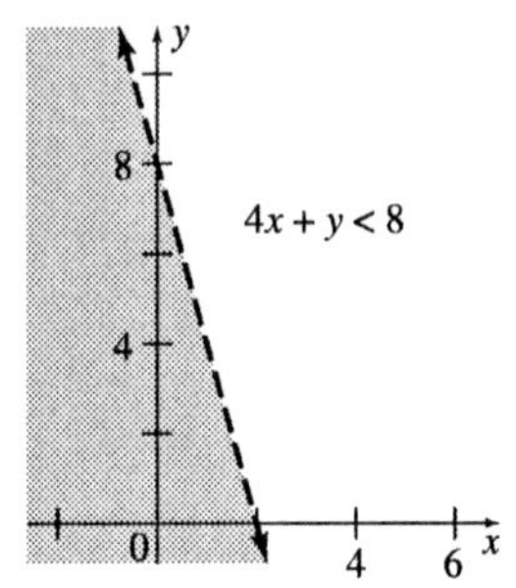

8. $2x - y > 2$

The boundary is the line $2x-y=2$. Graph a dashed line using the points $(0,-2)$ and $(1,0)$. Use $(0,0)$ as a test point to get $0-0>2$, which is false. Shade the half-plane that does not contain $(0,0)$, or all points below the line.

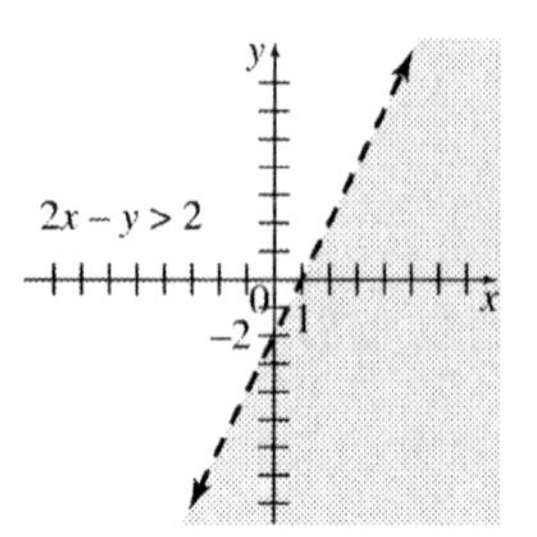

9. $x + 3y \geq -2$

The graph includes the line $x+3y=-2$, whose intercepts are the points $\left(0,-\frac{2}{3}\right)$ and $(-2,0)$. Graph $x+3y=-2$ as a solid line and use the origin as a test point. Since $0+3(0)\geq -2$ is true, shade the half-plane containing $(0,0)$, or all points above the line.

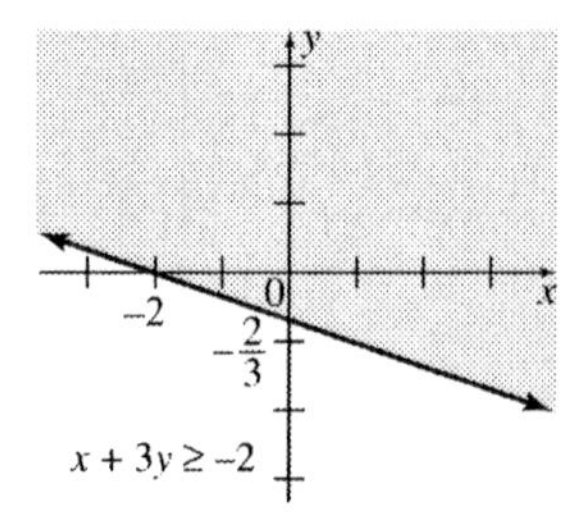

10. $2x + 3y \leq 6$

The boundary is the line $2x+3y=6$. Graph a solid line using $(0,2)$ and $(3,0)$. Use $(0,0)$ as a test point to get $0+0\leq 6$, which is true. Shade all points below the line, or the half-plane containing $(0,0)$.

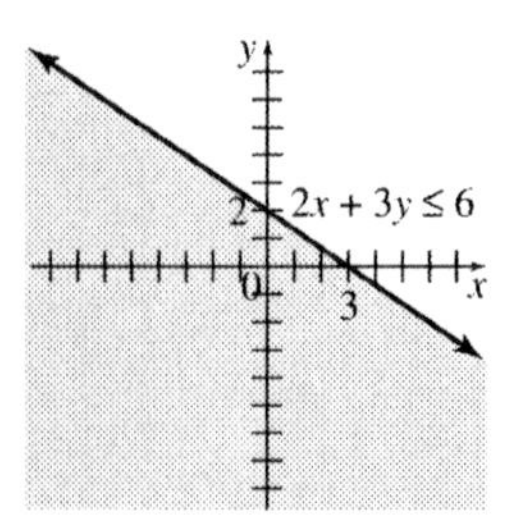

11. $x \leq 3y$

Graph $x = 3y$ as a solid line through the points $(0,0)$ and $(3,1)$. Since this line contains the origin, some point other than $(0,0)$ must be used as a test point. If we use the point $(1,2)$, we obtain $1 \leq 3(2)$ or $1 \leq 6$, a true statement. Shade the half-plane containing $(1,2)$, or all points above the line.

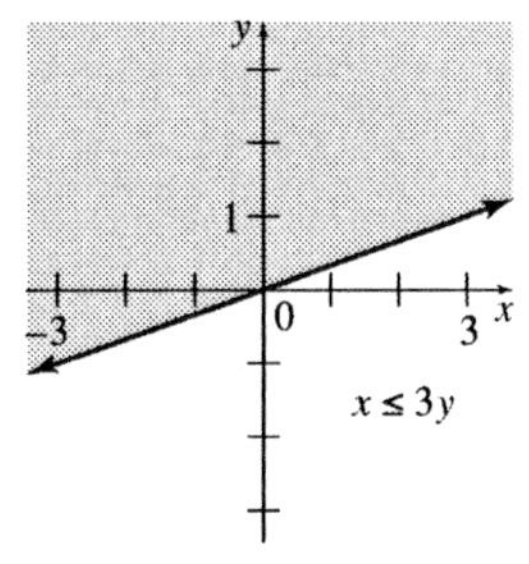

12. $2x \geq y$

The boundary is $2x = y$. Graph a solid line using the points $(0,0)$ and $(2,4)$. Since $(0,0)$ is on the line, use $(3,1)$ as a test point to get $2 \cdot 3 \geq 1$, which is true. Shade the half-plane containing $(3,1)$, or all points below the line.

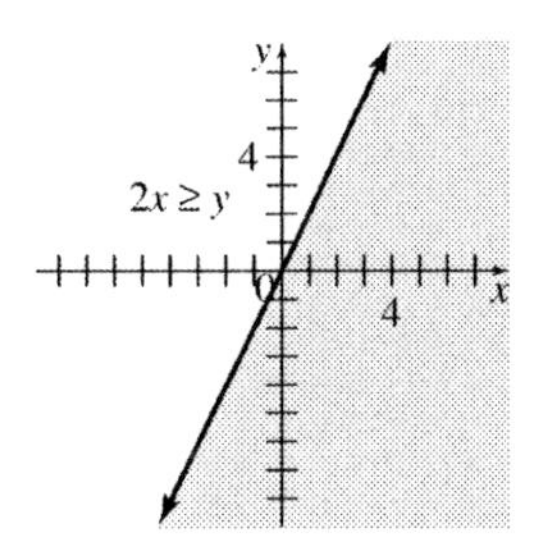

13. $x + y \leq 0$

Graph $x + y = 0$ as a solid line through the points $(0,0)$ and $(1,-1)$. This line contains $(0,0)$. If we use $(-1,0)$ as a test point, we obtain $-1 + 0 \leq 0$ or $-1 \leq 0$, a true statement. Shade the half-plane containing $(-1,0)$, or all points below the line.

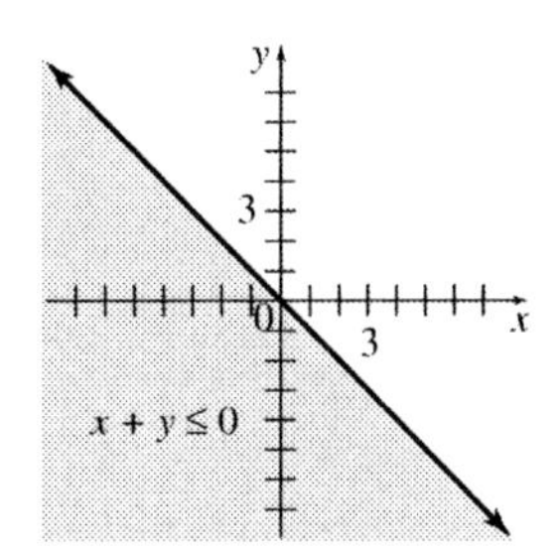

14. $3x + 2y \geq 0$

The boundary is $3x + 2y = 0$. Graph a solid line using $(0,0)$ and $(2,-3)$. Use $(4,1)$ as a test point to get $12 + 2 \geq 0$, which is true. Shade the half-plane containing $(4,1)$, or all points above the line.

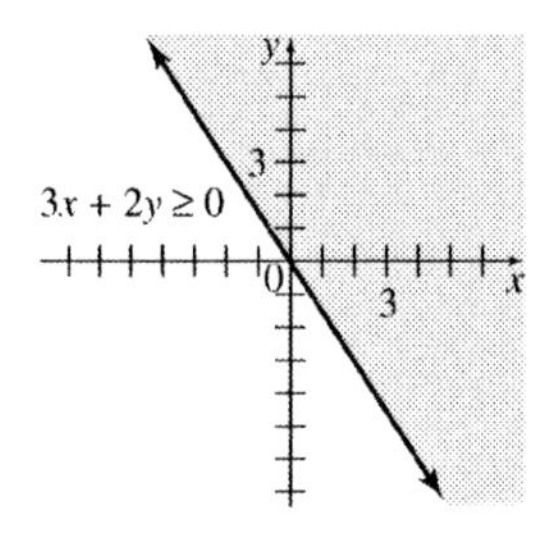

15. $y < x$

Graph $y = x$ as a dashed line through the points $(0,0)$ and $(1,1)$. Since this line contains the origin, choose a point other than $(0,0)$ as a test point. If we use $(2,3)$, we obtain $3 < 2$, which is false. Shade the half-plane that does not contain $(2,3)$, or all points below the line.

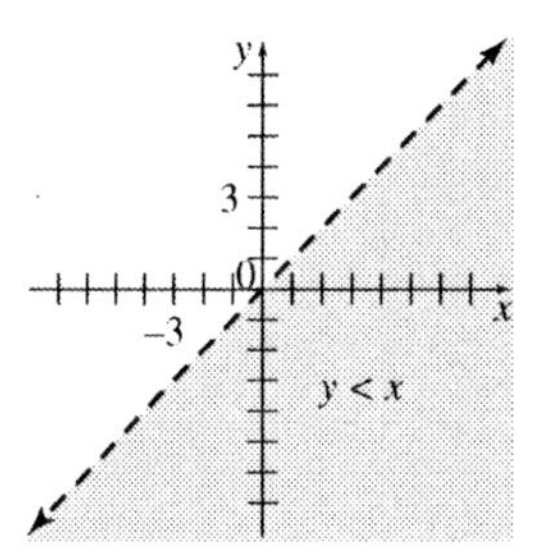

16. $y > 5x$

The boundary is $y = 5x$. Graph a dashed line using the points $(0,0)$ and $(2,10)$. Use $(0,4)$ as a test point to get $4 > 0$, which is true. Shade the half-plane containing $(0,4)$, or all points above the line.

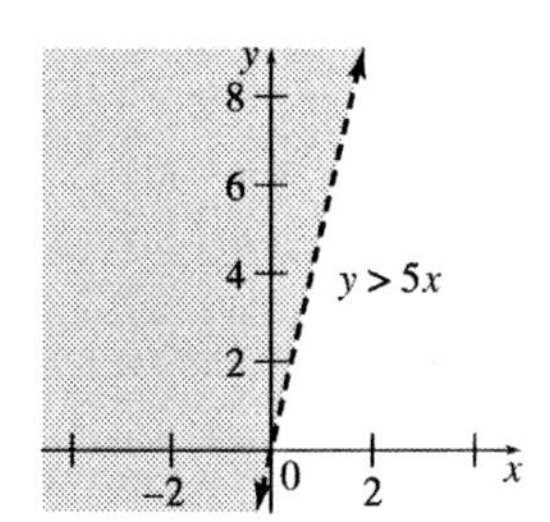

17. $x < 4$

Graph $x = 4$ as a dashed line. This is the vertical line crossing the x-axis at the point $(4, 0)$. Using $(0, 0)$ as a test point, we obtain $0 < 4$, which is true. Shade the half-plane containing $(0, 0)$, or all points to the left of the line.

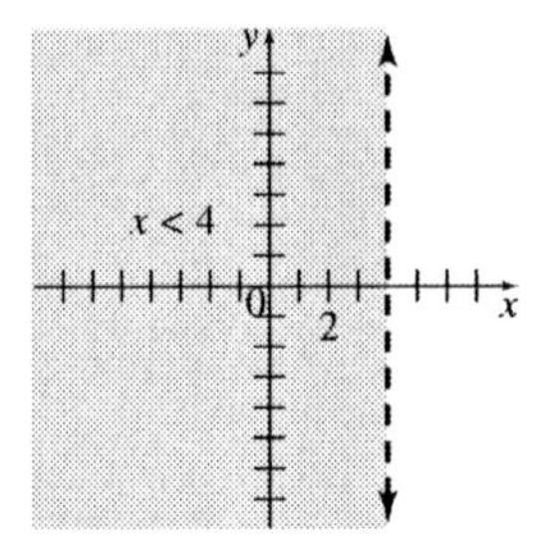

18. $y > 5$

The boundary is $y = 5$, a horizontal dashed line. $y > 5$ is the set of points in the half-plane above this line.

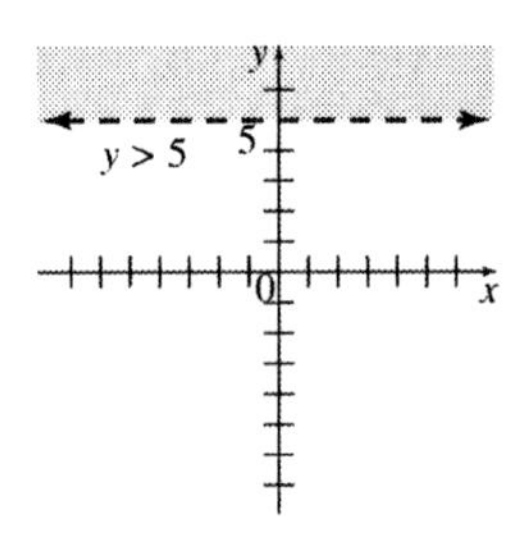

19. $y \leq -2$

Graph $y = -2$ as a solid horizontal line through the point $(0, -2)$. Using the origin as a test point, we obtain $0 \leq -2$, which is false. Shade the half-plane that does not contain $(0, 0)$, or all points below the line.

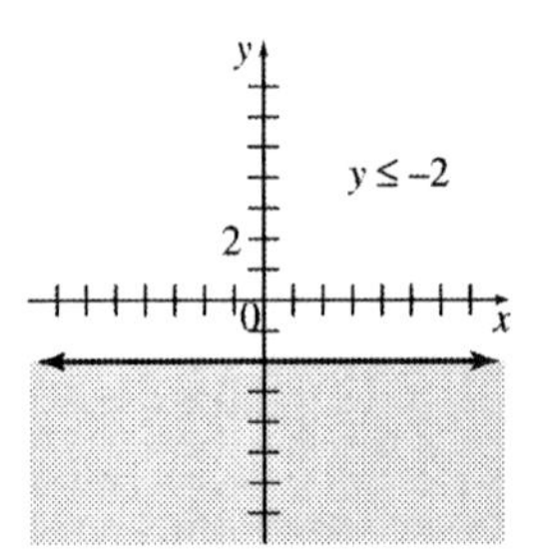

20. $x \geq -4$

The boundary is $x = -4$, a solid vertical line. The graph of $x \geq -4$ is the set of points that are on or to the right of this line.

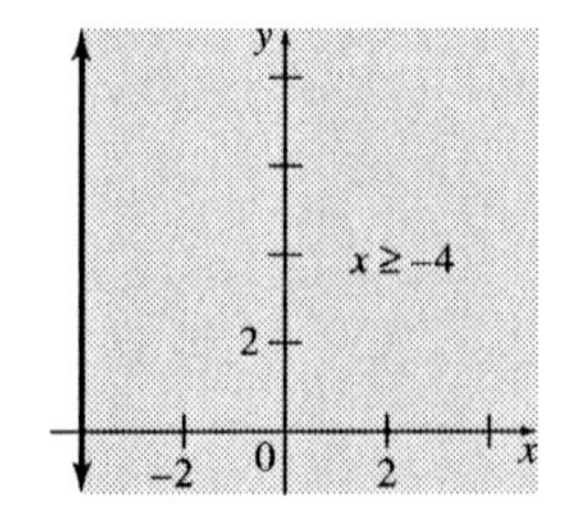

21. $x + y \leq 1$
$x - y \geq 2$

Graph the solid lines

$$x + y = 1 \text{ and}$$
$$x - y = 2.$$

$0 + 0 \leq 1$ is true, and $0 - 0 \geq 2$ is false. In each case, the graph is the region below the line. Shade the overlapping part of these two half-planes, which is the region below both lines. The shaded region is the feasible region for this system.

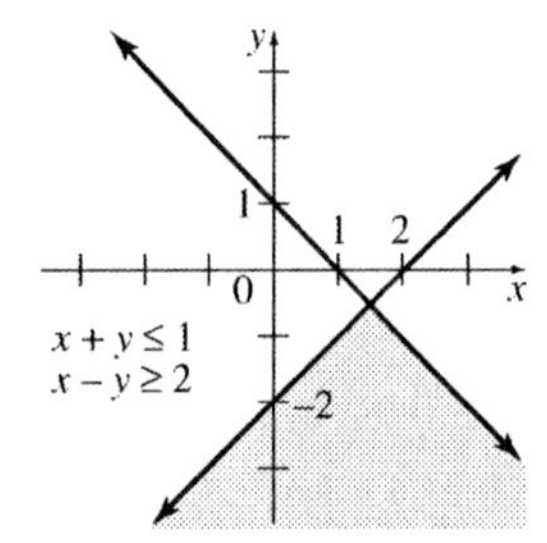

22. $4x - y < 6$
$3x + y < 9$

Graph $4x - y < 6$ as the half-plane above the dashed line $4x - y = 6$. Graph $3x + y < 9$ as the half-plane below the dashed line $3x + y = 9$. Shade the overlapping part of these two half-planes to show the feasible region for this system.

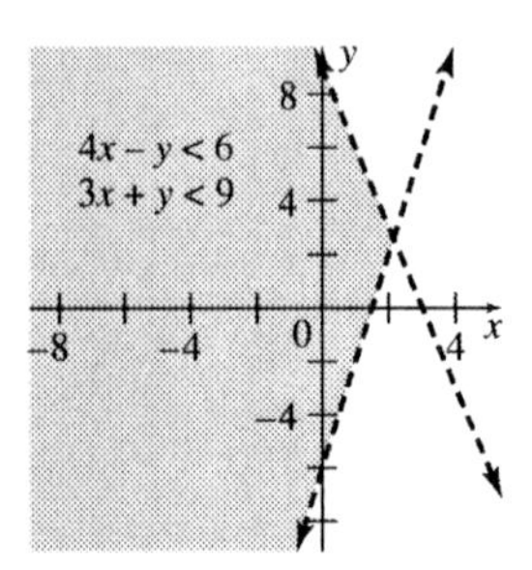

23. $x + 3y \leq 6$
$2x + 4y \geq 7$

Graph the solid lines $x + 3y = 6$ and $2x + 4y = 7$. Use $(0, 0)$ as a test point. $0 + 0 \leq 6$ is true, and $0+0 \geq 7$ is false. Shade all points below $x+3y = 6$ and above $2x + 4y = 7$. The feasible region is the overlap of the two half-planes.

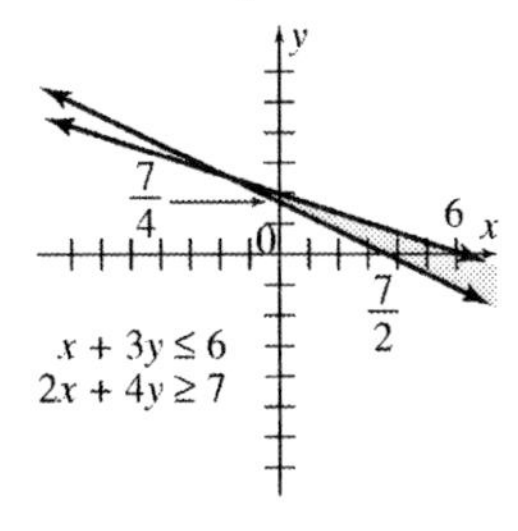

24. $-x - y < 5$
$2x - y < 4$

Graph $-x - y < 5$ as the half-plane above the dashed line $-x - y = 5$. Graph $2x - y < 4$ as the half-plane above the dashed line $2x-y = 4$. Shade the overlapping part of these two half-planes to show the feasible region.

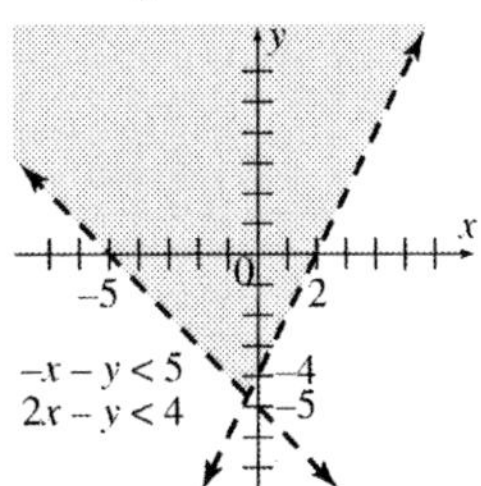

25. $x + y \leq 7$
$x - y \leq -4$
$4x + y \geq 0$

The graph of $x + y \leq 7$ consists of the solid line $x + y = 7$ and all the points below it. The graph of $x - y \leq -4$ consists of the solid line $x - y = -4$ and all the points above it. The graph of $4x + y \geq 0$ consists of the solid line $4x + y = 0$ and all the points above it. The feasible region is the overlapping part of these three half-planes.

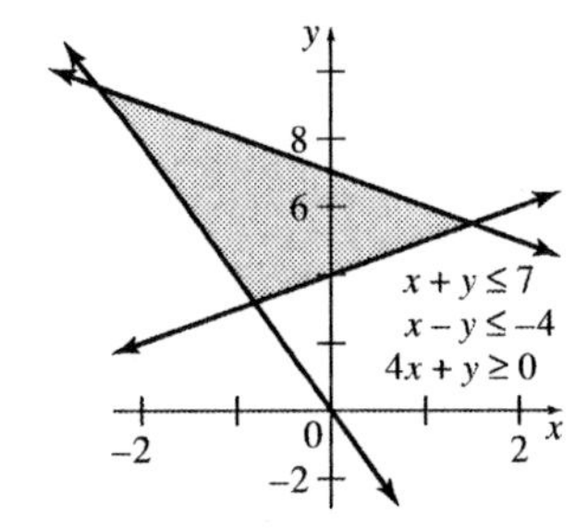

26. $3x - 2y \geq 6$
$x + y \leq -5$
$y \leq 4$

Graph the solid lines $3x - 2y = 6$, $x + y = -5$, and $y = 4$. Use $(0, 0)$ as a test point. $0 - 0 \geq 6$ is false, $0+0 \leq -5$ is false, and $0 \leq 4$ is true. Shade all points below each line. The feasible region is the overlap of the three half-planes.

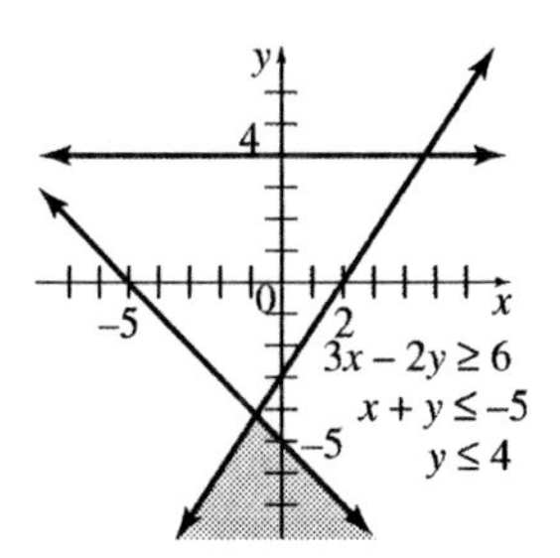

27. $-2 < x < 3$
$-1 \leq y \leq 5$
$2x + y < 6$

The graph of $-2 < x < 3$ is the region between the vertical lines $x = -2$ and $x = 3$, but not including the lines themselves (so the two vertical boundaries are drawn as dashed lines). The graph of $-1 \leq y \leq 5$ is the region between the horizontal lines $y = -1$ and $y = 5$, including the lines (so the two horizontal boundaries are drawn as solid lines). The graph of $2x+y < 6$ is the region below the line $2x + y = 6$ (so the boundary is drawn as a dashed line). Shade the region common to all three graphs to show the feasible region.

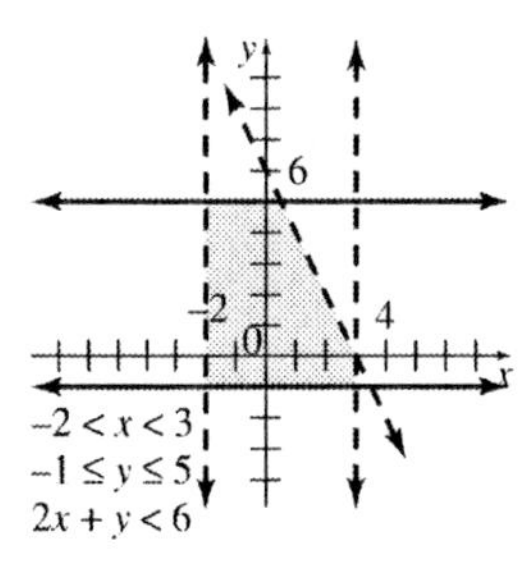

28. $1 < x < 4$
$y > 2$
$x > y$

The inequality $1 < x < 4$ defines a vertical region from $x = 1$ to $x = 4$ with dashed boundary lines $x = 1$ and $x = 4$. The inequality $y > 2$ defines the half-plane above the dashed line $y = 2$.
For $x > y$, use $(4, 1)$ as a test point. $4 > 1$ is true.

Shade all points below $x > y$. The feasible region is a small triangle bordered above by $x > y$, below by $y = 2$, and on the right by $x = 4$. $x = 1$ does not affect the feasible region.

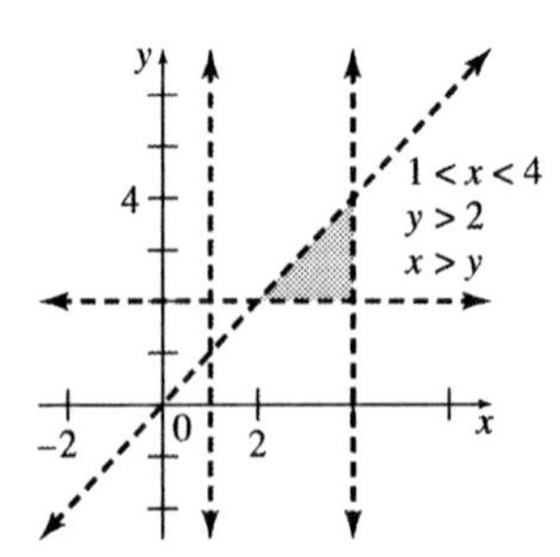

29. $y - 2x \leq 4$
$y \geq 2 - x$
$x \geq 0$
$y \geq 0$

The graph of $y - 2x \leq 4$ consists of the boundary line $y - 2x = 4$ and the region below it. The graph of $y \geq 2 - x$ consists of the boundary line $y = 2 - x$ and the region above it. The inequalities $x \geq 0$ and $y \geq 0$ restrict the feasible region to the first quadrant. Shade the region in the first quadrant where the first two graphs overlap to show the feasible region.

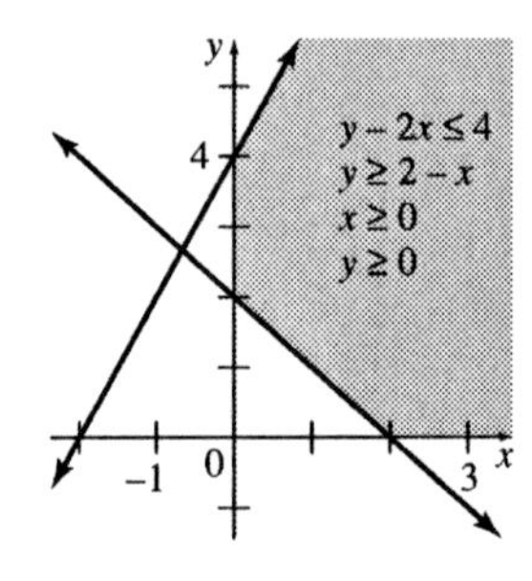

30. $2x + 3y \leq 12$
$2x + 3y > -6$
$3x + \ y < \ 4$
$x \geq 0$
$y \geq 0$

The inequalities $x \geq 0$ and $y \geq 0$ restrict the feasible region to the first quadrant. Graph $2x + 3y = 12$ as a solid line, $2x + 3y = -6$ as a dashed line, and $3x + y = 4$ as a dashed line. $2x + 3y = -6$ does not cross quadrant I and has no effect on the answer. For $2x + 3y = 12$ and $3x + y = 4$, use test point $(0, 0)$. $0 + 0 \leq 12$ is true, and $0 + 0 < 4$ is true. Shade all points below each line and in quadrant I. The feasible region is the overlap of these regions.

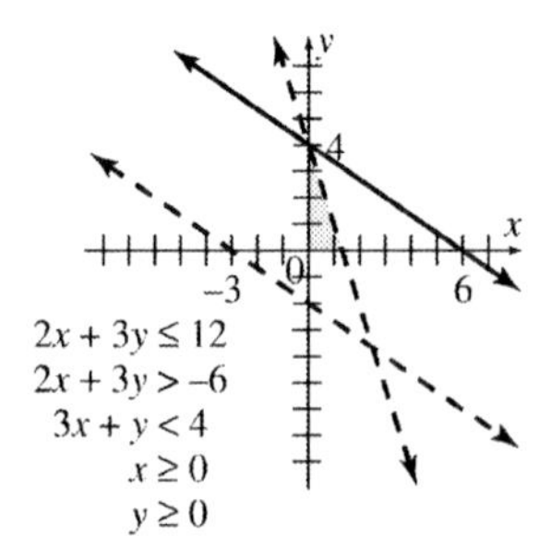

31. $3x + 4y > 12$
$2x - 3y < 6$
$0 \leq y \leq 2$
$x \geq 0$

$3x + 4y > 12$ is the set of points above the dashed line $3x + 4y = 12$; $2x - 3y < 6$ is the set of points above the dashed line $2x - 3y = 6$; $0 \leq y \leq 2$ is the set of points lying on or between the horizontal lines $y = 0$ and $y = 2$; and $x \geq 0$ consists of all the points on or to the right of the y-axis. Shade the feasible region, which is the triangular region satisfying all of the inequalities.

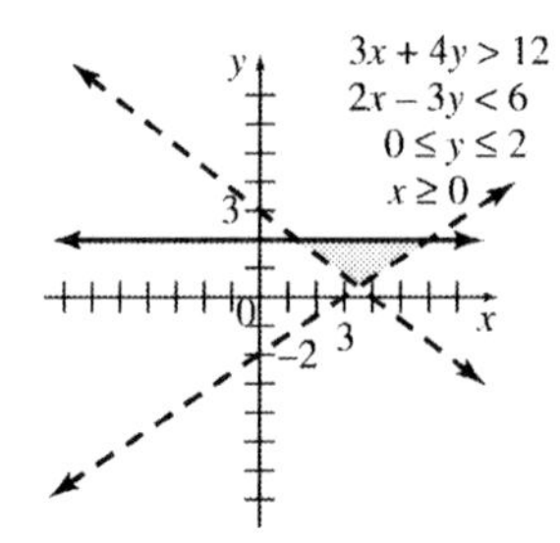

32. $0 \leq x \leq 9$
$x - 2y \geq 4$
$3x + 5y \leq 30$
$y \geq 0$

$0 \leq x \leq 9$ and $y \geq 0$ restrict the region to the first quadrant. Graph $x = 9$, $x - 2y = 4$, and $3x + 5y = 30$ as solid lines. Use test point $(0, 0)$. $0 - 0 \geq 4$ is false, and $0 + 0 \leq 30$ is true. Shade all points from $x = 0$ to $x = 9$, below $x - 2y = 4$, and below $3x + 5y = 30$. The feasible region is the region in the first quadrant that is bounded above by $x - 2y = 4$ and $3x + 5y = 30$, below by $y = 0$, and on the right by $x = 9$.

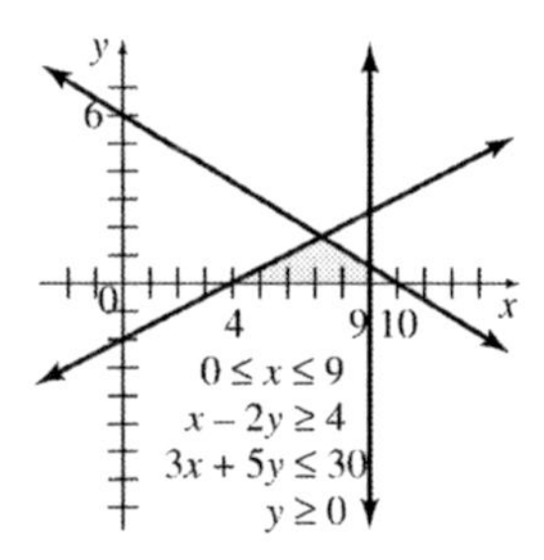

33. $2x - 6y > 12$

Use a graphing calculator. The boundary line is the graph of $2x - 6y = 12$. Solve this equation for y.

$$-6y = -2x + 12$$
$$y = \frac{-2}{-6}x + \frac{12}{-6}$$
$$y = \frac{1}{3}x - 2$$

Enter $y_1 = \frac{1}{3}x - 2$ and graph it. Using the origin as a test point, we obtain $0 > 12$, which is false. Shade the region that does not contain the origin.

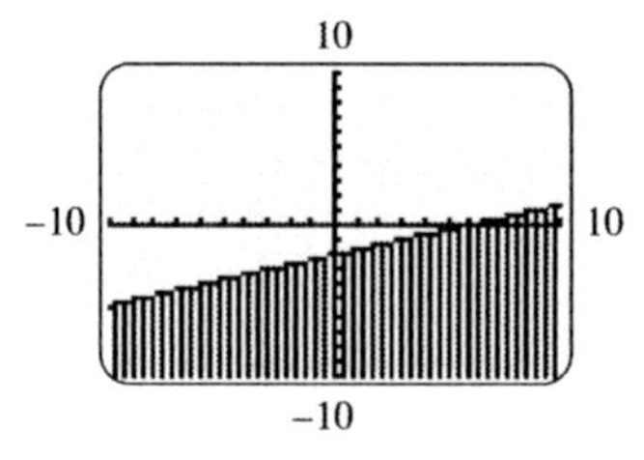

34. $4x - 3y < 12$

Use a graphing calculator. The boundary line is the graph of $4x - 3y = 12$. Solve this equation for y.

$$-3y = -4x + 12$$
$$y = \frac{-4}{-3}x + \frac{12}{-3}$$
$$y = \frac{4}{3}x - 4$$

Enter $y_1 = \frac{4}{3}x - 4$ and graph it. Using the origin as a test point, we obtain $0 < 12$, which is true. Shade the region that contains the origin.

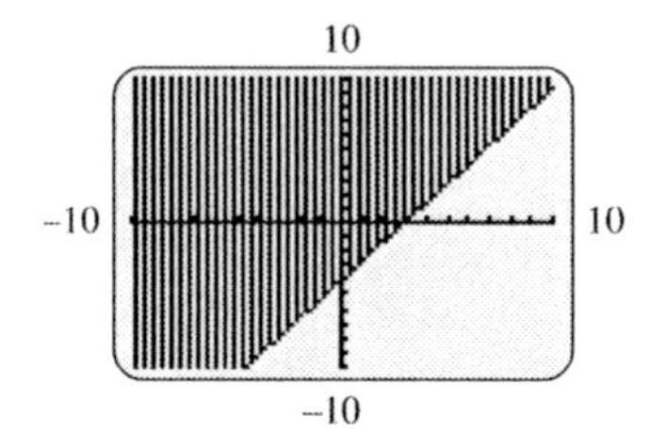

35. $3x - 4y < 6$
$2x + 5y > 15$

Use a graphing calculator. One boundary line is the graph of $3x - 4y = 6$. Solve this equation for y.

$$-4y = -3x + 6$$
$$y = \frac{-3}{-4}x + \frac{6}{-4}$$
$$y = \frac{3}{4}x - \frac{3}{2}$$

Enter $y_1 = \frac{3}{4}x - \frac{3}{2}$ and graph it. Using the origin as a test point, we obtain $0 < 6$, which is true. Shade the region that contains the origin.
The other boundary line is the graph of $2x + 5y = 15$. Solve this equation for y.

$$5y = -2x + 15$$
$$y = -\frac{2}{5}x + 3$$

Enter $y_2 = -\frac{2}{5}x + 3$ and graph it. Using the origin as a test point, we obtain $0 > 15$, which is false. Shade the region that does not contain the origin. The overlap of the two graphs is the feasible region.

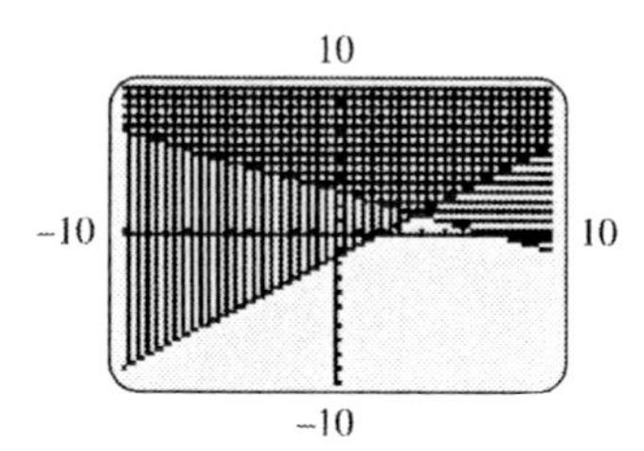

36. $6x - 4y > 8$
$2x + 5y < 5$

Use a graphing calculator. One boundary line is the graph of $6x - 4y = 8$. Solve this equation for y.

$$-4y = -6x + 8$$
$$y = \frac{-6}{-4}x + \frac{8}{-4}$$
$$y = \frac{3}{2}x - 2$$

Enter $y_1 = \frac{3}{2}x - 2$ and graph it. Using the origin as a test point, we obtain $0 > 8$, which is false. Shade the region that does not contain the origin.

The other boundary line is the graph of $2x+5y = 5$. Solve this equation for y.

$$5y = -2x + 5$$
$$y = -\frac{2}{5}x + 1$$

Enter $y_2 = -\frac{2}{5}x+1$ and graph it. Using the origin as a test point, we obtain $0 < 5$, which is true. Shade the region that contains the origin. The overlap of the two graphs is the feasible region.

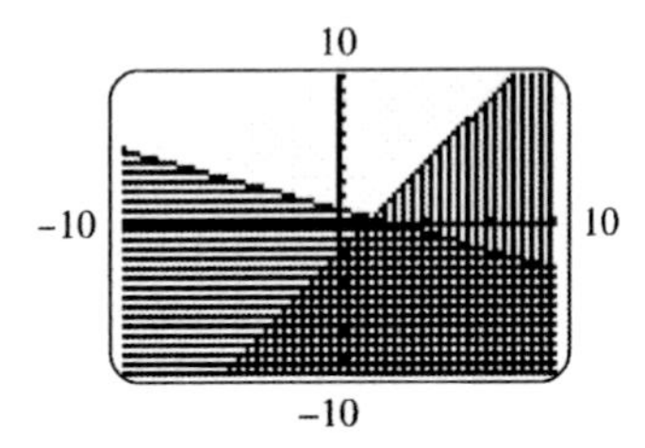

37. The region B is described by the inequalities

$$\begin{aligned} x + 3y &\le 6 \\ x + y &\le 3 \\ x - 2y &\le 2 \\ x &\ge 0 \\ y &\ge 0. \end{aligned}$$

The region C is described by the inequalities

$$\begin{aligned} x + 3y &\ge 6 \\ x + y &\ge 3 \\ x - 2y &\le 2 \\ x &\ge 0 \\ y &\ge 0. \end{aligned}$$

The region D is described by the inequalities

$$\begin{aligned} x + 3y &\le 6 \\ x + y &\ge 3 \\ x - 2y &\le 2 \\ x &\ge 0 \\ y &\ge 0. \end{aligned}$$

The region E is described by the inequalities

$$\begin{aligned} x + 3y &\le 6 \\ x + y &\le 3 \\ x - 2y &\ge 2 \\ x &\ge 0 \\ y &\ge 0. \end{aligned}$$

The region F is described by the inequalities

$$\begin{aligned} x + 3y &\le 6 \\ x + y &\ge 3 \\ x - 2y &\ge 2 \\ x &\ge 0 \\ y &\ge 0. \end{aligned}$$

The region G is described by the inequalities

$$\begin{aligned} x + 3y &\ge 6 \\ x + y &\ge 3 \\ x - 2y &\ge 2 \\ x &\ge 0 \\ y &\ge 0. \end{aligned}$$

38. **(a)**

	Glazed	Unglazed	Maximum
Number Made	x	y	
Time on Wheel	$\frac{1}{2}$	1	8
Time in Kiln	1	6	20

(b) On the wheel, x glazed planters require $\frac{1}{2} \cdot x = \frac{1}{2}x$ hr and y unglazed planters require $1 \cdot y = y$ hr. Since the wheel is available for at most 8 hr per day,

$$\frac{1}{2}x + y \le 8.$$

In the kiln, x glazed planters require $1 \cdot x = x$ hr and y unglazed planters require $6 \cdot y = 6y$ hr. Since the kiln is available for at most 20 hr per day,

$$x + 6y \le 20.$$

Since it is not possible to produce a negative number of pots,

$$x \ge 0 \text{ and y} \ge 0.$$

Thus, we have the system

$$\begin{aligned} \frac{1}{2}x + y &\le 8 \\ x + 6y &\le 20 \\ x &\ge 0 \\ y &\ge 0. \end{aligned}$$

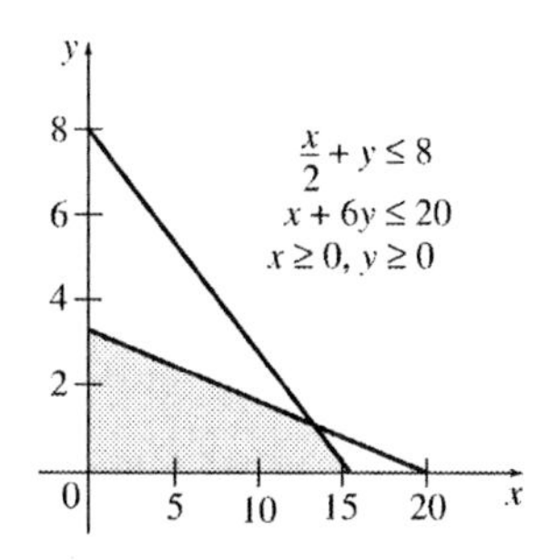

(c) Yes, 5 glazed and 2 unglazed planters can be made, since the point $(5, 2)$ lies within the feasible region.

From the graph, it looks like the point $(10, 2)$ might lie right on a boundary of the feasible region. However, $(10, 2)$ does not satisfy the inequality $x + 6y \le 20$, so the point is definitely outside the feasible region. Therefore, 10 glazed and 2 unglazed planters cannot be made.

39. (a)

	Shawls	Afghans	Total
Number Made	x	y	
Spinning Time	1	2	≤ 8
Dyeing Time	1	1	≤ 6
Weaving Time	1	4	≤ 14

(b)
$$\begin{aligned} x + 2y &\le 8 && \textit{Spinning inequality} \\ x + y &\le 6 && \textit{Dyeing inequality} \\ x + 4y &\le 14 && \textit{Weaving inequality} \\ x &\ge 0 && \textit{Ensures a nonnegative} \\ y &\ge 0 && \textit{number of each} \end{aligned}$$

Graph the solid lines $x + 2y = 8$, $x + y = 6$, $x + 4y = 14$, $x = 0$, and $y = 0$, and shade the appropriate half-planes to get the feasible region.

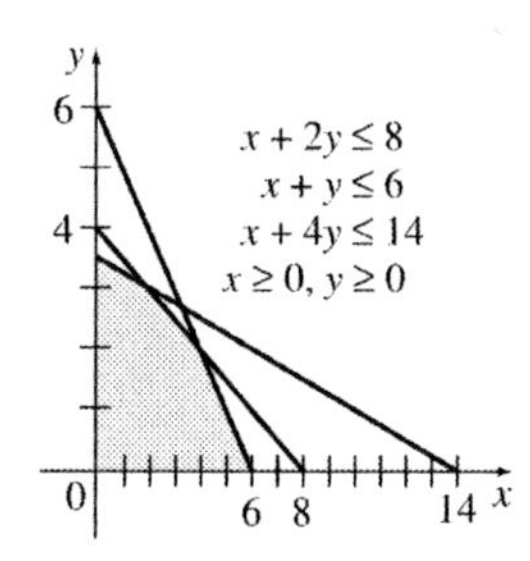

(c) Yes, 3 shawls and 2 afghans can be made because this corresponds to the point $(3, 2)$, which is in the feasible region.

No, 4 shawls and 3 afghans cannot be made because this corresponds to the point $(4, 3)$, which is not in the feasible region.

40. (a)
$$\begin{aligned} x &\ge 3000 \\ y &\ge 5000 \\ x + y &\le 10{,}000 \end{aligned}$$

(b) The first inequality gives the half-plane to the right of the vertical line $x = 3000$, including the points on the line. The second inequality gives the half-plane above the horizontal line $y = 5000$, including the points on the line. The third inequality gives the half-plane below the line $x + y \le 10{,}000$, including the points on the line. Shade the region where the three half-planes overlap to show the feasible region.

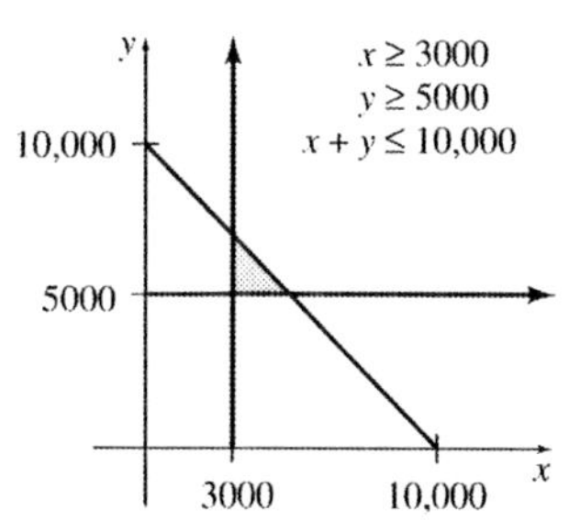

41. (a) The first sentence of the problem tells us that a total of \$30 million or $x + y \le 30$ has been set aside for loans. The second sentence of the problem gives $x \ge 4y$. The third and fourth sentences give

$$0.06x + 0.08y \ge 1.6$$

Also, $x \ge 0$ and $y \ge 0$ ensure nonnegative numbers. Thus,

$$\begin{aligned} x + y &\le 30 \\ x &\ge 4y \\ 0.06x + 0.08y &\ge 1.6 \\ x &\ge 0 \\ y &\ge 0 \end{aligned}$$

(b) Using the above system, graph solid lines and shade appropriate half-planes to get the feasible region.

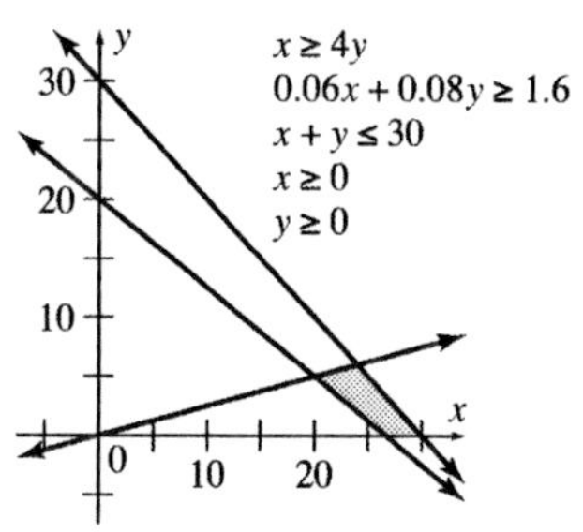

42. **(a)**

$$x \geq 1000$$
$$y \geq 800$$
$$x + y \leq 2400$$

(b) The first inequality gives the set of points on and to the right of the vertical line $x = 1000$. The second inequality gives the set of points on and above the horizontal line $y = 800$. The third inequality gives the set of points on and below the line $x + y = 2400$. Shade the region where the three graphs overlap to show the feasible region.

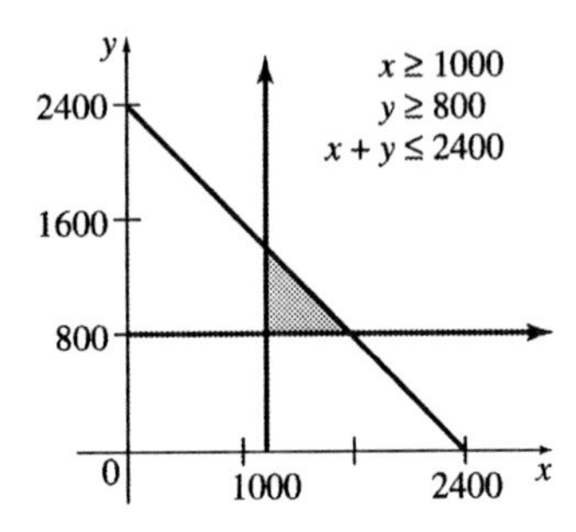

43. **(a)** The second sentence of the problem tells us that the number of M3 Power™ razors is never more than half the number of Fusion Power™ razors or $x \leq \frac{1}{2}y$. The third sentence tells us that a total of at most 800 razors can be produced per week or $x + y \leq 800$. The inequalities $x \geq 0$ and $y \geq 0$ ensure nonnegative numbers. Thus,

$$x \leq \frac{1}{2}y$$
$$x + y \leq 800$$
$$x \geq 0$$
$$y \geq 0.$$

(b)

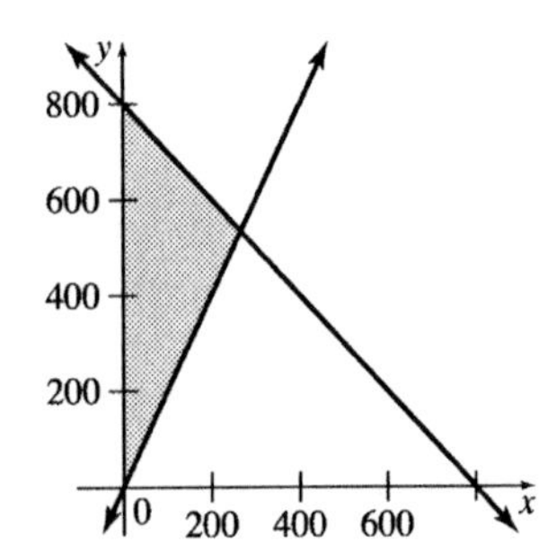

44. **(a)**

	Number	Emissions	Cost
Type 1	x	0.5	0.16
Type 2	y	0.3	0.20
Maximum		1.8	0.8

The manufacturer produces at least 3.2 million barrels annually, so

$$x + y \geq 3.2.$$

Operating costs are not to exceed \$0.8 million, so $0.16x + 0.20y \leq 0.8$. Total emissions must not exceed 1.8 million lb, so $0.5x + 0.3y \leq 1.8$. We obtain the system

$$x + y \geq 3.2$$
$$0.16x + 0.20y \leq 0.8$$
$$0.5x + 0.3y \leq 1.8$$
$$x \geq 0$$
$$y \geq 0.$$

(b) Using the above system, graph solid lines and shade appropriate half-planes to get the feasible region.

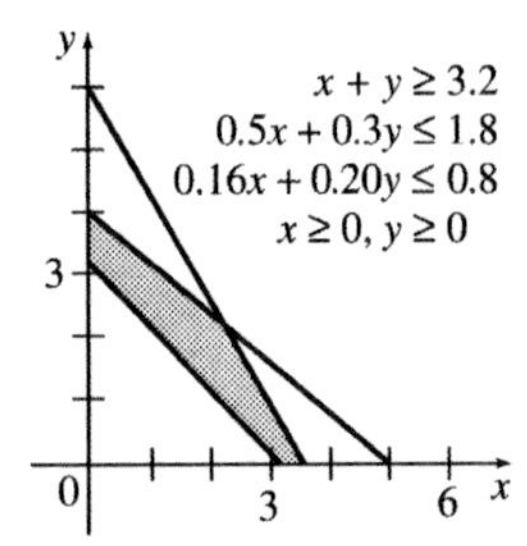

45. **(a)** The problem tells us that each ounce of fruit supplies 1 unit of protein and each ounce of nuts supplies 1 unit of protein. Thus, $1x + 1y$ is the number of units of protein per package. Since each package must provide at least 7 units of protein, we get the inequality $x + y \geq 7$. Similarly, we get the inequalities $2x + y \geq 10$ for carbohydrates and $x + y \leq 9$ for fat. The inequalities $x \geq 0$ and $y \geq 0$ ensure nonnegative numbers. Thus,

$$x + y \geq 7$$
$$2x + y \geq 10$$
$$x + y \leq 9$$
$$x \geq 0$$
$$y \geq 0.$$

(b)

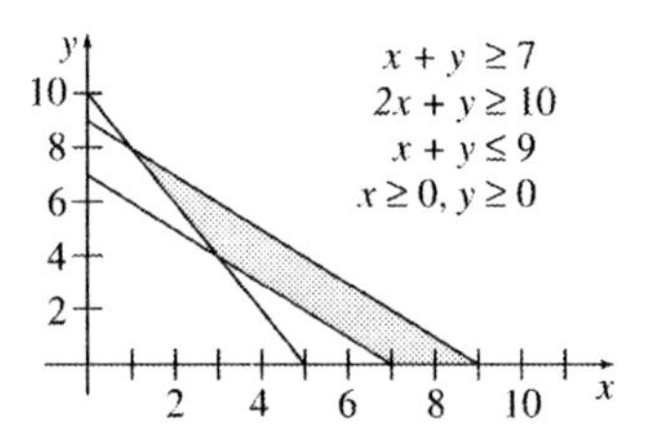

3.2 Solving Linear Programming Problems Graphically

1. (a)

Corner Point	Value of $z = 3x + 2y$
$(0, 5)$	$3(0) + 2(5) = 10$ Minimum
$(3, 8)$	$3(3) + 2(8) = 25$
$(7, 4)$	$3(7) + 2(4) = 29$ Maximum
$(4, 1)$	$3(4) + 2(1) = 14$

The maximum value of 29 occurs at $(7, 4)$. The minimum value of 10 occurs at $(0, 5)$.

(b)

Corner Point	Value of $z = x + 4y$
$(0, 5)$	$0 + 4(5) = 20$
$(3, 8)$	$3 + 4(8) = 35$ Maximum
$(7, 4)$	$7 + 4(4) = 23$
$(4, 1)$	$4 + 4(1) = 8$ Minimum

The maximum value of 35 occurs at $(3, 8)$. The minimum value of 8 occurs at $(4, 1)$.

2. (a)

Corner Point	Value of $z = x + 4y$
$(1, 4)$	$1 + 4(4) = 17$
$(2, 8)$	$2 + 4(8) = 34$ Maximum
$(4, 6)$	$4 + 4(6) = 28$
$(4, 1)$	$4 + 4(1) = 8$ Minimum

The maximum value of 34 occurs at $(2, 8)$. The minimum value of 8 occurs at $(4, 1)$.

(b)

Corner Point	Value of $z = 5x + 2y$
$(1, 4)$	$5(1) + 2(4) = 13$ Minimum
$(2, 8)$	$5(2) + 2(8) = 26$
$(4, 6)$	$5(4) + 2(6) = 32$ Maximum
$(4, 1)$	$5(4) + 2(1) = 22$

The maximum value of 32 occurs at $(4, 6)$. The minimum value of 13 occurs at $(1, 4)$.

3. **(a)**

Corner Point	Value of $z = 0.40x + 0.75y$	
$(0, 0)$	$0.40(0) + 0.75(0) = 0$	Minimum
$(0, 12)$	$0.40(0) + 0.75(12) = 9$	Maximum
$(4, 8)$	$0.40(4) + 0.75(8) = 7.6$	
$(7, 3)$	$0.40(7) + 0.75(3) = 5.05$	
$(8, 0)$	$0.40(8) + 0.75(0) = 3.2$	

The maximum value of 9 occurs at $(0, 12)$. The minimum value of 0 occurs at $(0, 0)$.

(b)

Corner Point	Value of $z = 1.50x + 0.25y$	
$(0, 0)$	$1.50.(0) + 0.25(0) = 0$	Minimum
$(0, 12)$	$1.50(0) + 0.25(12) = 3$	
$(4, 8)$	$1.50(4) + 0.25(8) = 8$	
$(7, 3)$	$1.50(7) + 0.25(3) = 11.25$	
$(8, 0)$	$1.50(8) + 0.25(0) = 12$	Maximum

The maximum value of 12 occurs at $(8, 0)$. The minimum value of 0 occurs at $(0, 0)$.

4. **(a)**

Corner Point	Value of $z = 0.35x + 1.25y$	
$(0, 0)$	$0.35(0) + 1.25(0) = 0$	Minimum
$(0, 15)$	$0.35(0) + 1.25(15) = 18.75$	
$(6, 18)$	$0.35(6) + 1.25(18) = 24.6$	Maximum
$(10, 9)$	$0.35(10) + 1.25(9) = 14.75$	
$(12, 0)$	$0.35(12) + 1.25(0) = 4.2$	

The maximum value of 24.6 at $(6, 18)$; the minimum is 0 at $(0, 0)$. The minimum value of 0 occurs at $(0, 0)$.

(b)

Corner Point	Value of $z = 1.5x + 0.5y$	
$(0, 0)$	$1.5(0) + 0.5(0) = 0$	Minimum
$(0, 15)$	$1.5(0) + 0.5(15) = 7.5$	
$(6, 18)$	$1.5(6) + 0.5(18) = 18$	Maximum
$(10, 9)$	$1.5(10) + 0.5(9) = 19.5$	
$(12, 0)$	$1.5(12) + 0.5(0) = 18$	

The maximum value of 19.5 occurs at $(10, 9)$. The minimum value of 0 occurs at $(0, 0)$.

5.

(a) Corner Point	Value of $z = 4x + 2y$	
$(0, 8)$	$4(0) + 2(8) = 16$	Minimum
$(3, 4)$	$4(3) + 2(4) = 20$	
$(\frac{13}{2}, 2)$	$4\left(\frac{13}{2}\right) + 2(2) = 30$	
$(12, 0)$	$4(12) + 2(0) = 48$	

The minimum value is 16 at $(0, 8)$. Since the feasible region is unbounded, there is no maximum value.

(b)

Corner Point	Value of $z = 2x + 3y$
$(0, 8)$	$2(0) + 3(8) = 24$
$(3, 4)$	$2(3) + 3(4) = 18$ Minimum
$\left(\frac{13}{2}, 2\right)$	$2\left(\frac{13}{2}\right) + 3(2) = 19$
$(12, 0)$	$2(12) + 3(0) = 24$

The minimum value is 18 at $(3, 4)$; there is no maximum value since the feasible region is unbounded.

(c)

Corner Point	Value of $z = 2x + 4y$
$(0, 8)$	$2(0) + 4(8) = 32$
$(3, 4)$	$2(3) + 4(4) = 22$
$\left(\frac{13}{2}, 2\right)$	$2\left(\frac{13}{2}\right) + 4(2) = 21$ Minimum
$(12, 0)$	$2(12) + 4(0) = 24$

The minimum value is 21 at $\left(\frac{13}{2}, 2\right)$; there is no maximum value since the feasible region is unbounded.

(d)

Corner Point	Value of $z = x + 4y$
$(0, 8)$	$0 + 4(8) = 32$
$(3, 4)$	$3 + 4(4) = 19$
$\left(\frac{13}{2}, 2\right)$	$\frac{13}{2} + 4(2) = \frac{29}{2}$
$(12, 0)$	$12 + 4(0) = 12$ Minimum

The minimum value is 12 at $(12, 0)$; there is no maximum value since the feasible region is unbounded.

6. (a) $z = 4x + y$

Corner Point	Value of $z = 4x + y$
$(0, 10)$	$4(0) + 10 = 10$ Minimum
$(2, 4)$	$4(2) + 4 = 12$
$(5, 2)$	$4(5) + 2 = 22$
$(15, 0)$	$4(15) + 0 = 60$

The minimum value is 10 at $(0, 10)$. There is no maximum because the feasible region is unbounded.

(b) $z = 5x + 6y$

Corner Point	Value of $z = 5x + 6y$
$(0, 10)$	$5(0) + 6(10) = 60$
$(2, 4)$	$5(2) + 6(4) = 34$ Minimum
$(5, 2)$	$5(5) + 6(2) = 37$
$(15, 0)$	$5(15) + 6(0) = 75$

The minimum value is 34 at $(2, 4)$. There is no maximum because the feasible region is unbounded.

(c) $z = x + 2y$

Corner Point	Value of $z = x + 2y$
$(0, 10)$	$0 + 2(10) = 20$
$(2, 4)$	$2 + 2(4) = 10$
$(5, 2)$	$5 + 2(2) = 9$ Minimum
$(15, 0)$	$15 + 2(0) = 15$

The minimum value is 9 at $(5, 2)$. There is no maximum because the feasible region is unbounded.

(d) $z = x + 6y$

Corner Point	Value of $z = x + 6y$
$(0, 10)$	$0 + 6(10) = 60$
$(2, 4)$	$2 + 6(4) = 26$
$(5, 2)$	$5 + 6(2) = 17$
$(15, 0)$	$15 + 6(0) = 15$ Minimum

The minimum value is 15 at $(15, 0)$. There is no maximum because the feasible region is unbounded.

7. Minimize $z = 4x + 7y$

subject to:
$$\begin{aligned} x - y &\geq 1 \\ 3x + 2y &\geq 18 \\ x &\geq 0 \\ y &\geq 0. \end{aligned}$$

Sketch the feasible region.

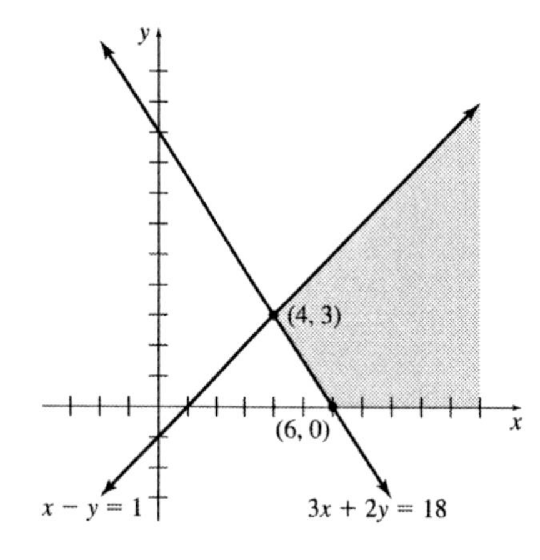

The sketch shows that the feasible region is unbounded. The corner points are $(4, 3)$ and $(6, 0)$. The corner point $(4, 3)$ can be found by solving the system

$$\begin{aligned} x - y &= 1 \\ 3x + 2y &= 18. \end{aligned}$$

Use the corner points to find the minimum value of the objective function.

Corner Point	Value of $z = 4x + 7y$
$(4, 3)$	$4(4) + 7(3) = 37$
$(6, 0)$	$4(6) + 7(0) = 24$ Minimum

The minimum value is 24 when $x = 6$ and $y = 0$.

8. Minimize $z = x + 3y$

subject to:
$$\begin{aligned} x + y &\leq 10 \\ 5x + 2y &\geq 20 \\ -x + 2y &\geq 0 \\ x &\geq 0 \\ y &\geq 0. \end{aligned}$$

Graph the feasible region, and identify the corner points. The corner point $\left(\frac{20}{3}, \frac{10}{3}\right)$ can be found by solving the system

$$\begin{aligned} x + \quad y &= 10 \\ -x + 2y &= \quad 0, \end{aligned}$$

and the corner point $\left(\frac{10}{3}, \frac{5}{3}\right)$ can be found by solving the system

$$\begin{aligned} 5x + 2y &= 20 \\ -x + 2y &= \quad 0. \end{aligned}$$

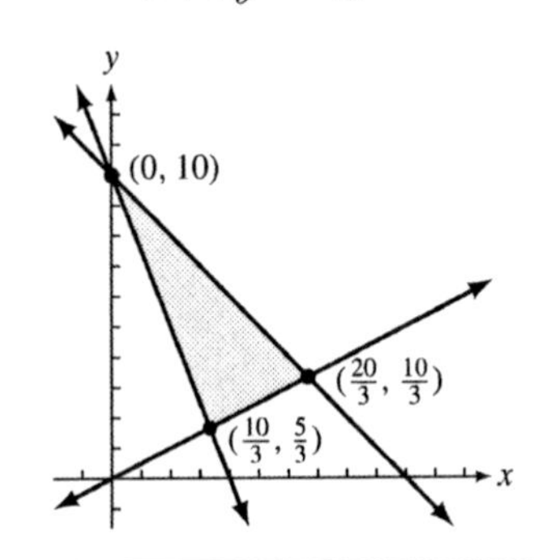

Corner Point	Value of $z = x + 3y$
$(0, 10)$	$0 + 3(10) = 30$
$\left(\frac{20}{3}, \frac{10}{3}\right)$	$\frac{20}{3} + 3\left(\frac{10}{3}\right) = \frac{50}{3}$
$\left(\frac{10}{3}, \frac{5}{3}\right)$	$\frac{10}{3} + 3\left(\frac{5}{3}\right) = \frac{25}{3}$ Minimum

The minimum value is $\frac{25}{3}$ when $x = \frac{10}{3}$ and $y = \frac{5}{3}$.

9. Maximize $z = 5x + 2y$

subject to:
$$\begin{aligned} 4x - y &\leq 16 \\ 2x + y &\geq 11 \\ x &\geq 3 \\ y &\leq 8. \end{aligned}$$

Sketch the feasible region.

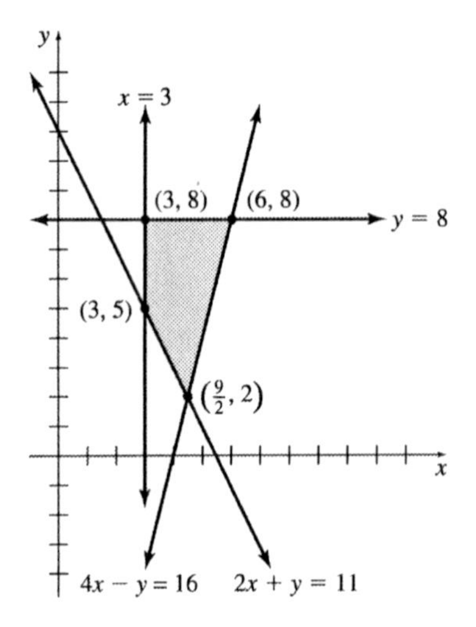

The sketch shows that the feasible region is bounded. The corner points are: $(3, 5)$, the intersection of $2x + y = 11$ and $x = 3$; $(3, 8)$, the intersection of $x = 3$ and $y = 8$; $(6, 8)$, the intersection of $y = 8$ and $4x - y = 16$; and $\left(\frac{9}{2}, 2\right)$, the intersection of $4x - y = 16$ and $2x + y = 11$. Use the corner points to find the maximum value of the objective function.

Corner Point	Value of $z = 5x + 2y$
$(3, 5)$	$5(3) + 2(5) = 25$
$(3, 8)$	$5(3) + 2(8) = 31$
$(6, 8)$	$5(6) + 2(8) = 46$ Maximum
$\left(\frac{9}{2}, 2\right)$	$5\left(\frac{9}{2}\right) + 2(2) = 26.5$

The maximum value is 46 when $x = 6$ and $y = 8$.

10. Maximize $z = 10x + 8y$

subject to:
$$\begin{aligned} 2x + 3y &\leq 100 \\ 5x + 4y &\leq 200 \\ x &\geq 10 \\ 0 \leq y &\leq 20. \end{aligned}$$

Graph the feasible region, and identify the corner points. The corner point $(20, 20)$ can be found by solving the system

$$\begin{aligned} 2x + 3y &= 100 \\ y &= \quad 20, \end{aligned}$$

and the corner point $\left(\frac{200}{7}, \frac{100}{7}\right)$ can be found by solving the system

$$\begin{aligned} 2x + 3y &= 100 \\ 5x + 4y &= 200. \end{aligned}$$

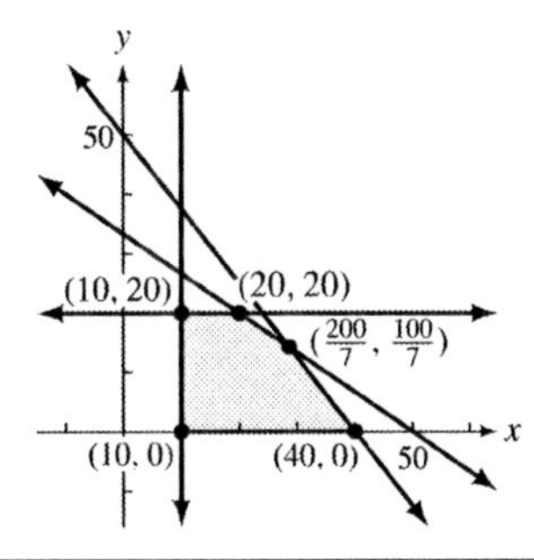

Corner Point	Value of $z = 10x + 8y$
$(10, 0)$	$10(10) + 8(0) = 100$
$(10, 20)$	$10(10) + 8(20) = 260$
$(20, 20)$	$10(20) + 8(20) = 360$
$\left(\frac{200}{7}, \frac{100}{7}\right)$	$10\left(\frac{200}{7}\right) + 8\left(\frac{100}{7}\right) = 400$ Maximum
$(40, 0)$	$10(40) + 8(0) = 400$ Maximum

The maximum value is 400 when $x = \frac{200}{7}$ and $y = \frac{100}{7}$, as well as when $x = 40$ and $y = 0$ and at all points in between.

11. Maximize $z = 10x + 10y$

$$\begin{aligned} \text{subject to: } 5x + 8y &\geq 200 \\ 25x - 10y &\geq 250 \\ x + y &\leq 150 \\ x &\geq 0 \\ y &\geq 0. \end{aligned}$$

Sketch the feasible region.

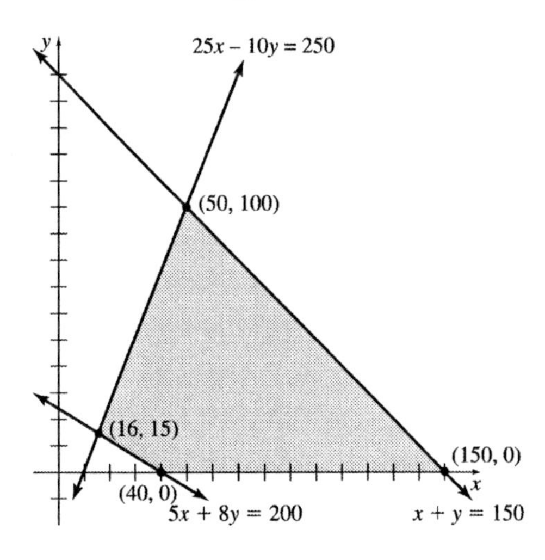

The sketch shows that the feasible region is bounded. The corner points are: $(16, 15)$, the intersection of $5x + 8y = 200$ and $25x - 10y = 250$; $(50, 100)$, the intersection of $25x - 10y = 250$ and $x + y = 150$; $(150, 0)$; and $(40, 0)$. Use the corner points to find the maximum value of the objective function.

Corner Point	Value of $z = 10x + 10y$
$(16, 15)$	$10(16) + 10(15) = 310$
$(50, 100)$	$10(50) + 10(100) = 1500$ Maximum
$(150, 0)$	$10(150) + 10(0) = 1500$ Maximum
$(40, 0)$	$10(40) + 10(0) = 400$

The maximum value is 1500 when $x = 50$ and $y = 100$, as well as when $x = 150$ and $y = 0$ and all points on the line between.

12. Maximize $z = 4x + 5y$

$$\begin{aligned} \text{subject to: } 10x - 5y &\leq 100 \\ 20x + 10y &\geq 150 \\ x + y &\geq 12 \\ x &\geq 0 \\ y &\geq 0. \end{aligned}$$

Graph the feasible region and identify the corner points. The corner point $\left(\frac{32}{3}, \frac{4}{3}\right)$ can be found by solving the system

$$\begin{aligned} 10x - 5y &= 100 \\ x + y &= 12, \end{aligned}$$

and the corner point $(3, 9)$ can be found by solving the system

$$\begin{aligned} 20x + 10y &= 150 \\ x + y &= 12. \end{aligned}$$

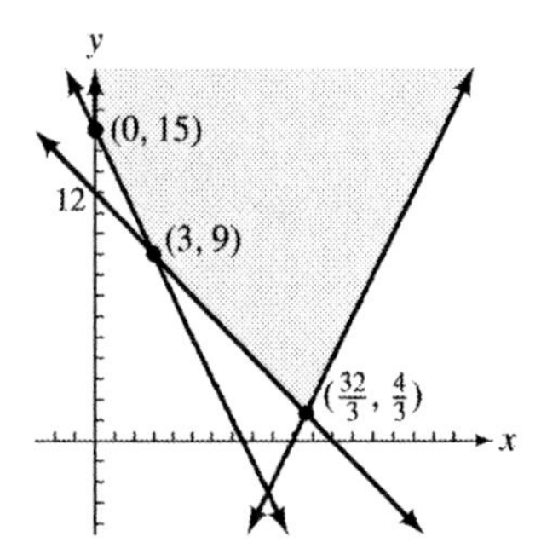

Since the region is unbounded, there is no maximum value, hence no solution.

13. Maximize $z = 3x + 6y$

$$\begin{aligned} \text{subject to: } 2x - 3y &\leq 12 \\ x + y &\geq 5 \\ 3x + 4y &\geq 24 \\ x &\geq 0 \\ y &\geq 0. \end{aligned}$$

Sketch the feasible region.

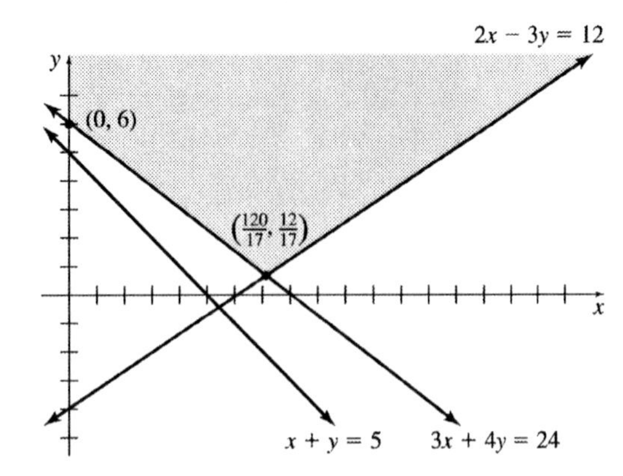

The graph shows that the feasible region is unbounded. Therefore, there is no maximum value of the objective function on the feasible region, hence, no solution.

14. Maximize $z = 4x + 6y$

subject to: $3 \leq x + y \leq 10$
$x - y \geq 3$
$x \geq 0$
$y \geq 0.$

Sketch the feasible region.

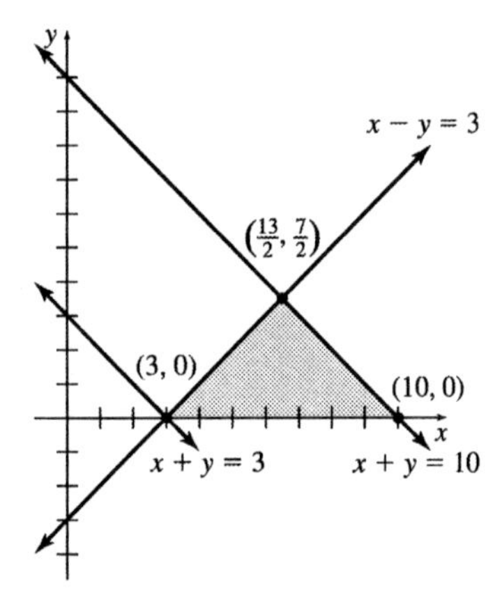

The graph shows that the feasible region is bounded. The corner points are: $(3, 0)$; $(\frac{13}{2}, \frac{7}{2})$, the intersection of $x + y = 10$ and $x - y = 3$; and $(10, 0)$. Use the corner points to find the maximum value of the objective function.

Corner Point	Value of $z = 4x + 6y$
$(3, 0)$	$4(3) + 6(0) = 12$
$(\frac{13}{2}, \frac{7}{2})$	$4(\frac{13}{2}) + 6(\frac{7}{2}) = 47$ Maximum
$(10, 0)$	$4(10) + 6(0) = 40$

The maximum value is 47 when $x = \frac{13}{2}$ and $y = \frac{7}{2}$.

15. Maximize $z = 10x + 12y$ subject to the following sets of constraints, with $x \geq 0$ and $y \geq 0$.

(a) $x + y \leq 20$
$x + 3y \leq 24$

Sketch the feasible region in the first quadrant, and identify the corner points at $(0, 0)$, $(0, 8)$, $(18, 2)$, which is the intersection of $x+y = 20$ and $x+3y = 24$, and $(20, 0)$.

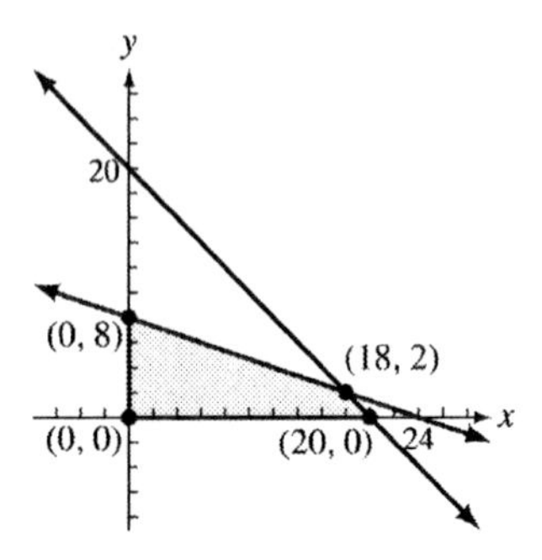

Corner Point	Value of $z = 10x + 12y$
$(0, 0)$	$10(0) + 12(0) = 0$
$(0, 8)$	$10(0) + 12(8) = 96$
$(18, 2)$	$10(18) + 12(2) = 204$ Maximum
$(20, 0)$	$10(20) + 12(0) = 200$

The maximum value of 204 occurs when $x = 18$ and $y = 2$.

(b) $3x + y \leq 15$
$x + 2y \leq 18$

Sketch the feasible region in the first quadrant, and identify the corner points. The corner point $(\frac{12}{5}, \frac{39}{5})$ can be found by solving the system

$$\begin{aligned} 3x + y &= 15 \\ x + 2y &= 18. \end{aligned}$$

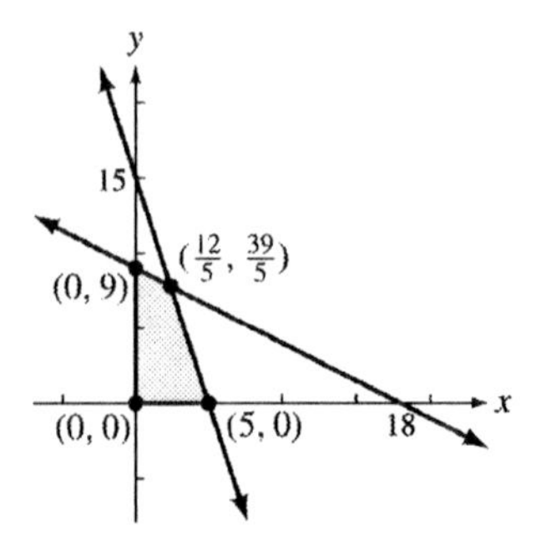

Corner Point	Value of $z = 10x + 12y$
$(0, 0)$	$10(0) + 12(0) = 0$
$(0, 9)$	$10(0) + 12(9) = 108$
$\left(\frac{12}{5}, \frac{39}{5}\right)$	$10\left(\frac{12}{5}\right) + 12\left(\frac{39}{5}\right) = \frac{588}{5} = 117\frac{3}{5}$ Maximum
$(5, 0)$	$10(5) + 12(0) = 50$

The maximum value of $\frac{588}{5}$ occurs when $x = \frac{12}{5}$ and $y = \frac{39}{5}$.

(c) $2x + 5y \geq 22$
$4x + 3y \leq 28$
$2x + 2y \leq 17$

Sketch the feasible region in the first quadrant, and identify the corner points. The corner point $\left(\frac{5}{2}, 6\right)$ can be found by solving the system

$$4x + 3y = 28$$
$$2x + 2y = 17,$$

and the corner point $\left(\frac{37}{7}, \frac{16}{7}\right)$ can be found by solving the system

$$2x + 5y = 22$$
$$4x + 3y = 28.$$

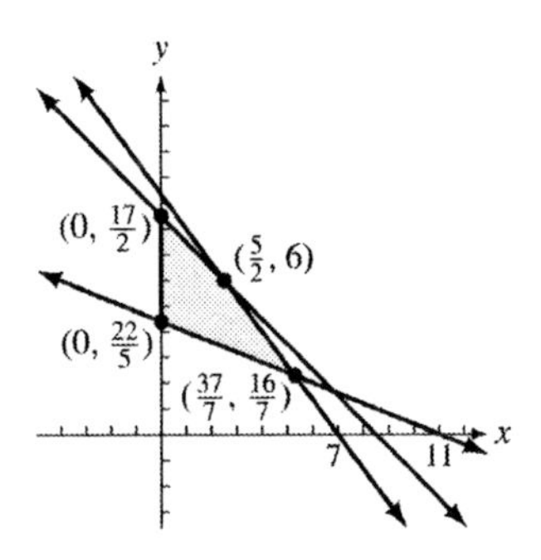

Corner Point	Value of $z = 10x + 12y$
$\left(0, \frac{22}{5}\right)$	$10(0) + 12\left(\frac{22}{5}\right) = \frac{264}{5} = 52.8$
$\left(0, \frac{17}{2}\right)$	$10(0) + 12\left(\frac{17}{2}\right) = 102$ Maximum
$\left(\frac{5}{2}, 6\right)$	$10\left(\frac{5}{2}\right) + 12(6) = 97$
$\left(\frac{37}{7}, \frac{16}{7}\right)$	$10\left(\frac{37}{7}\right) + 12\left(\frac{16}{7}\right) = \frac{562}{7} \approx 80.3$

The maximum value of 102 occurs when $x = 0$ and $y = \frac{17}{2}$.

16. Minimize $z = 3x + 2y$ subject to the following constraints, with $x \geq 0$ and $y \geq 0$.

(a) $10x + 7y \leq 42$
$4x + 10y \geq 35$

Graph the feasible region and identify the corner points. The corner point $\left(\frac{175}{72}, \frac{91}{36}\right)$ can be found by solving the system

$$10x + 7y = 42$$
$$4x + 10y = 35$$

by the elimination method.

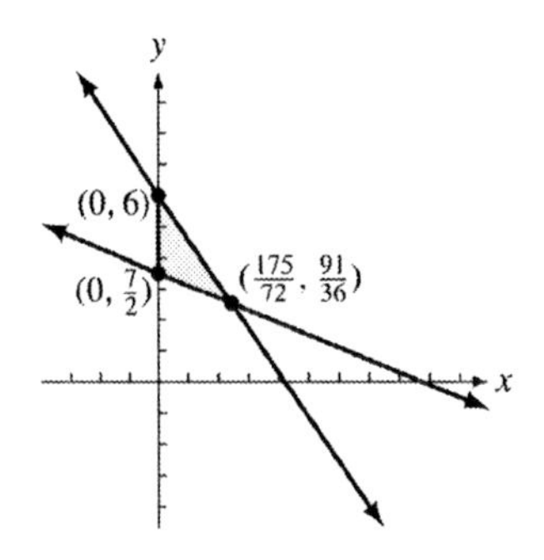

Corner Point	Value of $z = 3x + 2y$
$\left(0, \frac{7}{2}\right)$	$3(0) + 2\left(\frac{7}{2}\right) = 7$ Minimum
$(0, 6)$	$3(0) + 2(6) = 12$
$\left(\frac{175}{72}, \frac{91}{36}\right)$	$3\left(\frac{175}{72}\right) + 2\left(\frac{91}{36}\right) = \frac{889}{72} \approx 12.35$

The minimum value is 7 when $x = 0$ and $y = \frac{7}{2}$.

(b) $6x + 5y \geq 25$
$2x + 6y \geq 15$

Graph the feasible region, and identify the corner points. The corner point $\left(\frac{75}{26}, \frac{20}{13}\right)$ can be found by solving the system

$$6x + 5y = 25$$
$$2x + 6y = 15$$

by the elimination method.

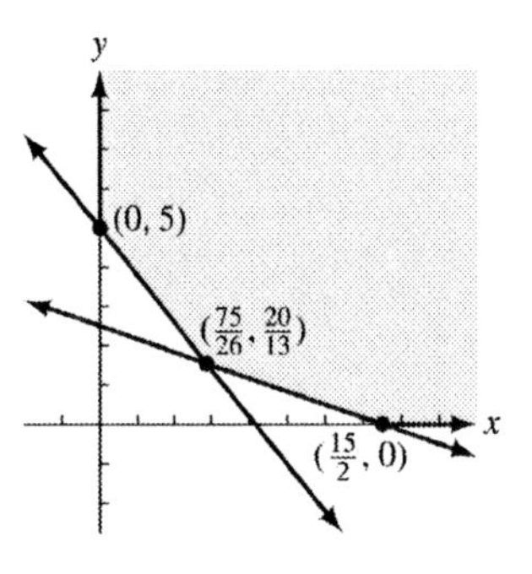

Corner Point	Value of $z = 3x + 2y$
$(0, 5)$	$3(0) + 2(5) = 10$ Minimum
$\left(\frac{15}{2}, 0\right)$	$3\left(\frac{15}{2}\right) + 2(0) = \frac{45}{2} = 22.5$
$\left(\frac{75}{26}, \frac{20}{13}\right)$	$3\left(\frac{75}{26}\right) + 2\left(\frac{20}{13}\right) = \frac{305}{26} \approx 11.7$

The minimum value is 10 when $x = 0$ and $y = 5$.

(c) $x + 2y \geq 10$
$2x + y \geq 12$
$x - y \leq 8$

Graph the region and identify the corner points. The corner point $\left(\frac{14}{3}, \frac{8}{3}\right)$ can be found by solving the system

$$x + 2y = 10$$
$$2x + y = 12,$$

and the corner point $\left(\frac{26}{3}, \frac{2}{3}\right)$ can be found by solving the system

$$x + 2y = 10$$
$$x - y = 8.$$

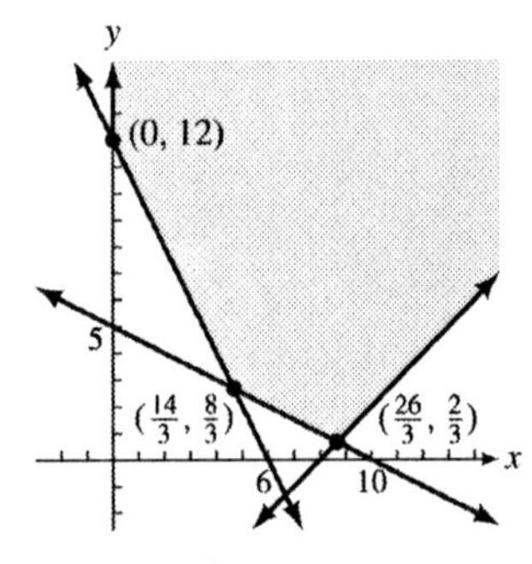

Corner Point	Value of $z = 3x + 2y$
$\left(\frac{14}{3}, \frac{8}{3}\right)$	$3\left(\frac{14}{3}\right) + 2\left(\frac{8}{3}\right) = \frac{58}{3} = 19\frac{1}{3}$ Minimum
$\left(\frac{26}{3}, \frac{2}{3}\right)$	$3\left(\frac{26}{3}\right) + 2\left(\frac{2}{3}\right) = \frac{82}{3} = 27\frac{1}{3}$
$(0, 12)$	$3(0) + 2(12) = 24$

The minimum value is $\frac{58}{3}$ when $x = \frac{14}{3}$ and $y = \frac{8}{3}$.

17. Maximize $z = c_1x_1 + c_2x_2$

subject to: $2x_1 + x_2 \leq 11$
$-x_1 + 2x_2 \leq 2$
$x_1 \geq 0,\ x_2 \geq 0.$

Sketch the feasible region.

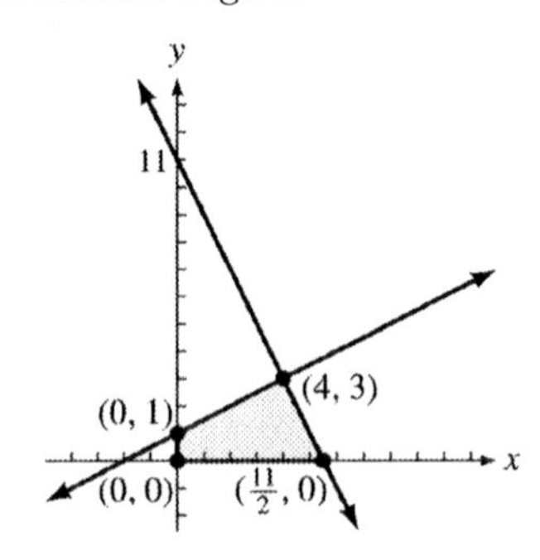

The region is bounded, with corner points $(0, 0)$, $(0, 1)$, $(4, 3)$, and $\left(\frac{11}{2}, 0\right)$.

Corner Point	Value of $z = c_1x_1 + c_2x_2$
$(0, 0)$	$c_1(0) + c_2(0) = 0$
$(0, 1)$	$c_1(0) + c_2(1) = c_2$
$(4, 3)$	$c_1(4) + c_2(3) = 4c_1 + 3c_2$
$\left(\frac{11}{2}, 0\right)$	$c_1\left(\frac{11}{2}\right) + c_2(0) = \frac{11}{2}c_1$

If we are to have $(x_1, x_2) = (4, 3)$ as an optimal solution, then it must be true that both $4c_1 + 3c_2 \geq c_2$ and $4c_1 + 3c_2 \geq \frac{11}{2}c_1$, because the value of z at $(4, 3)$ cannot be smaller than the other values of z in the table. Manipulate the symbols in these two inequalities in order to isolate $\frac{c_1}{c_2}$ in each; keep in mind the given information that $c_2 > 0$ when performing division by c_2. First,

$$4c_1 + 3c_2 \geq c_2$$
$$4c_1 \geq -2c_2$$
$$\frac{4c_1}{4c_2} \geq \frac{-2c_2}{4c_2}$$
$$\frac{c_1}{c_2} \geq -\frac{1}{2}.$$

Then,

$$4c_1 + 3c_2 \geq \frac{11}{2}c_1$$
$$-\frac{3}{2}c_1 + 3c_2 \geq 0$$
$$3c_1 - 6c_2 \leq 0$$
$$3c_1 \leq 6c_2$$
$$\frac{3c_1}{3c_2} \leq \frac{6c_2}{3c_2}$$
$$\frac{c_1}{c_2} \leq 2.$$

Since $\frac{c_1}{c_2} \geq -\frac{1}{2}$ and $\frac{c_1}{c_2} \leq 2$, the desired range for $\frac{c_1}{c_2}$ is $\left[-\frac{1}{2}, 2\right]$, which corresponds to choice (b).

3.3 Applications of Linear Programming

1. Let x represent the number of product A made and y represent the number of product B. Each item of A uses 3 hr on the machine, so $2x$ represents the total hours required for x items of product A. Similarly, $5y$ represents the total hours used for product B. There are only 60 hr available, so

$$3x + 5y \leq 60.$$

2. Let x represent the number of cows. Then $\frac{1}{3}x$ is the number of acres used by x cows. Let y represent the number of sheep. Then $\frac{1}{4}y$ is the number of acres used by y sheep. There are at least 120 acres of pasture, so the inequality is

$$\frac{1}{3}x + \frac{1}{4}y \geq 120.$$

3. Let $x =$ the amount of calcium carbonate supplement
and $y =$ the amount of calcimum citrate supplement.

Then $600x$ represents the number of units of calcium provided by the calcium carbonate supplement and $250y$ represents the number of units provided by the calcium citrate supplement. Since at least 1500 units are needed per day,

$$600x + 250y \geq 1500.$$

4. If x represents the number of small computers sold, then $3x$ is the number of hours spent. If y represents the number of large computers sold, then $5y$ is the number of hours spent. Since Pauline works no more than 45 hr/wk, the inequality is

$$3x + 5y \leq 45.$$

5. Let x represent the number of pounds of \$8 coffee and y represent the number of pounds of \$10 coffee. Since the mixture must weigh at least 40 lb,

$$x + y \geq 40.$$

(Notice that the price per pound is not used in setting up this inequality.)

6. Let x represent the number of gallons of light oil and y represent the number of gallons of heavy oil. The total must not exceed 120 gal, so the inequality is

$$x + y \leq 120.$$

(Note that the price per gallon is not used in setting up this inequality.)

7. Let $x =$ the number of engines to ship to plant I
and $y =$ the number of engines to ship to plant II.

Minimize $z = 30x + 40y$

subject to:
$$\begin{aligned} x &\geq 45 \\ y &\geq 32 \\ x + y &\leq 90 \\ 20x + 15y &\geq 1200 \\ x &\geq 0. \\ y &\geq 0. \end{aligned}$$

Sketch the feasible region in quadrant I, and identify the corner points.

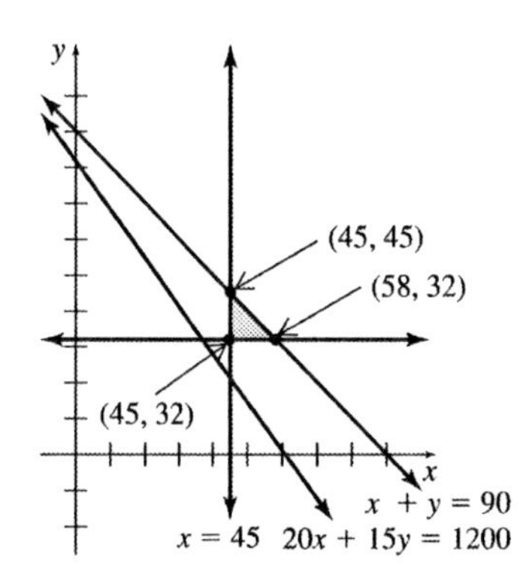

The corner points are: $(45, 32)$, the intersection of $x = 45$ and $y = 32$; $(45, 45)$, the intersection of $x = 45$ and $x + y = 90$; and $(58, 32)$, the intersection of $x + y = 90$ and $y = 32$. Use the corner points to find the minimum value of the objective function.

Corner Point	Value of $z = 30x + 40y$	
$(45, 32)$	$30(45) + 40(32) = 2630$	Minimum
$(45, 45)$	$30(45) + 40(45) = 3150$	
$(58, 32)$	$30(58) + 40(32) = 3020$	

The minimum value is \$2630, which occurs when 45 engines are shipped to plant I and 32 engines are shipped to plant II.

8. Let $x =$ the number of refrigerators to ship to warehouse A
and $y =$ the number of refrigerators to ship to warehouse B.

Minimize $z = 12x + 10y$

subject to:
$$\begin{aligned} x + y &\geq 100 \\ x &\leq 75 \\ y &\leq 80 \\ 4x + 2y &\geq 300 \\ x &\geq 0 \\ y &\geq 0. \end{aligned}$$

Graph the feasible region in quadrant I, and identify the corner points.

$$\begin{aligned} x + \ \ y &= 100 \\ 4x + 2y &= 300. \end{aligned}$$

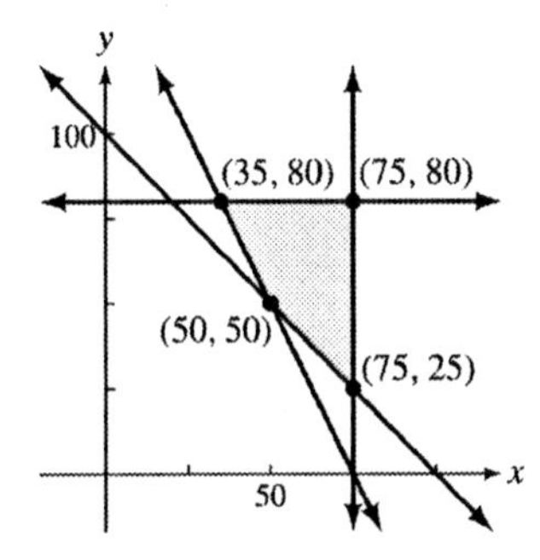

The corner points are: $(35, 80)$, which is the intersection of $y = 80$ and $4x + 2y = 300$; $(75, 80)$; $(75, 25)$, which is the intersection of $x = 75$ and $x + y = 100$; and $(50, 50)$, which is the intersection of $x + y = 100$ and $4x + 2y = 300$.

Corner Point	Value of $z = 12x + 10y$
$(35, 80)$	1220
$(75, 80)$	1700
$(75, 25)$	1150
$(50, 50)$	1100 Minimum

Ship 50 refrigerators to warehouse A and 50 to warehouse B for a minimum cost of $1100.

9. Let $x =$ the number of units of policy A
and $y =$ the number of units of policy B.

(a) Minimize $z = 50x + 40y$

subject to:

$$\begin{aligned} 10{,}000x + \ \ 15{,}000y &\geq 300{,}000 \\ 180{,}000x + 120{,}000y &\geq 3{,}000{,}000 \\ x &\geq 0 \\ y &\geq 0. \end{aligned}$$

Sketch the feasible region in quadrant I, and identify the corner points. The corner point $(6, 16)$ can be found by solving the system

$$\begin{aligned} 10{,}000x + \ \ 15{,}000y &= 300{,}000 \\ 180{,}000x + 120{,}000y &= 3{,}000{,}000, \end{aligned}$$

which can be simplified as

$$\begin{aligned} 2x + 3y &= 60 \\ 3x + 2y &= 50. \end{aligned}$$

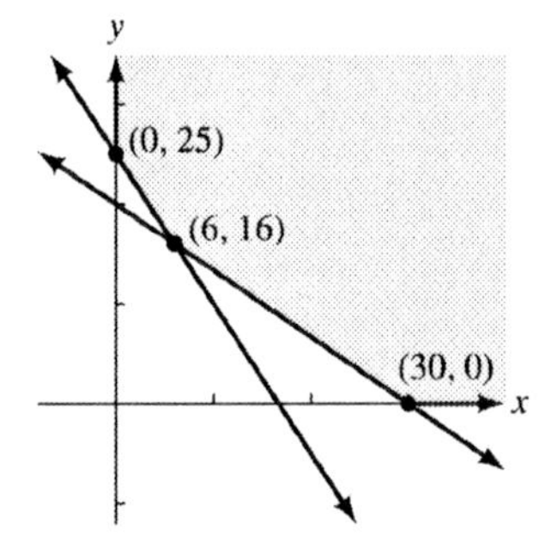

Corner Point	Value of $z = 50x + 40y$
$(0, 25)$	$50(0) + 40(25) = 1000$
$(6, 16)$	$50(6) + 40(16) = 940$ Minimum
$(30, 0)$	$50(30) + 40(0) = 1500$

The minimum cost is $940, which occurs when 6 units of policy A and 16 units of policy B are purchased.

(b) The objective function changes to $z = 25x + 40y$, but the constraints remain the same. Use the same corner points as in part (a).

Corner Point	Value of $z = 25x + 40y$
$(0, 25)$	$25(0) + 40(25) = 1000$
$(6, 16)$	$25(6) + 40(16) = 790$
$(30, 0)$	$25(30) + 40(0) = 750$ Minimum

The minimum cost is $750, which occurs when 30 units of policy A and no units of policy B are purchased.

10. **(a)** Let $x =$ the number of Flexscan sets produced and $y =$ the number of Panoramic I sets produced.

Maximize $z = 350x + 500y$

subject to:
$$5x + 7y \leq 3600$$
$$x + 2y \leq 900$$
$$4x + 4y \leq 2600$$
$$x \geq 0$$
$$y \geq 0.$$

Graph the feasible region and identify the corner points.

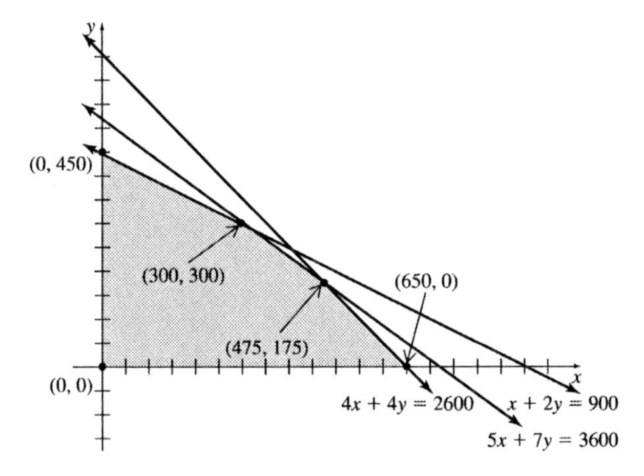

The corner points are $(0, 0)$; $(0, 450)$; $(300, 300)$, the intersection of $x + 2y = 900$ and $5x + 7y = 3600$; $(475, 175)$, the intersection of $5x+7y = 3600$ and $4x + 4y = 2600$; and $(650, 0)$. Use the corner points to find the maximum value of the objective function.

Corner Point	Value of $z = 350x + 500y$
$(0, 0)$	$350(0) + 500(0) = 0$
$(0, 450)$	$350(0) + 500(450) = 225,000$
$(300, 300)$	$350(300) + 500(300) = 255,000$ Maximum
$(475, 175)$	$350(475) + 500(175) = 253,750$
$(650, 0)$	$350(650) + 500(0) = 227,500$

The maximum profit is $255,000 when 300 Flexscan sets and 300 Panoramic I sets are producted.

(b) The objective function is now $z = 450x+500y$. The corner points remain the same.

Corner Point	Value of $z = 450x + 500y$
$(0, 0)$	$450(0) + 500(0) = 0$
$(0, 450)$	$450(0) + 500(450) = 225,000$
$(300, 300)$	$450(300) + 500(300) = 285,000$
$(475, 175)$	$450(475) + 500(175) = 301,250$ Maximum
$(650, 0)$	$450(650) + 500(0) = 292,500$

A maximum profit of $301,250 when 475 Flexscan and 175 Panoramic I sets are produced.

(c) In the solution to part (a), 300 Flexscan and 300 Panoramic I sets are produced.

Assembly line:	$5(300) + 7(300) = 3600 \leq 3600$
Cabinet shop:	$300 + 2(300) = 900 \leq 900$
Testing and packing:	$4(300) + 4(300) = 2400 \leq 2600$

There are $2600 - 2400$ or 200 unused hours in testing and packing.

In the solution to part (b), 475 Flexscan and 175 Panoramic I sets are produced.

Assembly line:	$5(475) + 7(175) = 3600 \leq 3600$
Cabinet shop:	$475 + 2(175) = 825 \leq 900$
Testing and packing:	$4(475) + 4(175) = 2600 \leq 2600$

There are $900 - 825$ or 75 unused hours in the cabinet shop.

11. Let $x =$ the number of type I bolts and $y =$ the number of type II bolts.

Maximize $z = 0.15x + 0.20y$

subject to:
$$0.2x + 0.2y \leq 300$$
$$0.6x + 0.2y \leq 720$$
$$0.04x + 0.08y \leq 100$$
$$x \geq 0$$
$$y \geq 0.$$

Graph the feasible region and identify the corner points.

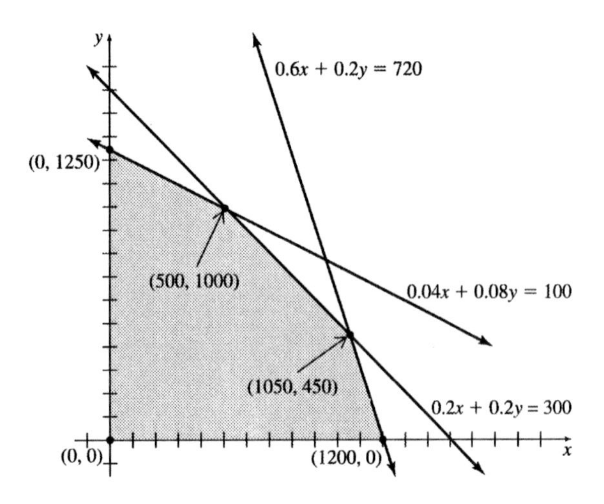

The corner points are $(0,0)$; $(0,1250)$; $(500,1000)$, the intersection of $0.04x+0.08y=100$ and $0.2x+0.2y=300$; $(1050,450)$, the intersection of $0.2x+0.2y=300$ and $0.6x+0.2y=720$; and $(1200,0)$. Use the corner points to find the maximum value of the objective function.

Corner Point	Value of $z = 0.15x + 0.90y$
$(0,0)$	$0.15(0)+0.20(0) = 0$
$(0,1250)$	$0.15(0)+0.20(1250) = 250$
$(500,1000)$	$0.15(500)+0.20(1000) = 275$ Maximum
$(1050,450)$	$0.15(1050)+0.20(450) = 247.5$
$(1200,0)$	$0.15(1200)+0.20(0) = 180$

The shop should manufacture 500 type I bolts and 1000 type II bolts to maximize revenue.

(b) The maximum revenue is \$275.

(c) Notice that each one-cent increase in the selling price of type I bolts increases the value of z at $(500,1000)$ by \$5 and at $(1050,450)$ by \$10.50. (At $(0,1200)$, there would be no increase in z.) Therefore, the corner point $(1050,450)$ will begin to maximize the revenue when n, the number of one-cent increases, is larger than the solution to the following equation.

$$
\begin{aligned}
(0.15+0.01n)(1050)+0.20(450) &= (0.15+0.01n)(500) \\
&\quad + 0.20(1000) \\
(0.15+0.01n)(550) &= 110 \\
5.5n &= 27.5 \\
n &= 5
\end{aligned}
$$

Therefore, the selling price of the type I bolts can increase up to $0.15+0.01(5) = 0.20$, or 20¢, before a different number of each type of bolts should be produced to maximize the revenue. If the price of the type I bolts exceeds 20¢, then it is more profitable to produce 1050 type I bolts and 450 type II bolts.

12. Let $x =$ the number of gallons of gasoline in millions to produce each day
and $y =$ the number of gallons of fuel oil in millions to produce each day.

Maximize $z = 1.25x + 1.00y$

subject to:

$$
\begin{aligned}
x &\geq 2y \\
y &\geq 3 \\
x &\leq 6.4 \\
0.25x + 1y &\leq 4.65 \\
x &\geq 0 \\
y &\geq 0.
\end{aligned}
$$

Graph the feasible region in quadrant I, and find the corner points.

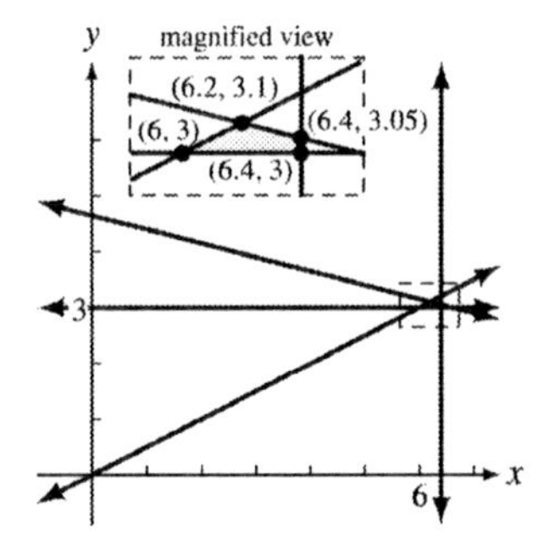

Corner Point	Value of $z = 1.25x + 1.00y$
$(6,3)$	10.5
$(6.2,3.1)$	10.85
$(6.4,3.05)$	11.05 Maximum
$(6.4,3)$	11

Produce 6.4 million gal of gasoline and 3.05 million gal of fuel oil for a maximum revenue of \$11.05 million (or \$11,050,000).

13. (a) Let $x =$ the number of kg of the half-and-half mixture
and $y =$ the number of kg of the second mixture.

Maximize $z = 7x + 9.5y$

subject to: $\frac{1}{2}x + \frac{3}{4}y \leq 150$
$\frac{1}{2}x + \frac{1}{4}y \leq 90$
$x \geq 0$
$y \geq 0.$

Sketch the feasible region and identify the corner points.

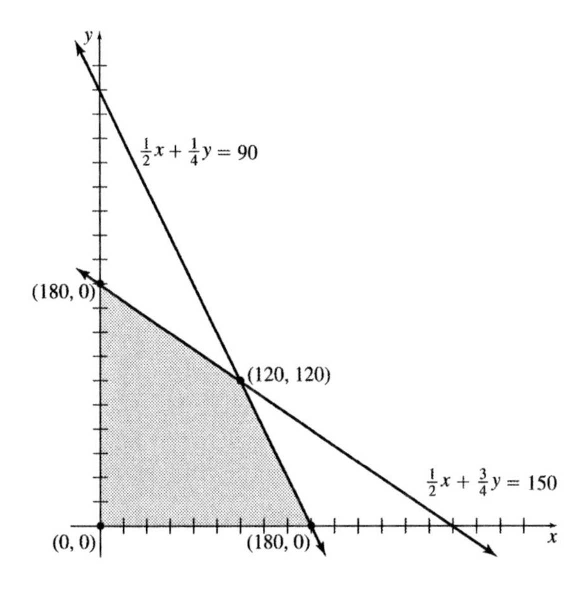

The corner points are $(0,0)$; $(0,200)$; $(120,120)$, the intersection of $\frac{1}{2}x + \frac{3}{4}y = 150$ and $\frac{1}{2}x + \frac{1}{4}y = 90$; and $(180,0)$. Use the corner points to find the maximum value of the objective function.

Corner Point	Value of $z = 7x + 9.5y$
$(0,0)$	$7(0) + 9.5(0) = 0$
$(0,200)$	$7(0) + 9.5(200) = 1900$
$(120,120)$	$7(120) + 9.5(120) = 1980$ Maximum
$(180,0)$	$7(180) + 9.5(0) = 1260$

The candy company should prepare 120 kg of the half-and-half mixture and 120 kg of the second mixture for a maximum revenue of $1980.

(b) The objective function to be maximized is now $z = 7x + 11y$. The corner points remain the same.

Corner Point	Value of $z = 7x + 11y$
$(0,0)$	$7(0) + 11(0) = 0$
$(0,200)$	$7(0) + 11(200) = 2200$ Maximum
$(120,120)$	$7(120) + 11(120) = 2160$
$(180,0)$	$7(180) + 11(0) = 1260$

In order to maximize the revenue under the altered conditions, the candy company should prepare 0 kg of the half-and-half mixture and 200 kg of the second mixture for a maximum revenue of $2200.

14. Let $x =$ the number of hectares of coffee and $y =$ the number of hectares of cocoa.

Maximize $z = 220x + 550y$

subject to: $x + y \leq 500,000$
$x \geq 100,000$
$200,000 \leq y \leq 270,000$
$2x + 5y \leq 1,750,000$
$x \geq 0$
$y \geq 0.$

Graph the feasible region in quadrant I, and identify the corner points.

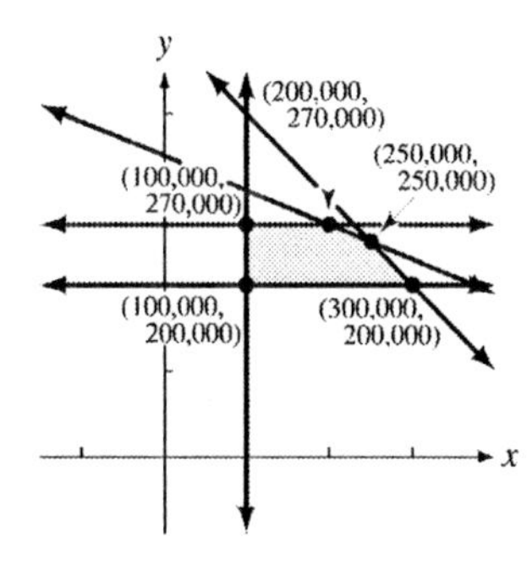

Corner Point	Value of $z = 220x + 550y$
(100,000, 200,000)	132,000,000
(100,000, 270,000)	170,500,000
(200,000, 270,000)	192,500,000 Maximum
(250,000, 250,000)	192,500,000 Maximum
(300,000, 200,000)	176,000,000

A maximum profit of $192,500,000 is obtained by growing 250,000 hectares of each crop or by growing 200,000 hectares of coffee and 270,000 hectares of cocoa (or any point on the line between these two points).

15. **(a)** Let $x =$ the number of gallons from dairy I and $y =$ the number of gallons from dairy II.

Maximize $z = 0.037x + 0.032y$

subject to: $0.60x + 0.20y \leq 36$
$x \leq 50$
$y \leq 80$
$x + y \leq 100$
$x \geq 0$
$y \geq 0.$

Sketch the feasible region, and identify the corner points.

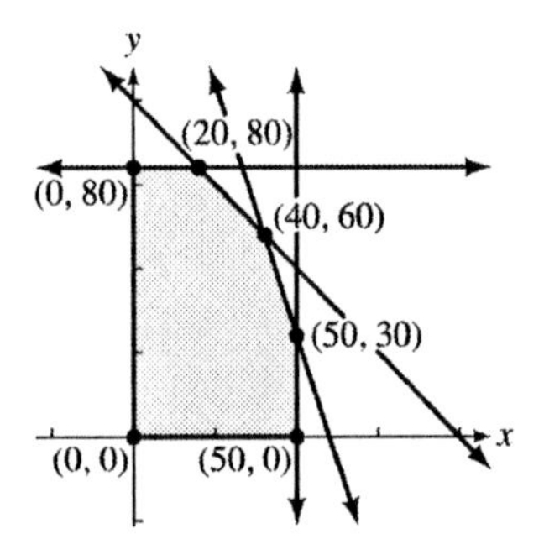

Corner Point	Value of $z = 0.037x + 0.032y$
$(0, 0)$	0
$(0, 80)$	2.56
$(20, 80)$	3.30
$(40, 60)$	3.40 Maximum
$(50, 30)$	2.81
$(50, 0)$	1.85

The maximum amount of butterfat is 3.4%, which occurs when 40 gal are purchased from dairy I and 60 gal are purchased from dairy II.

(b) In the solution to part (a), Mostpure uses 40 gallons from dairy I with a capacity for 50 gallons. Therefore, there is an excess capacity of 10 gallons from dairy I. Similarly, there is an excess capacity of $80 - 60$ or 20 gallons from dairy II.

16. Let $x =$ the number of boxes shipped from warehouse I to San Jose
and $y =$ the number of boxes shipped from warehouse I to Memphis.

Then, $350 - x$ is the number of boxes shipped from warehouse II to San Jose. $300 - y$ is the number of boxes shipped from warehouse II to Memphis.

The constraints are represented by the following inequalities:

$$x + y \leq 370$$
$$(350 - x) + (300 - y) \leq 290 \text{ or } x + y \geq 360$$
$$x \leq 350$$
$$y \leq 300$$
$$x \geq 0$$
$$y \geq 0.$$

Minimize the shipping cost

$$z = 0.25x + 0.22y + 0.23(350 - x) + 0.21(300 - y)$$

or

$$z = 0.02x + 0.01y + 143.5$$

subject to the above constraints.

Graph the feasible region in quadrant I, and identify the corner points.

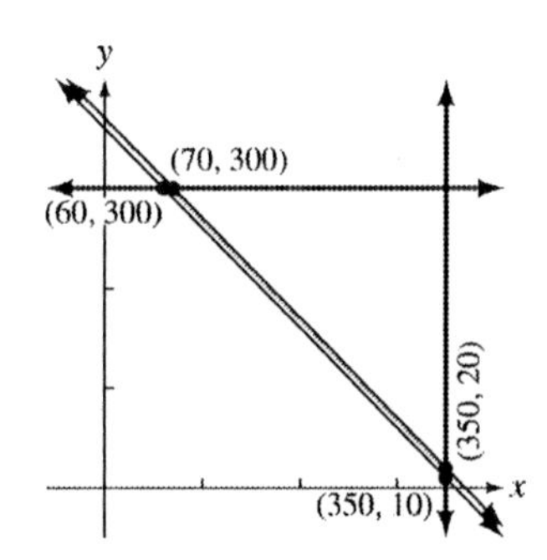

Corner Point	Value of $z = 0.02x + 0.01y + 143.5$
$(60, 300)$	147.7 Minimum
$(70, 300)$	147.9
$(350, 20)$	150.7
$(350, 10)$	150.6

Thus, a minimum cost of \$147.70 is obtained when 60 boxes are shipped from warehouse I to San Jose, 300 boxes are shipped from warehouse I to Memphis, and 290 boxes are shipped from warehouse II to San Jose. Notice that no boxes are sent from warehouse II to Memphis.

17. Let $x =$ the amount (in millions) invested in U.S. Treasury bonds
and $y =$ the amount (in millions) invested in mutual funds.

Maximize $z = 0.04x + 0.08y$

subject to:

$$\begin{aligned} x + y &\le 30 \\ x &\ge 5 \\ y &\ge 10 \\ 100x + 200y &\ge 5000 \\ x &\ge 0 \\ y &\ge 0. \end{aligned}$$

Sketch the feasible region, and identify the corner points.

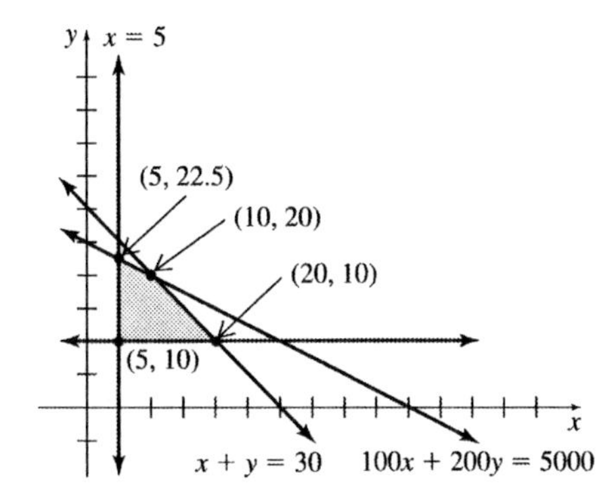

The corner points are $(5, 10)$; $(5, 22.5)$, the intersection of $x = 5$ and $100x + 200y = 5000$; $(10, 20)$, the intersection of $100x + 200y = 5000$ and $x + y = 30$; and $(20, 10)$. Use the corner points to find the maximum value of the objective function.

Corner Point	Value of $z = 0.04x + 0.08y$
$(5, 10)$	$0.04(5) + 0.08(10) = 1$
$(5, 22.5)$	$0.04(5) + 0.08(22.5) = 2$ Maximum
$(10, 20)$	$0.04(10) + 0.08(20) = 2$ Maximum
$(20, 10)$	$0.04(20) + 0.08(10) = 1.6$

The maximum annual interest of \$2 million can be achieved by investing \$5 million in U.S. Treasurey bonds and \$22.5 million in mutual funds, or \$10 million in bonds and \$20 million in mutual funds (or in any solution on the line between those two points).

18. 1 Zeta + 2 Beta must not exceed 1000; thus (b) is the correct choice.

19. Beta is limited to 400 units per day, so Beta $\le$ 400. The correct answer is choice (a).

20. \$4.00 Zeta + \$5.25 Beta equals the total contribution margin; (c) is the correct choice.

21. (a) Let $x =$ the number of pill 1
and $y =$ the number of pill 2.

Minimize $z = 0.15x + 0.30y$

subject to:

$$\begin{aligned} 8x + 2y &\ge 16 \\ x + y &\ge 5 \\ 2x + 7y &\ge 20 \\ x &\ge 0 \\ y &\ge 0. \end{aligned}$$

Sketch the feasible region in quadrant I.

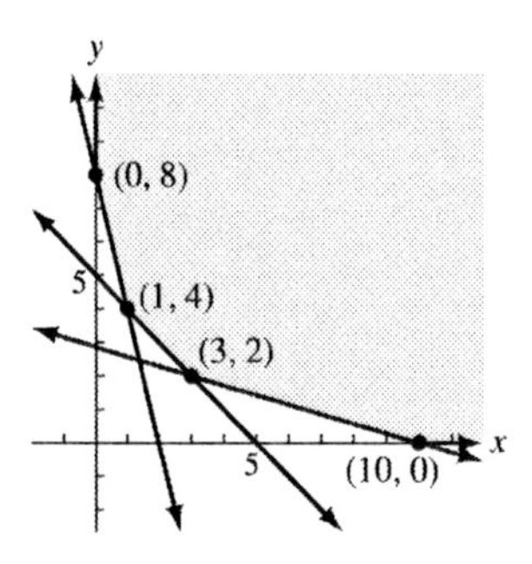

The corner points $(0, 8)$ and $(10, 0)$ can be identified from the graph. The coordinates of the corner point $(1, 4)$ can be found by solving the system

$$\begin{aligned} 8x + 2y &= 16 \\ x + y &= 5. \end{aligned}$$

The coordinates of the corner point $(3, 2)$ can be found by solving the system

$$\begin{aligned} 2x + 7y &= 20 \\ x + y &= 5. \end{aligned}$$

Corner Point	Value of $z = 0.15x + 0.30y$
$(1, 4)$	1.35
$(3, 2)$	1.05 Minimum
$(0, 8)$	2.40
$(10, 0)$	1.50

A minimum daily cost of \$1.05 is incurred by taking three of pill 1 and two of pill 2.

(b) In the solution to part (a), Mark receives $8(3) + 2(2)$ or 28 units of vitamin A. This is a surplus of $28 - 16$ or 12 units of vitamin A.

22. Let $x =$ the number of species I prey and $y =$ the number of species II prey.

		Protein	Fat
Species	I	5	2
	II	3	4

Minimize $z = 2x + 3y$

subject to:
$$5x + 3y \geq 10$$
$$2x + 4y \geq 8$$
$$x \geq 0$$
$$y \geq 0.$$

Graph the feasible region in quadrant I, and identify the corner points $\left(0, \frac{10}{3}\right)$, $(4, 0)$, and the intersection of $5x + 3y = 10$ and $2x + 4y = 8$, which is $\left(\frac{8}{7}, \frac{10}{7}\right)$.

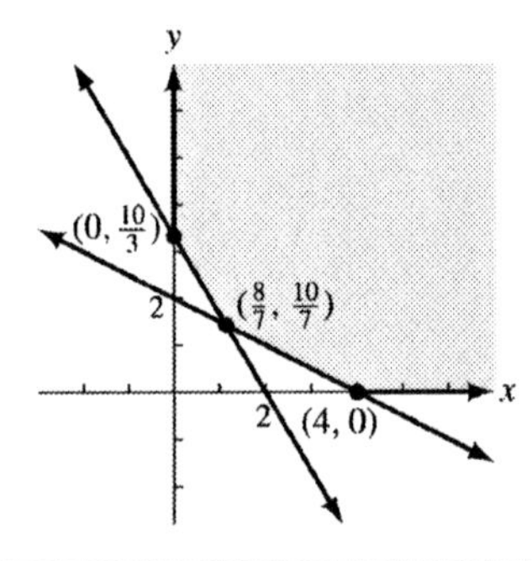

Corner Point	Value of $z = 2x + 3y$
$\left(0, \frac{10}{3}\right)$	10
$(4, 0)$	8
$\left(\frac{8}{7}, \frac{10}{7}\right)$	$\frac{46}{7}$ Minimum

The minimum value is $\frac{46}{7} \approx 6.57$ units of energy. $\frac{8}{7}$ units of species I and $\frac{10}{7}$ units of species II will meet the daily food requirements with the least expenditure of energy. However, a predator probably can catch and digest only whole numbers of prey. This problem shows that it is important to consider whether a model produces a realistic answer to a problem.

23. Let $x =$ the number of ounces of fruit and $y =$ the number of ounces of nuts.

Minimize $z = 20x + 30y$

subject to:
$$3y \geq 6$$
$$2x + y \geq 10$$
$$x + 2y \leq 9$$
$$x \geq 0$$
$$y \geq 0.$$

Sketch the feasible region, and identify the corner points.

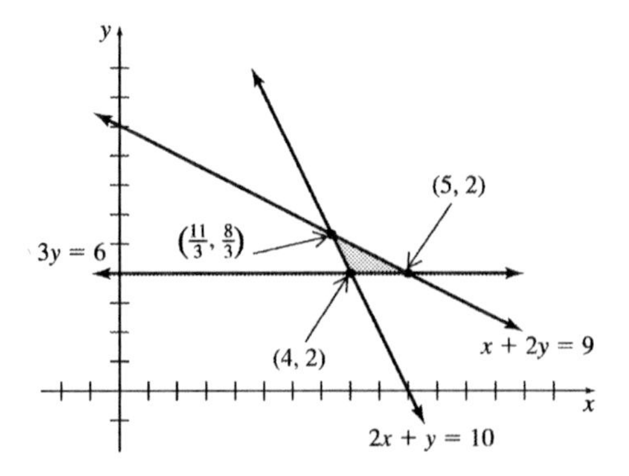

The corner points are: $(4, 2)$, the intersection of $y = 2$ and $2x + y = 10$; $\left(\frac{11}{3}, \frac{8}{3}\right)$,the intersection of $2x + y = 10$ and $x + 2y = 9$; and $(5, 2)$, the intersection of $x + 2y = 9$ and $y = 2$. Use the corner points to find the minimum value of the objective function.

Corner Point	Value of $z = 20x + 30y$
$(4, 2)$	$20(4) + 30(2) = 140$ Minimum
$\left(\frac{11}{3}, \frac{8}{3}\right)$	$20\left(\frac{11}{3}\right) + 30\left(\frac{8}{3}\right) = \frac{460}{3} \approx 153$
$(5, 2)$	$20(5) + 30(2) = 160$

The dietician should use 4 ounces of fruit and 2 ounces of nuts for a minimum of 140 calories.

24. **(a)** Let $x =$ the number of Brand X pills and $y =$ the number of Brand Y pills.

Minimize $z = 0.05x + 0.04y$

subject to:
$$3000x + 1000y \geq 6000$$
$$45x + 50y \geq 195$$
$$75x + 200y \geq 600$$
$$x \geq 0$$
$$y \geq 0.$$

Graph the feasible region in quadrant I.

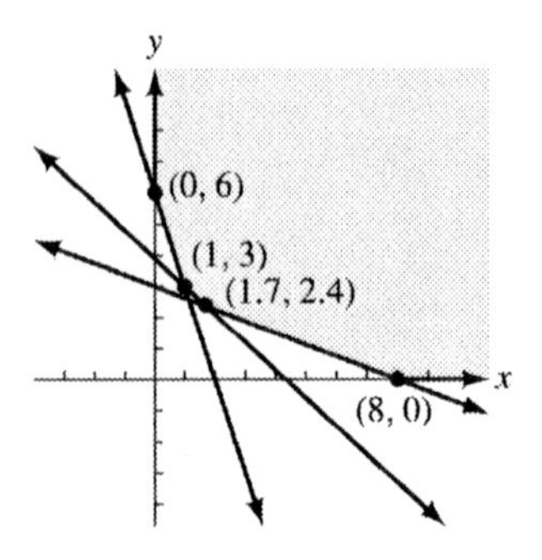

The corner points $(0, 6)$ and $(8, 0)$ can be identified from the graph. The coordinates of the corner point $(1, 3)$ can be found by solving the system

$$\begin{aligned} 45x + 50y &= 195 \\ 3000x + 1000y &= 6000. \end{aligned}$$

The approximate coordinates of the corner point $(1.7, 2.4)$ can be found by solving the system

$$\begin{aligned} 45x + 50y &= 195 \\ 75x + 200y &= 600. \end{aligned}$$

Corner Point	Value of $z = 0.05x + 0.04y$
$(1, 3)$	0.17 Minimum
$(1.7, 2.4)$	0.18
$(8, 0)$	0.40
$(0, 6)$	0.24

A minimum daily cost of 17¢ is incurred by taking 1 Brand X pill and 3 Brand Y pills.

(b) In the solution to part (a), Ms. Oliveras receives $75(1) + 200(3)$ or 675 USP units of vitamin D. This is a surplus of $675 - 600$ or 75 USP units of vitamin D.

25. Let $x =$ the number of units of plants and $y =$ the number of animals.

Minimize $z = 30x + 15y$
subject to:
$$\begin{aligned} 30x + 20y &\geq 360 \\ 10x + 25y &\geq 300 \\ y &\geq 8 \\ 0 \leq x &\leq 25 \\ 0 \leq y &\leq 25. \end{aligned}$$

Sketch the feasible region in quadrant I.

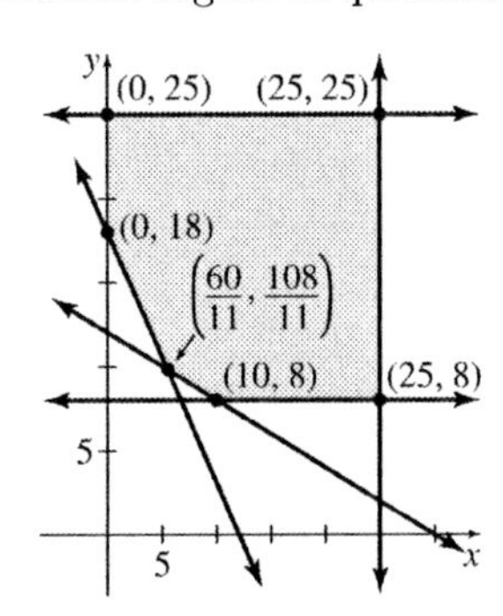

The corner points $(0, 18)$, $(0, 25)$, $(25, 25)$, and $(25, 8)$ can be determined from the graph. The corner point $\left(\frac{60}{11}, \frac{108}{11}\right)$ can be found by solving the system

$$\begin{aligned} 30x + 20y &= 360 \\ 10x + 25y &= 300. \end{aligned}$$

The corner point $(10, 8)$ can be found by solving the system

$$\begin{aligned} 10x + 25y &= 300 \\ y &= 8. \end{aligned}$$

Corner Point	Value of $z = 30x + 15y$	
$(0, 18)$	270	Minimum
$(0, 25)$	375	
$(25, 25)$	1125	
$(25, 8)$	870	
$\left(\frac{60}{11}, \frac{108}{11}\right)$	$\frac{3420}{11} \approx 310.91$	
$(10, 8)$	420	

The minimum labor is 270 hours and is achieved when 0 units of plants and 18 animals are collected.

26. Let $x =$ the number of square feet of window space and $y =$ the number of square feet of wall space.

Maximize $z = x + y$

subject to:
$$\begin{aligned} x &\geq \frac{1}{6}y \\ 10x + 20y &\leq 12{,}000 \\ 0.32x + 0.20y &\leq 160 \\ x &\geq 0 \\ y &\geq 0. \end{aligned}$$

Graph the feasible region on a graphing calculator and identify the corner points.

Corner Point	Value of $z = x + y$
$(0, 0)$	0
$(92.31, 553.85)$	646.16
$(181.82, 509.09)$	690.91 Maximum
$(500, 0)$	500

The maximum total area is 690.91 sq ft occurring when 181.82 sq ft is used for windows and 509.09 sq ft is used for walls.

Chapter 3 Review Exercises

2. There is no limit to the number of constraints in the graphical method. We are, however, limited to two variables.

3. $y \geq 2x + 3$

Graph $y = 2x + 3$ as a solid line, using the intercepts $(0, 3)$ and $\left(-\frac{3}{2}, 0\right)$. Using the origin as a test point, we get $0 \geq 2(0) + 3$ or $0 \geq 3$, which is false. Shade the region that does not contain the origin, that is, the half-plane above the line.

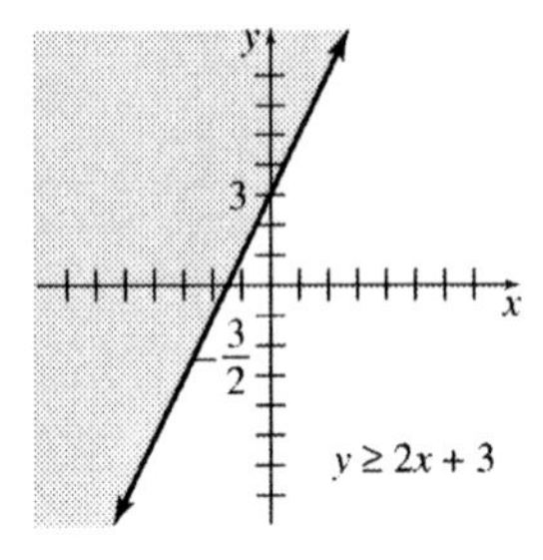

4. $5x - 2y \leq 10$

Graph $5x - 2y = 10$ as a solid line using the points $(2, 0)$ and $(0, -5)$. The test point $(0, 0)$ gives $0 \leq 10$, which is true. Shade the half-plane containing $(0, 0)$, that is, all points above the line.

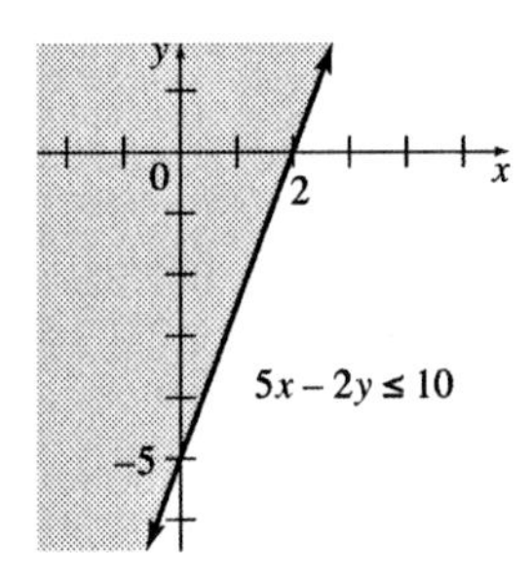

5. $2x + 6y \leq 8$

Graph $2x + 6y = 8$ as a solid line, using the intercepts $(0, \frac{4}{3})$ and $(4, 0)$. Using the origin as a test point, we get $0 \leq 8$, which is true. Shade the region that contains the origin, that is, the half-plane below the line.

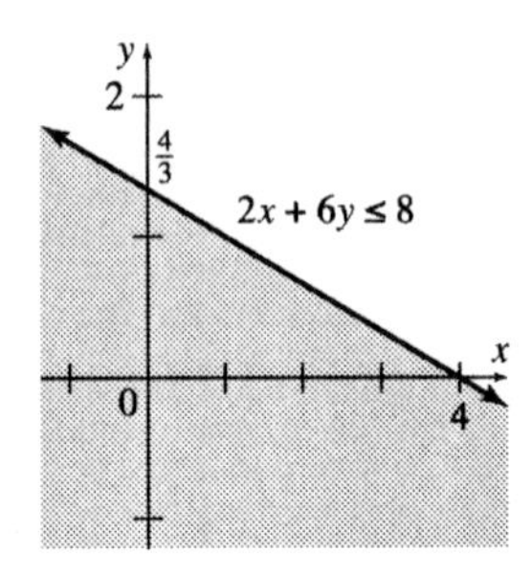

6. $2x - 6y \geq 18$

Graph $2x - 6y = 18$ as a solid line using the points $(9, 0)$ and $(0, -3)$. The test point $(0, 0)$ gives $0 \geq 18$, which is false. Shade the half-plane that does not contain $(0, 0)$, that is, all points below the line.

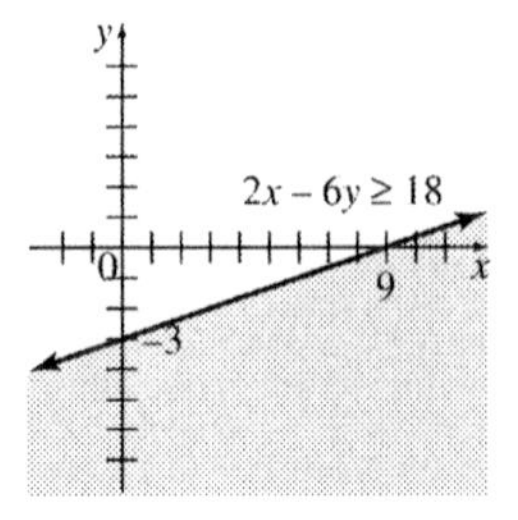

7. $y \geq x$

Graph $y = x$ as a solid line. Since this line contains the origin, choose a point other than $(0, 0)$ as a test point. If we use $(1, 4)$, we get $4 \geq 1$, which is true. Shade the region that contains the test point, that is, the half-plane above the line.

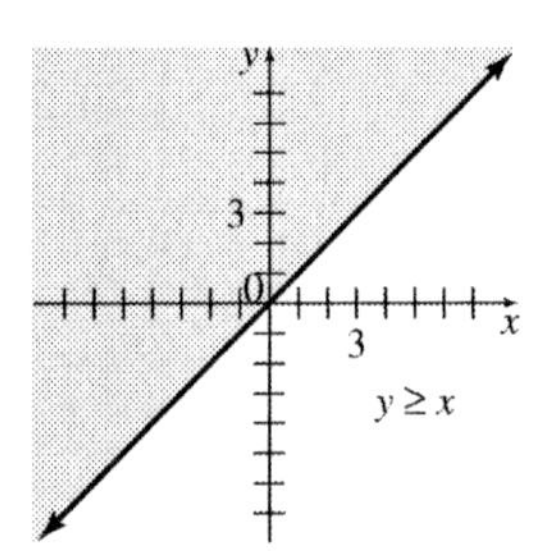

8. $y \geq -2$

Graph the horizontal solid line $y = -2$, and shade the half-plane above the line.

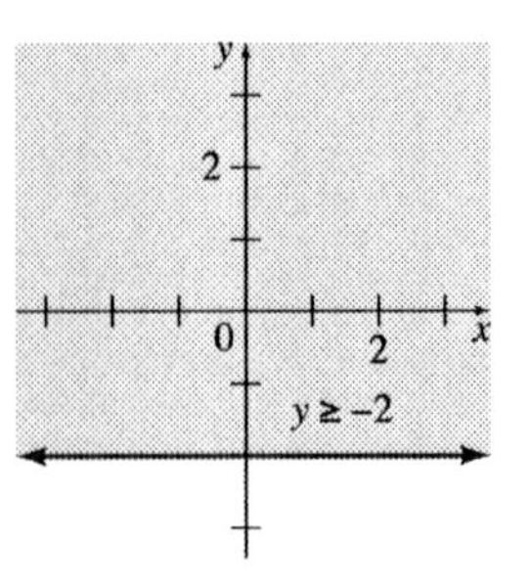

9. $x + y \le 6$
$2x - y \ge 3$

$x + y \le 6$ is the half-plane on or below the line $x + y = 6$; $2x - y \ge 3$ is the half-plane on or below the line $2x - y = 3$. Shade the overlapping part of these two half-planes, which is the region below both lines. The only corner point is the intersection of the two boundary lines, the point $(3, 3)$.

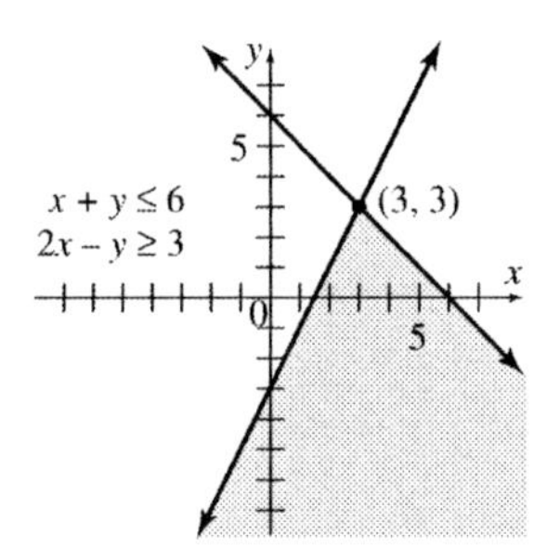

10. $3x + 2y \ge 12$
$4x - 5y \le 20$

Graph $3x + 2y = 12$ as a solid line using $(4, 0)$ and $(0, 6)$, and graph $4x - 5y = 20$ as a solid line using $(5, 0)$ and $(0, -4)$. The test point $(0, 0)$ gives $0 + 0 \ge 12$, which is false, and $0 - 0 \le 20$, which is true. Shade the half-planes above $3x + 2y = 12$ and above $4x - 5y = 20$. The final shaded region is the overlapping part of these two half-planes, which is the region above both lines.
The only corner point is the intersection of the two boundary lines. To find the coordinates of this point, solve the system

$$3x + 2y = 12$$
$$4x - 5y = 20.$$

The corner point is $\left(\frac{100}{23}, -\frac{12}{23}\right)$.

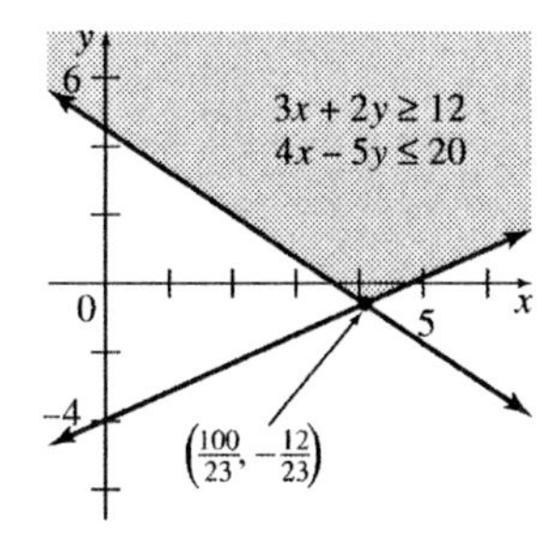

11. $-4 \le x \le 2$
$-1 \le y \le 3$
$x + y \le 4$

$-4 \le x \le 2$ is the rectangular region lying on or between the two vertical lines, $x = -4$ and $x = 2$; $-1 \le y \le 3$ is the rectangular region lying on or between the two horizontal lines, $y = -1$ and $y = 3$; $x + y \le 4$ is the half-plane lying on or below the line $x + y = 4$. Shade the overlapping part of these three regions. The corner points are $(-4, -1)$, $(-4, 3)$, $(1, 3)$, $(2, 2)$, and $(2, -1)$.

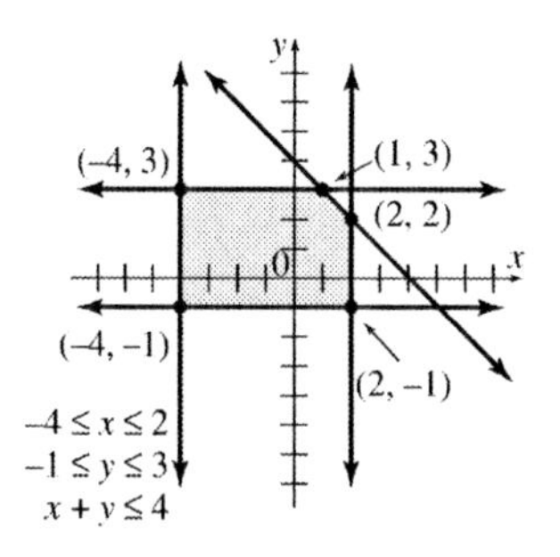

12. $2 \le x \le 5$
$1 \le y \le 7$
$x - y \le 3$

Graph $x = 2$, $x = 5$, $y = 1$, $y = 7$, and $x - y = 3$ as solid lines. $(0, 0)$ can be used as a test point for each inequality to help graph the feasible region. The corner points are $(2, 1)$, $(2, 7)$, $(5, 7)$, $(5, 2)$, and $(4, 1)$.

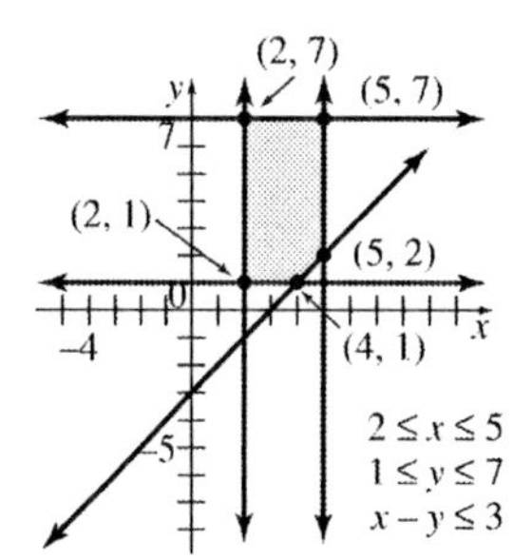

13. $x + 2y \le 4$
$5x - 6y \le 12$
$x \ge 0$
$y \ge 0$

$x + 2y \le 4$ is the half-plane on or below the line $x + 2y = 4$; $5x - 6y \le 12$ is the half-plane on or above the line $5x - 6y = 12$; $x \ge 0$ and $y \ge 0$ together restrict the graph to the first quadrant. Shade the portion of the first quadrant where the half-planes overlap. The corner points are $(0, 0)$,

$(0,2)$, $\left(\frac{12}{5},0\right)$, and $\left(3,\frac{1}{2}\right)$, which can be found by solving the system

$$\begin{aligned} x + 2y &= 4 \\ 5x - 6y &= 12. \end{aligned}$$

14. $x + 2y \le 4$
$2x - 3y \le 6$
$x \ge 0$
$y \ge 0$

Graph $x + 2y = 4$ and $2x - 3y = 6$ as solid lines. The inequalities $x \ge 0$ and $y \ge 0$ restrict the region to quadrant I. Use $(0,0)$ as a test point to get $0 + 0 \le 4$ and $0 - 0 \le 6$, which are true. The feasible region contains all points on or below $x + 2y = 4$ and on or above $2x - 3y = 6$ in quadrant I.

The corner points $(0,0)$, $(0,2)$, and $(3,0)$ can be identified from the graph. The fourth corner point, $\left(\frac{24}{7},\frac{2}{7}\right)$, is the intersection of the lines $x + 2y = 4$ and $2x - 3y = 6$.

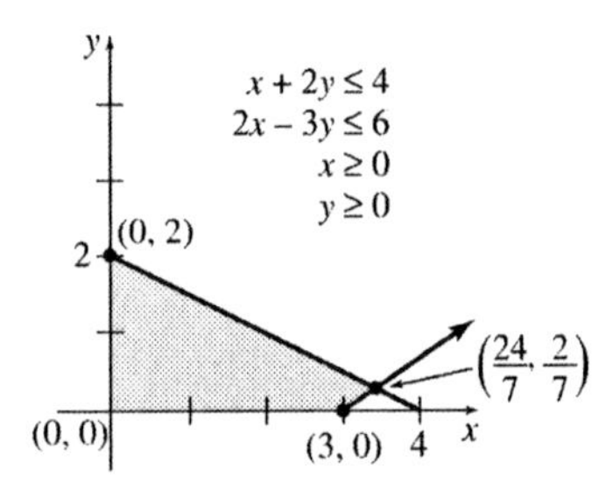

15. Evaluate the objective function $z = 2x + 4y$ at each corner point.

Corner Point	Value of $z = 2x + 4y$	
$(0,0)$	$2(0) + 4(0) = 0$	Minimum
$(0,4)$	$2(0) + 4(4) = 16$	
$(3,4)$	$2(3) + 4(4) = 22$	Maximum
$(6,2)$	$2(6) + 4(2) = 20$	
$(4, 0)$	$2(4) + 4(0) = 8$	

The maximum value 22 occurs at $(3,4)$, and the minimum value of 0 occurs at $(0,0)$.

16. Evaluate the objective function $z = 2x + 4y$ at all the corner points.

Corner Point	Value of $z = 2x + 4y$	
$(0,8)$	$2(0) + 4(8) = 32$	
$(8,8)$	$2(8) + 4(8) = 48$	Maximum
$(5,2)$	$2(5) + 4(2) = 18$	
$(2,0)$	$2(2) + 4(0) = 4$	Minimum

The maximum is 48 at $(8,8)$; the minimum is 4 at $(2,0)$.

17. Maximize $z = 2x + 4y$

subject to: $3x + 2y \le 12$
$5x + y \ge 5$
$x \ge 0$
$y \ge 0.$

Sketch the feasible region in quadrant I.

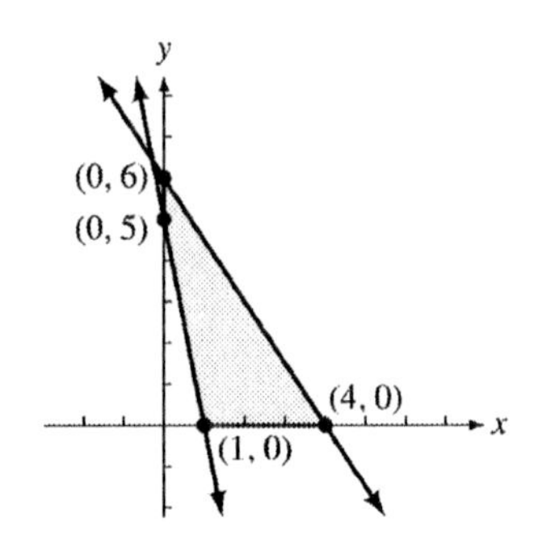

The corner points are $(0,5)$, $(0,6)$, $(4,0)$, and $(1,0)$.

Corner Point	Value of $z = 2x + 4y$	
$(0,5)$	20	
$(0,6)$	24	Maximum
$(4,0)$	8	
$(1,0)$	2	

The maximum value is 24 at $(0,6)$.

18. Minimize $z = 5x + 3y$

subject to:
$$\begin{aligned} 8x + 5y &\geq 40 \\ 4x + 10y &\geq 40 \\ x &\geq 0 \\ y &\geq 0. \end{aligned}$$

Graph the feasible region, and identify corner points.

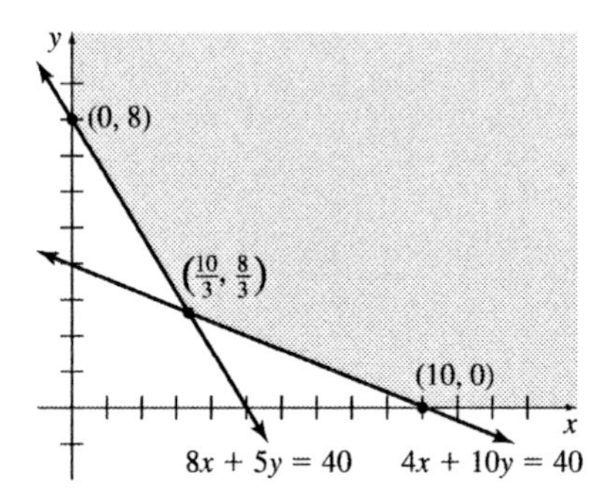

The corner points are: $(0, 8)$; $(\frac{10}{3}, \frac{8}{3})$, the intersection of $8x+5y = 40$ and $4x+10y = 40$; and $(10, 0)$. Use the corner points to find the minimum value of the objective function.

Corner Point	Value of $z = 5x + 3y$
$(0, 8)$	$5(0) + 3(8) = 24$ Minimum
$(\frac{10}{3}, \frac{8}{3})$	$5(\frac{10}{3}) + 3(\frac{8}{3}) = \frac{10}{3} \approx 25$
$(10, 0)$	$5(10) + 3(0) = 50$

The minimum value is 24 at $(0, 8)$.

19. Minimize $z = 4x + 2y$

subject to:
$$\begin{aligned} x + y &\leq 50 \\ 2x + y &\geq 20 \\ x + 2y &\geq 30 \\ x &\geq 0 \\ y &\geq 0. \end{aligned}$$

Sketch the feasible region.

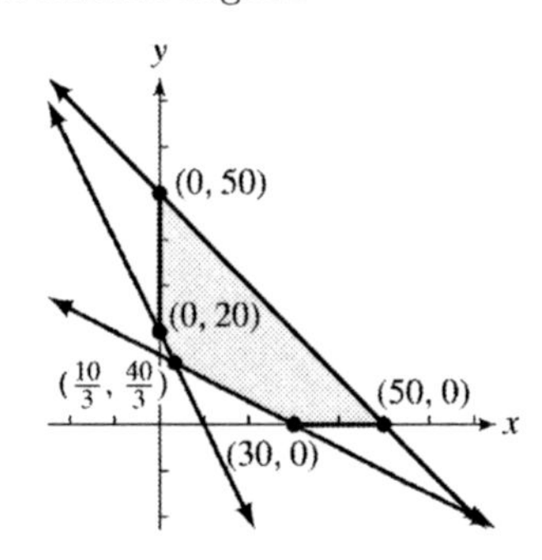

The corner points are $(0, 20)$, $(\frac{10}{3}, \frac{40}{3})$, $(30, 0)$, $(50, 0)$, and $(0, 50)$. The corner point $(\frac{10}{3}, \frac{40}{3})$ can be found by solving the system

$$\begin{aligned} 2x + \quad y &= 20 \\ x + 2y &= 30. \end{aligned}$$

Corner Point	Value of $z = 4x + 2y$
$(0, 20)$	40 Minimum
$(\frac{10}{3}, \frac{40}{3})$	40 Minimum
$(30, 0)$	120
$(50, 0)$	200
$(0, 50)$	100

Thus, the minimum value is 40 and occurs at every point on the line segment joining $(0, 20)$ and $(\frac{10}{3}, \frac{40}{3})$.

20. Maximize $z = 8x + 4y$

subject to:
$$\begin{aligned} 3x + 12y &\leq 36 \\ x + y &\leq 4 \\ x &\geq 0 \\ y &\geq 0. \end{aligned}$$

Graph the feasible region, and identify the corner points.

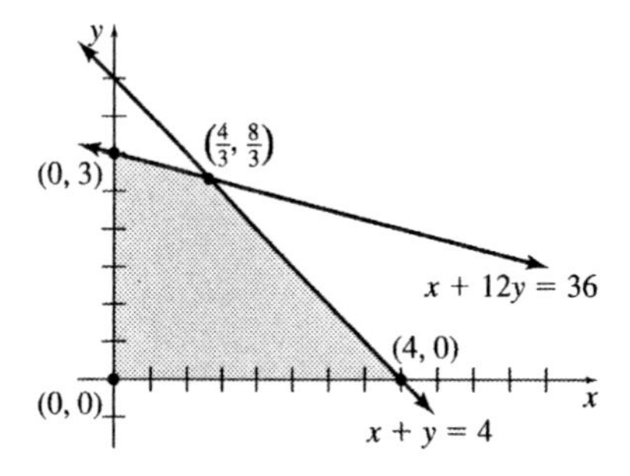

The corner points are: $(0, 0)$; $(0, 3)$; $(\frac{4}{3}, \frac{8}{3})$, the intersection of $3x + 12y = 36$ and $x + y = 4$; and $(4, 0)$. Use the corner points to find the maximum value of the objective function.

Corner Point	Value of $z = 8x + 4y$
$(0, 0)$	$8(0) + 4(0) = 0$
$(0, 3)$	$8(0) + 4(3) = 12$
$(\frac{4}{3}, \frac{8}{3})$	$8(\frac{4}{3}) + 4(\frac{8}{3}) = \frac{64}{3} \approx 21$
$(4, 0)$	$8(4) + 4(0) = 32$ Maximum

The maximum value is 32 at $(4, 0)$.

23. Maximize $z = 2x + 5y$

subject to:
$$3x + 2y \le 6$$
$$-x + 2y \le 4$$
$$x \ge 0$$
$$y \ge 0.$$

(a) Sketch the feasible region. All corner points except one can be read from the graph. Solving the system

$$3x + 2y = 6$$
$$-x + 2y = 4$$

gives the final corner point, $\left(\frac{1}{2}, \frac{9}{4}\right)$.

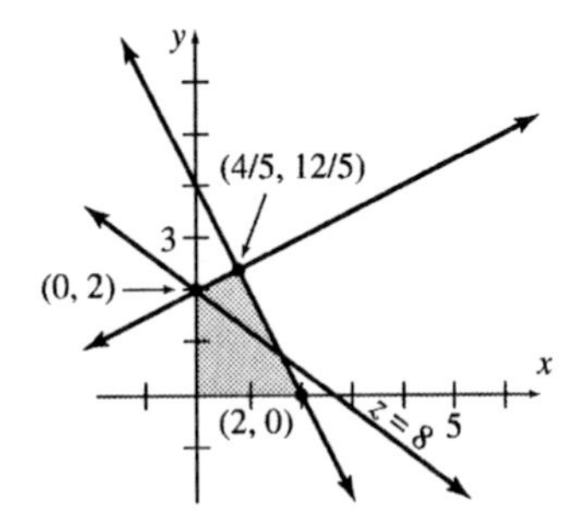

(b)

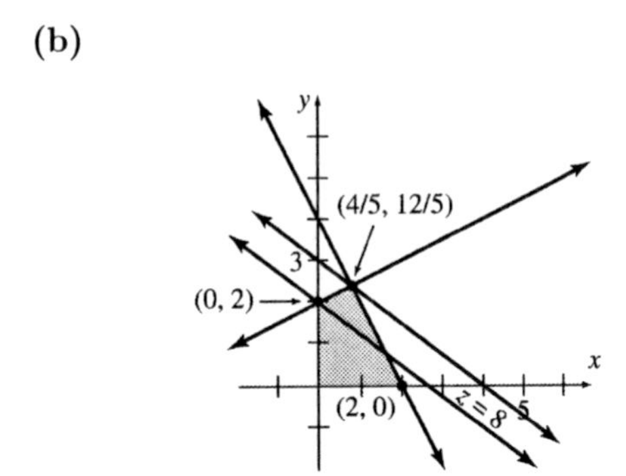

24. Maximize $z = 8x + 4y$

subject to:
$$3x + 12y \le 36$$
$$x + y \le 4$$
$$x \ge 0$$
$$y \ge 0.$$

Using the method of Exercise 23, $z = 32$ or $8x + 4y = 32$ is the line that is as far from the origin as possible but still touches the feasible region. It touches the feasible region at $(4, 0)$. Note that a value of z greater than 32, such as $z = 34$, will produce a line that does not intersect the feasible region, while a value of z less than 32, such as $z = 30$, will produce a line that intersects the feasible region in more than one point.

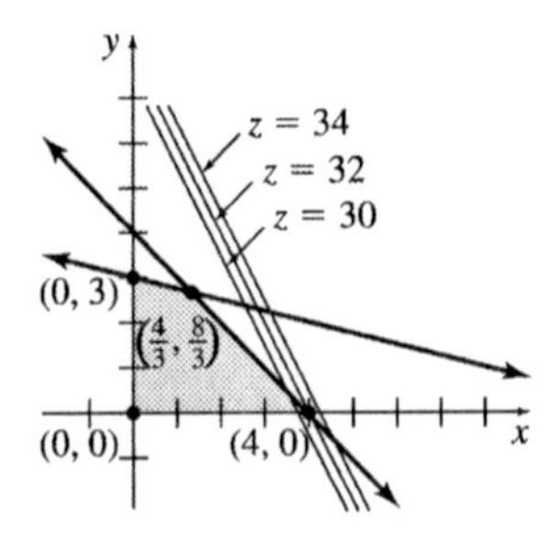

The maximum value of z is 32 when $x = 4$ and $y = 0$.

25. Let $x =$ the number of batches of cakes and $y =$ the number of batches of cookies.

Then we have the following inequalities.

$$2x + \frac{3}{2}y \le 15 \quad \text{(oven time)}$$
$$3x + \frac{2}{3}y \le 13 \quad \text{(decorating)}$$
$$x \ge 0$$
$$y \ge 0$$

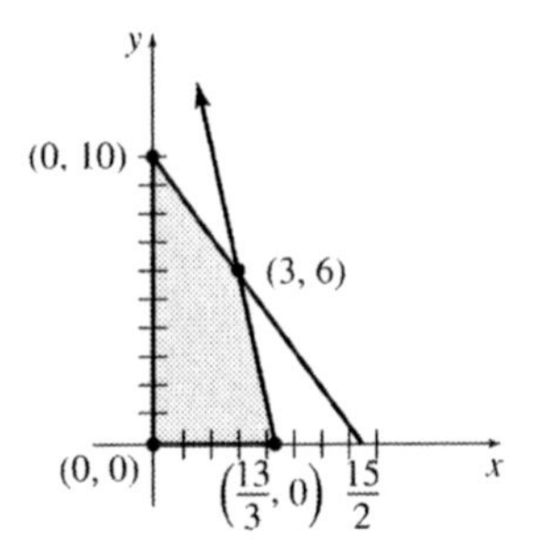

26. Let $x =$ the number of Mighty Meaty pizzas and $y =$ the number of Very Veggie pizzas.

The system of inequalities is

$$x \ge 4$$
$$y \ge 6$$
$$3x + 2y \le 60$$
$$2x + 4y \le 80.$$

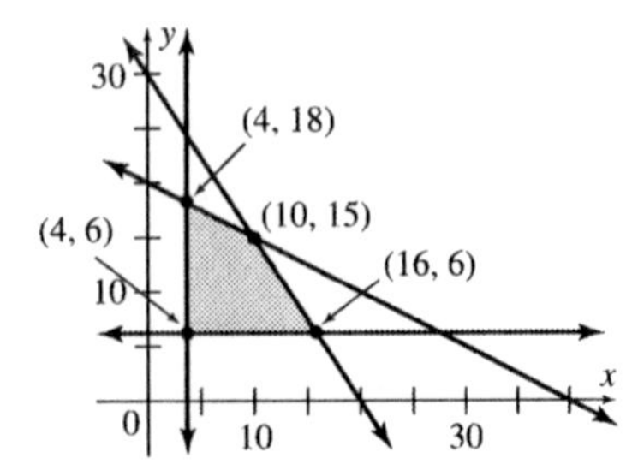

27. (a) From the graph for Exercise 25, the corner points are $(0, 10)$, $(3, 6)$, $\left(\frac{13}{3}, 0\right)$, and $(0, 0)$. Since x was the number of batches of cakes and y the number of batches of cookies, the revenue function is

$$z = 30x + 20y.$$

Evaluate this objective function at each corner point.

Corner Point	Value of $z = 30x + 20y$
$(0, 10)$	200
$(3, 6)$	210 Maximum
$\left(\frac{13}{3}, 0\right)$	130
$(0, 0)$	0

Therefore, 3 batches of cakes and 6 batches of cookies should be made to produce a maximum profit of \$210.

(b) Note that each \$1 increase in the price of cookies increases the profit by \$10 at $(0, 10)$ and by \$6 at $(3, 6)$. (The increase has no effect at the other corner points since, for those, $y = 0$.) Therefore, the corner point $(0, 10)$ will begin to maximize the profit when x, the number of one-dollar increases, is larger than the solution to the following equation.

$$\begin{aligned} 30(0) + (20 + 1x)(10) &= 30(3) + (20 + 1x)(6) \\ (20 + x)(4) &= 90 \\ 4x &= 10 \\ x &= 2.5 \end{aligned}$$

If the profit per batch of cookies increases by more than \$2.50 (to \$22.50), then it will be more profitable to make 10 batches of cookies and no batches of cake.

28. Maximize $z = 15x + 12y$.

Identify the corner points from the graph of the feasible region in Exercise 26.

Corner Point	Value of $z = 15x + 12y$
$(4, 6)$	$15(4) + 12(6) = 132$
$(4, 18))$	$15(4) + 12(18) = 276$
$(10, 15)$	$15(10) + 12(15) = 330$ Maximum
$(16, 6)$	$15(16) + 12(6) = 312$

DeMarco's pizza shop should make 10 Mighty Meaty pizzas and 15 Very Veggie pizzas for a maximum revenue of \$330.

29. Let $x =$ number of packages of gardening mixture
and $y =$ number of packages of potting mixture.

Maximize $z = 3x + 5y$

subject to:
$$\begin{aligned} 2x + y &\le 16 \\ x + 2y &\le 11 \\ x + 3y &\le 15 \\ x &\ge 0 \\ y &\ge 0. \end{aligned}$$

Sketch the feasible region in quadrant I.

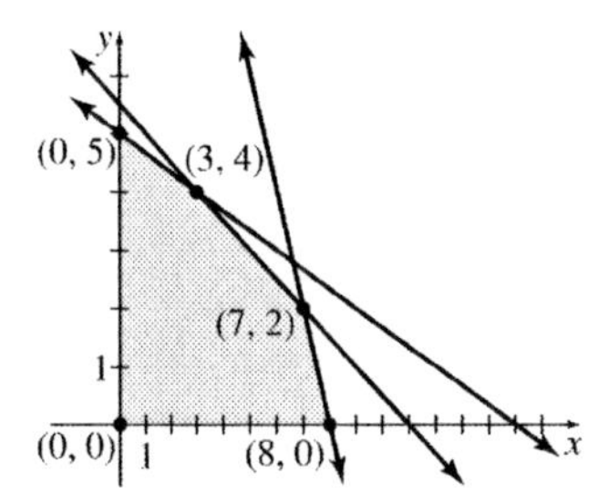

The corner points $(0, 0)$, $(0, 5)$, and $(8, 0)$ can be identified from the graph. The corner point $(3, 4)$ can be found by solving the system

$$\begin{aligned} x + 2y &= 11 \\ x + 3y &= 15. \end{aligned}$$

The corner point $(7, 2)$ can be found by solving the system

$$\begin{aligned} 2x + y &= 16 \\ x + 2y &= 11. \end{aligned}$$

Corner Point	Value of $z = 3x + 5y$
$(0, 0)$	0
$(0, 5)$	25
$(3, 4)$	29
$(7, 2)$	31 Maximum
$(8, 0)$	24

A maximum income of \$31 can be achieved by preparing 7 packages of gardening mixture and 2 packages of potting mixture.

30. Let $x =$ the number of Atlantic boathouses and $y =$ the number of Pacific boathouses.

Minimize $z = 30{,}000x + 40{,}000y$
subject to: $1000x + 2000y \geq 8000$
$3000x + 3000y \geq 18{,}000$
$2000x + 3000y \geq 15{,}000$
$x \geq 0$
$y \geq 0.$

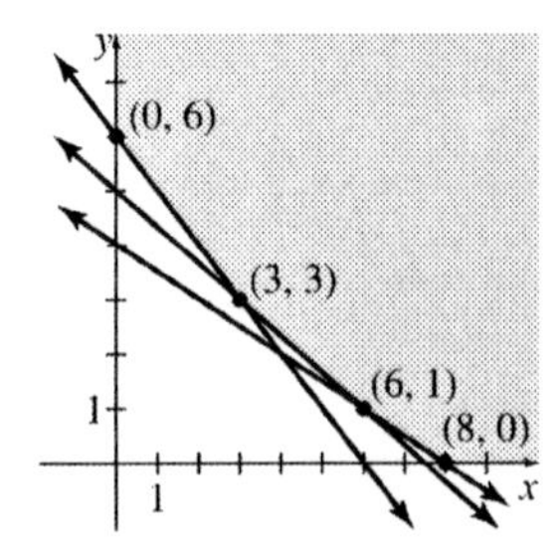

The corner points $(0, 6)$ and $(8, 0)$ can be identified from the graphs. The coordinates of the corner point $(3, 3)$ can be found by solving the system

$$3000x + 3000y = 18{,}000$$
$$2000x + 3000y = 15{,}000.$$

The coordinates of the point $(6, 1)$ can be found by solving the system

$$1000x + 2000y = 8000$$
$$2000x + 3000y = 15{,}000.$$

Corner Point	Value of $z = 30{,}000x + 40{,}000y$
$(0, 6)$	240,000
$(3, 3)$	210,000 Minimum
$(6, 1)$	220,000
$(8, 0)$	240,000

A minimum cost of \$210,000 is incurred by building 3 of each model.

31. Let $x =$ number of runs of type I and $y =$ number of runs of type II.

Minimize $z = 15{,}000x + 6000y$
subject to: $3000x + 3000y \geq 18{,}000$
$2000x + 1000y \geq 7000$
$2000x + 3000y \geq 14{,}000$
$x \geq 0$
$y \geq 0.$

Sketch the feasible region in quadrant I.

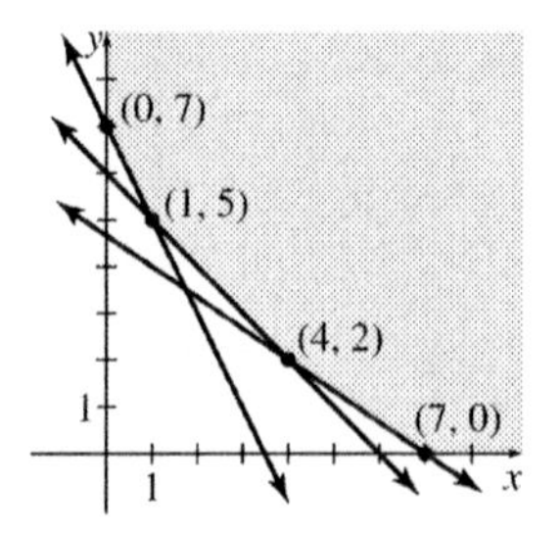

The corner points $(0, 7)$ and $(7, 0)$ can be identified from the graph. The corner point $(1, 5)$ can be found by solving the system

$$3000x + 3000y = 18{,}000$$
$$2000x + 1000y = 7000.$$

The corner point $(4, 2)$ can be found by solving the system

$$3000x + 3000y = 18{,}000$$
$$2000x + 3000y = 14{,}000.$$

Corner Point	Value of $z = 15{,}000x + 6000y$
$(0, 7)$	42,000 Minimum
$(1, 5)$	45,000
$(4, 2)$	72,000
$(7, 0)$	105,000

The company should produce 0 runs of type I and 7 runs of type II for a minimum cost of \$42,000.

32. Let $x =$ ounces of Health Trough and $y =$ ounces of Power Gunk.

Minimize $z = 8x + 4y$
subject to: $30x + 10y \geq 360$
$10x + 10y \geq 160$
$10x + 30y \geq 240$
$x \geq 0$
$y \geq 0.$

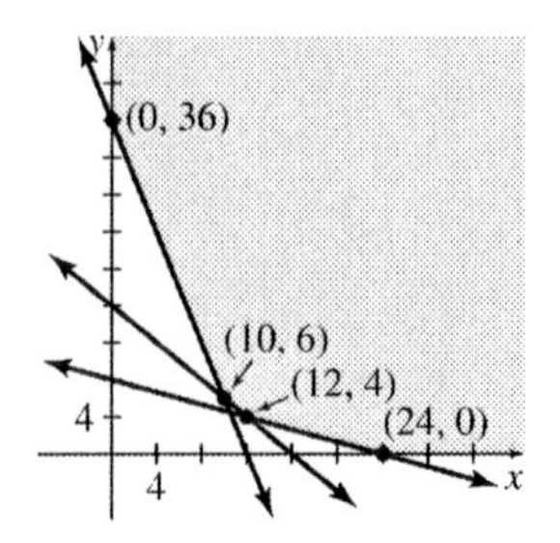

The corner points $(0, 36)$ and $(24, 0)$ can be identified from the graph. The coordinates of the corner point $(10, 6)$ can be found by solving the following system.

$$30x + 10y = 360$$
$$10x + 10y = 160.$$

The coordinates of the corner point $(12, 4)$ can be found by solving the system

$$10x + 10y = 160$$
$$10x + 30y = 240.$$

Corner Point	Value of $z = 8x + 4y$
$(0, 36)$	144
$(10, 6)$	104 Minimum
$(12, 4)$	112
$(24, 0)$	192

Ten ounces of Health Trough and six ounces of Power Gunk should be used for a minimum cholesterol intake of 104 mg.

33. Let $x =$ the number of acres devoted to millet
and $y =$ the number of acres devoted to wheat.

Maximize $z = 400x + 800y$
subject to: $36x + 8y \leq 48$
$x + y \leq 2$
$x \geq 0$
$y \geq 0.$

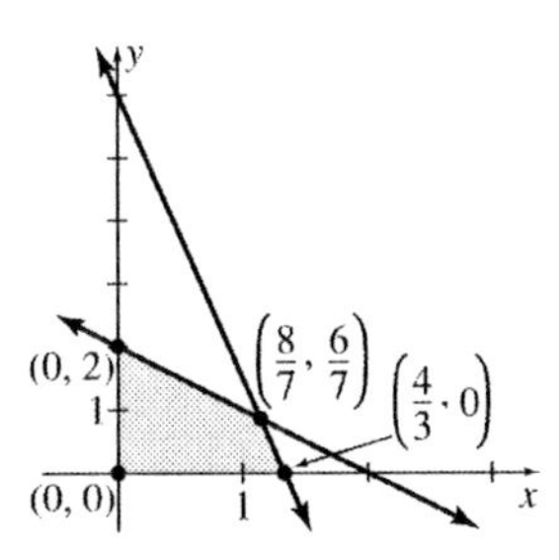

The corner points $(0, 0)$ and $(0, 2)$ can be identified from the graph. The corner point $(\frac{4}{3}, 0)$ can be found by solving the system

$$36x + 8y = 48$$
$$y = 0.$$

The corner point $(\frac{8}{7}, \frac{6}{7})$ can be found by solving the system

$$36x + 8y = 48$$
$$x + y = 2.$$

Corner Point	Value of $z = 400x + 800y$
$(0, 0)$	0
$(0, 2)$	1600 Maximum
$(\frac{8}{7}, \frac{6}{7})$	$\frac{8000}{7}$
$(\frac{4}{3}, 0)$	$\frac{1600}{3}$

The maximum amount of grain is 1600 pounds and can be obtained by planting 2 acres of wheat and no millet.

34. Let $x =$ the number of hours Ron should spend with his math tutor
and $y =$ the number of hours he should spend with his accounting tutor.

The number of points he expects to gain on the two tests combined is $z = 3x + 5y$. The given information translates into the following problem.

Maximize $z = 3x + 5y$

subject to: $20x + 40y \leq 220$ (finances)
$x + \frac{1}{2}y \leq 8$ (aspirin)
$x + 3y \leq 15$ (sleep)

$x \geq 0$
$y \geq 0.$

Sketch the feasible region.

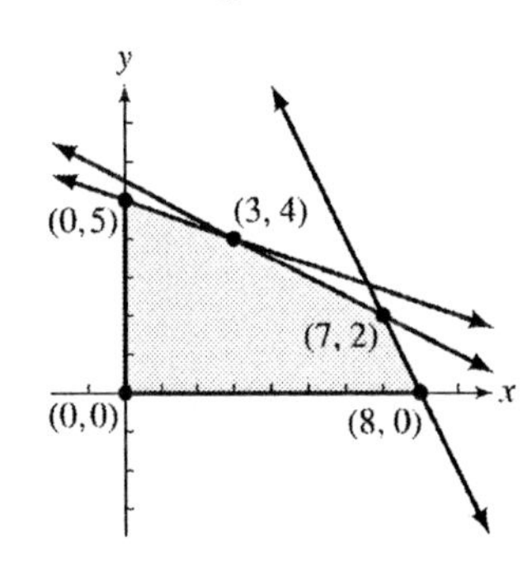

The corner points of the feasible region are $(0, 0)$, $(0, 5)$, $(3, 4)$, $(7, 2)$, and $(8, 0)$. Evaluate the objective function at each corner point.

Corner Point	Value of $z = 3x + 5y$
$(0, 0)$	0
$(0, 5)$	25
$(3, 4)$	29
$(7, 2)$	31 Maximum
$(8, 0)$	24

Therefore, Ron should spend 7 hours with the math tutor and 2 hours with the accounting tutor in order to gain a maximum of 31 points.

Chapter 4

LINEAR PROGRAMMING: THE SIMPLEX METHOD

4.1 Slack Variables and the Pivot

1. $x_1 + 2x_2 \leq 6$

Add s_1 to the given inequality to obtain

$$x_1 + 2x_2 + s_1 = 6.$$

2. $6x_1 + 2x_2 \leq 50$

Add s_1 to the given inequality to obtain

$$6x_1 + 2x_2 + s_1 = 50.$$

3. $2.3x_1 + 5.7x_2 + 1.8x_3 \leq 17$

Add s_1 to the given inequality to obtain

$$2.3x_1 + 5.7x_2 + 1.8x_3 + s_1 = 17.$$

4. $8x_1 + 6x_2 + 5x_3 \leq 250$

Add s_1 to the given inequality to obtain

$$8x_1 + 6x_2 + 5x_3 + s_1 = 250.$$

5. **(a)** Since there are three constraints to be converted into equations, we need three slack variables.

(b) We use s_1, s_2, and s_3 for the slack variables.

(c) The equations are

$$\begin{aligned} 2x_1 + 3x_2 + s_1 \qquad\qquad &= 15 \\ 4x_1 + 5x_2 \qquad + s_2 \qquad &= 35 \\ x_1 + 6x_2 \qquad\qquad + s_3 &= 20. \end{aligned}$$

6. Maximize $z = 1.2x_1 + 3.5x_2$

subject to: $2.4x_1 + 1.5x_2 \leq 10$

$1.7x_1 + 1.9x_2 \leq 15$

with $x_1 \geq 0, x_2 \geq 0.$

(a) We need one slack variable for each inequality. Thus, 2 are needed.

(b) We will use s_1 and s_2 for the slack variables.

(c) $2.4x_1 + 1.5x_2 \leq 10$ becomes

$$2.4x_1 + 1.5x_2 + s_1 = 10.$$

$1.7x_1 + 1.9x_2 \leq 15$ becomes

$$1.7x_1 + 1.9x_2 + s_2 = 15.$$

7. **(a)** There are two constraints to be converted into equations, so we must introduce two slack variables.

(b) Call the slack variables s_1 and s_2.

(c) The equations are

$$\begin{aligned} 7x_1 + 6x_2 + 8x_3 + s_1 \qquad &= 118 \\ 4x_1 + 5x_2 + 10x_3 \qquad + s_2 &= 220. \end{aligned}$$

8. Maximize $z = 12x_1 + 15x_2 + 10x_3$

subject to: $2x_1 + 2x_2 + x_3 \leq 8$

$x_1 + 4x_2 + 3x_3 \leq 12$

with $x_1 \geq 0, x_2 \geq 0, x_3 \geq 0.$

(a) There are two inequalities, so 2 slack variables are needed.

(b) Use s_1 and s_2 for the slack variables.

(c) $$\begin{aligned} 2x_1 + 2x_2 + x_3 + s_1 \qquad &= 8 \\ x_1 + 4x_2 + 3x_3 \qquad + s_2 &= 12 \end{aligned}$$

9.

$$\begin{array}{cccccc|c} x_1 & x_2 & x_3 & s_1 & s_2 & z & \\ 1 & 0 & 4 & 5 & 1 & 0 & 8 \\ 3 & 1 & 1 & 2 & 0 & 0 & 4 \\ \hline -2 & 0 & 2 & 3 & 0 & 1 & 28 \end{array}$$

The variables x_2 and s_2 are basic variables, because the columns for these variables have all zeros except for one nonzero entry. If the remaining variables x_1, x_3, and s_1 are zero, then $x_2 = 4$ and $s_2 = 8$. From the bottom row, $z = 28$. The basic feasible solution is $x_1 = 0, x_2 = 4, x_3 = 0, s_1 = 0, s_2 = 8$, and $z = 28$.

10.

$$\begin{array}{cccccc|c} x_1 & x_2 & x_3 & s_1 & s_2 & z & \\ 1 & 5 & 0 & 1 & 2 & 0 & 6 \\ 0 & 2 & 1 & 2 & 3 & 0 & 15 \\ \hline 0 & 4 & 0 & 1 & -2 & 1 & 64 \end{array}$$

x_1 and x_3 are the basic variables. The solution is $x_1 = 6, x_2 = 0, x_3 = 15, s_1 = 0, s_2 = 0$, and $z = 64$.

11.

$$\begin{array}{ccccccc|c} x_1 & x_2 & x_3 & s_1 & s_2 & s_3 & z & \\ 6 & 2 & 2 & 3 & 0 & 0 & 0 & 16 \\ 2 & 2 & 0 & 1 & 0 & 5 & 0 & 35 \\ 2 & 1 & 0 & 3 & 1 & 0 & 0 & 6 \\ \hline -3 & -2 & 0 & 2 & 0 & 0 & 3 & 36 \end{array}$$

The basic variables are x_3, s_2, and s_3. If x_1, x_2, and s_1 are zero, then $2x_3 = 16$, so $x_3 = 8$. Similarly, $s_2 = 6$ and $5s_3 = 35$, so $s_3 = 7$. From the bottom row, $3z = 36$, so $z = 12$. The basic feasible solution is $x_1 = 0, x_2 = 0, x_3 = 8, s_1 = 0, s_2 = 6, s_3 = 7$, and $z = 12$.

12.

$$\begin{array}{ccccccc|c} x_1 & x_2 & x_3 & s_1 & s_2 & s_3 & z & \\ 0 & 2 & 0 & 5 & 2 & 2 & 0 & 15 \\ 0 & 3 & 1 & 0 & 1 & 2 & 0 & 2 \\ 7 & 4 & 0 & 0 & 3 & 5 & 0 & 35 \\ \hline 0 & -4 & 0 & 0 & 4 & 3 & 2 & 40 \end{array}$$

x_1, x_3, and s_1 are the basic variables. The solution is $x_1 = 5, x_2 = 0, x_3 = 2, s_1 = 3, s_2 = 0, s_3 = 0$, and $z = 20$.

13.

$$\begin{array}{cccccc|c} x_1 & x_2 & x_3 & s_1 & s_2 & z & \\ 1 & 2 & 4 & 1 & 0 & 0 & 56 \\ 2 & \boxed{2} & 1 & 0 & 1 & 0 & 40 \\ \hline -1 & -3 & -2 & 0 & 0 & 1 & 0 \end{array}$$

Clear the x_2 column.

$$\begin{array}{r} \\ -R_2+R_1 \rightarrow R_1 \\ \\ \\ \end{array} \begin{array}{cccccc|c} x_1 & x_2 & x_3 & s_1 & s_2 & z & \\ -1 & 0 & 3 & 1 & -1 & 0 & 16 \\ 2 & \boxed{2} & 1 & 0 & 1 & 0 & 40 \\ \hline -1 & -3 & -2 & 0 & 0 & 1 & 0 \end{array}$$

$$\begin{array}{r} \\ \\ \\ 3R_2+2R_3 \rightarrow R_3 \end{array} \begin{array}{cccccc|c} x_1 & x_2 & x_3 & s_1 & s_2 & z & \\ -1 & 0 & 3 & 1 & -1 & 0 & 16 \\ 2 & 2 & 1 & 0 & 1 & 0 & 40 \\ \hline 4 & 0 & -1 & 0 & 3 & 2 & 120 \end{array}$$

x_2 and s_1 are now basic. The solution is $x_1 = 0, x_2 = 20, x_3 = 0, s_1 = 16, s_2 = 0$, and $z = 60$.

14.

$$\begin{array}{cccccc|c} x_1 & x_2 & x_3 & s_1 & s_2 & z & \\ 2 & 3 & 4 & 1 & 0 & 0 & 18 \\ 6 & \boxed{3} & 2 & 0 & 1 & 0 & 15 \\ \hline -1 & -6 & -2 & 0 & 0 & 1 & 0 \end{array}$$

Clear the x_2 column.

$$\begin{array}{r} \\ -R_2+R_1 \rightarrow R_1 \\ \\ 2R_2+R_3 \rightarrow R_3 \end{array} \begin{array}{cccccc|c} x_1 & x_2 & x_3 & s_1 & s_2 & z & \\ -4 & 0 & 2 & 1 & -1 & 0 & 3 \\ 6 & \boxed{3} & 2 & 0 & 1 & 0 & 15 \\ \hline 11 & 0 & 2 & 0 & 2 & 1 & 30 \end{array}$$

x_2 and s_1 are now basic. Thus, the solution is $x_1 = 0, x_2 = 5, x_3 = 0, s_1 = 3, s_2 = 0$, and $z = 30$.

15.

$$\begin{array}{ccccccc|c} x_1 & x_2 & x_3 & s_1 & s_2 & s_3 & z & \\ 2 & 2 & \boxed{1} & 1 & 0 & 0 & 0 & 12 \\ 1 & 2 & 3 & 0 & 1 & 0 & 0 & 45 \\ 3 & 1 & 1 & 0 & 0 & 1 & 0 & 20 \\ \hline -2 & -1 & -3 & 0 & 0 & 0 & 1 & 0 \end{array}$$

Clear the x_3 column.

$$\begin{array}{r} \\ \\ -3R_1+R_2 \rightarrow R_2 \\ -R_1+R_3 \rightarrow R_3 \\ 3R_1+R_4 \rightarrow R_4 \end{array} \begin{array}{ccccccc|c} x_1 & x_2 & x_3 & s_1 & s_2 & s_3 & z & \\ 2 & 2 & 1 & 1 & 0 & 0 & 0 & 12 \\ -5 & -4 & 0 & -3 & 1 & 0 & 0 & 9 \\ 1 & -1 & 0 & -1 & 0 & 1 & 0 & 8 \\ \hline 4 & 5 & 0 & 3 & 0 & 0 & 1 & 36 \end{array}$$

x_3, s_2, and s_3 are now basic. The solution is $x_1 = 0, x_2 = 0, x_3 = 12, s_1 = 0, s_2 = 9, s_3 = 8$, and $z = 36$.

16.

$$\begin{array}{ccccccc|c} x_1 & x_2 & x_3 & s_1 & s_2 & s_3 & z & \\ 4 & 2 & 3 & 1 & 0 & 0 & 0 & 22 \\ 2 & 2 & \boxed{5} & 0 & 1 & 0 & 0 & 28 \\ 1 & 3 & 2 & 0 & 0 & 1 & 0 & 45 \\ \hline -3 & -2 & -4 & 0 & 0 & 0 & 1 & 0 \end{array}$$

Clear the x_3 column.

$$\begin{array}{r} \\ -3R_2+5R_1 \rightarrow R_1 \\ \\ -2R_2+5R_3 \rightarrow R_3 \\ 4R_2+5R_4 \rightarrow R_4 \end{array} \begin{array}{ccccccc|c} x_1 & x_2 & x_3 & s_1 & s_2 & s_3 & z & \\ 14 & 4 & 0 & 5 & -3 & 0 & 0 & 26 \\ 2 & 2 & \boxed{5} & 0 & 1 & 0 & 0 & 28 \\ 1 & 11 & 0 & 0 & -2 & 5 & 0 & 169 \\ \hline -7 & -2 & 0 & 0 & 4 & 0 & 5 & 112 \end{array}$$

x_3, s_1, and s_3 are now basic. Thus, the solution is $x_1 = 0, x_2 = 0, x_3 = \frac{28}{5}, s_1 = \frac{26}{5}, s_2 = 0, s_3 = \frac{169}{5}$, and $z = \frac{112}{5}$.

17.

$$\begin{array}{ccccccc} x_1 & x_2 & x_3 & s_1 & s_2 & s_3 & z \end{array}$$

$$\left[\begin{array}{ccccccc|c} 2 & \boxed{2} & 3 & 1 & 0 & 0 & 0 & 500 \\ 4 & 1 & 1 & 0 & 1 & 0 & 0 & 300 \\ 7 & 2 & 4 & 0 & 0 & 1 & 0 & 700 \\ \hline -3 & -4 & -2 & 0 & 0 & 0 & 1 & 0 \end{array}\right]$$

Clear the x_2 column.

$$\begin{array}{r} \\ -R_1 + 2R_2 \to R_2 \\ -R_1 + R_3 \to R_3 \\ 2R_1 + R_4 \to R_4 \end{array} \left[\begin{array}{ccccccc|c} 2 & \boxed{2} & 3 & 1 & 0 & 0 & 0 & 500 \\ 6 & 0 & -1 & -1 & 2 & 0 & 0 & 100 \\ 5 & 0 & 1 & -1 & 0 & 1 & 0 & 200 \\ \hline 1 & 0 & 4 & 2 & 0 & 0 & 1 & 1000 \end{array}\right]$$

(columns: x_1 x_2 x_3 s_1 s_2 s_3 z)

x_2, s_2, and s_3 are now basic. Thus, the solution is $x_1 = 0, x_2 = 250, x_3 = 0, s_1 = 0, s_2 = 50, s_3 = 200$, and $z = 1000$.

18.

$$\begin{array}{cccccccc} x_1 & x_2 & x_3 & x_4 & s_1 & s_2 & s_3 & z \end{array}$$

$$\left[\begin{array}{cccccccc|c} 1 & 2 & 3 & 1 & 1 & 0 & 0 & 0 & 115 \\ 2 & 1 & 8 & 5 & 0 & 1 & 0 & 0 & 200 \\ \boxed{1} & 0 & 1 & 0 & 0 & 0 & 1 & 0 & 50 \\ \hline -2 & -1 & -1 & -1 & 0 & 0 & 0 & 1 & 0 \end{array}\right]$$

Clear the x_1 column.

$$\begin{array}{r} -R_3 + R_1 \to R_1 \\ -2R_3 + R_2 \to R_2 \\ \\ 2R_3 + R_4 \to R_4 \end{array} \left[\begin{array}{cccccccc|c} 0 & 2 & 2 & 1 & 1 & 0 & -1 & 0 & 65 \\ 0 & 1 & 6 & 5 & 0 & 1 & -2 & 0 & 100 \\ 1 & 0 & 1 & 0 & 0 & 0 & 1 & 0 & 50 \\ \hline 0 & -1 & 1 & -1 & 0 & 0 & 2 & 1 & 100 \end{array}\right]$$

(columns: x_1 x_2 x_3 x_4 s_1 s_2 s_3 z)

x_1, s_1, and s_2 are now basic. Thus, the solution is $x_1 = 50, x_2 = 0, x_3 = 0, x_4 = 0, s_1 = 65, s_2 = 100, s_3 = 0$, and $z = 100$.

19. Find $x_1 \geq 0$ and $x_2 \geq 0$ such that

$$\begin{aligned} 4x_1 + 2x_2 &\leq 5 \\ x_1 + 2x_2 &\leq 4 \end{aligned}$$

and $z = 7x_1 + x_2$ is maximized.

We need two slack variables, s_1 and s_2. Then the problem can be restated as:

Find $x_1 \geq 0, x_2 \geq 0, s_1 \geq 0$, and $s_2 \geq 0$ such that

$$\begin{aligned} 4x_1 + 2x_2 + s_1 \qquad &= 5 \\ x_1 + 2x_2 \qquad + s_2 &= 4. \end{aligned}$$

and $z = 7x_1 + x_2$ is maximized.

Rewrite the objective function as

$$-7x_1 - x_2 + z = 0.$$

The initial simplex tableau is

$$\begin{array}{ccccc} x_1 & x_2 & s_1 & s_2 & z \end{array}$$

$$\left[\begin{array}{ccccc|c} 4 & 2 & 1 & 0 & 0 & 5 \\ 1 & 2 & 0 & 1 & 0 & 4 \\ \hline -7 & -1 & 0 & 0 & 1 & 0 \end{array}\right].$$

20. Find $x_1 \geq 0$ and $x_2 \geq 0$ such that

$$\begin{aligned} 2x_1 + 3x_2 &\leq 100 \\ 5x_1 + 4x_2 &\leq 200 \end{aligned}$$

and $z = x_1 + 3x_2$ is maximized. We need two slack variables. Add s_1 and s_2 to get the system

$$\begin{aligned} 2x_1 + 3x_2 + s_1 \qquad\qquad &= 100 \\ 5x_1 + 4x_2 \qquad + s_2 \qquad &= 200 \\ -x_1 - 3x_2 \qquad\qquad + z &= 0. \end{aligned}$$

The initial simplex tableau is

$$\begin{array}{ccccc} x_1 & x_2 & s_1 & s_2 & z \end{array}$$

$$\left[\begin{array}{ccccc|c} 2 & 3 & 1 & 0 & 0 & 100 \\ 5 & 4 & 0 & 1 & 0 & 200 \\ \hline -1 & -3 & 0 & 0 & 1 & 0 \end{array}\right].$$

21. Find $x_1 \geq 0$ and $x_2 \geq 0$ such that

$$\begin{aligned} x_1 + x_2 &\leq 10 \\ 5x_1 + 2x_2 &\leq 20 \\ x_1 + 2x_2 &\leq 36 \end{aligned}$$

and $z = x_1 + 3x_2$ is maximized.

Using slack variables s_1, s_2, and s_3, the problem can be restated as:

Find $x_1 \geq 0, x_2 \geq 0, s_1 \geq 0, s_2 \geq 0$, and $s_3 \geq 0$ such that

$$\begin{aligned} x_1 + x_2 + s_1 \qquad\qquad &= 10 \\ 5x_1 + 2x_2 \qquad + s_2 \qquad &= 20 \\ x_1 + 2x_2 \qquad\qquad + s_3 &= 36 \end{aligned}$$

and $z = x_1 + 3x_2$ is maximized.

Rewrite the objective function as

$$-x_1 - 3x_2 + z = 0.$$

The initial simplex tableau is

$$\begin{array}{cccccc} x_1 & x_2 & s_1 & s_2 & s_3 & z \end{array}$$

$$\left[\begin{array}{cccccc|c} 1 & 1 & 1 & 0 & 0 & 0 & 10 \\ 5 & 2 & 0 & 1 & 0 & 0 & 20 \\ 1 & 2 & 0 & 0 & 1 & 0 & 36 \\ \hline -1 & -3 & 0 & 0 & 0 & 1 & 0 \end{array}\right].$$

22. Find $x_1 \geq 0$ and $x_2 \geq 0$ such that

$$\begin{aligned} x_1 + x_2 &\leq 25 \\ 4x_1 + 3x_2 &\leq 48 \end{aligned}$$

and $z = 5x_1 + 3x_2$ is maximized.

We add s_1 and s_2 to get the system

$$\begin{aligned} x_1 + x_2 + s_1 \qquad\qquad &= 25 \\ 4x_1 + 3x_2 \qquad + s_2 \qquad &= 48 \\ -5x_1 - 3x_2 \qquad\qquad + z &= 0. \end{aligned}$$

The initial simplex tableau is

$$\begin{array}{c} \begin{matrix} x_1 & x_2 & s_1 & s_2 & z & \end{matrix} \\ \left[\begin{array}{rrrrr|r} 1 & 1 & 1 & 0 & 0 & 25 \\ 4 & 3 & 0 & 1 & 0 & 48 \\ \hline -5 & -3 & 0 & 0 & 1 & 0 \end{array}\right]. \end{array}$$

23. Find $x_1 \geq 0$ and $x_2 \geq 0$ such that

$$\begin{aligned} 3x_1 + x_2 &\leq 12 \\ x_1 + x_2 &\leq 15 \end{aligned}$$

and $z = 2x_1 + x_2$ is maximized.

Using slack variables s_1 and s_2, the problem can be restated as:

Find $x_1 \geq 0, x_2 \geq 0, s_1 \geq 0$, and $s_2 \geq 0$ such that

$$\begin{aligned} 3x_1 + x_2 + s_1 \qquad &= 12 \\ x_1 + x_2 \qquad + s_2 &= 15 \end{aligned}$$

and $z = 2x_1 + x_2$ is maximized.

Rewrite the objective function as

$$-2x_1 - x_2 + z = 0.$$

The initial simplex tableau is

$$\begin{array}{c} \begin{matrix} x_1 & x_2 & s_1 & s_2 & z & \end{matrix} \\ \left[\begin{array}{rrrrr|r} 3 & 1 & 1 & 0 & 0 & 12 \\ 1 & 1 & 0 & 1 & 0 & 15 \\ \hline -2 & -1 & 0 & 0 & 1 & 0 \end{array}\right]. \end{array}$$

24. Find $x_1 \geq 0$ and $x_2 \geq 0$ such that

$$\begin{aligned} 10x_1 + 4x_2 &\leq 100 \\ 20x_1 + 10x_2 &\leq 150 \end{aligned}$$

and $z = 4x_1 + 5x_2$ is maximized.
Add s_1 and s_2 to get

$$\begin{aligned} 10x_1 + 4x_2 + s_1 \qquad\qquad &= 100 \\ 20x_1 + 10x_2 \qquad + s_2 \qquad &= 150 \\ -4x_1 - 5x_2 \qquad\qquad + z &= 0. \end{aligned}$$

The initial simplex tableau is

$$\begin{array}{c} \begin{matrix} x_1 & x_2 & s_1 & s_2 & z & \end{matrix} \\ \left[\begin{array}{rrrrr|r} 10 & 4 & 1 & 0 & 0 & 100 \\ 20 & 10 & 0 & 1 & 0 & 150 \\ \hline -4 & -5 & 0 & 0 & 1 & 0 \end{array}\right]. \end{array}$$

25. Let x_1 represent the number of simple figures, x_2 the number of figures with additions, and x_3 the number of computer-drawn sketches. Organize the information in a table.

	Simple Figures	Figures with Additions	Computer-Drawn Sketches	Maximum Allowed
Cost	20	35	60	2200
Royalties	95	200	325	

The cost constraint is

$$20x_1 + 35x_2 + 60x_3 \leq 2200.$$

The limit of 400 figures leads to the constraint

$$x_1 + x_2 + x_3 \leq 400.$$

The other stated constraints are

$$x_3 \leq x_1 + x_2 \text{ and } x_1 \geq 2x_2,$$

and these can be rewritten in standard form as

$$-x_1 - x_2 + x_3 \leq 0 \text{ and } -x_1 + 2x_2 \leq 0$$

respectively. The problem may be stated as:

Find $x_1 \geq 0, x_2 \geq 0$, and $x_3 \geq 0$ such that

$$\begin{aligned} 20x_1 + 35x_2 + 60x_3 &\leq 2200 \\ x_1 + x_2 + x_3 &\leq 400 \\ -x_1 - x_2 + x_3 &\leq 0 \\ -x_1 + 2x_2 \qquad &\leq 0 \end{aligned}$$

and $z = 95x_1 + 200x_2 + 325x_3$ is maximized.

Introduce slack variables s_1, s_2, s_3, and s_4, and the problem can be restated as:

Find $x_1 \geq 0, x_2 \geq 0, x_3 \geq 0, s_1 \geq 0, s_2 \geq 0, s_3 \geq 0$, and $s_4 \geq 0$ such that

$$\begin{aligned} 20x_1 + 35x_2 + 60x_3 + s_1 &= 2200 \\ x_1 + x_2 + x_3 + s_2 &= 400 \\ -x_1 - x_2 + x_3 + s_3 &= 0 \\ -x_1 + 2x_2 + s_4 &= 0 \end{aligned}$$

and $z = 95x_1 + 200x_2 + 325x_3$ is maximized.

Rewrite the objective function as

$$-95x_1 - 200x_2 - 325x_3 + z = 0.$$

The initial simplex tableau is

$$\begin{array}{c} \begin{matrix} x_1 & x_2 & x_3 & s_1 & s_2 & s_3 & s_4 & z \end{matrix} \\ \left[\begin{array}{cccccccc|c} 20 & 35 & 60 & 1 & 0 & 0 & 0 & 0 & 2200 \\ 1 & 1 & 1 & 0 & 1 & 0 & 0 & 0 & 400 \\ -1 & -1 & 1 & 0 & 0 & 1 & 0 & 0 & 0 \\ -1 & 2 & 0 & 0 & 0 & 0 & 1 & 0 & 0 \\ \hline -95 & -200 & -325 & 0 & 0 & 0 & 0 & 1 & 0 \end{array}\right] \end{array}.$$

26. Let x_1 represent the number of racing bicycles, x_2 the number of touring bicycles, and x_3 the number of mountain bicycles. Organize the information in a table.

	Racing	Touring	Mountain	Amount Available
Steel	17	27	34	91,800
Aluminum	12	21	15	42,000
Profit	\$8	\$12	\$22	

Using this information, the problem may be stated as:

Find $x_1 \geq 0, x_2 \geq 0$, and $x_3 \geq 0$ such that

$$\begin{aligned} 17x_1 + 27x_2 + 34x_3 &\leq 91{,}800 \\ 12x_1 + 21x_2 + 15x_3 &\leq 42{,}000 \end{aligned}$$

and $z = 8x_1 + 12x_2 + 22x_3$ is maximized.

Introduce slack variables s_1 and s_2, and the problem can be restated as:

Find $x_1 \geq 0, x_2 \geq 0, x_3 \geq 0, s_1 \geq 0$, and $s_2 \geq 0$ such that

$$\begin{aligned} 17x_1 + 27x_2 + 34x_3 + s_1 &= 91{,}800 \\ 12x_1 + 21x_2 + 15x_3 + s_2 &= 42{,}000 \end{aligned}$$

and $z = 8x_1 + 12x_2 + 22x_3$ is maximized.

Rewrite the objective function as

$$-8x_1 - 12x_2 - 22x_3 + z = 0.$$

The initial simplex tableau is

$$\begin{array}{c} \begin{matrix} x_1 & x_2 & x_3 & s_1 & s_2 & z \end{matrix} \\ \left[\begin{array}{cccccc|c} 17 & 27 & 34 & 1 & 0 & 0 & 91{,}800 \\ 12 & 21 & 15 & 0 & 1 & 0 & 42{,}000 \\ \hline -8 & -12 & -22 & 0 & 0 & 1 & 0 \end{array}\right] \end{array}.$$

27. Let x_1 represent the number of redwood tables, x_2 the number of stained Douglas fir tables, and x_3 the number of stained white spruce tables. Organize the information in a table.

	Redwood	Douglas Fir	White Spruce	Maximum Available
Assembly Time	8	7	8	90 8-hr days = 720 hr
Staining Time	0	2	2	60 8-hr days = 480 hr
Cost	\$159	\$138.85	\$129.35	\$15,000

The limit of 720 hr for carpenters leads to the constraint

$$8x_1 + 7x_2 + 8x_3 \leq 720.$$

The limit of 480 hr for staining leads to the constraint

$$2x_2 + 2x_3 \leq 480.$$

The cost constraint is

$$159x_1 + 138.85x_2 + 129.35x_3 \leq 15{,}000.$$

The problem may be stated as:

Find $x_1 \geq 0, x_2 \geq 0$, and $x_3 \geq 0$ such that

$$\begin{aligned} 8x_1 + 7x_2 + 8x_3 &\leq 720 \\ 2x_2 + 2x_3 &\leq 480 \\ 159x_1 + 138.85x_2 + 129.35x_3 &\leq 15{,}000 \end{aligned}$$

and $z = x_1 + x_2 + x_3$ is maximized.

Introduce slack variables s_1, s_2, and s_3, and the problem can be restated as:

Find $x_1 \geq 0, x_2 \geq 0, x_3 \geq 0, s_1 \geq 0, s_2 \geq 0$, and $s_3 \geq 0$ such that

$$\begin{aligned} 8x_1 + 7x_2 + 8x_3 + s_1 &= 720 \\ 2x_2 + 2x_3 + s_2 &= 480 \\ 159x_1 + 138.85x_2 + 129.35x_3 + s_3 &= 15{,}000 \end{aligned}$$

and $z = x_1 + x_2 + x_3$ is maximized.

Rewrite the objective function as

$$-x_1 - x_2 - x_3 + z = 0.$$

The initial simplex tableau is

$$\begin{array}{c} \begin{matrix} x_1 & x_2 & x_3 & s_1 & s_2 & s_3 & z \end{matrix} \\ \left[\begin{array}{ccccccc|c} 8 & 7 & 8 & 1 & 0 & 0 & 0 & 720 \\ 0 & 2 & 2 & 0 & 1 & 0 & 0 & 480 \\ 159 & 138.85 & 129.35 & 0 & 0 & 1 & 0 & 15{,}000 \\ \hline -1 & -1 & -1 & 0 & 0 & 0 & 1 & 0 \end{array}\right]. \end{array}$$

28. Let x_1 represent the number of Basic sets, x_2 the number of Regular sets, and x_3 the number of Deluxe sets. Organize the information in a table.

	Basic Set	Regular Set	Deluxe Set	Number Available
Utility Knife	2	2	3	800
Chef's Knife	1	1	1	400
Slicer	0	1	1	200
Profit	\$30	\$40	\$60	

Using this information, the problem may be stated as:

Find $x_1 \geq 0, x_2 \geq 0$, and $x_3 \geq 0$ such that

$$\begin{aligned} 2x_1 + 2x_2 + 3x_3 &\leq 800 \\ x_1 + x_2 + x_3 &\leq 400 \\ x_2 + x_3 &\leq 200 \end{aligned}$$

and $z = 30x_1 + 40x_2 + 60x_3$ is maximized.

Introduce slack variables s_1, s_2, and s_3, and the problem can be restated as:

Find $x_1 \geq 0, x_2 \geq 0, x_3 \geq 0, s_1 \geq 0, s_2 \geq 0$, and $s_3 \geq 0$ such that

$$\begin{aligned} 2x_1 + 2x_2 + 3x_3 + s_1 &= 800 \\ x_1 + x_2 + x_3 + s_2 &= 400 \\ x_2 + x_3 + s_3 &= 200 \end{aligned}$$

and $z = 30x_1 + 40x_2 + 60x_3$ is maximized.

Rewrite the objective function as

$$-30x_1 - 40x_2 - 60x_3 + z = 0.$$

The initial simplex tableau is

$$\begin{array}{c} \begin{matrix} x_1 & x_2 & x_3 & s_1 & s_2 & s_3 & z \end{matrix} \\ \left[\begin{array}{ccccccc|c} 2 & 2 & 3 & 1 & 0 & 0 & 0 & 800 \\ 1 & 1 & 1 & 0 & 1 & 0 & 0 & 400 \\ 0 & 1 & 1 & 0 & 0 & 1 & 0 & 200 \\ \hline -30 & -40 & -60 & 0 & 0 & 0 & 1 & 0 \end{array}\right]. \end{array}$$

29. Let x_1 = the number of newspaper ads,
x_2 = the number of internet banners,
and x_3 = the number of TV ads.

Organize the information in a table.

	Newspaper Ads	Internet Banners	TV Ads
Cost per Ad	400	20	2000
Maximum Number	30	60	10
Women Seeing Ad	4000	3000	10,000

The cost constraint is

$$400x_1 + 20x_2 + 2000x_3 \leq 8000$$

The constraints on the numbers of ads is

$$\begin{aligned} x_1 &\leq 30 \\ x_2 &\leq 60 \\ x_3 &\leq 10. \end{aligned}$$

The problem may be stated as:
Find $x_1 \geq 0, x_2 \geq 0$, and $x_3 \geq 0$ such that

$$\begin{aligned} 400x_1 + 20x_2 + 2000x_3 &\leq 8000 \\ x_1 &\leq 30 \\ x_2 &\leq 60 \\ x_3 &\leq 10 \end{aligned}$$

and $z = 4000x_1 + 3000x_2 + 10{,}000x_3$ is maximized.

Introduce slack variables s_1, s_2, s_3 and s_4, and the problem can be restated as:

Find $x_1 \geq 0, x_2 \geq 0, x_3 \geq 0, s_1 \geq 0, s_2 \geq 0, s_3 \geq 0$, and $s_4 \geq 0$ such that

$$\begin{aligned} 400x_1 + 20x_2 + 2000x_3 + s_1 &= 8000 \\ x_1 + s_2 &= 30 \\ x_2 + s_3 &= 60 \\ x_3 + s_4 &= 10 \end{aligned}$$

and $z = 4000x_1 + 3000x_2 + 10{,}000x_3$ is maximized.

Rewrite the objective function as

$$-4000x_1 - 3000x_2 - 10{,}000x_3 + z = 0.$$

The initial simplex tableau is

x_1	x_2	x_3	s_1	s_2	s_3	s_4	z	
400	20	2000	1	0	0	0	0	8000
1	0	0	0	1	0	0	0	30
0	1	0	0	0	1	0	0	60
0	0	1	0	0	0	1	0	10
−4000	−3000	−10,000	0	0	0	0	1	0

4.2 Maximization Problems

1.

x_1	x_2	x_3	s_1	s_2	z	
1	4	4	1	0	0	16
2	1	5	0	1	0	20
−3	−1	−2	0	0	1	0

The most negative indicator is −3, in the first column. Find the quotients $\frac{16}{1} = 16$ and $\frac{20}{2} = 10$; since 10 is the smaller quotient, 2 in row 2, column 1 is the pivot.

	x_1	x_2	x_3	s_1	s_2	z	
$\frac{16}{1} = 16$	1	4	4	1	0	0	16
$\frac{20}{2} = 10$	$\boxed{2}$	1	5	0	1	0	20
	−3	−1	−2	0	0	1	0

Performing row transformations, we get the following tableau.

	x_1	x_2	x_3	s_1	s_2	z	
$-R_2 + 2R_1 \to R_1$	0	7	3	2	−1	0	12
	2	1	5	0	1	0	20
$3R_2 + 2R_3 \to R_3$	0	1	11	0	3	2	60

All of the numbers in the last row are nonnegative, so we are finished pivoting. Create a 1 in the columns corresponding to x_1, s_1 and z.

	x_1	x_2	x_3	s_1	s_2	z	
$\frac{1}{2}R_1 \to R_1$	0	$\frac{7}{2}$	$\frac{3}{2}$	1	$-\frac{1}{2}$	0	6
$\frac{1}{2}R_2 \to R_2$	1	$\frac{1}{2}$	$\frac{5}{2}$	0	$\frac{1}{2}$	0	10
$\frac{1}{2}R_3 \to R_3$	0	$\frac{1}{2}$	$\frac{11}{2}$	0	$\frac{3}{2}$	1	30

The maximum value is 30 and occurs when $x_1 = 10, x_2 = 0, x_3 = 0, s_1 = 6$, and $s_2 = 0$.

2.

x_1	x_2	x_3	s_1	s_2	z	
3	3	2	1	0	0	18
2	2	3	0	1	0	16
−4	−6	−2	0	0	1	0

The most negative indicator is −6, in the second column. Find the quotients $\frac{18}{3} = 6$ and $\frac{16}{2} = 8$; since 6 is the smaller quotient, 3 in row 1, column 2 is the pivot.

	x_1	x_2	x_3	s_1	s_2	z	
$\frac{18}{3} = 6$	3	$\boxed{3}$	2	1	0	0	18
$\frac{16}{2} = 8$	2	2	3	0	1	0	16
	−4	−6	−2	0	0	1	0

	x_1	x_2	x_3	s_1	s_2	z	
	3	3	2	1	0	0	18
$-2R_1 + 3R_2 \to R_2$	0	0	5	−2	3	0	12
$2R_1 + R_3 \to R_3$	2	0	2	2	0	1	36

All of the numbers in the last row are nonnegative, so we are finished pivoting. Create a 1 in the columns corresponding to x_2 and s_2.

	x_1	x_2	x_3	s_1	s_2	z	
$\frac{1}{3}R_1 \to R_1$	1	1	$\frac{2}{3}$	$\frac{1}{3}$	0	0	6
$\frac{1}{3}R_2 \to R_2$	0	0	$\frac{5}{3}$	$-\frac{2}{3}$	1	0	4
	2	0	2	2	0	1	36

The maximum value is 36 when $x_1 = 0, x_2 = 6, x_3 = 0, s_1 = 0$, and $s_2 = 4$.

3.

x_1	x_2	s_1	s_2	s_3	z	
1	3	1	0	0	0	12
2	1	0	1	0	0	10
1	1	0	0	1	0	4
−2	−1	0	0	0	1	0

The most negative indicator is −2, in the first column. Find the quotients $\frac{12}{1} = 12$, $\frac{10}{2} = 5$, and $\frac{4}{1} = 4$; since 4 is the smallest quotient, 1 in row 3, column 1 is the pivot.

x_1	x_2	s_1	s_2	s_3	z	
1	3	1	0	0	0	12
2	1	0	1	0	0	10
$\boxed{1}$	1	0	0	1	0	4
−2	−1	0	0	0	1	0

	x_1	x_2	s_1	s_2	s_3	z	
$-R_3 + R_1 \to R_1$	0	2	1	0	−1	0	8
$-2R_3 + R_2 \to R_2$	0	−1	0	1	−2	0	2
	1	1	0	0	1	0	4
$2R_3 + R_4 \to R_4$	0	1	0	0	2	1	8

This is a final tableau since all of the numbers in the last row are nonnegative. The maximum value is 8 when $x_1 = 4, x_2 = 0, s_1 = 8, s_2 = 2$, and $s_3 = 0$.

4.

$$\begin{array}{c} \\ \\ \\ \\ \\ \end{array}\begin{array}{ccccccc|c} x_1 & x_2 & x_3 & s_1 & s_2 & s_3 & z & \\ 2 & 1 & 2 & 1 & 0 & 0 & 0 & 25 \\ 4 & 3 & 2 & 0 & 1 & 0 & 0 & 40 \\ 3 & 1 & 6 & 0 & 0 & 1 & 0 & 60 \\ \hline -4 & -2 & -3 & 0 & 0 & 0 & 1 & 0 \end{array}$$

The most negative indicator is -4, in the first column. Find the quotients $\frac{25}{2} = 12.5$, $\frac{40}{4} = 10$, and $\frac{60}{3} = 20$; since 10 is the smallest quotient, 4 in row 2, column 1 is the pivot.

$$\begin{array}{ccccccc|c} x_1 & x_2 & x_3 & s_1 & s_2 & s_3 & z & \\ 2 & 1 & 2 & 1 & 0 & 0 & 0 & 25 \\ \boxed{4} & 3 & 2 & 0 & 1 & 0 & 0 & 40 \\ 3 & 1 & 6 & 0 & 0 & 1 & 0 & 60 \\ \hline -4 & -2 & -3 & 0 & 0 & 0 & 1 & 0 \end{array}$$

Performing row transformations, we get the following tableau.

$$\begin{array}{r} \\ -R_2+2R_1 \to R_1 \\ \\ -3R_2+4R_3 \to R_3 \\ R_2+R_4 \to R_4 \end{array}\begin{array}{ccccccc|c} x_1 & x_2 & x_3 & s_1 & s_2 & s_3 & z & \\ 0 & -1 & 2 & 2 & -1 & 0 & 0 & 10 \\ 4 & 3 & 2 & 0 & 1 & 0 & 0 & 40 \\ 0 & -5 & 18 & 0 & -3 & 4 & 0 & 120 \\ \hline 0 & 1 & -1 & 0 & 1 & 0 & 1 & 40 \end{array}$$

Since there is still a negative indicator, we must repeat the process. Find the quotients $\frac{10}{2} = 5$, $\frac{40}{2} = 20$, and $\frac{120}{18} \approx 6.7$; since 5 is the smallest quotient, 2 in row 1, column 3 is the pivot.

$$\begin{array}{ccccccc|c} x_1 & x_2 & x_3 & s_1 & s_2 & s_3 & z & \\ 0 & -1 & \boxed{2} & 2 & -1 & 0 & 0 & 10 \\ 4 & 3 & 2 & 0 & 1 & 0 & 0 & 40 \\ 0 & -5 & 18 & 0 & -3 & 4 & 0 & 120 \\ \hline 0 & 1 & -1 & 0 & 1 & 0 & 1 & 40 \end{array}$$

Performing row transformations, we get the following tableau.

$$\begin{array}{r} \\ \\ -R_1+R_2 \to R_2 \\ -9R_1+R_3 \to R_3 \\ R_1+2R_4 \to R_4 \end{array}\begin{array}{ccccccc|c} x_1 & x_2 & x_3 & s_1 & s_2 & s_3 & z & \\ 0 & -1 & 2 & 2 & -1 & 0 & 0 & 10 \\ 4 & 4 & 0 & -2 & 2 & 0 & 0 & 30 \\ 0 & 4 & 0 & -18 & 6 & 4 & 0 & 30 \\ \hline 0 & 1 & 0 & 2 & 1 & 0 & 2 & 90 \end{array}$$

All of the numbers in the last row are nonnegative, so we are finished pivoting. Create a 1 in the columns corresponding to x_1, x_3, s_3, and z.

$$\begin{array}{r} \\ \frac{1}{2}R_1 \to R_1 \\ \frac{1}{4}R_2 \to R_2 \\ \frac{1}{4}R_3 \to R_3 \\ \frac{1}{2}R_4 \to R_4 \end{array}\begin{array}{ccccccc|c} x_1 & x_2 & x_3 & s_1 & s_2 & s_3 & z & \\ 0 & -\frac{1}{2} & 1 & 1 & -\frac{1}{2} & 0 & 0 & 5 \\ 1 & 1 & 0 & -\frac{1}{2} & \frac{1}{2} & 0 & 0 & \frac{15}{2} \\ 0 & 1 & 0 & -\frac{9}{2} & \frac{3}{2} & 1 & 0 & \frac{15}{2} \\ \hline 0 & \frac{1}{2} & 0 & 1 & \frac{1}{2} & 0 & 1 & 45 \end{array}$$

The maximum is 45 when $x_1 = \frac{15}{2}, x_2 = 0$, $x_3 = 5, s_1 = 0, s_2 = 0$, and $s_3 = \frac{15}{2}$.

5.

$$\begin{array}{ccccccc|c} x_1 & x_2 & x_3 & s_1 & s_2 & s_3 & z & \\ 2 & 2 & 8 & 1 & 0 & 0 & 0 & 40 \\ 4 & -5 & 6 & 0 & 1 & 0 & 0 & 60 \\ 2 & -2 & 6 & 0 & 0 & 1 & 0 & 24 \\ \hline -14 & -10 & -12 & 0 & 0 & 0 & 1 & 0 \end{array}$$

The most negative indicator is -14, in the first column. Find the quotients $\frac{40}{2} = 20$, $\frac{60}{4} = 15$, and $\frac{24}{2} = 12$; since 12 is the smallest quotient, 2 in row 3, column 1 is the pivot.

$$\begin{array}{ccccccc|c} x_1 & x_2 & x_3 & s_1 & s_2 & s_3 & z & \\ 2 & 2 & 8 & 1 & 0 & 0 & 0 & 40 \\ 4 & -5 & 6 & 0 & 1 & 0 & 0 & 60 \\ \boxed{2} & -2 & 6 & 0 & 0 & 1 & 0 & 24 \\ \hline -14 & -10 & -12 & 0 & 0 & 0 & 1 & 0 \end{array}$$

Performing row transformations, we get the following tableau.

$$\begin{array}{r} \\ -R_3+R_1 \to R_1 \\ -2R_3+R_2 \to R_2 \\ \\ 7R_3+R_4 \to R_4 \end{array}\begin{array}{ccccccc|c} x_1 & x_2 & x_3 & s_1 & s_2 & s_3 & z & \\ 0 & \boxed{4} & 2 & 1 & 0 & -1 & 0 & 16 \\ 0 & -1 & -6 & 0 & 1 & -2 & 0 & 12 \\ 2 & -2 & 6 & 0 & 0 & 1 & 0 & 24 \\ \hline 0 & -24 & 30 & 0 & 0 & 7 & 1 & 168 \end{array}$$

Since there is still a negative indicator, we must repeat the process. The second pivot is the 4 in column 2, since $\frac{16}{4}$ is the only nonnegative quotient in the only column with a negative indicator. Performing row transformations again, we get the following tableau.

$$\begin{array}{r} \\ \\ R_1+4R_2 \to R_2 \\ R_1+2R_3 \to R_3 \\ 6R_1+R_4 \to R_4 \end{array}\begin{array}{ccccccc|c} x_1 & x_2 & x_3 & s_1 & s_2 & s_3 & z & \\ 0 & 4 & 2 & 1 & 0 & -1 & 0 & 16 \\ 0 & 0 & -22 & 1 & 4 & -9 & 0 & 64 \\ 4 & 0 & 14 & 1 & 0 & 1 & 0 & 64 \\ \hline 0 & 0 & 42 & 6 & 0 & 1 & 1 & 264 \end{array}$$

All of the numbers in the last row are nonnegative, so we are finished pivoting. Create a 1 in the columns corresponding to x_1, x_2, and s_2.

$$\begin{array}{l} \\ \frac{1}{4}R_1 \to R_1 \\ \frac{1}{4}R_2 \to R_2 \\ \frac{1}{4}R_3 \to R_3 \\ \\ \end{array} \begin{array}{c} \begin{array}{ccccccc} x_1 & x_2 & x_3 & s_1 & s_2 & s_3 & z \end{array} \\ \left[\begin{array}{ccccccc|c} 0 & 1 & \frac{1}{2} & \frac{1}{4} & 0 & -\frac{1}{4} & 0 & 4 \\ 0 & 0 & -\frac{11}{2} & \frac{1}{4} & 1 & -\frac{9}{4} & 0 & 16 \\ 1 & 0 & \frac{7}{2} & \frac{1}{4} & 0 & \frac{1}{4} & 0 & 16 \\ \hline 0 & 0 & 42 & 6 & 0 & 1 & 1 & 264 \end{array}\right] \end{array}$$

The maximum value is 264 and occurs when $x_1 = 16, x_2 = 4, x_3 = 0, s_1 = 0, s_2 = 16$, and $s_3 = 0$.

6.

$$\begin{array}{c} \begin{array}{cccccc} x_1 & x_2 & x_3 & s_1 & s_2 & z \end{array} \\ \left[\begin{array}{cccccc|c} 3 & 2 & 4 & 1 & 0 & 0 & 18 \\ 2 & \boxed{1} & 5 & 0 & 1 & 0 & 8 \\ \hline -1 & -4 & -2 & 0 & 0 & 1 & 0 \end{array}\right] \end{array}$$

The most negative indicator is -4. Of the quotients $\frac{18}{2} = 9$ and $\frac{8}{1} = 8$, the smallest is 8, so pivot on the 1 in row 2, column 2.

$$\begin{array}{l} -2R_2 + R_1 \to R_1 \\ \\ 4R_2 + R_3 \to R_3 \end{array} \begin{array}{c} \begin{array}{cccccc} x_1 & x_2 & x_3 & s_1 & s_2 & z \end{array} \\ \left[\begin{array}{cccccc|c} -1 & 0 & -6 & 1 & -2 & 0 & 2 \\ 2 & 1 & 5 & 0 & 1 & 0 & 8 \\ \hline 7 & 0 & 18 & 0 & 4 & 1 & 32 \end{array}\right] \end{array}$$

This solution is optimal. The basic variables are x_2 and s_1. The maximum is 32 when $x_1 = 0, x_2 = 8, x_3 = 0, s_1 = 2$, and $s_2 = 0$.

7.

$$\begin{array}{ll} \text{Maximize} & z = 3x_1 + 5x_2 \\ \text{subject to:} & 4x_1 + x_2 \leq 25 \\ & 2x_1 + 3x_2 \leq 15 \\ \text{with} & x_1 \geq 0, x_2 \geq 0. \end{array}$$

Two slack variables, s_1 and s_2, need to be introduced. The problem can be restated as:

$$\begin{array}{ll} \text{Maximize} & z = 3x_1 + 5x_2 \\ \text{subject to:} & 4x_1 + x_2 + s_1 \qquad = 25 \\ & 2x_1 + 3x_2 \qquad + s_2 = 15 \\ \text{with} & x_1 \geq 0, x_2 \geq 0, s_1 \geq 0, s_2 \geq 0. \end{array}$$

Rewrite the objective function as

$$-3x_1 - 5x_2 + z = 0.$$

The initial simplex tableau follows.

$$\begin{array}{c} \begin{array}{ccccc} x_1 & x_2 & s_1 & s_2 & z \end{array} \\ \left[\begin{array}{ccccc|c} 4 & 1 & 1 & 0 & 0 & 25 \\ 2 & 3 & 0 & 1 & 0 & 15 \\ \hline -3 & -5 & 0 & 0 & 1 & 0 \end{array}\right] \end{array}$$

The most negative indicator is -5, in the second column. To select the pivot from column 2, find the quotients $\frac{25}{1} = 25$ and $\frac{15}{3} = 5$. The smaller quotient is 5, so 3 is the pivot.

$$\begin{array}{c} \begin{array}{ccccc} x_1 & x_2 & s_1 & s_2 & z \end{array} \\ \left[\begin{array}{ccccc|c} 4 & 1 & 1 & 0 & 0 & 25 \\ 2 & \boxed{3} & 0 & 1 & 0 & 15 \\ \hline -3 & -5 & 0 & 0 & 1 & 0 \end{array}\right] \end{array}$$

$$\begin{array}{l} -R_2 + 3R_1 \to R_1 \\ \\ 5R_2 + 3R_3 \to R_3 \end{array} \begin{array}{c} \begin{array}{ccccc} x_1 & x_2 & s_1 & s_2 & z \end{array} \\ \left[\begin{array}{ccccc|c} 10 & 0 & 3 & -1 & 0 & 60 \\ 2 & 3 & 0 & 1 & 0 & 15 \\ \hline 1 & 0 & 0 & 5 & 3 & 75 \end{array}\right] \end{array}$$

All of the indicators are nonnegative. Create a 1 in the columns corresponding to x_2, s_1, and z.

$$\begin{array}{l} \frac{1}{3}R_1 \to R_1 \\ \frac{1}{3}R_2 \to R_2 \\ \\ \frac{1}{3}R_3 \to R_3 \end{array} \begin{array}{c} \begin{array}{ccccc} x_1 & x_2 & s_1 & s_2 & z \end{array} \\ \left[\begin{array}{ccccc|c} \frac{10}{3} & 0 & 1 & -\frac{1}{3} & 0 & 20 \\ \frac{2}{3} & 1 & 0 & \frac{1}{3} & 0 & 5 \\ \hline \frac{1}{3} & 0 & 0 & \frac{5}{3} & 1 & 25 \end{array}\right] \end{array}$$

The maximum value is 25 when $x_1 = 0$, $x_2 = 5, s_1 = 20$, and $s_2 = 0$.

8.

$$\begin{array}{ll} \text{Maximize} & z = 5x_1 + 2x_2 \\ \text{subject to:} & 2x_1 + 4x_2 \leq 15 \\ & 3x_1 + x_2 \leq 10 \\ \text{with} & x_1 \geq 0, x_2 \geq 0. \end{array}$$

Two slack variables s_1 and s_2 need to be introduced. The problem can be restated as:

$$\begin{array}{ll} \text{Maximize} & z = 5x_1 + 2x_2 \\ \text{subject to:} & 2x_1 + 4x_2 + s_1 \qquad = 15 \\ & 3x_1 + x_2 \qquad + s_2 = 10 \\ \text{with} & x_1 \geq 0, x_2 \geq 0, s_1 \geq 0, s_2 \geq 0. \end{array}$$

Rewrite the objective function as

$$-5x_1 - 2x_2 + z = 0.$$

The initial simplex tableau as follows.

$$\begin{array}{c} \begin{array}{ccccc} x_1 & x_2 & s_1 & s_2 & z \end{array} \\ \left[\begin{array}{ccccc|c} 2 & 4 & 1 & 0 & 0 & 15 \\ 3 & 1 & 0 & 1 & 0 & 10 \\ \hline -5 & -2 & 0 & 0 & 1 & 0 \end{array}\right] \end{array}$$

The most negative indicator is -5 in the first column. To select the pivot from column 1, find the quotients $\frac{15}{2}$ and $\frac{10}{3}$, so 3 is the pivot.

$$\begin{array}{c} \\ \\ \\ \\ \end{array}\begin{array}{ccccc|c} x_1 & x_2 & s_1 & s_2 & z & \\ 2 & 4 & 1 & 0 & 0 & 15 \\ \boxed{3} & 1 & 0 & 1 & 0 & 10 \\ \hline -5 & -2 & 0 & 0 & 1 & 0 \end{array}$$

$$\begin{array}{r} \\ -2R_2 + 3R_1 \rightarrow R_1 \\ \\ 5R_2 + 3R_3 \rightarrow R_3 \end{array}\begin{array}{ccccc|c} x_1 & x_2 & s_1 & s_2 & z & \\ 0 & 10 & 3 & -2 & 0 & 25 \\ 3 & 1 & 0 & 1 & 0 & 10 \\ \hline 0 & -1 & 0 & 5 & 3 & 50 \end{array}$$

Since there is still a negative indicator, we must repeat the process. Find the quotients $\frac{25}{10}$ and $\frac{10}{1}$. Since the smaller quotient $\frac{25}{10}$, the 10 in row 1, column 2 is the pivot.

$$\begin{array}{ccccc|c} x_1 & x_2 & s_1 & s_2 & z & \\ 0 & \boxed{10} & 3 & -2 & 0 & 25 \\ 3 & 1 & 0 & 1 & 0 & 10 \\ \hline 0 & -1 & 0 & 5 & 3 & 50 \end{array}$$

$$\begin{array}{r} \\ \\ -R_1 + 10R_2 \rightarrow R_2 \\ R_1 + 10R_3 \rightarrow R_3 \end{array}\begin{array}{ccccc|c} x_1 & x_2 & s_1 & s_2 & z & \\ 0 & 10 & 3 & -2 & 0 & 25 \\ 30 & 0 & -3 & 12 & 0 & 75 \\ \hline 0 & 0 & 3 & 48 & 30 & 525 \end{array}$$

All of the indicators are nonnegative. Create a 1 in the columns corresponding to x_1, x_2, and z.

$$\begin{array}{r} \\ \frac{1}{10}R_1 \rightarrow R_1 \\ \frac{1}{30}R_2 \rightarrow R_2 \\ \frac{1}{30}R_3 \rightarrow R_3 \end{array}\begin{array}{ccccc|c} x_1 & x_2 & s_1 & s_2 & z & \\ 0 & 1 & \frac{3}{10} & -\frac{1}{5} & 0 & \frac{5}{2} \\ 1 & 0 & -\frac{1}{10} & \frac{2}{5} & 0 & \frac{5}{2} \\ \hline 0 & 0 & \frac{1}{10} & \frac{8}{5} & 1 & \frac{35}{2} \end{array}$$

The maximum value is 17.5 when $x_1 = 2.5, x_2 = 2.5, s_1 = 0$, and $s_2 = 0$.

9. Maximize $z = 10x_1 + 12x_2$

subject to:
$$4x_1 + 2x_2 \le 20$$
$$5x_1 + x_2 \le 50$$
$$2x_1 + 2x_2 \le 24$$

with $x_1 \ge 0, x_2 \ge 0$.

Three slack variables, s_1, s_2, and s_3, need to be introduced. The initial tableau is as follows.

$$\begin{array}{cccccc|c} x_1 & x_2 & s_1 & s_2 & s_3 & z & \\ 4 & 2 & 1 & 0 & 0 & 0 & 20 \\ 5 & 1 & 0 & 1 & 0 & 0 & 50 \\ 2 & 2 & 0 & 0 & 1 & 0 & 24 \\ \hline -10 & -12 & 0 & 0 & 0 & 1 & 0 \end{array}$$

The most negative indicator is -12, in column 2.

The quotients are $\frac{20}{2} = 10$, $\frac{50}{1} = 50$, and $\frac{24}{2} = 12$; the smallest is 10, so 2 in row 1, column 2 is the pivot.

$$\begin{array}{cccccc|c} x_1 & x_2 & s_1 & s_2 & s_3 & z & \\ 4 & \boxed{2} & 1 & 0 & 0 & 0 & 20 \\ 5 & 1 & 0 & 1 & 0 & 0 & 50 \\ 2 & 2 & 0 & 0 & 1 & 0 & 24 \\ \hline -10 & -12 & 0 & 0 & 0 & 1 & 0 \end{array}$$

$$\begin{array}{r} \\ \\ -R_1 + 2R_2 \rightarrow R_2 \\ -R_1 + R_3 \rightarrow R_3 \\ 6R_1 + R_4 \rightarrow R_4 \end{array}\begin{array}{cccccc|c} x_1 & x_2 & s_1 & s_2 & s_3 & z & \\ 4 & 2 & 1 & 0 & 0 & 0 & 20 \\ 6 & 0 & -1 & 2 & 0 & 0 & 80 \\ -2 & 0 & -1 & 0 & 1 & 0 & 4 \\ \hline 14 & 0 & 6 & 0 & 0 & 1 & 120 \end{array}$$

All of the indicators are nonnegative, so we are finished pivoting. Create a 1 in the columns corresponding to x_2 and s_2.

$$\begin{array}{r} \\ \frac{1}{2}R_1 \rightarrow R_1 \\ \frac{1}{2}R_2 \rightarrow R_2 \\ \\ \\ \end{array}\begin{array}{cccccc|c} x_1 & x_2 & s_1 & s_2 & s_3 & z & \\ 2 & 1 & \frac{1}{2} & 0 & 0 & 0 & 10 \\ 3 & 0 & -\frac{1}{2} & 1 & 0 & 0 & 40 \\ -2 & 0 & -1 & 0 & 1 & 0 & 4 \\ \hline 14 & 0 & 6 & 0 & 0 & 1 & 120 \end{array}$$

The maximum value is 120 when $x_1 = 0$, $x_2 = 10, s_1 = 0, s_2 = 40$, and $s_3 = 4$.

10. Maximize $z = 1.5x_1 + 4.2x_2$

subject to:
$$2.8x_1 + 3.4x_2 \le 21$$
$$1.4x_1 + 2.2x_2 \le 11$$

with $x_1 \ge 0, x_2 \ge 0$.

The initial tableau follows.

$$\begin{array}{ccccc|c} x_1 & x_2 & s_1 & s_2 & z & \\ 2.8 & 3.4 & 1 & 0 & 0 & 21 \\ 1.4 & \boxed{2.2} & 0 & 1 & 0 & 11 \\ \hline -1.5 & -4.2 & 0 & 0 & 1 & 0 \end{array}$$

Pivot on the 2.2 in row 2, column 2.

$$\begin{array}{r} \\ -1.7R_2 + 1.1R_1 \rightarrow R_1 \\ \\ 2.1R_2 + 1.1R_3 \rightarrow R_3 \end{array}\begin{array}{ccccc|c} x_1 & x_2 & s_1 & s_2 & z & \\ 0.7 & 0 & 1.1 & -1.7 & 0 & 4.4 \\ 1.4 & 2.2 & 0 & 1 & 0 & 11 \\ \hline 1.29 & 0 & 0 & 2.1 & 1.1 & 23.1 \end{array}$$

All of the indicators are nonnegative. Create a 1 in the columns corresponding to x_2, s_2, and z.

$$\begin{array}{r} \\ \frac{1}{1.1}R_1 \rightarrow R_1 \\ \frac{1}{2.2}R_2 \rightarrow R_2 \\ \frac{1}{1.1}R_3 \rightarrow R_3 \end{array}\begin{array}{ccccc|c} x_1 & x_2 & s_1 & s_2 & z & \\ \frac{7}{11} & 0 & 1 & -\frac{17}{11} & 0 & 4 \\ \frac{7}{11} & 1 & 0 & \frac{5}{11} & 0 & 5 \\ \hline \frac{129}{110} & 0 & 0 & \frac{21}{11} & 1 & 21 \end{array}$$

The maximum is 21 when $x_1 = 0, x_2 = 5, s_1 = 4$, and $s_2 = 0$.

11. Maximize $z = 8x_1 + 3x_2 + x_3$
subject to: $x_1 + 6x_2 + 8x_3 \leq 118$
$x_1 + 5x_2 + 10x_3 \leq 220$
with $x_1 \geq 0, x_2 \geq 0, x_3 \geq 0$.

Two slack variables, s_1 and s_2, need to be introduced. The initial simplex tableau is as follows.

x_1	x_2	x_3	s_1	s_2	z	
$\boxed{1}$	6	8	1	0	0	118
1	5	10	0	1	0	220
−8	−3	−1	0	0	1	0

The most negative indicator is −8, in the first column. The quotients are $\frac{118}{1} = 118$ and $\frac{220}{1} = 220$; since 118 is the smaller, 1 in row 1, column 1 is the pivot. Performing row transformations, we get the following tableau.

	x_1	x_2	x_3	s_1	s_2	z	
	1	6	8	1	0	0	118
$-R_1 + R_2 \rightarrow R_2$	0	−1	2	−1	1	0	102
$8R_1 + R_3 \rightarrow R_3$	0	45	63	8	0	1	944

All of the indicators are nonnegative, so we are finished pivoting. The maximum value is 944 when $x_1 = 118, x_2 = 0, x_3 = 0, s_1 = 0$, and $s_2 = 102$.

12. Maximize $z = 8x_1 + 10x_2 + 7x_3$
subject to: $x_1 + 3x_2 + 2x_3 \leq 10$
$x_1 + 5x_2 + x_3 \leq 8$
with $x_1 \geq 0, x_2 \geq 0, x_3 \geq 0$.

The initial tableau is as follows.

x_1	x_2	x_3	s_1	s_2	z	
1	3	2	1	0	0	10
1	$\boxed{5}$	1	0	1	0	8
−8	−10	−7	0	0	1	0

Pivot on the 5 in row 2, column 2.

	x_1	x_2	x_3	s_1	s_2	z	
$-3R_2 + 5R_1 \rightarrow R_1$	2	0	7	5	−3	0	26
	$\boxed{1}$	5	1	0	1	0	8
$2R_2 + R_3 \rightarrow R_3$	−6	0	−5	0	2	1	16

Pivot on the 1 in row 2, column 1.

	x_1	x_2	x_3	s_1	s_2	z	
$-2R_2 + R_1 \rightarrow R_1$	0	−10	5	5	−5	0	10
	1	5	1	0	1	0	8
$6R_2 + R_3 \rightarrow R_3$	0	30	1	0	8	1	64

Create a 1 in the column corresponding to s_1.

$$\begin{array}{l} \\ \\ \frac{1}{5}R_1 \to R_1 \\ \\ \end{array} \begin{array}{cccccc|c} x_1 & x_2 & x_3 & s_1 & s_2 & z & \\ \hline 0 & -2 & 1 & 1 & -1 & 0 & 2 \\ 1 & 5 & 1 & 0 & 1 & 0 & 8 \\ \hline 1 & 30 & 1 & 0 & 8 & 1 & 64 \end{array}$$

The maximum value is 64 when $x_1 = 8, x_2 = 0, x_3 = 0, s_1 = 2$, and $s_2 = 0$.

13. Maximize $z = 10x_1 + 15x_2 + 10x_3 + 5x_4$
subject to: $x_1 + x_2 + x_3 + x_4 \le 300$
$x_1 + 2x_2 + 3x_3 + x_4 \le 360$
with $x_1 \ge 0, x_2 \ge 0, x_3 \ge 0, x_4 \ge 0$.

The initial tableau is as follows.

$$\begin{array}{ccccccc|c} x_1 & x_2 & x_3 & x_4 & s_1 & s_2 & z & \\ 1 & 1 & 1 & 1 & 1 & 0 & 0 & 300 \\ 1 & \boxed{2} & 3 & 1 & 0 & 1 & 0 & 360 \\ \hline -10 & -15 & -10 & -5 & 0 & 0 & 1 & 0 \end{array}$$

In the column with the most negative indicator, -15, the quotients are $\frac{300}{1} = 300$ and $\frac{360}{2} = 180$. The smaller quotient is 180, so the 2 in row 2, column 2, is the pivot.

$$\begin{array}{l} \\ -R_2 + 2R_1 \to R_1 \\ \\ 15R_2 + 2R_3 \to R_3 \end{array} \begin{array}{ccccccc|c} x_1 & x_2 & x_3 & x_4 & s_1 & s_2 & z & \\ \boxed{1} & 0 & -1 & 1 & 2 & -1 & 0 & 240 \\ 1 & 2 & 3 & 1 & 0 & 1 & 0 & 360 \\ \hline -5 & 0 & 25 & 5 & 0 & 15 & 2 & 5400 \end{array}$$

Pivot on the 1 in row 1, column 1.

$$\begin{array}{l} \\ \\ -R_1 + R_2 \to R_2 \\ 5R_1 + R_3 \to R_3 \end{array} \begin{array}{ccccccc|c} x_1 & x_2 & x_3 & x_4 & s_1 & s_2 & z & \\ 1 & 0 & -1 & 1 & 2 & -1 & 0 & 240 \\ 0 & 2 & 4 & 0 & -2 & 2 & 0 & 120 \\ \hline 0 & 0 & 20 & 10 & 10 & 10 & 2 & 6600 \end{array}$$

Create a 1 in the columns corresponding to x_2 and z.

$$\begin{array}{l} \\ \\ \frac{1}{2}R_2 \to R_2 \\ \frac{1}{2}R_3 \to R_3 \end{array} \begin{array}{ccccccc|c} x_1 & x_2 & x_3 & x_4 & s_1 & s_2 & z & \\ 1 & 0 & -1 & 1 & 2 & -1 & 0 & 240 \\ 0 & 1 & 2 & 0 & -1 & 1 & 0 & 60 \\ \hline 0 & 0 & 10 & 5 & 5 & 5 & 1 & 3300 \end{array}$$

The maximum value is 3300 when $x_1 = 240, x_2 = 60, x_3 = 0, x_4 = 0, s_1 = 0$, and $s_2 = 0$.

14. Maximize $z = x_1 + x_2 + 4x_3 + 5x_4$

subject to:
$$\begin{aligned} x_1 + 2x_2 + 3x_3 + x_4 &\le 115 \\ 2x_1 + x_2 + 8x_3 + 5x_4 &\le 200 \\ x_1 + x_3 &\le 50 \end{aligned}$$

with $x_1 \ge 0, x_2 \ge 0, x_3 \ge 0, x_4 \ge 0.$

$$\begin{array}{c} \begin{array}{cccccccc} x_1 & x_2 & x_3 & x_4 & s_1 & s_2 & s_3 & z \end{array} \\ \left[\begin{array}{cccccccc|c} 1 & 2 & 3 & 1 & 1 & 0 & 0 & 0 & 115 \\ 2 & 1 & 8 & \boxed{5} & 0 & 1 & 0 & 0 & 200 \\ 1 & 0 & 1 & 0 & 0 & 0 & 1 & 0 & 50 \\ \hline -1 & -1 & -4 & -5 & 0 & 0 & 0 & 1 & 0 \end{array}\right] \end{array}$$

Pivot on the 5 in row 2, column 4

$$\begin{array}{r} \\ -R_2+5R_1 \to R_1 \\ \\ \\ R_2+R_4 \to R_4 \end{array} \begin{array}{c} \begin{array}{cccccccc} x_1 & x_2 & x_3 & x_4 & s_1 & s_2 & s_3 & z \end{array} \\ \left[\begin{array}{cccccccc|c} 3 & 9 & 7 & 0 & 5 & -1 & 0 & 0 & 375 \\ 2 & 1 & 8 & 5 & 0 & 1 & 0 & 0 & 200 \\ 1 & 0 & 1 & 0 & 0 & 0 & 1 & 0 & 50 \\ \hline 1 & 0 & 4 & 0 & 0 & 1 & 0 & 1 & 200 \end{array}\right] \end{array}$$

Create a 1 in the columns corresponding to x_4 and s_1.

$$\begin{array}{r} \\ \\ \frac{1}{5}R_1 \to R_1 \\ \frac{1}{5}R_2 \to R_2 \\ \\ \end{array} \begin{array}{c} \begin{array}{cccccccc} x_1 & x_2 & x_3 & x_4 & s_1 & s_2 & s_3 & z \end{array} \\ \left[\begin{array}{cccccccc|c} \frac{3}{5} & \frac{9}{5} & \frac{7}{5} & 0 & 1 & -\frac{1}{5} & 0 & 0 & 75 \\ \frac{2}{5} & \frac{1}{5} & \frac{8}{5} & 1 & 0 & \frac{1}{5} & 0 & 0 & 40 \\ 1 & 0 & 1 & 0 & 0 & 0 & 1 & 0 & 50 \\ \hline 1 & 0 & 4 & 0 & 0 & 1 & 0 & 1 & 200 \end{array}\right] \end{array}$$

This solution is optimal. The maximum is 200 when $x_1 = 0, x_2 = 0, x_3 = 0, x_4 = 40, s_1 = 75, s_2 = 0$, and $s_3 = 50$.

15. Maximize $z = 4x_1 + 6x_2$

subject to:
$$\begin{aligned} x_1 - 5x_2 &\le 25 \\ 4x_1 - 3x_2 &\le 12 \end{aligned}$$

with $x_1 \ge 0, x_2 \ge 0.$

$$\begin{array}{c} \begin{array}{ccccc} x_1 & x_2 & s_1 & s_2 & z \end{array} \\ \left[\begin{array}{ccccc|c} 1 & -5 & 1 & 0 & 0 & 25 \\ 4 & -3 & 0 & 1 & 0 & 12 \\ \hline -4 & -6 & 0 & 0 & 1 & 0 \end{array}\right] \end{array}$$

The most negative indicator is -6. The negative quotients $25/(-5)$ and $12/(-3)$ indicate an unbounded feasible region, so there is no unique optimum solution.

16. Maximize $z = 2x_1 + 5x_2 + x_3$

subject to:
$$\begin{aligned} x_1 - 5x_2 + 2x_3 &\le 30 \\ 4x_1 - 3x_2 + 6x_3 &\le 72 \end{aligned}$$

with $x_1 \ge 0, x_2 \ge 0, x_3 \ge 0.$

$$\begin{array}{c} \begin{array}{cccccc} x_1 & x_2 & x_3 & s_1 & s_2 & z \end{array} \\ \left[\begin{array}{cccccc|c} 1 & -5 & 2 & 1 & 0 & 0 & 30 \\ 4 & -3 & 6 & 0 & 1 & 0 & 72 \\ \hline -2 & -5 & -1 & 0 & 0 & 1 & 0 \end{array}\right] \end{array}$$

The most negative indicator is -5. The negative quotients $30/(-5)$ and $72/(-3)$ indicate an unbounded feasible region, so there is no unique optimum solution.

17. Maximize $z = 37x_1 + 34x_2 + 36x_3 + 30x_4 + 35x_5$
subject to:
$$16x_1 + 19x_2 + 23x_3 + 15x_4 + 21x_5 \le 42{,}000$$
$$15x_1 + 10x_2 + 19x_3 + 23x_4 + 10x_5 \le 25{,}000$$
$$9x_1 + 16x_2 + 14x_3 + 12x_4 + 11x_5 \le 23{,}000$$
$$18x_1 + 20x_2 + 15x_3 + 17x_4 + 19x_5 \le 36{,}000$$
with $x_1 \ge 0, x_2 \ge 0, x_3 \ge 0, x_4 \ge 0, x_5 \ge 0.$

Four slack variables, s_1, s_2, s_3, and s_4, need to be introduced. The initial simplex tableau follows.

$$\begin{array}{ccccccccccc} x_1 & x_2 & x_3 & x_4 & x_5 & s_1 & s_2 & s_3 & s_4 & z & \\ \left[\begin{array}{cccccccccc|c} 16 & 19 & 23 & 15 & 21 & 1 & 0 & 0 & 0 & 0 & 42{,}000 \\ 15 & 10 & 19 & 23 & 10 & 0 & 1 & 0 & 0 & 0 & 25{,}000 \\ 9 & 16 & 14 & 12 & 11 & 0 & 0 & 1 & 0 & 0 & 23{,}000 \\ 18 & 20 & 15 & 17 & 19 & 0 & 0 & 0 & 1 & 0 & 36{,}000 \\ \hline -37 & -34 & -36 & -30 & -35 & 0 & 0 & 0 & 0 & 1 & 0 \end{array}\right] \end{array}$$

Using a graphing calculator or computer program, the maximum value is found to be 70,818.18 when $x_1 = 181.82, x_2 = 0, x_3 = 454.55, x_4 = 0, x_5 = 1363.64, s_1 = 0, s_2 = 0, s_3 = 0$, and $s_4 = 0$.

18. Maximize $z = 2.0x_1 + 1.7x_2 + 2.1x_3 + 2.4x_4 + 2.2x_5$
subject to:
$$12x_1 + 10x_2 + 11x_3 + 12x_4 + 13x_5 \le 4250$$
$$8x_1 + 8x_2 + 7x_3 + 18x_4 + 5x_5 \le 4130$$
$$9x_1 + 10x_2 + 12x_3 + 11x_4 + 8x_5 \le 3500$$
$$5x_1 + 3x_2 + 4x_3 + 5x_4 + 4x_5 \le 1600$$
with $x_1 \ge 0, x_2 \ge 0, x_3 \ge 0, x_4 \ge 0, x_5 \ge 0.$

Four slack variables, s_1, s_2, s_3, and s_4, need to be introduced. The initial simplex tableau follows.

$$\begin{array}{ccccccccccc} x_1 & x_2 & x_3 & x_4 & x_5 & s_1 & s_2 & s_3 & s_4 & z & \\ \left[\begin{array}{cccccccccc|c} 12 & 10 & 11 & 12 & 13 & 1 & 0 & 0 & 0 & 0 & 4250 \\ 8 & 8 & 7 & 18 & 5 & 0 & 1 & 0 & 0 & 0 & 4130 \\ 9 & 10 & 12 & 11 & 8 & 0 & 0 & 1 & 0 & 0 & 3500 \\ 5 & 3 & 4 & 5 & 4 & 0 & 0 & 0 & 1 & 0 & 1600 \\ \hline -2.0 & -1.7 & -2.1 & -2.4 & -2.2 & 0 & 0 & 0 & 0 & 1 & 0 \end{array}\right] \end{array}$$

Using a graphing calculator or computer program, the maximum value is found to be 795.68 when $x_1 = 0$, $x_2 = 0, x_3 = 46.97, x_4 = 176.72, x_5 = 124.05, s_1 = 0, s_2 = 0, s_3 = 0$, and $s_4 = 32.31$.

21. Organize the information in a table.

	Church Group	Labor Union	Maximum Time Available
Letter Writing	2	2	16
Follow-up	1	3	12
Money Raised	\$100	\$200	

Let x_1 and x_2 be the number of church groups and labor unions contacted respectively. We need two slack variables, s_1 and s_2.

Maximize $z = 100x_1 + 200x_2$
subject to:
$$2x_1 + 2x_2 + s_1 = 16$$
$$x_1 + 3x_2 + s_2 = 12$$
with $x_1 \ge 0, x_2 \ge 0, s_1 \ge 0, s_2 \ge 0.$

The initial simplex tableau is as follows.

$$\begin{array}{c} \\ \\ \\ \end{array}\left[\begin{array}{cccccc|c} x_1 & x_2 & s_1 & s_2 & z & & \\ 2 & 2 & 1 & 0 & 0 & & 16 \\ 1 & \boxed{3} & 0 & 1 & 0 & & 12 \\ \hline -100 & -200 & 0 & 0 & 1 & & 0 \end{array}\right]$$

Pivot on the 3 in row 2, column 2.

$$\begin{array}{r} \\ -2R_2 + 3R_1 \rightarrow R_1 \\ \\ 200R_2 + 3R_3 \rightarrow R_3 \end{array}\left[\begin{array}{ccccc|c} x_1 & x_2 & s_1 & s_2 & z & \\ \boxed{4} & 0 & 3 & -2 & 0 & 24 \\ 1 & 3 & 0 & 1 & 0 & 12 \\ \hline -100 & 0 & 0 & 200 & 3 & 2400 \end{array}\right]$$

Pivot on the 4 in row 1, column 1.

$$\begin{array}{r} \\ \\ -R_1 + 4R_2 \rightarrow R_2 \\ 25R_1 + R_3 \rightarrow R_3 \end{array}\left[\begin{array}{ccccc|c} x_1 & x_2 & s_1 & s_2 & z & \\ 4 & 0 & 3 & -2 & 0 & 24 \\ 0 & 12 & -3 & 6 & 0 & 24 \\ \hline 0 & 0 & 75 & 150 & 3 & 3000 \end{array}\right]$$

This is a final tableau, since all of the indicators are nonnegative. Create a 1 in the columns corresponding to x_1, x_2, and z.

$$\begin{array}{r} \\ \frac{1}{4}R_1 \rightarrow R_1 \\ \frac{1}{12}R_2 \rightarrow R_2 \\ \frac{1}{3}R_3 \rightarrow R_3 \end{array}\left[\begin{array}{ccccc|c} x_1 & x_2 & s_1 & s_2 & z & \\ 1 & 0 & \frac{3}{4} & -\frac{1}{2} & 0 & 6 \\ 0 & 1 & -\frac{1}{4} & \frac{1}{2} & 0 & 2 \\ \hline 0 & 0 & 25 & 50 & 1 & 1000 \end{array}\right]$$

The maximum amount of money raised is \$1000/mo when $x_1 = 6$ and $x_2 = 2$, that is, when 6 churches and 2 labor unions are contacted.

22. **(a)** Let x_1 be the number of Flexscan sets and x_2 be the number of Panoramic I sets. The problem can be stated as follows.

$$\begin{array}{ll} \text{Maximize } z = 350x_1 + 500x_2 & \\ \text{subject to:} & 5x_1 + 7x_2 \leq 3600 \\ & x_1 + 2x_2 \leq 900 \\ & 4x_1 + 4x_2 \leq 2600 \\ \text{with} & x_1 \geq 0, x_2 \geq 0. \end{array}$$

Since there are three constraints, introduce slack variables s_1, s_2, and s_3 and set up the initial tableau.

$$\left[\begin{array}{cccccc|c} x_1 & x_2 & s_1 & s_2 & s_3 & z & \\ 5 & 7 & 1 & 0 & 0 & 0 & 3600 \\ 1 & \boxed{2} & 0 & 1 & 0 & 0 & 900 \\ 4 & 4 & 0 & 0 & 1 & 0 & 2600 \\ \hline -350 & -500 & 0 & 0 & 0 & 1 & 0 \end{array}\right]$$

Pivot on the 2 in row 2, column 2.

$$\begin{array}{r} \\ -7R_2 + 2R_1 \rightarrow R_1 \\ \\ -2R_2 + R_3 \rightarrow R_3 \\ 250R_2 + R_4 \rightarrow R_4 \end{array}\left[\begin{array}{cccccc|c} x_1 & x_2 & s_1 & s_2 & s_3 & z & \\ \boxed{3} & 0 & 2 & -7 & 0 & 0 & 900 \\ 1 & 2 & 0 & 1 & 0 & 0 & 900 \\ 2 & 0 & 0 & -2 & 1 & 0 & 800 \\ \hline -100 & 0 & 0 & 250 & 0 & 1 & 225{,}000 \end{array}\right]$$

Pivot on the 3 in row 1, column 1.

$$
\begin{array}{r}
\\
\\
-R_1 + 3R_2 \rightarrow R_2 \\
-2R_1 + 3R_3 \rightarrow R_3 \\
100R_1 + 3R_4 \rightarrow R_4
\end{array}
\begin{array}{cccccc|r}
x_1 & x_2 & s_1 & s_2 & s_3 & z & \\
3 & 0 & 2 & -7 & 0 & 0 & 900 \\
0 & 6 & -2 & 10 & 0 & 0 & 1800 \\
0 & 0 & -4 & 8 & 3 & 0 & 600 \\
\hline
0 & 0 & 200 & 50 & 0 & 3 & 765{,}000
\end{array}
$$

Create a 1 in the columns corresponding to x_1, x_2, and z.

$$
\begin{array}{r}
\\
\frac{1}{3}R_1 \rightarrow R_1 \\
\frac{1}{6}R_2 \rightarrow R_2 \\
\\
\frac{1}{3}R_4 \rightarrow R_4
\end{array}
\begin{array}{cccccc|r}
x_1 & x_2 & s_1 & s_2 & s_3 & z & \\
1 & 0 & \frac{2}{3} & -\frac{7}{3} & 0 & 0 & 300 \\
0 & 1 & -\frac{2}{3} & \frac{5}{3} & 0 & 0 & 300 \\
0 & 0 & -4 & 8 & 3 & 0 & 600 \\
\hline
0 & 0 & \frac{200}{3} & \frac{50}{3} & 0 & 1 & 255{,}000
\end{array}
$$

The optimal solution is \$255,000 when 300 Flexscan and 300 Panoramic I sets are produced. (This agrees with the graphical solution found in Exercise 10 of Section 3.3.)

(b) Since $5x_1 + 7x_2 + s_1 = 3600$, let $x_1 = 300$ and $x_2 = 300$ and solve for s_1.

$$
\begin{aligned}
5(300) + 7(300) + s_1 &= 3600 \\
s_1 &= 0
\end{aligned}
$$

Similarly, find s_2 and s_3.

$$
\begin{aligned}
x_1 + 2x_2 + s_2 &= 900 \\
300 + 2(300) + s_2 &= 900 \\
s_2 &= 0
\end{aligned}
$$

and

$$
\begin{aligned}
4x_1 + 4x_2 + s_3 &= 2600 \\
4(300) + 4(300) + s_3 &= 2600 \\
s_3 &= 200.
\end{aligned}
$$

There are 200 leftover hours in the testing and packing department.

23. **(a)** Let x_1 be the number of Royal Flush poker sets, x_2 be the number of Deluxe Diamond sets, and x_3 be the number of Full House sets. The problem can be stated as follows.

$$
\begin{array}{lrcrcrcr}
\text{Maximize } z = 38x_1 + 22x_2 + 12x_3 & & & & & & & \\
\text{subject to:} & 1000x_1 & + & 600x_2 & + & 300x_3 & \leq & 2{,}800{,}000 \\
 & 4x_1 & + & 2x_2 & + & 2x_3 & \leq & 10{,}000 \\
 & 10x_1 & + & 5x_2 & + & 5x_3 & \leq & 25{,}000 \\
 & 2x_1 & + & x_2 & + & x_3 & \leq & 6000 \\
\text{with} & \multicolumn{7}{l}{x_1 \geq 0, x_2 \geq 0, x_3 \geq 0.}
\end{array}
$$

Since there are four constraints, introduce slack variables, s_1, s_2, s_3, and s_4 and set up the initial simplex tableau.

$$
\begin{array}{cccccccc|r}
x_1 & x_2 & x_3 & s_1 & s_2 & s_3 & s_4 & z & \\
1000 & 600 & 300 & 1 & 0 & 0 & 0 & 0 & 2{,}800{,}000 \\
4 & 2 & 2 & 0 & 1 & 0 & 0 & 0 & 10{,}000 \\
10 & 5 & 5 & 0 & 0 & 1 & 0 & 0 & 25{,}000 \\
2 & 1 & 1 & 0 & 0 & 0 & 1 & 0 & 6000 \\
\hline
-38 & -22 & -12 & 0 & 0 & 0 & 0 & 1 & 0
\end{array}
$$

Using a graphing calculator or computer program, the maximum profit is \$104,000 and is obtained when 1000 Royal Flush poker sets, 3000 Deluxe Diamond poker sets, and no Full House poker sets are assembled.

(b) According to the poker chip constraint:

$$\begin{aligned} 1000(1000) + 600(3000) + 300(0) + s_2 &= 2{,}800{,}000 \\ s_1 &= 0. \end{aligned}$$

So all of the poker chips are used. Checking the card constraint:

$$\begin{aligned} 4(1000) + 2(3000) + 2(0) + s_2 &= 10{,}000 \\ s_2 &= 0. \end{aligned}$$

So all of the poker chips are used. Checking the dice constraint:

$$\begin{aligned} 10(1000) + 5(3000) + 5(0) + s_3 &= 25{,}000 \\ s_3 &= 0. \end{aligned}$$

So all of the dice are used. Finally, checking the dealer button constraint:

$$\begin{aligned} 2(1000) + 3000 + 0 + s_4 &= 6000 \\ s_4 &= 1000. \end{aligned}$$

This means there are 1000 unused dealer buttons.

24. (a) Let x_1 be the number of loaves of raisin bread and x_2 be the number of raisin cakes.

Then
$$\begin{aligned} x_1 + 5x_2 &\le 150 \\ x_1 + 2x_2 &\le 90 \end{aligned}$$
and
$$2x_1 + x_2 \le 150.$$

To maximize $z = 1.75x_1 + 4x_2$, add s_1, s_2, and s_3 as slack variables. The initial tableau will be as follows.

$$\begin{array}{c} \\ \\ \\ \\ \end{array}\left[\begin{array}{ccccccc|c} x_1 & x_2 & s_1 & s_2 & s_3 & z & \\ 1 & \boxed{5} & 1 & 0 & 0 & 0 & 150 \\ 1 & 2 & 0 & 1 & 0 & 0 & 90 \\ 2 & 1 & 0 & 0 & 1 & 0 & 150 \\ \hline -\frac{7}{4} & -4 & 0 & 0 & 0 & 1 & 0 \end{array}\right]$$

Pivot on the 5 in row 1, column 2.

$$\begin{array}{r} \\ -2R_1 + 5R_2 \to R_2 \\ -R_1 + 5R_3 \to R_3 \\ 4R_1 + 5R_4 \to R_4 \end{array}\left[\begin{array}{cccccc|c} 1 & 5 & 1 & 0 & 0 & 0 & 150 \\ \boxed{3} & 0 & -2 & 5 & 0 & 0 & 150 \\ 9 & 0 & -1 & 0 & 5 & 0 & 600 \\ \hline -\frac{19}{4} & 0 & 4 & 0 & 0 & 5 & 600 \end{array}\right]$$

(columns: $x_1, x_2, s_1, s_2, s_3, z$)

Pivot on the 3 in row 2, column 1.

$$\begin{array}{r} -R_2 + 3R_1 \to R_1 \\ \\ -3R_2 + R_3 \to R_3 \\ \frac{19}{4}R_2 + 3R_4 \to R_4 \end{array}\left[\begin{array}{cccccc|c} 0 & 15 & 5 & -5 & 0 & 0 & 300 \\ 3 & 0 & -2 & 5 & 0 & 0 & 150 \\ 0 & 0 & 5 & -15 & 5 & 0 & 150 \\ \hline 0 & 0 & \frac{5}{2} & \frac{95}{4} & 0 & 15 & \frac{5025}{2} \end{array}\right]$$

(columns: $x_1, x_2, s_1, s_2, s_3, z$)

Create a 1 in the columns corresponding to x_1, x_2, s_3, and z.

$$\begin{array}{l} \\ \frac{1}{15}R_1 \to R_1 \\ \frac{1}{3}R_2 \to R_2 \\ \frac{1}{5}R_3 \to R_3 \\ \\ \frac{1}{15}R_4 \to R_4 \end{array} \begin{array}{c} \begin{array}{cccccc} x_1 & x_2 & s_1 & s_2 & s_3 & z \end{array} \\ \left[\begin{array}{cccccc|c} 0 & 1 & \frac{1}{3} & -\frac{1}{3} & 0 & 0 & 20 \\ 1 & 0 & -\frac{2}{3} & \frac{5}{3} & 0 & 0 & 50 \\ 0 & 0 & 1 & -3 & 1 & 0 & 30 \\ \hline 0 & 0 & \frac{1}{6} & \frac{19}{12} & 0 & 1 & \frac{335}{2} \end{array}\right] \end{array}$$

The optimal solution occurs when $x_1 = 50$ and $x_2 = 20$; that is, when 50 loaves of raisin bread and 20 raisin cakes are baked.

(b) $\frac{335}{2} = 167.5$; the maximum gross income is \$167.50.

(c) When $x_1 = 50$ and $x_2 = 20$, the number of units used are as follows.

Flour: $50 + 5(20) = 150$

This is the total amount of available flour.

Sugar: $50 + 2(20) = 90$

This is the total amount of available sugar.

Raisins: $2(50) + 20 = 120$

This leaves 150 – 120, or 30 units, of raisins.

Since

$$\begin{aligned} 2x_1 + x_2 + s_3 &= 150, \\ 2(50) + 20 + s_3 &= 150 \\ s_3 &= 30. \end{aligned}$$

25. (a) Let x_1 represent the number of racing bicycles, x_2 the number of touring bicycles, and x_3 the number of mountain bicycles.

From Exercise 26 in Section 4.1, the initial simplex tableau is as follows.

$$\begin{array}{c} \begin{array}{cccccc} x_1 & x_2 & x_3 & s_1 & s_2 & z \end{array} \\ \left[\begin{array}{cccccc|c} 17 & 27 & \boxed{34} & 1 & 0 & 0 & 91{,}800 \\ 12 & 21 & 15 & 0 & 1 & 0 & 42{,}000 \\ \hline -8 & -12 & -22 & 0 & 0 & 1 & 0 \end{array}\right] \end{array}$$

Pivot on the 34 in row 1, column 3.

$$\begin{array}{l} \\ \\ -15R_1 + 34R_2 \to R_2 \\ 11R_1 + 17R_3 \to R_3 \end{array} \begin{array}{c} \begin{array}{cccccc} x_1 & x_2 & x_3 & s_1 & s_2 & z \end{array} \\ \left[\begin{array}{cccccc|c} 17 & 27 & 34 & 1 & 0 & 0 & 91{,}800 \\ 153 & 309 & 0 & -15 & 34 & 0 & 51{,}000 \\ \hline 51 & 93 & 0 & 11 & 0 & 17 & 1{,}009{,}800 \end{array}\right] \end{array}$$

This is a final tableau, since all of the indicators are nonnegative. Create a 1 in the columns corresponding to x_3, s_2, and z.

$$\begin{array}{l} \\ \frac{1}{34}R_1 \to R_1 \\ \frac{1}{34}R_2 \to R_2 \\ \frac{1}{17}R_3 \to R_3 \end{array} \begin{array}{c} \begin{array}{cccccc} x_1 & x_2 & x_3 & s_1 & s_2 & z \end{array} \\ \left[\begin{array}{cccccc|c} \frac{1}{2} & \frac{27}{34} & 1 & \frac{1}{34} & 0 & 0 & 2700 \\ \frac{9}{2} & \frac{309}{34} & 0 & -\frac{15}{34} & 1 & 0 & 1500 \\ \hline 3 & \frac{93}{17} & 0 & \frac{11}{17} & 0 & 1 & 59{,}400 \end{array}\right] \end{array}$$

From the tableau, $x_1 = 0, x_2 = 0$, and $x_3 = 2700$. The company should make no racing or touring bicycles and 2700 mountain bicycles.

(b) From the third row of the final tableau, the maximum profit is \$59,400.

(c) When $x_1 = 0, x_2 = 0$, and $x_3 = 2700$, the number of units of steel used is

$$17(0) + 27(0) + 34(2700) = 91{,}800$$

which is all the steel available. The number of units of aluminum used is

$$12(0) + 21(0) + 15(2700) = 40{,}500$$

which leaves $42{,}000 - 40{,}500 = 1500$ units of aluminum unused.

Checking the second constraint:

$$\begin{aligned} 12x_1 + 21x_2 + 15x_3 + s_2 &= 42{,}000 \\ 12(0) + 21(0) + 15(2700) + s_2 &= 42{,}000 \\ s_2 &= 1500. \end{aligned}$$

26. **(a)** The tableau and set up were explained in Exercise 28 of Section 4.1.

$$\begin{array}{c} \\ \\ \\ \\ \\ \end{array}\left[\begin{array}{ccccccc|c} x_1 & x_2 & x_3 & s_1 & s_2 & s_3 & z & \\ 2 & 2 & 3 & 1 & 0 & 0 & 0 & 800 \\ 1 & 1 & 1 & 0 & 1 & 0 & 0 & 400 \\ 0 & 1 & \boxed{1} & 0 & 0 & 1 & 0 & 200 \\ \hline -30 & -40 & -60 & 0 & 0 & 0 & 1 & 0 \end{array}\right]$$

Pivot on the 1 in row 3, column 3.

$$\begin{array}{r} \\ -3R_3 + R_1 \to R_1 \\ -R_3 + R_2 \to R_2 \\ \\ 60R_3 + R_4 \to R_4 \end{array}\left[\begin{array}{ccccccc|c} x_1 & x_2 & x_3 & s_1 & s_2 & s_3 & z & \\ \boxed{2} & -1 & 0 & 1 & 0 & -3 & 0 & 200 \\ 1 & 0 & 0 & 0 & 1 & -1 & 0 & 200 \\ 0 & 1 & 1 & 0 & 0 & 1 & 0 & 200 \\ \hline -30 & 20 & 0 & 0 & 0 & 60 & 1 & 12{,}000 \end{array}\right]$$

Pivot on the 2 in row 1, column 1.

$$\begin{array}{r} \\ \\ -R_1 + 2R_2 \to R_2 \\ \\ 15R_1 + R_4 \to R_4 \end{array}\left[\begin{array}{ccccccc|c} x_1 & x_2 & x_3 & s_1 & s_2 & s_3 & z & \\ 2 & -1 & 0 & 1 & 0 & -3 & 0 & 200 \\ 0 & 1 & 0 & -1 & 2 & 1 & 0 & 200 \\ 0 & 1 & 1 & 0 & 0 & 1 & 0 & 200 \\ \hline 0 & 5 & 0 & 15 & 0 & 15 & 1 & 15{,}000 \end{array}\right]$$

Create a 1 in the column corresponding to x_1.

$$\begin{array}{r} \\ \\ \frac{1}{2}R_1 \to R_1 \\ \\ \\ \end{array}\left[\begin{array}{ccccccc|c} x_1 & x_2 & x_3 & s_1 & s_2 & s_3 & z & \\ 1 & -\frac{1}{2} & 0 & \frac{1}{2} & 0 & -\frac{3}{2} & 0 & 100 \\ 0 & 1 & 0 & -1 & 2 & 1 & 0 & 200 \\ 0 & 1 & 1 & 0 & 0 & 1 & 0 & 200 \\ \hline 0 & 5 & 0 & 15 & 0 & 15 & 1 & 15{,}000 \end{array}\right]$$

The maximum profit is \$15,000 when $x_1 = 100, x_2 = 0$, and $x_3 = 200$, that is, when 100 basic sets, no regular sets, and 200 deluxe sets are made.

(b) Even though regular sets make a larger profit, there are only 200 slicers available. Since slicers are used in regular and deluxe sets, and deluxe sets account for \$20 more profit, slicers should be used in deluxe sets (as many as possible) with any leftovers used in regular sets.

27. **(a)** Let x_1 be the number of newspaper ads, x_2 be the number of Internet banner ads, and x_3 be the number of TV ads. From

x_1	x_2	x_3	s_1	s_2	s_3	s_4	z	
400	20	2000	1	0	0	0	0	8000
1	0	0	0	1	0	0	0	30
0	1	0	0	0	1	0	0	60
0	0	1	0	0	0	1	0	10
−4000	−3000	−10,000	0	0	0	0	1	0

Pivot on the 2000 in row 1, column 3.

	x_1	x_2	x_3	s_1	s_2	s_3	s_4	z	
	400	20	2000	1	0	0	0	0	8000
	1	0	0	0	1	0	0	0	30
	0	1	0	0	0	1	0	0	60
$-R_1 + 2000R_4 \to R_4$	−400	−20	0	−1	0	0	2000	0	12,000
$5R_1 + R_5 \to R_5$	−2000	−2900	0	5	0	0	0	1	40,000

Pivot on the 1 in row 3, column 2.

	x_1	x_2	x_3	s_1	s_2	s_3	s_4	z	
$-20R_3 + R_1 \to R_1$	400	0	2000	1	0	−20	0	0	6800
	1	0	0	0	1	0	0	0	30
	0	1	0	0	0	1	0	0	60
$20R_3 + R_4 \to R_4$	−400	0	0	−1	0	20	2000	0	13,200
$2900R_3 + R_5 \to R_5$	−2000	0	0	5	0	2900	0	1	214,000

Pivot on the 400 in row 1, column 1.

	x_1	x_2	x_3	s_1	s_2	s_3	s_4	z	
	400	0	2000	1	0	−20	0	0	6800
$-R_1 + 400R_2 \to R_2$	0	0	−2000	−1	400	20	0	0	5200
	0	1	0	0	0	1	0	0	60
$R_1 + R_4 \to R_4$	0	0	2000	0	0	0	2000	0	20,000
$5R_1 + R_5 \to R_5$	0	0	10,000	10	0	2800	0	1	248,000

Create a 1 in the columns corresponding to x_1, s_2, and s_4.

	x_1	x_2	x_3	s_1	s_2	s_3	s_4	z	
$\frac{1}{400}R_1 \to R_1$	1	0	5	$\frac{1}{400}$	0	$-\frac{1}{20}$	0	0	17
$\frac{1}{400}R_2 \to R_2$	0	0	−5	$-\frac{1}{400}$	1	$\frac{1}{20}$	0	0	13
	0	1	0	0	0	1	0	0	60
$\frac{1}{2000}R_4 \to R_4$	0	0	1	0	0	0	1	0	10
	0	0	10,000	10	0	2800	0	1	248,000

This is the final tableau. The maximum exposure is 248,000 women when 17 newspaper ads, 60 Internet banner ads, and no TV ads are used.

28. **(a)** Let x_1 represent the number of toy trucks and x_2 the number of toy fire engines.

$$\begin{array}{lrl}\text{Maximize} & z = 8.50x_1 + 12.10x_2 & \\ \text{subject to:} & -2x_1 + 3x_2 \leq & 0 \\ & x_1 \quad\quad \leq & 6700 \\ & x_2 \leq & 5500 \\ & x_1 + \quad x_2 \leq & 12,000 \\ \text{with} & x_1 \geq 0, x_2 \geq 0. & \end{array}$$

This exercise should be solved by graphing calculator or computer methods. The answer is to produce 6700 trucks and 4467 fire engines for a maximum profit of $110,997.

(b) Many solutions are possible.

(c) Many solutions are possible.

29. **(a)** The coefficients of the objective function are the profit coefficients from the table: 5, 4, and 3; choice (3) is correct.

(b) The constraints are the available man-hours for the 2 departments, 400 and 600; choice (4) is correct.

(c) $2X_1 + 3X_2 + 1X_3 \leq 400$ is the constraint on department 1; choice (3) is correct.

30. **(a)** Look at the first table, which has to do with the profits. The profit-maximization formula is

$$\$2\text{A} + \$5\text{B} + \$4\text{C} = X,$$

so the answer is choice (1).

(b) Look at the "Painting" row of the second chart. The "Painting" constraint is

$$1\text{A} + 2\text{B} + 2\text{C} \leq 38{,}000,$$

so the answer is choice (3).

31. Maximize $z = 100x + 200y$

$$\begin{array}{ll}\text{subject to:} & 2x + 2y \leq 16 \\ & x + 3y \leq 12 \\ \text{with} & x \geq 0, y \geq 0.\end{array}$$

Using Excel, we enter the variables x and y in cells A1 and B1, respectively. Enter the x- and y-coordinates of the initial corner point of the feasible region, $(0, 0)$, in cells A2 and B2, respectively, and NAME these cells x and y, respectively. In cells C2, C4, C5, C6, and C7, enter the formula for the function to maximize and each of the constraints: $100x + 200y, 2x + 2y, x + 3y, x$, and y. Since x and y have been set to 0, all the cells containing formulas should also show the value 0, as below.

	A	B	C
1	x	y	
2	0	0	0
3			
4			0
5			0
6			0
7			0

Using the SOLVER, ask Excel to maximize the value in cell C2 subject to the constraints C4 $\leq$ 16, C5 $\leq$ 12, C6 $\geq$ 0, C7 $\geq$ 0. Make sure you have checked off the box *Assume Linear Model* in SOLVER OPTIONS.

Excel returns the following values and allows you to choose a report.

	A	B	C
1	x	y	
2	6	2	1000
3			
4			16
5			12
6			6
7			2

Select the sensitivity report. The report will appear on a new sheet of the spread sheet.

Adjustable Cells

Cell	Name	Final Value	Reduced Cost	Objective Coefficient	Allowable Increase	Allowable Decrease
A2	x	6	0	100	100	33.33333333
B2	y	2	0	200	100	100

Constraints

Cell	Name	Final Value	Shadow Price	Constraint R.H. Side	Allowable Increase	Allowable Decrease
C4		16	25	16	8	8
C5		12	50	12	12	4
C6		6	0	0	6	1E+30
C7		2	0	0	2	1E+30

The church group's allowable increase is $100 and the allowable decrease is $33.33. So their contribution can be as high as $100 + $100 = $200 or as low as $100 − $33.33 = $66.67 and the original solution is still optimal. The unions' allowable increase is $100 and the allowable decrease is $100. So their contribution can be as high as $200 + $100 = $300 or as low as $200 − $100 = $100 and the original solution is still optimal.

32. Maximize $z = 350x + 500y$

subject to:
$$\begin{aligned} 5x + 7y &\le 3600 \\ x + 2y &\le 900 \\ 4x + 4y &\le 2600 \end{aligned}$$
with $x \ge 0, y \ge 0.$

Using Excel, we enter the variables x and y in cells A1 and B1, respectively. Enter the x- and y-coordinates of the initial corner point of the feasible region, $(0, 0)$, in cells A2 and B2, respectively, and NAME these cells x and y, respectively. In cells C2, C4, C5, C6, C7, and C8, enter the formula for the function to maximize and each of the constraints: $350x + 500y, 5x + 7y, x + 2y, 4x + 4y, x$, and y. Since x and y have been set to 0, all the cells containing formulas should also show the value 0, as below.

	A	B	C
1	x	y	
2	0	0	0
3			
4			0
5			0
6			0
7			0
8			0

Using the SOLVER, ask Excel to maximize the value in cell C2 subject to the constraints C4 $\leq$ 3600, C5 $\leq$ 900,C6 $\leq$ 3600,C7 $\geq$ 0, C8 $\geq$ 0. Make sure you have checked off the box *Assume Linear Model* in SOLVER OPTIONS.

Excel returns the following values and allows you to choose a report.

	A	B	C
1	x	y	
2	300	300	255000
3			
4			3600
5			900
6			2400
7			300
8			300

Select the sensitivity report. The report will appear on a new sheet of the spread sheet.

Adjustable Cells

Cell	Name	Final Value	Reduced Cost	Objective Coefficient	Allowable Increase	Allowable Decrease
\$A\$2	x	300	0	350	7.142857143	100
\$B\$2	y	300	0	500	200	10

Constraints

Cell	Name	Final Value	Shadow Price	Constraint R.H. Side	Allowable Increase	Allowable Decrease
\$C\$8		3600	66.66666667	3600	150	450
\$C\$4		900	16.66666667	900	128.5714286	75
\$C\$7		2400	0	2600	1E+30	200
\$C\$5		300	0	0	300	1E+30
\$C\$6		300	0	0	300	1E+30

For the Flexscan sets, the allowable increase is \$7.14 and the allowable decrease is \$100. So the profit from the bargain sets can be as high as \$350 + \$7.14 = \$357.14 or as low as \$350 – \$100 = \$250 and the original solution is still optimal. For the Panoramic I sets, the allowable increase is \$200 and the allowable decrease is \$10. So the profit from the Panoramic I sets can be as high as \$500 + \$200 = \$700 or as low as \$500 – \$10 = \$490 and the original solution is still optimal.

33. Let x_1 = number of hours running, x_2 be the number of hours biking, and x_3 be the number hours walking. The problem can be stated as follows.

$$\begin{aligned}
\text{Maximize}\quad & z = 531x_1 + 472x_2 + 354x_3 \\
\text{subject to:}\quad & x_1 + x_2 + x_3 \le 15 \\
& x_1 \le 3 \\
& 2x_2 - x_3 \le 0 \\
\text{with}\quad & x_1 \ge 0, x_2 \ge 0, x_3 \ge 0.
\end{aligned}$$

We need three slack variables, s_1, s_2, and s_3. The initial simplex tableau as follows.

$$\begin{array}{c}
\begin{matrix} x_1 & x_2 & x_3 & s_1 & s_2 & s_3 & z & \end{matrix} \\
\left[\begin{array}{ccccccc|c}
1 & 1 & 1 & 1 & 0 & 0 & 0 & 15 \\
\boxed{1} & 0 & 0 & 0 & 1 & 0 & 0 & 3 \\
0 & 2 & -1 & 0 & 0 & 1 & 0 & 0 \\ \hline
-531 & -472 & -354 & 0 & 0 & 0 & 1 & 0
\end{array}\right]
\end{array}$$

Pivot on the 1 in row 2, column 1.

$$\begin{array}{r}
-R_2 + R_1 \to R_1 \\ \\ \\ 531R_2 + R_4 \to R_4
\end{array}
\left[\begin{array}{ccccccc|c}
x_1 & x_2 & x_3 & s_1 & s_2 & s_3 & z & \\
0 & 1 & 1 & 1 & -1 & 0 & 0 & 12 \\
1 & 0 & 0 & 0 & 1 & 0 & 0 & 3 \\
0 & \boxed{2} & -1 & 0 & 0 & 1 & 0 & 0 \\ \hline
0 & -472 & -354 & 0 & 351 & 0 & 1 & 1593
\end{array}\right]$$

Pivot on the 2 in row 3, column 2.

$$\begin{array}{r}
-R_3 + 2R_1 \to R_1 \\ \\ \\ 236R_3 + R_4 \to R_4
\end{array}
\left[\begin{array}{ccccccc|c}
x_1 & x_2 & x_3 & s_1 & s_2 & s_3 & z & \\
0 & 0 & \boxed{3} & 2 & -2 & -1 & 0 & 24 \\
1 & 0 & 0 & 0 & 1 & 0 & 0 & 3 \\
0 & 2 & -1 & 0 & 0 & 1 & 0 & 0 \\ \hline
0 & 0 & -590 & 0 & 531 & 236 & 1 & 1593
\end{array}\right]$$

Finally pivot on the 3 in row 1, column 3.

$$\begin{array}{r}
\\ \\ R_1 + 3R_3 \to R_3 \\ 590R_1 + 3R_4 \to R_4
\end{array}
\left[\begin{array}{ccccccc|c}
x_1 & x_2 & x_3 & s_1 & s_2 & s_3 & z & \\
0 & 1 & 3 & 2 & -2 & -1 & 0 & 24 \\
1 & 0 & 0 & 0 & 1 & 0 & 0 & 3 \\
0 & 6 & 0 & 2 & -2 & 2 & 0 & 24 \\ \hline
0 & 0 & 0 & 1180 & 413 & 118 & 3 & 18{,}939
\end{array}\right]$$

Create a 1 in the columns corresponding to x_2, x_3, and z.

$$\begin{array}{r}
\frac{1}{3}R_1 \to R_1 \\ \\ \frac{1}{6}R_3 \to R_3 \\ \frac{1}{3}R_4 \to R_4
\end{array}
\left[\begin{array}{ccccccc|c}
x_1 & x_2 & x_3 & s_1 & s_2 & s_3 & z & \\
0 & 0 & 1 & \frac{2}{3} & -\frac{2}{3} & -\frac{1}{3} & 0 & 8 \\
1 & 0 & 0 & 0 & 1 & 0 & 0 & 3 \\
0 & 1 & 0 & \frac{1}{3} & -\frac{1}{3} & \frac{1}{3} & 0 & 4 \\ \hline
0 & 0 & 0 & \frac{1180}{3} & \frac{413}{3} & \frac{118}{3} & 1 & 6313
\end{array}\right]$$

Rachel should run 3 hours, bike 4 hours, and walk 8 hours for a maximum calorie expenditure of 6313 calories.

34. **(a)** Let x_1 represent the number of hours doing calisthenics, x_2 be the number of hours swimming, and x_3 be the number of hours playing the drums. The problem can be stated as follows.

$$\begin{array}{lrl} \text{Maximize} & z = & 388x_1 + 518x_2 + 345x_3 \\ \text{subject to:} & & x_1 + x_2 + x_3 \leq 10 \\ & & -x_1 + 2x_2 - x_3 \leq 0 \\ & & x_3 \leq 4 \\ \text{with} & & x_1 \geq 0, x_2 \geq 0, x_3 \geq 0. \end{array}$$

We need three slack variables. The initial simplex tableau is as follows.

$$\begin{array}{c} \begin{array}{ccccccc} x_1 & x_2 & x_3 & s_1 & s_2 & s_3 & z \end{array} \\ \left[\begin{array}{ccccccc|c} 1 & 1 & 1 & 1 & 0 & 0 & 0 & 10 \\ -1 & \boxed{2} & -1 & 0 & 1 & 0 & 0 & 0 \\ 0 & 0 & 1 & 0 & 0 & 1 & 0 & 4 \\ \hline -388 & -518 & -345 & 0 & 0 & 0 & 1 & 0 \end{array}\right] \end{array}$$

Pivot on the 2 in row 2, column 2.

$$\begin{array}{r} -R_2 + 2R_1 \rightarrow R_1 \\ \\ \\ 259R_2 + R_4 \rightarrow R_4 \end{array} \left[\begin{array}{ccccccc|c} x_1 & x_2 & x_3 & s_1 & s_2 & s_3 & z & \\ \boxed{3} & 0 & 3 & 2 & -1 & 0 & 0 & 20 \\ -1 & 2 & -1 & 0 & 1 & 0 & 0 & 0 \\ 0 & 0 & 1 & 0 & 0 & 1 & 0 & 4 \\ \hline -647 & 0 & -604 & 0 & 259 & 0 & 1 & 0 \end{array}\right]$$

Pivot on the 3 in row 1, column 1.

$$\begin{array}{r} \\ R_1 + 3R_2 \rightarrow R_2 \\ \\ 647R_1 + 3R_4 \rightarrow R_4 \end{array} \left[\begin{array}{ccccccc|c} x_1 & x_2 & x_3 & s_1 & s_2 & s_3 & z & \\ 3 & 0 & 3 & 2 & -1 & 0 & 0 & 20 \\ 0 & 6 & 0 & 2 & 2 & 0 & 0 & 20 \\ 0 & 0 & 1 & 0 & 0 & 1 & 0 & 4 \\ \hline 0 & 0 & 129 & 1294 & 130 & 0 & 3 & 12{,}940 \end{array}\right]$$

Create a 1 in the columns corresponding to x_1, x_2, and z.

$$\begin{array}{r} \frac{1}{3}R_1 \rightarrow R_1 \\ \frac{1}{6}R_2 \rightarrow R_2 \\ \\ \frac{1}{3}R_4 \rightarrow R_4 \end{array} \left[\begin{array}{ccccccc|c} x_1 & x_2 & x_3 & s_1 & s_2 & s_3 & z & \\ 1 & 0 & 1 & \frac{2}{3} & -\frac{1}{3} & 0 & 0 & \frac{20}{3} \\ 0 & 1 & 0 & \frac{1}{3} & \frac{1}{3} & 0 & 0 & \frac{10}{3} \\ 0 & 0 & 1 & 0 & 0 & 1 & 0 & 4 \\ \hline 0 & 0 & 43 & \frac{1294}{3} & \frac{130}{3} & 0 & 1 & \frac{12{,}940}{3} \end{array}\right]$$

Joe should do $\frac{20}{3}$ hours of calisthenics, $\frac{10}{3}$ hours of swimming, and 0 hours of playing the drums for a maximum calorie expenditure of $\frac{12{,}940}{3}$ or $4313\frac{1}{3}$ calories.

35. **(a)** Let x_1 = amount of P, x_2 = amount of Q, x_3 = amount of R, and x_4 = amount of S (all in kilograms).

We desire to maximize

$$z = 90x_1 + 70x_2 + 60x_3 + 50x_4$$

subject to:

$$\begin{aligned} 0.375x_3 + 0.625x_4 &\le 500 \\ 0.75x_2 + 0.5x_3 + 0.375x_4 &\le 600 \\ x_1 + 0.25x_2 + 0.125x_3 &\le 300 \end{aligned}$$

with $x_1 \ge 0, x_2 \ge 0, x_3 \ge 0, x_4 \ge 0$.

If we rewrite the constraints as

$$\begin{aligned} \frac{3}{8}x_3 + \frac{5}{8}x_4 &\le 500 \\ \frac{3}{4}x_2 + \frac{1}{2}x_3 + \frac{3}{8}x_4 &\le 600 \\ x_1 + \frac{1}{4}x_2 + \frac{1}{8}x_3 &\le 300, \end{aligned}$$

and then multiply each inequality by the least common denominator, 8, we get a set of constraints without fractions.

$$\begin{aligned} 3x_3 + 5x_4 &\le 4000 \\ 6x_2 + 4x_3 + 3x_4 &\le 4800 \\ 8x_1 + 2x_2 + x_3 &\le 2400 \end{aligned}$$

We need three slack variables. The initial simplex tableau is as follows.

x_1	x_2	x_3	x_4	s_1	s_2	s_3	z	
0	0	3	5	1	0	0	0	4000
0	6	4	3	0	1	0	0	4800
$\boxed{8}$	2	1	0	0	0	1	0	2400
−90	−70	−60	−50	0	0	0	1	0

The first pivot is the 8 in row 3, column 1.

	x_1	x_2	x_3	x_4	s_1	s_2	s_3	z	
	0	0	3	$\boxed{5}$	1	0	0	0	4000
	0	6	4	3	0	1	0	0	4800
	8	2	1	0	0	0	1	0	2400
$45R_3 + 4R_4 \to R_4$	0	−190	−195	−200	0	0	45	4	108,000

Pivot on the 5 in row 1, column 4.

	x_1	x_2	x_3	x_4	s_1	s_2	s_3	z	
	0	0	3	5	1	0	0	0	4000
$-3R_1 + 5R_2 \to R_2$	0	$\boxed{30}$	11	0	−3	5	0	0	12,000
	8	2	1	0	0	0	1	0	2400
$40R_1 + R_4 \to R_4$	0	−190	−75	0	40	0	45	4	268,000

Pivot on the 30 in row 2, column 2.

$$\begin{array}{r} \\ \\ \\ -R_2+15R_3 \rightarrow R_3 \\ 19R_2+\ \ 3R_4 \rightarrow R_4 \end{array}
\begin{array}{c} \begin{array}{cccccccc} x_1 & x_2 & x_3 & x_4 & s_1 & s_2 & s_3 & z \end{array} \\
\left[\begin{array}{cccccccc|c}
0 & 0 & 3 & 5 & 1 & 0 & 0 & 0 & 4000 \\
0 & 30 & \boxed{11} & 0 & -3 & 5 & 0 & 0 & 12{,}000 \\
120 & 0 & 4 & 0 & 3 & -5 & 15 & 0 & 24{,}000 \\ \hline
0 & 0 & -16 & 0 & 63 & 95 & 135 & 12 & 1{,}032{,}000
\end{array}\right] \end{array}$$

Pivot on the 11 in row 2, column 3.

$$\begin{array}{r} \\ -3R_2+11R_1 \rightarrow R_1 \\ \\ -4R_2+11R_3 \rightarrow R_3 \\ 16R_2+11R_4 \rightarrow R_4 \end{array}
\begin{array}{c} \begin{array}{cccccccc} x_1 & x_2 & x_3 & x_4 & s_1 & s_2 & s_3 & z \end{array} \\
\left[\begin{array}{cccccccc|c}
0 & -90 & 0 & 55 & 20 & -15 & 0 & 0 & 8000 \\
0 & 30 & 11 & 0 & -3 & 5 & 0 & 0 & 12{,}000 \\
1320 & -120 & 0 & 0 & 45 & -75 & 165 & 0 & 216{,}000 \\ \hline
0 & 480 & 0 & 0 & 645 & 1125 & 1485 & 132 & 11{,}544{,}000
\end{array}\right] \end{array}$$

$$\begin{array}{r} \\ \frac{1}{55}R_1 \rightarrow R_1 \\ \frac{1}{11}R_2 \rightarrow R_2 \\ \frac{1}{1320}R_3 \rightarrow R_3 \\ \frac{1}{132}R_4 \rightarrow R_4 \end{array}
\begin{array}{c} \begin{array}{cccccccc} x_1 & x_2 & x_3 & x_4 & s_1 & s_2 & s_3 & z \end{array} \\
\left[\begin{array}{cccccccc|c}
0 & -\frac{18}{11} & 0 & 1 & \frac{4}{11} & -\frac{3}{11} & 0 & 0 & \frac{1600}{11} \\
0 & \frac{30}{11} & 1 & 0 & -\frac{3}{11} & \frac{5}{11} & 0 & 0 & \frac{12{,}000}{11} \\
1 & -\frac{1}{11} & 0 & 0 & \frac{3}{88} & -\frac{15}{264} & \frac{1}{8} & 0 & \frac{1800}{11} \\ \hline
0 & \frac{40}{11} & 0 & 0 & \frac{215}{44} & \frac{1125}{132} & \frac{45}{4} & 1 & \frac{962{,}000}{11}
\end{array}\right] \end{array}$$

This final tableau gives the solution $x_1 = \frac{1800}{11} \approx 163.6, x_2 = 0, x_3 = \frac{12{,}000}{11} \approx 1090.9, x_4 = \frac{1600}{11} \approx 145.5$, and $z = \frac{962{,}000}{11} \approx 87,454.5$. Produce 163.6 kg of food P, none of food Q, 1090.9 kg of R, and 145.5 kg of S.

(b) The maximum total growth value is read from the bottom row of the final tableau: $\frac{962{,}000}{11} \approx 87{,}454.5$.

(c) When $x_1 = \frac{1800}{11}, x_2 = 0, x_3 = \frac{12{,}000}{11}$, and $x_4 = \frac{1600}{11}$, the number of units of nutrient A used is

$$0.375\left(\frac{12{,}000}{11}\right) + 0.625\left(\frac{1600}{11}\right) = 500$$

which is the total amount of nutrient A available. The number of units of nutrient B used is

$$0.75(0) + 0.5\left(\frac{12{,}000}{11}\right) + 0.375\left(\frac{1600}{11}\right) = 600$$

which is all the units of nutrient B. The amount of nutrient C used is

$$\left(\frac{1800}{11}\right) + 0.25(0) + 0.125\left(\frac{12{,}000}{11}\right) = 300$$

which is all of the nutrient C. So none of the nutrients are left over.

36. (a) Let x_1 represent the number of species A, x_2 represent the number of species B, and x_3 represent the number of species C.

$$\begin{array}{ll} \text{Maximize} & z = 1.62x_1 + 2.14x_2 + 3.01x_3 \\ \text{subject to:} & 1.32x_1 + \ \ 2.1x_2 + 0.86x_3 \leq 490 \\ & 2.9x_1 + 0.95x_2 + 1.52x_3 \leq 897 \\ & 1.75x_1 + \ \ 0.6x_2 + 2.01x_3 \leq 653 \\ \text{with} & x_1 \geq 0, x_2 \geq 0, x_3 \geq 0. \end{array}$$

Use a graphing calculator or computer to solve this problem and find that the answer is to stock none of species A, 114 of species B, and 291 of species C for a maximum combined weight of 1119.72 kg.

(b) When $x_1 = 0$, $x_2 = 114$, and $x_2 = 291$, the number of units used are as follows.

Food I: $1.32(0) + 2.1 + (114) + 0.86(291) = 489.66$

or 490 units, which is the total amount available of Food I.

Food II: $2.9(0) + 0.95(114) + 1.52(291) = 550.62$

or 551 units, which leaves 897 – 551, or 346 units of Food II available.

Food III: $1.75(0) + 0.6(114) + 2.01(291) = 653.31$

or 653 units, which is the total amount available of Food III.

(c) Many answers are possible. The idea is to choose average weights for species B and C that are considerably smaller than the average weight chosen for species A, so that species A dominates the objective function.

(d) Many answers are possible. The idea is to choose average weights for species A and B that are considerably smaller than the average weight chosen for species C.

37. Let x_1 represent the number of minutes for the senator, x_2 the number of minutes for the congresswoman, and x_3 the number of minutes for the governor.

Of the half-hour show's time, at most only $30 - 3 = 27$ min are available to be allotted to the politicians. The given information leads to the inequality

$$x_1 + x_2 + x_3 \leq 27$$

and the inequalities

$$x_1 \geq 2x_3 \quad \text{and} \quad x_1 + x_3 \geq 2x_2,$$

and we are to maximize the objective function

$$z = 35x_1 + 40x_2 + 45x_3.$$

Rewrite the equation as

$$x_3 \leq 27 - x_1 - x_2$$

and the inequalities as

$$-x_1 + 2x_3 \leq 0 \quad \text{and} \quad -x_1 + 2x_2 - x_3 \leq 0.$$

Substitute $27 - x_1 - x_2$ for x_3 in the objective function and the inequalities, and the problem is as follows.

$$\begin{array}{ll} \text{Maximize} & z = 35x_1 + 40x_2 + 45x_3 \\ \text{subject to:} & -x_1 \qquad\quad + 2x_3 \leq 0 \\ & -x_1 + 2x_2 - \ \ x_3 \leq 0 \\ & x_1 + \ \ x_2 + \ \ x_3 \leq 27 \\ \text{with} & x_1 \geq 0, x_2 \geq 0, x_3 \geq 0. \end{array}$$

We need three slack variables. The initial simplex tableau is as follows.

$$\begin{array}{c} \\ \\ \\ \\ \\ \end{array}\begin{array}{ccccccc|c} x_1 & x_2 & x_3 & s_1 & s_2 & s_3 & z & \\ \hline -1 & 0 & 2 & 1 & 0 & 0 & 0 & 0 \\ -1 & \boxed{2} & -1 & 0 & 1 & 0 & 0 & 0 \\ 1 & 1 & 1 & 0 & 0 & 1 & 0 & 27 \\ \hline -35 & -40 & -45 & 0 & 0 & 0 & 1 & 0 \end{array}$$

Pivot on the 2 in row 2, column 2.

$$\begin{array}{r} \\ \\ \\ -R_2 + 2R_3 \rightarrow R_3 \\ 20R_2 + R_4 \rightarrow R_4 \end{array}\begin{array}{ccccccc|c} x_1 & x_2 & x_3 & s_1 & s_2 & s_3 & z & \\ \hline -1 & 0 & \boxed{2} & 1 & 0 & 0 & 0 & 0 \\ -1 & 2 & -1 & 0 & 1 & 0 & 0 & 0 \\ 3 & 0 & 3 & 0 & -1 & 2 & 0 & 54 \\ \hline -55 & 0 & -65 & 0 & 20 & 0 & 1 & 0 \end{array}$$

Pivot on the 2 in row 1, column 3.

$$\begin{array}{r} \\ \\ R_1 + 2R_2 \rightarrow R_2 \\ -3R_1 + 2R_3 \rightarrow R_3 \\ 65R_1 + 2R_4 \rightarrow R_4 \end{array}\begin{array}{ccccccc|c} x_1 & x_2 & x_3 & s_1 & s_2 & s_3 & z & \\ \hline -1 & 0 & 2 & 1 & 0 & 0 & 0 & 0 \\ -3 & 4 & 0 & 1 & 2 & 0 & 0 & 0 \\ \boxed{9} & 0 & 0 & -3 & -2 & 4 & 0 & 108 \\ \hline -175 & 0 & 0 & 65 & 40 & 0 & 2 & 0 \end{array}$$

Pivot on the 9 in row 3, column 1.

$$\begin{array}{r} \\ R_3 + 9R_1 \rightarrow R_1 \\ R_3 + 3R_2 \rightarrow R_2 \\ \\ 175R_3 + 9R_4 \rightarrow R_4 \end{array}\begin{array}{ccccccc|c} x_1 & x_2 & x_3 & s_1 & s_2 & s_3 & z & \\ \hline 0 & 0 & 18 & 6 & -2 & 4 & 0 & 108 \\ 0 & 12 & 0 & 0 & 4 & 4 & 0 & 108 \\ 9 & 0 & 0 & -3 & -2 & 4 & 0 & 108 \\ \hline 0 & 0 & 0 & 60 & 10 & 700 & 18 & 18{,}900 \end{array}$$

Create a 1 in the columns corresponding to x_1, x_2, x_3, and z.

$$\begin{array}{r} \\ \frac{1}{18} R_1 \rightarrow R_1 \\ \frac{1}{12} R_2 \rightarrow R_2 \\ \frac{1}{9} R_3 \rightarrow R_3 \\ \frac{1}{18} R_4 \rightarrow R_4 \end{array}\begin{array}{ccccccc|c} x_1 & x_2 & x_3 & s_1 & s_2 & s_3 & z & \\ \hline 0 & 0 & 1 & \frac{1}{3} & -\frac{1}{9} & \frac{2}{9} & 0 & 6 \\ 0 & 1 & 0 & 0 & \frac{1}{3} & \frac{1}{3} & 0 & 9 \\ 1 & 0 & 0 & -\frac{1}{3} & -\frac{2}{9} & \frac{4}{9} & 0 & 12 \\ \hline 0 & 0 & 0 & \frac{10}{3} & \frac{5}{9} & \frac{350}{9} & 1 & 1050 \end{array}$$

The maximum value of z is 1050 when $x_1 = 12, x_2 = 9$, and $x_3 = 6$. That is, for a maximum of 1,050,000 viewers, the time allotments should be 12 minutes for the senator, 9 minutes for the congresswoman, and 6 minutes for the governor.

38. **(a)** Let x_1 = number of large fund-raising parties, x_2 = number of letters requesting funds, and x_3 = number of dinner parties.

$$\begin{aligned} \text{Maximize} \quad & z = 200{,}000x_1 + 100{,}000x_2 + 600{,}000x_3 \\ \text{subject to:} \quad & x_1 + x_2 + x_3 \le 25 \\ & 3000x + 1000x_2 + 12{,}000x_3 \le 102{,}000 \\ \text{with} \quad & x_1 \ge 0, x_2 \ge 0, x_3 \ge 0. \end{aligned}$$

We need two slack variables. The initial simplex tableau is as follows.

$$\begin{array}{c} \begin{array}{cccccc} x_1 & x_2 & x_3 & s_1 & s_2 & z \end{array} \\ \left[\begin{array}{cccccc|c} 1 & 1 & 1 & 1 & 0 & 0 & 25 \\ 3000 & 1000 & \boxed{12,000} & 0 & 1 & 0 & 102{,}000 \\ \hline -200,000 & -100,000 & -600,000 & 0 & 0 & 1 & 0 \end{array}\right] \end{array}$$

Pivot on the 12,000 in row 2, column 3.

$$\begin{array}{r} \mathrm{R}_2 + (-12,000\mathrm{R}_1) \to \mathrm{R}_1 \\ \\ 50\mathrm{R}_2 + \mathrm{R}_3 \to \mathrm{R}_3 \end{array} \left[\begin{array}{cccccc|c} \boxed{-9000} & -11,000 & 0 & -12,000 & 1 & 0 & -198,000 \\ 3000 & 1000 & 12,000 & 0 & 1 & 0 & 102{,}000 \\ \hline -50,000 & -50,000 & 0 & 0 & 50 & 1 & 5{,}100{,}000 \end{array}\right]$$

Pivot on -9000 in row 1, column 1.

$$\begin{array}{r} \\ \mathrm{R}_1 + 3\mathrm{R}_2 \to \mathrm{R}_2 \\ 50\mathrm{R}_1 + (-9)\mathrm{R}_3 \to \mathrm{R}_3 \end{array} \left[\begin{array}{cccccc|c} -9000 & -11,000 & 0 & -12,000 & 1 & 0 & -198,000 \\ 0 & -8000 & 36,000 & -12,000 & 4 & 0 & 108{,}000 \\ \hline 0 & -100,000 & 0 & -600,000 & -400 & -9 & -55{,}800{,}000 \end{array}\right]$$

Create a 1 in the columns corresponding to x_1, x_3, and z.

$$\begin{array}{r} -\frac{1}{9000}\mathrm{R}_1 \to \mathrm{R}_1 \\ \frac{1}{36{,}000}\mathrm{R}_2 \to \mathrm{R}_2 \\ -\frac{1}{9}\mathrm{R}_3 \to \mathrm{R}_3 \end{array} \left[\begin{array}{cccccc|c} 1 & \frac{11}{9} & 0 & \frac{4}{3} & -\frac{1}{9000} & 0 & 22 \\ 0 & -\frac{2}{9} & 1 & -\frac{1}{3} & \frac{1}{9000} & 0 & 3 \\ \hline 0 & \frac{100{,}000}{9} & 0 & \frac{200{,}000}{3} & \frac{400}{9} & 1 & 6{,}200{,}000 \end{array}\right]$$

The maximum amount of money is \$6,200,000 when $x_1 = 22, x_2 = 0$, and $x_3 = 3$, that is, when 22 fund-raising parties, no mailings, and 3 dinner parties are planned.

4.3 Minimization Problems; Duality

1. To form the transpose of a matrix, the rows of the original matrix are written as the columns of the transpose. The transpose of

$$\begin{bmatrix} 1 & 2 & 3 \\ 3 & 2 & 1 \\ 1 & 10 & 0 \end{bmatrix}$$

is

$$\begin{bmatrix} 1 & 3 & 1 \\ 2 & 2 & 10 \\ 3 & 1 & 0 \end{bmatrix}.$$

2. The transpose of a matrix is found by exchanging the rows and columns. The transpose of

$$\begin{bmatrix} 3 & 4 & -2 & 0 & 1 \\ 2 & 0 & 11 & 5 & 7 \end{bmatrix}$$

is

$$\begin{bmatrix} 3 & 2 \\ 4 & 0 \\ -2 & 11 \\ 0 & 5 \\ 1 & 7 \end{bmatrix}.$$

3. The transpose of

$$\begin{bmatrix} 4 & 5 & -3 & 15 \\ 7 & 14 & 20 & -8 \\ 5 & 0 & -2 & 23 \end{bmatrix}$$

is

$$\begin{bmatrix} 4 & 7 & 5 \\ 5 & 14 & 0 \\ -3 & 20 & -2 \\ 15 & -8 & 23 \end{bmatrix}.$$

4. The transpose of

$$\begin{bmatrix} 1 & 11 & 15 \\ 0 & 10 & -6 \\ 4 & 12 & -2 \\ 1 & -1 & 13 \\ 2 & 25 & -1 \end{bmatrix}$$

is

$$\begin{bmatrix} 1 & 0 & 4 & 1 & 2 \\ 11 & 10 & 12 & -1 & 25 \\ 15 & -6 & -2 & 13 & -1 \end{bmatrix}.$$

5. Maximize $z = 4x_1 + 3x_2 + 2x_3$
subject to: $x_1 + x_2 + x_3 \le 5$
$x_1 + x_2 \le 4$
$2x_1 + x_2 + 3x_3 \le 15$
with $x_1 \ge 0, x_2 \ge 0, x_3 \ge 0.$

To form the dual, first write the augmented matrix for the given problem.

$$\left[\begin{array}{ccc|c} 1 & 1 & 1 & 5 \\ 1 & 1 & 0 & 4 \\ 2 & 1 & 3 & 15 \\ \hline 4 & 3 & 2 & 0 \end{array}\right]$$

Then form the transpose of this matrix.

$$\left[\begin{array}{ccc|c} 1 & 1 & 2 & 4 \\ 1 & 1 & 1 & 3 \\ 1 & 0 & 3 & 2 \\ \hline 5 & 4 & 15 & 0 \end{array}\right]$$

The dual problem is stated from this second matrix (using y instead of x).

Minimize $w = 5y_1 + 4y_2 + 15y_3$
subject to: $y_1 + y_2 + 2y_3 \ge 4$
$y_1 + y_2 + y_3 \ge 3$
$y_1 + 3y_3 \ge 2$
with $y_1 \ge 0, y_2 \ge 0, y_3 \ge 0.$

6. Maximize $z = 2x_1 + 7x_2 + 4x_3$
subject to: $4x_1 + 2x_2 + x_3 \le 26$
$x_1 + 7x_2 + 8x_3 \le 33$
with $x_1 \ge 0, x_2 \ge 0, x_3 \ge 0.$

To find the dual, first write the augmented matrix for the problem.

$$\left[\begin{array}{ccc|c} 4 & 2 & 1 & 26 \\ 1 & 7 & 8 & 33 \\ \hline 2 & 7 & 4 & 0 \end{array}\right]$$

Then form the transpose of this matrix.

$$\left[\begin{array}{cc|c} 4 & 1 & 2 \\ 2 & 7 & 7 \\ 1 & 8 & 4 \\ \hline 26 & 33 & 0 \end{array}\right]$$

The dual problem is:

Minimize $w = 26y_1 + 33y_2$
subject to: $4y_1 + y_2 \ge 2$
$2y_1 + 7y_2 \ge 7$
$y_1 + 8y_2 \ge 4$
with $y_1 \ge 0, y_2 \ge 0.$

7. Minimize $w = 3y_1 + 6y_2 + 4y_3 + y_4$
subject to: $y_1 + y_2 + y_3 + y_4 \geq 150$
$2y_1 + 2y_2 + 3y_3 + 4y_4 \geq 275$
with $y_1 \geq 0, y_2 \geq 0, y_3 \geq 0, y_4 \geq 0.$

To find the dual problem, first write the augmented matrix for the problem.

$$\left[\begin{array}{cccc|c} 1 & 1 & 1 & 1 & 150 \\ 2 & 2 & 3 & 4 & 275 \\ \hline 3 & 6 & 4 & 1 & 0 \end{array}\right]$$

Then form the transpose of this matrix.

$$\left[\begin{array}{cc|c} 1 & 2 & 3 \\ 1 & 2 & 6 \\ 1 & 3 & 4 \\ 1 & 4 & 1 \\ \hline 150 & 275 & 0 \end{array}\right]$$

The dual problem is

Maximize $z = 150x_1 + 275x_2$
subject to: $x_1 + 2x_2 \leq 3$
$x_1 + 2x_2 \leq 6$
$x_1 + 3x_2 \leq 4$
$x_1 + 4x_2 \leq 1$
with $x_1 \geq 0, x_2 \geq 0.$

8. Minimize $w = y_1 + y_2 + 4y_3$
subject to: $y_1 + 2y_2 + 3y_3 \geq 115$
$2y_1 + y_2 + 8y_3 \geq 200$
$y_1 + y_3 \geq 50$
with $y_1 \geq 0, y_2 \geq 0, y_3 \geq 0.$

Write the augmented matrix for the problem.

$$\left[\begin{array}{ccc|c} 1 & 2 & 3 & 115 \\ 2 & 1 & 8 & 200 \\ 1 & 0 & 1 & 50 \\ \hline 1 & 1 & 4 & 0 \end{array}\right]$$

Form the transpose of this matrix.

$$\left[\begin{array}{ccc|c} 1 & 2 & 1 & 1 \\ 2 & 1 & 0 & 1 \\ 3 & 8 & 1 & 4 \\ \hline 115 & 200 & 50 & 0 \end{array}\right]$$

The dual problem is:

Maximize $z = 115x_1 + 200x_2 + 50x_3$
subject to: $x_1 + 2x_2 + x_3 \leq 1$
$2x_1 + x_2 \leq 1$
$3x_1 + 8x_2 + x_3 \leq 4$
with $x_1 \geq 0, x_2 \geq 0, x_3 \geq 0.$

9. Find $y_1 \geq 0$ and $y_2 \geq 0$ such that

$$2y_1 + 3y_2 \geq 6$$
$$2y_1 + y_2 \geq 7$$

and $w = 5y_1 + 2y_2$ is minimized.

Write the augmented matrix for this problem.

$$\left[\begin{array}{cc|c} 2 & 3 & 6 \\ 2 & 1 & 7 \\ \hline 5 & 2 & 0 \end{array}\right]$$

Form the transpose of this matrix.

$$\left[\begin{array}{cc|c} 2 & 2 & 5 \\ 3 & 1 & 2 \\ \hline 6 & 7 & 0 \end{array}\right]$$

Use this matrix to write the dual problem.

Find $x_1 \geq 0$ and $x_2 \geq 0$ such that

$$2x_1 + 2x_2 \leq 5$$
$$3x_1 + x_2 \leq 2$$

and $z = 6x_1 + 7x_2$ is maximized.

Introduce slack variables s_1 and s_2. The initial tableau is as follows.

$$\begin{array}{c} \begin{matrix} x_1 & x_2 & s_1 & s_2 & z \end{matrix} \\ \left[\begin{array}{ccccc|c} 2 & 2 & 1 & 0 & 0 & 5 \\ 3 & \boxed{1} & 0 & 1 & 0 & 2 \\ \hline -6 & -7 & 0 & 0 & 1 & 0 \end{array}\right] \end{array}$$

Pivot on the 1 in row 2, column 2, since that column has the most negative indicator and that row has the smallest nonnegative quotient.

$$\begin{array}{r} -2R_2 + R_1 \rightarrow R_1 \\ \\ 7R_2 + R_3 \rightarrow R_3 \end{array} \begin{array}{c} \begin{matrix} x_1 & x_2 & s_1 & s_2 & z \end{matrix} \\ \left[\begin{array}{ccccc|c} -4 & 0 & 1 & -2 & 0 & 1 \\ 3 & 1 & 0 & 1 & 0 & 2 \\ \hline 15 & 0 & 0 & 7 & 1 & 14 \end{array}\right] \end{array}$$

The minimum value of w is the same as the maximum value of z. The minimum value of w is 14 when $y_1 = 0$ and $y_2 = 7$. (Note that the values of y_1 and y_2 are given by the entries in the bottom row of the columns corresponding to the slack variables in the final tableau.)

10. Find $y_1 \geq 0$ and $y_2 \geq 0$ such that

$$2y_1 + 3y_2 \geq 15$$
$$5y_1 + 6y_2 \geq 35$$

and $w = 2y_1 + 3y_2$ is minimized.

Write the augmented matrix for this problem.

$$\left[\begin{array}{cc|c} 2 & 3 & 15 \\ 5 & 6 & 35 \\ \hline 2 & 3 & 0 \end{array}\right]$$

Form the transpose to get the matrix for the dual problem.

$$\left[\begin{array}{cc|c} 2 & 5 & 2 \\ 3 & 6 & 3 \\ \hline 15 & 35 & 0 \end{array}\right]$$

Use this matrix to write the dual problem:

Find $x_1 \geq 0$ and $x_2 \geq 0$ such that

$$2x_1 + 5x_2 \leq 2$$
$$3x_1 + 6x_2 \leq 3$$

and $z = 15x_1 + 35x_2$ is maximized.

Introduce slack variables and write the initial tableau.

$$\begin{array}{c} \\ \\ \\ \end{array}\begin{array}{c} \begin{array}{cccccc} x_1 & x_2 & s_1 & s_2 & z & \end{array} \\ \left[\begin{array}{ccccc|c} 2 & \boxed{5} & 1 & 0 & 0 & 2 \\ 3 & 6 & 0 & 1 & 0 & 3 \\ \hline -15 & -35 & 0 & 0 & 1 & 0 \end{array}\right] \end{array}$$

Pivot on the 5 in row 1, column 2.

$$\begin{array}{r} \\ -6R_1 + 5R_2 \to R_2 \\ 7R_1 + R_3 \to R_3 \end{array} \left[\begin{array}{ccccc|c} x_1 & x_2 & s_1 & s_2 & z & \\ 2 & 5 & 1 & 0 & 0 & 2 \\ \boxed{3} & 0 & -6 & 5 & 0 & 3 \\ \hline -1 & 0 & 7 & 0 & 1 & 14 \end{array}\right]$$

Because the quotients in the pivot column are the same, we have a choice for the second pivot. Choose the 3 in row 2, column 1, as the second pivot.

$$\begin{array}{r} -2R_2 + 3R_1 \to R_1 \\ \\ R_2 + 3R_3 \to R_3 \end{array} \left[\begin{array}{ccccc|c} 0 & 15 & 15 & -10 & 0 & 0 \\ 3 & 0 & -6 & 5 & 0 & 3 \\ \hline 0 & 0 & 15 & 5 & 3 & 45 \end{array}\right]$$

(columns: x_1, x_2, s_1, s_2, z)

Create a 1 in the columns corresponding to x_1, x_2, and z.

$$\begin{array}{r} \frac{1}{15}R_1 \to R_1 \\ \frac{1}{3}R_2 \to R_2 \\ \frac{1}{3}R_3 \to R_3 \end{array} \left[\begin{array}{ccccc|c} 0 & 1 & 1 & -\frac{2}{3} & 0 & 0 \\ 1 & 0 & -2 & \frac{5}{3} & 0 & 1 \\ \hline 0 & 0 & 5 & \frac{5}{3} & 1 & 15 \end{array}\right]$$

(columns: x_1, x_2, s_1, s_2, z)

The minimum is 15 when $y_1 = 5$ and $y_2 = \frac{5}{3}$.

For the second pivot, if the 2 in row 1, column 1, was chosen instead, the minimum would still be 15 but would occur when $y_1 = \frac{15}{2}$ and $y_2 = 0$. So, any point on the line segment between $\left(5, \frac{5}{3}\right)$ and $\left(\frac{15}{2}, 0\right)$ is a solution.

11. Find $y_1 \geq 0$ and $y_2 \geq 0$ such that

$$10y_1 + 5y_2 \geq 100$$
$$20y_1 + 10y_2 \geq 150$$

and $w = 4y_1 + 5y_2$ is minimized.

Write the augmented matrix for this problem.

$$\left[\begin{array}{cc|c} 10 & 5 & 100 \\ 20 & 10 & 150 \\ \hline 4 & 5 & 0 \end{array}\right]$$

Form the transpose of this matrix.

$$\left[\begin{array}{cc|c} 10 & 20 & 4 \\ 5 & 10 & 5 \\ \hline 100 & 150 & 0 \end{array}\right]$$

Write the dual problem from this matrix.

Find $x_1 \geq 0$ and $x_2 \geq 0$ such that

$$10x_1 + 20x_2 \leq 4$$
$$5x_1 + 10x_2 \leq 5$$

and $z = 100x_1 + 150x_2$ is maximized.

The initial simplex tableau is as follows.

$$\left[\begin{array}{ccccc|c} x_1 & x_2 & s_1 & s_2 & z & \\ 10 & \boxed{20} & 1 & 0 & 0 & 4 \\ 5 & 10 & 0 & 1 & 0 & 5 \\ \hline -100 & -150 & 0 & 0 & 1 & 0 \end{array}\right]$$

Pivot on the 20 in row 1, column 2.

$$\begin{array}{r} \\ -R_1 + 2R_1 \to R_2 \\ 15R_1 + 2R_3 \to R_3 \end{array} \left[\begin{array}{ccccc|c} \boxed{10} & 20 & 1 & 0 & 0 & 4 \\ 0 & 0 & -1 & 2 & 0 & 6 \\ \hline -50 & 0 & 15 & 0 & 2 & 60 \end{array}\right]$$

(columns: x_1, x_2, s_1, s_2, z)

Pivot on the 10 in row 1, column 1.

$$\begin{array}{r} \\ \\ 5R_1 + R_3 \to R_3 \end{array} \left[\begin{array}{ccccc|c} x_1 & x_2 & s_1 & s_2 & z & \\ 10 & 20 & 1 & 0 & 0 & 4 \\ 0 & 0 & -1 & 2 & 0 & 6 \\ \hline 0 & 100 & 20 & 0 & 2 & 80 \end{array}\right]$$

Create a 1 in the columns corresponding to x_1, s_2, and z.

$$\begin{array}{r} \frac{1}{10}R_1 \to R_1 \\ \frac{1}{2}R_2 \to R_2 \\ \frac{1}{2}R_3 \to R_3 \end{array} \left[\begin{array}{ccccc|c} 1 & 2 & \frac{1}{10} & 0 & 0 & \frac{2}{5} \\ 0 & 0 & -\frac{1}{2} & 1 & 0 & 3 \\ \hline 0 & 50 & 10 & 0 & 1 & 40 \end{array}\right]$$

(columns: x_1, x_2, s_1, s_2, z)

The minimum value of w is 40 when $y_1 = 10$ and $y_2 = 0$. (These values of y_1 and y_2 are read from the last row of the columns corresponding to s_1 and s_2 in the final tableau.)

12. Minimize $w = 29y_1 + 10y_2$

subject to: $3y_1 + 2y_2 \geq 2$

$5y_1 + y_2 \geq 3$

with $y_1 \geq 0, y_2 \geq 0.$

Write the augmented matrix for this problem.

$$\left[\begin{array}{cc|c} 3 & 2 & 2 \\ 5 & 1 & 3 \\ \hline 29 & 10 & 0 \end{array}\right]$$

From the transpose to get the matrix for the dual problem.

$$\left[\begin{array}{cc|c} 3 & 5 & 29 \\ 2 & 1 & 10 \\ \hline 2 & 3 & 0 \end{array}\right]$$

Write the dual problem from this matrix:

Maximize $z = 2x_1 + 3x_2$

subject to: $3x_1 + 5x_2 \leq 29$

$2x_1 + x_2 \leq 10$

with $x_1 \geq 0, x_2 \geq 0.$

Write the initial tableau.

$$\left[\begin{array}{ccccc|c} x_1 & x_2 & s_1 & s_2 & z & \\ 3 & \boxed{5} & 1 & 0 & 0 & 29 \\ 2 & 1 & 0 & 1 & 0 & 10 \\ \hline -2 & -3 & 0 & 0 & 1 & 0 \end{array}\right]$$

Pivot on the 5 in row 1, column 2.

$$\begin{array}{r} \\ \\ -R_1 + 5R_2 \to R_2 \\ 3R_1 + 5R_3 \to R_3 \end{array} \left[\begin{array}{ccccc|c} x_1 & x_2 & s_1 & s_2 & z & \\ 3 & 5 & 1 & 0 & 0 & 29 \\ \boxed{7} & 0 & -1 & 5 & 0 & 21 \\ \hline -1 & 0 & 3 & 0 & 5 & 87 \end{array}\right]$$

Pivot on the 7 in row 2, column 1.

$$\begin{array}{r} \\ -3R_2 + 7R_1 \to R_1 \\ \\ R_2 + 7R_3 \to R_3 \end{array} \left[\begin{array}{ccccc|c} x_1 & x_2 & s_1 & s_2 & z & \\ 0 & 35 & 10 & -15 & 0 & 140 \\ 7 & 0 & -1 & 5 & 0 & 21 \\ \hline 0 & 0 & 20 & 5 & 35 & 630 \end{array}\right]$$

Create a 1 in the columns corresponding to x_1, x_2, and z.

$$\begin{array}{r} \\ \frac{1}{35}R_1 \to R_1 \\ \frac{1}{7}R_2 \to R_2 \\ \frac{1}{35}R_3 \to R_3 \end{array} \left[\begin{array}{ccccc|c} x_1 & x_2 & s_1 & s_2 & z & \\ 0 & 1 & \frac{2}{7} & -\frac{3}{7} & 0 & 4 \\ 1 & 0 & -\frac{1}{7} & \frac{5}{7} & 0 & 3 \\ \hline 0 & 0 & \frac{4}{7} & \frac{1}{7} & 1 & 18 \end{array}\right]$$

The minimum is 18 when $y_1 = \frac{4}{7}$ and $y_2 = \frac{1}{7}$.

13. Minimize $w = 2y_1 + y_2 + 3y_3$

subject to: $y_1 + y_2 + y_3 \geq 100$

$2y_1 + y_2 \geq 50$

with $y_1 \geq 0, y_2 \geq 0, y_3 \geq 0.$

Write the augmented matrix.

$$\left[\begin{array}{ccc|c} 1 & 1 & 1 & 100 \\ 2 & 1 & 0 & 50 \\ \hline 2 & 1 & 3 & 0 \end{array}\right]$$

Form the transpose of this matrix.

$$\left[\begin{array}{cc|c} 1 & 2 & 2 \\ 1 & 1 & 1 \\ 1 & 0 & 3 \\ \hline 100 & 50 & 0 \end{array}\right]$$

The dual problem is as follows.

Maximize $z = 100x_1 + 50x_2$

subject to: $x_1 + 2x_2 \leq 2$

$x_1 + x_2 \leq 1$

$x_1 \leq 3$

with $x_1 \geq 0, x_2 \geq 0.$

The initial simplex tableau is as follows.

$$\left[\begin{array}{cccccc|c} x_1 & x_2 & s_1 & s_2 & s_3 & z & \\ 1 & 2 & 1 & 0 & 0 & 0 & 2 \\ \boxed{1} & 1 & 0 & 1 & 0 & 0 & 1 \\ 1 & 0 & 0 & 0 & 1 & 0 & 3 \\ \hline -100 & -50 & 0 & 0 & 0 & 1 & 0 \end{array}\right]$$

Pivot on the 1 in row 2, column 1.

$$\begin{array}{r} \\ -R_2+R_1 \to R_1 \\ \\ -R_2+R_3 \to R_3 \\ 100R_2+R_4 \to R_4 \end{array} \begin{array}{c} \begin{array}{cccccc} x_1 & x_2 & s_1 & s_2 & s_3 & z \end{array} \\ \left[\begin{array}{cccccc|c} 0 & 1 & 1 & -1 & 0 & 0 & 1 \\ 1 & 1 & 0 & 1 & 0 & 0 & 1 \\ 0 & -1 & 0 & -1 & 1 & 0 & 2 \\ \hline 0 & 50 & 0 & 100 & 0 & 1 & 100 \end{array}\right] \end{array}$$

The minimum value of w is 100 when $y_1 = 0, y_2 = 100$, and $y_3 = 0$.

14. Minimize $w = 3y_1 + 2y_2$
subject to:
$y_1 + 2y_2 \geq 10$
$y_1 + y_2 \geq 8$
$2y_1 + y_2 \geq 12$
with $y_1 \geq 0, y_2 \geq 0$.

Write the augmented matrix.

$$\left[\begin{array}{cc|c} 1 & 2 & 10 \\ 1 & 1 & 8 \\ 2 & 1 & 12 \\ \hline 3 & 2 & 0 \end{array}\right]$$

Transpose to get the matrix for the dual problem.

$$\left[\begin{array}{ccc|c} 1 & 1 & 2 & 3 \\ 2 & 1 & 1 & 2 \\ \hline 10 & 8 & 12 & 0 \end{array}\right]$$

Write the dual problem:

Maximize $z = 10x_1 + 8x_2 + 12x_3$
subject to:
$x_1 + x_2 + 2x_3 \leq 3$
$2x_1 + x_2 + x_3 \leq 2$
with $x_1 \geq 0, x_2 \geq 0, x_3 \geq 0$.

Write the initial tableau.

$$\begin{array}{c} \begin{array}{cccccc} x_1 & x_2 & x_3 & s_1 & s_2 & z \end{array} \\ \left[\begin{array}{cccccc|c} 1 & 1 & \boxed{2} & 1 & 0 & 0 & 3 \\ 2 & 1 & 1 & 0 & 1 & 0 & 2 \\ \hline -10 & -8 & -12 & 0 & 0 & 1 & 0 \end{array}\right] \end{array}$$

Pivot on the 2 in row 1, column 3.

$$\begin{array}{r} \\ \\ 2R_2 - R_1 \to R_2 \\ R_3 + 6R_1 \to R_3 \end{array} \begin{array}{c} \begin{array}{cccccc} x_1 & x_2 & x_3 & s_1 & s_2 & z \end{array} \\ \left[\begin{array}{cccccc|c} 1 & 1 & 2 & 1 & 0 & 0 & 3 \\ \boxed{3} & 1 & 0 & -1 & 2 & 0 & 1 \\ \hline -4 & -2 & 0 & 6 & 0 & 1 & 18 \end{array}\right] \end{array}$$

Pivot on the 3 in row 2, column 1.

$$\begin{array}{r} \\ 3R_1 - R_2 \to R_1 \\ \\ 4R_2 + 3R_3 \to R_3 \end{array} \begin{array}{c} \begin{array}{cccccc} x_1 & x_2 & x_3 & s_1 & s_2 & z \end{array} \\ \left[\begin{array}{cccccc|c} 0 & 2 & 6 & 4 & -2 & 0 & 8 \\ 3 & 1 & 0 & -1 & 2 & 0 & 1 \\ \hline 0 & -2 & 0 & 14 & 8 & 3 & 58 \end{array}\right] \end{array}$$

Pivot on the 1 in row 2, column 2.

$$\begin{array}{r} \\ R_1 - 2R_2 \to R_1 \\ \\ R_3 + 2R_2 \to R_3 \end{array} \begin{array}{c} \begin{array}{cccccc} x_1 & x_2 & x_3 & s_1 & s_2 & z \end{array} \\ \left[\begin{array}{cccccc|c} -6 & 0 & 6 & 6 & -6 & 0 & 6 \\ 3 & 1 & 0 & -1 & 2 & 0 & 1 \\ \hline 6 & 0 & 0 & 12 & 12 & 3 & 60 \end{array}\right] \end{array}$$

Create a 1 in the columns corresponding to x_2, x_3, and z.

$$\begin{array}{r} \\ \frac{1}{6}R_1 \to R_1 \\ \\ \frac{1}{3}R_3 \to R_3 \end{array} \begin{array}{c} \begin{array}{cccccc} x_1 & x_2 & x_3 & s_1 & s_2 & z \end{array} \\ \left[\begin{array}{cccccc|c} -1 & 0 & 1 & 1 & -1 & 0 & 1 \\ 3 & 1 & 0 & -1 & 2 & 0 & 1 \\ \hline 2 & 0 & 0 & 4 & 4 & 1 & 20 \end{array}\right] \end{array}$$

This solution is optimal. The minimum is 20 when $y_1 = 4$ and $y_2 = 4$.

15. Minimize $z = x_1 + 2x_2$
subject to:
$-2x_1 + x_2 \geq 1$
$x_1 - 2x_2 \geq 1$
with $x_1 \geq 0, x_2 \geq 0$.

A quick sketch of the constraints $-2x_1 + x_2 \geq 1$ and $x_1 - 2x_2 \geq 1$ will verify that the two corresponding half planes do not overlap in the first quadrant of the x_1x_2-plane. Therefore, this problem (P) has no feasible solution. The dual of the given problem is as follows:

Maximize $w = y_1 + y_2$
subject to:
$-2y_1 + y_2 \leq 1$
$y_1 - 2y_2 \leq 2$
with $y_1 \geq 0, y_2 \geq 0$.

A quick sketch here will verify that there is a feasible region in the y_1y_2-plane, and it is unbounded. Therefore, there is no maximum value of w in this problem (D).

(P) has no feasible solution and the objective function of (D) is unbounded; this is choice (a).

16. (a) Let y_1 = the number of units of regular beer and y_2 = the number of units of light beer.

Minimize $w = 32{,}000y_1 + 50{,}000y_2$

Subject to:

$$\begin{array}{rcrl} y_1 & & & \geq 10 \\ & & y_2 & \geq 15 \\ y_1 & + & y_2 & \geq 45 \\ 120{,}000y_1 & + & 300{,}000y_2 & \geq 9{,}000{,}000 \\ y_1 & + & y_2 & \geq 20 \end{array}$$

with $y_1 \geq 0, y_2 \geq 0.$

Write the augmented matrix for this problem.

$$\left[\begin{array}{cc|c} 1 & 0 & 10 \\ 0 & 1 & 15 \\ 1 & 1 & 45 \\ 120{,}000 & 300{,}000 & 9{,}000{,}000 \\ 1 & 1 & 20 \\ \hline 32{,}000 & 50{,}000 & 0 \end{array}\right]$$

Form the transpose of this matrix for the dual problem.

$$\left[\begin{array}{ccccc|c} 1 & 0 & 1 & 120{,}000 & 1 & 32{,}000 \\ 0 & 1 & 1 & 300{,}000 & 1 & 50{,}000 \\ \hline 10 & 15 & 45 & 9{,}000{,}000 & 20 & 0 \end{array}\right]$$

The dual problem is

Maximize $z = 10x_1 + 15x_2 + 45x_3 + 9{,}000{,}000x_4 + 20x_5$

subject to:

$$\begin{array}{l} x_1 + x_3 + 120{,}000x_4 + x_5 \leq 32{,}000 \\ x_2 + x_3 + 300{,}000x_4 + x_5 \leq 50{,}000 \end{array}$$

with $x_1 \geq 0, x_2 \geq 0, x_3 \geq 0, x_4 \geq 0, x_5 \geq 0.$

Write the initial simplex tableau.

$$\begin{array}{c} \begin{array}{ccccccccc} x_1 & x_2 & x_3 & x_4 & x_5 & s_1 & s_2 & z & \end{array} \\ \left[\begin{array}{cccccccc|c} 1 & 0 & 1 & 120{,}000 & 1 & 1 & 0 & 0 & 32{,}000 \\ 0 & 1 & 1 & \boxed{300{,}000} & 1 & 0 & 1 & 0 & 50{,}000 \\ \hline -10 & -15 & -45 & -9{,}000{,}000 & -20 & 0 & 0 & 1 & 0 \end{array}\right] \end{array}$$

Pivot on the 300,000 in row 2, column 3.

$$\begin{array}{r} -2R_2+5R_1 \rightarrow R_1 \\ \\ 30R_2+R_3 \rightarrow R_3 \end{array} \left[\begin{array}{cccccccc|c} 5 & -2 & \boxed{3} & 0 & 3 & 5 & -2 & 0 & 60{,}000 \\ 0 & 1 & 1 & 300{,}000 & 1 & 0 & 1 & 0 & 50{,}000 \\ \hline -10 & 15 & -15 & 0 & 10 & 0 & 30 & 1 & 1{,}500{,}000 \end{array}\right]$$

(columns: $x_1, x_2, x_3, x_4, x_5, s_1, s_2, z$)

Pivot on the 3 in row 1, column 3.

$$\begin{array}{r} \\ -R_1+3R_2 \rightarrow R_2 \\ 5R_1+R_3 \rightarrow R_3 \end{array} \left[\begin{array}{cccccccc|c} 5 & -2 & 3 & 0 & 3 & 5 & -2 & 0 & 60{,}000 \\ -5 & 5 & 0 & 900{,}000 & 0 & -5 & 5 & 0 & 90{,}000 \\ \hline 15 & 5 & 0 & 0 & 25 & 25 & 20 & 1 & 1{,}800{,}000 \end{array}\right]$$

(columns: $x_1, x_2, x_3, x_4, x_5, s_1, s_2, z$)

Create a 1 in the columns corresponding to x_3 and x_4.

$$\begin{array}{r} \frac{1}{3}R_1 \to R_1 \\ \frac{1}{900{,}000}R_3 \to R_3 \\ \\ \end{array} \begin{array}{c} \\ \left[\begin{array}{cccccccc|c} x_1 & x_2 & x_3 & x_4 & x_5 & s_1 & s_2 & z & \\ \frac{5}{3} & -\frac{2}{3} & 1 & 0 & 1 & \frac{5}{3} & -\frac{2}{3} & 0 & 20{,}000 \\ -\frac{1}{180{,}000} & \frac{1}{180{,}000} & 0 & 1 & 0 & -\frac{1}{180{,}000} & \frac{1}{180{,}000} & 0 & \frac{1}{10} \\ \hline 15 & 5 & 0 & 0 & 25 & 25 & 20 & 1 & 1{,}800{,}000 \end{array}\right] \end{array}$$

The minimum value of w is 1,800,000 when $y_1 = 25$ and $y_2 = 20$.
Therefore, 25 units of regular beer and 20 units of light beer should be made for a minimum cost of \$1,800,000.

(b) The shadow cost for revenue is $\frac{1}{10}$ dollar or \$0.10. An increase in \$500,000 in revenue will increase costs to

$$\$1{,}800{,}000 + \$0.10(500{,}000) = \$1{,}850{,}000.$$

17. (a) Let y_1 = the number of small test tubes and y_2 = the number of large test tubes.

Minimize $w = 18y_1 + 15y_2$

Subject to:

$$\begin{aligned} y_1 \quad\quad &\geq 900 \\ y_2 &\geq 600 \\ y_1 + y_2 &\geq 2700 \\ y_1 \quad\quad &\geq 2y_2 \end{aligned}$$

with $y_1 \geq 0, y_2 \geq 0$.

The last constraint can be written as

$$y_1 - 2y_2 \geq 0.$$

Write the augmented matrix for this problem.

$$\left[\begin{array}{cc|c} 1 & 0 & 900 \\ 0 & 1 & 600 \\ 1 & 1 & 2700 \\ 1 & -2 & 0 \\ \hline 18 & 15 & 0 \end{array}\right]$$

Transpose to get the matrix for the dual problem.

$$\left[\begin{array}{cccc|c} 1 & 0 & 1 & 1 & 18 \\ 0 & 1 & 1 & -2 & 15 \\ \hline 900 & 600 & 2700 & 0 & 0 \end{array}\right]$$

Write the dual problem.

Maximize $z = 900x_1 + 600x_2 + 2700x_3$

Subject to:

$$\begin{aligned} x_1 \quad + x_3 + x_4 &\leq 18 \\ x_2 + x_3 - 2x_4 &\leq 15 \end{aligned}$$

with $x_1 \geq 0, x_2 \geq 0, x_3 \geq 0, x_4 \geq 0$

Write the initial simplex tableau.

$$\left[\begin{array}{ccccccc|c} x_1 & x_2 & x_3 & x_4 & s_1 & s_2 & z & \\ 1 & 0 & 1 & 1 & 1 & 0 & 0 & 18 \\ 0 & 1 & \boxed{1} & -2 & 0 & 1 & 0 & 15 \\ \hline -900 & -600 & -2700 & 0 & 0 & 0 & 1 & 0 \end{array}\right]$$

Pivot on the 1 in row 2, column 3.

$$\begin{array}{r} \\ -R_2+R_1\rightarrow R_1 \\ \\ 2700R_2+R_3\rightarrow R_3 \end{array} \begin{array}{c} \begin{array}{ccccccc} x_1 & x_2 & x_3 & x_4 & s_1 & s_2 & z \end{array} \\ \left[\begin{array}{ccccccc|c} 1 & -1 & 0 & \boxed{3} & 1 & -1 & 0 & 3 \\ 0 & 1 & 1 & -2 & 0 & 1 & 0 & 15 \\ \hline -900 & 2100 & 0 & -5400 & 0 & 2700 & 1 & 40{,}500 \end{array}\right] \end{array}$$

Pivot on the 3 in row 1, column 4.

$$\begin{array}{r} \\ \\ 2R_1+3R_2\rightarrow R_2 \\ 1800R_1+R_3\rightarrow R_3 \end{array} \begin{array}{c} \begin{array}{ccccccc} x_1 & x_2 & x_3 & x_4 & s_1 & s_2 & z \end{array} \\ \left[\begin{array}{ccccccc|c} 1 & -1 & 0 & 3 & 1 & -1 & 0 & 3 \\ 2 & 1 & 3 & 0 & 2 & 1 & 0 & 51 \\ \hline 900 & 300 & 0 & 0 & 1800 & 900 & 1 & 45{,}900 \end{array}\right] \end{array}$$

Create a 1 in the columns corresponding to x_3 and x_4.

$$\begin{array}{r} \\ \frac{1}{3}R_1\rightarrow R_1 \\ \frac{1}{3}R_2\rightarrow R_2 \\ \\ \end{array} \begin{array}{c} \begin{array}{ccccccc} x_1 & x_2 & x_3 & x_4 & s_1 & s_2 & z \end{array} \\ \left[\begin{array}{ccccccc|c} \frac{1}{3} & -\frac{1}{3} & 0 & 1 & \frac{1}{3} & -\frac{1}{3} & 0 & 1 \\ \frac{2}{3} & \frac{1}{3} & 1 & 0 & \frac{2}{3} & \frac{1}{3} & 0 & 17 \\ \hline 900 & 300 & 0 & 0 & 1800 & 900 & 1 & 45{,}900 \end{array}\right] \end{array}$$

The minimum cost is 45,900¢, or \$459, when 1800 small test tubes and 900 test tubes are ordered.

(b) The shadow cost for the test tubes is \$0.17. An increase in the minimum number of test tubes by $(3000 - 2700) = 300$ will increase the cost to

$$\$459 + \$0.17(300) = \$510.$$

18. (a) The initial matrix for the original problem is

$$\left[\begin{array}{ccc|c} 1 & 1 & 1 & 100 \\ 400 & 160 & 280 & 20{,}000 \\ \hline 120 & 40 & 60 & 0 \end{array}\right].$$

The transposed matrix, for the dual problem, is

$$\left[\begin{array}{cc|c} 1 & 400 & 120 \\ 1 & 160 & 40 \\ 1 & 280 & 60 \\ \hline 100 & 20{,}000 & 0 \end{array}\right].$$

$$\begin{array}{ll} \text{Minimize} & w = 100y_1 + 20{,}000y_2 \\ \text{subject to:} & y_1 + 400y_2 \geq 120 \\ & y_1 + 160y_2 \geq 40 \\ & y_1 + 280y_2 \geq 60 \\ \text{with} & y_1 \geq 0, y_2 \geq 0. \end{array}$$

(b) We apply the simplex algorithm to the original maximization problem. The initial tableau is

$$\begin{array}{c} \begin{matrix} x_1 & x_2 & x_3 & s_1 & s_2 & z \end{matrix} \\ \left[\begin{array}{cccccc|c} 1 & 1 & 1 & 1 & 0 & 0 & 100 \\ \boxed{400} & 160 & 280 & 0 & 1 & 0 & 20{,}000 \\ \hline -120 & -40 & -60 & 0 & 0 & 1 & 0 \end{array}\right] \end{array}$$

Pivot on the 400 in row 2, column 1.

$$\begin{array}{r} 400R_1 - R_2 \rightarrow R_1 \\ \\ \frac{3}{10}R_2 + R_3 \rightarrow R_3 \end{array} \left[\begin{array}{cccccc|c} x_1 & x_2 & x_3 & s_1 & s_2 & z & \\ 0 & 240 & 120 & 400 & -1 & 0 & 20{,}000 \\ 400 & 160 & 280 & 0 & 1 & 0 & 20{,}000 \\ \hline 0 & 8 & 24 & 0 & 0.3 & 1 & 6000 \end{array}\right]$$

Create a 1 in the columns corresponding to x_1 and s_1.

$$\begin{array}{r} \frac{1}{400}R_1 \rightarrow R_1 \\ \frac{1}{400}R_2 \rightarrow R_2 \\ \\ \end{array} \left[\begin{array}{cccccc|c} x_1 & x_2 & x_3 & s_1 & s_2 & z & \\ 0 & 0.6 & 0.3 & 1 & -\frac{1}{400} & 0 & 50 \\ 1 & 0.4 & 0.7 & 0 & \frac{1}{400} & 0 & 50 \\ \hline 0 & 8 & 24 & 0 & 0.3 & 1 & 6000 \end{array}\right]$$

This solution is optimal. A maximum profit of \$6000 is achieved by planting 50 acres of potatoes, 0 acres of corn, and 0 acres of cabbage.

From the dual solution, the shadow cost of acreage is 0 and of capital is $\frac{3}{10}$.

$$\text{New profit} = 6000 + 0(-10) + \left(\frac{3}{10}\right)1000 = \$6300$$

Now calculate the number of acres of each:

$$\begin{aligned} \text{Profit} &= 120\text{P} + 40\text{C} + 60\text{B} \\ 6300 &= 120\text{P} + 40(0) + 60(0) \\ \text{P} &= 52.5. \end{aligned}$$

The farmer will make a profit of \$6300 by planting 52.5 acres of potatoes and no corn or cabbage.

(c) $\text{New profit} = 6000 + 0(10) + \frac{3}{10}(-1000)$

$= \$5700$

Calculate the number of acres of each:

$$\begin{aligned} \text{Profit} &= 120\text{P} + 40\text{C} + 60\text{B} \\ 5700 &= 120\text{P} + 40(0) + 60(0) \\ \text{P} &= 47.5. \end{aligned}$$

The farmer will make a profit of \$5700 by planting 47.5 acres of potatoes and no corn or cabbage.

19. (a) Maximize $x_1 + 1.5x_2 = z$
subject to:
$$x_1 + 2x_2 \le 200$$
$$4x_1 + 3x_2 \le 600$$
$$0 \le x_2 \le 90$$
with $x_1 \ge 0$.

(b) Write the initial tableau.

$$\begin{array}{cccccc|c} x_1 & x_2 & s_1 & s_2 & s_3 & z & \\ 1 & 2 & 1 & 0 & 0 & 0 & 200 \\ 4 & 3 & 0 & 1 & 0 & 0 & 600 \\ 0 & \boxed{1} & 0 & 0 & 1 & 0 & 90 \\ \hline -1 & -1.5 & 0 & 0 & 0 & 1 & 0 \end{array}$$

Pivot on the 1 in row 3, column 2.

$$\begin{array}{l} -2R_3 + R_1 \to R_1 \\ -3R_3 + R_2 \to R_2 \\ \\ 1.5R_3 + R_4 \to R_4 \end{array} \begin{array}{cccccc|c} x_1 & x_2 & s_1 & s_2 & s_3 & z & \\ \boxed{1} & 0 & 1 & 0 & -2 & 0 & 20 \\ 4 & 0 & 0 & 1 & -3 & 0 & 330 \\ 0 & 1 & 0 & 0 & 1 & 0 & 90 \\ \hline -1 & 0 & 0 & 0 & 1.5 & 1 & 135 \end{array}$$

Pivot on the 1 in row 1, column 1.

$$\begin{array}{l} \\ -4R_1 + R_2 \to R_2 \\ \\ R_1 + R_4 \to R_4 \end{array} \begin{array}{cccccc|c} x_1 & x_2 & s_1 & s_2 & s_3 & z & \\ 1 & 0 & 1 & 0 & -2 & 0 & 20 \\ 0 & 0 & -4 & 1 & \boxed{5} & 0 & 250 \\ 0 & 1 & 0 & 0 & 1 & 0 & 90 \\ \hline 0 & 0 & 1 & 0 & -0.5 & 1 & 155 \end{array}$$

Pivot on the 5 in row 2, column 5.

$$\begin{array}{l} \frac{2}{5}R_2 + R_1 \to R_1 \\ \frac{1}{5}R_2 \to R_2 \\ -\frac{1}{5}R_2 + R_3 \to R_3 \\ \frac{1}{10}R_2 + R_4 \to R_4 \end{array} \begin{array}{cccccc|c} x_1 & x_2 & s_1 & s_2 & s_3 & z & \\ 1 & 0 & -\frac{3}{5} & \frac{2}{5} & 0 & 0 & 120 \\ 0 & 0 & -\frac{4}{5} & \frac{1}{5} & 1 & 0 & 50 \\ 0 & 1 & \frac{4}{5} & -\frac{1}{5} & 0 & 0 & 40 \\ \hline 0 & 0 & 0.6 & 0.1 & 0 & 1 & 180 \end{array}$$

The maximum profit is \$180 when $x_1 = 120$ and $x_2 = 40$, that is, when 120 bears and 40 monkeys are produced.

(c) The corresponding dual problem is as follows:

Minimize $w = 200y_1 + 600y_2 + 90y_3$
subject to:
$$y_1 + 4y_2 \ge 1$$
$$2y_1 + 3y_2 + y_3 \ge 1.5$$
with $y_1 \ge 0, y_2 \ge 0, y_3 \ge 0$.

(d) From the given final tableau, the optimal solution to the dual problem is $y_1 = 0.6, y_2 = 0.1, y_3 = 0$, and $w = 180$.

(e) The shadow value for felt is 0.6; an increase in supply of 10 units of felt will increase profit to

$$\$180 + 0.6(10) = \$186.$$

(f) The shadow values are 0.1 for stuffing and 0 for trim. If stuffing and trim are each decreased by 10 units, the profit will be

$$\$180 - 0.1(10) - 0(10) = \$179.$$

20. Let $y_1 =$ the number of political interviews conducted
and $y_2 =$ the number of market interviews conducted.

The problem is:

$$\begin{array}{ll} \text{Minimize} & w = 45y_1 + 55y_2 \\ \text{subject to:} & y_1 + y_2 \geq 8 \\ & 8y_1 + 10y_2 \geq 60 \\ & 6y_1 + 5y_2 \geq 40 \\ \text{with} & y_1 \geq 0, y_2 \geq 0. \end{array}$$

Write the augmented matrix.

$$\left[\begin{array}{cc|c} 1 & 1 & 8 \\ 8 & 10 & 60 \\ 6 & 5 & 40 \\ \hline 45 & 55 & 0 \end{array}\right]$$

Transpose to get the matrix for the dual problem.

$$\left[\begin{array}{ccc|c} 1 & 8 & 6 & 45 \\ 1 & 10 & 5 & 55 \\ \hline 8 & 60 & 40 & 0 \end{array}\right]$$

Write the dual problem:

$$\begin{array}{ll} \text{Maximize} & z = 8x_1 + 60x_2 + 40x_3 \\ \text{subject to:} & x_1 + 8x_2 + 6x_3 \leq 45 \\ & x_1 + 10x_2 + 5x_3 \leq 55 \\ \text{with} & x_1 \geq 0, x_2 \geq 0, x_3 \geq 0. \end{array}$$

Write the initial tableau.

$$\begin{array}{c} \\ \\ \\ \end{array}\begin{array}{cccccc|c} x_1 & x_2 & x_3 & s_1 & s_2 & z & \\ 1 & 8 & 6 & 1 & 0 & 0 & 45 \\ 1 & \boxed{10} & 5 & 0 & 1 & 0 & 55 \\ \hline -8 & -60 & -40 & 0 & 0 & 1 & 0 \end{array}$$

Pivot on the 10 in row 2, column 2.

$$\begin{array}{r} \\ -4R_2+5R_1 \to R_1 \\ \\ 6R_2+R_3 \to R_3 \end{array}\begin{array}{cccccc|c} x_1 & x_2 & x_3 & s_1 & s_2 & z & \\ 1 & 0 & \boxed{10} & 5 & -4 & 0 & 5 \\ 1 & 10 & 5 & 0 & 1 & 0 & 55 \\ \hline -2 & 0 & -10 & 0 & 6 & 1 & 330 \end{array}$$

Pivot on the 10 in row 1, column 3.

$$\begin{array}{r} \\ \\ -R_1+2R_2 \to R_2 \\ R_1+R_3 \to R_3 \end{array}\begin{array}{cccccc|c} x_1 & x_2 & x_3 & s_1 & s_2 & z & \\ \boxed{1} & 0 & 10 & 5 & -4 & 0 & 5 \\ 1 & 20 & 0 & -5 & 6 & 0 & 105 \\ \hline -1 & 0 & 0 & 5 & 2 & 1 & 335 \end{array}$$

Pivot on the 1 in row 1, column 1.

$$\begin{array}{r} \\ \\ -R_1+R_2 \to R_2 \\ R_1+R_3 \to R_3 \end{array}\begin{array}{cccccc|c} x_1 & x_2 & x_3 & s_1 & s_2 & z & \\ 1 & 0 & 10 & 5 & -4 & 0 & 5 \\ 0 & 20 & -10 & -10 & \boxed{10} & 0 & 100 \\ \hline 0 & 0 & 10 & 10 & -2 & 1 & 340 \end{array}$$

Pivot on the 10 in row 2, column 5.

$$\begin{array}{r} \\ 2R_2+5R_1 \to R_1 \\ \\ R_2+5R_3 \to R_3 \end{array}\begin{array}{cccccc|c} x_1 & x_2 & x_3 & s_1 & s_2 & z & \\ 5 & 40 & 30 & 5 & 0 & 0 & 225 \\ 0 & 20 & -10 & -10 & 10 & 0 & 100 \\ \hline 0 & 20 & 40 & 40 & 0 & 5 & 1800 \end{array}$$

Create a 1 in the columns corresponding to x_1, s_2, and z.

$$\begin{array}{r} \\ \frac{1}{5}R_1 \to R_1 \\ \frac{1}{10}R_2 \to R_2 \\ \frac{1}{5}R_3 \to R_3 \end{array}\begin{array}{cccccc|c} x_1 & x_2 & x_3 & s_1 & s_2 & z & \\ 1 & 8 & 6 & 1 & 0 & 0 & 45 \\ 0 & 2 & -1 & -1 & 1 & 0 & 10 \\ \hline 0 & 4 & 8 & 8 & 0 & 1 & 360 \end{array}$$

The minimum time spent is 360 min when $y_1 = 8$ and $y_2 = 0$, that is, when 8 political interviews and no market interviews are done.

21. (a) Let $y_1 =$ the number of grams of soybean meal,
$y_2 =$ the number of grams of meat byproducts
and $y_3 =$ the number of grams of grain.

$$\begin{array}{ll} \text{Minimize} & w = 8y_1 + 9y_2 + 10y_3 \\ \text{subject to:} & 2.5y_1 + 4.5y_2 + 5y_3 \geq 54 \\ & 5y_1 + 3y_2 + 10y_3 \geq 60 \\ \text{with} & y_1 \geq 0, y_2 \geq 0, y_3 \geq 0. \end{array}$$

Write the augmented matrix for this problem.

$$\left[\begin{array}{ccc|c} 2.5 & 4.5 & 5 & 54 \\ 5 & 3 & 10 & 60 \\ \hline 8 & 9 & 10 & 0 \end{array}\right]$$

Transpose to get the matrix for the dual problem.

$$\left[\begin{array}{cc|c} 2.5 & 5 & 8 \\ 4.5 & 3 & 9 \\ 5 & 10 & 10 \\ \hline 54 & 60 & 0 \end{array}\right]$$

Write the dual problem.

$$\begin{array}{ll} \text{Maximize} & z = 54x_1 + 60x_2 \\ \text{subject to:} & 2.5x_1 + 5x_2 \leq 8 \\ & 4.5x_1 + 3x_2 \leq 9 \\ & 5x_1 + 10x_2 \leq 10 \\ \text{with} & x_1 \geq 0, x_2 \geq 0. \end{array}$$

Write the initial tableau.

$$\begin{array}{c} \\ \\ \\ \\ \\ \end{array}\begin{array}{cccccc|c} x_1 & x_2 & s_1 & s_2 & s_3 & z & \\ 2.5 & 5 & 1 & 0 & 0 & 0 & 8 \\ 4.5 & 3 & 0 & 1 & 0 & 0 & 9 \\ 5 & \boxed{10} & 0 & 0 & 1 & 0 & 10 \\ \hline -54 & -60 & 0 & 0 & 0 & 1 & 0 \end{array}$$

To eliminate the decimal entries, multiply rows 1 and 2 by 2.

$$\begin{array}{cccccc|c} x_1 & x_2 & s_1 & s_2 & s_3 & z & \\ 5 & 10 & 2 & 0 & 0 & 0 & 16 \\ 9 & 6 & 0 & 2 & 0 & 0 & 18 \\ 5 & \boxed{10} & 0 & 0 & 1 & 0 & 10 \\ \hline -54 & -60 & 0 & 0 & 0 & 1 & 0 \end{array}$$

Pivot on the 10 in row 3, column 2.

$$\begin{array}{r} \\ -R_3 + R_1 \to R_1 \\ -3R_3 + 5R_2 \to R_2 \\ \\ 6R_3 + R_4 \to R_4 \end{array}\begin{array}{cccccc|c} x_1 & x_2 & s_1 & s_2 & s_3 & z & \\ 0 & 0 & 2 & 0 & -1 & 0 & 6 \\ \boxed{30} & 0 & 0 & 10 & -3 & 0 & 60 \\ 5 & 10 & 0 & 0 & 1 & 0 & 10 \\ \hline -24 & 0 & 0 & 0 & 6 & 1 & 60 \end{array}$$

Pivot on the 30 in row 2, column 1.

$$\begin{array}{r} \\ \\ \\ -R_2 + 6R_3 \to R_3 \\ 4R_2 + 5R_4 \to R_4 \end{array}\begin{array}{cccccc|c} x_1 & x_2 & s_1 & s_2 & s_3 & z & \\ 0 & 0 & 2 & 0 & -1 & 0 & 6 \\ 30 & 0 & 0 & 10 & -3 & 0 & 60 \\ 0 & 60 & 0 & -10 & 9 & 0 & 0 \\ \hline 0 & 0 & 0 & 40 & 18 & 5 & 540 \end{array}$$

Create a 1 in the columns representing x_1, x_2, s_1, and z.

$$\begin{array}{r} \\ \frac{1}{2}R_1 \to R_1 \\ \frac{1}{30}R_2 \to R_2 \\ \frac{1}{60}R_3 \to R_3 \\ \frac{1}{5}R_4 \to R_4 \end{array}\begin{array}{cccccc|c} x_1 & x_2 & s_1 & s_2 & s_3 & z & \\ 0 & 0 & 1 & 0 & -\frac{1}{2} & 0 & 3 \\ 1 & 0 & 0 & \frac{1}{3} & -\frac{1}{10} & 0 & 2 \\ 0 & 1 & 0 & -\frac{1}{6} & \frac{3}{20} & 0 & 0 \\ \hline 0 & 0 & 0 & 8 & 3.6 & 1 & 108 \end{array}$$

The minimum cost is obtained when 0g of soybean meal, 8g of meat by products, and 3.6g of grain are used, or 0g of soybean meal, 0g of meat by products and 10.8g of grain are used.

(b) The minimum cost is $1.08.

(c) After the initial pivot, the tableau is

$$\begin{array}{cccccc|c} x_1 & x_2 & s_1 & s_2 & s_3 & z & \\ 0 & 0 & 2 & 0 & -1 & 0 & 6 \\ 30 & 0 & 0 & 10 & -3 & 0 & 60 \\ \boxed{5} & 10 & 0 & 0 & 1 & 0 & 10 \\ \hline -24 & 0 & 0 & 0 & 6 & 1 & 60 \end{array}$$

Now pivot on the 5 in row 3, column 1.

$$\begin{array}{r} \\ \\ -6R_3 + R_2 \to R_2 \\ \\ 24R_3 + 5R_4 \to R_4 \end{array}\begin{array}{cccccc|c} x_1 & x_2 & s_1 & s_2 & s_3 & z & \\ 0 & 0 & 2 & 0 & -1 & 0 & 6 \\ 0 & -60 & 0 & 10 & -9 & 0 & 0 \\ 5 & 10 & 0 & 0 & 1 & 0 & 10 \\ \hline 0 & 240 & 0 & 0 & 54 & 5 & 540 \end{array}$$

$$\begin{array}{r} \\ \\ \\ \\ \frac{1}{5}R_4 \to R_4 \end{array}\begin{array}{cccccc|c} x_1 & x_2 & s_1 & s_2 & s_3 & z & \\ 0 & 0 & 2 & 0 & -1 & 0 & 6 \\ 0 & -60 & 0 & 10 & -9 & 0 & 0 \\ 5 & 10 & 0 & 0 & 1 & 0 & 10 \\ \hline 0 & 48 & 0 & 0 & 10.8 & 1 & 108 \end{array}$$

The minimum cost is $108 when $y_1 = 0, y_2 = 8$ and $y_3 = 10.8$, that is, when 0 grams of soybean meal, 0 grams of meat by-products, and 10.8 grams of grain are mixed.

22. Organize the information in a table.

	Units of Nutrient A (per bag)	Units of Nutrient B (per bag)	Cost (per bag)
Feed 1	1	2	$3
Feed 2	3	1	$2
Minimum	7	4	

Let $y_1 =$ the number of bags of feed 1 and $y_2 =$ the number of bags of feed 2.

(a) We want the cost to equal $7 for 7 units of A and 4 units of B exactly. Therefore, use a system of equations rather than a system of inequalities.

$$\begin{aligned} 3y_1 + 2y_2 &= 7 \\ y_1 + 3y_2 &= 7 \\ 2y_1 + y_2 &= 4 \end{aligned}$$

Use Gauss-Jordan elimination to solve this system of equations.

$$\left[\begin{array}{cc|c} 3 & 2 & 7 \\ 1 & 3 & 7 \\ 2 & 1 & 4 \end{array}\right]$$

$$\begin{array}{r} \\ -R_1 + 3R_2 \to R_2 \\ -2R_1 + 3R_3 \to R_3 \end{array} \left[\begin{array}{cc|c} 3 & 2 & 7 \\ 0 & 7 & 14 \\ 0 & -1 & -2 \end{array}\right]$$

$$\begin{array}{r} -2R_2 + 7R_1 \to R_1 \\ \\ R_2 + 7R_3 \to R_3 \end{array} \left[\begin{array}{cc|c} 21 & 0 & 21 \\ 0 & 7 & 14 \\ 0 & 0 & 0 \end{array}\right]$$

$$\begin{array}{r} \frac{1}{21}R_1 \to R_1 \\ \frac{1}{7}R_2 \to R_2 \\ \\ \end{array} \left[\begin{array}{cc|c} 1 & 0 & 1 \\ 0 & 1 & 2 \\ 0 & 0 & 0 \end{array}\right]$$

Thus, $y_1 = 1$ and $y_2 = 2$, so use 1 bag of feed 1 and 2 bags of feed 2. The cost will be $3(1) + 2(2) = \$7$ as desired. The number of units of A is $1(1) + 3(2) = 7$, and the number of units of B is $2(1) + 1(2) = 4$.

(b)

	Units of Nutrient A (per bag)	Units of Nutrient B (per bag)	Cost (per bag)
Feed 1	1	2	\$3
Feed 2	3	1	\$2
Minimum	5	4	

The problem is:

$$\begin{array}{ll} \text{Minimize} & w = 3y_1 + 2y_2 \\ \text{subject to:} & y_1 + 3y_2 \geq 5 \\ & 2y_1 + y_2 \geq 4 \\ \text{with} & y_1 \geq 0, y_2 \geq 0. \end{array}$$

The dual problem is as follows.

$$\begin{array}{ll} \text{Maximize} & z = 5x_1 + 4x_2 \\ \text{subject to:} & x_1 + 2x_2 \leq 3 \\ & 3x_1 + x_2 \leq 2 \\ \text{with} & x_1 \geq 0, x_2 \geq 0. \end{array}$$

The initial tableau is as follows.

$$\begin{array}{c} \begin{array}{ccccc} x_1 & x_2 & s_1 & s_2 & z \end{array} \\ \left[\begin{array}{ccccc|c} 1 & 2 & 1 & 0 & 0 & 3 \\ \boxed{3} & 1 & 0 & 1 & 0 & 2 \\ \hline -5 & -4 & 0 & 0 & 1 & 0 \end{array}\right] \end{array}$$

Pivot as indicated.

$$\begin{array}{r} -R_2 + 3R_1 \to R_1 \\ \\ 5R_2 + 3R_3 \to R_3 \end{array} \begin{array}{c} \begin{array}{ccccc} x_1 & x_2 & s_1 & s_2 & z \end{array} \\ \left[\begin{array}{ccccc|c} 0 & \boxed{5} & 3 & -1 & 0 & 7 \\ 3 & 1 & 0 & 1 & 0 & 2 \\ \hline 0 & -7 & 0 & 5 & 3 & 10 \end{array}\right] \end{array}$$

$$\begin{array}{r} \\ -R_1 + 5R_2 \to R_2 \\ 7R_1 + 5R_3 \to R_3 \end{array} \begin{array}{c} \begin{array}{ccccc} x_1 & x_2 & s_1 & s_2 & z \end{array} \\ \left[\begin{array}{ccccc|c} 0 & 5 & 3 & -1 & 0 & 7 \\ 15 & 0 & -3 & 6 & 0 & 3 \\ \hline 0 & 0 & 21 & 18 & 15 & 99 \end{array}\right] \end{array}$$

Create a 1 in the columns corresponding to x_1, x_2, and z.

$$\begin{array}{r} \frac{1}{5}R_1 \to R_1 \\ \frac{1}{15}R_2 \to R_2 \\ \frac{1}{15}R_3 \to R_3 \end{array} \begin{array}{c} \begin{array}{ccccc} x_1 & x_2 & s_1 & s_2 & z \end{array} \\ \left[\begin{array}{ccccc|c} 0 & 1 & \frac{3}{5} & -\frac{1}{5} & 0 & \frac{7}{5} \\ 1 & 0 & -\frac{1}{5} & \frac{2}{5} & 0 & \frac{1}{5} \\ \hline 0 & 0 & \frac{7}{5} & \frac{6}{5} & 1 & \frac{33}{5} \end{array}\right] \end{array}$$

Reading from the final column of the final tableau, $x_2 = \$1.40$ is the cost of nutrient B and $x_1 = \$0.20$ is the cost of nutrient A. With 5 units of A and 4 units of B, this gives a minimum cost of

$$5(\$0.20) + 4(\$1.40) = \$6.60$$

as given in the lower right corner. 1.4 (or $\frac{7}{5}$) bags of feed 1 and 1.2 (or $\frac{6}{5}$) bags of feed 2 should be used.

23. Let y_1 = the number of large bowls.
y_2 = the number of small bowls.
y_3 = the number of pots for plants.

$$\begin{array}{ll} \text{Minimize} & w = 5y_1 + 6y_2 + 4y_3 \\ \text{subject to:} & 3y_1 + 2y_2 + 4y_3 \geq 72 \\ & 6y_1 + 6y_2 + 2y_3 \geq 108 \\ \text{with} & y_1 \geq 0, y_2 \geq 0, y_3 \geq 0. \end{array}$$

Write the augmented matrix for this problem.

$$\left[\begin{array}{ccc|c} 3 & 2 & 4 & 72 \\ 6 & 6 & 2 & 108 \\ \hline 5 & 6 & 4 & 0 \end{array}\right]$$

Transpose to get the matrix for the dual problem.

$$\left[\begin{array}{cc|c} 3 & 6 & 5 \\ 2 & 6 & 6 \\ 4 & 2 & 4 \\ \hline 72 & 108 & 0 \end{array}\right]$$

Write the dual problem.

$$\begin{array}{ll} \text{Maximize} & z = 72x_1 + 108x_2 \\ \text{subject to:} & 3x_1 + 6x_2 \le 5 \\ & 2x_1 + 6x_2 \le 6 \\ & 4x_1 + 2x_2 \le 4 \\ \text{with} & x_1 \ge 0, x_2 \ge 0. \end{array}$$

Write the initial tableau.

$$\begin{array}{c} \begin{array}{cccccccc} x_1 & x_2 & s_1 & s_2 & s_3 & z & & \end{array} \\ \left[\begin{array}{cccccc|c} 3 & \boxed{6} & 1 & 0 & 0 & 0 & 5 \\ 2 & 6 & 0 & 1 & 0 & 0 & 6 \\ 4 & 2 & 0 & 0 & 1 & 0 & 4 \\ \hline -72 & -108 & 0 & 0 & 0 & 1 & 0 \end{array}\right] \end{array}$$

Pivot on the 6 in row 1, column 2.

$$\begin{array}{r} \\ \frac{1}{6}\text{R}_1 \to \text{R}_1 \\ -\text{R}_1 + \text{R}_2 \to \text{R}_2 \\ -\frac{1}{3}\text{R}_1 + \text{R}_3 \to \text{R}_3 \\ 18\text{R}_1 + \text{R}_4 \to \text{R}_4 \end{array} \begin{array}{c} \begin{array}{cccccc} x_1 & x_2 & s_1 & s_2 & s_3 & z \end{array} \\ \left[\begin{array}{cccccc|c} \frac{1}{2} & 1 & \frac{1}{6} & 0 & 0 & 0 & \frac{5}{6} \\ -1 & 0 & -1 & 1 & 0 & 0 & 1 \\ \boxed{3} & 0 & -\frac{1}{3} & 0 & 1 & 0 & \frac{7}{3} \\ \hline -18 & 0 & 18 & 0 & 0 & 1 & 90 \end{array}\right] \end{array}$$

Pivot on the 3 in row 3, column 1.

$$\begin{array}{r} \\ -\frac{1}{6}\text{R}_3 + \text{R}_1 \to \text{R}_1 \\ \frac{1}{3}\text{R}_3 + \text{R}_2 \to \text{R}_2 \\ \frac{1}{3}\text{R}_3 \to \text{R}_3 \\ 6\text{R}_3 + \text{R}_4 \to \text{R}_4 \end{array} \begin{array}{c} \begin{array}{cccccc} x_1 & x_2 & s_1 & s_2 & s_3 & z \end{array} \\ \left[\begin{array}{cccccc|c} 0 & 1 & \frac{2}{9} & 0 & -\frac{1}{6} & 0 & \frac{4}{9} \\ 0 & 0 & -\frac{10}{9} & 1 & \frac{1}{3} & 0 & \frac{16}{9} \\ 1 & 0 & -\frac{1}{9} & 0 & \frac{1}{3} & 0 & \frac{7}{9} \\ \hline 0 & 0 & 16 & 0 & 6 & 1 & 104 \end{array}\right] \end{array}$$

The minimum time is 104 hours when $y_1 = 16, y_2 = 0$, and $y_3 = 6$, that is, when 16 large bowls, 0 small bowls, and 6 pots for flowers are made.

24. Let $y_1 =$ the number of minutes spent walking, $y_2 =$ the number of minutes spent cycling, and $y_3 =$ the number of minutes spent swimming.

$$\begin{array}{ll} \text{Minimize} & w = y_1 + y_2 + y_3 \\ \text{subject to:} & 3.5y_1 + 4y_2 + 8y_3 \ge 1500 \\ & y_1 + y_2 \ge 3y_3 \\ & y_1 \ge 30 \\ \text{with} & y_1 \ge 0, y_2 \ge 0, y_3 \ge 0. \end{array}$$

The second constraint can be written as

$$y_1 + y_2 - 3y_3 \ge 0.$$

Write the augmented matrix for this problem.

$$\left[\begin{array}{ccc|c} 3.5 & 4 & 8 & 1500 \\ 1 & 1 & -3 & 0 \\ 1 & 0 & 0 & 30 \\ \hline 1 & 1 & 1 & 0 \end{array}\right]$$

Transpose to get the matrix for the dual problem.

$$\left[\begin{array}{ccc|c} 3.5 & 1 & 1 & 1 \\ 4 & 1 & 0 & 1 \\ 8 & -3 & 0 & 1 \\ \hline 1500 & 0 & 30 & 0 \end{array}\right]$$

Write the dual problem.

$$\begin{array}{ll} \text{Maximize} & z = 1500x_1 + 30x_3 \\ \text{subject to:} & 3.5x_1 + x_2 + x_3 \le 1 \\ & 4x_1 + x_2 \le 1 \\ & 8x_1 - 3x_2 \le 1 \\ \text{with} & x_1 \ge 0, s_2 \ge 0, x_3 \ge 0. \end{array}$$

Write the initial simplex tableau.

$$\begin{array}{c} \begin{array}{ccccccc} x_1 & x_2 & x_3 & x_4 & s_1 & s_2 & z \end{array} \\ \left[\begin{array}{ccccccc|c} 3.5 & 1 & 1 & 1 & 0 & 0 & 0 & 1 \\ 4 & 1 & 0 & 0 & 1 & 0 & 0 & 1 \\ 8 & -3 & 0 & 0 & 0 & 1 & 0 & 1 \\ \hline -1500 & 0 & -30 & 0 & 0 & 0 & 1 & 0 \end{array}\right] \end{array}$$

Using a graphing calculator or computer program, such as Solver in Microsoft Excel, we obtain the optimal answer: 30 minutes walking, 197.25 minutes cycling, and 75.75 minutes swimming for a total minimum time of 303 minutes per week.

25. Let $y_1 =$ the number of #1 pills and $y_2 =$ the number of #2 pills.

Organize the given information in a table.

	Vitamin A	Vitamin B_1	Vitamin C	Cost
#1	8	1	2	$0.10
#2	2	1	7	$0.20
Total Needed	16	5	20	

The problem is:

$$\begin{array}{ll} \text{Minimize} & w = 0.1y_1 + 0.2y_2 \\ \text{subject to:} & 8y_1 + 2y_2 \ge 16 \\ & y_1 + y_2 \ge 5 \\ & 2y_1 + 7y_2 \ge 20 \\ \text{with} & y_1 \ge 0, y_2 \ge 0\ . \end{array}$$

The dual problem is as follows.

$$\begin{array}{ll} \text{Maximize} & z = 16x_1 + 5x_2 + 20x_3 \\ \text{subject to:} & 8x_1 + x_2 + 2x_3 \le 0.1 \\ & 2x_1 + x_2 + 7x_3 \le 0.2 \\ \text{with} & x_1 \ge 0, x_2 \ge 0. \end{array}$$

The initial tableau is as follows.

$$\begin{array}{c} \\ \\ \\ \end{array}\begin{array}{cccccc|c} x_1 & x_2 & x_3 & s_1 & s_2 & z & \\ \hline 8 & 1 & 2 & 1 & 0 & 0 & 0.1 \\ 2 & 1 & \boxed{7} & 0 & 1 & 0 & 0.2 \\ \hline -16 & -5 & -20 & 0 & 0 & 1 & 0 \end{array}$$

Pivot as indicated.

$$\begin{array}{r} \\ -2R_2 + 7R_1 \rightarrow R_1 \\ \\ 20R_2 + 7R_3 \rightarrow R_3 \end{array}\begin{array}{cccccc|c} x_1 & x_2 & x_3 & s_1 & s_2 & z & \\ \hline \boxed{52} & 5 & 0 & 7 & -2 & 0 & 0.3 \\ 2 & 1 & 7 & 0 & 1 & 0 & 0.2 \\ \hline -72 & -15 & 0 & 0 & 20 & 7 & 4 \end{array}$$

$$\begin{array}{r} \\ \\ -R_1 + 26R_2 \rightarrow R_2 \\ 18R_1 + 13R_3 \rightarrow R_3 \end{array}\begin{array}{cccccc|c} x_1 & x_2 & x_3 & s_1 & s_2 & z & \\ \hline 52 & \boxed{5} & 0 & 7 & -2 & 0 & 0.3 \\ 0 & 21 & 182 & -7 & 28 & 0 & 4.9 \\ \hline 0 & -105 & 0 & 126 & 224 & 91 & 57.4 \end{array}$$

$$\begin{array}{r} \\ \\ -21R_1 + 5R_2 \rightarrow R_2 \\ 21R_1 + R_3 \rightarrow R_3 \end{array}\begin{array}{cccccc|c} x_1 & x_2 & x_3 & s_1 & s_2 & z & \\ \hline 52 & 5 & 0 & 7 & -2 & 0 & 0.3 \\ -1092 & 0 & 910 & -182 & 182 & 0 & 18.2 \\ \hline 1092 & 0 & 0 & 273 & 182 & 91 & 63.7 \end{array}$$

Create a 1 in the columns corresponding to x_2, x_3, and z.

$$\begin{array}{r} \\ \frac{1}{5}R_1 \rightarrow R_1 \\ \frac{1}{910}R_2 \rightarrow R_2 \\ \frac{1}{91}R_3 \rightarrow R_3 \end{array}\begin{array}{cccccc|c} x_1 & x_2 & x_3 & s_1 & s_2 & z & \\ \hline \frac{52}{5} & 1 & 0 & \frac{7}{5} & -\frac{2}{5} & 0 & 0.06 \\ -\frac{6}{5} & 0 & 1 & -\frac{1}{5} & \frac{1}{5} & 0 & 0.02 \\ \hline 12 & 0 & 0 & 3 & 2 & 1 & 0.7 \end{array}$$

From the last row, the minimum value is 0.7 when $y_1 = 3$ and $y_2 = 2$. Mark should buy 3 of pill #1 and 2 of pill #2 for a minimum cost of 70¢.

26. Let $y_1 =$ the number of units of ingredient I;
$y_2 =$ the number of units of ingredient II;
and $y_3 =$ the number of units of ingredient III.

The problem is:

$$\begin{array}{ll} \text{Minimize} & w = 4y_1 + 7y_2 + 5y_3 \\ \text{subject to:} & 4y_1 + y_2 + 10y_3 \geq 10 \\ & 3y_1 + 2y_2 + y_3 \geq 12 \\ & 4y_2 + 5y_3 \geq 20 \\ \text{with} & y_1 \geq 0, y_2 \geq 0, y_3 \geq 0\,. \end{array}$$

The dual problem is as follows.

$$\begin{array}{lrl} \text{Maximize} & z = & 10x_1 + 12x_2 + 20x_3 \\ \text{subject to:} & & 4x_1 + 3x_2 \le 4 \\ & & x_1 + 2x_2 + 4x_3 \le 7 \\ & & 10x_1 + x_2 + 5x_3 \le 5 \\ \text{with} & & x_1 \ge 0, x_2 \ge 0, x_3 \ge 0. \end{array}$$

The initial tableau is as follows.

$$\begin{array}{c} \begin{array}{ccccccc|c} x_1 & x_2 & x_3 & s_1 & s_2 & s_3 & z & \end{array} \\ \left[\begin{array}{ccccccc|c} 4 & 3 & 0 & 1 & 0 & 0 & 0 & 4 \\ 1 & 2 & 4 & 0 & 1 & 0 & 0 & 7 \\ 10 & 1 & \boxed{5} & 0 & 0 & 1 & 0 & 5 \\ \hline -10 & -12 & -20 & 0 & 0 & 0 & 1 & 0 \end{array}\right] \end{array}$$

Pivot as indicated.

$$\begin{array}{r} \\ -4\text{R}_3 + 5\text{R}_2 \to \text{R}_2 \\ \\ 4\text{R}_3 + \text{R}_4 \to \text{R}_4 \end{array} \left[\begin{array}{ccccccc|c} 4 & \boxed{3} & 0 & 1 & 0 & 0 & 0 & 4 \\ -35 & 6 & 0 & 0 & 5 & -4 & 0 & 15 \\ 10 & 1 & 5 & 0 & 0 & 1 & 0 & 5 \\ \hline 30 & -8 & 0 & 0 & 0 & 4 & 1 & 20 \end{array}\right]$$

(columns: $x_1, x_2, x_3, s_1, s_2, s_3, z$)

$$\begin{array}{r} \\ -2\text{R}_1 + \text{R}_2 \to \text{R}_2 \\ -\text{R}_1 + 3\text{R}_3 \to \text{R}_3 \\ 8\text{R}_1 + 3\text{R}_4 \to \text{R}_4 \end{array} \left[\begin{array}{ccccccc|c} 4 & 3 & 0 & 1 & 0 & 0 & 0 & 4 \\ -43 & 0 & 0 & -2 & 5 & -4 & 0 & 7 \\ 26 & 0 & 15 & -1 & 0 & 3 & 0 & 11 \\ \hline 122 & 0 & 0 & 8 & 0 & 12 & 3 & 92 \end{array}\right]$$

(columns: $x_1, x_2, x_3, s_1, s_2, s_3, z$)

Create a 1 in the columns corresponding to x_2, x_3, and z.

$$\begin{array}{r} \frac{1}{3}\text{R}_1 \to \text{R}_1 \\ \\ \frac{1}{15}\text{R}_3 \to \text{R}_3 \\ \frac{1}{3}\text{R}_4 \to \text{R}_4 \end{array} \left[\begin{array}{ccccccc|c} \frac{4}{3} & 1 & 0 & \frac{1}{3} & 0 & 0 & 0 & \frac{4}{3} \\ -43 & 0 & 0 & -2 & 5 & -4 & 0 & 7 \\ \frac{26}{15} & 0 & 1 & -\frac{1}{15} & 0 & \frac{1}{5} & 0 & \frac{11}{5} \\ \hline \frac{122}{3} & 0 & 0 & \frac{8}{3} & 0 & 4 & 1 & \frac{92}{3} \end{array}\right]$$

(columns: $x_1, x_2, x_3, s_1, s_2, s_3, z$)

From the last row, the minimum value is $\frac{92}{3}$ when $y_1 = \frac{8}{3}, y_2 = 0$, and $y_3 = 4$. The biologist can meet his needs at a minimum cost of $30.67 by using $\frac{8}{3}$ units of ingredient I and 4 units of ingredient III. (Ingredient II should not be used at all.)

4.4 Nonstandard Problems

1. $2x_1 + 3x_2 \le 8$
$x_1 + 4x_2 \ge 7$

Introduce the slack variable s_1 and the surplus variable s_2 to obtain the following equations:

$$\begin{aligned} 2x_1 + 3x_2 + s_1 \quad &= 8 \\ x_1 + 4x_2 \quad - s_2 &= 7. \end{aligned}$$

2. $3x_1 + 7x_2 \le 9$
$4x_1 + 5x_2 \ge 11$

We need one slack variable, s_1, and one surplus variable, s_2. The system becomes

$$\begin{aligned} 3x_1 + 7x_2 + s_1 \quad &= 9 \\ 4x_1 + 5x_2 \quad - s_2 &= 11. \end{aligned}$$

3. $2x_1 + x_2 + 2x_3 \le 50$
$x_1 + 3x_2 + x_3 \ge 35$
$x_1 + 2x_2 \ge 15$

Introduce the slack variable s_1 and the surplus variables s_2 and s_3 to obtain the following equations:

$$\begin{aligned} 2x_1 + x_2 + 2x_3 + s_1 \quad &= 50 \\ x_1 + 3x_2 + x_3 \quad - s_2 &= 35 \\ x_1 + 2x_2 \quad - s_3 &= 15. \end{aligned}$$

4. $2x_1 + x_3 \le 40$
$x_1 + x_2 \ge 18$
$x_1 + x_3 \ge 20$

We need one slack variable, s_1, and two surplus variables, s_2 and s_3.
The system becomes

$$\begin{aligned} 2x_1 + x_3 + s_1 \quad &= 40 \\ x_1 + x_2 \quad - s_2 &= 18 \\ x_1 + x_3 \quad - s_3 &= 20. \end{aligned}$$

5. Minimize $w = 3y_1 + 4y_2 + 5y_3$
subject to:
$y_1 + 2y_2 + 3y_3 \ge 9$
$y_2 + 2y_3 \ge 8$
$2y_1 + y_2 + 2y_3 \ge 6$
with $y_1 \ge 0, y_2 \ge 0, y_3 \ge 0$.

Change this to a maximization problem by letting $z = -w$. The problem can now be stated equivalently as follows:

Maximize $z = -3y_1 - 4y_2 - 5y_3$
subject to:
$y_1 + 2y_2 + 3y_3 \ge 9$
$y_2 + 2y_3 \ge 8$
$2y_1 + y_2 + 2y_3 \ge 6$
with $y_1 \ge 0, y_2 \ge 0, y_3 \ge 0$.

6. Minimize $w = 8y_1 + 3y_2 + y_3$
subject to:
$7y_1 + 6y_2 + 8y_3 \ge 18$
$4y_1 + 5y_2 + 10y_3 \ge 20$
with $y_1 \ge 0, y_2 \ge 0, y_3 \ge 0$.

To minimize $w = 8y_1 + 3y_2 + y_3$,
we maximize $z = -w = -8y_1 - 3y_2 - y_3$.
The constraints are not changed.

7. Minimize $w = y_1 + 2y_2 + y_3 + 5y_4$
subject to:
$y_1 + y_2 + y_3 + y_4 \ge 50$
$3y_1 + y_2 + 2y_3 + y_4 \ge 100$
with $y_1 \ge 0, y_2 \ge 0, y_3 \ge 0, y_4 \ge 0$.

Change this to a maximization problem by letting $z = -w$. The problem can now be stated equivalently as follows:

Maximize $z = -y_1 - 2y_2 - y_3 - 5y_4$
subject to:
$y_1 + y_2 + y_3 + y_4 \ge 50$
$3y_1 + y_2 + 2y_3 + y_4 \ge 100$
with $y_1 \ge 0, y_2 \ge 0, y_3 \ge 0, y_4 \ge 0$.

8. Minimize $w = y_1 + y_2 + 7y_3$
subject to:
$5y_1 + 2y_2 + y_3 \ge 125$
$4y_1 + y_2 + 6y_3 \le 75$
$6y_1 + 8y_2 \ge 50$
with $y_1 \ge 0, y_2 \ge 0, y_3 \ge 0$.

To minimize $w = y_1 + y_2 + 7y_3$,
we maximize $z = -w = -y_1 - y_2 - 7y_3$.
The constraints are not changed.

9. Find $x_1 \ge 0$ and $x_2 \ge 0$ such that

$$\begin{aligned} x_1 + 2x_2 &\ge 24 \\ x_1 + x_2 &\le 40 \end{aligned}$$

and $z = 12x_1 + 10x_2$ is maximized.

Subtracting the surplus variable s_1 and adding the slack variable s_2 leads to the equations

$$\begin{aligned} x_1 + 2x_2 - s_1 \quad &= 24 \\ x_1 + x_2 \quad + s_2 &= 40. \end{aligned}$$

The initial simplex tableau is as follows.

x_1	x_2	s_1	s_2	z	
[1]	2	−1	0	0	24
1	1	0	1	0	40
−12	−10	0	0	1	0

The initial basic solution is not feasible since $s_1 = -24$ is negative, so row transformations must be used. Pivot on the 1 in row 1, column 1, since it is the positive entry that is farthest to the left in the first row (the row containing the -1) and since, in the first column, $\frac{24}{1} = 24$ is a smaller quotient than $\frac{40}{1} = 40$. After row transformations, we obtain the following tableau.

$$\begin{array}{r} \\ \\ -R_1 + R_2 \to R_2 \\ \\ 12R_1 + R_3 \to R_3 \end{array} \begin{array}{c} \begin{array}{ccccc} x_1 & x_2 & s_1 & s_2 & z \end{array} \\ \left[\begin{array}{ccccc|c} 1 & 2 & -1 & 0 & 0 & 24 \\ 0 & -1 & \boxed{1} & 1 & 0 & 16 \\ \hline 0 & 14 & -12 & 0 & 1 & 288 \end{array}\right] \end{array}$$

The basic solution is now feasible, but the problem is not yet finished since there is a negative indicator. Continue in the usual way. The 1 in column 3 is the next pivot. After row transformations, we get the following tableau.

$$\begin{array}{r} \\ R_1 + R_2 \to R_1 \\ \\ 12R_2 + R_3 \to R_3 \end{array} \begin{array}{c} \begin{array}{ccccc} x_1 & x_2 & s_1 & s_2 & z \end{array} \\ \left[\begin{array}{ccccc|c} 1 & 1 & 0 & 1 & 0 & 40 \\ 0 & -1 & 1 & 1 & 0 & 16 \\ \hline 0 & 2 & 0 & 12 & 1 & 480 \end{array}\right] \end{array}$$

This is a final tableau since the entries in the last row are all nonnegative. The maximum value is 480 when $x_1 = 40$ and $x_2 = 0$.

10. Find $x_1 \geq 0$ and $x_2 \geq 0$ such that

$$\begin{aligned} 2x_1 + x_2 &\geq 2 \\ 2x_1 + 5x_2 &\leq 80 \end{aligned}$$

and $z = 6x_1 + 2x_2$ is maximized.

Introducing one surplus variable and one slack variable, the system becomes

$$\begin{aligned} 2x_1 + x_2 - s_1 &= \\ 2x_1 + 5x_2 + s_2 &= 80. \end{aligned}$$

The initial simplex tableau is

$$\begin{array}{c} \begin{array}{ccccc} x_1 & x_2 & s_1 & s_2 & z \end{array} \\ \left[\begin{array}{ccccc|c} \boxed{2} & 1 & -1 & 0 & 0 & 2 \\ 2 & 5 & 0 & 1 & 0 & 80 \\ \hline -6 & -2 & 0 & 0 & 1 & 0 \end{array}\right] \end{array}.$$

The initial basic solution is not feasible since $s_1 = -2$. Pivot on the 2 in row 1, column 1.

$$\begin{array}{r} \\ \\ -R_1 + R_2 \to R_2 \\ 3R_1 + R_3 \to R_3 \end{array} \begin{array}{c} \begin{array}{ccccc} x_1 & x_2 & s_1 & s_2 & z \end{array} \\ \left[\begin{array}{ccccc|c} 2 & 1 & -1 & 0 & 0 & 2 \\ 0 & 4 & \boxed{1} & 1 & 0 & 78 \\ \hline 0 & 1 & -3 & 0 & 1 & 6 \end{array}\right] \end{array}$$

Pivot on the 1 in row 2, column 3.

$$\begin{array}{r} \\ R_2 + R_1 \to R_1 \\ \\ 3R_2 + R_3 \to R_3 \end{array} \begin{array}{c} \begin{array}{ccccc} x_1 & x_2 & s_1 & s_2 & z \end{array} \\ \left[\begin{array}{ccccc|c} 2 & 5 & 0 & 1 & 0 & 80 \\ 0 & 4 & 1 & 1 & 0 & 78 \\ \hline 0 & 13 & 0 & 3 & 1 & 240 \end{array}\right] \end{array}$$

Create a 1 in the column corresponding to x_1.

$$\begin{array}{r} \\ \frac{1}{2}R_1 \to R_1 \\ \\ \\ \end{array} \begin{array}{c} \begin{array}{ccccc} x_1 & x_2 & s_1 & s_2 & z \end{array} \\ \left[\begin{array}{ccccc|c} 1 & \frac{5}{2} & 0 & \frac{1}{2} & 0 & 40 \\ 0 & 4 & 1 & 1 & 0 & 78 \\ \hline 0 & 13 & 0 & 3 & 1 & 240 \end{array}\right] \end{array}$$

The maximum is 240 when $x_1 = 40$ and $x_2 = 0$.

11. Find $x_1 \geq 0, x_2 \geq 0$, and $x_3 \geq 0$ such that

$$\begin{aligned} x_1 + x_2 + x_3 &\leq 150 \\ x_1 + x_2 + x_3 &\geq 100 \end{aligned}$$

and $z = 2x_1 + 5x_2 + 3x_3$ is maximized.

The initial tableau is as follows.

$$\begin{array}{c} \begin{array}{cccccc} x_1 & x_2 & x_3 & s_1 & s_2 & z \end{array} \\ \left[\begin{array}{cccccc|c} 1 & 1 & 1 & 1 & 0 & 0 & 150 \\ \boxed{1} & 1 & 1 & 0 & -1 & 0 & 100 \\ \hline -2 & -5 & -3 & 0 & 0 & 1 & 0 \end{array}\right] \end{array}$$

Note that s_1 is a slack variable, while s_2 is a surplus variable. The initial basic solution is not feasible, since $s_2 = -100$ is negative. Pivot on the 1 in row 2, column 1.

$$\begin{array}{r} \\ -R_2 + R_1 \to R_1 \\ \\ 2R_2 + R_3 \to R_3 \end{array} \begin{array}{c} \begin{array}{cccccc} x_1 & x_2 & x_3 & s_1 & s_2 & z \end{array} \\ \left[\begin{array}{cccccc|c} 0 & 0 & 0 & 1 & 1 & 0 & 50 \\ 1 & \boxed{1} & 1 & 0 & -1 & 0 & 100 \\ \hline 0 & -3 & -1 & 0 & -2 & 1 & 200 \end{array}\right] \end{array}$$

Pivot on the 1 in row 2, column 2.

$$\begin{array}{r} \\ \\ \\ 3R_2 + R_3 \to R_3 \end{array} \begin{array}{c} \begin{array}{cccccc} x_1 & x_2 & x_3 & s_1 & s_2 & z \end{array} \\ \left[\begin{array}{cccccc|c} 0 & 0 & 0 & 1 & \boxed{1} & 0 & 50 \\ 1 & 1 & 1 & 0 & -1 & 0 & 100 \\ \hline 3 & 0 & 2 & 0 & -5 & 1 & 500 \end{array}\right] \end{array}$$

Pivot on the 1 in row 1, column 5.

$$\begin{array}{r} \\ \\ R_1 + R_2 \to R_2 \\ 5R_1 + R_3 \to R_3 \end{array} \begin{array}{c} \begin{array}{cccccc} x_1 & x_2 & x_3 & s_1 & s_2 & z \end{array} \\ \left[\begin{array}{cccccc|c} 0 & 0 & 0 & 1 & 1 & 0 & 50 \\ 1 & 1 & 1 & 1 & 0 & 0 & 150 \\ \hline 3 & 0 & 2 & 5 & 0 & 1 & 750 \end{array}\right] \end{array}$$

This is a final tableau. The maximum value is 750 when $x_1 = 0, x_2 = 150$, and $x_3 = 0$.

12. Find $x_1 \geq 0, x_2 \geq 0$, and $x_3 \geq 0$ such that

$$\begin{aligned} x_1 + x_2 + x_3 &\leq 15 \\ 4x_1 + 4x_2 + 2x_3 &\geq 48 \end{aligned}$$

and $z = 2x_1 + x_2 + 3x_3$ is maximized.

The initial simplex tableau is

$$\begin{array}{c} \begin{array}{cccccc|c} x_1 & x_2 & x_3 & s_1 & s_2 & z & \\ \end{array} \\ \left[\begin{array}{cccccc|c} 1 & 1 & \boxed{1} & 1 & 0 & 0 & 15 \\ 4 & 4 & 2 & 0 & -1 & 0 & 48 \\ \hline -2 & -1 & -3 & 0 & 0 & 1 & 0 \end{array}\right]. \end{array}$$

The initial basic solution is not feasible since $s_2 = -48$. Pivot on the 1 in row 1, column 3.

$$\begin{array}{r} \\ -2R_1 + R_2 \to R_2 \\ 3R_1 + R_3 \to R_3 \end{array} \left[\begin{array}{cccccc|c} x_1 & x_2 & x_3 & s_1 & s_2 & z & \\ 0 & 1 & 1 & 1 & 0 & 0 & 15 \\ \boxed{2} & 2 & 0 & -2 & -1 & 0 & 18 \\ \hline 1 & 2 & 0 & 3 & 0 & 1 & 45 \end{array}\right]$$

The initial basic solution is still not feasible since $s_2 = -18$. To choose a pivot, locate the positive entry farthest to the left in row 2. The 2 in row 2, column 1, determines the pivot column and is also the pivot element, since it is forms the smaller quotient.

$$\begin{array}{r} -R_2 + 2R_1 \to R_1 \\ \\ -R_2 + 2R_3 \to R_3 \end{array} \left[\begin{array}{cccccc|c} 0 & 0 & 2 & 4 & 1 & 0 & 12 \\ 2 & 2 & 0 & -2 & -1 & 0 & 18 \\ 0 & 2 & 0 & 8 & 1 & 2 & 72 \end{array}\right] \quad (x_1, x_2, x_3, s_1, s_2, z)$$

The solution is feasible since all variables and indicators are nonnegative. Therefore, create a 1 in the columns corresponding to x_1, x_3, and z.

$$\begin{array}{r} \frac{1}{2}R_1 \to R_1 \\ \frac{1}{2}R_2 \to R_2 \\ \frac{1}{2}R_3 \to R_3 \end{array} \left[\begin{array}{cccccc|c} 0 & 0 & 1 & 2 & \frac{1}{2} & 0 & 6 \\ 1 & 1 & 0 & -1 & -\frac{1}{2} & 0 & 9 \\ \hline 0 & 1 & 0 & 4 & \frac{1}{2} & 1 & 36 \end{array}\right] \quad (x_1, x_2, x_3, s_1, s_2, z)$$

The maximum is 36 when $x_1 = 9, x_2 = 0$, and $x_3 = 6$.

13. Find $x_1 \geq 0$ and $x_2 \geq 0$ such that

$$\begin{aligned} x_1 + x_2 &\leq 100 \\ 2x_1 + 3x_2 &\leq 75 \\ x_1 + 4x_2 &\geq 50 \end{aligned}$$

and $z = 5x_1 - 3x_2$ is maximized.

The initial simplex tableau is

$$\left[\begin{array}{cccccc|c} x_1 & x_2 & s_1 & s_2 & s_3 & z & \\ 1 & 1 & 1 & 0 & 0 & 0 & 100 \\ \boxed{2} & 3 & 0 & 1 & 0 & 0 & 75 \\ 1 & 4 & 0 & 0 & -1 & 0 & 50 \\ \hline -5 & 3 & 0 & 0 & 0 & 1 & 0 \end{array}\right].$$

The initial basic solution is not feasible since $s_3 = -50$. Pivot on the 2 in row 2, column 1.

$$\begin{array}{r} -R_2 + 2R_1 \to R_1 \\ \\ -R_2 + 2R_3 \to R_3 \\ 5R_2 + 2R_4 \to R_4 \end{array} \left[\begin{array}{cccccc|c} 0 & -1 & 2 & -1 & 0 & 0 & 125 \\ 2 & 3 & 0 & 1 & 0 & 0 & 75 \\ 0 & \boxed{5} & 0 & -1 & -2 & 0 & 25 \\ \hline 0 & 21 & 0 & 5 & 0 & 2 & 375 \end{array}\right]. \quad (x_1, x_2, x_3, s_1, s_2, z)$$

This solution is still not feasible since $s_3 = -\frac{25}{2}$. Pivot on the 5 in row 3, column 2.

$$\begin{array}{r} R_3 + 5R_1 \to R_1 \\ -3R_3 + 5R_2 \to R_2 \\ \\ -21R_3 + 5R_4 \to R_4 \end{array} \left[\begin{array}{cccccc|c} 0 & 0 & 10 & -6 & -2 & 0 & 650 \\ 10 & 0 & 0 & 8 & 6 & 0 & 300 \\ 0 & \boxed{5} & 0 & -1 & -2 & 0 & 25 \\ \hline 0 & 0 & 0 & 46 & 42 & 10 & 1350 \end{array}\right] \quad (x_1, x_2, x_3, s_1, s_2, z)$$

Create a 1 in the columns corresponding to x_1, x_2, s_1, and z.

$$\begin{array}{r} \frac{1}{10}R_1 \to R_1 \\ \frac{1}{10}R_2 \to R_2 \\ \frac{1}{5}R_3 \to R_3 \\ \frac{1}{10}R_4 \to R_4 \end{array} \left[\begin{array}{cccccc|c} 0 & 0 & 1 & -\frac{3}{5} & -\frac{1}{5} & 0 & 65 \\ 1 & 0 & 0 & \frac{4}{5} & \frac{3}{5} & 0 & 30 \\ 0 & 1 & 0 & -\frac{1}{5} & -\frac{2}{5} & 0 & 5 \\ \hline 0 & 0 & 0 & \frac{23}{5} & \frac{21}{5} & 1 & 135 \end{array}\right]. \quad (x_1, x_2, x_3, s_1, s_2, z)$$

This is a final tableau. The maximum is 135 when $x_1 = 30, x_2 = 5$.

14. Find $x_1 \geq 0$ and $x_2 \geq 0$ such that

$$\begin{aligned} x_1 + 2x_2 &\leq 18 \\ x_1 + 3x_2 &\geq 12 \\ 2x_1 + 2x_2 &\leq 24 \end{aligned}$$

and $z = 5x_1 - 10x_2$ is maximized.
Introduce slack and surplus variables to get the system

$$\begin{aligned} x_1 + 2x_2 + s_1 \qquad\qquad &= 18 \\ x_1 + 3x_2 \qquad - s_2 \qquad &= 12 \\ 2x_1 + 2x_2 \qquad\qquad + s_3 &= 24. \end{aligned}$$

The initial tableau is

$$\begin{array}{cccccc|c} x_1 & x_2 & s_1 & s_2 & s_3 & z & \\ \hline 1 & 2 & 1 & 0 & 0 & 0 & 18 \\ \boxed{1} & 3 & 0 & -1 & 0 & 0 & 12 \\ 2 & 2 & 0 & 0 & 1 & 0 & 24 \\ \hline -5 & 10 & 0 & 0 & 0 & 1 & 0 \end{array}.$$

$s_2 = -12$ is not a feasible solution. Pivot on the 1 in row 1, column 1.

$$\begin{array}{l|cccccc|c} & x_1 & x_2 & s_1 & s_2 & s_3 & z & \\ \hline -R_2 + R_1 \to R_1 & 0 & -1 & 1 & 1 & 0 & 0 & 6 \\ & 1 & 3 & 0 & -1 & 0 & 0 & 12 \\ -2R_2 + R_3 \to R_3 & 0 & -4 & 0 & \boxed{2} & 1 & 0 & 0 \\ \hline 5R_2 + R_4 \to R_4 & 0 & 25 & 0 & -5 & 0 & 1 & 60 \end{array}$$

Pivot on the 2 in row 3, column 4.

$$\begin{array}{l|cccccc|c} & x_1 & x_2 & s_1 & s_2 & s_3 & z & \\ \hline -R_3 + 2R_1 \to R_1 & 0 & 6 & 2 & 0 & -1 & 0 & 12 \\ R_3 + 2R_2 \to R_2 & 2 & 2 & 0 & 0 & 1 & 0 & 24 \\ & 0 & -4 & 0 & 2 & 1 & 0 & 0 \\ \hline 5R_3 + 2R_4 \to R_4 & 0 & 30 & 0 & 0 & 5 & 2 & 120 \end{array}$$

$$\begin{array}{l|cccccc|c} & x_1 & x_2 & s_1 & s_2 & s_3 & z & \\ \hline \frac{1}{2}R_1 \to R_1 & 0 & 3 & 1 & 0 & -\frac{1}{2} & 0 & 6 \\ \frac{1}{2}R_2 \to R_2 & 1 & 1 & 0 & 0 & \frac{1}{2} & 0 & 12 \\ \frac{1}{2}R_3 \to R_3 & 0 & -2 & 0 & 1 & \frac{1}{2} & 0 & 0 \\ \hline \frac{1}{2}R_4 \to R_4 & 0 & 15 & 0 & 0 & \frac{5}{2} & 1 & 60 \end{array}$$

The maximum is 60 when $x_1 = 12$ and $x_2 = 0$.

15. Find $y_1 \geq 0, y_2 \geq 0$, and $y_3 \geq 0$ such that

$$\begin{aligned} 5y_1 + \ \ 3y_2 + 2y_3 &\leq 150 \\ 5y_1 + 10y_2 + 3y_3 &\geq \ \ 90 \end{aligned}$$

and $w = 10y_1 + 12y_2 + 10y_3$ is minimized.
Let $z = -w = -10y - 12y_2 - 10y_3$. Maximize z.
The initial simplex tableau is

$$\begin{array}{cccccc|c} y_1 & y_2 & y_3 & s_1 & s_2 & z & \\ \hline 5 & 3 & 2 & 1 & 0 & 0 & 150 \\ \boxed{5} & 10 & 3 & 0 & -1 & 0 & 90 \\ \hline 10 & 12 & 10 & 0 & 0 & 1 & 0 \end{array}$$

The initial basic solution is not feasible since $s_2 = -90$. Pivot on the 5 in row 2, column 1.

$$\begin{array}{l|cccccc|c} & y_1 & y_2 & y_3 & s_1 & s_2 & z & \\ \hline -R_2 + R_1 \to R_1 & 0 & -7 & -1 & 1 & 1 & 0 & 60 \\ & 5 & \boxed{10} & 3 & 0 & -1 & 0 & 90 \\ \hline -2R_2 + R_3 \to R_3 & 0 & -8 & 4 & 0 & 2 & 1 & -180 \end{array}$$

Pivot on the 10 in row 2, column 2.

$$\begin{array}{l|cccccc|c} & y_1 & y_2 & y_3 & s_1 & s_2 & z & \\ \hline 7R_2 + 10R_1 \to R_1 & 35 & 0 & 11 & 10 & 3 & 0 & 1230 \\ & 5 & 10 & 3 & 0 & -1 & 0 & 90 \\ \hline 8R_2 + 10R_3 \to R_3 & 40 & 0 & 64 & 0 & 12 & 10 & -1080 \end{array}$$

Create a 1 in the columns corresponding to y_2, s_1, and z.

$$\begin{array}{l|cccccc|c} & x_1 & x_2 & s_1 & s_2 & s_3 & z & \\ \hline \frac{1}{10}R_1 \to R_1 & \frac{7}{2} & 0 & \frac{11}{10} & 1 & \frac{3}{10} & 0 & 123 \\ \frac{1}{10}R_2 \to R_2 & \frac{1}{2} & 1 & \frac{3}{10} & 0 & -\frac{1}{10} & 0 & 9 \\ \hline \frac{1}{10}R_3 \to R_3 & 4 & 0 & \frac{32}{5} & 0 & \frac{6}{5} & 1 & -108 \end{array}$$

This is a final tableau. The minimum is 108 when $y_1 = 0, y_2 = 9$, and $y_3 = 0$.

16. Minimize $w = 3y_1 + 2y_2 + 3y_3$

subject to: $2y_1 + 3y_2 + 6y_3 \le 60$

$y_1 + 4y_2 + 5y_3 \ge 40$

with $y_1 \ge 0, y_2 \ge 0, y_3 \ge 0$

Let $z = -w = -3y_1 - 2y_2 - 3y_3$. Maximize z.

The initial simplex tableau is

$$\begin{array}{c} \\ \\ \\ \\ \end{array}\begin{array}{cccccc|c} y_1 & y_2 & y_3 & s_1 & s_2 & z & \\ \boxed{2} & 3 & 6 & 1 & 0 & 0 & 60 \\ 1 & 4 & 5 & 0 & -1 & 0 & 40 \\ \hline 3 & 2 & 3 & 0 & 0 & 1 & 0 \end{array}$$

The initial basic solution is not feasible since $s_2 = -40$. Pivot on the 2 in row 1, column 1.

$$\begin{array}{r} \\ \\ -R_1 + 2R_2 \to R_2 \\ -3R_1 + 2R_3 \to R_3 \end{array}\begin{array}{cccccc|c} y_1 & y_2 & y_3 & s_1 & s_2 & z & \\ 2 & 3 & 6 & 1 & 0 & 0 & 60 \\ 0 & 5 & \boxed{4} & -1 & -2 & 0 & 20 \\ \hline 0 & -5 & -12 & -3 & 0 & 2 & -180 \end{array}$$

There are negative indicators, so now pivot on the 4 in row 2, column 3.

$$\begin{array}{r} \\ -3R_2 + 2R_1 \to R_1 \\ \\ 3R_2 + R_3 \to R_3 \end{array}\begin{array}{cccccc|c} y_1 & y_2 & y_3 & s_1 & s_2 & z & \\ 4 & -9 & 0 & \boxed{5} & 6 & 0 & 60 \\ 0 & 5 & 4 & -1 & -2 & 0 & 20 \\ \hline 0 & 10 & 0 & -6 & -6 & 2 & -120 \end{array}$$

Pivot on the 5 in row 1, column 4.

$$\begin{array}{r} \\ \\ R_1 + 5R_2 \to R_2 \\ 6R_1 + 5R_3 \to R_3 \end{array}\begin{array}{cccccc|c} y_1 & y_2 & y_3 & s_1 & s_2 & z & \\ 4 & -9 & 0 & 5 & 6 & 0 & 60 \\ 4 & \boxed{16} & 20 & 0 & -4 & 0 & 160 \\ \hline 24 & -4 & 0 & 0 & 6 & 10 & -240 \end{array}$$

Pivot on the 16 in row 2, column 2.

$$\begin{array}{r} \\ 9R_2 + 16R_1 \to R_1 \\ \\ R_2 + 4R_3 \to R_3 \end{array}\begin{array}{cccccc|c} y_1 & y_2 & y_3 & s_1 & s_2 & z & \\ \boxed{100} & 0 & 180 & 80 & 60 & 0 & 2400 \\ 4 & 16 & 20 & 0 & -4 & 0 & 160 \\ \hline 100 & 0 & 20 & 0 & 20 & 40 & -800 \end{array}$$

$$\begin{array}{r} \\ \frac{1}{80}R_1 \to R_1 \\ \frac{1}{16}R_2 \to R_2 \\ \frac{1}{40}R_3 \to R_3 \end{array}\begin{array}{cccccc|c} y_1 & y_2 & y_3 & s_1 & s_2 & z & \\ \frac{5}{4} & 0 & \frac{9}{4} & 1 & \frac{3}{4} & 0 & 30 \\ \frac{1}{4} & 1 & \frac{5}{4} & 0 & -\frac{1}{4} & 0 & 10 \\ \hline \frac{5}{2} & 0 & \frac{1}{2} & 0 & \frac{1}{2} & 1 & -20 \end{array}$$

The minimum is $w = 20$ when $y_1 = 0$, $y_2 = 10$, and $y_3 = 0$.

17. Maximize $z = 3x_1 + 2x_2$

subject to:
$$x_1 + x_2 = 50$$
$$4x_1 + 2x_2 \geq 120$$
$$5x_1 + 2x_2 \leq 200$$
with $x_1 \geq 0, x_2 \geq 0.$

The artificial variable a_1 is used to rewrite $x_1 + x_2 = 50$ as $x_1 + x_2 + a_1 = 50$; note that a_1 must equal 0 for this equation to be a true statement. Also the surplus variable s_1 and the slack variable s_2 are needed. The initial tableau is as follows.

$$\begin{array}{c} \\ \\ \\ \\ \\ \end{array}\begin{array}{cccccc|c} x_1 & x_2 & a_1 & s_1 & s_2 & z & \\ 1 & 1 & 1 & 0 & 0 & 0 & 50 \\ \boxed{4} & 2 & 0 & -1 & 0 & 0 & 120 \\ 5 & 2 & 0 & 0 & 1 & 0 & 200 \\ \hline -3 & -2 & 0 & 0 & 0 & 1 & 0 \end{array}$$

The initial basic solution is not feasible. Pivot on the 4 in row 2, column 1.

$$\begin{array}{r} \\ -R_2 + 4R_1 \rightarrow R_1 \\ \\ -5R_2 + 4R_3 \rightarrow R_3 \\ 3R_2 + 4R_4 \rightarrow R_4 \end{array}\begin{array}{cccccc|c} x_1 & x_2 & a_1 & s_1 & s_2 & z & \\ 0 & 2 & 4 & 1 & 0 & 0 & 80 \\ 4 & 2 & 0 & -1 & 0 & 0 & 120 \\ 0 & -2 & 0 & \boxed{5} & 4 & 0 & 200 \\ \hline 0 & -2 & 0 & -3 & 0 & 4 & 360 \end{array}$$

The basic solution is now feasible, but there are negative indicators. Pivot on the 5 in row 3, column 4 (which is the column with the most negative indicator and the row with the smallest nonnegative quotient).

$$\begin{array}{r} \\ -R_3 + 5R_1 \rightarrow R_1 \\ R_3 + 5R_2 \rightarrow R_2 \\ \\ 3R_3 + 5R_4 \rightarrow R_4 \end{array}\begin{array}{cccccc|c} x_1 & x_2 & a_1 & s_1 & s_2 & z & \\ 0 & \boxed{12} & 20 & 0 & -4 & 0 & 200 \\ 20 & 8 & 0 & 0 & 4 & 0 & 800 \\ 0 & -2 & 0 & 5 & 4 & 0 & 200 \\ \hline 0 & -16 & 0 & 0 & 12 & 20 & 2400 \end{array}$$

Pivot on the 12 in row 1, column 2.

$$\begin{array}{r} \\ \\ -2R_1 + 3R_2 \rightarrow R_2 \\ R_1 + 6R_3 \rightarrow R_3 \\ 4R_1 + 3R_4 \rightarrow R_4 \end{array}\begin{array}{cccccc|c} x_1 & x_2 & a_1 & s_1 & s_2 & z & \\ 0 & 12 & 20 & 0 & -4 & 0 & 200 \\ 60 & 0 & -40 & 0 & 20 & 0 & 2000 \\ 0 & 0 & 20 & 30 & 20 & 0 & 1400 \\ \hline 0 & 0 & 80 & 0 & 20 & 60 & 8000 \end{array}$$

We now have $a_1 = 0$, so drop the a_1 column.

$$\begin{array}{ccccc|c} x_1 & x_2 & s_1 & s_2 & z & \\ 0 & 12 & 0 & -4 & 0 & 200 \\ 60 & 0 & 0 & 20 & 0 & 2000 \\ 0 & 0 & 30 & 20 & 0 & 1400 \\ \hline 0 & 0 & 0 & 20 & 60 & 8000 \end{array}$$

We are finished pivoting. Create a 1 in the columns corresponding to x_1, x_2, s_1, and z.

$$\begin{array}{l} \\ \frac{1}{12}R_1 \to R_1 \\ \frac{1}{60}R_2 \to R_2 \\ \frac{1}{30}R_3 \to R_3 \\ \frac{1}{60}R_4 \to R_4 \end{array} \begin{array}{c} \begin{array}{cccccc} x_1 & x_2 & s_1 & s_2 & z & \end{array} \\ \left[\begin{array}{ccccc|c} 0 & 1 & 0 & -\frac{1}{3} & 0 & \frac{50}{3} \\ 1 & 0 & 0 & \frac{1}{3} & 0 & \frac{100}{3} \\ 0 & 0 & 1 & \frac{2}{3} & 0 & \frac{140}{3} \\ \hline 0 & 0 & 0 & \frac{1}{3} & 1 & \frac{400}{3} \end{array}\right] \end{array}$$

The maximum value is $\frac{400}{3}$ when $x_1 = \frac{100}{3}$ and $x_2 = \frac{50}{3}$.

18. Maximize $z = 5x_1 + 7x_2$

subject to:

$$\begin{aligned} x_1 + x_2 &= 15 \\ 2x_1 + 4x_2 &\geq 30 \\ 3x_1 + 5x_2 &\geq 10 \end{aligned}$$

with $x_1 \geq 0, x_2 \geq 0$.

With artificial, slack, and surplus variables, we have

$$\begin{aligned} x_1 + x_2 + a \qquad\qquad &= 15 \\ 2x_1 + 4x_2 \qquad - s_1 \qquad &= 30 \\ 3x_1 + 5x_2 \qquad\qquad - s_2 &= 10. \end{aligned}$$

The initial tableau is

$$\begin{array}{c} \begin{array}{ccccccc} x_1 & x_2 & s_1 & s_2 & a & z & \end{array} \\ \left[\begin{array}{cccccc|c} \boxed{1} & 1 & 0 & 0 & 1 & 0 & 15 \\ 2 & 4 & -1 & 0 & 0 & 0 & 30 \\ 3 & 5 & 0 & -1 & 0 & 0 & 10 \\ \hline -5 & -7 & 0 & 0 & 0 & 1 & 0 \end{array}\right] \end{array}.$$

First, eliminate the artificial variable a. Pivot on the 1 in row 1, column 1.

$$\begin{array}{r} \\ \\ -2R_1 + R_2 \to R_2 \\ -3R_1 + R_3 \to R_3 \\ 5R_1 + R_4 \to R_4 \end{array} \begin{array}{c} \begin{array}{ccccccc} x_1 & x_2 & s_1 & s_2 & a & z & \end{array} \\ \left[\begin{array}{cccccc|c} 1 & 1 & 0 & 0 & 1 & 0 & 15 \\ 0 & 2 & -1 & 0 & -2 & 0 & 0 \\ 0 & 2 & 0 & -1 & -3 & 0 & 35 \\ \hline 0 & -2 & 0 & 0 & 5 & 1 & 75 \end{array}\right] \end{array}$$

Now $a = 0$, so we can drop the a column.

$$\begin{array}{c} \begin{array}{cccccc} x_1 & x_2 & s_1 & s_2 & z & \end{array} \\ \left[\begin{array}{ccccc|c} 1 & 1 & 0 & 0 & 0 & 15 \\ 0 & \boxed{2} & -1 & 0 & 0 & 0 \\ 0 & 2 & 0 & -1 & 0 & 35 \\ \hline 0 & -2 & 0 & 0 & 1 & 75 \end{array}\right] \end{array}$$

Because $s_2 = -35$,we choose the 2 in row 2, column 2, as the next pivot. (Note that $s_1 = 0$.)

$$\begin{array}{r} \\ -R_2 + 2R_1 \to R_1 \\ \\ R_2 - R_3 \to R_3 \\ R_2 + R_4 \to R_4 \end{array} \begin{array}{c} \begin{array}{cccccc} x_1 & x_2 & s_1 & s_2 & z & \end{array} \\ \left[\begin{array}{ccccc|c} 2 & 0 & \boxed{1} & 0 & 0 & 30 \\ 0 & 2 & -1 & 0 & 0 & 0 \\ 0 & 0 & -1 & 1 & 0 & 35 \\ \hline 0 & 0 & -1 & 0 & 1 & 75 \end{array}\right] \end{array}$$

Pivot on the 1 in row 1, column 3.

$$\begin{array}{l} \\ \\ R_1 + R_2 \rightarrow R_2 \\ R_1 + R_3 \rightarrow R_3 \\ R_1 + R_4 \rightarrow R_4 \end{array} \begin{array}{c} \begin{array}{ccccc} x_1 & x_2 & s_1 & s_2 & z \end{array} \\ \left[\begin{array}{ccccc|c} 2 & 0 & 1 & 0 & 0 & 30 \\ 2 & 2 & 0 & 0 & 0 & 30 \\ 2 & 0 & 0 & 1 & 0 & 65 \\ \hline 2 & 0 & 0 & 0 & 1 & 105 \end{array}\right] \end{array}$$

Create a 1 in the column for x_2.

$$\begin{array}{l} \\ \\ \\ \frac{1}{2}R_2 \rightarrow R_2 \\ \\ \end{array} \begin{array}{c} \begin{array}{ccccc} x_1 & x_2 & s_1 & s_2 & z \end{array} \\ \left[\begin{array}{ccccc|c} 2 & 0 & 1 & 0 & 0 & 30 \\ 1 & 1 & 0 & 0 & 0 & 15 \\ 2 & 0 & 0 & 1 & 0 & 65 \\ \hline 2 & 0 & 0 & 0 & 1 & 105 \end{array}\right] \end{array}$$

The maximum is 105 when $x_1 = 0$ and $x_2 = 15$.

19. Minimize $w = 32y_1 + 40y_2 + 48y_3$

subject to:
$$20y_1 + 10y_2 + 5y_3 = 200$$
$$25y_1 + 40y_2 + 50y_3 \leq 500$$
$$18y_1 + 24y_2 + 12y_3 \geq 300$$

with $y_1 \geq 0, y_2 \geq 0, y_3 \geq 0$

With artificial, slack, and surplus variables, this problem becomes

Maximize $z = -32y_1 - 40y_2 - 48y_3$

subject to:
$$\begin{aligned} 20y_1 + 10y_2 + 5y_3 + a_1 \qquad\qquad &= 200 \\ 25y_1 + 40y_2 + 50y_3 + \qquad s_1 \qquad &= 500 \\ 18y_1 + 24y_2 + 12y_3 \qquad\qquad - s_2 &= 300. \end{aligned}$$

The initial tableau is as follows.

$$\begin{array}{c} \begin{array}{ccccccc} y_1 & y_2 & y_3 & a_1 & s_1 & s_2 & z \end{array} \\ \left[\begin{array}{ccccccc|c} \boxed{20} & 10 & 5 & 1 & 0 & 0 & 0 & 200 \\ 25 & 40 & 50 & 0 & 1 & 0 & 0 & 500 \\ 18 & 24 & 12 & 0 & 0 & -1 & 0 & 300 \\ \hline 32 & 40 & 48 & 0 & 0 & 0 & 1 & 0 \end{array}\right] \end{array}$$

The initial basic tableau is not feasible. Pivot on the 20 in row 1, column 1.

$$\begin{array}{r} \\ \\ -5R_1 + 4R_2 \rightarrow R_2 \\ -9R_1 + 10R_3 \rightarrow R_3 \\ -8R_1 + 5R_4 \rightarrow R_4 \end{array} \begin{array}{c} \begin{array}{ccccccc} y_1 & y_2 & y_3 & a_1 & s_1 & s_2 & z \end{array} \\ \left[\begin{array}{ccccccc|c} 20 & 10 & 5 & 1 & 0 & 0 & 0 & 200 \\ 0 & 110 & 175 & -5 & 4 & 0 & 0 & 1000 \\ 0 & 150 & 75 & -9 & 0 & -10 & 0 & 1200 \\ \hline 0 & 120 & 200 & -8 & 0 & 0 & 5 & -1600 \end{array}\right] \end{array}$$

Eliminate the a_1 column.

$$\begin{array}{c} \begin{array}{cccccc} y_1 & y_2 & y_3 & s_1 & s_2 & z \end{array} \\ \left[\begin{array}{cccccc|c} 20 & 10 & 5 & 0 & 0 & 0 & 200 \\ 0 & 110 & 175 & 4 & 0 & 0 & 1000 \\ 0 & \boxed{150} & 75 & 0 & -10 & 0 & 1200 \\ \hline 0 & 120 & 200 & 0 & 0 & 5 & -1600 \end{array}\right] \end{array}$$

Pivot on the 150 in row 3, column 2.

$$\begin{array}{r} \\ -R_3+15R_1 \to R_1 \\ -11R_3+15R_2 \to R_2 \\ \\ -4R_3+5R_4 \to R_4 \end{array} \begin{array}{c} \begin{array}{cccccc|c} y_1 & y_2 & y_3 & s_1 & s_2 & z & \end{array} \\ \left[\begin{array}{cccccc|c} 300 & 0 & 0 & 0 & 10 & 0 & 1800 \\ 0 & 0 & 1800 & 60 & 110 & 0 & 1800 \\ 0 & 150 & 75 & 0 & -10 & 0 & 1200 \\ \hline 0 & 0 & 700 & 0 & 40 & 25 & -12,800 \end{array}\right] \end{array}$$

Create ones in the columns corresponding to y_1, y_2, s_1, and z.

$$\begin{array}{r} \\ \frac{1}{300}R_1 \to R_1 \\ \frac{1}{60}R_2 \to R_2 \\ \frac{1}{150}R_3 \to R_3 \\ \frac{1}{25}R_4 \to R_4 \end{array} \begin{array}{c} \begin{array}{cccccc|c} y_1 & y_2 & y_3 & s_1 & s_2 & z & \end{array} \\ \left[\begin{array}{cccccc|c} 1 & 0 & 0 & 0 & \frac{1}{30} & 0 & 6 \\ 0 & 0 & 30 & 1 & \frac{11}{6} & 0 & 30 \\ 0 & 1 & \frac{1}{2} & 0 & -\frac{1}{15} & 0 & 8 \\ \hline 0 & 0 & 28 & 0 & \frac{8}{5} & 1 & -512 \end{array}\right] \end{array}$$

This is a final tableau. The minimum value is 512 when $y_1 = 6$, $y_2 = 8$, and $y_3 = 0$.

20. Minimize $w = 15y_1 + 12y_2 + 18y_3$

subject to:
$$\begin{aligned} y_1 + 2y_2 + 3y_3 &\le 12 \\ 3y_1 + y_2 + 3y_3 &\ge 18 \\ y_1 + y_2 + y_3 &= 10 \end{aligned}$$

with $y_1 \ge 0, y_2 \ge 0, y_3 \ge 0$

Let $z = -w = -15y_1 - 12y_2 - 18y_3$ and maximize z. Introduce the slack variable s_1, the surplus variable s_2, and the artificial variable a_1. The initial tableau is as follows.

$$\begin{array}{c} \begin{array}{ccccccc|c} y_1 & y_2 & y_3 & s_1 & s_2 & a_1 & z & \end{array} \\ \left[\begin{array}{ccccccc|c} 1 & 2 & 3 & 1 & 0 & 0 & 0 & 12 \\ 3 & 1 & 3 & 0 & -1 & 0 & 0 & 18 \\ \boxed{1} & 1 & 1 & 0 & 0 & 1 & 0 & 10 \\ \hline 15 & 12 & 18 & 0 & 0 & 0 & 1 & 0 \end{array}\right] \end{array}$$

First, eliminate the artificial variable a_1. Pivot on the 1 in row 3, column 1.

$$\begin{array}{r} \\ -R_3+R_1 \to R_1 \\ -3R_3+R_2 \to R_2 \\ \\ -15R_3+R_4 \to R_4 \end{array} \begin{array}{c} \begin{array}{ccccccc|c} y_1 & y_2 & y_3 & s_1 & s_2 & a_1 & z & \end{array} \\ \left[\begin{array}{ccccccc|c} 0 & 1 & 2 & 1 & 0 & -1 & 0 & 2 \\ 0 & -2 & 0 & 0 & -1 & -3 & 0 & -12 \\ 1 & 1 & 1 & 0 & 0 & 1 & 0 & 10 \\ \hline 0 & -3 & 3 & 0 & 0 & -15 & 1 & -150 \end{array}\right] \end{array}$$

Now $a_1 = 0$, so we can drop the a_1 column.

$$\begin{array}{c} \begin{array}{cccccc|c} y_1 & y_2 & y_3 & s_1 & s_2 & z & \end{array} \\ \left[\begin{array}{cccccc|c} 0 & \boxed{1} & 2 & 1 & 0 & 0 & 2 \\ 0 & -2 & 0 & 0 & -1 & 0 & -12 \\ 1 & 1 & 1 & 0 & 0 & 0 & 10 \\ \hline 0 & -3 & 3 & 0 & 0 & 1 & -150 \end{array}\right] \end{array}$$

Pivot on the 1 in row 1, column 2.

$$
\begin{array}{r}
\\
\\
2R_1 + R_2 \to R_2 \\
-R_1 + R_3 \to R_3 \\
3R_1 + R_4 \to R_4
\end{array}
\begin{array}{cccccc|c}
y_1 & y_2 & y_3 & s_1 & s_2 & z & \\
0 & 1 & 2 & 1 & 0 & 0 & 2 \\
0 & 0 & 4 & 2 & -1 & 0 & -8 \\
1 & 0 & -1 & -1 & 0 & 0 & 8 \\
\hline
0 & 0 & 9 & 3 & 0 & 1 & -144
\end{array}
$$

The maximum value of $z = -w$ is -144.
Therefore, the minimum value of w is 144 when
$y_1 = 8, y_2 = 2$, and $y_3 = 0$.

23. (a) Let $y_1 =$ amount shipped from S_1 to D_1,
$y_2 =$ amount shipped from S_1 to D_2,
$y_3 =$ amount shipped from S_2 to D_1,
and $y_4 =$ amount shipped from S_2 to D_2.

Minimize $w = 30y_1 + 20y_2 + 25y_3 + 22y_4$

subject to:
$$
\begin{aligned}
y_1 + y_3 &\geq 3000 \\
y_2 + y_4 &\geq 5000 \\
y_1 + y_2 &\leq 5000 \\
y_3 + y_4 &\leq 5000 \\
2y_1 + 6y_2 + 5y_3 + 4y_4 &\leq 40{,}000
\end{aligned}
$$
with $y_1 \geq 0, y_2 \geq 0, y_3 \geq 0, y_4 \geq 0.$

Maximize $z = -w = -30y_1 - 20y_2 - 25y_3 - 22y_4$.

$$
\begin{array}{cccccccccc|c}
y_1 & y_2 & y_3 & y_4 & s_1 & s_2 & s_3 & s_4 & s_5 & z & \\
\boxed{1} & 0 & 1 & 0 & -1 & 0 & 0 & 0 & 0 & 0 & 3000 \\
0 & 1 & 0 & 1 & 0 & -1 & 0 & 0 & 0 & 0 & 5000 \\
1 & 1 & 0 & 0 & 0 & 0 & 1 & 0 & 0 & 0 & 5000 \\
0 & 0 & 1 & 1 & 0 & 0 & 0 & 1 & 0 & 0 & 5000 \\
2 & 6 & 5 & 4 & 0 & 0 & 0 & 0 & 1 & 0 & 40{,}000 \\
\hline
30 & 20 & 25 & 22 & 0 & 0 & 0 & 0 & 0 & 1 & 0
\end{array}
$$

Pivot on the 1 in row 1, column 1 since the feasible solution has a negative value, $s_1 = -3000$.

$$
\begin{array}{r}
\\
\\
\\
-R_1 + R_3 \to R_3 \\
\\
-2R_1 + R_5 \to R_5 \\
-30R_1 + R_6 \to R_6
\end{array}
\begin{array}{cccccccccc|c}
y_1 & y_2 & y_3 & y_4 & s_1 & s_2 & s_3 & s_4 & s_5 & z & \\
1 & 0 & 1 & 0 & -1 & 0 & 0 & 0 & 0 & 0 & 3000 \\
0 & 1 & 0 & 1 & 0 & -1 & 0 & 0 & 0 & 0 & 5000 \\
0 & \boxed{1} & -1 & 0 & 1 & 0 & 1 & 0 & 0 & 0 & 2000 \\
0 & 0 & 1 & 1 & 0 & 0 & 0 & 1 & 0 & 0 & 5000 \\
0 & 6 & 3 & 4 & 2 & 0 & 0 & 0 & 1 & 0 & 34{,}000 \\
\hline
0 & 20 & -5 & 22 & 30 & 0 & 0 & 0 & 0 & 1 & -90{,}000
\end{array}
$$

Since the feasible solution has a negative value ($s_2 = -5000$), pivot on the 1 in row 3, column 2.

	y_1	y_2	y_3	y_4	s_1	s_2	s_3	s_4	s_5	z	
	1	0	1	0	−1	0	0	0	0	0	3000
$-R_3 + R_2 \to R_2$	0	0	1	1	−1	−1	−1	0	0	0	3000
	0	1	−1	0	1	0	1	0	0	0	2000
	0	0	1	1	0	0	0	1	0	0	5000
$-6R_3 + R_5 \to R_5$	0	0	**[9]**	4	−4	0	−6	0	1	0	22,000
$-20R_3 + R_6 \to R_6$	0	0	15	22	10	0	−20	0	0	1	−130,000

Since the feasible solution has a negative value ($s_2 = -3000$), pivot on the 9 in row 5, column 3.

	y_1	y_2	y_3	y_4	s_1	s_2	s_3	s_4	s_5	z	
$-R_5 + 9R_1 \to R_1$	9	0	0	−4	−5	0	6	0	−1	0	5000
$-R_5 + 9R_2 \to R_2$	0	0	0	**[5]**	−5	−9	−3	0	−1	0	5000
$R_5 + 9R_3 \to R_3$	0	9	0	4	5	0	3	0	1	0	40,000
$-R_5 + 9R_4 \to R_4$	0	0	0	5	4	0	6	9	−1	0	23,000
	0	0	9	4	−4	0	−6	0	1	0	22,000
$-5R_5 + 3R_6 \to R_6$	0	0	0	46	50	0	−30	0	−5	3	−500,000

Pivot on the 5 in row 2, column 4.

	y_1	y_2	y_3	y_4	s_1	s_2	s_3	s_4	s_5	z	
$4R_2 + 5R_1 \to R_1$	45	0	0	0	−45	−36	18	0	−9	0	45,000
	0	0	0	5	−5	−9	−3	0	−1	0	5000
$-4R_2 + 5R_3 \to R_3$	0	45	0	0	45	36	27	0	9	0	180,000
$-R_2 + R_4 \to R_4$	0	0	0	0	9	9	**[9]**	9	0	0	18,000
$-4R_2 + 5R_5 \to R_5$	0	0	45	0	0	36	−18	0	9	0	90,000
$-46R_2 + 5R_6 \to R_6$	0	0	0	0	480	414	−12	0	21	15	−2,730,000

Pivot on the 9 in row 4, column 7.

	y_1	y_2	y_3	y_4	s_1	s_2	s_3	s_4	s_5	z	
$-2R_4 + R_1 \to R_1$	45	0	0	0	−63	−54	0	−18	−9	0	9000
$R_4 + 3R_2 \to R_2$	0	0	0	15	−6	−18	0	9	−3	0	33,000
$-3R_4 + R_3 \to R_3$	0	45	0	0	18	9	0	−27	9	0	126,000
	0	0	0	0	9	9	9	9	0	0	18,000
$2R_4 + R_5 \to R_5$	0	0	45	0	18	54	0	18	9	0	126,000
$4R_4 + 3R_6 \to R_6$	0	0	0	0	1476	450	0	36	63	45	−8,118,000

Create a 1 in the columns corresponding to y_1, y_2, y_3, y_4, and z.

	y_1	y_2	y_3	y_4	s_1	s_2	s_3	s_4	s_5	z	
$\frac{1}{45}R_1 \to R_1$	1	0	0	0	$-\frac{7}{5}$	$-\frac{6}{5}$	0	$-\frac{2}{5}$	$-\frac{1}{5}$	0	200
$\frac{1}{15}R_2 \to R_2$	0	0	0	1	$-\frac{2}{5}$	$-\frac{6}{5}$	0	$\frac{3}{5}$	$-\frac{1}{5}$	0	2200
$\frac{1}{45}R_3 \to R_3$	0	1	0	0	$\frac{2}{5}$	$\frac{1}{5}$	0	$-\frac{3}{5}$	$\frac{1}{5}$	0	2800
	0	0	0	0	9	9	9	9	0	0	18,000
$\frac{1}{45}R_5 \to R_5$	0	0	1	0	$\frac{2}{5}$	$\frac{6}{5}$	0	$\frac{2}{5}$	$\frac{1}{5}$	0	2800
$\frac{1}{45}R_6 \to R_6$	0	0	0	0	$\frac{164}{5}$	10	0	$\frac{4}{5}$	$\frac{7}{5}$	1	−180,400

Here, $y_1 = 200, y_2 = 2800, y_3 = 2800, y_4 = 2200$, and $-z = w = 180{,}400$. So, ship 200 barrels of oil from supplier S_1 to distributor D_1. Ship 2800 barrels of oil from supplier S_1 to distributor D_2. Ship 2800 barrels of oil from supplier S_2 to distributor D_1. Ship 2200 barrels of oil from supplier S_2 to distributor D_2. The minimum cost is $180,400.

(b) From the final tableau, $9s_3 = 18{,}000$, so $s_3 = 2000$. Therefore, S_1 could furnish 2000 more barrels of oil.

24. Let $y_1 =$ amount shipped from S_1 to D_1,
$y_2 =$ amount shipped from S_1 to D_2,
$y_3 =$ amount shipped from S_2 to D_1,
and $y_4 =$ amount shipped from S_2 to D_2.

$$\begin{array}{ll}
\text{Minimize} & w = 30y_1 + 20y_2 + 25y_3 + 22y_4 \\
\text{subject to:} & y_1 + y_3 \geq 3000 \\
 & y_2 + y_4 \geq 5000 \\
 & y_1 + y_2 = 5000 \\
 & y_3 + y_4 = 5000 \\
 & 2y_1 + 6y_2 + 5y_3 + 4y_4 \leq 40{,}000 \\
\text{with} & y_1 \geq 0, y_2 \geq 0, y_3 \geq 0, y_4 \geq 0.
\end{array}$$

Maximize $z = -w = -30y_1 - 20y_2 - 25y_3 - 22y_4$.

$$\begin{array}{cccccccccc|c}
y_1 & y_2 & y_3 & y_4 & s_1 & s_2 & s_3 & a_1 & a_2 & z & \\
1 & 0 & 1 & 0 & -1 & 0 & 0 & 0 & 0 & 0 & 3000 \\
0 & 1 & 0 & 1 & 0 & -1 & 0 & 0 & 0 & 0 & 5000 \\
\boxed{1} & 1 & 0 & 0 & 0 & 0 & 0 & 1 & 0 & 0 & 5000 \\
0 & 0 & 1 & 1 & 0 & 0 & 0 & 0 & 1 & 0 & 5000 \\
2 & 6 & 5 & 4 & 0 & 0 & 1 & 0 & 0 & 0 & 40{,}000 \\
\hline
30 & 20 & 25 & 22 & 0 & 0 & 0 & 0 & 0 & 1 & 0
\end{array}$$

Pivot on the 1 in row 3, column 1 to remove the a columns.

$$\begin{array}{r|cccccccccc|c}
 & y_1 & y_2 & y_3 & y_4 & s_1 & s_2 & s_3 & a_1 & a_2 & z & \\
-R_1 + R_3 \to R_1 & 0 & 1 & -1 & 0 & 1 & 0 & 0 & 1 & 0 & 0 & 2000 \\
 & 0 & 1 & 0 & 1 & 0 & -1 & 0 & 0 & 0 & 0 & 5000 \\
 & 1 & 1 & 0 & 0 & 0 & 0 & 0 & 1 & 0 & 0 & 5000 \\
 & 0 & 0 & 1 & 1 & 0 & 0 & 0 & 0 & 1 & 0 & 5000 \\
-2R_3 + R_5 \to R_5 & 0 & 4 & 5 & 4 & 0 & 0 & 1 & -2 & 0 & 0 & 30{,}000 \\
\hline
-30R_3 + R_6 \to R_6 & 0 & -10 & 25 & 22 & 0 & 0 & 0 & -30 & 0 & 1 & -150{,}000
\end{array}$$

Column a_1 can be removed since $a_1 = 0$.

$$\begin{array}{ccccccccc|c}
y_1 & y_2 & y_3 & y_4 & s_1 & s_2 & s_3 & a_2 & z & \\
0 & 1 & -1 & 0 & 1 & 0 & 0 & 0 & 0 & 2000 \\
0 & 1 & 0 & 1 & 0 & -1 & 0 & 0 & 0 & 5000 \\
1 & 1 & 0 & 0 & 0 & 0 & 0 & 0 & 0 & 5000 \\
0 & 0 & \boxed{1} & 1 & 0 & 0 & 0 & 1 & 0 & 5000 \\
0 & 4 & 5 & 4 & 0 & 0 & 1 & 0 & 0 & 30{,}000 \\
\hline
0 & -10 & 25 & 22 & 0 & 0 & 0 & 0 & 1 & -150{,}000
\end{array}$$

Pivot on the 1 in row 4, column 3.

$$\begin{array}{r|ccccccccc|r|}
 & y_1 & y_2 & y_3 & y_4 & s_1 & s_2 & s_3 & a_2 & z & \\
R_4+R_1\to R_1 & 0 & 1 & 0 & 1 & 1 & 0 & 0 & 1 & 0 & 7000 \\
 & 0 & \boxed{1} & 0 & 1 & 0 & -1 & 0 & 0 & 0 & 5000 \\
 & 1 & 1 & 0 & 0 & 0 & 0 & 0 & 0 & 0 & 5000 \\
 & 0 & 0 & 1 & 1 & 0 & 0 & 0 & 1 & 0 & 5000 \\
-5R_4+R_5\to R_5 & 0 & 4 & 0 & -1 & 0 & 0 & 1 & -5 & 0 & 5000 \\ \hline
-25R_4+R_6\to R_6 & 0 & -10 & 0 & -3 & 0 & 0 & 0 & -25 & 1 & -275,000
\end{array}$$

Column a_2 can be removed since $a_2 = 0$. Pivot on the 1 in row 2, column 2 since the basic solution is not yet feasible ($s_2 = -5000$).

$$\begin{array}{r|cccccccc|r|}
 & y_1 & y_2 & y_3 & y_4 & s_1 & s_2 & s_3 & z & \\
-R_2+R_1\to R_1 & 0 & 0 & 0 & 0 & 1 & 1 & 0 & 0 & 2000 \\
 & 0 & 1 & 0 & 1 & 0 & -1 & 0 & 0 & 5000 \\
-R_2+R_3\to R_3 & 1 & 0 & 0 & -1 & 0 & 1 & 0 & 0 & 0 \\
 & 0 & 0 & 1 & 1 & 0 & 0 & 0 & 0 & 5000 \\
-4R_2+R_5\to R_5 & 0 & 0 & 0 & \boxed{-5} & 0 & 4 & 1 & 0 & -15,000 \\ \hline
10R_2+R_6\to R_6 & 0 & 0 & 0 & 7 & 0 & -10 & 0 & 1 & -225,000
\end{array}$$

Pivot on the -5 in row 5, column 4.

$$\begin{array}{r|cccccccc|r|}
 & y_1 & y_2 & y_3 & y_4 & s_1 & s_2 & s_3 & z & \\
 & 0 & 0 & 0 & 0 & 1 & \boxed{1} & 0 & 0 & 2000 \\
R_5+5R_2\to R_2 & 0 & 5 & 0 & 0 & 0 & -1 & 1 & 0 & 10,000 \\
R_5-5R_3\to R_3 & -5 & 0 & 0 & 0 & 0 & -1 & 1 & 0 & -15,000 \\
R_5+5R_4\to R_4 & 0 & 0 & 5 & 0 & 0 & 4 & 1 & 0 & 10,000 \\
 & 0 & 0 & 0 & -5 & 0 & 4 & 1 & 0 & -15,000 \\ \hline
7R_5+5R_6\to R_6 & 0 & 0 & 0 & 0 & 0 & -22 & 7 & 5 & -1,230,000
\end{array}$$

Pivot on the 1 in row 1, column 6.

$$\begin{array}{r|cccccccc|r|}
 & y_1 & y_2 & y_3 & y_4 & s_1 & s_2 & s_3 & z & \\
 & 0 & 0 & 0 & 0 & 1 & 1 & 0 & 0 & 2000 \\
R_1+R_2\to R_2 & 0 & 5 & 0 & 0 & 1 & 0 & 1 & 0 & 12,000 \\
R_1+R_3\to R_3 & -5 & 0 & 0 & 0 & 1 & 0 & 1 & 0 & -13,000 \\
-4R_1+R_4\to R_4 & 0 & 0 & 5 & 0 & -4 & 0 & 1 & 0 & 2000 \\
-4R_1+R_5\to R_5 & 0 & 0 & 0 & -5 & -4 & 0 & 1 & 0 & -23,000 \\ \hline
22R_1+R_6\to R_6 & 0 & 0 & 0 & 0 & 22 & 0 & 7 & 5 & -1,186,000
\end{array}$$

$$\begin{array}{r|cccccccc|r|}
 & y_1 & y_2 & y_3 & y_4 & s_1 & s_2 & s_3 & z & \\
 & 0 & 0 & 0 & 0 & 1 & 1 & 0 & 0 & 2000 \\
\frac{1}{5}R_2\to R_2 & 0 & 1 & 0 & 0 & \frac{1}{5} & 0 & \frac{1}{5} & 0 & 2400 \\
-\frac{1}{5}R_3\to R_3 & 1 & 0 & 0 & 0 & -\frac{1}{5} & 0 & -\frac{1}{5} & 0 & 2600 \\
\frac{1}{5}R_4\to R_4 & 0 & 0 & 1 & 0 & -\frac{4}{5} & 0 & \frac{1}{5} & 0 & 400 \\
-\frac{1}{5}R_5\to R_5 & 0 & 0 & 0 & 1 & \frac{4}{5} & 0 & -\frac{1}{5} & 0 & 4600 \\ \hline
\frac{1}{5}R_6\to R_6 & 0 & 0 & 0 & 0 & \frac{22}{5} & 0 & \frac{7}{5} & 1 & -237,200
\end{array}$$

Here, $y_1 = 2600, y_2 = 2400, y_3 = 400, y_4 = 4600$, and $z = -w = 237,200$. Therefore, ship 2600 barrels from S_1 to D_1, 2400 barrels from S_1 to D_2, 400 barrels from S_2 to D_1, and 4600 barrels from S_2 to D_2 for a minimum cost of \$237,200.

25. Let $x_1 =$ the number of million dollars for home loans
and $x_2 =$ the number of million dollars for commercial loans.

$$\begin{array}{ll}
\text{Maximize} & z = 0.12x_1 + 0.10x_2 \\
\text{subject to:} & x_1 \geq 4x_2 \text{ or } x_1 - 4x_2 \geq 0 \\
 & x_1 + x_2 \geq 10 \\
 & 3x_1 + 2x_2 \leq 72 \\
 & x_1 + x_2 \leq 25 \\
\text{with} & x_1 \geq 0, x_2 \geq 0.
\end{array}$$

$$\begin{array}{c}
\begin{array}{ccccccc|c} x_1 & x_2 & s_1 & s_2 & s_3 & s_4 & z & \end{array} \\
\left[\begin{array}{ccccccc|c}
1 & -4 & -1 & 0 & 0 & 0 & 0 & 0 \\
1 & 1 & 0 & -1 & 0 & 0 & 0 & 10 \\
3 & 2 & 0 & 0 & 1 & 0 & 0 & 72 \\
1 & 1 & 0 & 0 & 0 & 1 & 0 & 25 \\ \hline
-0.12 & -0.10 & 0 & 0 & 0 & 0 & 1 & 0
\end{array}\right]
\end{array}$$

Eliminate the decimals in the last row by multiplying by 100

$$\begin{array}{c}
\begin{array}{ccccccc|c} x_1 & x_2 & s_1 & s_2 & s_3 & s_4 & z & \end{array} \\
\left[\begin{array}{ccccccc|c}
1 & -4 & -1 & 0 & 0 & 0 & 0 & 0 \\
\boxed{1} & 1 & 0 & -1 & 0 & 0 & 0 & 10 \\
3 & 2 & 0 & 0 & 1 & 0 & 0 & 72 \\
1 & 1 & 0 & 0 & 0 & 1 & 0 & 25 \\ \hline
-12 & -10 & 0 & 0 & 0 & 0 & 100 & 0
\end{array}\right]
\end{array}$$

Pivot on the 1 in row 2, column 1.

$$\begin{array}{r}
-R_2 + R_1 \rightarrow R_1 \\
\\
-3R_2 + R_3 \rightarrow R_3 \\
-R_2 + R_4 \rightarrow R_4 \\
12R_2 + R_5 \rightarrow R_5
\end{array}
\left[\begin{array}{ccccccc|c}
x_1 & x_2 & s_1 & s_2 & s_3 & s_4 & z & \\
0 & -5 & -1 & 1 & 0 & 0 & 0 & -10 \\
1 & 1 & 0 & -1 & 0 & 0 & 0 & 10 \\
0 & -1 & 0 & \boxed{3} & 1 & 0 & 0 & 42 \\
0 & 0 & 0 & 1 & 0 & 1 & 0 & 15 \\ \hline
0 & 2 & 0 & -12 & 0 & 0 & 100 & 120
\end{array}\right]$$

Pivot on the 3 in row 3, column 4.

$$\begin{array}{r}
-R_3 + 3R_1 \rightarrow R_1 \\
R_3 + 3R_2 \rightarrow R_2 \\
\\
-R_3 + 3R_4 \rightarrow R_4 \\
4R_3 + R_5 \rightarrow R_5
\end{array}
\left[\begin{array}{ccccccc|c}
x_1 & x_2 & s_1 & s_2 & s_3 & s_4 & z & \\
0 & -14 & -3 & 0 & -1 & 0 & 0 & -72 \\
3 & 2 & 0 & 0 & -2 & 0 & 0 & 72 \\
0 & -1 & 0 & 3 & 1 & 0 & 0 & 42 \\
0 & \boxed{1} & 0 & 0 & -1 & 3 & 0 & 3 \\ \hline
0 & -2 & 0 & 0 & 4 & 0 & 100 & 288
\end{array}\right]$$

Pivot on the 1 in row 4, column 2.

$$\begin{array}{r}
14R_4 + R_1 \rightarrow R_1 \\
-2R_4 + R_2 \rightarrow R_2 \\
R_4 + R_3 \rightarrow R_3 \\
\\
2R_4 + R_5 \rightarrow R_5
\end{array}
\left[\begin{array}{ccccccc|c}
x_1 & x_2 & s_1 & s_2 & s_3 & s_4 & z & \\
0 & 0 & -3 & 0 & -15 & 42 & 0 & -30 \\
3 & 0 & 0 & 0 & 0 & -6 & 0 & 66 \\
0 & 0 & 0 & 3 & 0 & 3 & 0 & 45 \\
0 & 1 & 0 & 0 & -1 & 3 & 0 & 3 \\ \hline
0 & 0 & 0 & 0 & 2 & 6 & 100 & 294
\end{array}\right]$$

Create a 1 in the columns corresponding to x_1 and z.

$$
\begin{array}{r}
\\
\\
\frac{1}{3}R_2 \to R_2 \\
\\
\\
\frac{1}{100}R_5 \to R_5
\end{array}
\begin{array}{c}
\begin{array}{ccccccc|c}
x_1 & x_2 & s_1 & s_2 & s_3 & s_4 & z & \\
\end{array}\\
\left[\begin{array}{ccccccc|c}
0 & 0 & -3 & 0 & -15 & 42 & 0 & -30 \\
1 & 0 & 0 & 0 & 0 & -2 & 0 & 22 \\
0 & 0 & 0 & 3 & 0 & 3 & 0 & 45 \\
0 & 1 & 0 & 0 & -1 & 3 & 0 & 3 \\
\hline
0 & 0 & 0 & 0 & 0.02 & 0.06 & 1 & 2.94
\end{array}\right]
\end{array}
$$

Here, $x_1 = 22, x_2 = 3$, and $z = 2.94$. Make \$22 million (\$22,000,000) in home loans and \$3 million (\$3,000,000) in commercial loans for a maximum return of \$2.94 million, or \$2,940,000.

26. Let x_1 = the number of pounds of bluegrass seed,
x_2 = the number of pounds of rye seed,
and x_3 = the number of pounds of Bermuda seed.

If each batch must contain at least 25% bluegrass seed, then

$$
\begin{aligned}
y_1 &\geq 0.25(y_1 + y_2 + y_3) \\
0.75y_1 - 0.25y_2 - 0.25y_3 &\geq 0.
\end{aligned}
$$

And if the amount of Bermuda must be no more than $\frac{2}{3}$ the amount of rye, then

$$
\begin{aligned}
y_3 &\leq \frac{2}{3}y_2 \\
-2y_2 + 3y_3 &= 0.
\end{aligned}
$$

Using these forms for our constraints, we can now state the problem as follows.

$$
\begin{array}{ll}
\text{Minimize} & w = 16y_1 + 14y_2 + 12y_3 \\
\text{subject to:} & 0.75y_1 - 0.25y_2 - 0.25y_3 \geq 0 \\
& \qquad\quad -2y_2 + 3y_3 \leq 0 \\
& \quad y_1 + y_2 + y_3 \geq 6000 \\
\text{with} & y_1 \geq 0,\ y_2 \geq 0,\ y_3 \geq 0.
\end{array}
$$

The initial simplex tableau is

$$
\begin{array}{c}
\begin{array}{ccccccc|c}
y_1 & y_2 & y_3 & s_1 & s_2 & s_3 & z & \\
\end{array}\\
\left[\begin{array}{ccccccc|c}
0.75 & -0.25 & -0.25 & -1 & 0 & 0 & 0 & 0 \\
0 & -2 & 3 & 0 & 1 & 0 & 0 & 0 \\
\boxed{1} & 1 & 1 & 0 & 0 & -1 & 0 & 6000 \\
\hline
16 & 14 & 12 & 0 & 0 & 0 & 1 & 0
\end{array}\right]
\end{array}
$$

Since $s_3 = -6000$, the basic solution is not feasible. So pivot on the 1 in row 3, column 1.

$$
\begin{array}{r}
\\
0.75R_3 - R_1 \to R_1 \\
\\
\\
-16R_3 + R_4 \to R_4
\end{array}
\begin{array}{c}
\begin{array}{ccccccc|c}
y_1 & y_2 & y_3 & s_1 & s_2 & s_3 & z & \\
\end{array}\\
\left[\begin{array}{ccccccc|c}
0 & 1 & 1 & 1 & 0 & -0.75 & 0 & 4500 \\
0 & -2 & \boxed{3} & 0 & 1 & 0 & 0 & 0 \\
1 & 1 & 1 & 0 & 0 & -1 & 0 & 6000 \\
\hline
0 & -2 & -4 & 0 & 0 & 16 & 1 & -96{,}000
\end{array}\right]
\end{array}
$$

All of the variables are now nonnegative so choose the pivot by locating the most negative number in the bottom row and forming the quotients. Pivot on the 3 in row 2, column 3.

$$
\begin{array}{r}
\\
-R_2+3R_1 \to R_1 \\
\\
-R_2+3R_3 \to R_3 \\
4R_2+3R_4 \to R_4
\end{array}
\begin{array}{c}
\begin{array}{ccccccc} y_1 & y_2 & y_3 & s_1 & s_2 & s_3 & z \end{array} \\
\left[\begin{array}{ccccccc|c}
0 & \boxed{5} & 0 & 3 & -1 & -2.25 & 0 & 13{,}500 \\
0 & -2 & 3 & 0 & 1 & 0 & 0 & 0 \\
3 & 5 & 0 & 0 & -1 & -3 & 0 & 18{,}000 \\
\hline
0 & -14 & 0 & 0 & 4 & 48 & 3 & -288{,}000
\end{array}\right]
\end{array}
$$

Pivot on the 5 in row 1, column 2.

$$
\begin{array}{r}
\\
\\
2R_1+5R_2 \to R_2 \\
-R_1+R_3 \to R_3 \\
14R_1+5R_4 \to R_4
\end{array}
\begin{array}{c}
\begin{array}{ccccccc} y_1 & y_2 & y_3 & s_1 & s_2 & s_3 & z \end{array} \\
\left[\begin{array}{ccccccc|c}
0 & 5 & 0 & 3 & -1 & -2.25 & 0 & 13{,}500 \\
0 & 0 & 15 & 6 & 3 & -4.5 & 0 & 27{,}000 \\
3 & 0 & 0 & -3 & 0 & -0.75 & 0 & 4500 \\
\hline
0 & 0 & 0 & 42 & 6 & 208.5 & 15 & -1{,}251{,}000
\end{array}\right]
\end{array}
$$

Create a 1 in the columns corresponding to $y_1, y_2, y_3,$ and z.

$$
\begin{array}{r}
\\
\frac{1}{5}R_1 \to R_1 \\
\frac{1}{15}R_2 \to R_2 \\
\frac{1}{3}R_3 \to R_3 \\
\frac{1}{15}R_4 \to R_4
\end{array}
\begin{array}{c}
\begin{array}{ccccccc} y_1 & y_2 & y_3 & s_1 & s_2 & s_3 & z \end{array} \\
\left[\begin{array}{ccccccc|c}
0 & 1 & 0 & 0.6 & -0.2 & -0.45 & 0 & 2700 \\
0 & 0 & 1 & 0.4 & 0.2 & -0.3 & 0 & 1800 \\
1 & 0 & 0 & -1 & 0 & -0.25 & 0 & 1500 \\
\hline
0 & 0 & 0 & 2.8 & 0.4 & 13.9 & 1 & -83{,}400
\end{array}\right]
\end{array}
$$

Here, $y_1 = 1500$, $y_2 = 2700$, $y_3 = 1800$, and $z = -w = 83{,}400$. Therefore, use 1500 lb of bluegrass, 2700 lb of rye, and 1800 lb of Bermuda for a minimum cost of \$834.

27. Let $x_1 =$ the number of pounds of bluegrass seed,
$x_2 =$ the number of pounds of rye seed,
and $x_3 =$ the number of pounds of Bermuda seed.

If each batch must contain at least 25% bluegrass seed, then

$$
\begin{aligned}
y_1 &\geq 0.25(y_1 + y_2 + y_3) \\
0.75y_1 - 0.25y_2 - 0.25y_3 &\geq 0.
\end{aligned}
$$

And if the amount of Bermuda must be no more than $\frac{2}{3}$ the amount of rye, then

$$
\begin{aligned}
y_3 &\leq \frac{2}{3}y_2 \\
-2y_2 + 3y_3 &= 0.
\end{aligned}
$$

Using these forms for our constraints, we can now state the problem as follows.

$$
\begin{array}{ll}
\text{Minimize} & w = 16y_1 + 14y_2 + 12y_3 \\
\text{subject to:} & 0.75y_1 - 0.25y_2 - 0.25y_3 \geq 0 \\
 & \qquad\quad - \; 2y_2 + \;\; 3y_3 \leq 0 \\
 & \quad y_1 + \quad\;\; y_2 + \quad\;\; y_3 \geq 6000 \\
\text{with} & y_1 \geq 0,\ y_2 \geq 0,\ y_3 \geq 0.
\end{array}
$$

The initial simplex tableau is

$$\begin{array}{c}
\begin{array}{cccccccc}
y_1 & y_2 & y_3 & s_1 & s_2 & a & z & \\
\end{array}\\
\left[\begin{array}{ccccccc|c}
0.75 & -0.25 & -0.25 & -1 & 0 & 0 & 0 & 0 \\
0 & -2 & 3 & 0 & 1 & 0 & 0 & 0 \\
\boxed{1} & 1 & 1 & 0 & 0 & 1 & 0 & 6000 \\
\hline
16 & 14 & 12 & 0 & 0 & 0 & 1 & 0
\end{array}\right]
\end{array}$$

First eliminate the artificial variable a. Pivot on the 1 in row 3, column 1.

$$\begin{array}{r}
0.75R_3 - R_1 \to R_1 \\ \\ \\ -16R_3 + R_4 \to R_4
\end{array}
\begin{array}{c}
\begin{array}{cccccccc}
y_1 & y_2 & y_3 & s_1 & s_2 & a & z & \\
\end{array}\\
\left[\begin{array}{ccccccc|c}
0 & 1 & 1 & 1 & 0 & 0.75 & 0 & 4500 \\
0 & -2 & 3 & 0 & 1 & 0 & 0 & 0 \\
1 & 1 & 1 & 0 & 0 & 1 & 0 & 6000 \\
\hline
0 & -2 & -4 & 0 & 0 & -16 & 1 & -96{,}000
\end{array}\right]
\end{array}$$

Since $a = 0$, we can drop the a column.

$$\begin{array}{c}
\begin{array}{ccccccc}
y_1 & y_2 & y_3 & s_1 & s_2 & z & \\
\end{array}\\
\left[\begin{array}{cccccc|c}
0 & 1 & 1 & 1 & 0 & 0 & 4500 \\
0 & -2 & \boxed{3} & 0 & 1 & 0 & 0 \\
1 & 1 & 1 & 0 & 0 & 0 & 6000 \\
\hline
0 & -2 & -4 & 0 & 0 & 1 & -96{,}000
\end{array}\right]
\end{array}$$

Pivot on the 3 in row 2, column 3.

$$\begin{array}{r}
-R_2 + 3R_1 \to R_1 \\ \\ -R_2 + 3R_3 \to R_3 \\ 4R_2 + 3R_4 \to R_4
\end{array}
\begin{array}{c}
\begin{array}{ccccccc}
y_1 & y_2 & y_3 & s_1 & s_2 & z & \\
\end{array}\\
\left[\begin{array}{cccccc|c}
0 & \boxed{5} & 0 & 3 & -1 & 0 & 13{,}500 \\
0 & -2 & 3 & 0 & 1 & 0 & 0 \\
3 & 5 & 0 & 0 & -1 & 0 & 18{,}000 \\
\hline
0 & -14 & 0 & 0 & 4 & 3 & -288{,}000
\end{array}\right]
\end{array}$$

Pivot on the 5 in row 1, column 2.

$$\begin{array}{r}
\\ 2R_1 + 5R_2 \to R_2 \\ -R_1 + R_3 \to R_3 \\ 14R_1 + 5R_4 \to R_4
\end{array}
\begin{array}{c}
\begin{array}{ccccccc}
y_1 & y_2 & y_3 & s_1 & s_2 & z & \\
\end{array}\\
\left[\begin{array}{cccccc|c}
0 & 5 & 0 & 3 & -1 & 0 & 13{,}500 \\
0 & 0 & 15 & 6 & 3 & 0 & 27{,}000 \\
3 & 0 & 0 & -3 & 0 & 0 & 4500 \\
\hline
0 & 0 & 0 & 42 & 6 & 15 & -1{,}251{,}000
\end{array}\right]
\end{array}$$

Create a 1 in the columns corresponding to $y_1, y_2, y_3,$ and z.

$$\begin{array}{r}
\frac{1}{5}R_1 \to R_1 \\ \frac{1}{15}R_2 \to R_2 \\ \frac{1}{3}R_3 \to R_3 \\ \frac{1}{15}R_4 \to R_4
\end{array}
\begin{array}{c}
\begin{array}{ccccccc}
x_1 & x_2 & x_3 & s_1 & s_2 & z & \\
\end{array}\\
\left[\begin{array}{cccccc|c}
0 & 1 & 0 & 0.6 & -0.2 & 0 & 2700 \\
0 & 0 & 1 & 0.4 & 0.2 & 0 & 1800 \\
1 & 0 & 0 & -1 & 0 & 0 & 1500 \\
\hline
0 & 0 & 0 & 2.8 & 0.4 & 1 & -83{,}400
\end{array}\right]
\end{array}$$

Here, $y_1 = 1500$, $y_2 = 2700$, $y_3 = 1800$, and $z = -w = 83{,}400$. Therefore, use 1500 lb of bluegrass, 2700 lb of rye, and 1800 lb of Bermuda for a minimum cost of \$834.

28. Let x_1 = the amount invested in government securities,
x_2 = the amount invested in municipal bonds,
and x_3 = the amount invested in mutual funds.

Maximize $z = 0.07x_1 + 0.06x_2 + 0.10x_3$

subject to:

$$\begin{array}{rcrcrl} x_1 & + & x_2 & + & x_3 & = 100{,}000 \\ x_1 & & & & & \geq 40{,}000 \\ & & x_2 & + & x_3 & \geq 50{,}000 \\ 0.02x_1 & + & 0.01x_2 & + & 0.03x_3 & \leq 2400 \text{ or } 2x_1 + x_2 + 3x_3 \leq 240{,}000 \end{array}$$

with $x_1 \geq 0,\ x_2 \geq 0,\ x_3 \geq 0.$

$$\begin{array}{c} \begin{array}{cccccccc|c} x_1 & x_2 & x_3 & a_1 & s_1 & s_2 & s_3 & z & \end{array} \\ \left[\begin{array}{cccccccc|r} \boxed{1} & 1 & 1 & 1 & 0 & 0 & 0 & 0 & 100{,}000 \\ 1 & 0 & 0 & 0 & -1 & 0 & 0 & 0 & 40{,}000 \\ 0 & 1 & 1 & 0 & 0 & -1 & 0 & 0 & 50{,}000 \\ 2 & 1 & 3 & 0 & 0 & 0 & 1 & 0 & 240{,}000 \\ \hline -0.07 & -0.06 & -0.10 & 0 & 0 & 0 & 0 & 1 & 0 \end{array}\right] \end{array}$$

Pivot on the 1 in row 1, column 1.

$$\begin{array}{r} \\ R_1 + (-R_2) \to R_2 \\ \\ -2R_1 + R_4 \to R_4 \\ 7R_1 + 100R_5 \to R_5 \end{array} \left[\begin{array}{cccccccc|r} x_1 & x_2 & x_3 & a_1 & s_1 & s_2 & s_3 & z & \\ 1 & 1 & 1 & 1 & 0 & 0 & 0 & 0 & 100{,}000 \\ 0 & 1 & 1 & 1 & 1 & 0 & 0 & 0 & 60{,}000 \\ 0 & 1 & \boxed{1} & 0 & 0 & -1 & 0 & 0 & 50{,}000 \\ 0 & -1 & 1 & -2 & 0 & 0 & 1 & 0 & 40{,}000 \\ \hline 0 & 1 & -3 & 7 & 0 & 0 & 0 & 100 & 700{,}000 \end{array}\right]$$

Since $a_1 = 0$, we can now eliminate column a_1. Pivot on the 1 in row 3, column 3 since the basic solution is not feasible $(s_2 = -50{,}000)$.

$$\begin{array}{r} -R_3 + R_1 \to R_1 \\ -R_3 + R_2 \to R_2 \\ \\ R_3 - R_4 \to R_4 \\ 3R_3 + R_5 \to R_5 \end{array} \left[\begin{array}{ccccccc|r} x_1 & x_2 & x_3 & s_1 & s_2 & s_3 & z & \\ 1 & 0 & 0 & 0 & 1 & 0 & 0 & 50{,}000 \\ 0 & 0 & 0 & 1 & 1 & 0 & 0 & 10{,}000 \\ 0 & 1 & 1 & 0 & -1 & 0 & 0 & 50{,}000 \\ 0 & \boxed{2} & 0 & 0 & -1 & -1 & 0 & 10{,}000 \\ \hline 0 & 4 & 0 & 0 & -3 & 0 & 100 & 850{,}000 \end{array}\right]$$

Pivot on the 2 in row 4, column 2 since the basic solution is not feasible $(s_3 = -10{,}000)$.

$$\begin{array}{r} \\ \\ -R_4 + 2R_3 \to R_3 \\ \\ -2R_4 + R_5 \to R_5 \end{array} \left[\begin{array}{ccccccc|r} x_1 & x_2 & x_3 & s_1 & s_2 & s_3 & z & \\ 1 & 0 & 0 & 0 & 1 & 0 & 0 & 50{,}000 \\ 0 & 0 & 0 & 1 & \boxed{1} & 0 & 0 & 10{,}000 \\ 0 & 0 & 2 & 0 & -1 & 1 & 0 & 90{,}000 \\ 0 & 2 & 0 & 0 & -1 & -1 & 0 & 10{,}000 \\ \hline 0 & 0 & 0 & 0 & -1 & 2 & 100 & 830{,}000 \end{array}\right]$$

Since all basic solutions are feasible, continue with the simplex method by pivoting on the 1 in row 2, column 5.

	x_1	x_2	x_3	s_1	s_2	s_3	z	
$-R_2 + R_1 \to R_1$	1	0	0	−1	0	0	0	40,000
	0	0	0	1	1	0	0	10,000
$R_2 + R_3 \to R_3$	0	0	2	1	0	1	0	100,000
$R_2 + R_4 \to R_4$	0	2	0	1	0	−1	0	20,000
$R_2 + R_5 \to R_5$	0	0	0	1	0	2	100	840,000

Create a 1 in the columns corresponding to x_2, x_3, and z.

	x_1	x_2	x_3	s_1	s_2	s_3	z	
	1	0	0	−1	0	0	0	40,000
	0	0	0	1	1	0	0	10,000
$\frac{1}{2}R_3 \to R_3$	0	0	1	$\frac{1}{2}$	0	$\frac{1}{2}$	0	50,000
$\frac{1}{2}R_4 \to R_4$	0	1	0	$\frac{1}{2}$	0	$-\frac{1}{2}$	0	10,000
$\frac{1}{100}R_5 \to R_5$	0	0	0	0.01	0	0.02	1	8400

Here, $x_1 = 40,000$, $x_2 = 10,000$, $x_3 = 50,000$, and $z = 8400$. Therefore, invest \$40,000 in government securities, \$10,000 in municipal bonds, and \$50,000 in mutual funds for maximum interest of \$8400.

29. (a) Let $x_1 =$ the number of computers shipped from W_1 to D_1,
$x_2 =$ the number of computers shipped from W_1 to D_2,
$x_3 =$ the number of computers shipped from W_2 to D_1,
and $x_4 =$ the number of computers shipped from W_2 to D_2.

Minimize $w = 14x_1 + 12x_2 + 12x_3 + 10x_4$
subject to: $x_1 + x_3 \geq 32$
$x_2 + x_4 \geq 20$
$x_1 + x_2 \leq 25$
$x_3 + x_4 \leq 30$
with $x_1 \geq 0, x_2 \geq 0, x_3 \geq 0, x_4 \geq 0.$

Maximize $z = -w = -14x_1 - 12x_2 - 12x_3 - 10x_4$.

x_1	x_2	x_3	x_4	s_1	s_2	s_3	s_4	z	
[1]	0	1	0	−1	0	0	0	0	32
0	1	0	1	0	−1	0	0	0	20
1	1	0	0	0	0	1	0	0	25
0	0	1	1	0	0	0	1	0	30
14	12	12	10	0	0	0	0	1	0

Since the basic solution is not feasible ($s_1 = -32$), pivot on the 1 in row 1, column 1.

	x_1	x_2	x_3	x_4	s_1	s_2	s_3	s_4	z	
	1	0	1	0	−1	0	0	0	0	32
	0	[1]	0	1	0	−1	0	0	0	20
$R_1 - R_3 \to R_3$	0	−1	1	0	−1	0	−1	0	0	7
	0	0	1	1	0	0	0	1	0	30
$-14R_1 + R_5 \to R_5$	0	12	−2	10	14	0	0	0	1	−448

Pivot on the 1 in row 2, column 2 since $s_2 = -20$.

$$
\begin{array}{r}
\\ \\ \\ R_2 + R_3 \to R_3 \\ \\ -12R_2 + R_5 \to R_5
\end{array}
\begin{array}{c}
\begin{array}{ccccccccc} x_1 & x_2 & x_3 & x_4 & s_1 & s_2 & s_3 & s_4 & z \end{array} \\
\left[\begin{array}{ccccccccc|c}
1 & 0 & 1 & 0 & -1 & 0 & 0 & 0 & 0 & 32 \\
0 & 1 & 0 & 1 & 0 & -1 & 0 & 0 & 0 & 20 \\
0 & 0 & \boxed{1} & 1 & -1 & -1 & -1 & 0 & 0 & 27 \\
0 & 0 & 1 & 1 & 0 & 0 & 0 & 1 & 0 & 30 \\
\hline
0 & 0 & -2 & -2 & 14 & 12 & 0 & 0 & 1 & -688
\end{array}\right]
\end{array}
$$

Pivot on the 1 in row 3, column 3 since $s_3 = -27$.

$$
\begin{array}{r}
\\ -R_3 + R_1 \to R_1 \\ \\ \\ -R_3 + R_4 \to R_4 \\ 2R_3 + R_5 \to R_5
\end{array}
\begin{array}{c}
\begin{array}{ccccccccc} x_1 & x_2 & x_3 & x_4 & s_1 & s_2 & s_3 & s_4 & z \end{array} \\
\left[\begin{array}{ccccccccc|c}
1 & 0 & 0 & -1 & 0 & 1 & 1 & 0 & 0 & 5 \\
0 & 1 & 0 & 1 & 0 & -1 & 0 & 0 & 0 & 20 \\
0 & 0 & 1 & 1 & -1 & -1 & -1 & 0 & 0 & 27 \\
0 & 0 & 0 & 0 & 1 & 1 & \boxed{1} & 1 & 0 & 3 \\
\hline
0 & 0 & 0 & 0 & 12 & 10 & -2 & 0 & 1 & -634
\end{array}\right]
\end{array}
$$

Pivot on the 1 in row 4, column 7.

$$
\begin{array}{r}
\\ -R_4 + R_1 \to R_1 \\ \\ R_4 + R_3 \to R_3 \\ \\ 2R_4 + R_5 \to R_5
\end{array}
\begin{array}{c}
\begin{array}{ccccccccc} x_1 & x_2 & x_3 & x_4 & s_1 & s_2 & s_3 & s_4 & z \end{array} \\
\left[\begin{array}{ccccccccc|c}
1 & 0 & 0 & -1 & -1 & 0 & 0 & -1 & 0 & 2 \\
0 & 1 & 0 & 1 & 0 & -1 & 0 & 0 & 0 & 20 \\
0 & 0 & 1 & 1 & 0 & 0 & 0 & 1 & 0 & 30 \\
0 & 0 & 0 & 0 & 1 & 1 & 1 & 1 & 0 & 3 \\
\hline
0 & 0 & 0 & 0 & 14 & 12 & 0 & 2 & 1 & -628
\end{array}\right]
\end{array}
$$

Here, $x_1 = 2, x_2 = 20, x_3 = 30, x_4 = 0$, and $z = -w = 628$. Therefore, ship 2 computers from W_1 to D_1, 20 computers from W_1 to D_2, 30 computers from W_2 to D_1, and 0 computers from W_2 to D_2 for a minimum cost of \$628.

(b) From the final tableau, $s_3 = 3$. Therefore, warehouse W_1has three more computers that it could ship.

30. Let $x_1 =$ the amount of chemical I,
$x_2 =$ the amount of chemical II,
and $x_3 =$ the amount of chemical III.

$$
\begin{array}{lr}
\text{Minimize} & w = 1.09x_1 + 0.87x_2 + 0.65x_3 \\
\text{subject to:} & x_1 + x_2 + x_3 \geq 750 \\
 & 0.09x_1 + 0.04x_2 + 0.03x_3 \geq 30 \\
 & 3x_2 = 4x_3 \\
\text{with} & x_1 \geq 0,\ x_2 \geq 0,\ x_3 \geq 0.
\end{array}
$$

Use a graphing calculator or computer to find that we should use 59.21 kg of chemical I, 394.74 kg of chemical II, and 296.05 kg of chemical III for a minimum cost of \$600.39.

31. Let $y_1 =$ the number of ounces of ingredient I,
$y_2 =$ the number of ounces of ingredient II,
and $y_3 =$ the number of ounces of ingredient III.

The problem is:

$$\begin{array}{ll} \text{Minimize} & w = 0.30y_1 + 0.09y_2 + 0.27y_3 \\ \text{subject to:} & y_1 + y_2 + y_3 \geq 10 \\ & y_1 + y_2 + y_3 \leq 15 \\ & y_1 \geq \frac{1}{4}y_2 \\ & y_3 \geq y_1 \\ \text{with} & y_1 \geq 0, y_2 \geq 0, y_3 \geq 0. \end{array}$$

Use a graphing calculator or computer to find that the minimum is $w = 1.55$ when $y_1 = \frac{5}{3}, y_2 = \frac{20}{3}$, and $y_3 = \frac{5}{3}$. Therefore, the additive should consist of $\frac{5}{3}$ oz of ingredient I, $\frac{20}{3}$ oz of ingredient II, and $\frac{5}{3}$ oz of ingredient III, for a minimum cost of \$1.55/gal. The amount of additive that should be used per gallon of gasoline is $\frac{5}{3} + \frac{20}{3} + \frac{5}{3} = 10$ oz.

32. Let y_1 = the number of gallons of ingredient 1, y_2 = the number of gallons of ingredient 2, y_3 = the number of gallons of ingredient 3, y_4 = the number of gallons of ingredient 4, y_5 = the number of gallons of ingredient 5, and y_6 = the number of gallons of water.

Note that 10%(15,000) = 1500, and 0.01(15,000) = 150.

The problem becomes:

Minimize

$$w = 0.48y_1 + 0.32y_2 + 0.53y_3 + 0.28y_4 + 0.43y_5 + 0.04y_6$$

subject to:

$$\begin{array}{llllllll} 0.28y_1 & +0.19y_2 & +0.43y_3 & +0.57y_4 & +0.22y_5 & & \leq & 1500 \\ & & y_3 & + y_4 & & & \geq & 150 \\ & y_2 & & & + y_5 & & \geq & 150 \\ y_1 & & & + y_4 & & & \geq & 150 \\ y_1 & + y_2 & + y_3 & + y_4 & + y_5 & + y_6 & = & 15{,}000 \end{array}$$

with $y_1 \geq 0, y_2 \geq 0, y_3 \geq 0, y_4 \geq 0, y_5 \geq 0, y_6 \geq 0$.

This exercise should be solved by graphing calculator or computer methods. The answer is to use 0 gal of ingredient 1, 150 gal of 2, 0 gal of 3, 150 gal of 4, 0 gal of 5, and 14,700 gal of water for a minimum cost of \$678.

33. (a) Let $x_1 =$ the number of hours spent doing calisthenics,
$x_2 =$ the number of hours spent swimming,
and $x_3 =$ the number of hours spent playing the drums.

The problem can be stated as follows.

$$\begin{array}{ll} \text{Maximize} & z = 388x_1 + 518x_2 + 345x_3 \\ \text{subject to:} & x_1 + x_2 + x_3 \leq 10 \\ & x_1 - 2x_2 + x_3 \geq 0 \\ & x_3 \leq 4 \\ & x_3 \geq 1. \\ \text{with} & x_1 \geq 0, x_2 \geq 0, x_3 \geq 0. \end{array}$$

The initial simplex tableau is

$$
\begin{array}{c}
\begin{array}{cccccccc|c}
x_1 & x_2 & x_3 & s_1 & s_2 & s_3 & s_4 & z & \\
\end{array}\\
\left[\begin{array}{cccccccc|c}
1 & 1 & 1 & 1 & 0 & 0 & -1 & 0 & 10 \\
1 & -2 & 1 & 0 & -1 & 0 & 0 & 0 & 0 \\
0 & 0 & 1 & 0 & 0 & 1 & 0 & 0 & 4 \\
0 & 0 & \boxed{1} & 0 & 0 & 0 & -1 & 0 & 1 \\
\hline
-388 & -518 & -345 & 0 & 0 & 0 & 0 & 1 & 0
\end{array}\right]
\end{array}
$$

Since $s_4 = 1$, the initial basic solution is not feasible. So pivot on the 1 in row 4, column 3.

$$
\begin{array}{r}
\\
-R_4 + R_1 \rightarrow R_1 \\
R_4 - R_2 \rightarrow R_2 \\
-R_4 + R_3 \rightarrow R_3 \\
\\
345R_4 + R_5 \rightarrow R_5
\end{array}
\left[\begin{array}{cccccccc|c}
x_1 & x_2 & x_3 & s_1 & s_2 & s_3 & s_4 & z & \\
1 & 1 & 0 & 1 & 0 & 0 & 0 & 0 & 9 \\
-1 & \boxed{2} & 0 & 0 & 1 & 0 & -1 & 0 & 1 \\
0 & 0 & 0 & 0 & 0 & 1 & 1 & 0 & 3 \\
0 & 0 & 1 & 0 & 0 & 0 & -1 & 0 & 1 \\
\hline
-388 & -518 & 0 & 0 & 0 & 0 & -345 & 1 & 345
\end{array}\right]
$$

Pivot on the 2 in row 2, column 2.

$$
\begin{array}{r}
\\
-R_2 + 2R_1 \rightarrow R_1 \\
\\
\\
\\
259R_2 + R_5 \rightarrow R_5
\end{array}
\left[\begin{array}{cccccccc|c}
x_1 & x_2 & x_3 & s_1 & s_2 & s_3 & s_4 & z & \\
\boxed{3} & 0 & 0 & 2 & -1 & 0 & 1 & 0 & 17 \\
-1 & 2 & 0 & 0 & 1 & 0 & -1 & 0 & 1 \\
0 & 0 & 0 & 0 & 0 & 1 & 1 & 0 & 3 \\
0 & 0 & 1 & 0 & 0 & 0 & -1 & 0 & 1 \\
\hline
-647 & 0 & 0 & 0 & 259 & 0 & -604 & 1 & 604
\end{array}\right]
$$

Pivot on the 3 in row 1, column 1.

$$
\begin{array}{r}
\\
\\
R_1 + 3R_2 \rightarrow R_2 \\
\\
\\
647R_1 + 3R_5 \rightarrow R_5
\end{array}
\left[\begin{array}{cccccccc|c}
x_1 & x_2 & x_3 & s_1 & s_2 & s_3 & s_4 & z & \\
3 & 0 & 0 & 2 & -1 & 0 & 1 & 0 & 17 \\
0 & 6 & 0 & 2 & 2 & 0 & -2 & 0 & 20 \\
0 & 0 & 0 & 0 & 0 & 1 & 1 & 0 & 3 \\
0 & 0 & 1 & 0 & 0 & 0 & -1 & 0 & 1 \\
\hline
0 & 0 & 0 & 1294 & 130 & 0 & -1165 & 3 & 12{,}811
\end{array}\right]
$$

Create a 1 in the columns corresponding to x_1, x_2, and z.

$$
\begin{array}{r}
\\
\frac{1}{3}R_1 \rightarrow R_1 \\
\frac{1}{6}R_2 \rightarrow R_2 \\
\\
\\
\frac{1}{3}R_5 \rightarrow R_5
\end{array}
\left[\begin{array}{cccccccc|c}
x_1 & x_2 & x_3 & s_1 & s_2 & s_3 & s_4 & z & \\
1 & 0 & 0 & \frac{2}{3} & -\frac{1}{3} & 0 & \frac{1}{3} & 0 & \frac{17}{3} \\
0 & 1 & 0 & \frac{1}{3} & \frac{1}{3} & 0 & -\frac{1}{3} & 0 & \frac{10}{3} \\
0 & 0 & 0 & 0 & 0 & 1 & 1 & 0 & 3 \\
0 & 0 & 1 & 0 & 0 & 0 & -1 & 0 & 1 \\
\hline
0 & 0 & 0 & \frac{1294}{3} & \frac{130}{3} & 0 & -\frac{1165}{3} & 1 & \frac{12{,}811}{3}
\end{array}\right]
$$

Joe should spend $\frac{17}{3}$ hours doing calisthenics, $\frac{10}{3}$ hours swimming, and 1 hour playing drums for a maximum calorie expenditure of $\frac{12{,}811}{3}$ or $4270\frac{1}{3}$ calories.

Chapter 4 Review Exercises

1. The simplex method should be used for problems with more than two variables or problems with two variables and many constants.

2. If a surplus variable cannot be made nonnegative, then the inequality which represents one of the constraints can never exist. This means that no solution is possible.

3. (a) Maximize $z = 2x_1 + 7x_2$

subject to:
$$\begin{aligned} 4x_1 + 6x_2 &\le 60 \\ 3x_1 + x_2 &\le 18 \\ 2x_1 + 5x_2 &\le 20 \\ x_1 + x_2 &\le 15 \end{aligned}$$
with $x_1 \ge 0,\ x_2 \ge 0.$

Adding slack variables s_1, s_2, s_3, and s_4, we obtain the following equations.

$$\begin{aligned} 4x_1 + 6x_2 + s_1 \qquad\qquad &= 60 \\ 3x_1 + x_2 \qquad + s_2 \qquad &= 18 \\ 2x_1 + 5x_2 \qquad\qquad + s_3 &= 20 \\ x_1 + x_2 \qquad\qquad\qquad + s_4 &= 15. \end{aligned}$$

(b) The initial simplex tableau is as follows.

$$\begin{array}{c} \begin{matrix} x_1 & x_2 & s_1 & s_2 & s_3 & s_4 & z & \end{matrix} \\ \left[\begin{array}{rrrrrrr|r} 4 & 6 & 1 & 0 & 0 & 0 & 0 & 60 \\ 3 & 1 & 0 & 1 & 0 & 0 & 0 & 18 \\ 2 & 5 & 0 & 0 & 1 & 0 & 0 & 20 \\ 1 & 1 & 0 & 0 & 0 & 1 & 0 & 15 \\ \hline -2 & -7 & 0 & 0 & 0 & 0 & 1 & 0 \end{array}\right]. \end{array}$$

4. Maximize $z = 25x_1 + 30x_2$

subject to:
$$\begin{aligned} 3x_1 + 5x_2 &\le 47 \\ x_1 + x_2 &\le 25 \\ 5x_1 + 2x_2 &\le 35 \\ 2x_1 + x_2 &\le 30 \end{aligned}$$
with $x_1 \ge 0,\ x_2 \ge 0.$

(a) Add s_1, s_2, s_3, and s_4 as slack variables to obtain

$$\begin{aligned} 3x_1 + 5x_2 + s_1 \qquad\qquad &= 47 \\ x_1 + x_2 \qquad + s_2 \qquad &= 25 \\ 5x_1 + 2x_2 \qquad\qquad + s_3 &= 35 \\ 2x_1 + x_2 \qquad\qquad\qquad + s_4 &= 30. \end{aligned}$$

(b) The initial tableau is

$$\begin{array}{c} \begin{matrix} x_1 & x_2 & s_1 & s_2 & s_3 & s_4 & z & \end{matrix} \\ \left[\begin{array}{rrrrrrr|r} 3 & 5 & 1 & 0 & 0 & 0 & 0 & 47 \\ 1 & 1 & 0 & 1 & 0 & 0 & 0 & 25 \\ 5 & 2 & 0 & 0 & 1 & 0 & 0 & 35 \\ 2 & 1 & 0 & 0 & 0 & 1 & 0 & 30 \\ \hline -25 & -30 & 0 & 0 & 0 & 0 & 1 & 0 \end{array}\right]. \end{array}$$

5. Maximize $z = 5x_1 + 8x_2 + 6x_3$

subject to:
$$\begin{aligned} x_1 + x_2 + x_3 &\le 90 \\ 2x_1 + 5x_2 + x_3 &\le 120 \\ x_1 + 3x_2 \qquad &\ge 80 \end{aligned}$$
with $x_1 \ge 0, x_2 \ge 0, x_3 \ge 0.$

(a) Adding the slack variables s_1 and s_2 and subtracting the surplus variable s_3, we obtain the following equations:

$$\begin{aligned} x_1 + x_2 + x_3 + s_1 \qquad\qquad &= 90 \\ 2x_1 + 5x_2 + x_3 \qquad + s_2 \qquad &= 120 \\ x_1 + 3x_2 \qquad\qquad\qquad - s_3 &= 80. \end{aligned}$$

(b) The initial tableau is

$$\begin{array}{c} \begin{matrix} x_1 & x_2 & x_3 & s_1 & s_2 & s_3 & z & \end{matrix} \\ \left[\begin{array}{rrrrrrr|r} 1 & 1 & 1 & 1 & 0 & 0 & 0 & 90 \\ 2 & 5 & 1 & 0 & 1 & 0 & 0 & 120 \\ 1 & 3 & 0 & 0 & 0 & -1 & 0 & 80 \\ \hline -5 & -8 & -6 & 0 & 0 & 0 & 1 & 0 \end{array}\right]. \end{array}$$

6. Maximize $z = 4x_1 + 6x_2 + 8x_3$

subject to:
$$\begin{aligned} x_1 + x_2 + 2x_3 &\ge 200 \\ 8x_1 \qquad + 6x_3 &\le 400 \\ 3x_1 + 5x_2 + x_3 &\le 300 \end{aligned}$$
with $x_1 \ge 0,\ x_2 \ge 0,\ x_3 \ge 0.$

(a) Introduce s_1 as a surplus variable and s_2 and s_3 as slack variables to obtain the following equations.

$$\begin{aligned} x_1 + x_2 + 2x_3 - s_1 \qquad\qquad &= 200 \\ 8x_1 \qquad + 6x_3 \qquad + s_2 \qquad &= 400 \\ 3x_1 + 5x_2 + x_3 \qquad\qquad + s_3 &= 300. \end{aligned}$$

(b) The initial tableau is as follows.

$$\begin{array}{c} \begin{matrix} x_1 & x_2 & x_3 & s_1 & s_2 & s_3 & z & \end{matrix} \\ \left[\begin{array}{rrrrrrr|r} 1 & 1 & 2 & -1 & 0 & 0 & 0 & 200 \\ 8 & 0 & 6 & 0 & 1 & 0 & 0 & 400 \\ 3 & 5 & 1 & 0 & 0 & 1 & 0 & 300 \\ \hline -4 & -6 & -8 & 0 & 0 & 0 & 1 & 0 \end{array}\right]. \end{array}$$

7.

$$\begin{array}{cccccc|c} x_1 & x_2 & x_3 & s_1 & s_2 & z & \\ 4 & 5 & 2 & 1 & 0 & 0 & 18 \\ 2 & 8 & \boxed{6} & 0 & 1 & 0 & 24 \\ \hline -5 & -3 & -6 & 0 & 0 & 1 & 0 \end{array}$$

The most negative entry in the last row is −6, and the smaller of the two quotients is $\frac{24}{6} = 4$. Hence, the 6 in row 2, column 3, is the first pivot. Performing row transformations leads to the following tableau.

$$\begin{array}{l} -R_2 + 3R_1 \rightarrow R_1 \\ \\ R_2 + R_3 \rightarrow R_3 \end{array} \begin{array}{cccccc|c} x_1 & x_2 & x_3 & s_1 & s_2 & z & \\ \boxed{10} & 7 & 0 & 3 & -1 & 0 & 30 \\ 2 & 8 & 6 & 0 & 1 & 0 & 24 \\ \hline -3 & 5 & 0 & 0 & 1 & 1 & 24 \end{array}$$

Pivot on the 10 in row 1, column 1.

$$\begin{array}{l} \\ -R_1 + 5R_2 \rightarrow R_2 \\ 3R_1 + 10R_3 \rightarrow R_3 \end{array} \begin{array}{cccccc|c} x_1 & x_2 & x_3 & s_1 & s_2 & z & \\ 10 & 7 & 0 & 3 & -1 & 0 & 30 \\ 0 & 33 & 30 & -3 & 6 & 0 & 90 \\ \hline 0 & 71 & 0 & 9 & 7 & 10 & 330 \end{array}$$

Create a 1 in the columns corresponding to x_1, x_3, and z.

$$\begin{array}{l} \frac{1}{10}R_1 \rightarrow R_1 \\ \frac{1}{30}R_2 \rightarrow R_2 \\ \frac{1}{10}R_3 \rightarrow R_3 \end{array} \begin{array}{cccccc|c} x_1 & x_2 & x_3 & s_1 & s_2 & z & \\ 1 & \frac{7}{10} & 0 & \frac{3}{10} & -\frac{1}{10} & 0 & 3 \\ 0 & \frac{11}{10} & 1 & -\frac{1}{10} & \frac{1}{5} & 0 & 3 \\ \hline 0 & \frac{71}{10} & 0 & \frac{9}{10} & \frac{7}{10} & 1 & 33 \end{array}$$

The maximum value is 33 when $x_1 = 3, x_2 = 0, x_3 = 3, s_1 = 0$, and $s_2 = 0$.

8.

$$\begin{array}{ccccc|c} x_1 & x_2 & s_1 & s_2 & z & \\ 2 & \boxed{7} & 1 & 0 & 0 & 14 \\ 2 & 3 & 0 & 1 & 0 & 10 \\ \hline -2 & -4 & 0 & 0 & 1 & 0 \end{array}$$

The most negative indicator is in the second column. The smaller quotient is $\frac{14}{7} = 2$. Pivot on the 7 in row 1, column 2.

$$\begin{array}{l} \\ -3R_1 + 7R_2 \rightarrow R_2 \\ 4R_1 + 7R_3 \rightarrow R_3 \end{array} \begin{array}{ccccc|c} x_1 & x_2 & s_1 & s_2 & z & \\ 2 & 7 & 1 & 0 & 0 & 14 \\ \boxed{8} & 0 & -3 & 7 & 0 & 28 \\ \hline -6 & 0 & 4 & 0 & 7 & 56 \end{array}$$

Pivot on the 8 in row 2, column 1.

$$\begin{array}{l} -R_2 + 4R_1 \rightarrow R_1 \\ \\ 3R_2 + 4R_3 \rightarrow R_3 \end{array} \begin{array}{ccccc|c} x_1 & x_2 & s_1 & s_2 & z & \\ 0 & 28 & 7 & -7 & 0 & 28 \\ 8 & 0 & -3 & 7 & 0 & 28 \\ \hline 0 & 0 & 7 & 21 & 28 & 308 \end{array}$$

Create a 1 in the columns corresponding to x_1, x_2, and z.

$$\begin{array}{l} \\ \frac{1}{28}R_1 \to R_1 \\ \frac{1}{8}R_2 \to R_2 \\ \frac{1}{28}R_3 \to R_3 \end{array} \begin{array}{c} \begin{array}{ccccc} x_1 & x_2 & s_1 & s_2 & z \end{array} \\ \left[\begin{array}{ccccc|c} 0 & 1 & \frac{1}{4} & -\frac{1}{4} & 0 & 1 \\ 1 & 0 & -\frac{3}{8} & \frac{7}{8} & 0 & \frac{7}{2} \\ \hline 0 & 0 & \frac{1}{4} & \frac{3}{4} & 1 & 11 \end{array}\right] \end{array}$$

The maximum value is 11 when $x_1 = \frac{7}{2}$, $x_2 = 1$, $s_1 = 0$, and $s_2 = 0$.

9.

$$\begin{array}{c} \begin{array}{ccccccc} x_1 & x_2 & x_3 & s_1 & s_2 & s_3 & z \end{array} \\ \left[\begin{array}{ccccccc|c} 1 & 2 & 2 & 1 & 0 & 0 & 0 & 50 \\ \boxed{3} & 1 & 0 & 0 & 1 & 0 & 0 & 20 \\ 1 & 0 & 2 & 0 & 0 & -1 & 0 & 15 \\ \hline -5 & -3 & -2 & 0 & 0 & 0 & 1 & 0 \end{array}\right] \end{array}$$

The initial basic solution is not feasible since $s_3 = -15$. In the third row where the negative coefficient appears, the nonnegative entry that appears farthest to the left is the 1 in the first column. In the first column, the smallest nonnegative quotient is $\frac{20}{3}$. Pivot on the 3 in row 2, column 1.

$$\begin{array}{r} \\ -R_2 + 3R_1 \to R_1 \\ \\ -R_2 + 3R_3 \to R_3 \\ 5R_2 + 3R_4 \to R_4 \end{array} \begin{array}{c} \begin{array}{ccccccc} x_1 & x_2 & x_3 & s_1 & s_2 & s_3 & z \end{array} \\ \left[\begin{array}{ccccccc|c} 0 & 5 & 6 & 3 & -1 & 0 & 0 & 130 \\ 3 & 1 & 0 & 0 & 1 & 0 & 0 & 20 \\ 0 & -1 & \boxed{6} & 0 & -1 & -3 & 0 & 25 \\ \hline 0 & -4 & -6 & 0 & 5 & 0 & 3 & 100 \end{array}\right] \end{array}$$

Continue by pivoting on each circled entry.

$$\begin{array}{r} \\ -R_3 + R_2 \to R_1 \\ \\ \\ R_3 + R_4 \to R_4 \end{array} \begin{array}{c} \begin{array}{ccccccc} x_1 & x_2 & x_3 & s_1 & s_2 & s_3 & z \end{array} \\ \left[\begin{array}{ccccccc|c} 0 & \boxed{6} & 0 & 3 & 0 & 3 & 0 & 105 \\ 3 & 1 & 0 & 0 & 1 & 0 & 0 & 20 \\ 0 & -1 & 6 & 0 & -1 & -3 & 0 & 25 \\ \hline 0 & -5 & 0 & 0 & 4 & -3 & 3 & 125 \end{array}\right] \end{array}$$

The basic solution is now feasible, but there are negative indicators.
Continue pivoting.

$$\begin{array}{r} \\ \\ -R_1 + 6R_2 \to R_2 \\ R_1 + 6R_3 \to R_3 \\ 5R_1 + 6R_4 \to R_4 \end{array} \begin{array}{c} \begin{array}{ccccccc} x_1 & x_2 & x_3 & s_1 & s_2 & s_3 & z \end{array} \\ \left[\begin{array}{ccccccc|c} 0 & 6 & 0 & 3 & 0 & \boxed{3} & 0 & 105 \\ 18 & 0 & 0 & -3 & 6 & -3 & 0 & 15 \\ 0 & 0 & 36 & 3 & 0 & -15 & 0 & 255 \\ \hline 0 & 0 & 0 & 15 & 24 & -3 & 18 & 1275 \end{array}\right] \end{array}$$

$$\begin{array}{r} \\ \\ R_1 + R_2 \to R_2 \\ 5R_1 + R_3 \to R_3 \\ R_1 + R_4 \to R_4 \end{array} \begin{array}{c} \begin{array}{ccccccc} x_1 & x_2 & x_3 & s_1 & s_2 & s_3 & z \end{array} \\ \left[\begin{array}{ccccccc|c} 0 & 6 & 0 & 3 & 0 & 3 & 0 & 105 \\ 18 & 6 & 0 & 0 & 6 & 0 & 0 & 120 \\ 0 & 30 & 36 & 18 & 0 & 0 & 0 & 780 \\ \hline 0 & 6 & 0 & 18 & 24 & 0 & 18 & 1380 \end{array}\right] \end{array}$$

Create a 1 in the columns corresponding to x_1, x_3, s_3, and z.

	x_1	x_2	x_3	s_1	s_2	s_3	z	
$\frac{1}{3}R_1 \to R_1$	0	2	0	1	0	1	0	35
$\frac{1}{18}R_2 \to R_2$	1	.33	0	0	.33	0	0	6.67
$\frac{1}{36}R_3 \to R_3$	0	.83	1	.5	0	0	0	21.67
$\frac{1}{18}R_4 \to R_4$	0	.33	0	1	1.33	0	1	76.67

The maximum value is about 76.67 when $x_1 \approx 6.67, x_2 = 0, x_3 \approx 21.67, s_1 = 0, s_2 = 0$, and $s_3 = 35$.

10.

x_1	x_2	s_1	s_2	s_3	z	
3	[6]	−1	0	0	0	28
1	1	0	1	0	0	12
2	1	0	0	1	0	16
−1	−2	0	0	0	1	0

Pivot on the 6 in row 1, column 2.

	x_1	x_2	s_1	s_2	s_3	z	
	3	6	−1	0	0	0	28
$-R_1 + 6R_2 \to R_2$	3	0	[1]	6	0	0	44
$-R_1 + 6R_3 \to R_3$	9	0	1	0	6	0	68
$R_1 + 3R_4 \to R_4$	0	0	−1	0	0	3	28

Pivot on the 1 in row 2, column 3.

	x_1	x_2	s_1	s_2	s_3	z	
$R_2 + R_1 \to R_1$	6	6	0	6	0	0	72
	3	0	1	6	0	0	44
$-R_2 + R_3 \to R_3$	6	0	0	−6	6	0	24
$R_2 + R_4 \to R_4$	3	0	0	6	0	3	72

	x_1	x_2	s_1	s_2	s_3	z	
$\frac{1}{6}R_1 \to R_1$	1	1	0	1	0	0	12
	3	0	1	6	0	0	44
$\frac{1}{6}R_3 \to R_3$	1	0	0	−1	1	0	4
$\frac{1}{3}R_4 \to R_4$	1	0	0	2	0	1	24

The maximum is 24 when $x_1 = 0,\ x_2 = 12,$
$s_1 = 44,\ s_2 = 0$, and $s_3 = 4$.

11. Minimize $w = 10y_1 + 15y_2$
subject to: $y_1 + y_2 \geq 17$
$5y_1 + 8y_2 \geq 42$
with $y_1 \geq 0, y_2 \geq 0.$

Using the dual method:

To form the dual, write the augmented matrix for the given problem.

$$\left[\begin{array}{cc|c} 1 & 1 & 17 \\ 5 & 8 & 42 \\ \hline 10 & 15 & 0 \end{array}\right]$$

Form the transpose of this matrix.

$$\left[\begin{array}{cc|c} 1 & 5 & 10 \\ 1 & 8 & 15 \\ \hline 17 & 42 & 0 \end{array}\right]$$

Write the dual problem.

Maximize $z = 17x_1 + 42x_2$
subject to: $x_1 + 5x_2 \leq 10$
$x_1 + 8x_2 \leq 15$
with $x_1 \geq 0, x_2 \geq 0.$

The initial simplex tableau is as follows.

$$\begin{array}{c} \begin{array}{ccccc} x_1 & x_2 & s_1 & s_2 & z \end{array} \\ \left[\begin{array}{ccccc|c} 1 & 5 & 1 & 0 & 0 & 10 \\ 1 & \boxed{8} & 0 & 1 & 0 & 15 \\ \hline -17 & -42 & 0 & 0 & 1 & 0 \end{array}\right] \end{array}$$

Pivot on the 8 in row 2 column 2.

$$\begin{array}{c} -5R_2 + 8R_1 \to R_1 \\ \\ 21R_2 + 4R_3 \to R_3 \end{array} \quad \begin{array}{c} \begin{array}{ccccc} x_1 & x_2 & s_1 & s_2 & z \end{array} \\ \left[\begin{array}{ccccc|c} \boxed{3} & 0 & 8 & -5 & 0 & 5 \\ 1 & 8 & 0 & 1 & 0 & 15 \\ \hline -47 & 0 & 0 & 21 & 4 & 315 \end{array}\right] \end{array}$$

Pivot on the 3 in row 1, column 1.

$$\begin{array}{c} \\ -R_1 + 3R_2 \to R_2 \\ \\ 47R_1 + 3R_3 \to R_3 \end{array} \quad \begin{array}{c} \begin{array}{ccccc} x_1 & x_2 & s_1 & s_2 & z \end{array} \\ \left[\begin{array}{ccccc|c} 3 & 0 & 8 & -5 & 0 & 5 \\ 0 & 24 & -8 & \boxed{8} & 0 & 40 \\ \hline 0 & 0 & 376 & -172 & 12 & 1180 \end{array}\right] \end{array}$$

Pivot on the 8 in row 2, column 4.

$$\begin{array}{c} 5R_2 + 8R_1 \to R_1 \\ \\ 43R_2 + 2R_3 \to R_3 \end{array} \quad \begin{array}{c} \begin{array}{ccccc} x_1 & x_2 & s_1 & s_2 & z \end{array} \\ \left[\begin{array}{ccccc|c} 24 & 120 & 24 & 0 & 0 & 240 \\ 0 & 24 & -8 & 8 & 0 & 40 \\ \hline 0 & 1032 & 408 & 0 & 24 & 4080 \end{array}\right] \end{array}$$

Create a 1 in the columns corresponding to x_1, x_2, and z.

$$\begin{array}{l} \frac{1}{24}R_1 \to R_1 \\ \frac{1}{8}R_2 \to R_2 \\ \frac{1}{24}R_3 \to R_3 \end{array} \quad \begin{array}{c} \begin{matrix} x_1 & x_2 & s_1 & s_2 & z \end{matrix} \\ \left[\begin{array}{ccccc|c} 1 & 5 & 1 & 0 & 0 & 10 \\ 0 & 3 & -1 & 1 & 0 & 5 \\ \hline 0 & 43 & 17 & 0 & 1 & 170 \end{array}\right] \end{array}$$

The minimum value is 170 when $y_1 = 17$ and $y_2 = 0$.

Using the method of 4.4:

Change the objective function to

$$\text{Maximize } z = -w = -10y_1 - 15y_2.$$

The constraints are not changed.

The initial simplex tableau is as follows.

$$\begin{array}{c} \begin{matrix} y_1 & y_2 & s_1 & s_2 & z \end{matrix} \\ \left[\begin{array}{ccccc|c} 1 & 1 & -1 & 0 & 0 & 17 \\ \boxed{5} & 8 & 0 & -1 & 0 & 42 \\ \hline 10 & 15 & 0 & 0 & 1 & 0 \end{array}\right] \end{array}$$

The solution is not feasible since $s_1 = -17$ and $s_2 = -42$. Pivot on the 5 in row 2, column 1.

$$\begin{array}{l} -R_2 + 5R_1 \to R_1 \\ \\ -2R_2 + R_3 \to R_3 \end{array} \quad \begin{array}{c} \begin{matrix} y_1 & y_2 & s_1 & s_2 & z \end{matrix} \\ \left[\begin{array}{ccccc|c} 0 & -3 & -5 & 1 & 0 & 43 \\ 5 & 8 & 0 & -1 & 0 & 42 \\ \hline 0 & -1 & 0 & 2 & 1 & -84 \end{array}\right] \end{array}$$

The solution is still not feasible since $s_1 = -\frac{43}{5}$. But there are no positive entries to the left of the -5 in column 3 so it is not possible to choose a pivot element. The method of 4.4 fails to provide a solution in this case.

12. Minimize $\quad w = 22y_1 + 44y_2 + 33y_3$

subject to:

$$\begin{aligned} y_1 + 2y_2 + y_3 &\geq 3 \\ y_1 \qquad\quad + y_3 &\geq 3 \\ 3y_1 + 2y_2 + 2y_3 &\geq 8 \end{aligned}$$

with $\quad y_1 \geq 0,\ y_2 \geq 0,\ y_3 \geq 0.$

Using the dual method:

To form the dual, write the augmented matrix for the given problem.

$$\left[\begin{array}{ccc|c} 1 & 2 & 1 & 3 \\ 1 & 0 & 1 & 3 \\ 3 & 2 & 2 & 8 \\ \hline 22 & 44 & 33 & 0 \end{array}\right]$$

Form the transpose of the matrix.

$$\left[\begin{array}{ccc|c} 1 & 1 & 3 & 22 \\ 2 & 0 & 2 & 44 \\ 1 & 1 & 2 & 33 \\ \hline 3 & 3 & 8 & 0 \end{array}\right]$$

Write the dual problem.

$$\begin{array}{lrl} \text{Maximize} & z = 3x_1 + 3x_2 + 8x_3 & \\ \text{subject to:} & x_1 + x_2 + 3x_3 & \le 22 \\ & 2x_1 + 2x_3 & \le 44 \\ & x_1 + x_2 + 2x_3 & \le 33 \\ \text{with} & x_1 \ge 0,\ x_2 \ge 0,\ x_3 \ge 0. & \end{array}$$

The initial simplex tableau is as follows.

$$\begin{array}{ccccccc|c} x_1 & x_2 & x_3 & s_1 & s_2 & s_3 & z & \\ 1 & 1 & \boxed{3} & 1 & 0 & 0 & 0 & 22 \\ 2 & 0 & 2 & 0 & 1 & 0 & 0 & 44 \\ 1 & 1 & 2 & 0 & 0 & 1 & 0 & 33 \\ \hline -3 & -3 & -8 & 0 & 0 & 0 & 1 & 0 \end{array}$$

Pivot on the 3 in row 1, column 3.

$$\begin{array}{l} \\ \\ -2R_1 + 3R_2 \to R_2 \\ -2R_1 + 3R_3 \to R_3 \\ 8R_1 + 3R_4 \to R_4 \end{array} \begin{array}{ccccccc|c} x_1 & x_2 & x_3 & s_1 & s_2 & s_3 & z & \\ 1 & \boxed{1} & 3 & 1 & 0 & 0 & 0 & 22 \\ 4 & -2 & 0 & -2 & 3 & 0 & 0 & 88 \\ 1 & 1 & 0 & -2 & 0 & 3 & 0 & 55 \\ \hline -1 & -1 & 0 & 8 & 0 & 0 & 3 & 176 \end{array}$$

There is a choice of pivot columns; choose column 2. Pivot on the 1 in row 1, column 2.

$$\begin{array}{l} \\ \\ 2R_1 + R_2 \to R_2 \\ -R_1 + R_3 \to R_3 \\ R_1 + R_4 \to R_4 \end{array} \begin{array}{ccccccc|c} x_1 & x_2 & x_3 & s_1 & s_2 & s_3 & z & \\ 1 & 1 & 3 & 1 & 0 & 0 & 0 & 22 \\ 6 & 0 & 6 & 0 & 3 & 0 & 0 & 132 \\ 0 & 0 & -3 & -3 & 0 & 3 & 0 & 33 \\ \hline 0 & 0 & 3 & 9 & 0 & 0 & 3 & 198 \end{array}$$

Create a 1 in the columns corresponding to s_2, s_3, and z.

$$\begin{array}{l} \\ \\ \frac{1}{3}R_2 \to R_2 \\ \frac{1}{3}R_3 \to R_3 \\ \frac{1}{3}R_4 \to R_4 \end{array} \begin{array}{ccccccc|c} x_1 & x_2 & x_3 & s_1 & s_2 & s_3 & z & \\ 1 & 1 & 3 & 1 & 0 & 0 & 0 & 22 \\ 2 & 0 & 2 & 0 & 1 & 0 & 0 & 44 \\ 0 & 0 & -1 & -1 & 0 & 1 & 0 & 11 \\ \hline 0 & 0 & 1 & 3 & 0 & 0 & 1 & 66 \end{array}$$

The minimum value is 66 when $y_1 = 3, y_2 = 0$, and $y_3 = 0$.

Using the method of 4.4:

Change the objective function to

$$\text{Maximize} \quad z = -w = -22y_1 - 44y_2 - 33y_3.$$

The constraints are not changed.

The initial simplex tableau is as follows.

$$\begin{array}{ccccccc|c} y_1 & y_2 & y_3 & s_1 & s_2 & s_3 & z & \\ \boxed{1} & 2 & 1 & -1 & 0 & 0 & 0 & 3 \\ 1 & 0 & 1 & 0 & -1 & 0 & 0 & 3 \\ 3 & 2 & 2 & 0 & 0 & -1 & 0 & 8 \\ \hline 22 & 44 & 33 & 0 & 0 & 0 & 1 & 0 \end{array}$$

The solution is not feasible since $s_1 = -3, s_2 = -3$, and $s_3 = -8$. Pivot on the 1 in row 1, column 1.

$$\begin{array}{l} \\ \\ -R_1+R_2 \to R_2 \\ 3R_1-R_3 \to R_3 \\ -22R_1+R_4 \to R_4 \end{array} \begin{array}{c} \begin{array}{ccccccc} y_1 & y_2 & y_3 & s_1 & s_2 & s_3 & z \end{array} \\ \left[\begin{array}{ccccccc|c} 1 & 2 & 1 & -1 & 0 & 0 & 0 & 3 \\ 0 & -2 & 0 & 1 & -1 & 0 & 0 & 0 \\ 0 & 4 & 1 & -3 & 0 & 1 & 0 & 1 \\ \hline 0 & 0 & 11 & 22 & 0 & 0 & 1 & -66 \end{array}\right] \end{array}$$

The solution is feasible and there are no negative indicators so the solution is optimal. Create a 1 in the column corresponding to s_2.

$$\begin{array}{l} \\ \\ \\ -R_2 \to R_2 \\ \\ \end{array} \begin{array}{c} \begin{array}{ccccccc} y_1 & y_2 & y_3 & s_1 & s_2 & s_3 & z \end{array} \\ \left[\begin{array}{ccccccc|c} 1 & 2 & 1 & -1 & 0 & 0 & 0 & 3 \\ 0 & 2 & 0 & -1 & 1 & 0 & 0 & 0 \\ 0 & 4 & 1 & -3 & 0 & 1 & 0 & 1 \\ \hline 0 & 0 & 11 & 22 & 0 & 0 & 1 & -66 \end{array}\right] \end{array}$$

Since $z = -w = -66$, the minimum value is 66 when $y_1 = 3, y_2 = 0$, and $y_3 = 0$.

13. Minimize $w = 7y_1 + 2y_2 + 3y_3$

subject to:

$$\begin{aligned} y_1 + y_2 + 2y_3 &\geq 48 \\ y_1 + y_2 \qquad &\geq 12 \\ y_3 &\geq 10 \\ 3y_1 \qquad + y_3 &\geq 30 \end{aligned}$$

with $y_1 \geq 0, _2 \geq 0, y_3 \geq 0.$

Using the dual method:

To form the dual, write the augmented matrix for the given problem.

$$\left[\begin{array}{ccc|c} 1 & 1 & 2 & 48 \\ 1 & 1 & 0 & 12 \\ 0 & 0 & 1 & 10 \\ 3 & 0 & 1 & 30 \\ \hline 7 & 2 & 3 & 0 \end{array}\right]$$

Form the transpose of this matrix.

$$\left[\begin{array}{cccc|c} 1 & 1 & 0 & 3 & 7 \\ 1 & 1 & 0 & 0 & 2 \\ 2 & 0 & 1 & 1 & 3 \\ \hline 48 & 12 & 10 & 30 & 0 \end{array}\right]$$

Write the dual problem.

Maximize $z = 48x_1 + 12x_2 + 10x_3 + 30x_4$

subject to:

$$\begin{aligned} x_1 + x_2 \qquad + 3x_4 &\leq 7 \\ x_1 + x_2 \qquad\qquad &\leq 2 \\ 2x_1 \qquad + x_3 + x_4 &\leq 3 \end{aligned}$$

with $x_1 \geq 0, x_2 \geq 0, x_3 \geq 0, x_4 \geq 0.$

The initial simplex tableau is as follows.

$$\begin{array}{c} \\ \\ \\ \\ \\ \end{array}\begin{array}{cccccccc|c} x_1 & x_2 & x_3 & x_4 & s_1 & s_2 & s_3 & z & \\ 1 & 1 & 0 & 3 & 1 & 0 & 0 & 0 & 7 \\ 1 & 1 & 0 & 0 & 0 & 1 & 0 & 0 & 2 \\ \boxed{2} & 0 & 1 & 1 & 0 & 0 & 1 & 0 & 3 \\ \hline -48 & -12 & -10 & -30 & 0 & 0 & 0 & 1 & 0 \end{array}$$

Pivot on the 2 in row 3, column 1.

$$\begin{array}{c} \\ -R_3 + 2R_1 \to R_1 \\ -R_3 + 2R_2 \to R_2 \\ \\ 24R_3 + R_4 \to R_4 \end{array}\begin{array}{cccccccc|c} x_1 & x_2 & x_3 & x_4 & s_1 & s_2 & s_3 & z & \\ 0 & 2 & -1 & 5 & 2 & 0 & -1 & 0 & 11 \\ 0 & \boxed{2} & -1 & -1 & 0 & 2 & -1 & 0 & 1 \\ 2 & 0 & 1 & 1 & 0 & 0 & 1 & 0 & 3 \\ \hline 0 & -12 & 14 & -6 & 0 & 0 & 24 & 1 & 72 \end{array}$$

Pivot on the 2 in row 2, column 2.

$$\begin{array}{c} \\ -R_2 + R_1 \to R_1 \\ \\ \\ 6R_2 + R_4 \to R_4 \end{array}\begin{array}{cccccccc|c} x_1 & x_2 & x_3 & x_4 & s_1 & s_2 & s_3 & z & \\ 0 & 0 & 0 & \boxed{6} & 2 & -2 & 0 & 0 & 10 \\ 0 & 2 & -1 & -1 & 0 & 2 & -1 & 0 & 1 \\ 2 & 0 & 1 & 1 & 0 & 0 & 1 & 0 & 3 \\ \hline 0 & 0 & 8 & -12 & 0 & 12 & 18 & 1 & 78 \end{array}$$

Pivot on the 6 in row 1, column 4.

$$\begin{array}{c} \\ \\ R_1 + 6R_2 \to R_2 \\ -R_1 + 6R_3 \to R_3 \\ 2R_1 + R_4 \to R_4 \end{array}\begin{array}{cccccccc|c} x_1 & x_2 & x_3 & x_4 & s_1 & s_2 & s_3 & z & \\ 0 & 0 & 0 & 6 & 2 & -2 & 0 & 0 & 10 \\ 0 & 12 & -6 & 0 & 2 & 10 & -6 & 0 & 16 \\ 12 & 0 & 6 & 0 & -2 & 2 & 6 & 0 & 8 \\ \hline 0 & 0 & 8 & 0 & 4 & 8 & 18 & 1 & 98 \end{array}$$

Create a 1 in the columns corresponding to x_1, x_2, and x_4.

$$\begin{array}{c} \\ \frac{1}{6}R_1 \to R_1 \\ \frac{1}{12}R_2 \to R_2 \\ \frac{1}{12}R_3 \to R_3 \\ \\ \end{array}\begin{array}{cccccccc|c} x_1 & x_2 & x_3 & x_4 & s_1 & s_2 & s_3 & z & \\ 0 & 0 & 0 & 1 & \frac{1}{3} & -\frac{1}{3} & 0 & 0 & \frac{5}{3} \\ 0 & 1 & -\frac{1}{2} & 0 & \frac{1}{6} & \frac{5}{6} & -\frac{1}{2} & 0 & \frac{4}{3} \\ 1 & 0 & \frac{1}{2} & 0 & -\frac{1}{6} & \frac{1}{6} & \frac{1}{2} & 0 & \frac{2}{3} \\ \hline 0 & 0 & 8 & 0 & 4 & 8 & 18 & 1 & 98 \end{array}$$

The minimum value is 98 when $y_1 = 4, y_2 = 8$, and $y_3 = 18$.

Using the method of 4.4:

Change the objective function to

$$\text{Maximize } z = -w = -7y_1 - 2y_2 - 3y_3.$$

The constraints are not changed.

The initial simplex tableau is as follows.

y_1	y_2	y_3	s_1	s_2	s_3	s_4	z	
1	1	2	−1	0	0	0	0	48
1	1	0	0	−1	0	0	0	12
0	0	1	0	0	−1	0	0	10
3	0	1	0	0	0	−1	0	30
7	2	3	0	0	0	0	1	0

The solution is not feasible since $s_1 = -48, s_2 = -12, s_3 = -10$, and $s_4 = -30$. Pivot on the 3 in row 4, column 1.

	y_1	y_2	y_3	s_1	s_2	s_3	s_4	z	
$-R_4 + 3R_1 \rightarrow R_1$	0	3	5	−3	0	0	1	0	114
$-R_4 + 3R_2 \rightarrow R_2$	0	3	−1	0	−3	0	1	0	6
	0	0	1	0	0	−1	0	0	10
	3	0	1	0	0	0	−1	0	30
$-7R_4 + 3R_5 \rightarrow R_5$	0	6	2	0	0	0	7	3	−210

The solution is still not feasible since $s_1 = -38, s_2 = -2$, and $s_3 = -10$. Pivot on the 3 in row 1, column 2.

	y_1	y_2	y_3	s_1	s_2	s_3	s_4	z	
	0	3	5	−3	0	0	1	0	114
$R_1 - R_2 \rightarrow R_2$	0	0	6	−3	3	0	0	0	108
	0	0	1	0	0	−1	0	0	10
	3	0	1	0	0	0	−1	0	30
$-2R + R_5 \rightarrow R_5$	0	0	−8	6	0	0	5	3	−438

Again, the solution is not feasible since $s_3 = -10$ and $s_4 = -30$. Pivot on the 1 in row 3, column 3.

	y_1	y_2	y_3	s_1	s_2	s_3	s_4	z	
$-5R_3 + R_1 \rightarrow R_1$	0	3	0	−3	0	5	1	0	64
$-6R_3 + R_2 \rightarrow R_2$	0	0	0	−3	3	6	0	0	48
	0	0	1	0	0	−1	0	0	10
$-R_3 + R_4 \rightarrow R_4$	3	0	0	0	0	1	−1	0	20
$8R_3 + R_5 \rightarrow R_5$	0	0	0	6	0	−8	5	3	−358

The solution is feasible because all variables are nonnegative. But it is still not optimal. Pivot on the 6 in row 2, column 6.

	y_1	y_2	y_3	s_1	s_2	s_3	s_4	z	
$-5R_2 + 6R_1 \rightarrow R_1$	0	18	0	−3	−15	0	6	0	144
	0	0	0	−3	3	6	0	0	48
$R_2 + 6R_3 \rightarrow R_3$	0	0	6	−3	3	0	0	0	108
$-R_2 + 6R_4 \rightarrow R_4$	18	0	0	3	−3	0	−6	0	72
$4R_2 + 3R_5 \rightarrow R_5$	0	0	0	6	12	0	15	9	−882

Create a 1 in the columns corresponding to y_1, y_2, y_3, s_3 and z.

$$\begin{array}{l} \\ \frac{1}{18}R_1 \to R_1 \\ \frac{1}{6}R_2 \to R_2 \\ \frac{1}{6}R_3 \to R_3 \\ \frac{1}{18}R_4 \to R_4 \\ \frac{1}{9}R_5 \to R_5 \end{array}
\begin{array}{c} \begin{array}{cccccccc|c} y_1 & y_2 & y_3 & s_1 & s_2 & s_3 & s_4 & z & \end{array} \\ \left[\begin{array}{cccccccc|c} 0 & 1 & 0 & -\frac{1}{6} & -\frac{5}{6} & 0 & \frac{1}{3} & 0 & 8 \\ 0 & 0 & 0 & -\frac{1}{2} & \frac{1}{2} & 1 & 0 & 0 & 8 \\ 0 & 0 & 1 & -\frac{1}{2} & \frac{1}{2} & 0 & 0 & 0 & 18 \\ 1 & 0 & 0 & \frac{1}{6} & -\frac{1}{6} & 0 & -\frac{1}{3} & 0 & 4 \\ \hline 0 & 0 & 0 & \frac{2}{3} & \frac{4}{3} & 0 & \frac{5}{3} & 1 & -98 \end{array}\right] \end{array}$$

Since $z = -w = -98$, the minimum value is 98 when $y_1 = 4, y_2 = 8$, and $y_3 = 18$.

14.

$$\begin{array}{c} \begin{array}{cccccc|c} y_1 & y_2 & y_3 & s_1 & s_2 & z & \end{array} \\ \left[\begin{array}{cccccc|c} 0 & 1 & 0 & 5 & 3 & 0 & 7 \\ 1 & 0 & 0 & -2 & 1 & 0 & 15 \\ 0 & 0 & 1 & -6 & 2 & 0 & 23 \\ \hline 0 & 0 & 0 & 2 & 9 & 1 & -53 \end{array}\right] \end{array}$$

Here y_1, y_2, and y_3 are basic. Since $z = -w$, a maximum of -53 gives a minimum of 53 when $y_1 = 15$, $y_2 = 7$, $y_3 = 23$, $s_1 = 0$, and $s_2 = 0$.

15.

$$\begin{array}{c} \begin{array}{ccccccc|c} y_1 & y_2 & s_1 & s_2 & s_3 & s_4 & z & \end{array} \\ \left[\begin{array}{ccccccc|c} 0 & 0 & 3 & 0 & 1 & 1 & 0 & 2 \\ 1 & 0 & -2 & 0 & 2 & 0 & 0 & 8 \\ 0 & 1 & 7 & 0 & 0 & 0 & 0 & 12 \\ 0 & 0 & 1 & 1 & -4 & 0 & 0 & 1 \\ \hline 0 & 0 & 5 & 0 & 8 & 0 & 1 & -62 \end{array}\right] \end{array}$$

From this final tableau, read that the maximum value of $z = -w$ is -62 when $y_1 = 8$, $y_2 = 12, s_1 = 0, s_2 = 1, s_3 = 0$, and $s_4 = 2$. Therefore, the minimum value of w is 62 when $y_1 = 8, y_2 = 12, s_1 = 0, s_2 = 1, s_3 = 0$, and $s_4 = 2$.

16.

$$\begin{array}{c} \begin{array}{cccccc|c} y_1 & y_2 & y_3 & s_1 & s_2 & z & \end{array} \\ \left[\begin{array}{cccccc|c} 0 & 0 & 1 & -1 & 2 & 0 & 14 \\ 1 & 2 & 0 & 0 & 4 & 0 & 11 \\ \hline 0 & 3 & 0 & 10 & 6 & 1 & -120 \end{array}\right] \end{array}$$

Here y_1 and y_3 are basic. Since $z = -w$, a maximum of -120 gives a minimum of 120 when $y_1 = 11$, $y_2 = 0$, $y_3 = 14$, $s_1 = 0$, and $s_2 = 0$.

17.

$$\begin{array}{c} \begin{array}{ccccc|c} x_1 & x_2 & s_1 & s_2 & z & \end{array} \\ \left[\begin{array}{ccccc|c} 5 & 10 & 1 & 0 & 0 & 120 \\ \boxed{10} & 15 & 0 & -1 & 0 & 200 \\ \hline -20 & -30 & 0 & 0 & 1 & 0 \end{array}\right] \end{array}$$

The initial tableau is not feasible. Pivot on the 10 in row 2, column 1.

$$\begin{array}{l} \\ -R_2 + 2R_1 \to R_1 \\ \\ 2R_2 + R_3 \to R_3 \end{array}
\begin{array}{c} \begin{array}{ccccc|c} x_1 & x_2 & s_1 & s_2 & z & \end{array} \\ \left[\begin{array}{ccccc|c} 0 & 5 & 2 & \boxed{1} & 0 & 40 \\ 10 & 15 & 0 & -1 & 0 & 200 \\ \hline 0 & 0 & 0 & -2 & 1 & 400 \end{array}\right] \end{array}$$

The basic solution is feasible, but there are negative indicators. Pivot on the 1 in row 1, column 4.

$$\begin{array}{r} \\ \\ R_2+2R_1 \to R_2 \\ 2R_1+R_3 \to R_3 \end{array} \begin{array}{c} \begin{array}{ccccc} x_1 & x_2 & s_1 & s_2 & z \end{array} \\ \left[\begin{array}{ccccc|c} 0 & 5 & 2 & 1 & 0 & 40 \\ 10 & 20 & 2 & 0 & 0 & 240 \\ \hline 0 & 10 & 4 & 0 & 1 & 480 \end{array}\right] \end{array}$$

Create a one in the column corresponding to x_1.

$$\begin{array}{r} \\ \\ \tfrac{1}{10}R_2 \to R_2 \\ \\ \end{array} \begin{array}{c} \begin{array}{ccccc} x_1 & x_2 & s_1 & s_2 & z \end{array} \\ \left[\begin{array}{ccccc|c} 0 & 5 & 2 & 1 & 0 & 40 \\ 1 & 2 & \frac{1}{5} & 0 & 0 & 24 \\ \hline 0 & 10 & 4 & 0 & 1 & 480 \end{array}\right] \end{array}$$

The maximum value is $z = 480$ when $x_1 = 24$ and $x_2 = 0$.

18. Minimize $w = 4y_1 + 2y_2$
subject to:
$$y_1 + 3y_2 \geq 6$$
$$2y_1 + 8y_2 \leq 21$$
$$y_1 \geq 0,\ y_2 \geq 0$$

Let $z = -w = -4y_1 - 2y_2$ and maximize z.
Introduce the surplus variable s_1 and the slack variable s_2. The initial tableau is as follows.

$$\begin{array}{c} \begin{array}{ccccc} y_1 & y_2 & s_1 & s_2 & z \end{array} \\ \left[\begin{array}{ccccc|c} \boxed{1} & 3 & -1 & 0 & 0 & 6 \\ 2 & 8 & 0 & 1 & 0 & 21 \\ \hline 4 & 2 & 0 & 0 & 1 & 0 \end{array}\right] \end{array}$$

The initial basic solution is not feasible since $s_1 = -6$. Pivot on the 1 in row 1, column 1.

$$\begin{array}{r} \\ \\ -2R_1+R_2 \to R_2 \\ -4R_1+R_3 \to R_3 \end{array} \begin{array}{c} \begin{array}{ccccc} y_1 & y_2 & s_1 & s_2 & z \end{array} \\ \left[\begin{array}{ccccc|c} 1 & \boxed{3} & -1 & 0 & 0 & 6 \\ 0 & 2 & 2 & 1 & 0 & 9 \\ \hline 0 & -10 & 4 & 0 & 1 & -24 \end{array}\right] \end{array}$$

Pivot on the 3 in row 1, column 2.

$$\begin{array}{r} \\ \\ -2R_1+3R_2 \to R_2 \\ 10R_1+3R_3 \to R_3 \end{array} \begin{array}{c} \begin{array}{ccccc} y_1 & y_2 & s_1 & s_2 & z \end{array} \\ \left[\begin{array}{ccccc|c} 1 & 3 & -1 & 0 & 0 & 6 \\ -2 & 0 & 8 & 3 & 0 & 15 \\ \hline 10 & 0 & 2 & 0 & 3 & -12 \end{array}\right] \end{array}$$

Create a 1 in the columns corresponding to y_2, s_2, and z.

$$\begin{array}{r} \\ \tfrac{1}{3}R_1 \to R_1 \\ \tfrac{1}{3}R_2 \to R_2 \\ \tfrac{1}{3}R_3 \to R_3 \end{array} \begin{array}{c} \begin{array}{ccccc} y_1 & y_2 & s_1 & s_2 & z \end{array} \\ \left[\begin{array}{ccccc|c} \frac{1}{3} & 1 & -\frac{1}{3} & 0 & 0 & 2 \\ -\frac{2}{3} & 0 & \frac{8}{3} & 1 & 0 & 5 \\ \hline \frac{10}{3} & 0 & \frac{2}{3} & 0 & 1 & -4 \end{array}\right] \end{array}$$

The maximum value of $z = -w$ is -4. Therefore, the minimum value of w is 4 when $y_1 = 0$ and $y_2 = 2$.

19. Maximize $\quad z = 10x_1 + 12x_2$

subject to: $2x_1 + 2x_2 = 17$

$2x_1 + 5x_2 \geq 22$

$4x_1 + 3x_2 \leq 28$

with $\quad x_1 \geq 0, x_2 \geq 0.$

Introduce artificial variable a, surplus variable s_1, and slack variable s_2. The initial simplex tableau as follows.

$$\begin{array}{cccccc|c}
x_1 & x_2 & a & s_1 & s_2 & z & \\
\boxed{2} & 2 & 1 & 0 & 0 & 0 & 17 \\
2 & 5 & 0 & -1 & 0 & 0 & 22 \\
4 & 3 & 0 & 0 & 1 & 0 & 28 \\
\hline
-10 & -12 & 0 & 0 & 0 & 1 & 0
\end{array}$$

First, eliminate the artificial variable a. Pivot on the 2 in row 1, column 1.

$$\begin{array}{r|cccccc|c}
 & x_1 & x_2 & a & s_1 & s_2 & z & \\
 & 2 & 2 & 1 & 0 & 0 & 0 & 17 \\
-R_1 + R_2 \to R_2 & 0 & 3 & -1 & -1 & 0 & 0 & 5 \\
2R_1 - R_3 \to R_3 & 0 & 1 & 2 & 0 & -1 & 0 & 6 \\
\hline
5R_1 + R_4 \to R_4 & 0 & -2 & 5 & 0 & 0 & 1 & 85
\end{array}$$

Now $a = 0$, so we can drop the a column.

$$\begin{array}{ccccc|c}
x_1 & x_2 & s_1 & s_2 & z & \\
2 & 2 & 0 & 0 & 0 & 17 \\
0 & \boxed{3} & -1 & 0 & 0 & 5 \\
0 & 1 & 0 & -1 & 0 & 6 \\
\hline
0 & -2 & 0 & 0 & 1 & 85
\end{array}$$

Because $s_1 = -5$, we choose the 3 in row 2, column 2, as the next pivot.

$$\begin{array}{r|ccccc|c}
 & x_1 & x_2 & s_1 & s_2 & z & \\
-2R_2 + 3R_1 \to R_1 & 6 & 0 & 2 & 0 & 0 & 41 \\
 & 0 & 3 & -1 & 0 & 0 & 5 \\
-R_2 + 3R_3 \to R_3 & 0 & 0 & \boxed{1} & -3 & 0 & 13 \\
\hline
2R_2 + 3R_4 \to R_4 & 0 & 0 & -2 & 0 & 3 & 265
\end{array}$$

The solution is still not feasible since $s_2 = -\frac{13}{3}$. Pivot on the 1 in row 3, column 3.

$$\begin{array}{r|ccccc|c}
 & x_1 & x_2 & s_1 & s_2 & z & \\
-2R_3 + R_1 \to R_1 & 6 & 0 & 0 & \boxed{6} & 0 & 15 \\
R_3 + R_2 \to R_2 & 0 & 3 & 0 & -3 & 0 & 18 \\
 & 0 & 0 & 1 & -3 & 0 & 13 \\
\hline
2R_3 + R_4 \to R_4 & 0 & 0 & 0 & -6 & 3 & 291
\end{array}$$

The solution is now feasible but is not yet optimal. Pivot on the 6 in row 1, column 4.

$$\begin{array}{r|ccccc|c}
 & x_1 & x_2 & s_1 & s_2 & z & \\
 & 6 & 0 & 0 & 6 & 0 & 15 \\
R_1 + 2R_2 \to R_2 & 6 & 6 & 0 & 0 & 0 & 51 \\
R_1 + 2R_3 \to R_3 & 6 & 0 & 2 & 0 & 0 & 41 \\
\hline
R_1 + R_4 \to R_4 & 6 & 0 & 0 & 0 & 3 & 306
\end{array}$$

Create a 1 in the columns corresponding to x_2, s_1, s_2, and z.

$$\begin{array}{l} \\ \frac{1}{6}R_1 \to R_1 \\ \frac{1}{6}R_2 \to R_2 \\ \frac{1}{2}R_3 \to R_3 \\ \frac{1}{3}R_4 \to R_4 \end{array} \begin{array}{c} \begin{array}{ccccccc} x_1 & x_2 & s_1 & s_2 & z & & \end{array} \\ \left[\begin{array}{ccccc|c} 1 & 0 & 0 & 1 & 0 & \frac{5}{2} \\ 1 & 1 & 0 & 0 & 0 & \frac{17}{2} \\ 3 & 0 & 1 & 0 & 0 & \frac{41}{2} \\ \hline 2 & 0 & 0 & 0 & 1 & 102 \end{array}\right] \end{array}$$

The maximum is 102 when $x_1 = 0$ and $x_2 = \frac{17}{2}$.

20. Minimize $w = 24y_1 + 30y_2 + 36y_3$

subject to:

$$\begin{aligned} 5y_1 + 10y_2 + 15y_3 &\geq 1200 \\ y_1 + y_2 + y_3 &\leq 50 \\ y_1 \geq 0, \ y_2 \geq 0, \ y_3 &\geq 0 \end{aligned}$$

Let $z = -w = -24y_1 - 30y_2 - 36y_3$ and maximize z.
Introduce surplus variable s_1 and slack variable s_2.
The initial tableau is as follows.

$$\begin{array}{c} \begin{array}{ccccccc} y_1 & y_2 & y_3 & s_1 & s_2 & z & \end{array} \\ \left[\begin{array}{cccccc|c} 5 & 10 & 15 & -1 & 0 & 0 & 1200 \\ \boxed{1} & 1 & 1 & 0 & 1 & 0 & 50 \\ \hline 24 & 30 & 36 & 0 & 0 & 1 & 0 \end{array}\right] \end{array}$$

The initial basic solution is not feasible since $s_1 = -1200$.
Pivot on the 1 in row 2, column 1.

$$\begin{array}{l} \\ -5R_2 + R_1 \to R_1 \\ \\ -24R_2 + R_3 \to R_3 \end{array} \begin{array}{c} \begin{array}{ccccccc} y_1 & y_2 & y_3 & s_1 & s_2 & z & \end{array} \\ \left[\begin{array}{cccccc|c} 0 & 5 & 10 & -1 & -5 & 0 & 950 \\ 1 & \boxed{1} & 1 & 0 & 1 & 0 & 50 \\ \hline 0 & 6 & 12 & 0 & -24 & 1 & -1200 \end{array}\right] \end{array}$$

Pivot on the 1 in row 2, column 2.

$$\begin{array}{l} \\ -5R_2 + R_1 \to R_1 \\ \\ -6R_2 + R_3 \to R_3 \end{array} \begin{array}{c} \begin{array}{ccccccc} y_1 & y_2 & y_3 & s_1 & s_2 & z & \end{array} \\ \left[\begin{array}{cccccc|c} -5 & 0 & 5 & -1 & -10 & 0 & 700 \\ 1 & 1 & \boxed{1} & 0 & 1 & 0 & 50 \\ \hline -6 & 0 & 6 & 0 & -30 & 1 & -1500 \end{array}\right] \end{array}$$

Pivot on the 1 in row 2, column 3.

$$\begin{array}{l} \\ -5R_2 + R_1 \to R_1 \\ \\ -6R_2 + R_3 \to R_3 \end{array} \begin{array}{c} \begin{array}{ccccccc} y_1 & y_2 & y_3 & s_1 & s_2 & z & \end{array} \\ \left[\begin{array}{cccccc|c} -10 & -5 & 0 & -1 & -15 & 0 & 450 \\ 1 & 1 & 1 & 0 & 1 & 0 & 50 \\ \hline -12 & -6 & 0 & 0 & -36 & 1 & -1800 \end{array}\right] \end{array}$$

Now $s_1 = -450$ is not a feasible solution, but it is not possible to choose a pivot point. Therefore there is no solution.

21. Any maximizing or minimizing problems can be solved using slack, surplus, and artificial variables. Slack variables are used in problems involving "$\leq$" constraints. Surplus variables are used in problems involving "$\geq$" constraints. Artificial variables are used in problems involving "=" constraints.

22. A dual can be used to solve any standard minimization problem.

23.
$$\left[\begin{array}{cccccc|c} 4 & 2 & 3 & 1 & 0 & 0 & 9 \\ 5 & 4 & 1 & 0 & 1 & 0 & 10 \\ \hline -6 & -7 & -5 & 0 & 0 & 1 & 0 \end{array}\right]$$

(a) The 1 in column 4 and the 1 in column 5 indicate that the constraints involve $\leq$. The problem being solved with this tableau is:

$$\begin{array}{ll} \text{Maximize} & z = 6x_1 + 7x_2 + 5x_3 \\ \text{subject to:} & 4x_1 + 2x_2 + 3x_3 \leq 9 \\ & 5x_1 + 4x_2 + x_3 \leq 10 \\ \text{with} & x_1 \geq 0, x_2 \geq 0, x_3 \geq 0. \end{array}$$

(b) If the 1 in row 1, column 4 was -1 rather than 1, then the first constraint would have a surplus variable rather than a slack variable, which means the first constraint would be $4x_1 + 2x_2 + 3x_3 \geq 9$ instead of $4x_1 + 2x_2 + 3x_3 \leq 9$.

(c)
$$\begin{array}{c} \begin{array}{ccccccc} x_1 & x_2 & x_3 & s_1 & s_2 & z & \end{array} \\ \left[\begin{array}{cccccc|c} 3 & 0 & 5 & 2 & -1 & 0 & 8 \\ 11 & 10 & 0 & -1 & 3 & 0 & 21 \\ \hline 47 & 0 & 0 & 13 & 11 & 10 & 227 \end{array}\right] \end{array}$$

From this tableau, the solution is $x_1 = 0$, $x_2 = \frac{21}{10} = 2.1, x_3 = \frac{8}{5} = 1.6$, and $z = \frac{227}{10} = 22.7$.

(d) The dual of the original problem is as follows:

$$\begin{array}{ll} \text{Minimize} & w = 9y_1 + 10y_2 \\ \text{subject to:} & 4y_1 + 5y_2 \geq 6 \\ & 2y_1 + 4y_2 \geq 7 \\ & 3y_1 + y_2 \geq 5 \\ \text{with} & y_1 \geq 0, y_2 \geq 0. \end{array}$$

(e) From the tableau in part (c), the solution of the dual in part (d) is $y_1 = \frac{13}{10} = 1.3, y_2 = \frac{11}{10} = 1.1$, and $w = \frac{227}{10} = 22.7$.

24. (a) Find matrices A, B, C, and X such that the problem

$$\begin{array}{ll} \text{Maximize} & z = 3x_1 + 2x_2 + x_3 \\ \text{subject to:} & 2x_1 + x_2 + x_3 \le 150 \\ & 2x_1 + 2x_2 + 8x_3 \le 200 \\ & 2x_1 + 3x_2 + x_3 \le 320 \\ \text{with} & x_1 \ge 0,\ x_2 \ge 0,\ x_3 \ge 0 \end{array}$$

can be written as

$$\begin{array}{ll} \text{Maximize} & CX \\ \text{subject to:} & AX \le B \\ \text{with} & X \ge O. \end{array}$$

$$A = \begin{bmatrix} 2 & 1 & 1 \\ 2 & 2 & 8 \\ 2 & 3 & 1 \end{bmatrix},\ B = \begin{bmatrix} 150 \\ 200 \\ 320 \end{bmatrix},$$

$$C = \begin{bmatrix} 3 & 2 & 1 \end{bmatrix},\ X = \begin{bmatrix} x_1 \\ x_2 \\ x_3 \end{bmatrix}$$

(b) To write the dual, write the augmented matrix for the given problem.

$$\left[\begin{array}{ccc|c} 2 & 1 & 1 & 150 \\ 2 & 2 & 8 & 200 \\ 2 & 3 & 1 & 320 \\ \hline 3 & 2 & 1 & 0 \end{array}\right]$$

Now form the transpose.

$$\left[\begin{array}{ccc|c} 2 & 2 & 2 & 3 \\ 1 & 2 & 3 & 2 \\ 1 & 8 & 1 & 1 \\ \hline 150 & 200 & 320 & 0 \end{array}\right]$$

The dual is now stated as:

$$\begin{array}{ll} \text{Minimize} & w = 150y_1 + 200y_2 + 320y_3 \\ \text{subject to:} & 2y_1 + 2y_2 + 2y_3 \ge 3 \\ & y_1 + 2y_2 + 3y_3 \ge 2 \\ & y_1 + 8y_2 + y_3 \ge 1 \\ \text{with} & y_1 \ge 0,\ y_2 \ge 0,\ y_3 \ge 0. \end{array}$$

This can be stated as:

$$\begin{array}{ll} \text{Minimize} & B^T Y \\ \text{subject to:} & A^T Y \ge C \\ \text{with} & Y \ge O. \end{array}$$

25. (a) Let x_1 = the number of cake plates, x_2 = the number of bread plates, and x_3 = the number of dinner plates.

(b) The objective function to maximize is $z = 15x_1 + 12x_2 + 5x_3$.

(c) The constraints are

$$\begin{aligned} 15x_1 + 10x_2 + 8x_3 &\le 1500 \\ 5x_1 + 4x_2 + 4x_3 &\le 2700 \\ 6x_1 + 5x_2 + 5x_3 &\le 1200. \end{aligned}$$

26. (a) Let x_1 = the amount invested in oil leases; x_2 = the amount invested in bonds; and x_3 = the amount invested in stock.

(b) We want to maximize

$$z = 0.15x_1 + 0.09x_2 + 0.05x_3.$$

(c) The constraints are

$$\begin{aligned} x_1 + x_2 + x_3 &\le 50{,}000 \\ x_1 + x_2 &\le 15{,}000 \\ x_1 + x_3 &\le 25{,}000. \end{aligned}$$

27. (a) Let x_1 = number of gallons of fruity wine and x_2 = number of gallons of crystal wine.

(b) The profit function is

$$z = 12x_1 + 15x_2.$$

(c) The ingredients available are the limitations; the constraints are

$$\begin{aligned} 2x_1 + x_2 &\le 110 \\ 2x_1 + 3x_2 &\le 125 \\ 2x_1 + x_2 &\le 90. \end{aligned}$$

28. (a) Let y_1 = the number of kilograms of canned whole tomatoes produced and y_2 = the number of kilograms of tomato sauce produced.

(b) The minimum cost function is

$$w = 4y_1 + 3.25y_2.$$

(c) The constraints are

$$\begin{aligned} y_1 + y_2 &\le 3{,}000{,}000 \\ y_1 &\ge 800{,}000 \\ y_2 &\ge 80{,}000 \\ 6y_1 + 3y_2 &\ge 6{,}600{,}000. \end{aligned}$$

29. Maximize $z = 15x_1 + 12x_2 + 5x_3$

$$\begin{array}{ll} \text{subject to:} & 15x_1 + 10x_2 + 8x_3 \le 1500 \\ & 5x_1 + 4x_2 + 4x_3 \le 2700 \\ & 6x_1 + 5x_2 + 5x_3 \le 1200 \\ \text{with} & x_1 \ge 0, x_2 \ge 0, x_3 \ge 0. \end{array}$$

The initial tableau is as follows.

$$\begin{array}{c} \begin{array}{ccccccc} x_1 & x_2 & x_3 & s_1 & s_2 & s_3 & z \end{array} \\ \left[\begin{array}{ccccccc|c} \boxed{15} & 10 & 8 & 1 & 0 & 0 & 0 & 1500 \\ 5 & 4 & 4 & 0 & 1 & 0 & 0 & 2700 \\ 6 & 5 & 5 & 0 & 0 & 1 & 0 & 1200 \\ \hline -15 & -12 & -5 & 0 & 0 & 0 & 1 & 0 \end{array}\right]. \end{array}$$

Pivot on the 15 in row 1, column 1.

$$\begin{array}{r} \\ \\ -R_1 + 3R_2 \to R_2 \\ -2R_1 + 5R_3 \to R_3 \\ R_1 + R_4 \to R_4 \end{array} \begin{array}{c} \begin{array}{ccccccc} x_1 & x_2 & x_3 & s_1 & s_2 & s_3 & z \end{array} \\ \left[\begin{array}{ccccccc|c} 15 & \boxed{10} & 8 & 1 & 0 & 0 & 0 & 1500 \\ 0 & 2 & 4 & -1 & 3 & 0 & 0 & 6600 \\ 0 & 5 & 9 & -2 & 0 & 5 & 0 & 3000 \\ \hline 0 & -2 & 3 & 1 & 0 & 0 & 1 & 1500 \end{array}\right] \end{array}$$

Pivot on the 10 in row 1, column 2.

$$\begin{array}{r} \\ \\ -R_1 + 5R_2 \to R_2 \\ -R_1 + 2R_3 \to R_3 \\ R_1 + 5R_4 \to R_4 \end{array} \begin{array}{c} \begin{array}{ccccccc} x_1 & x_2 & x_3 & s_1 & s_2 & s_3 & z \end{array} \\ \left[\begin{array}{ccccccc|c} 15 & 10 & 8 & 1 & 0 & 0 & 0 & 1500 \\ -15 & 0 & 12 & -6 & 15 & 0 & 0 & 31{,}500 \\ -15 & 0 & 10 & -5 & 0 & 10 & 0 & 4500 \\ \hline 15 & 0 & 23 & 6 & 0 & 0 & 5 & 9000 \end{array}\right] \end{array}$$

Create a 1 in the columns corresponding to x_2, s_2, s_3, and z.

$$\begin{array}{r} \\ \frac{1}{10}R_1 \to R_1 \\ \frac{1}{15}R_2 \to R_2 \\ \frac{1}{10}R_3 \to R_3 \\ \frac{1}{5}R_4 \to R_4 \end{array} \begin{array}{c} \begin{array}{ccccccc} x_1 & x_2 & x_3 & s_1 & s_2 & s_3 & z \end{array} \\ \left[\begin{array}{ccccccc|c} \frac{3}{2} & 1 & \frac{4}{5} & \frac{1}{10} & 0 & 0 & 0 & 150 \\ -1 & 0 & \frac{4}{5} & -\frac{2}{5} & 1 & 0 & 0 & 2100 \\ -\frac{3}{2} & 0 & 1 & -\frac{1}{2} & 0 & 1 & 0 & 450 \\ \hline 3 & 0 & \frac{23}{5} & \frac{6}{5} & 0 & 0 & 1 & 1800 \end{array}\right] \end{array}$$

The maximum profit of $1800 when no cake plates, 150 bread plates, and no dinner places are produced.

30. Based on the information given in Exercise 26, the initial tableau is as follows.

$$
\begin{array}{rrrrrrr|r}
x_1 & x_2 & x_3 & s_1 & s_2 & s_3 & z & \\
\hline
1 & 1 & 1 & 1 & 0 & 0 & 0 & 50{,}000 \\
\boxed{1} & 1 & 0 & 0 & 1 & 0 & 0 & 15{,}000 \\
1 & 0 & 1 & 0 & 0 & 1 & 0 & 25{,}000 \\
\hline
-0.15 & -0.09 & -0.05 & 0 & 0 & 0 & 1 & 0
\end{array}
$$

Continue by pivoting on each indicated entry.

$$
\begin{array}{r}
\\
-R_2+R_1 \to R_1 \\
\\
-R_2+R_3 \to R_3 \\
0.15R_2+R_4 \to R_4
\end{array}
\begin{array}{rrrrrrr|r}
x_1 & x_2 & x_3 & s_1 & s_2 & s_3 & z & \\
\hline
0 & 0 & 1 & 1 & -1 & 0 & 0 & 35{,}000 \\
1 & 1 & 0 & 0 & 1 & 0 & 0 & 15{,}000 \\
0 & -1 & \boxed{1} & 0 & -1 & 1 & 0 & 10{,}000 \\
\hline
0 & 0.06 & -0.05 & 0 & 0.15 & 0 & 1 & 2250
\end{array}
$$

$$
\begin{array}{r}
\\
-R_3+R_1 \to R_1 \\
\\
\\
0.05R_3+R_4 \to R_4
\end{array}
\begin{array}{rrrrrrr|r}
x_1 & x_2 & x_3 & s_1 & s_2 & s_3 & z & \\
\hline
0 & 1 & 0 & 1 & 0 & -1 & 0 & 25{,}000 \\
1 & 1 & 0 & 0 & 1 & 0 & 0 & 15{,}000 \\
0 & -1 & 1 & 0 & -1 & 1 & 0 & 10{,}000 \\
\hline
0 & 0.01 & 0 & 0 & 0.1 & 0.05 & 1 & 2750
\end{array}
$$

The maximum value is $z = 2750$ when $x_1 = 15{,}000$, $x_2 = 0$, and $x_3 = 10{,}000$. He should invest $15,000 in oil leases and $10,000 in stock for a maximum return of $2750.

31. Based on Exercise 27, the initial tableau is

$$
\begin{array}{rrrrrr|r}
x_1 & x_2 & s_1 & s_2 & s_3 & z & \\
\hline
2 & 1 & 1 & 0 & 0 & 0 & 110 \\
2 & \boxed{3} & 0 & 1 & 0 & 0 & 125 \\
2 & 1 & 0 & 0 & 1 & 0 & 90 \\
\hline
-12 & -15 & 0 & 0 & 0 & 1 & 0
\end{array}.
$$

Locating the first pivot in the usual way, it is found to be the 3 in row 2, column 2. After row transformations, we get the next tableau.

$$
\begin{array}{r}
\\
-R_2+3R_1 \to R_1 \\
\\
-R_2+3R_3 \to R_3 \\
5R_2+R_4 \to R_4
\end{array}
\begin{array}{rrrrrr|r}
x_1 & x_2 & s_1 & s_2 & s_3 & z & \\
\hline
4 & 0 & 3 & -1 & 0 & 0 & 205 \\
2 & 3 & 0 & 1 & 0 & 0 & 125 \\
\boxed{4} & 0 & 0 & -1 & 3 & 0 & 145 \\
\hline
-2 & 0 & 0 & 5 & 0 & 1 & 625
\end{array}
$$

Pivot on the 4 in row 3, column 1.

$$
\begin{array}{r}
\\
-R_3+R_1 \to R_1 \\
-R_3+2R_2 \to R_2 \\
\\
R_3+2R_4 \to R_4
\end{array}
\begin{array}{rrrrrr|r}
x_1 & x_2 & s_1 & s_2 & s_3 & z & \\
\hline
0 & 0 & 3 & 0 & -3 & 0 & 60 \\
0 & 6 & 0 & 3 & -3 & 0 & 105 \\
4 & 0 & 0 & -1 & 3 & 0 & 145 \\
\hline
0 & 0 & 0 & 9 & 3 & 2 & 1395
\end{array}
$$

	x_1	x_2	s_1	s_2	s_3	z	
$\frac{1}{3}R_1 \to R_1$	0	0	1	0	-1	0	20
$\frac{1}{6}R_2 \to R_2$	0	1	0	$\frac{1}{2}$	$-\frac{1}{2}$	0	$\frac{35}{2}$
$\frac{1}{4}R_3 \to R_3$	1	0	0	$-\frac{1}{4}$	$\frac{3}{4}$	0	$\frac{145}{4}$
$\frac{1}{2}R_4 \to R_4$	0	0	0	$\frac{9}{2}$	$\frac{3}{2}$	1	$\frac{1395}{2}$

The final tableau gives the solution $x_1 = \frac{145}{4}, x_2 = \frac{35}{2}$, and $z = \frac{1395}{2} = 697.5$. 36.25 gal of fruity wine and 17.5 gal of crystal wine should be produced for a maximum profit of \$697.50.

32. Based on Exercise 28, the initial tableau is as follows.

y_1	y_2	s_1	s_2	s_3	s_4	z	
1	1	1	0	0	0	0	3,000,000
[1]	0	0	-1	0	0	0	800,000
0	1	0	0	-1	0	0	80,000
6	3	0	0	0	-1	0	6,600,000
4	3.25	0	0	0	0	1	0

Pivot on the 1 in row 2, column 1 since the basic solution is not feasible.

	y_1	y_2	s_1	s_2	s_3	s_4	z	
$-R_2 + R_1 \to R_1$	0	1	1	1	0	0	0	2,200,000
	1	0	0	-1	0	0	0	800,000
	0	[1]	0	0	-1	0	0	80,000
$-6R_2 + R_4 \to R_4$	0	3	0	6	0	-1	0	1,800,000
$-4R_2 + R_5 \to R_5$	0	3.25	0	4	0	0	1	$-3{,}200{,}000$

Pivot on the 1 in row 3, column 2 since the basic solution is not feasible.

	y_1	y_2	s_1	s_2	s_3	s_4	z	
$-R_3 + R_1 \to R_1$	0	0	1	1	1	0	0	1,400,000
	1	0	0	-1	0	0	0	800,000
	0	1	0	0	-1	0	0	80,000
$-3R_3 + R_4 \to R_4$	0	0	0	[6]	3	-1	0	1,560,000
$-3.25R_3 + R_5 \to R_5$	0	0	0	4	3.25	0	1	$-3{,}460{,}000$

Pivot on the 6 in row 4, column 4 since basic solution is not feasible.

	y_1	y_2	s_1	s_2	s_3	s_4	z	
$R_4 + (-6R_1) \to R_1$	0	0	-6	0	-3	-1	0	$-6{,}840{,}000$
$R_4 + 6R_2 \to R_2$	6	0	0	0	3	-1	0	6,360,000
	0	1	0	0	-1	0	0	80,000
	0	0	0	6	3	-1	0	1,560,000
$2R_4 + 3R_5 \to R_5$	0	0	0	0	-3.75	-2	-3	13,500,000

Create a 1 in the columns corresponding to y_1, y_2, s_1, s_2, and z.

$$\begin{array}{r} \\ -\frac{1}{6}R_1 \to R_1 \\ \frac{1}{6}R_2 \to R_2 \\ \\ \frac{1}{6}R_4 \to R_4 \\ -\frac{1}{3}R_5 \to R_5 \end{array} \begin{array}{c} \begin{array}{ccccccc|c} y_1 & y_2 & s_1 & s_2 & s_3 & s_4 & z & \end{array} \\ \left[\begin{array}{ccccccc|c} 0 & 0 & 1 & 0 & \frac{1}{2} & \frac{1}{6} & 0 & 1{,}140{,}000 \\ 1 & 0 & 0 & 0 & \frac{1}{2} & -\frac{1}{6} & 0 & 1{,}060{,}000 \\ 0 & 1 & 0 & 0 & -1 & 0 & 0 & 80{,}000 \\ 0 & 0 & 0 & 1 & \frac{1}{2} & -\frac{1}{6} & 0 & 260{,}000 \\ \hline 0 & 0 & 0 & 0 & 1.25 & \frac{2}{3} & 1 & -4{,}500{,}000 \end{array}\right] \end{array}$$

The final tableau gives the solution $y_2 = 1{,}060{,}000$, $y_2 = 80{,}000$, and $z = 4{,}500{,}000$. Use 1,060,000 kg of whole tomatoes and 80,000 kg for sauce for a minimum cost of \$4,500,000.

33. **(a)** Let $y_1 =$ the number of cases of corn,
$y_2 =$ the number of cases of beans,
and $y_3 =$ the number of cases of carrots.

Minimize $w = 10y_1 + 15y_2 + 25y_3$
subject to: $y_1 + y_2 + y_3 \geq 1000$
$y_1 \geq 2y_2$
$y_3 \geq 340$
with $y_1 \geq 0, y_2 \geq 0.$

The second constraint can be rewritten as $y_1 - 2y_2 \geq 0$. Change this to a maximization problem by letting $z = -w = -10y_1 - 15y_2 - 25y_3$. Now maximize $z = -10y_1 - 15y_2 - 25y_3$ subject to the constraints above. Begin by inserting surplus variables to set up the first tableau.

$$\begin{array}{c} \begin{array}{ccccccc|c} y_1 & y_2 & y_3 & s_1 & s_2 & s_3 & z & \end{array} \\ \left[\begin{array}{ccccccc|c} \boxed{1} & 1 & 1 & -1 & 0 & 0 & 0 & 1000 \\ 1 & -2 & 0 & 0 & -1 & 0 & 0 & 0 \\ 0 & 0 & 1 & 0 & 0 & -1 & 0 & 340 \\ \hline 10 & 15 & 25 & 0 & 0 & 0 & 1 & 0 \end{array}\right] \end{array}$$

Multiply row 2 by -1 so that s_2 is positive.

$$\begin{array}{r} \\ \\ -R_2 \to R_2 \\ \\ \\ \end{array} \begin{array}{c} \begin{array}{ccccccc|c} y_1 & y_2 & y_3 & s_1 & s_2 & s_3 & z & \end{array} \\ \left[\begin{array}{ccccccc|c} \boxed{1} & 1 & 1 & -1 & 0 & 0 & 0 & 1000 \\ -1 & 2 & 0 & 0 & 1 & 0 & 0 & 0 \\ 0 & 0 & 1 & 0 & 0 & -1 & 0 & 340 \\ \hline 10 & 15 & 25 & 0 & 0 & 0 & 1 & 0 \end{array}\right] \end{array}$$

Pivot on the 1 in row 1, column 1.

$$\begin{array}{r} \\ \\ R_1 + R_2 \to R_2 \\ \\ -10R_1 + R_4 \to R_4 \end{array} \begin{array}{c} \begin{array}{ccccccc|c} y_1 & y_2 & y_3 & s_1 & s_2 & s_3 & z & \end{array} \\ \left[\begin{array}{ccccccc|c} 1 & 1 & 1 & -1 & 0 & 0 & 0 & 1000 \\ 0 & 3 & 1 & -1 & 1 & 0 & 0 & 1000 \\ 0 & 0 & \boxed{1} & 0 & 0 & -1 & 0 & 340 \\ \hline 0 & 5 & 15 & 10 & 0 & 0 & 1 & -10{,}000 \end{array}\right] \end{array}$$

Pivot on the 1 in row 3, column 3.

$$\begin{array}{r} \\ -R_3 + R_1 \to R_1 \\ -R_3 + R_2 \to R_2 \\ \\ -15R_3 + R_4 \to R_4 \end{array} \begin{array}{c} \begin{array}{ccccccc|c} y_1 & y_2 & y_3 & s_1 & s_2 & s_3 & z & \end{array} \\ \left[\begin{array}{ccccccc|c} 1 & 1 & 0 & -1 & 0 & 1 & 0 & 660 \\ 0 & 3 & 0 & -1 & 1 & 1 & 0 & 660 \\ 0 & 0 & 1 & 0 & 0 & -1 & 0 & 340 \\ \hline 0 & 5 & 0 & 10 & 0 & 15 & 1 & -15{,}100 \end{array}\right] \end{array}$$

The maximum value of z is $-15{,}100$ when $y_1 = 660, y_2 = 0$, and $y_3 = 340$. Hence the minimum value of w is 15,100 when $y_1 = 660, y_2 = 0$, and $y_3 = 340$.

(b) The dual problem is as follows.

$$\begin{array}{ll} \text{Maximize} & z = 1000x_1 + 340x_3 \\ \text{subject to:} & x_1 + \ x_2 \leq 10 \\ & x_1 - 2x_2 \leq 15 \\ & x_1 + x_3 \leq 25 \\ \text{with} & x_1 \geq 0, x_2 \geq 0, x_3 \geq 0. \end{array}$$

The initial simplex tableau is as follows.

x_1	x_2	x_3	s_1	s_2	s_3	z	
[1]	1	0	1	0	0	0	10
1	−2	0	0	1	0	0	15
1	0	1	0	0	1	0	25
−1000	0	−340	0	0	0	1	0

Pivot on the 1 in row 1, column 1.

	x_1	x_2	x_3	s_1	s_2	s_3	z	
	1	1	0	1	0	0	0	10
$-R_1 + R_2 \to R_2$	0	−3	0	−1	1	0	0	5
$-R_1 + R_3 \to R_3$	0	−1	[1]	−1	0	1	0	15
$1000R_1 + R_4 \to R_4$	0	1000	−340	1000	0	0	1	10,000

Pivot on the 1 in row 3, column 3.

	x_1	x_2	x_3	s_1	s_2	s_3	z	
	1	1	0	1	0	0	0	10
	0	−3	0	−1	1	0	0	5
	0	−1	1	−1	0	1	0	15
$340R_3 + R_4 \to R_4$	0	660	0	660	0	340	1	15,100

The minimum value of w is 15,100 when $y_1 = 660, y_2 = 0$, and $y_3 = 340$, that is, 660 cases of corn, 0 cases of beans, and 340 cases of carrots should be produced to minimize costs, and the minimum cost is \$15,100.

34. Let $y_1 =$ the number of packages of Sun Hill and $y_2 =$ the number of packages of Bear Valley.

The problem is:

$$\begin{array}{ll} \text{Minimize} & w = 3y_1 + 2y_2 \\ \text{subject to:} & 10y_1 + 2y_2 \geq 20 \\ & 4y_1 + 4y_2 \geq 24 \\ & 2y_1 + 8y_2 \geq 24 \\ \text{with} & y_1 \geq 0, y_2 \geq 0. \end{array}$$

(a) Change this to a maximization problem by letting $z = -w = -3y_1 - 2y_2$. Now maximize $z = -3y_1 - 2y_2$ subject to the constraints above. Begin by inserting surplus variables to set up the first tableau.

The initial simplex tableau is as follows.

y_1	y_2	s_1	s_2	s_3	z	
[10]	2	−1	0	0	0	20
4	4	0	−1	0	0	24
2	8	0	0	−1	0	24
3	2	0	0	0	1	0

Pivot on the 10 in row 1, column 1.

$$\begin{array}{r} \\ \\ -4R_1 + 10R_2 \to R_2 \\ -R_1 + 5R_3 \to R_3 \\ -3R_1 + 10R_4 \to R_4 \end{array} \begin{array}{cccccc|c} y_1 & y_2 & s_1 & s_2 & s_3 & z & \\ \hline 10 & 2 & -1 & 0 & 0 & 0 & 20 \\ 0 & 32 & 4 & -10 & 0 & 0 & 160 \\ 0 & \boxed{38} & 1 & 0 & -5 & 0 & 100 \\ \hline 0 & 14 & 3 & 0 & 0 & 10 & -60 \end{array}$$

Pivot on the 38 in row 3, column 2.

$$\begin{array}{r} \\ -R_3 + 19R_1 \to R_1 \\ -16R_3 + 19R_2 \to R_2 \\ \\ -7R_3 + 19R_4 \to R_4 \end{array} \begin{array}{cccccc|c} y_1 & y_2 & s_1 & s_2 & s_3 & z & \\ \hline 190 & 0 & -20 & 0 & 5 & 0 & 280 \\ 0 & 0 & \boxed{60} & -190 & 80 & 0 & 1440 \\ 0 & 38 & 1 & 0 & -5 & 0 & 100 \\ \hline 0 & 0 & 50 & 0 & 35 & 190 & -1840 \end{array}$$

Pivot on the 60 in row 2, column 3.

$$\begin{array}{r} \\ R_2 + 3R_1 \to R_1 \\ \\ -R_2 + 60R_3 \to R_3 \\ -5R_2 + 6R_4 \to R_4 \end{array} \begin{array}{cccccc|c} y_1 & y_2 & s_1 & s_2 & s_3 & z & \\ \hline 570 & 0 & 0 & -190 & 95 & 0 & 2280 \\ 0 & 0 & 60 & -190 & \boxed{80} & 0 & 1440 \\ 0 & 2280 & 0 & 190 & -380 & 0 & 4560 \\ \hline 0 & 0 & 0 & 950 & -190 & 1140 & -18,240 \end{array}$$

Pivot on the 80 in row 2, column 5.

$$\begin{array}{r} \\ -19R_2 + 16R_1 \to R_1 \\ \\ 19R_2 + 4R_3 \to R_3 \\ 19R_2 + 8R_4 \to R_4 \end{array} \begin{array}{cccccc|c} y_1 & y_2 & s_1 & s_2 & s_3 & z & \\ \hline 9120 & 0 & -1140 & 570 & 0 & 0 & 9120 \\ 0 & 0 & 60 & -190 & 80 & 0 & 1440 \\ 0 & 9120 & 1140 & -2850 & 0 & 0 & 45,600 \\ \hline 0 & 0 & 1140 & 3990 & 0 & 9120 & -118,560 \end{array}$$

Create a 1 in the columns corresponding to y_1, y_2, and z.

$$\begin{array}{r} \\ \frac{1}{9120}R_1 \to R_1 \\ \\ \frac{1}{9120}R_3 \to R_3 \\ \frac{1}{9120}R_4 \to R_4 \end{array} \begin{array}{cccccc|c} y_1 & y_2 & s_1 & s_2 & s_3 & z & \\ \hline 1 & 0 & -\frac{1}{8} & \frac{1}{16} & 0 & 0 & 1 \\ 0 & 0 & 60 & -190 & 80 & 0 & 1440 \\ 0 & 1 & \frac{1}{8} & -\frac{5}{16} & 0 & 0 & 5 \\ \hline 0 & 0 & \frac{1}{8} & \frac{7}{16} & 0 & 1 & -13 \end{array}$$

The maximum value of z is -13 when $y_1 = 1$ and $y_2 = 5$. Hence the minimum value of w is 13 when $y_1 = 1$ and $y_2 = 5$. Thus the minimum cost is \$13 for 1 package of Sun Hill and 5 packages of Bear Valley.

(b) The dual problem is as follows.

$$\begin{array}{ll} \text{Maximize} & z = 20x_1 + 24x_2 + 24x_3 \\ \text{subject to:} & 10x_1 + 4x_2 + 2x_3 \le 3 \\ & 2x_1 + 4x_2 + 8x_3 \le 2 \\ \text{with} & x_1 \ge 0, x_2 \ge 0, x_3 \ge 0. \end{array}$$

The initial simplex tableau is as follows.

$$\begin{array}{cccccc|c} x_1 & x_2 & x_3 & s_1 & s_2 & z & \\ \hline 10 & 4 & 2 & 1 & 0 & 0 & 3 \\ 2 & \boxed{4} & 8 & 0 & 1 & 0 & 2 \\ \hline -20 & -24 & -24 & 0 & 0 & 1 & 0 \end{array}$$

Pivot about the 4 in row 2, column 2.

$$\begin{array}{l} -R_2 + R_1 \to R_1 \\ \\ 6R_2 + R_3 \to R_3 \end{array} \begin{array}{c} \begin{matrix} x_1 & x_2 & x_3 & s_1 & s_2 & z & \end{matrix} \\ \left[\begin{array}{cccccc|c} \boxed{8} & 0 & -6 & 1 & -1 & 0 & 1 \\ 2 & 4 & 8 & 0 & 1 & 0 & 2 \\ \hline -8 & 0 & 24 & 0 & 6 & 1 & 12 \end{array}\right] \end{array}$$

Pivot about the 8 in row 1, column 1.

$$\begin{array}{l} \\ -R_1 + 4R_2 \to R_2 \\ R_1 + R_3 \to R_3 \end{array} \begin{array}{c} \begin{matrix} x_1 & x_2 & x_3 & s_1 & s_2 & z & \end{matrix} \\ \left[\begin{array}{cccccc|c} 8 & 0 & -6 & 1 & -1 & 0 & 1 \\ 0 & 16 & 38 & -1 & 5 & 0 & 7 \\ \hline 0 & 0 & 18 & 1 & 5 & 1 & 13 \end{array}\right] \end{array}$$

$$\begin{array}{l} \frac{1}{8}R_1 \to R_1 \\ \frac{1}{16}R_2 \to R_2 \\ \\ \end{array} \begin{array}{c} \begin{matrix} x_1 & x_2 & x_3 & s_1 & s_2 & z & \end{matrix} \\ \left[\begin{array}{cccccc|c} 1 & 0 & -\frac{3}{4} & \frac{1}{8} & -\frac{1}{8} & 0 & \frac{1}{8} \\ 0 & 1 & \frac{19}{8} & -\frac{1}{16} & \frac{5}{16} & 0 & \frac{7}{16} \\ \hline 0 & 0 & 18 & 1 & 5 & 1 & 13 \end{array}\right] \end{array}$$

The minimum value of w is 13 when $y_1 = 1$ and $y_2 = 5$, that is, you should buy 1 package of Sun Hill and 5 packages of Bear Valley for a minimum cost of \$13.

(c) The shadow cost for peanuts is based on the variable x_1 and can be read from the final simplex tableau: $\frac{1}{8}$. To get 8 more ounces of peanuts will cost an additional $8\left(\frac{1}{8}\right) = \$1$, so the total cost will then be \$14.

35. Let $x_1 =$ the number of hours doing tai chi,
$x_2 =$ the number of hours riding a unicycle,
and $x_3 =$ the number of hours fencing.

If Ginger wants the total time doing tai chi to be at least twice as long as she rides a unicycle, then

$$x_1 \geq 2x_2$$
$$\text{or } -x_1 + 2x_2 \leq 0.$$

The problem can be stated as follows.

Maximize $z = 236x_1 + 295x_2 + 354x_3$

subject to:
$$\begin{aligned} x_1 + x_2 + x_3 &\leq 10 \\ x_3 &\leq 2 \\ -x_1 + 2x_2 &\leq 0 \end{aligned}$$

with $x_1 \geq 0, x_2 \geq 0, x_3 \geq 0.$

The initial simplex tableau is as follows.

$$\begin{array}{c} \begin{matrix} x_1 & x_2 & x_3 & s_1 & s_2 & s_3 & z & \end{matrix} \\ \left[\begin{array}{ccccccc|c} 1 & 1 & 1 & 1 & 0 & 0 & 0 & 10 \\ 0 & 0 & \boxed{1} & 0 & 1 & 0 & 0 & 2 \\ -1 & 2 & 0 & 0 & 0 & 1 & 0 & 0 \\ \hline -236 & -295 & -354 & 0 & 0 & 0 & 1 & 0 \end{array}\right] \end{array}$$

Pivot on the 1 in row 2, column 3.

$$\begin{array}{l} -R_2 + R_1 \to R_1 \\ \\ \\ 354R_2 + R_4 \to R_4 \end{array} \begin{array}{c} \begin{matrix} x_1 & x_2 & x_3 & s_1 & s_2 & s_3 & z & \end{matrix} \\ \left[\begin{array}{ccccccc|c} 1 & 1 & 0 & 1 & -1 & 0 & 0 & 8 \\ 0 & 0 & 1 & 0 & 1 & 0 & 0 & 2 \\ -1 & \boxed{2} & 0 & 0 & 0 & 1 & 0 & 0 \\ \hline -236 & -295 & 0 & 0 & 354 & 0 & 1 & 708 \end{array}\right] \end{array}$$

Pivot on the 2 in row 3, column 2.

$$\begin{array}{r|ccccccc|c|}
 & x_1 & x_2 & x_3 & s_1 & s_2 & s_3 & z & \\
-R_3 + 2R_1 \rightarrow R_1 & \boxed{3} & 0 & 0 & 2 & -2 & -1 & 0 & 16 \\
 & 0 & 0 & 1 & 0 & 1 & 0 & 0 & 2 \\
 & -1 & 2 & 0 & 0 & 0 & 1 & 0 & 0 \\
\hline
295R_3 + 2R_4 \rightarrow R_4 & -767 & 0 & 0 & 0 & 708 & 295 & 2 & 1416
\end{array}$$

Pivot on the 3 in row 1, column 1.

$$\begin{array}{r|ccccccc|c|}
 & x_1 & x_2 & x_3 & s_1 & s_2 & s_3 & z & \\
 & 3 & 0 & 0 & 2 & -2 & -1 & 0 & 16 \\
 & 0 & 0 & 1 & 0 & 1 & 0 & 0 & 2 \\
R_1 + 3R_3 \rightarrow R_3 & 0 & 6 & 0 & 2 & -2 & 2 & 0 & 16 \\
\hline
767R_1 + 3R_4 \rightarrow R_4 & 0 & 0 & 0 & 1534 & 590 & 118 & 6 & 16{,}520
\end{array}$$

Create a 1 in the columns corresponding to x_1, x_2, and z.

$$\begin{array}{r|ccccccc|c|}
 & x_1 & x_2 & x_3 & s_1 & s_2 & s_3 & z & \\
\frac{1}{3}R_1 \rightarrow R_1 & 1 & 0 & 0 & \frac{2}{3} & -\frac{2}{3} & -\frac{1}{3} & 0 & \frac{16}{3} \\
 & 0 & 0 & 1 & 0 & 1 & 0 & 0 & 2 \\
\frac{1}{6}R_3 \rightarrow R_3 & 0 & 1 & 0 & \frac{1}{3} & -\frac{1}{3} & \frac{1}{3} & 0 & \frac{8}{3} \\
\hline
\frac{1}{6}R_4 \rightarrow R_4 & 0 & 0 & 0 & \frac{767}{3} & \frac{295}{3} & \frac{59}{3} & 1 & \frac{8260}{3}
\end{array}$$

Ginger will burn a maximum of $2753\frac{1}{3}$ calories if she does $\frac{16}{3}$ hours of tai chi, $\frac{8}{3}$ hours riding a unicycle, and 2 hours fencing.

Extended Application: Using Integer Programming in the Stock–Cutting Problem

1. **(a)** With Plan A you will need to buy 8 timbers: one cut will give you the two 4-ft lengths, two more cuts will give you two each of the 3-ft and 5-ft lengths, the two 3-ft pieces will come out of another full length, leaving 2 ft over, and all four 6-ft lengths will come out of 8-ft pieces. Your total waste amounts to 10 ft.

(b) There's no advantage to Plan B; you still need 8 pieces of lumber: two cuts will give you four 4-ft lengths, two more cuts will give you two each of the 3-ft and 5-ft lengths, the two 5-ft lengths will come out of 8-ft pieces as will each of the two 6-ft lengths, leaving a total waste of 10 ft.

(c) If the original timbers were 9 ft in length, you could but 6 timbers and cut the lengths for either Plan A or Plan B with no waste.

2. Four patterns not in the minimizer's list are, for example,

$14|14|33|33|, 31|33|33|, 33|33|33|$, and $14|17|31|33|$.

3. The patterns are 31|33|36, 17|17|33|33, 14|17|33|36, and 14|14|36|36.

4. $\dfrac{808}{35{,}600} \approx 2.3\%$

5. A leftover piece less than 14 inches wide can't be used for any standard width, but a leftover piece of 22 inches, for example, could be cut to make either the 14-inch or the 17-inch standard width. So it might be better to reserve the choice about how to cut this leftover until more orders come in.

6. The highest value is 34: choose weights 2, 2.5 and 4.5.

Chapter 5

MATHEMATICS OF FINANCE

5.1 Simple and Compound Interest

5. \$25,000 at 3% for 9 mo

Use the formula for simple interest.

$$\begin{aligned} I &= Prt \\ &= 25{,}000(0.03)\left(\frac{9}{12}\right) \\ &= 562.50 \end{aligned}$$

The simple interest is \$562.50.

6. \$4289 at 4.5% for 9 wk

Use the formula for simple interest.

$$\begin{aligned} &= Prt \\ &= 4289(0.045)\left(\frac{35}{52}\right) \\ &\approx 129.91 \end{aligned}$$

The simple interest is \$129.91.

7. \$1974 at 6.3% for 25 wk

Use the formula for simple interest.

$$\begin{aligned} I &= Prt \\ &= 1974(0.063)\left(\frac{25}{52}\right) \\ &\approx 59.79 \end{aligned}$$

The simple interest is \$59.79.

8. \$6125 at 1.25% for 6 mo

Use the formula for simple interest.

$$\begin{aligned} I &= Prt \\ &= 6125(0.0125)\left(\frac{6}{12}\right) \\ &\approx 38.28 \end{aligned}$$

The simple interest is \$38.28.

9. \$8192.17 at 3.1% for 72 days

Use the formula for simple interest.

$$\begin{aligned} I &= Prt \\ &= 8192.17(0.031)\left(\frac{72}{360}\right) \\ &\approx 50.79 \end{aligned}$$

The simple interest is \$50.79.

10. \$7236.15 at 4.25% for 30 days
Use the formula for simple interest.

$$\begin{aligned} I &= Prt \\ &= 7236.15(0.0425)\left(\frac{30}{360}\right) \\ &\approx 25.63 \end{aligned}$$

The simple interest is \$25.63.

11. Use the formula for future value for simple interest.

$$\begin{aligned} A &= P(1+rt) \\ &= 3125\left[1+0.0285\left(\frac{7}{12}\right)\right] \\ &\approx 3176.95 \end{aligned}$$

The maturity value is \$3176.95. The interest earned is $3176.95 - 3125 = \$51.95$.

12. Use the formula for future value for simple interest.

$$\begin{aligned} A &= P(1+rt) \\ &= 12{,}000\left[1+0.053\left(\frac{11}{12}\right)\right] \\ &= 12{,}583 \end{aligned}$$

The maturity value is \$12,583. The interest earned is $12{,}583 - 12{,}000 = \$583$.

13. Use the formula for simple interest.

$$I = Prt$$
$$56.25 = 1500r\left(\frac{6}{12}\right)$$
$$r = 0.075$$

The interest rate was 7.5%.

14. Use the formula for simple interest.

$$I = Prt$$
$$1057.50 = 23{,}500r\left(\frac{9}{12}\right)$$
$$r = 0.06$$

The interest rate was 6%.

19. Use the formula for compound amount with $P = 1000$, $i = 0.06$, and $n = 8$.

$$\begin{aligned} A &= P(1+i)^n \\ &= 1000(1+0.06)^8 \\ &\approx 1593.85 \end{aligned}$$

The compound amount is \$1593.85. The interest earned is 1593.85 – 1000 = \$593.85.

20. Use the formula for compound amount with $P = 1000$, $i = 0.045$, and $n = 6$.

$$\begin{aligned} A &= P(1+i)^n \\ &= 1000(1+0.045)^6 \\ &\approx 1302.26 \end{aligned}$$

The compound amount is \$1302.26. The interest earned is 1302.26 – 1000 = \$302.26.

21. Use the formula for compound amount with

$P = 470, i = \frac{0.054}{2} = 0.027$, and $n = 12(2) = 24$.

$$\begin{aligned} A &= P(1+i)^n \\ &= 470(1+0.027)^{24} \\ &\approx 890.82 \end{aligned}$$

The compound amount is \$890.82. The interest earned is 890.82 – 470 = \$420.82.

22. Use the formula for compound amount with $P = 15{,}000$, $i = \frac{0.06}{12} = 0.005$, and $n = 10(12) = 120$.

$$\begin{aligned} A &= P(1+i)^n \\ &= 15{,}000(1+0.005)^{120} \\ &\approx 27{,}290.95 \end{aligned}$$

The compound amount is \$27,290.95. The interest earned is 27,290.95 – 15,000 = \$12,290.95.

23. Use the formula for compound amount with $P = 8500, i = \frac{0.08}{4} = 0.02$, and $n = 5(4) = 20$.

$$\begin{aligned} A &= P(1+i)^n \\ &= 8500(1+0.02)^{20} \\ &\approx 12{,}630.55 \end{aligned}$$

The compound amount is \$12,630.55. The interest earned is 12,630.55 – 8500 = \$4130.55.

24. Use the formula for compound amount with $P = 9100, i = \frac{0.064}{4} = 0.016$, and $n = 9(4) = 36$.

$$\begin{aligned} A &= P(1+i)^n \\ &= 9100(1+0.016)^{36} \\ &\approx 16{,}114.43 \end{aligned}$$

The compound amount is \$16,114.43. The interest earned is 16,114.43 – 9100 = \$7014.43.

25. Use the formula for present value for compound interest with $A = 12{,}820.77, i = 0.048$, and $n = 6$.

$$\begin{aligned} P &= \frac{A}{(1+r)^n} \\ &= \frac{12{,}820.77}{(1+0.048)^6} \\ &\approx 9677.13 \end{aligned}$$

The present value \$9677.13.

26. Use the formula for present value for compound interest with $A = 36{,}527.13, i = 0.053$, and $n = 10$.

$$\begin{aligned} P &= \frac{A}{(1+r)^n} \\ &= \frac{36{,}527.13}{(1+0.053)^{10}} \\ &\approx 21{,}793.74. \end{aligned}$$

The present value \$21,793.74.

27. Use the formula for present value for compound interest with $A = 2000, i = \frac{0.06}{2} = 0.03$, and $n = 8(2) = 16$.

$$\begin{aligned} P &= \frac{A}{(1+r)^n} \\ &= \frac{2000}{(1+0.03)^{16}} \\ &\approx 1246.33 \end{aligned}$$

The present value \$1246.33.

28. Use the formula for present value for compound interest with $A = 2000, i = \frac{0.07}{2} = 0.035$, and $n = 8(2) = 16$.

$$\begin{aligned} P &= \frac{A}{(1+r)^n} \\ &= \frac{2000}{(1+0.035)^{16}} \\ &\approx 1153.41 \end{aligned}$$

The present value \$1153.41.

29. Use the formula for present value for compound interest with $A = 8800, i = \frac{0.05}{4} = 0.0125$, and $n = 5(4) = 20$.

$$\begin{aligned} P &= \frac{A}{(1+r)^n} \\ &= \frac{8800}{(1+0.0125)^{20}} \\ &\approx 6864.08 \end{aligned}$$

The present value \$6864.08.

30. Use the formula for present value for compound interest with $A = 7500, i = \frac{0.055}{4} = 0.01375$, and $n = 9(4) = 36$.

$$\begin{aligned} P &= \frac{A}{(1+r)^n} \\ &= \frac{7500}{(1+0.01375)^{36}} \\ &\approx 4587.23 \end{aligned}$$

The present value \$4587.23.

32. The effective interest rate $\left(1+\frac{i}{n}\right)^n - 1$ equals $1 + n\left(\frac{i}{n}\right) +$ other terms -1. This equals $i+$ other terms, which is greater than the stated interest rate i.

33. 4% compounded quarterly.

Use the formula for effective rate with $r = 0.04$ and $m = 4$.

$$\begin{aligned} r_e &= \left(1+\frac{r}{m}\right)^m - 1 \\ &= \left(1+\frac{0.04}{4}\right)^4 - 1 \\ &\approx 0.04060 \end{aligned}$$

The effective rate is about 4.06%.

34. 6% compounded quarterly.

Use the formula for effective rate with $r = 0.06$ and $m = 4$.

$$\begin{aligned} r_e &= \left(1+\frac{r}{m}\right)^m - 1 \\ &= \left(1+\frac{0.06}{4}\right)^4 - 1 \\ &\approx 0.06136 \end{aligned}$$

The effective rate is about 6.136%, or rounding to two decimal places, 6.14%.

35. 7.25% compounded semiannually.

Use the formula for effective rate with $r = 0.0725$ and $m = 2$.

$$\begin{aligned} r_e &= \left(1+\frac{r}{m}\right)^m - 1 \\ &= \left(1+\frac{0.0725}{2}\right)^2 - 1 \\ &\approx 0.07381 \end{aligned}$$

The effective rate is about 7.381%, or rounding to two decimal places, 7.38%.

36. 6.25% compounded semiannually.

Use the formula for effective rate with $r = 0.0625$ and $m = 2$.

$$\begin{aligned} r_e &= \left(1+\frac{r}{m}\right)^m - 1 \\ &= \left(1+\frac{0.0625}{2}\right)^2 - 1 \\ &\approx 0.06348 \end{aligned}$$

The effective rate is about 6.348%, or rounding to two decimal places, 6.35%.

37. Start by finding the total amount repaid. Use the formula for future value for simple interest, with $P = 2700$, $r = 0.062$, and $t = \frac{9}{12}$.

$$A = P(1 + rt)$$
$$= 7200\left[1 + 0.062\left(\frac{9}{12}\right)\right]$$
$$= 7534.80$$

Amy repaid her father \$7534.80. To find the amount of this which was interest, subtract the original loan amount from the repayment amount.

$$7534.80 - 7200 = 334.80$$

Of the amount repaid, \$334.80 was interest.

38. To find the total amount paid, use the formula for future value for simple interest, with $P = 321{,}812.85$, $r = 0.134$, and $t = \frac{29}{365}$.

$$A = P(1 + i)^n$$
$$= 321{,}812.85\left[1 + 0.134\left(\frac{29}{365}\right)\right]$$
$$\approx 325{,}239.05$$

The company paid \$325,239.05.

39. The interest earned was

$$\$1521.25 - \$1500 = \$21.25$$

Use the formula for simple interest, with $I = 21.25$, $P = 1500$, and $t = \frac{75}{360}$.

$$I = Prt$$
$$21.25 = 1500r\left(\frac{75}{360}\right)$$
$$0.068 = r$$

The interest rate was 6.8%.

40. The interest earned is

$$\$10{,}000 - \$5988.02 = \$4011.98$$

Use the formula for simple interest, with $I = 4011.98$, $P = 5988.02$, and $t = 10$.

$$I = Prt$$
$$4011.98 = 5988.02r(10)$$
$$0.067 \approx r$$

The interest rate was about 6.7%.

41. The total cost of the 8 computers is $\$2309(8) = \$18{,}472$. We want to find the present value of 18,472 dollars compounded at interest rate $i = \frac{0.0479}{12}$ per month for $n = 6$ months.

$$P = \frac{A}{(1 + i)^n}$$
$$= \frac{18{,}472}{\left(1 + \frac{0.0479}{12}\right)^6}$$
$$\approx 18{,}035.71$$

The department should deposit \$18,035.71 now.

42. Start by finding the total interest earned.

$$I = (\$24 - \$22) + \$0.50 = \$2.50$$

Now use the formula for simple interest, with $I = 2.50$, $P = 22$, and $t = 1$.

$$I = Prt$$
$$2.50 = 22r(1)$$
$$0.11364 \approx r$$

The interest rate was about 11.36% or, rounding to one decimal place, 11.4%.

43. Use the formula for compound amount with $P = 50{,}000$, $i = \frac{r}{m} = \frac{0.08}{12} = 0.00\overline{6}$, and $n = mt = 12(6) = 72$.

$$A = P(1 + i)^n$$
$$= 50{,}000(1 + 0.00\overline{6})^{72}$$
$$\approx 80{,}675.11$$

The amount of interest is found by subtracting.

$$I = A - P$$
$$= 80{,}675.11 - 50{,}000$$
$$= 30{,}675.11$$

The interest earned was \$30,675.11.

44. **(a)** Use the formula for compound amount with $P = 42$ and $i = 0.58$.

$$A = P(1 + i)^n$$
$$A = 42(1 + 0.58)^n$$

Graph $y_1 = 42(1 + 0.58)^x$ and $y_2 = 1000$.

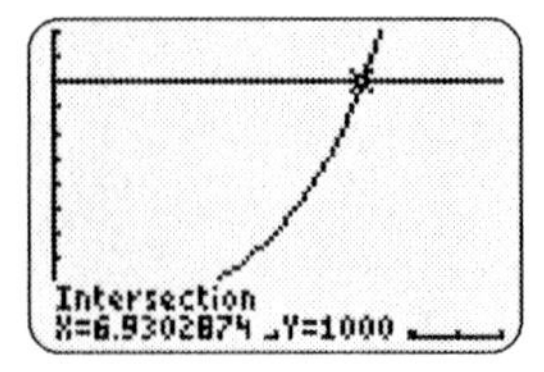

The graphs intersect at $(6.9302874, 1000)$. Thus, 6.93 yr after July 16, 1997, or in June 2004, Bill Gates would be a trillionaire. At that time Mr. Gates would be 48 years old.

(b) Use the formula for compound amount with $P = 42$ and $i = 0.105$.

$$A = P(1+i)^n$$
$$A = 42(1+0.105)^n$$

Graph $y_1 = 42(1+0.105)^x$ and $y_2 = 1000$.

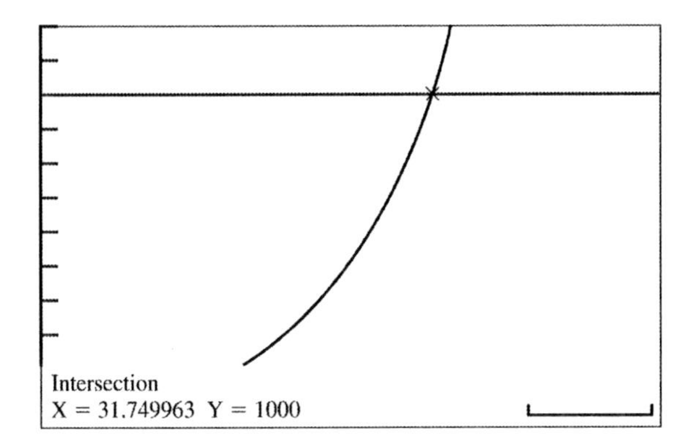

The graphs intersect at $(31.749963, 1000)$. Thus, 31.75 yr after July 16, 1997, or in April 2029, Bill Gates would be a trillionaire. At that time Mr. Gates would be 73 yr old.

(c) January 1, 2022, is 24.46 yr after July 16, 1997. Thus, $t = 24.46$. Since we are compounding once a year, there are 24.46 periods. Thus $n = 24.46$. Use the formula for compound amount with $P = 42$.

$$A = P(1+i)^n$$
$$A = 42(1+i)^{24.46}$$

Graph $y_1 = 42(1+x)^{24.46}$ and $y_2 = 1000$.

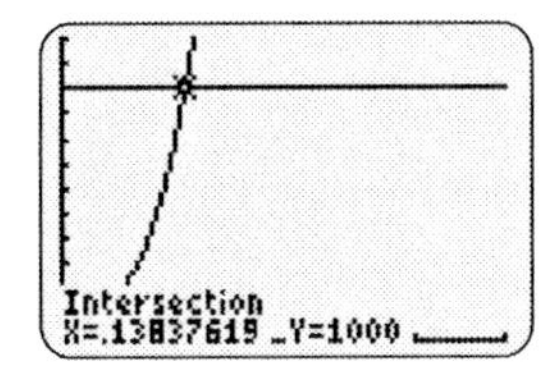

The graphs intersect at $(0.13837619, 1000)$. Thus, $i = 0.138$. 13.8% growth would be necessary for Bill Gates to be a trillionaire by January 1, 2022.

(d) Use the formula for compound amount with $P = 40.7$ (billion), $A = 50$ (billion) and $n = 3$.

$$A = P(1+i)^n$$
$$50 = 40.7(1+i)^3$$
$$\left(\frac{50}{40.7}\right)^{1/3} = 1+i$$
$$0.07101 \approx i$$

The rate of growth was almost exactly 7.1%.

45. (a) Use the Rule of 72 to find the doubling time.

$$\text{Doubling time} = \frac{72}{4.5} = 16$$

It takes about 16 years for the trust fund to double in size, from \$10,000 to \$20,000. The grandchild will be 16 years old.

(b) Use the formula for compound amount with $P = 10{,}000$, $i = \frac{0.045}{12}$, and $n = 16(12) = 192$.

$$A = P(1+i)^n$$
$$= 10{,}000\left(1+\frac{0.045}{12}\right)^{192}$$
$$\approx 20{,}516.69$$

The actual amount in the trust fund after 16 years is \$20,516.69. Obviously, it actually takes slightly less than 16 years for the fund to reach \$20,000.

46. Use the formula for compound amount with $P = 40{,}000$, $i = \frac{0.0654}{12}$, and $n = 6$.

$$A = P(1+i)^n$$
$$= 40{,}000\left(1+\frac{0.0654}{12}\right)^6$$
$$\approx 41{,}325.95$$

When Kelly begins paying off his loan, he will owe \$41,325.95.

47. Use the formula for present value for compound interest with $A = 30{,}000$, $i = \frac{0.055}{4} = 0.01375$, and $n = 5(4) = 20$.

$$P = \frac{A}{(1+r)^n}$$
$$= \frac{30{,}000}{(1+0.01375)^{20}}$$
$$\approx 22{,}829.89$$

The present value is \$22,829.89, or rounding up to the nearest cent (to make sure that the investment really grows to \$30,000), \$22,829.90. That is how much of the inherited \$25,000 Phyllis should invest in order to have \$30,000 for a down payment in 5 years.

48. Substitute $P = 10{,}000$, $i = \frac{0.06}{2}$, and $n = 2(3) = 6$ in the formula for compound amount.

$$\begin{aligned} A &= P(1+i)^n \\ &= 10{,}000\left(1+\frac{0.06}{2}\right)^6 \\ &= 10{,}000(1.03)^6 \\ &\approx 11{,}940.52 \end{aligned}$$

She should contribute about \$11,940.52 in 3 yr.

49. (a) Use the formula for compound amount to find the value of \$1000 in 5 yr.

$$\begin{aligned} A &= P(1+i)^n \\ &= 1000(1.06)^5 \\ &\approx 1338.23 \end{aligned}$$

In 5 yr, \$1000 will be worth \$1338.23. Since this is larger than the \$1210 one would receive in 5 yr, it would be more profitable to take the \$1000 now.

50. For each quoted effective rate, find the corresponding nominal rate by using the formula for effective rate. Regardless of the CD's term, m always equals 4, since compounding is always quarterly.

For the 6-month CD, use $r_e = 0.025$.

$$\begin{aligned} r_e &= \left(1+\frac{r}{m}\right)^m - 1 \\ 0.025 &= \left(1+\frac{r}{4}\right)^4 - 1 \\ (1+0.025)^{1/4} &= 1+\frac{r}{4}. \\ 0.02477 &\approx r \end{aligned}$$

For the 6-month CD, the nominal rate is about 2.48%.

For the 9-month CD, use $r_e = 0.051$.

$$\begin{aligned} r_e &= \left(1+\frac{r}{m}\right)^m - 1 \\ 0.051 &= \left(1+\frac{r}{4}\right)^4 - 1 \\ (1+0.051)^{1/4} &= 1+\frac{r}{4}. \\ 0.050053 &\approx r \end{aligned}$$

For the 9-month CD, the nominal rate is about 5.01%.

For the 1-year CD, use $r_e = 0.0425$ and $m = 4$.

$$\begin{aligned} r_e &= \left(1+\frac{r}{m}\right)^m - 1 \\ 0.0425 &= \left(1+\frac{r}{4}\right)^4 - 1 \\ (1+0.0425)^{1/4} &= 1+\frac{r}{4}. \\ 0.04184 &\approx r \end{aligned}$$

For the 1-year CD, the nominal rate is about 4.18%.

For the 2-year CD, use $r_e = 0.045$.

$$\begin{aligned} r_e &= \left(1+\frac{r}{m}\right)^m - 1 \\ 0.045 &= \left(1+\frac{r}{4}\right)^4 - 1 \\ (1+0.045)^{1/4} &= 1+\frac{r}{4}. \\ 0.04426 &\approx r \end{aligned}$$

For the 2-year CD, the nominal rate is about 4.43%.

For the 3-year CD, use $r_e = 0.0525$.

$$\begin{aligned} r_e &= \left(1+\frac{r}{m}\right)^m - 1 \\ 0.0525 &= \left(1+\frac{r}{4}\right)^4 - 1 \\ (1+0.0525)^{1/4} &= 1+\frac{r}{4}. \\ 0.05150 &\approx r \end{aligned}$$

For the 3-year CD, the nominal rate is about 5.15%.

51. The yield is the effective rate. Find the corresponding nominal rate by using the formula for effective rate. Use the formula for effective rate, with $r = 0.0546$ and $m = 12$.

$$r_e = \left(1 + \frac{r}{m}\right)^m - 1$$

$$0.0546 = \left(1 + \frac{r}{12}\right)^{12} - 1$$

$$(1 + 0.0546)^{1/12} = 1 + \frac{r}{12}$$

$$0.05328 \approx r$$

The effective rate is about 5.33%.

52. Start by finding the effective rate for the CD offered by Centennial Bank of Fountain Valley. Use the formula for effective rate, with $r = 0.055$ and $m = 12$.

$$r_e = \left(1 + \frac{r}{m}\right)^m - 1$$

$$= \left(1 + \frac{0.055}{12}\right)^{12} - 1$$

$$\approx 0.05641$$

The effective rate is about 5.64%.

Since the CD offered by First Source Bank of South Bend compound annually, the quoted rate of 5.63% is also the effective rate.

Centennial Bank of Fountain Valley pays a slightly higher effective rate.

53. Use 8% compounded quarterly for 20 yr. Then $i = \frac{0.08}{4} = 0.02$ and $n = 20(4) = 80$.

$$A = P(1+i)^n = P(1.02)^{80}$$

For \$10,000,

$$A = 10{,}000(1.02)^{80} \approx 48{,}754.39,$$

that is, \$48,754.39.

For \$149,000,

$$A = 149,000(1.02)^{80} \approx 726,440.43,$$

that is, \$726,440.43.

For \$1,000,000,

$$A = 1,000,000(1.02)^{80} \approx 4,875,439.16,$$

that is, \$4,875,439.16.

54. To find the number of years it will take prices to double at 4% annual inflation, find n in the equation

$$2 = (1 + 0.04)^n,$$

which simplifies to

$$2 = (1.04)^n.$$

By trying various values of n, find that $n = 18$ is approximately correct, because

$$1.04^{18} \approx 2.0258 \approx 2.$$

Prices will double in about 18 yr.

55. $2 = (1 + 0.05)^n$
$2 = (1.05)^n$

Try various values for n.

$$(1.05)^{14} \approx 1.979932 \approx 2$$

Thus, $n \approx 14$. It would take about 14 yr for the general level of prices in the economy to double at the annual inflation rate of 5%.

56. To find the number of years it will be until the generating capacity will need to be doubled, find n in the equation

$$2 = (1 + 0.06)^n,$$

which simplifies to

$$2 = (1.06)^n.$$

By trying various values of n, find that $n = 12$ is approximately correct, because

$$1.06^{12} \approx 2.0122 \approx 2.$$

The generating capacity will need to be doubled in about 12 yr.

57. Find n such that

$$2 = (1.02)^n$$

By trying various values of n, we see that $n \approx 35$ is approximately correct because

$$(1.02)^{35} \approx 1.999890 \approx 2.$$

It will take about 35 yr before the utilities will need to double their generating capacity.

58. Let $P = 150{,}000$, $i = -2.4\% = -.024$, and $n = 4$.

$$\begin{aligned} A &= P(1+i)^n \\ &= 150{,}000[1+(-.024)]^4 \\ &= 150{,}000(.976)^4 \\ &\approx 136{,}110.16 \end{aligned}$$

After 4 yr, the amount on deposit will be \$136,110.16.

59. Let $P = 150{,}000$, $i = -0.024$, and $n = 8$.

$$\begin{aligned} A &= P(1+i)^n \\ &= 150{,}000(1-0.024)^8 \\ &= 150{,}000(0.976)^8 \\ &= 123{,}506.50 \end{aligned}$$

After 8 yr, the amount on deposit will be \$123,506.50.

60. Use the formula

$$A = P(1+i)^n$$

with $A = 420{,}000{,}000$, $P = 100$, and $n = 160$.

$$\begin{aligned} 420{,}000{,}000 &= 100(1+r)^{160} \\ 4{,}200{,}000 &= (1+r)^{160} \\ 4{,}200{,}000^{1/160} &= 1+r \\ r &= 4{,}200{,}000^{1/160} - 1 \\ r &\approx 0.1000 \end{aligned}$$

The rate used was 10.00%.

61. Use the formula

$$A = P(1+i)^n$$

with $P = \frac{2}{8}$ cent $=$ \$0.0025 and $r = 0.04$ compounded quarterly for 2000 yr.

$$\begin{aligned} A &= 0.0025\left(1+\frac{0.04}{4}\right)^{4(2000)} \\ &= 0.0025(1.01)^{8000} \\ &\approx 9.31 \times 10^{31} \end{aligned}$$

The money would be worth $\$9.31 \times 10^{31}$ 2000 yr later.

62. First use the formula for simple interest where $P = 5200$, $r = 0.07$, and $t = \frac{10}{12}$.

$$\begin{aligned} A &= P(1+rt) \\ &= 5200\left[1+0.07\left(\frac{10}{12}\right)\right] \\ &\approx 5503.33 \end{aligned}$$

Now use the formula for compound interest with $P = 5503.33$, $i = \frac{0.063}{4}$, and $n = 5(4) = 20$.

$$\begin{aligned} A &= P(1+i)^n \\ &= 5503.33\left(1+\frac{0.063}{4}\right)^{20} \\ &= 5503.33(1.01575)^{20} \\ &\approx 7522.50 \end{aligned}$$

He will have \$7522.50 at the end of the 5 yr.

63. Use the formula

$$A = P(1+i)^n$$

with $P = 10{,}000$ and $r = 0.05$ for 10 yr.

(a) If interest is compounding annually,

$$\begin{aligned} A &= 10{,}000(1+0.05)^{10} \\ &\approx 16{,}288.95. \end{aligned}$$

The future value is \$16,288.95.

(b) If interest is compounding quarterly,

$$\begin{aligned} A &= 10{,}000\left(1+\frac{0.05}{4}\right)^{40} \\ &\approx 16{,}436.19. \end{aligned}$$

The future value is \$16,436.19.

(c) If interest is compounding monthly,

$$\begin{aligned} A &= 10{,}000\left(1+\frac{0.05}{12}\right)^{120} \\ &\approx 16{,}470.09. \end{aligned}$$

The future value is \$16,470.09.

(d) If interest is compounding daily,

$$\begin{aligned} A &= 10{,}000\left(1+\frac{0.05}{365}\right)^{3650} \\ &\approx 16{,}486.65. \end{aligned}$$

The future value is \$16,486.65.

65. First consider the case of earning interest at a rate of k per annum compounded quarterly for all 8 yr and earning \$2203.76 on the \$1000 investment.

$$\begin{aligned} 2203.76 &= 1000\left(1+\frac{k}{4}\right)^{8(4)} \\ 2.20376 &= \left(1+\frac{k}{4}\right)^{32} \end{aligned}$$

Use a calculator to raise both sides to the power $\frac{1}{32}$.

$$1.025 = 1 + \frac{k}{4}$$
$$0.025 = \frac{k}{4}$$
$$0.1 = k$$

Next consider the actual investments. The \$1000 was invested for the first 5 yr at a rate of j per annum compounded semiannually.

$$A = 1000\left(1 + \frac{j}{2}\right)^{5(2)}$$
$$A = 1000\left(1 + \frac{j}{2}\right)^{10}$$

This amount was then invested for the remaining 3 yr at $k = .1$ per annum compounded quarterly for a final compound amount of \$1990.76.

$$1990.76 = A\left(1 + \frac{0.1}{4}\right)^{3(4)}$$
$$1990.76 = A(1.025)^{12}$$
$$1480.24 \approx A$$

Recall that $A = 1000\left(1 + \frac{j}{2}\right)^{10}$ and substitute this value into the above equation.

$$1480.24 = 1000\left(1 + \frac{j}{2}\right)^{10}$$
$$1.48024 = \left(1 + \frac{j}{2}\right)^{10}$$

Use a calculator to raise both sides to the power $\frac{1}{10}$.

$$1.04 \approx 1 + \frac{j}{2}$$
$$0.04 = \frac{j}{2}$$
$$0.08 = j$$

The ratio of k to j is

$$\frac{k}{j} = \frac{0.1}{0.08} = \frac{10}{8} = \frac{5}{4}.$$

5.2 Future Value of an Annuity

1. $a = 3;\ r = 2$

The first five terms are

$$3,\ 3(2),\ 3(2)^2,\ 3(2)^3,\ 3(2)^4$$

or

$$3,\ 6,\ 12,\ 24,\ 48.$$

The fifth term is 48.

Or, use the formula $a_n = ar^{n-1}$ with $n = 5$.

$$a_5 = ar^{5-1} = 3(2)^4 = 3(16) = 48$$

2. $a = 7,\ r = 5$

$$a_n = ar^{n-1}$$
$$a_5 = 7(5)^4 = 4375$$

3. $a = -8;\ r = 3;\ n = 5$

$$a_5 = ar^{5-1} = -8(3)^4 = -8(81) = -648$$

The fifth term is -648.

4. $a = -6;\ r = 2$

$$a_5 = ar^4 = -6(2)^4 = -96$$

5. $a = 1;\ r = -3;\ n = 5$

$$a_5 = ar^{5-1} = 1(-3)^4 = 81$$

The fifth term is 81.

6. $a = 12;\ r = -2$

$$a_5 = ar^4 = 12(-2)^4 = 192.$$

7. $a = 256;\ r = \frac{1}{4};\ n = 5$

$$a_5 = ar^{5-1} = 256\left(\frac{1}{4}\right)^4 = 256\left(\frac{1}{256}\right) = 1$$

The fifth term is 1.

8. $a = 729;\ r = \frac{1}{3}$

$$a_5 = ar^4 = 729\left(\frac{1}{3}\right)^4 = 9$$

9. $a = 1;\ r = 2;\ n = 4$

To find the sum of the first 4 terms, S_4, use the formula for the sum of the first n terms of a geometric sequence.

$$S_n = \frac{a(r^n - 1)}{r - 1}$$
$$S_4 = \frac{1(2^4 - 1)}{2 - 1} = \frac{16 - 1}{1} = 15$$

10. $a = 4;\ r = 4;\ n = 4$

$$S_n = \frac{a(r^n - 1)}{r - 1}$$

$$S_4 = \frac{4(4^4 - 1)}{4 - 1} = 340$$

11. $a = 5;\ r = \frac{1}{5};\ n = 4$

$$S_n = \frac{a(r^n - 1)}{r - 1}$$

$$S_4 = \frac{5\left[\left(\frac{1}{5}\right)^4 - 1\right]}{\frac{1}{5} - 1} = \frac{5\left(-\frac{624}{625}\right)}{-\frac{4}{5}}$$

$$= \frac{-\frac{624}{125}}{-\frac{4}{5}} = \left(-\frac{624}{125}\right)\left(-\frac{5}{4}\right) = \frac{156}{25}$$

12. $a = 6;\ r = \frac{1}{2};\ n = 4$

$$S_n = \frac{a(r^n - 1)}{r - 1}$$

$$S_4 = \frac{6\left[\left(\frac{1}{2}\right)^4 - 1\right]}{\frac{1}{2} - 1} = \frac{6\left(-\frac{15}{16}\right)}{-\frac{1}{2}} = \frac{45}{4}$$

13. $a = 128;\ r = -\frac{3}{2};\ n = 4$

$$S_n = \frac{a(r^n - 1)}{r - 1}$$

$$S_4 = \frac{128\left[\left(-\frac{3}{2}\right)^4 - 1\right]}{-\frac{3}{2} - 1} = \frac{128\left(\frac{65}{16}\right)}{-\frac{5}{2}}$$

$$= -208$$

14. $a = 64;\ r = -\frac{3}{4};\ n = 4$

$$S_4 = \frac{64\left[\left(-\frac{3}{4}\right)^4 - 1\right]}{-\frac{3}{4} - 1} = \frac{64\left(-\frac{175}{256}\right)}{-\frac{7}{4}} = 25$$

15.
$$s_{\overline{n}|i} = \frac{(1+i)^n - 1}{i}$$

$$s_{\overline{12}|0.05} = \frac{(1+0.05)^{12} - 1}{0.05} \approx 15.91713$$

16.
$$s_{\overline{n}|i} = \frac{(1+i)^n - 1}{i}$$

$$s_{\overline{15}|0.04} = \frac{(1.04)^{15} - 1}{0.04} \approx 20.02359$$

17.
$$s_{\overline{n}|i} = \frac{(1+i)^n - 1}{i}$$

$$s_{\overline{10}|0.052} = \frac{(1+0.052)^{10} - 1}{0.052} \approx 12.69593$$

18. $s_{\overline{18}|0.015} = \dfrac{(1.015)^{18} - 1}{0.015} \approx 20.48938$

21. $R = 100;\ i = 0.06;\ n = 4$

Use the formula for the future value of an ordinary annuity.

$$S = R\left[\frac{(1+i)^n - 1}{i}\right]$$

$$= 100\left[\frac{(1.06)^4 - 1}{0.06}\right]$$

$$= 100\left(\frac{1.262477 - 1}{0.06}\right)$$

$$\approx 437.46$$

The future value is \$437.46.

22. $R = 1000;\ i = 0.06;\ n = 5$

Use the formula for the future value of an ordinary annuity.

$$S = Rs_{\overline{n}|i} = 1000s_{\overline{5}|0.06}$$

$$= 1000\left[\frac{(1.06)^5 - 1}{0.06}\right]$$

$$\approx 5637.09$$

The future value is \$5637.09.

23. $R = 25{,}000;\ i = 0.045;\ n = 36$

$$S = R\left[\frac{(1+i)^n - 1}{i}\right]$$

$$= 25{,}000\left[\frac{(1+0.045)^{36} - 1}{0.045}\right]$$

$$\approx 2{,}154{,}099.15$$

The future value is \$2,154,099.15.

24. $R = 29,500;\ i = 0.058;\ n = 15$

$$S = R\left[\frac{(1+i)^n - 1}{i}\right]$$

$$= 29,500\left[\frac{(1+0.058)^{15} - 1}{0.058}\right]$$

$$\approx 676{,}272.05$$

The future value is \$676,272.05.

25. $R = 9200$; 10% interest compounded semiannually for 7 yr

Interest of $\frac{10\%}{2} = 5\%$ is earned semiannually, so $i = 0.05$. In 7 yr, there are $7(2) = 14$ semiannual periods, so $n = 14$.

$$\begin{aligned} S &= R\left[\frac{(1+i)^n - 1}{i}\right] \\ &= 9200\left[\frac{(1.05)^{14} - 1}{0.05}\right] \\ &\approx 180,307.41 \end{aligned}$$

The future value is $180,307.41.
$9200 is contributed in each of 14 periods. The total contribution is

$$\$9200(14) = \$128{,}800.$$

The amount from interest is

$$\$180{,}307.41 - 128{,}800 = \$51{,}507.41$$

26. $R = 1250$; $i = \frac{0.05}{2} = 0.025$; $n = 18(2) = 36$

$$\begin{aligned} S &= R\left[\frac{(1+i)^n - 1}{i}\right] \\ &= 1250\left[\frac{(1+0.025)^{36} - 1}{0.025}\right] \\ &\approx 71{,}626.77 \end{aligned}$$

The future value is $71,626.77.

$1250 is contributed in each of 36 periods. The total contribution is

$$\$1250(36) = \$45{,}000.$$

The amount from interest is

$$\$71{,}626.77 - 45{,}000 = \$26{,}626.77$$

27. $R = 800$; 6.51% interest compounded semiannually for 12 yr

Interest of $\frac{6.51\%}{2}$ is earned semiannually, so $i = \frac{0.0651}{2} = 0.03255$. In 12 yr, there are $12(2) = 24$ semiannual periods, so $n = 24$.

$$\begin{aligned} S &= R\left[\frac{(1+i)^n - 1}{i}\right] \\ &= 800\left[\frac{(1+0.03255)^{24} - 1}{0.03255}\right] \\ &\approx 28{,}438.21 \end{aligned}$$

The future value is $28,438.21.

$800 is contributed in each of 24 periods. The total contribution is

$$\$800(24) = \$19{,}200.$$

The amount from interest is

$$\$28{,}438.21 - 19{,}200 = \$9238.21.$$

28. $R = 4600$; $i = \frac{0.0873}{4} = 0.021825$; $n = 9(4) = 36$

$$\begin{aligned} S &= R\left[\frac{(1+i)^n - 1}{i}\right] \\ &= 4600\left[\frac{(1+0.021825)^{36} - 1}{0.021825}\right] \\ &\approx 247{,}752.70 \end{aligned}$$

The future value is $247,752.70.

$4600 is contributed in each of 36 periods. The total contribution is

$$\$4600(36) = \$165{,}600.$$

The amount from interest is

$$\$247{,}752.70 - 165{,}600 = \$82{,}152.70.$$

29. $R = 12{,}000$; $i = \frac{0.048}{2} = 0.012$; $n = 16(4) = 64$

$$\begin{aligned} S &= R\left[\frac{(1+i)^n - 1}{i}\right] \\ &= 12{,}000\left[\frac{(1+0.012)^{64} - 1}{0.012}\right] \\ &\approx 1{,}145{,}619.96 \end{aligned}$$

The future value is $1,145,619.96.

$12,000 is contributed in each of 64 periods. The total contribution is

$$\$12{,}000(64) = \$768{,}000.$$

The amount from interest is

$$\$1{,}145{,}619.96 - 768{,}000 = \$377{,}619.96.$$

30. $R = 42{,}000$; $i = \frac{0.1005}{2} = 0.05025$; $n = 12(2) = 24$

$$S = R\left[\frac{(1+i)^n - 1}{i}\right]$$
$$= 42{,}000\left[\frac{(1+0.05025)^{24} - 1}{0.05025}\right]$$
$$\approx 1{,}875{,}230.74$$

The future value is $1,875,230.74.

$42,000 is contributed in each of 24 periods. The total contribution is

$$\$42{,}000(24) = \$1{,}008{,}000.$$

The amount from interest is

$$\$1{,}875{,}230.74 - 1{,}008{,}000 = \$867{,}230.74.$$

31. $R = 600$; $i = 0.06$; $n = 8$

To find the future value of an annuity due, use the formula for the future value of an ordinary annuity, but include one additional time period and subtract the amount of one payment.

$$S = R\left[\frac{(1+i)^{n+1} - 1}{i}\right] - R$$
$$= 600\left[\frac{(1+0.06)^9 - 1}{0.06}\right] - 600$$
$$\approx 6294.79$$

The future value is $6294.79.

32. $R = 1700$; $i = 0.04$; $n = 15$

To find the future value of an annuity due, use the formula for the future value of an ordinary annuity, but include one additional time period and subtract the amount of one payment.

$$S = R\left[\frac{(1+i)^{n+1} - 1}{i}\right] - R$$
$$= 1700\left[\frac{(1+0.04)^{16} - 1}{0.04}\right] - 1700$$
$$\approx 35{,}401.70$$

The future value is $35,401.70.

33. $R = 16{,}000$; $i = 0.05$; $n = 7$

$$S = R\left[\frac{(1+i)^{n+1} - 1}{i}\right] - R$$
$$= 16{,}000\left[\frac{(1+0.05)^8 - 1}{0.05}\right] - 16{,}000$$
$$\approx 136{,}785.74$$

The future value is $136,785.74.

34. $R = 4000$; $i = 0.06$; $n = 11$

$$S = R\left[\frac{(1+i)^{n+1} - 1}{i}\right] - R$$
$$= 4000\left[\frac{(1+0.06)^{12} - 1}{0.06}\right] - 4000$$
$$\approx 63{,}479.76$$

The future value is $63,479.76.

35. $R = 1000$; $i = \frac{0.0815}{2} = 0.04075$; $n = 9(2) = 18$

$$S = R\left[\frac{(1+i)^{n+1} - 1}{i}\right] - R$$
$$= 1000\left[\frac{(1+0.04075)^{19} - 1}{0.04075}\right] - 1000$$
$$\approx 26{,}874.97$$

The future value is $26,874.97.

$1000 is contributed in each of 18 periods. The total contribution is

$$\$1000(18) = \$18{,}000.$$

The amount from interest is

$$\$26{,}874.97 - 18{,}000 = \$8874.97.$$

36. $R = 750$; $i = \frac{0.059}{12} = 0.00491\overline{6}$; $n = 15(12) = 180$

$$S = R\left[\frac{(1+i)^{n+1} - 1}{i}\right] - R$$
$$= 750\left[\frac{(1+0.00491\overline{6})^{181} - 1}{0.00491\overline{6}}\right] - 750$$
$$\approx 217{,}328.08$$

The future value is $217,328.08.

$750 is contributed in each of 180 periods. The total contribution is

$$\$750(180) = \$135{,}000.$$

The amount from interest is

$$\$217{,}328.08 - 135{,}000 = \$82{,}328.08.$$

37. $R = 250$; $i = \frac{0.042}{2} = 0.0105$; $n = 12(4) = 48$

$$\begin{aligned} S &= R\left[\frac{(1+i)^{n+1}-1}{i}\right] - R \\ &= 250\left[\frac{(1+0.0105)^{49}-1}{0.0105}\right] - 250 \\ &\approx 15{,}662.40 \end{aligned}$$

The future value is $15,662.40.

$250 is contributed in each of 48 periods. The total contribution is

$$\$250(48) = \$12{,}000.$$

The amount from interest is

$$15{,}662.40 - 12{,}000 = \$3662.40.$$

38. $R = 1500$; $i = \frac{0.056}{2} = 0.028$; $n = 11(2) = 22$

$$\begin{aligned} S &= R\left[\frac{(1+i)^{n+1}-1}{i}\right] - R \\ &= 1500\left[\frac{(1+0.028)^{23}-1}{0.028}\right] - 1500 \\ &\approx 46{,}034.09 \end{aligned}$$

The future value is $46,034.09.

$1500 is contributed in each of 22 periods. The total contribution is

$$\$1500(22) = \$33{,}000.$$

The amount from interest is

$$\$46{,}034.09 - 33{,}000 = \$13{,}034.09.$$

39. $S = \$10{,}000$; interest is 5% compounded annually; payments are made at the end of each year for 12 yr.

This is a sinking fund. Use the formula for an ordinary annuity with $S = 10{,}000$, $i = 0.05$, and $n = 12$ to find the value of R, the amount of each payment.

$$\begin{aligned} 10{,}000 &= Rs_{\overline{12}|0.05} \\ R &= \frac{10{,}000}{s_{\overline{12}|0.05}} \\ &= \frac{10{,}000}{\frac{(1+0.05)^{12}-1}{0.05}} \\ &\approx 628.25 \end{aligned}$$

The required periodic payment is $628.25.

40. $S = \$150{,}000$; interest is 6% compounded semiannually; payments are made at the end of each semiannual period for 11 years

This is a sinking fund. Use the formula for an ordinary annuity with $S = 150{,}000$, $i = \frac{0.06}{2} = 0.03$, and $n = 11(2) = 22$ to find the value of R, the amount for each payment.

$$\begin{aligned} 150{,}000 &= Rs \\ &= \frac{150{,}000}{s_{\overline{22}|0.03}} \\ &= \frac{150{,}000}{\frac{(1+0.03)^{22}-1}{0.03}} \\ &\approx 4912.11 \end{aligned}$$

The required periodic payment is $4912.11.

42. $S = 8500$; $i = 0.08$; $n = 7$

$$\begin{aligned} R &= \frac{S}{s_{\overline{n}|i}} \\ &= \frac{8500}{s_{\overline{7}|0.08}} \\ &= \frac{8500(0.08)}{(1+0.08)^7 - 1} \\ &\approx 952.62 \end{aligned}$$

The payment is $952.62.

43. $2750; money earns 5% compounded annually; 5 annual payments

Let R be the amount of each payment.

$$\begin{aligned} 2750 &= Rs_{\overline{5}|0.05} \\ R &= \frac{2750}{s_{\overline{5}|0.05}} \\ &= \frac{2750}{\frac{(1+0.05)^5-1}{0.05}} \\ &\approx 497.68 \end{aligned}$$

The amount of each payment is $497.68.

44. $S = 75{,}000$; $i = \frac{0.06}{2} = 0.03$; $n = 4\frac{1}{2}(2) = 9$

$$\begin{aligned} R &= \frac{S}{s_{\overline{n}|i}} \\ &= \frac{75{,}000}{s_{\overline{9}|0.03}} \\ &= \frac{75{,}000(0.03)}{(1+0.03)^9 - 1} \\ &\approx 7382.54 \end{aligned}$$

The payment is \$7382.54.

45. \$25,000; money earns 5.7% compounded quarterly for $3\frac{1}{2}$ yr.

Thus, $i = \frac{0.057}{4} = 0.01425$ and $n = \left(3\frac{1}{2}\right)4 = 14$.

$$\begin{aligned} R &= \frac{25{,}000}{s_{\overline{14}|0.01425}} \\ &= \frac{25{,}000}{\frac{(1+0.01425)^{14}-1}{0.01425}} \\ &\approx 1626.16 \end{aligned}$$

The amount of each payment is \$1626.16.

46. \$65,000; money earns 7.5% compounded quarterly for $2\frac{1}{2}$years

Thus, $i = \frac{0.075}{4} = 0.01875$ and $n = \left(2\frac{1}{2}\right)4 = 10$.

$$\begin{aligned} R &= \frac{65{,}000}{s_{\overline{10}|0.01875}} \\ &= \frac{65{,}000}{\frac{(1+0.01875)^{10}-1}{0.01875}} \\ &\approx 5970.23 \end{aligned}$$

The amount of each payment is \$5970.23.

47. \$9000; money earns 4.8% compounded monthly for $2\frac{1}{2}$ years

Thus, $i = \frac{0.048}{12} = 0.004$ and $n = \left(2\frac{1}{2}\right)12 = 30$.

$$\begin{aligned} R &= \frac{9000}{s_{\overline{30}|0.004}} \\ &= \frac{9000}{\frac{(1+0.004)^{30}-1}{0.004}} \\ &\approx 282.96 \end{aligned}$$

The amount of each payment is \$282.96.

48. (a) $R = 12,000$; $i = 0.08$; $n = 9$

$$\begin{aligned} S &= R\left[\frac{(1+i)^n - 1}{i}\right] \\ &= 12,000\left[\frac{(1+0.08)^9 - 1}{0.08}\right] \\ &\approx 149{,}850.69 \end{aligned}$$

The final amount is \$149,850.69.

(b) $R = 12,000$; $i = 0.06$; $n = 9$

$$\begin{aligned} S &= R\left[\frac{(1+i)^n - 1}{i}\right] \\ &= 12{,}000\left[\frac{(1+0.06)^9 - 1}{0.06}\right] \\ &\approx 137{,}895.79 \end{aligned}$$

She will have \$137,895.79.

(c) The amount that would be lost is the difference between the two amounts in parts (a) and (b), which is

$$\$149{,}850.69 - 137{,}895.79 = \$11{,}954.90.$$

49. Use the formula for the future value of an ordinary annuity with $R = 100$, $i = \frac{0.0225}{12} = 0.001875$, and $n = 12(2) = 24$.

$$\begin{aligned} S &= R\left[\frac{(1+i)^n - 1}{i}\right] \\ &= 100\left[\frac{(1+.001875)^{24} - 1}{0.001875}\right] \\ &\approx 2452.47 \end{aligned}$$

The amount in the account after 2 years is \$2452.47.

Tom deposited \$100 in each of 24 periods. The total amount deposited was

$$\$100(24) = \$2400.$$

The amount of interest earned was

$$\$2452.47 - 2400 = \$52.47.$$

50. $R = 80$; $i = \frac{0.025}{12}$; $n = 3(12) + 9 = 45$

Because the deposits are made at the beginning of each month, this is an annuity due.

$$\begin{aligned} S &= R\left[\frac{(1+i)^{n+1}-1}{i}\right] - R \\ &= 80\left[\frac{(1+\frac{0.025}{12})^{46}-1}{\frac{0.025}{12}}\right] - 80 \\ &\approx 3777.89 \end{aligned}$$

The account will have $3777.89 in it.

51. $130.50 is invested each month at 4.8% compounded monthly for 40 yr. Thus, $i = \frac{0.048}{12} = 0.004$ and $n = 40(12) = 480$. Use the formula for the future value of an ordinary annuity.

$$\begin{aligned} S &= R\left[\frac{(1+i)^n-1}{i}\right] \\ &= 130.50\left[\frac{(1+0.004)^{480}-1}{0.004}\right] \\ &\approx 189{,}058.14 \end{aligned}$$

The account would be worth $189,058.14.

52. This may be considered an annuity due, since payments are made at the beginning of each year, starting with the day the daughter is born. However, a payment should not be subtracted at the end, since a twenty-second payment is made on her twenty-first birthday. Thus, the future value is given by

$$S = R\left[\frac{(1+i)^{n+1}-1}{i}\right],$$

where $R = 1000$; $i = 0.0525$; and $n = 21$. Therefore,

$$\begin{aligned} S &= 1000\left[\frac{(1.0525)^{22}-1}{0.0525}\right] \\ &\approx 39{,}664.40 \end{aligned}$$

There will be $39,664.40 in the account at the end of the day on the daughter's twenty-first birthday.

$1000 is contributed in each 22 periods. The total contribution is $22,000. Thus

$$\$39{,}664.40 - 22{,}000 = \$17{,}664.40.$$

53. For the first 15 yr, we have an ordinary annuity with $R = 2500$, $i = \frac{0.06}{4} = 0.015$, and $n = 15(4) = 60$. The amount on deposit after 15 yr is

$$\begin{aligned} S &= R\left[\frac{(1+i)^n-1}{i}\right] \\ &= 2500\left[\frac{(1+0.015)^{60}-1}{0.015}\right] \\ &\approx 240{,}536.63 \end{aligned}$$

For the remaining 5 yr, this amount earns compound interest at 6% compounded quarterly. To find the final amount on deposit, use the formula for the compound amount with $P = 240{,}536.63$, $i = \frac{0.06}{4} = 0.015$, and $n = 5(4) = 20$.

$$\begin{aligned} A &= P(1+i)^n \\ &= 240{,}536.63(1.015)^{20} \\ &\approx 323{,}967.96 \end{aligned}$$

The man will have about $323,967.96 in the account when he retires.

54. From ages 50 to 60, we have an ordinary annuity with $R = 3000$, $i = \frac{0.05}{4} = 0.0125$, and $n = 10(4) = 40$. Use the formula for the future value of an ordinary annuity.

$$\begin{aligned} S &= R\left[\frac{(1+i)^n-1}{i}\right] \\ &= 3000\left[\frac{(1.0125)^{40}-1}{0.0125}\right] \\ &\approx 154{,}468.67 \end{aligned}$$

85,851.20

At age 60, the value of the retirement account is $154,468.67. This amount now earns 6.9% interest compounded monthly for 5 yr. Use the formula for compound amount with $P = 154{,}468.67$, $i = \frac{0.069}{12} = 0.00575$, and $n = 5(12) = 60$ to find the value of this amount after 5 yr.

$$\begin{aligned} A &= P(1+i)^n \\ &= 154{,}468.67(1.00575)^{60} \\ &\approx 217{,}892.80 \end{aligned}$$

The value of the amount she withdraws from the retirement account will be $217,892.80 when she reaches 65.

$A = P(1+i)^n$

$85851.20\left(1 + \frac{.09}{12}\right)^{60}$

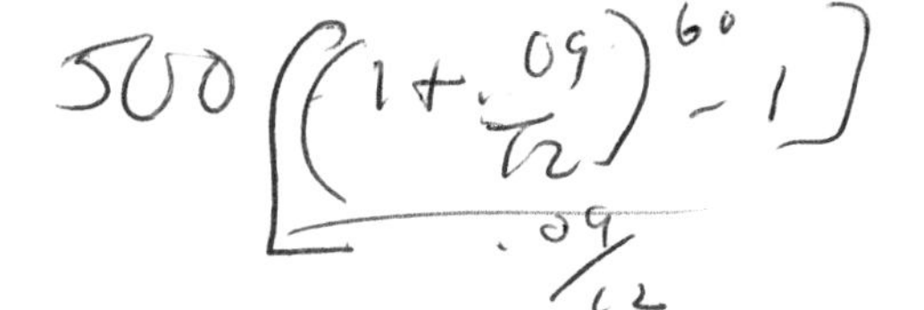

The deposits of \$300 at the end of each month into the mutual fund form another ordinary annuity. Use the formula for the future value of an ordinary annuity with $R = 300$, $i = \frac{0.069}{12} = 0.00575$, and $n = 12(5) = 60$.

$$\begin{aligned} S &= R\left[\frac{(1+i)^n - 1}{i}\right] \\ &= 300\left[\frac{(1.00575)^{60} - 1}{0.00575}\right] \\ &\approx 21{,}422.37 \end{aligned}$$

The value of this annuity after 5 yr is \$21,422.37.

The total amount in the mutual fund account when the woman reaches age 65 will be

$$\$217{,}892.80 + 21{,}422.37 = \$239{,}315.17.$$

55. For the first 8 yr, we have an annuity due with $R = 2435$, $i = \frac{0.06}{2} = 0.03$, and $n = 8(2) = 16$. The amount on deposit after 8 yr is

$$\begin{aligned} S &= R\left[\frac{(1+i)^{n+1} - 1}{i}\right] - R \\ &= 2435\left[\frac{(1+0.03)^{17} - 1}{0.03}\right] - 2435 \\ &\approx 50{,}554.47. \end{aligned}$$

For the remaining 5 yr, this amount, \$50,554.47, earns compound interest at 6% compounded semiannually. To find the final amount on deposit, use the formula for the compound amount with $P = 50{,}554.47$, $i = \frac{0.06}{2} = 0.03$, and $n = 5(2) = 10$.

$$\begin{aligned} A &= P(1+i)^n \\ &= 50{,}554.47(1.03)^{10} \\ &\approx 67{,}940.98 \end{aligned}$$

The final amount on deposit will be about \$67,940.98.

56. For the first 12 yr, we have an annuity due. To find the amount in this account after 12 yr, use the formula for the future value of an annuity due with $R = 10{,}000$, $i = 0.05$, and $n = 12$.

$$\begin{aligned} S &= R\left[\frac{(1+i)^{n+1} - 1}{i}\right] - R \\ &= 10{,}000\left[\frac{(1.05)^{13} - 1}{0.05}\right] - 10{,}000 \\ &\approx 167{,}129.83 \end{aligned}$$

This amount, \$167,129.83, now earns 6% interest compounded semiannually for another 9 yr, but no new deposits are made. Use the formula for compound amount with $P = 167{,}129.83$, $i = \frac{0.06}{2} = 0.03$, and $n = 9(2) = 18$.

$$\begin{aligned} A &= P(1+i)^n \\ &= 167{,}129.83(1.03)^{18} \\ &\approx 284{,}527.35 \end{aligned}$$

The final amount on deposit after 21 yr is \$284,527.35.

57. **(a)** This is a sinking fund with $S = 10{,}000$, $i = \frac{0.08}{4} = 0.02$, and $n = 8(4) = 32$. Let R represent the amount of each payment.

$$\begin{aligned} S &= Rs_{\overline{n}|i} \\ 10{,}000 &= Rs_{\overline{32}|0.02} \\ R &= \frac{10{,}000}{s_{\overline{32}|0.02}} \\ &= \frac{10{,}000(0.02)}{(1+0.02)^{32} - 1} \\ &\approx 226.11 \end{aligned}$$

If the money is deposited at 8% compounded quarterly, Greg's quarterly deposit will need to be about \$226.11.

(b) Here $S = 10{,}000$, $i = \frac{0.06}{4} = 0.015$, and $n = 8(4) = 32$. Let R represent the amount of each payment.

$$\begin{aligned} S &= Rs_{\overline{n}|i} \\ 10{,}000 &= Rs_{\overline{32}|0.015} \\ R &= \frac{10{,}000}{s_{\overline{32}|0.015}} \\ &= \frac{10{,}000(0.015)}{(1+0.015)^{32} - 1} \\ &\approx 245.77 \end{aligned}$$

If the money is deposited at 6% compounded quarterly, Greg's quarterly deposit will need to be about \$245.77.

58. This is a sinking fund with $S = 12{,}000$, $i = \frac{0.06}{2} = 003$, and $n = 4(2) = 8$.

$$\begin{aligned} R &= \frac{S}{s_{\overline{n}|i}} \\ &= \frac{12{,}000}{s_{\overline{8}|0.03}} \\ &= \frac{12{,}000(0.03)}{(1+0.03)^8 - 1} \\ &\approx 1349.48 \end{aligned}$$

Each payment should be $1349.48.

59. $S = 20{,}000$, $i = \frac{0.032}{4} = 0.008$, $n = 6(4) = 24$

Let R represent the amount of each payment.

$$\begin{aligned} S &= Rs_{\overline{n}|i} \\ 20{,}000 &= Rs_{\overline{24}|0.008} \\ R &= \frac{20{,}000}{Rs_{\overline{24}|0.008}} \\ &= \frac{20{,}000(0.008)}{(1+0.008)^{24} - 1} \\ &\approx 759.21 \end{aligned}$$

She must deposit about $759.21 at the end of each quarter.

60. $R = 1000$, $i = \frac{0.06}{4} = 0.015$, and $n = 25(4) = 100$.

$$\begin{aligned} S &= R\left[\frac{(1+i)^n - 1}{i}\right] \\ &= 1000\left[\frac{(1+0.015)^{100} - 1}{0.015}\right] \\ &\approx 228{,}803.04 \end{aligned}$$

There will be about $228,803.04 in the IRA.

The total amount deposited was $1000(100) = $100,000.

Thus, the amount of interest earned was

$$\$228{,}803.04 - 100{,}000 = \$128{,}803.04.$$

61. $R = 1000$, $i = \frac{0.08}{4} = 0.02$, and $n = 25(4) = 100$.

$$\begin{aligned} S &= R\left[\frac{(1+i)^n - 1}{i}\right] \\ &= 1000\left[\frac{(1+0.02)^{100} - 1}{0.02}\right] \\ &\approx 312{,}232.31 \end{aligned}$$

There will be about $312,232.31 in the IRA.

The total amount deposited was $1000(100) = $100,000.

Thus, the amount of interest earned was

$$\$312{,}232.31 - 100{,}000 = \$212{,}232.31.$$

62. $R = 1000$, $i = \frac{0.04}{4} = 0.01$, and $n = 100$.

$$\begin{aligned} S &= R\left[\frac{(1+i)^n - 1}{i}\right] \\ &= 1000\left[\frac{(1+0.01)^{100} - 1}{0.01}\right] \\ &\approx 170{,}481.38 \end{aligned}$$

There will be about $170,481.38 in the IRA.

The total amount deposited was $100,000.

Thus, the amount of interest earned was

$$\$170{,}481.38 - 100{,}000 = \$70{,}481.38.$$

63. $R = 1000$, $i = \frac{0.10}{4} = 0.025$, and $n = 100$.

$$\begin{aligned} S &= R\left[\frac{(1+i)^n - 1}{i}\right] \\ &= 1000\left[\frac{(1+0.025)^{100} - 1}{0.025}\right] \\ &\approx 432{,}548.65 \end{aligned}$$

There will be about $432,548.65 in the IRA.

The total amount deposited was $100,000.

Thus, the amount of interest earned was

$$\$432{,}548.65 - 100{,}000 = \$332{,}548.65.$$

64. Let $x =$ the annual interest rate.

$n = 20(12) = 240$

Graph $y_1 = 147,126$ and

$$y_2 = 300\left[\frac{\left(1+\frac{x}{12}\right)^{240} - 1}{\frac{x}{12}}\right].$$

The x-coordinate of the point of intersection is 0.06499984. Thus, the annual interest rate was about 6.5%.

65. Let $x =$ the annual interest rate.

$n = 30(12) = 360$

Graph $y_1 = 330,000$ and

$$y_2 = 250\left[\frac{\left(1+\frac{x}{12}\right)^{360} - 1}{\frac{x}{12}}\right].$$

The x-coordinate of the point of intersection is 0.0739706. Thus, she would need to earn an annual interest rate of about 7.397%.

66. **(a)** Compare the future amounts for an ordinary annuity with $R = 1{,}350{,}000$ and $i = 0.08$ to compound amounts with $P = 7{,}000{,}000$ and $i = .08$ for different values of n, starting with $n = 1$.

n	$S = R\left[\frac{(1+i)^n - 1}{i}\right]$	$A = P(1+i)^n$
1	$1{,}350{,}000\left[\frac{1.08 - 1}{0.08}\right]$	
	$= \$1{,}350{,}000.00$	\$7,560,000.00
2	$1{,}350{,}000\left[\frac{(1.08)^2 - 1}{0.08}\right]$	
	$= \$2{,}808{,}000.00$	\$8,164,800.00
3	$1{,}350{,}000\left[\frac{(1.08)^3 - 1}{0.08}\right]$	
	$= \$4{,}382{,}640.00$	\$8,817,984.00
4	$1{,}350{,}000\left[\frac{(1.08)^4 - 1}{0.08}\right]$	
	$= \$6{,}083{,}251.20$	\$9,523,422.72
5	$1{,}350{,}000\left[\frac{(1.08)^5 - 1}{0.08}\right]$	
	$= \$7{,}919{,}911.30$	\$10,285,296.54
6	$1{,}350{,}000\left[\frac{(1.08)^6 - 1}{.08}\right]$	
	$= \$9{,}903{,}504.20$	\$11,108,120.26
7	$1{,}350{,}000\left[\frac{(1.08)^7 - 1}{0.08}\right]$	
	$= \$12{,}045{,}784.54$	\$11,996,769.88

After 7 yr, the investors would do better by winning the lottery.

(b) Repeat the calculations from part (a), but change the interest rate to $i = 0.12$.

n	$S = R\left[\frac{(1+i)^n - 1}{i}\right]$	$A = P(1+i)^n$
1	\$1,350,000.00	\$7,840,000.00
2	\$2,862,000.00	\$8,780,800.00
3	\$4,555,440.00	\$9,834,496.00
4	\$6,452,092.80	\$11,014,635.52
5	\$8,576,343.94	\$12,336,391.78
6	\$10,955,505.21	\$13,816,758.80
7	\$13,620,165.83	\$15,474,769.85
8	\$16,604,585.73	\$17,331,742.23
9	\$19,947,136.02	\$19,411,551.30

After 9 yr, the investors would do better by winning the lottery.

67. This exercise should be solved by graphing calculator or computer methods. The answers, which may vary slightly, are as follows.

(a) The buyer's quarterly interest payment will be

$$\begin{aligned} I &= Prt \\ &= \$60{,}000(0.08)\frac{1}{4} \\ &= \$1200. \end{aligned}$$

(b) The buyer's semiannual payments into the sinking fund will be \$3511.58 for each of the first 13 payments and \$3511.59 for the last payment. A table showing the amount in the sinking fund after each deposit is as follows.

Payment Number	Amount of Deposit	Interest Earned	Total
1	\$3511.58	\$0	\$3511.58
2	\$3511.58	\$105.35	\$7128.51
3	\$3511.58	\$213.86	\$10,853.94
4	\$3511.58	\$325.62	\$14,691.14
5	\$3511.58	\$440.73	\$18,643.46
6	\$3511.58	\$559.30	\$22,714.34
7	\$3511.58	\$681.43	\$26,907.35
8	\$3511.58	\$807.22	\$31,226.15
9	\$3511.58	\$936.78	\$35,674.51
10	\$3511.58	\$1070.24	\$40,256.33
11	\$3511.58	\$1207.69	\$44,975.60
12	\$3511.58	\$1349.27	\$49,836.45
13	\$3511.58	\$1495.09	\$54,843.12
14	\$3511.59	\$1645.29	\$60,000.00

68. This exercise should be solved by graphing calculator or computer methods. The answers, which may vary slightly, are as follows.

(a) The amount of each interest payment is $120.

(b) The amount of each payment is $681.83, except the last payment, which is $681.80. A table showing the amount in the sinking fund after each deposit is as follows.

Payment Number	Amount of Deposit	Interest Earned	Total
1	$681.83	$0	$681.83
2	$681.83	$54.55	$1418.21
3	$681.83	$113.46	$2213.49
4	$681.83	$177.08	$3072.40
5	$681.81	$245.79	$4000.00

69. Using the compound amount formula the future value of the down payment, D, is given by

$$A = D(1+i)^n$$

The rest of the payments form an ordinary annuity with future value given by the formula

$$S = R\left[\frac{(1+i)^n - 1}{i}\right]$$

The future value of the loan, including the down payment, is the sum of the future value of the down payment and the future value of the annuity, or

$$S = D(1+i)^n + R\left[\frac{(1+i)^n - 1}{i}\right]$$

5.3 Present Value of an Annuity; Amortization

1. $\dfrac{1-(1+i)^{-n}}{i}$

is represented by $a_{\overline{n}|i}$, and it is choice (c).

2. The symbol $s_{\overline{n}|i}$ represents the expression

$$\frac{(1+i)^n - 1}{i},$$

which is choice (b).

3.
$$a_{\overline{n}|i} = \frac{1-(1+i)^{-n}}{i}$$
$$a_{\overline{15}|0.065} = \frac{1-(1+0.065)^{-15}}{0.065}$$
$$\approx 9.40267$$

4.
$$a_{\overline{n}|i} = \frac{1-(1+i)^{-n}}{i}$$
$$a_{\overline{10}|0.041} = \frac{1-(1+0.041)^{-10}}{0.041}$$
$$\approx 8.07067$$

5.
$$a_{\overline{n}|i} = \frac{1-(1+i)^{-n}}{i}$$
$$a_{\overline{18}|0.055} = \frac{1-(1+0.055)^{-18}}{0.055}$$
$$\approx 11.24607$$

6.
$$a_{\overline{n}|i} = \frac{1-(1+i)^{-n}}{i}$$
$$a_{\overline{32}|0.039} = \frac{1-(1+0.039)^{-32}}{0.039}$$
$$\approx 18.10334$$

9. Payments of $890 each year for 16 years at 6% compounded annually

Use the formula for present value of an annuity with $R = 890$, $i = 0.06$, and $n = 16$.

$$P = R\left[\frac{1-(1+i)^{-n}}{i}\right]$$
$$= 890\left[\frac{1-(1+0.06)^{-16}}{0.06}\right]$$
$$\approx 8994.25$$

The present value is $8994.25.

10. Payments of $1400 each year for 8 years at 6% compounded annually

Use the formula for present value of an annuity with $R = 1400$, $i = 0.06$, and $n = 8$.

$$P = R\left[\frac{1-(1+i)^{-n}}{i}\right]$$
$$= 1400\left[\frac{1-(1+0.06)^{-8}}{0.06}\right]$$
$$\approx 8693.71$$

The present value is $8693.71.

11. Payments of \$10,000 semiannually for 15 years at 5% compounded semiannually

Use the formula for present value of an annuity with $R = 10{,}000$, $i = \frac{0.05}{2} = 0.025$, and $n = 15(2) = 30$.

$$P = R\left[\frac{1-(1+i)^{-n}}{i}\right]$$
$$= 10{,}000\left[\frac{1-(1+0.025)^{-30}}{0.025}\right]$$
$$\approx 209{,}302.93$$

The present value is \$209,302.93.

12. Payments of \$50,000 quarterly for 10 years at 4% compounded quarterly

Use the formula for present value of an annuity with $R = 50{,}000$, $i = \frac{0.04}{4} = 0.01$, and $n = 10(4) = 40$.

$$P = R\left[\frac{1-(1+i)^{-n}}{i}\right]$$
$$= 50,000\left[\frac{1-(1+0.01)^{-40}}{0.01}\right]$$
$$\approx 1{,}641{,}734.31$$

The present value is \$1,641,734.31.

13. Payments of \$15,806 quarterly for 3 years at 6.8 compounded quarterly

Use the formula for present value of an annuity with $R = 15{,}806$, $i = \frac{0.068}{4} = 0.017$, and $n = 3(4) = 12$.

$$P = R\left[\frac{1-(1+i)^{-n}}{i}\right]$$
$$= 15{,}806\left[\frac{1-(1+0.017)^{-12}}{0.017}\right]$$
$$\approx 170{,}275.47$$

The present value is \$170,275.47.

14. Payments of \$18,579 every 6 months (semiannually) for 8 years at 5.4% compounded semiannually

Use the formula for present value of an annuity with $R = 18{,}579$, $i = \frac{0.054}{2} = 0.027$.

$$P = R\left[\frac{1-(1+i)^{-n}}{i}\right]$$
$$= 18{,}579\left[\frac{1-(1+0.027)^{-16}}{0.027}\right]$$
$$\approx 238{,}816.23$$

The present value is \$238,816.23.

15. 4% compounded annually

We want the present value, P, of an annuity with $R = 10{,}000$, $i = 0.04$, and $n = 15$.

$$P = R\left[\frac{1-(1+i)^{-n}}{i}\right]$$
$$= 10{,}000\left[\frac{1-(1.04)^{-15}}{0.04}\right]$$
$$\approx 111{,}183.87$$

The required lump sum is \$111,183.87.

16. We want the present value, P, of an annuity with $R = 10,000$, $i = 0.06$, and $n = 15$.

$$P = R\left[\frac{1-(1+i)^{-n}}{i}\right]$$
$$= 10{,}000\left[\frac{1-(1.06)^{-15}}{0.06}\right]$$
$$\approx 97,122.49$$

The required lump sum is \$97,122.49.

17. $P = 2500$, $i = \frac{0.06}{4} = 0.015$; $n = 6$

To find the payment amount, use the formula for amortization payments.

$$R = \frac{Pi}{1-(1+i)^{-n}}$$
$$R = \frac{2500(0.015)}{1-(1+0.015)^{-6}}$$
$$\approx 438.81$$

Each payment is \$438.81.

To find the total payments, multiply the amount of one payment by $n = 6$.

$$438.81(6) = 2632.86$$

The total payments come out to \$2632.86.

To find the total amount of interest paid, subtract the original loan amount from the total payments.

$$2632.86 - 2500 = 132.86$$

The total amount of interest paid is \$132.86.

18. $P = 41{,}000;\ i = \frac{0.08}{2} = 0.04;\ n = 10$

To find the payment amount, use the formula for amortization payments.

$$R = \frac{Pi}{1-(1+i)^{-n}}$$
$$R = \frac{41{,}000(0.04)}{1-(1+0.04)^{-10}}$$
$$\approx 5054.93$$

Each payment is $5054.93.

To find the total payments, multiply the amount of one payment by $n = 10$.

$$5054.93(10) = 50{,}549.30$$

The total payments come out to $50,549.30.

To find the total amount of interest paid, subtract the original loan amount from the total payments.

$$50{,}549.30 - 41{,}000 = 9549.30$$

The total amount of interest paid is $9549.30.

19. $P = 90{,}000;\ i = 0.06;\ n = 12$

To find the payment amount, use the formula for amortization payments.

$$R = \frac{Pi}{1-(1+i)^{-n}}$$
$$R = \frac{90{,}000(0.06)}{1-(1+0.06)^{-12}}$$
$$\approx 10{,}734.93$$

Each payment is $10,734.93.

To find the total payments, multiply the amount of one payment by $n = 12$.

$$10734.93(12) = 128{,}819.16$$

The total payments come out to $128,819.16.

To find the total amount of interest paid, subtract the original loan amount from the total payments.

$$128{,}819.16 - 90{,}000 = 38{,}819.16$$

The total amount of interest paid is $38,819.16.

20. $P = 140{,}000;\ i = \frac{0.08}{4} = 0.02;\ n = 15$

To find the payment amount, use the formula for amortization payments.

$$R = \frac{Pi}{1-(1+i)^{-n}}$$
$$R = \frac{140{,}000(0.02)}{1-(1+0.02)^{-15}}$$
$$\approx 10{,}895.57$$

Each payment is $10,895.57.

To find the total payments, multiply the amount of one payment by $n = 15$.

$$10{,}895.57(15) = 163{,}433.55$$

The total payments come out to $163,433.55.

To find the total amount of interest paid, subtract the original loan amount from the total payments

$$163{,}433.55 - 140{,}000 = 23{,}433.55$$

The total amount of interest paid is $23,433.55.

21. $P = 7400;\ i = \frac{0.062}{2} = 0.031;\ n = 18$

To find the payment amount, use the formula for amortization payments.

$$R = \frac{Pi}{1-(1+i)^{-n}}$$
$$R = \frac{7400(0.031)}{1-(1+0.031)^{-18}}$$
$$\approx 542.60$$

Each payment is $542.60.

To find the total payments, multiply the amount of one payment by $n = 18$.

$$542.60(18) = 9766.80$$

The total payments come out to $9766.80.

To find the total amount of interest paid, subtract the original loan amount from the total payments

$$9766.80 - 7400 = 2366.80$$

The total amount of interest paid is $2366.80.

22. $P = 5500$; $i = \frac{0.10}{12}$; $n = 24$

To find the payment amount, use the formula for amortization payments.

$$R = \frac{Pi}{1-(1+i)^{-n}}$$

$$R = \frac{5500(\frac{0.10}{12})}{1-(1+\frac{0.10}{12})^{-24}}$$

$$\approx 253.80$$

Each payment is \$253.80.

To find the total payments, multiply the amount of one payment by $n = 24$.

$$253.80(24) = 6091.20$$

The total payments come out to \$6091.20.

To find the total amount of interest paid, subtract the original loan amount from the total payments

$$6091.20 - 5500 = 591.20$$

The total amount of interest paid is \$591.20.

23. Look at the entry for payment number 4 under the heading "Interest for Period." The amount of interest included in the fourth payment is \$7.61.

24. The "Portion to Principal" column of the table indicates that \$87.10 of the 11th payment of \$88.85 is used to reduce the debt.

25. To find the amount of interest paid in the first 4 mo of the loan, add the entries for payments 1, 2, 3, and 4 under the heading "Interest for Period."

$$\$10.00 + 9.21 + 8.42 + 7.61 = \$35.24$$

In the first 4 mo of the loan, \$35.24 of interest is paid.

26. The amount of interest paid in the last 4 months of the loan is

$$\$3.47 + 2.61 + 1.75 + .88 = \$8.71.$$

27. First, find the value of the annuity at the end of 8 yr. Use the formula for future value of an ordinary annuity.

$$S = R\left[\frac{(1+i)^n - 1}{i}\right]$$

$$= 1000\left[\frac{(1+0.06)^8 - 1}{0.06}\right]$$

$$\approx 9897.47$$

The future value of the annuity is \$9897.47.

Now find the present value of \$9897.47 at 5% compounded annually for 8 yr. Use the formula for present value for compound interest.

$$P = \frac{A}{(1+i)^n} = \frac{9897.47}{(1.05)^8} \approx 6699.00$$

The required amount is \$6699.

28. \$4000 deposited every 6 mo for 10 yr at 6% compounded semiannually will be worth

$$4000 \cdot s_{\overline{20}|0.03} \approx \$107{,}481.50.$$

(Note that $i = \frac{0.06}{2} = 0.03$ and $n = 10(2) = 20$.)

For the lump sum investment of x dollars, use $i = \frac{0.08}{4} = 0.02$ and $n = 10(4) = 40$ in the formula $A = P(1+i)^n$. Our unknown amount x will be worth $x(1.02)^{40}$, so

$$x(1.02)^{40} = 107{,}481.50$$
$$x \approx 48{,}677.34.$$

About \$48,677.34 should be invested today.

29. $P = 199{,}000$; $i = \frac{0.0701}{12}$; $n = 25(12) = 300$
To find the payment amount, use the formula for amorization payments.

$$R = \frac{Pi}{1-(1+i)^{-n}}$$

$$R = \frac{199{,}000(\frac{0.0701}{12})}{1-(1+\frac{0.0701}{12})^{-300}}$$

$$\approx 1407.76$$

Each payment is \$1407.76.

To find the total payments, multiply the amount of one payment by $n = 300$.

$$1407.76(300) = 422{,}328$$

The total payments come out to \$422,328.

To find the total amount of interest paid, subtract the original loan amount from the total payments.

$$422{,}328 - 199{,}000 = 223{,}328$$

The total amount of interest paid is \$223,328.

30. $P = 175{,}000$, $i = \frac{0.0624}{12} = 0.0052$, $n = 30(12) = 360$

To find the payment amount, use the formula for amorization payments.

$$R = \frac{Pi}{1-(1+i)^{-n}}$$

$$R = \frac{175{,}000(0.0052)}{1-(1+0.0052)^{-360}}$$

$$\approx 1076.37$$

Each payment is \$1076.37.

To find the total payments, multiply the amount of one payment by $n = 360$.

$$1076.37(360) = 387{,}493.20$$

The total payments come out to \$387,493.20.

To find the total amount of interest paid, subtract the original loan amount from the total payments.

$$387{,}493.20 - 175{,}000 = 212{,}493.20$$

The total amount of interest paid is \$212,493.20.

31. $P = 253{,}000$, $i = \frac{0.0645}{12}$, $n = 30(12) = 360$

To find the payment amount, use the formula for amorization payments.

$$R = \frac{Pi}{1-(1+i)^{-n}}$$

$$R = \frac{253{,}000(\frac{0.0645}{12})}{1-(1+\frac{0.0645}{12})^{-360}}$$

$$\approx 1590.82$$

Each payment is \$1590.82.

To find the total payments, multiply the amount of one payment by $n = 360$.

$$1590.82(360) = 572{,}695.20$$

The total payments come out to \$572,695.20.

To find the total amount of interest paid, subtract the original loan amount from the total payments.

$$572{,}695.20 - 253{,}000 = 319{,}695.20$$

The total amount of interest paid is \$319,695.20.

32. $P = 310{,}000$, $i = \frac{0.0596}{12}$, $n = 25(12) = 300$

To find the payment amount, use the formula for amorization payments.

$$R = \frac{Pi}{1-(1+i)^{-n}}$$

$$R = \frac{310{,}000(\frac{0.0596}{12})}{1-(1+\frac{0.0596}{12})^{-300}}$$

$$\approx 1989.76$$

Each payment is \$1989.76.

To find the total payments, multiply the amount of one payment by $n = 300$.

$$1989.76(300) = 596{,}928$$

The total payments come out to \$596,928.

To find the total amount of interest paid, subtract the original loan amount from the total payments.

$$596{,}928 - 310{,}000 = 286{,}928$$

The total amount of interest paid is \$286,928.

33. From Example 3, $P = 220{,}000$ and $i = \frac{0.06}{12} = 0.005$. For a 15-year loan, use $n = 15(12) = 180$.

$$R = \frac{Pi}{1-(1+i)^{-n}}$$

$$= \frac{220{,}000(0.005)}{1-(1+0.005)^{-180}}$$

$$\approx 1856.49$$

The monthly payments would be \$1856.49. The family makes 180 payments of \$1856.49 each, for a total of \$334,168.20. Since the amount of the loan was \$220,000, the total interest paid is

$$334{,}168.20 - 220{,}000 = 114{,}168.20.$$

The total amount of interest paid is \$114,168.20.

The payments for the 15-year loan are

$$1856.49 - \$1319.01 = \$537.48$$

more than those for the 30-year loan in Example 3. However, the total interest paid is

$$254{,}843.60 - \$114{,}168.20 = \$140{,}675.40$$

less than for the 30-year loan in Example 3.

34. **(a)** $R = 30,\ i = 0.0125,\ n = 12(3) = 36$

Use the formula for the present value of an annuity

$$P = 30\left[\frac{1-(1+0.0125)^{-36}}{0.0125}\right] \approx 865.42$$

Since there was a down payment of \$600, the cost of the stereo system will be

$$\$865.42 + 600 = \$1465.42.$$

(b) Since a payment of \$30 was paid each month for 36 months, the total of the payments will be 36(\$30) = \$1080. From part (a), the cost of the stereo system will be \$865.42. Therefore, the total amount of interest paid will be

$$\$1080 - 865.42 = \$214.58.$$

35. **(a)** $P = 14{,}000,\ i = \frac{0.07}{12},\ n = 4(12) = 48$

$$\begin{aligned} R &= \frac{Pi}{1-(1+i)^{-n}} \\ &= \frac{14{,}000(\frac{0.07}{12})}{1-(1+\frac{0.07}{12})^{-48}} \\ &\approx 335.25 \end{aligned}$$

The amount of each payment is \$335.25.

(b) 48 payments of \$335.25 are made, and 48(\$335.25) = \$16,092. The total amount of interest Le will pay is \$16,092 – \$14,000 = \$2092.

36. **(a)** $P = 8430,\ i = \frac{0.27}{12},\ n = 3(12) = 36$

$$\begin{aligned} R &= \frac{Pi}{1-(1+i)^{-n}} \\ &= \frac{8430(\frac{0.27}{12})}{1-(1+\frac{0.27}{12})^{-36}} \\ &\approx 344.16 \end{aligned}$$

The amount of each payment is \$344.16.

(b) 36 payments of \$344.16 are made, and 36(\$344.16) = \$12,389.76. The total amount of interest Tom will have paid is \$12,389.76 – \$8430 = \$3959.76.

37. **(a)** $P = 20{,}000,\ i = \frac{0.019}{12},\ n = 36$

$$\begin{aligned} R &= \frac{Pi}{1-(1+i)^{-n}} \\ &= \frac{20{,}000(\frac{0.019}{12})}{1-(1+\frac{0.019}{12})^{-36}} \\ &\approx 571.98 \end{aligned}$$

The amount of each payment is \$571.98. Since 36 payments are made, the total amount paid will be 36(\$571.98) = \$20,591.28.

(b) $P = 15{,}000,\ i = \frac{0.0693}{12},\ n = 4(12) = 48$

$$\begin{aligned} R &= \frac{Pi}{1-(1+i)^{-n}} \\ &= \frac{20{,}000(\frac{0.0693}{12})}{1-(1+\frac{0.0693}{12})^{-48}} \\ &\approx 358.71 \end{aligned}$$

The amount of each payment will be \$358.71. Since 48 payments are made, the total amount paid will be 48(\$358.71) = \$17,218.08.

38. **(a)** With 0% financing, there is no interest. The payment is the loan amount divided by the number of payments.

$$R = \frac{28{,}000}{36} \approx 777.78$$

The payment amount is \$777.78.

(b) For the first option, $P = 26{,}000,\ i = \frac{0.0693}{12}$ $n = 4(12) = 48$.

$$\begin{aligned} R &= \frac{Pi}{1-(1+i)^{-n}} \\ &= \frac{26{,}000(\frac{0.0693}{12})}{1-(1+\frac{0.0693}{12})^{-48}} \\ &\approx 621.76 \end{aligned}$$

The amount of each payment will be \$621.76. Since 48 payments are made, the total amount paid will be 48(\$621.76) = \$29,844.48.

For the second option, $P = 26{,}000,\ i = \frac{0.0635}{12},$ $n = 5(12) = 60$.

$$\begin{aligned} R &= \frac{Pi}{1-(1+i)^{-n}} \\ &= \frac{26{,}000(\frac{0.0635}{12})}{1-(1+\frac{0.0635}{12})^{-60}} \\ &\approx 506.90 \end{aligned}$$

The amount of each payment will be $506.90. Since 60 payments are made, the total amount paid will be 60($506.90) = $30,414.

39. For parts (a) and (b), if $1 million is divided into 20 equal payments, each payment is $50,000.

(a) $i = 0.05,\ n = 20$

$$\begin{aligned} P &= R\left[\frac{1-(1+i)^{-n}}{i}\right] \\ &= 50{,}000\left[\frac{1-(1+0.05)^{-20}}{0.05}\right] \\ &\approx 623{,}110.52 \end{aligned}$$

The present value is $623,110.52.

(b) $i = 0.09,\ n = 20$

$$\begin{aligned} P &= R\left[\frac{1-(1+i)^{-n}}{i}\right] \\ &= 50{,}000\left[\frac{1-(1+0.09)^{-20}}{0.09}\right] \\ &\approx 456{,}427.28 \end{aligned}$$

The present value is $456,427.28.

For parts (c) and (d), if $1 million is divided into 25 equal payments, each payment is $40,000.

(c) $i = 0.05,\ n = 25$

$$\begin{aligned} P &= R\left[\frac{1-(1+i)^{-n}}{i}\right] \\ &= 40{,}000\left[\frac{1-(1+0.05)^{-25}}{0.05}\right] \\ &\approx 563{,}757.78 \end{aligned}$$

The present value is $563,757.78.

(d) $i = 0.09,\ n = 25$

$$\begin{aligned} P &= R\left[\frac{1-(1+i)^{-n}}{i}\right] \\ &= 40{,}000\left[\frac{1-(1+0.09)^{-25}}{0.09}\right] \\ &\approx 392{,}903.18 \end{aligned}$$

The present value is $392,903.18.

40. $P = 35{,}000$ at 7.43% compounded monthly for 10 yr. Thus, $i = \frac{0.0743}{12} = 0.006191\overline{6}$ and $n = 10(12) = 120$.

$$\begin{aligned} R &= \frac{Pi}{1-(1+i)^{-n}} \\ &= \frac{35{,}000(0.006191\overline{6})}{1-(1+0.006191\overline{6})^{-120}} \\ &\approx 414.18 \end{aligned}$$

The monthly payment is $414.18. The total interest is given by

$$120(414.18) - 35,000 = 14,701.60.$$

The total interest is $14, 701.60.

41. $P = 35{,}000$ at 7.43% compounded monthly for 20 yr. Thus, $i = \frac{0.0743}{12} = 0.006191\overline{6}$ and $n = 20(12) = 240$.

$$\begin{aligned} R &= \frac{Pi}{1-(1+i)^{-n}} \\ &= \frac{35{,}000(0.006191\overline{6})}{1-(1+0.006191\overline{6})^{-240}} \\ &\approx 280.46 \end{aligned}$$

The monthly payment is $280.46. The total interest is given by

$$240(280.46) - 35,000 = 32{,}310.40.$$

The total interest is $32, 310.40.

42. The amount of each annual payment is

$$R = \frac{4000}{a_{\overline{4}|0.08}} \approx \$1207.68.$$

On the first payment, the firm owes interest of

$$I = Prt = 4000(0.08)(1) = \$320.$$

Therefore, from the first payment, $320 goes to interest and the balance,

$$\$1207.68 - 320 = \$887.68,$$

goes to principal. The principal at the end of one year is

$$\$4000 - 887.68 = \$3112.32.$$

The interest for the second year is

$$I = Prt = 3112.32(0.08)(1) = \$248.99.$$

Of the second payment, \$248.99 goes to interest and

$$\$1207.68 - 248.99 = \$958.69$$

goes to principal. Continuing in this way, we obtain the following amortization schedule.

Payment Number	Amount of Payment	Interest for Period	Portion to Principal	Principal at End of Period
0	———	———	———	\$4000.00
1	\$1207.68	\$320.00	\$887.68	\$3112.32
2	\$1207.68	\$248.99	\$958.69	\$2153.63
3	\$1207.68	\$172.29	\$1035.39	\$1118.24
4	\$1207.70	\$89.46	\$1118.24	\$0.00

43. $P = 110{,}000$, $i = \frac{0.08}{2} = 0.04, n = 9$

$$R = \frac{110{,}000}{a_{\overline{9}|0.04}} \approx \$14{,}794.23$$

is the amount of each payment.

Of the first payment, the company owes interest of

$$I = Prt = 110{,}000(0.08)\left(\tfrac{1}{2}\right) = \$4400.$$

Therefore, from the first payment, \$4400 goes to interest, and the balance.

$$\$14,794.23 - 4400 = \$10,394.23$$

,goes to principal. The principal at the end of this period is

$$\$110{,}000 - 10{,}394.23 = \$99{,}605.77.$$

The interest for the second payment is

$$I = Prt = 99{,}605.77(0.08)\left(\tfrac{1}{2}\right) \approx \$3984.23$$

Of the second payment, \$3984.23 goes to interest and

$$\$14{,}794.23 - 3984.23 = \$10{,}810.00$$

goes to principal. Continue in this fashion to complete the amorization schedule for the first four payments.

Payment Number	Amount of Payment	Interest for Period	Portion to Principal	Principal at End of Period
0	———	———	———	\$110,000.00
1	\$14,794.23	\$4400.00	\$10,394.23	\$99,605.77
2	\$14,794.23	\$3984.23	\$10,810.00	\$88,795.77
3	\$14,794.23	\$3551.83	\$11,242.40	\$77,553.37
4	\$14,794.23	\$3102.13	\$11,692.10	\$65,861.27

44. $P = 1048(8) - 1200 = 7184, i = \frac{0.06}{12} = 0.005, n = 4(12) = 48$

$$R = \frac{7184}{a_{\overline{48}|0.005}} \approx \$168.72$$

is the amount of each payment.

Of the first payment, the company owes interest of

$$I = Prt = 7184(0.005)(1) = \$35.92.$$

Therefore, from the first payment, \$35.92 goes to interest and the balance,

$$\$168.72 - 35.92 = \$132.80,$$

goes to principal. The principal at the end of this period is

$$\$7184 - 132.80 = \$7051.20.$$

The interest for the second payment is

$$I = Prt = 7051.20(0.005)(1) \approx \$35.26.$$

Of the scond payment, \$35.26 goes to interest and

$$\$168.72 - 35.26 = \$133.46$$

goes to principal. Continue in this fashion to complete the amortization schedule for the first four payments.

Payment Number	Amount of Payment	Interest for Period	Portion to Principal	Principal at End of Period
0	———	———	———	\$7184.00
1	\$168.72	\$35.92	\$132.80	\$7051.20
2	\$168.72	\$35.26	\$133.46	\$6917.74
3	\$168.72	\$34.59	\$134.13	\$6783.61
4	\$168.72	\$33.92	\$134.80	\$6648.81

45. \$150,000 is the future value of an annuity over 79 yr compounded quarterly. So, there are 79(4) = 316 payment periods.

(a) The interest per quarter is $\frac{5.25\%}{4} = 1.3125\%$. Thus, $S = 150,000, n = 316, i = 0.013125$, and we must find the quarterly payment R in the formula

$$S = R\left[\frac{(1+i)^n - 1}{i}\right]$$

$$150{,}000 = R\left[\frac{(1.013125)^{316} - 1}{0.013125}\right]$$

$$R \approx 32.4923796$$

She would have to put \$32.49 into her savings at the end of every three months.

(b) For a 2% interest rate, the interest per quarter is $\frac{2\%}{4} = 0.5\%$. Thus, $S = 150{,}000$, $n = 316, i = 0.005$, and we must find the quarterly payment R in the formula

$$S = R\left[\frac{(1+i)^n - 1}{i}\right]$$
$$150{,}000 = R\left[\frac{(1.005)^{316} - 1}{0.005}\right]$$
$$R \approx 195.5222794$$

She would have to put $195.52 into her savings at the end of every three months.

For a 7% interest rate, the interest per quarter is $\frac{7\%}{4} = 1.75\%$. Thus, $S = 150{,}000$, $n = 316, i = 0.0175$, and we must find the quarterly payment R in the formula

$$S = R\left[\frac{(1+i)^n - 1}{i}\right]$$
$$150{,}000 = R\left[\frac{(1.0175)^{316} - 1}{0.0175}\right]$$
$$R \approx 10.9663932$$

She would have to put $10.97 into her savings at the end of every three months.

46. The total amount of the loan is

$$14{,}000 + 7200 - 1200 = 20{,}000.$$

We have $20,000 at 12% compounded semiannually for 5 yr.

(a) $i = \frac{0.08}{2} = 0.04$, $n = 5(2) = 10$

$$R = \frac{Pi}{1-(1+i)^{-n}}$$
$$= \frac{20{,}000(0.04)}{1-(1+0.04)^{-10}}$$
$$\approx 2465.82$$

The amount of each payment is $2465.82.

(b) Graph

$$y_1 = 2465.82\left[\frac{1-1.04^{-(10-x)}}{0.04}\right] \text{ and } y_2 = 5000.$$

The x-coordinate of the point of intersection is 7.8432905, or a little less than 8. Therefore, the loan is reduced below $5000 after 8 payments, at which time there will be 2 payments left.

47. Throughout this exercise, $i = \frac{0.065}{12}$ and $P =$ the total amount financed, which is

$$\$285{,}000 - 60{,}000 = \$225{,}000.$$

(a) $n = 15(12) = 180$

$$R = \frac{Pi}{1-(1+i)^{-n}}$$
$$= \frac{225{,}000(\frac{0.065}{12})}{1-(1+\frac{0.065}{12})^{-180}}$$
$$\approx 1959.99$$

The monthly payment is $1959.99.

$$\text{Total payments} = 180(\$1959.99) = \$352{,}798.20$$

$$\text{Total interest} = \$352{,}798.20 - 225{,}000 = \$127{,}798.20$$

(b) $n = 20(12) = 240$

$$R = \frac{Pi}{1-(1+i)^{-n}}$$
$$= \frac{225{,}000(\frac{0.065}{12})}{1-(1+\frac{0.065}{12})^{-240}}$$
$$\approx 1677.54$$

The monthly payment is $1677.54.

$$\text{Total payments} = 240(\$1677.54) = \$402{,}609.60$$

$$\text{Total interest} = \$402{,}609.60 - 225{,}000 = \$177{,}609.60$$

(c) $n = 25(12) = 300$

$$R = \frac{Pi}{1-(1+i)^{-n}}$$
$$= \frac{225{,}000(\frac{0.065}{12})}{1-(1+\frac{0.065}{12})^{-300}}$$
$$\approx 1519.22$$

The monthly payment is $1519.22.

$$\text{Total payments} = 300(\$1519.22) = \$455{,}766$$

$$\text{Total interest} = \$455{,}766 - 225{,}000 = \$230{,}766$$

(d) Graph

$$y_1 = 1677.54\left[\frac{1-\left(1+\frac{0.065}{12}\right)^{-(240-x)}}{\frac{0.065}{12}}\right] \text{ and}$$

$$y_2 = \frac{285{,}000 - 60{,}000}{2}.$$

The x-coordinate of the point of intersection is 156.44167, which rounds up to 157. Half the loan will be paid after 157 payments.

48. Throughout this exercise, $n = 30(12) = 360$ and P = the total amount financed, which is

$$\$225{,}000 - 50{,}000 = \$175{,}000.$$

(a) $i = \frac{0.06}{12} = 0.005$

$$R = \frac{Pi}{1-(1+i)^{-n}} = \frac{175{,}000(0.005)}{1-(1+0.005)^{-360}} \approx 1049.21$$

The monthly payment is \$1049.21.

$$\text{Total payments} = 360(\$1049.21) = \$377{,}715.60$$

$$\text{Total interest} = \$377{,}715.60 - 175{,}000 = \$202{,}715.60$$

(b) $i = \frac{0.065}{12}$

$$R = \frac{Pi}{1-(1+i)^{-n}} = \frac{175{,}000\left(\frac{0.065}{12}\right)}{1-\left(1+\frac{0.065}{12}\right)^{-360}} \approx 1106.12$$

The monthly payment is \$1106.12.

$$\text{Total payments} = 360(\$1106.12) = \$398{,}203.20$$

$$\text{Total interest} = \$398{,}203.20 - 175{,}000 = \$223{,}203.20$$

(c) $i = \frac{0.07}{12}$

$$R = \frac{Pi}{1-(1+i)^{-n}} = \frac{175{,}000\left(\frac{0.07}{12}\right)}{1-\left(1+\frac{0.07}{12}\right)^{-360}} \approx 1164.28$$

The monthly payment is \$1164.28.

$$\text{Total payments} = 360(\$1164.28) = \$419{,}140.80$$

$$\text{Total interest} = \$419{,}140.80 - 175{,}000 = \$244{,}140.80$$

(d) Graph

$$y_1 = 1164.28\left[\frac{1-\left(1+\frac{0.07}{12}\right)^{-(360-x)}}{\frac{0.07}{12}}\right] \text{ and}$$

$$y_2 = \frac{225{,}000 - 50{,}000}{2}.$$

The x-coordinate of the point of intersection is 260.80441, which rounds up to 261. Half the loan will be paid off after 261 payments.

49. $P = 150{,}000$, $i = \frac{0.082}{12}$, and $n = 30(12) = 360$.

$$R = \frac{Pi}{1-(1+i)^{-n}} = \frac{150{,}000\left(\frac{0.082}{12}\right)}{1-\left(1+\frac{0.082}{12}\right)^{-360}} \approx 1121.63$$

The monthly payment is \$1121.63.

$$\text{Total payments} = 360(\$1121.63) = \$403{,}786.80$$

$$\text{Total interest} = \$403{,}786.80 - 150{,}000 = \$253{,}786.80$$

(b) 15 years of payments means $15(12) = 180$ payments.

$$y_{15} = 1121.63\left[\frac{1-\left(1+\frac{0.082}{12}\right)^{-(360-180)}}{\frac{0.082}{12}}\right] \approx 115{,}962.66$$

The unpaid balance after 15 years is approximately \$115,962.66.

The total of the remaining 180 payments is

$$180(\$1121.63) = \$201{,}893.40.$$

(c) The unpaid balance from part (b) is the new loan amount. Now $P = 115{,}962.66$, $i = \frac{0.065}{12}$, and again $n = 30(12) = 360$.

$$\begin{aligned} R &= \frac{Pi}{1-(1+i)^{-n}} \\ &= \frac{115{,}962.66(\frac{0.065}{12})}{1-(1+\frac{0.065}{12})^{-360}} \\ &\approx 732.96 \end{aligned}$$

The new monthly payment would be \$732.96.

Total payments $= 360(\$732.96) + \$3400 = \$267{,}265.60$

(d) Again the unpaid balance from part (b) is the new loan amount. Again $P = 115{,}962.66$ and $i = \frac{0.065}{12}$, and this time $n = 15(12) = 180$.

$$\begin{aligned} R &= \frac{Pi}{1-(1+i)^{-n}} \\ &= \frac{115{,}962.66(\frac{0.065}{12})}{1-(1+\frac{0.065}{12})^{-180}} \\ &\approx 1010.16 \end{aligned}$$

The new monthly payment would be \$1010.16.

Total payments $= 180(\$1010.16) + \$4500 = \$186{,}328.80$

50. This is an amortization problem with $P = 25,000$. R represents the amount of each annual withdrawal.

(a) $i = 0.06,\ n = 8$

$$\begin{aligned} R &= \frac{Pi}{1-(1+i)^{-n}} \\ &= \frac{25{,}000(0.06)}{1-(1+0.06)^{-8}} \\ &\approx 4025.90 \end{aligned}$$

She will be able to withdraw about \$4025.90/yr for the 8 yr.

(b) $i = 0.06,\ n = 12$

$$\begin{aligned} R &= \frac{Pi}{1-(1+i)^{-n}} \\ &= \frac{25{,}000(0.06)}{1-(1+0.06)^{-12}} \\ &\approx 2981.93 \end{aligned}$$

She will be able to withdraw about \$2981.93/yr for the 12 yr.

51. This is just like a sinking fund in reverse.

(a) $P = 150,000,\ i = \frac{0.06}{2} = 0.03,\ n = 2(5) = 10$

$$\begin{aligned} R &= \frac{Pi}{1-(1+i)^{-n}} \\ &= \frac{150,000(.03)}{1-(1+0.03)^{-10}} \\ &\approx 17,584.58 \end{aligned}$$

The amount of each withdrawal is \$17,584.58.

(b) $P = 150,000,\ i = \frac{0.06}{2} = 0.03,\ n = 2(6) = 12$

$$\begin{aligned} R &= \frac{Pi}{1-(1+i)^{-n}} \\ &= \frac{150,000(0.03)}{1-(1+0.03)^{-12}} \\ &\approx 15,069.31 \end{aligned}$$

If the money must last 6 yr, the amount of each withdrawal is $15,069.31.

52. This exercise should be solved by graphing calculator or computer methods. The amortization schedule, which may vary slightly, is as follows.

Payment Number	Amount of Payment	Interest for Period	Portion to Principal	Principal at End of Period
0	—	—	—	$37,948.00
1	$5278.74	$2466.62	$2812.12	$35,135.88
2	$5278.74	$2283.83	$2994.91	$32,140.97
3	$5278.74	$2089.16	$3189.58	$28,951.40
4	$5278.74	$1881.84	$3396.90	$25,554.50
5	$5278.74	$1661.04	$3617.70	$21,936.80
6	$5278.74	$1425.89	$3852.85	$18,083.95
7	$5278.74	$1175.46	$4103.28	$13,980.67
8	$5278.74	$908.74	$4370.00	$9610.67
9	$5278.74	$624.69	$4654.05	$4956.62
10	$5278.80	$322.18	$4956.62	$0.00

53. This exercise should be solved by graphing calculator or computer methods. The amortization schedule, which may vary slightly, is as follows.

Payment Number	Amount of Payment	Interest for Period	Portion to Principal	Principal at End of Period
0	—	—	—	$4836.00
1	$585.16	$175.31	$409.85	$4426.15
2	$585.16	$160.45	$424.71	$4001.43
3	$585.16	$145.05	$440.11	$3561.32
4	$585.16	$129.10	$456.06	$3105.26
5	$585.16	$112.57	$472.59	$2632.67
6	$585.16	$95.43	$489.73	$2142.94
7	$585.16	$77.68	$507.48	$1635.46
8	$585.16	$59.29	$525.87	$1109.59
9	$585.16	$40.22	$544.94	$564.65
10	$585.12	$20.47	$564.65	$0.00

55. **(a)** Here $R = 1000$ and $i = 0.04$ and we have

$$P = \frac{R}{i} = \frac{100}{0.04} = 25{,}000$$

Therefore, the present value of the perpetuity is \$25,000.

(b) Here $R = 600$ and $i = \frac{0.06}{4} = 0.015$ and we have

$$P = \frac{R}{i} = \frac{600}{0.015} = 40{,}000$$

Therefore, the present value of the perpetuity is \$40,000.

Chapter 5 Review Exercises

1. $I = Prt$

$$= 15,903(0.06)\left(\frac{8}{12}\right)$$
$$= 636.12$$

The simple interest is \$636.12.

2. $I = Prt$

$$= 4902(0.054)\left(\frac{11}{12}\right)$$
$$\approx 242.65$$

The simple interest is \$242.65.

3. $I = Prt$

$$= 42,368(0.0522)\left(\frac{7}{12}\right)$$
$$\approx 1290.11$$

The simple interest is \$1290.11.

4. $I = Prt$

$$= 3478(0.068)\left(\frac{88}{360}\right)$$
$$\approx 57.81$$

The simple interest is \$57.81.

5. For a given amount of money at a given interest rate for a given time period greater than 1, compound interest produces more interest than simple interest.

6. \$2800 at 7% compounded annually for 10 yr

Use the formula for compound amount with $P = 2800$, $i = 0.07$, and $n = 10(1) = 10$.

$$\begin{aligned} A &= P(1+i)^n \\ &= 2800(1.07)^{10} \\ &\approx 5508.02 \end{aligned}$$

The compound amount is \$5508.02.

7. \$19,456.11 at 8% compounded semiannually for 7 yr

Use the formula for compound amount with $P = 19,456.11$, $i = \frac{0.08}{2} = 0.04$, and $n = 7(2) = 14$.

$$\begin{aligned} A &= P(1+i)^n \\ &= 19,456.11(1.04)^{14} \\ &\approx 33{,}691.69 \end{aligned}$$

The compound amount is \$33,691.69.

8. \$312.45 at 5.6% compounded semiannually for 16 yr

Use the formula for compound amount with $P = 312.45$, $i = \frac{0.056}{2} = 0.028$, and $n = 16(2) = 32$.

$$\begin{aligned} A &= P(1+i)^n \\ &= 312.45(1.028)^{32} \\ &\approx 756.07 \end{aligned}$$

The compound amount is \$756.07.

9. \$57,809.34 at 6% compounded quarterly for 5 yr

Use the formula for compound amount with $P = 57,809.34$, $i = \frac{0.06}{4} = 0.015$, and $n = 5(4) = 20$.

$$\begin{aligned} A &= P(1+i)^n \\ &= 57,809.34(1.015)^{20} \\ &\approx 77{,}860.80 \end{aligned}$$

The compound amount is \$77,860.80.

10. \$3954 at 8% compounded annually for 10 yr

Here $P = 3954$, $i = 0.08$, and $n = 10(1) = 10$. First, find the compound amount.

$$\begin{aligned} A &= P(1+i)^n \\ &= 3954(1.08)^{10} \\ &\approx 8536.39 \end{aligned}$$

The compound amount is \$8536.39. To find the amount of interest earned, subtract the initial deposit from the compound amount.

$$\text{Amount of interest} = A - P$$
$$= \$8536.39 - 3954$$
$$= \$4582.39$$

11. \$12,699.36 at 5% compounded semiannually for 7 yr

Here $P = 12,699.36$, $i = \frac{0.05}{2} = 0.025$, and $n = 7(2) = 14$. First find the compound amount.

$$A = P(1+i)^n$$
$$= 12,699.36(1.025)^{14}$$
$$\approx 17,943.86$$

The compound amount is \$17,943.86.

To find the amount of interest earned, subtract the initial deposit from the compound amount. The interest earned is

$$\$\,17,943.86 - 12,699.36 = \$5244.50.$$

12. \$12,903.45 at 6.4% compounded quarterly for 29 quarters

Here $P = 12,903.45$, $i = \frac{0.064}{4} = 0.016$, and $n = 29$.

$$A = P(1+i)^n$$
$$= 12,903.45\,(1.016)^{29}$$
$$\approx 20,446.71$$

The compound amount is \$20,446.71.

$$\text{Amount of interest} = A - P$$
$$= \$20,446.71 - 12,903.45$$
$$= \$7543.26$$

13. \$34,677.23 at 4.8% compounded monthly for 32 mo

Here $P = 34,677.23$, $i = \frac{0.048}{12} = 0.004$, and $n = 32$.

$$A = P(1+i)^n$$
$$= 34,677.23(1.004)^{32}$$
$$\approx 39,402.45$$

The compound amount is \$39,402.45

The interest earned is

$$\$39,402.45 - 34,677.23 = \$4725.22.$$

15. \$42,000 in 7 yr, 6% compounded monthly

Use the formula for present value for compound interest with $A = 42,000$, $i = \frac{0.06}{12} = 0.005$, and $n = 7(12) = 84$.

$$P = \frac{A}{(1+i)^n} = \frac{42,000}{(1.005)^{84}} \approx 27,624.86$$

The present value is \$27,624.86.

16. \$17,650 in 4 yr, 4% compounded quarterly

Use the formula for present value for compound interest with $A = 17,650$, $i = \frac{0.04}{4} = 0.01$, and $n = 4(4) = 16$.

$$P = \frac{A}{(1+i)^n}$$
$$= \frac{17,650}{(1.01)^{16}}$$
$$\approx 15,052.30$$

The present value is \$15,052.30.

17. \$1347.89 in 3.5 yr, 6.77% compounded semiannually

Use the formula for present value for compound interest with $A = 1347.89$, $i = \frac{0.0677}{2} = 0.03385$, and $n = 3.5(2) = 7$.

$$P = \frac{A}{(1+i)^n} = \frac{1347.89}{(1.03385)^7} \approx 1067.71$$

The present value is \$1067.71.

18. \$2388.90 in 44 mo, 5.93% compounded monthly

$A = 2388.90$, $i = \frac{5.93\%}{12} = \frac{0.0593}{12}$, $n = 44$

$$P = \frac{A}{(1+i)^n}$$
$$= \frac{2388.90}{\left(1 + \frac{0.0593}{12}\right)^{44}}$$
$$\approx 1923.09$$

The present value is \$1923.09.

19. $a = 2$; $r = 3$

The first five terms are

$$2,\ 2(3),\ 2(3)^2,\ 2(3)^3,\ \text{and } 2(3)^4,$$

or

$$2, 6, 18, 54, \text{ and } 162.$$

20. $a = 4,\ r = \frac{1}{2}$

The first four terms are

$$4, 4\left(\frac{1}{2}\right), 4\left(\frac{1}{2}\right)^2, 4\left(\frac{1}{2}\right)^3$$

or

$$4, 2, 1, \frac{1}{2}.$$

21. $a = -3;\ r = 2$

To find the sixth term, use the formula $a_n = ar^{n-1}$ with $a = -3,\ r = 2$, and $n = 6$.

$$a_6 = ar^{6-1} = -3(2)^5 = -3(32) = -96$$

22. $a = -2,\ r = -2$

For the fifth term, $n = 5$, so

$$a_5 = ar^{n-1} = -2(-2)^4 = -2(16) = -32.$$

The fifth term is -32.

23. $a = -3;\ r = 3$

To find the sum of the first 4 terms of this geometric sequence, use the formula $S_n = \frac{a(r^n-1)}{r-1}$ with $n = 4$.

$$S_4 = \frac{-3(3^4 - 1)}{3 - 1} = \frac{-3(80)}{2} = \frac{-240}{2} = -120$$

24. $a = 8000,\ r = -\frac{1}{2},\ n = 5$

$$S_n = \frac{a(r^n - 1)}{r - 1}$$

$$S_5 = \frac{8000\left[\left(-\frac{1}{2}\right)^5 - 1\right]}{-\frac{1}{2} - 1}$$

$$= \frac{8000\left(-\frac{33}{32}\right)}{-\frac{3}{2}} = \frac{-8250}{-\frac{3}{2}}$$

$$= (-8250)\left(-\frac{2}{3}\right) = 5500$$

25. $$s_{\overline{n}|i} = \frac{(1+i)^n - 1}{i}$$

$$s_{\overline{30}|0.02} = \frac{(1.02)^{30} - 1}{0.02} \approx 40.56808$$

26. $$s_{\overline{n}|i} = \frac{(1+i)^n - 1}{i}$$

$$s_{\overline{20}|0.06} = \frac{(1.06)^{20} - 1}{0.06} \approx 36.78559$$

28. $R = 500,\ i = \frac{0.06}{2} = 0.03,\ n = 10(2) = 20$

This is an ordinary annuity.

$$S = Rs_{\overline{n}|i}$$

$$S = 500s_{\overline{20}|0.03}$$

$$= 500\left[\frac{(1+0.03)^{20} - 1}{0.03}\right]$$

$$\approx 13{,}435.19$$

The future value is \$13,435.19.

The total amount deposited is \$500(20) = \$10,000. Thus, the amount of interest is

$$\$13{,}435.19 - 10{,}000 = \$3435.19.$$

29. $R = 1288, i = 0.04, n = 14$

This is an ordinary annuity.

$$S = Rs_{\overline{n}|i}$$

$$S = 1288s_{\overline{14}|0.04}$$

$$= 1288\left[\frac{(1+0.04)^{14} - 1}{0.04}\right]$$

$$\approx 23{,}559.98$$

The future value is \$23,559.98.

The total amount deposited is \$1288(14) = \$18,032. Thus, the amount of interest is

$$\$23{,}559.98 - 18{,}032 = \$5527.98.$$

30. $R = 4000,\ i = \frac{0.05}{4} = 0.0125,\ n = 7(4) = 28$

This is an ordinary annuity.

$$S = R\left[\frac{(1+i)^n - 1}{i}\right]$$

$$S = 4000\left[\frac{(1.0125)^{28} - 1}{0.0125}\right]$$

$$\approx 133{,}117.54$$

The future value is \$133,117.54.

The total amount deposited is \$4000(28) = \$112,000. Thus, the amount of interest is

$$\$133{,}117.54 - 112{,}000 = \$21{,}117.54.$$

31. $R = 233, i = \frac{0.048}{12} = 0.004, n = 4(12) = 48$

This is an ordinary annuity.

$$S = R\left[\frac{(1+i)^n - 1}{i}\right]$$

$$S = 233\left[\frac{(1.004)^{48} - 1}{0.004}\right]$$

$$\approx 12{,}302.78$$

The future value is \$12,302.78.

The total amount deposited is \$233(48) = \$11,184. Thus, the amount of interest is

$$\$12{,}302.78 - 11{,}184 = \$1118.78.$$

32. $R = 672,\ i = \frac{0.044}{4} = 0.011,\ n = 7(4) = 28$

This is an annuity due, so we use the formula for future value of an ordinary annuity, but include one additional time period and subtract the amount of one payment.

$$S = R\left[\frac{(1+i)^{n+1} - 1}{i}\right] - R$$

$$= 672\left[\frac{(1.011)^{29} - 1}{0.011}\right] - 672$$

$$\approx 22{,}136.73$$

The future value is \$22,136.73.

The total amount deposited is \$672(28) = \$18,816. Thus, the amount of interest is

$$\$22{,}136.73 - 18{,}816 = \$3320.73.$$

33. $R = 11{,}900,\ i = \frac{0.06}{12} = 0.005, n = 13$

This is an annuity due, so we use the formula for future value of an ordinary annuity, but include one additional time period and subtract the amount of one payment.

$$S = R\left[\frac{(1+i)^{n+1} - 1}{i}\right] - R$$

$$= 11{,}900\left[\frac{(1.005)^{14} - 1}{0.005}\right] - 11{,}900$$

$$\approx 160{,}224.29$$

The future value is \$160,224.29.

The total amount deposited is \$11,900(13) = \$154,700. Thus, the amount of interest is

$$\$160{,}224.29 - 154{,}700 = \$5524.29.$$

35. \$6500; money earns 5% compounded annually; 6 annual payments

$S = 6500, i = 0.05, n = 6$

Let R be the amount of each payment.

$$S = Rs_{\overline{n}|i}$$

$$R = \frac{6500}{s_{\overline{6}|0.05}}$$

$$= \frac{6500(0.05)}{(1.05)^6 - 1}$$

$$\approx 955.61$$

The amount of each payment is \$955.61.

36. 57,000; money earns 4% compounded semiannually for $8\frac{1}{2}$ years

$S = 57{,}000, i = \frac{0.04}{2} = 0.02,\ n = \left(8\frac{1}{2}\right)(2) = 17$

Let R be the amount of each payment.

$$S = Rs_{\overline{n}|i}$$

$$R = \frac{57{,}000}{s_{\overline{17}|0.02}}$$

$$= \frac{57{,}000(0.02)}{(1.02)^{17} - 1}$$

$$\approx 2848.28$$

The amount of each payment is \$2848.28.

37. \$233,188; money earns 5.2% compounded quarterly for $7\frac{3}{4}$

$S = 233{,}188, i = \frac{0.052}{4} = 0.013, n = \left(7\frac{3}{4}\right)(4) = 31$

Let R be the amount of each payment.

$$S = Rs_{\overline{n}|i}$$

$$R = \frac{233{,}188}{s_{\overline{31}|0.013}}$$

$$= \frac{233{,}188(0.013)}{(1.013)^{31} - 1}$$

$$\approx 6156.14$$

The amount of each payment is \$6156.14.

38. $1,056,788; money earns 7.2% compounded monthly for $4\frac{1}{2}$ years

$S = 1{,}056{,}788,\ i = \frac{0.072}{12} = 0.006,$

$n = \left(4\frac{1}{2}\right)(12) = 54$

Let R represent the amount of each payment.

$$\begin{aligned} S &= Rs_{\overline{n}|i} \\ R &= \frac{1{,}056{,}788}{s_{\overline{54}|0.006}} \\ &= \frac{1{,}056{,}788(0.006)}{(1.006)^{54} - 1} \\ &\approx 16{,}628.83 \end{aligned}$$

The amount of each payment is $16,628.83.

39. Deposits of $850 annually for 4 years at 6% compounded annually

Use the formula for the present value of an annuity with $R = 850, i = 0.06$, and $n = 4$.

$$\begin{aligned} P &= R\left[\frac{1-(1+i)^{-n}}{i}\right] \\ &= 850\left[\frac{1-(1+0.06)^{-4}}{0.06}\right] \\ &\approx 2945.34 \end{aligned}$$

The present value is $2945.34.

40. Deposits of $1500 quarterly for 7 years at 5% compounded annually

Use the formula for the present value of an annuity with $R = 1500,\ i = \frac{0.05}{4} = 0.0125,\ n = 7(4) = 28.$

$$\begin{aligned} P &= R\left[\frac{1-(1+i)^{-n}}{i}\right] \\ &= 1500\left[\frac{1-(1+0.0125)^{-28}}{0.0125}\right] \\ &\approx 35{,}253.78 \end{aligned}$$

The present value is $35,253.78.

41. Deposits of $4210 semiannually for 8 years at 4.2% compounded annually

Use the formula for the present value of an annuity with $R = 4210,\ i = \frac{0.042}{2} = 0.021,\ n = 8(2) = 16.$

$$\begin{aligned} P &= R\left[\frac{1-(1+i)^{-n}}{i}\right] \\ &= 4210\left[\frac{1-(1.021)^{-16}}{0.021}\right] \\ &\approx 56{,}711.93 \end{aligned}$$

The present value is $56,711.93.

42. Payments of $877.34 monthly for 17 months at an annuity at 6.4% compounded monthly

Use the formula for the present value of an annuity with $R = 877.34,\ i = \frac{0.064}{12} = 0.005\overline{3},\ n = 17.$

$$\begin{aligned} P &= R\left[\frac{1-(1+i)^{-n}}{i}\right] \\ P &= 877.34\left[\frac{1-(1+0.005\overline{3})^{-17}}{0.05\overline{3}}\right] \\ &\approx 14{,}222.42 \end{aligned}$$

The present value is $14,222.42.

43. Two types of loans that are commonly amortized are home loans and auto loans.

44. $P = 80{,}000,\ i = 0.05,\ n = 9$

$$\begin{aligned} R &= \frac{Pi}{1-(1+i)^{-n}} \\ &= \frac{80{,}000(0.05)}{1-(1.05)^{-9}} \\ &\approx 11{,}255.21 \end{aligned}$$

The amount of each payment is $11,255.21.

The total amount paid is $11,255.21(9) = $101,296.89. Thus, the total interest paid is

$$\$101{,}296.89 - 80{,}000 = \$21{,}296.89.$$

45. $P = 3200, i = \frac{0.08}{4} = 0.02, n = 12$

$$\begin{aligned} R &= \frac{Pi}{1-(1+i)^{-n}} \\ &= \frac{3200(0.02)}{1-(1.02)^{-12}} \\ &\approx 302.59 \end{aligned}$$

The amount of each payment is \$302.59.

The total amount paid is \$302.59(12) = \$3631.08. Thus, the total interest paid is

$$\$3631.08 - 3200 = \$431.08.$$

46. $P = 32{,}000,\ i = \frac{0.064}{4} = 0.016,\ n = 17$

$$\begin{aligned} R &= \frac{Pi}{1-(1+i)^{-n}} \\ &= \frac{32{,}000(0.016)}{1-(1.016)^{-17}} \\ &\approx 2164.87 \end{aligned}$$

The amount of each payment is \$2164.87.

The total amount paid is \$2164.87(17) = \$36,802.79. Thus, the total interest paid is

$$\$36{,}802.79 - 32{,}000 = \$4802.79.$$

47. $P = 51{,}607,\ i = \frac{0.08}{12} = 0.00\overline{6}, n = 32$

$$\begin{aligned} R &= \frac{Pi}{1-(1+i)^{-n}} \\ &= \frac{51{,}607(0.00\overline{6})}{1-(1.00\overline{6})^{-32}} \\ &\approx 1796.20 \end{aligned}$$

The amount of each payment is \$1796.20.

The total amount paid is \$1796.20(32) = \$57,478.40. Thus, the total interest paid is

$$\$57{,}478.40 - 51{,}607 = \$5871.40.$$

48. $P = 256{,}890,\ i = \frac{0.0596}{12} = 0.0049\overline{6},\ n = 25(12) = 300.$

$$\begin{aligned} R &= \frac{Pi}{1-(1+i)^{-n}} \\ &= \frac{256{,}890(0.0049\overline{6})}{1-(1.0049\overline{6})^{-300}} \\ &\approx 1648.87 \end{aligned}$$

The amount of each payment is \$1648.87.

The total amount paid is \$1648.87(300) = \$494,661. Thus, the total interest paid is

$$\$494{,}661 - 256{,}890 = \$237{,}771.$$

49. $P = 177{,}110,\ i = \frac{0.0668}{12} = 0.0055\overline{6}, n = 30(12) = 360$

$$\begin{aligned} R &= \frac{Pi}{1-(1+i)^{-n}} \\ &= \frac{177{,}110(0.0055\overline{6})}{1-(1.0055\overline{6})^{-360}} \\ &\approx 1140.50 \end{aligned}$$

The amount of each payment is \$1140.50.

The total amount paid is \$1140.50(360) = \$410,580. Thus, the total interest paid is

$$\$410{,}580 - 177{,}110 = \$233{,}470.$$

50. Look in the column titled "Interest for Period." \$896.06 of the fifth payment of \$1022.64 is interest.

51. The answer can be found in the table under payment number 12 in the column labeled "Portion to Principal." The amount of principal repayment included in the fifth payment is \$132.99.

52. In the first 3 months of the loan, the total amount of interest paid is

$$\$899.58 + 898.71 + 897.83 = \$2696.12.$$

53. The last entry in the column "Principal at End of Period," \$125,464.39, shows the debt remaining at the end of the first year (after 12 payments). Since the original debt (loan principal) was \$127,000, the amount by which the debt has been reduced at the end of the first year is

$$\$127{,}000 - 125{,}464.39 = \$1535.61.$$

54. Here $P = 5800$, $r = 5.3\% = 0.053$, and $t = \frac{10}{12}$.

$$\begin{aligned} I &= Prt \\ &= 5800(0.053)\left(\frac{10}{12}\right) \\ &\approx 256.17 \end{aligned}$$

The interest he will pay is \$256.17. The total amount he will owe is

$$\$5800 + 256.17 = \$6056.17.$$

55. Here $P = 9820$, $r = 6.7\% = 0.067$, and $t = \frac{7}{12}$.

$$\begin{aligned} I &= Prt \\ &= 9820(0.067)\left(\frac{7}{12}\right) \\ &\approx 383.80 \end{aligned}$$

The interest he will pay is \$383.80. The total amount he will owe in 7 mo is

$$\$9820 + 383.80 = \$10{,}203.80.$$

56. Here $P = 28{,}000$, $r = 6.5\% = 0.065$, and $I = 1365$.

Use the formula for simple interest.

$$\begin{aligned} I &= Prt \\ t &= \frac{I}{Pr} \\ &= \frac{1365}{28{,}000(0.065)} \\ &= 0.75 \end{aligned}$$

The loan is for 0.75 yr; convert this to months.

$$0.75 \text{ yr}\left(\frac{12 \text{ mo}}{1 \text{ yr}}\right) = 9 \text{ mo}$$

The loan is for 9 mo.

57. $P = 84{,}720$, $t = \frac{7}{12}$, $I = 4055.46$

Substitute these values into the formula for simple interest to find the value of r.

$$I = Prt$$

$$4055.46 = 84,720r\left(\frac{7}{12}\right)$$

$$\begin{aligned} 4055.46 &= 49,420r \\ 0.0821 &\approx r \end{aligned}$$

The interest rate is 8.21%.

58. $A = 7500$, $i = \frac{0.05}{2} = 0.025$, $n = 3(2) = 6$

Let P represent the lump sum.

$$\begin{aligned} A &= P(1+i)^n \\ P &= \frac{A}{(1+i)^n} \\ &= \frac{7500}{(1.025)^6} \\ &\approx 6467.23 \end{aligned}$$

She should deposit about \$6467.23 today.

59. In both cases use the formula for compound amount with $P = 500$ and $i = \frac{0.05}{4} = 0.0125$. For the investment at age 23 use $n = 42(4) = 168$.

$$\begin{aligned} A &= P(1+i)^n \\ &= 500(1+0.0125)^{168} \\ &\approx 4030.28 \end{aligned}$$

For the investment at age 40 use $n = 25(4) = 100$.

$$\begin{aligned} A &= P(1+i)^n \\ &= 500(1+0.0125)^{100} \\ &\approx 1731.70 \end{aligned}$$

The increased amount of money Tom will have if he invests now is

$$\$4030.28 - 1731.70 = \$2298.58.$$

60. Suppose you receive \$6000/yr at age 55 until age 75. Then $R = 6000$, $i = 0.08$, and $n = 20$.

$$S = 6000\left[\frac{(1+0.08)^{20}-1}{0.08}\right] \approx 274{,}571.79$$

You would receive a total of \$274,571.79.

Suppose you receive \$12,000/yr at age 65 until age 75. Then $R = 12,000$, $i = 0.08$, and $n = 10$.

$$S = 12,000\left[\frac{(1+0.08)^{10}-1}{0.08}\right] \approx 173{,}838.75$$

You would receive a total of \$173,838.75.

Receiving half the pension at 55 would produce the larger amount.

61. $R = 5000$, $i = \frac{0.10}{2} = 0.05$, $n = 7\frac{1}{2}(2) = 15$

This is an ordinary annuity.

$$S = R\left[\frac{(1+i)^n - 1}{i}\right]$$

$$\begin{aligned} S &= 5000\left[\frac{(1+0.05)^{15}-1}{0.05}\right] \\ &\approx 107{,}892.82 \end{aligned}$$

The future value is \$107,892.82. The amount of interest earned is

$$\$107{,}892.82 - 15(5000) = \$32{,}892.82.$$

62. Use the formula for amortization payments with $P = 28{,}000$, $i = \frac{0.08}{4} = 0.02$, and $n = 6\frac{1}{2}(4) = 26$.

$$R = \frac{Pi}{1-(1+i)^{-n}} = \frac{28{,}000(0.02)}{1-(1.02)^{-26}} \approx 1391.58$$

The amount of each payment is \$1391.58.

63. Use the formula for amortization payments with $P = 48{,}000$, $i = 0.065$, and $n = 7$.

$$\begin{aligned} R &= \frac{Pi}{1-(1+i)^{-n}} \\ &= \frac{48{,}000(0.065)}{1-(1.065)^{-7}} \\ &\approx 8751.91 \end{aligned}$$

The owner should deposit \$8751.91 at the end of each year.

The total amount deposited is \$8751.91(7) = \$61,263.37. Thus, the total interest paid is

$$\$61{,}263.37 - 48{,}000 = \$13{,}263.37.$$

64. Use the formula for compound amount with $P = 3250$, $i = 0.042$, and $n = 4$.

$$A = P(1+i)^n = 3250(1.042)^4 \approx 3831.37$$

Mark must pay back \$3831.37.

65. To find the effective rates use the formula $r_e = \left(1 + \frac{r}{m}\right)^m - 1$.

First Community Bank:

$$\begin{aligned} r_e &= \left(1 + \frac{0.0515}{4}\right)^4 - 1 \\ &\approx 0.052503 \\ &\approx 5.250\% \end{aligned}$$

UFB Direct.com:

$$\begin{aligned} r_e &= \left(1 + \frac{0.0513}{12}\right)^{12} - 1 \\ &\approx 0.052524 \\ &\approx 5.252\% \end{aligned}$$

UFB Direct.com has the higher effective rate, even though it has a lower stated rate.

66. Use the formula for amortization payments with $P = 315,700$, $i = \frac{0.075}{12} = 0.00625$, and $n = 300$.

$$\begin{aligned} R &= \frac{Pi}{1-(1+i)^{-n}} \\ &= \frac{315{,}700(0.00625)}{1-(1.00625)^{-300}} \\ &\approx 2333.00 \end{aligned}$$

Each monthly payment will be about \$2333.00. The total amount of interest will be

$$\$2333.00(300) - 315{,}700 = \$384{,}200.$$

67. **(a)** There is no interest with 0% financing, so the monthly payment is $\$20{,}000 \div 36 \approx \$555.56$.

The total payments will be \$20,000.

(b) 1.9% financing for 48 months:

$P = 20{,}000$, $i = \frac{0.019}{12} = 0.00158\overline{3}$, $n = 48$

$$\begin{aligned} P &= R\left[\frac{1-(1+i)^{-n}}{i}\right] \\ 20{,}000 &= R\left[\frac{1-(1+0.00158\overline{3})^{-48}}{0.00158\overline{3}}\right] \\ R &\approx 433.03 \end{aligned}$$

The monthly payments are \$433.03.

The total amount of the payments is \$433.03(48) = \$20,785.44.

2.9% financing for 60 months:

$P = 20{,}000$, $i = \frac{0.029}{12} = 0.00241\overline{6}, n = 60$

$$\begin{aligned} P &= R\left[\frac{1-(1+i)^{-n}}{i}\right] \\ 20{,}000 &= R\left[\frac{1-(1+0.00241\overline{6})^{-60}}{0.00241\overline{6},}\right] \\ R &\approx 358.49 \end{aligned}$$

The monthly payments are \$358.49.

The total amount of the payments is \$358.49(60) = \$21,509.40.

(c) $P = 18{,}000$, $i = \frac{0.0635}{12} = 0.005291\overline{6}, n = 48$

$$P = R\left[\frac{1-(1+i)^{-n}}{i}\right]$$

$$18{,}000 = R\left[\frac{1-(1+0.005291\overline{6})^{-48}}{0.005291\overline{6}}\right]$$

$$R \approx 425.62$$

The monthly payments are \$425.62.

The total amount of the payments is \$425.62(48) = \$20,429.76.

68. **(a)** There is no interest with 0% financing, so the monthly payment is $\$16{,}000 \div 36 \approx \$444.44$.

(b) $P = 15{,}000, i = \frac{0.0694}{12} = 0.005783\overline{3}, n = 48$

$$P = R\left[\frac{1-(1+i)^{-n}}{i}\right]$$

$$15{,}000 = R\left[\frac{1-(1+0.005783\overline{3})^{-48}}{0.005783\overline{3}}\right]$$

$$R \approx 358.78$$

The monthly payments are \$358.78.

(d) The monthly payment for $S = 15{,}000$ and $n = 48$ at interest rate i is

$$15{,}000 = R\left[\frac{1-(1+i)^{-48}}{i}\right]$$

$$R = \frac{15{,}000i}{1-(1+i)^{-48}}.$$

The total amount paid is

$$48R = 48\left[\frac{15{,}000i}{1-(1+i)^{-48}}\right].$$

To find i such that this total is 16,000, solve the equation

$$48\left[\frac{15{,}000i}{1-(1+i)^{-48}}\right] = 16{,}000.$$

Use a graphing calculator and enter each side of the equation as a function. Graph the two functions and locate the point of intersection.

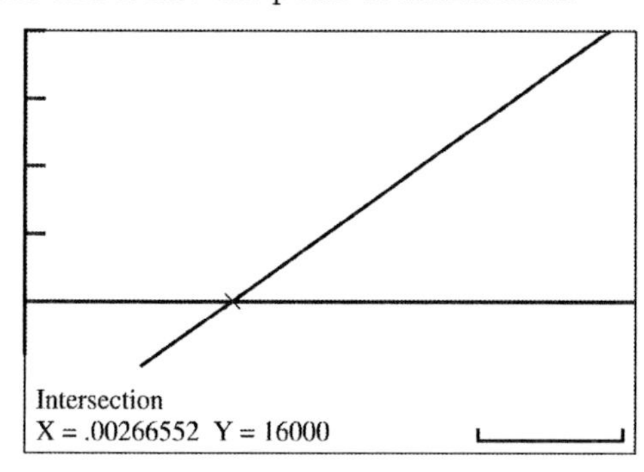

The graphs intersect at $x = i \approx 0.00266552$. This is the monthly interest rate so the annual rate is $0.00266552(12) \approx 0.0320$, or 3.2%. The bank's interest rate that would make the total amount of payments for the two options equal is 3.2%.

69. Amount of loan = \$191,000 − 40,000
= \$151,000

(a) Use the formula for amortization payments with $P = 151{,}000$, $i = \frac{0.065}{12} = 0.00541\overline{6}$, and $n = 30(12) = 360$.

$$R = \frac{Pi}{1-(1+i)^{-n}}$$

$$= \frac{151{,}000(0.00541\overline{6})}{1-(1.00541\overline{6})^{-360}}$$

$$\approx 954.42$$

The monthly payment for this mortgage is \$954.42.

(b) To find the amount of the first payment that goes to interest, use $I = Prt$ with $P = 151{,}000$, $i = 0.00541\overline{6}$, and $t = 1$.

$$I = 151{,}000(0.065)\left(\tfrac{1}{12}\right) = 817.92$$

Of the first payment, \$817.92 is interest.

(c) Using method 1, since 180 of 360 payments were made, there are 180 remaining payments. The present value is

$$954.42\left[\frac{1-(1.00541\overline{6})^{-180}}{0.00541\overline{6}}\right] \approx 109{,}563.99,$$

so the remaining balance is \$109,563.99.

Using method 2, since 180 payments were already made, we have

$$954.42\left[\frac{1-(1.00541\overline{6})^{-180}}{0.00541\overline{6}}\right] \approx 109{,}563.99.$$

She still owes

$$\$151{,}000 - 109{,}563.99 = \$41{,}436.01.$$

Furthermore, she owes the interest on this amount for 180 mo, for a total remaining balance of

$$41{,}436.01(1.00541\overline{6})^{180} = 109{,}565.13.$$

(d) Closing costs $= 3700 + 0.025(238{,}000)$
$= 3700 + 5950$
$= 9650$

Closing costs are $9650.

(e) Amount of money received
= Selling price – Closing costs
– Current mortgage balance

Using method 1, the amount received is

$238,000 – 9650 – 109,563.99 = $118,786.01.

Using method 2, the amount received is

$238,000 – 9650 – 109,565.13 = $118,784.87.

70. The death benefit grows to

$$10{,}000(1.05)^7 \approx 14{,}071.$$

This 14,071 is the present value of an annuity due with $P = 14{,}071$, $i = \frac{0.03}{12} = 0.0025$, and $n = 120$. Let X represent the amount of each monthly payment.

$$P = R \cdot a_{\overline{n+1}|i} - R$$
$$14{,}071 = X \cdot a_{\overline{121}|0.0025} - X$$
$$14{,}071 = (a_{\overline{121}|0.0025} - 1)X$$
$$14{,}071 \approx (104.301 - 1)X$$
$$14{,}071 \approx 103.301X$$
$$136 \approx X$$

Each payment is about $136, which corresponds to choice (d).

71. (a) Use the formula for effective rate with $r_e = 0.10$ and $m = 12$.

$$r_e = \left(1 + \frac{r}{m}\right)^m - 1$$
$$0.10 = \left(1 + \frac{r}{12}\right)^{12} - 1$$
$$1.10 = \left(1 + \frac{r}{12}\right)^{12}$$
$$(1.10)^{1/12} = 1 + \frac{r}{12}$$
$$1.007974 \approx 1 + \frac{r}{12}$$
$$0.007974 \approx \frac{r}{12}$$
$$0.095688 \approx r$$

The annual interest rate is 9.569%.

(b) Use the formula for amortization payments with $P = 140{,}000$, $i = \frac{0.06625}{12}$, and $n = 30(12) = 360$.

$$R = \frac{Pi}{1 - (1+i)^{-n}}$$
$$= \frac{140{,}000\left(\frac{0.06625}{12}\right)}{1 - \left(1 + \frac{0.06625}{12}\right)^{-360}}$$
$$\approx 896.44$$

Her monthly payment is $896.44.

(c) This investment is an annuity with $R = 1200 - 896.44 = 303.56$, $i = \frac{0.09569}{12}$, and $n = 30(12) = 360$. The future value is

$$S = R\left[\frac{(1+i)^n - 1}{i}\right]$$
$$= 303.56\left[\frac{\left(1 + \frac{0.09569}{12}\right)^{360} - 1}{\frac{0.09569}{12}}\right]$$
$$\approx 626{,}200.88$$

In 30 yr she will have $626,200.88 in the fund.

(d) Use the formula for amortization payments with $P = 140{,}000$, $i = \frac{0.0625}{12}$, and $n = 15(12) = 180$.

$$R = \frac{Pi}{1 - (1+i)^{-n}}$$
$$= \frac{140{,}000\left(\frac{0.0625}{12}\right)}{1 - \left(1 + \frac{0.0625}{12}\right)^{-180}}$$
$$\approx 1200.39$$

His monthly payment is $1200.39.

(e) This investment is an annuity with $R = 1200$, $i = \frac{0.09569}{12}$, and $n = 15(12) = 180$. The future value is

$$S = R\left[\frac{(1+i)^n - 1}{i}\right]$$
$$= 1200\left[\frac{\left(1 + \frac{0.09569}{12}\right)^{180} - 1}{\frac{0.09569}{12}}\right]$$
$$\approx 478{,}134.14$$

In 30 yr he will have $478,134.14.

(f) Sue is ahead by

$626,200.88 – 478,134.14 = $148,066.74.

Extended Application: Time, Money, and Polynomials

1.

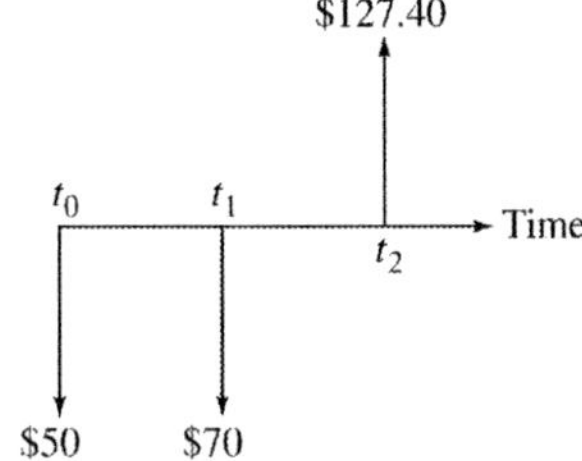

The polynomial equation is

$$50(1+i)^2 + 70(1+i) - 127.40 = 0.$$

Let $x = 1+i$. The equation becomes

$$50x^2 + 70x - 127.40 = 0.$$

Use the quadratic formula to solve the equation for x.

$$x = \frac{-b \pm \sqrt{b^2 - 4ac}}{2a}$$

$$x = \frac{-70 \pm \sqrt{70^2 - 4(50)(-127.40)}}{2(50)}$$

Reject $x = \frac{-70-\sqrt{30,380}}{100}$ because it is negative. Thus,

$$x = \frac{-70 + \sqrt{30,380}}{100} \approx 1.04298.$$

Since $x = 1+i$,

$$\begin{aligned} 1 + i &= 1.04298 \\ i &\approx 0.043. \end{aligned}$$

Thus, the YTM is 4.3%.

2. (a)

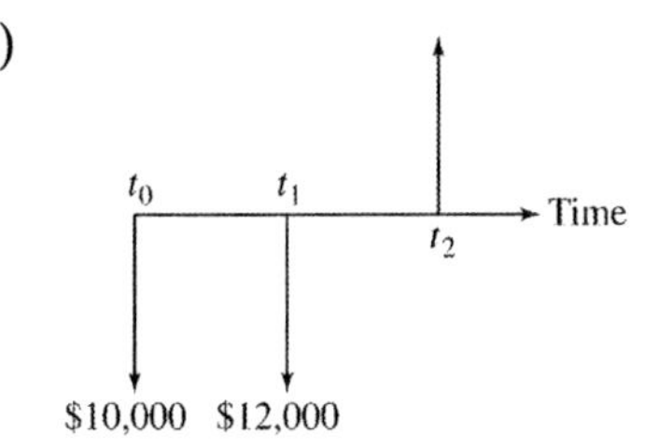

(b) $A = 1.05(10,000) + 0.045(1.05)(10,000)$
$\quad + 1.045(12,000)$
$\quad = 23,512.5$

At the end of the second year, $23,512.50 was in the account.

(c) The polynomial equation is

$10,000(1+i)^2 + 12,000(1+i) = 23,512.50 = 0.$

Let $x = 1+i$. The equation becomes

$$10,000x^2 + 12,000x - 23,512.50 = 0.$$

Use the quadratic formula to solve for x.

$$x = \frac{-12,000 \pm \sqrt{12,000^2 - 4(10,000)(-23, 512.50)}}{2(10,000)}$$

Reject

$$x = \frac{-12,000 - \sqrt{12,000^2 - 4(10,000)(-23,512.50)}}{20,000}$$

because it is negative. Thus,

$$x = \frac{-12,000 + \sqrt{12,000^2 - 4(10,000)(-23,512.50)}}{20,000}$$

$$\approx 1.04659.$$

Since $x = 1+i$,

$$\begin{aligned} 1 + i &= 1.04659 \\ i &= 0.04659. \end{aligned}$$

Thus, the YTM is 4.7%. As might be expected, the YTM is between 4.5% and 5%.

3. (a)

$5864.17

t_0 t_1 t_2 t_3 t_4 Time

$1025 $2200 $1850 $0

(b) The polynomial equation is

$$1025(1+i)^4 + 2200(1+i)^3 + 1850(1+i)^2 - 5864.17 = 0.$$

Let $x = 1+i$. The equation becomes

$$1025x^4 + 2200x^3 + 1850x^2 - 5864.17 = 0.$$

Let $f(x) = 1025x^4 + 2200x^3 + 1850x^2 - 5864.17$. Since $0 < i < 1$, then $1 < x < 2$ and

$$\begin{aligned} f(1) &= -789.17; \\ f(1.1) &= 803.2325; \\ f(1.05) &= -31.8761; \\ f(1.052) &= 0.00172. \end{aligned}$$

The YTM is approximately 5.2%.

4. (a)

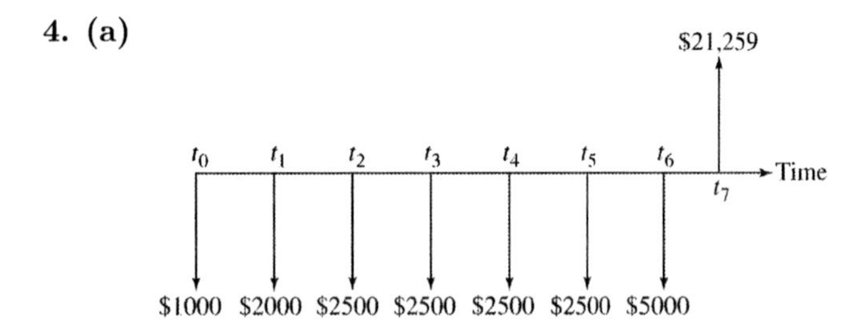

(b) The polynomial equation is

$$1000(1+i)^7 + 2000(1+i)^6 + 2500(1+i)^5 + 2500(1+i)^4 + 2500(1+i)^3 + 2500(1+i)^2 + 5000(1+i) - 21,259 = 0.$$

(c) Let $x = 1 + i$ and

$$f(x) = 1000(x^7 + 2x^6 + 2.5x^5 + 2.5x^4 + 2.5x^3 + 2.5x^2 + 5x - 21.259).$$

Then

$$f(1.0507) = 7.1216;$$
$$f(1.0505) = -6.9040.$$

Since $f(1.0507)$ is positive and $f(1.0505)$ is negative, the value of x that makes $f(x)$ zero is between 1.0507 and 1.0505.

$$1.0505 < 1 + i < 1.0507$$
$$0.0505 < i < 0.0507$$
$$5.05\% < i < 5.07\%$$

(d) Graph $y_1 = f(x)$. The graph intersects the x-axis at $x = 1.0505985$. Therefore, $i = 0.0505985$ or 5.06%.

5. (a)

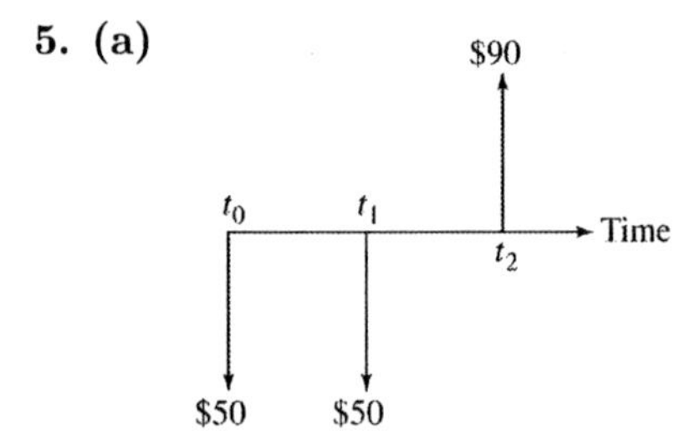

The polynomial equation is

$$50(1+i)^2 + 50(1+i) - 90 = 0.$$

Let $x = 1 + i$. The equation becomes

$$50x^2 + 50x - 90 = 0$$
$$5x^2 + 5x - 9 = 0.$$

Solve for x using the quadratic formula.

$$x = \frac{-5 \pm \sqrt{5^2 - 4(5)(-9)}}{2(5)}$$

$$x = \frac{-5 \pm \sqrt{205}}{10}$$

$$x = \frac{-5 + \sqrt{205}}{10} \approx 0.93178 \quad \text{or} \quad x = \frac{-5 - \sqrt{205}}{10} \approx -1.93178$$

Then

$$1 + i = 0.93178 \quad \text{or} \quad 1 + i = -1.93178$$
$$i = -0.06822 \qquad\qquad i = -2.93178$$
$$i \approx -6.8\% \quad \text{or} \quad i \approx -293.2\%.$$

(b) For $i = -6.8\%$ use the formula for compound amount for each $50 investment. For the first investment $P = 50$ and $n = 2$.

$$A = P(1+i)^n$$
$$= 50(1 - 0.068)^2$$
$$= 43.4312$$

For the second investment $P = 50$ and $n = 1$.

$$A = P(1+i)^n$$
$$= 50(1 - 0.068)^1$$
$$= 46.6$$

Each value of A seems to be a reasonable future value for the investment considered. Also, note that

$$43.4312 + 46.6 = 90.0312.$$

For $i = -293.2\%$ use the formula for compound amount for each $50 investment. For the first investment $P = 50$ and $n = 2$.

$$A = P(1+i)^n$$
$$= 50(1 - 2.932)^2$$
$$= 186.6312$$

For the second investment $P = 50$ and $n = 1$.

$$A = P(1+i)^n$$
$$= 50(1 - 2.932)^1$$
$$= -96.6$$

Although $186.6312 - 96.6 = 90.0312$, neither value seems like a reasonable future value for the investment considered. Only $i = -6.8\%$ seems a reasonable interpretation in the context to the problem.

Chapter 6

LOGIC

6.1 Statements and Quantifiers

1. Because the declarative sentence "Montevideo is the capital of Uruguay" has the property of being true or false, it is considered a statement. It is not compound.

2. Because the declarative sentence "John Marshall was not the first Chief Justice of the United States" has the property of being true or false, it is considered a statement.

3. "Don't cry for me Argentina" is not a declarative sentence and does not have the property of being true or false. Hence, it is not considered a statement.

4. "Do unto others as you would have them do unto you" is a command, not a declarative sentence and therefore, it is not a statement.

5. "$2+2=5$ and $3+3=7$" is a declarative sentence that is true and, therefore, is considered a statement. It is compound.

6. "$x<7$ or $x>14$" is a declarative sentence that is false and therefore, is considered a statement. It is compound.

7. "Where's the beef?" is a question, not a declarative sentence, and, therefore, is not considered a statement.

8. "Is that all there is?" is a question, not a declarative sentence, and therefore, is not considered a statement.

9. "I am not a crook" is a compound statement because it contains the logical connective "not."

10. "China has a population of over 1 billion, and so does India" is a compound statement because it contains the logical connective "and."

11. "She enjoys the comedy team of Penn and Teller" is not compound because only one assertion is being made.

12. "The New Hampshire motto is 'Live free or die.' is not compound because only one assertion is being made.

13. "If ever I would leave you, it wouldn't be in summer" is a compound statement because it consists of two simple statements combined by the connective "if ... then."

14. "If it's past 8:00, then we are late" is a compound statement because it consists of two simple statements combined by the connective "if ... then."

15. The negation of "My favorite flavor is chocolate" is "My favorite flavor is not chocolate."

16. The negation of "This is not the time to complain" is "This is the time to complain."

17. A negation for "$y>12$" (without using a slash sign) would be "$y \leq 12$."

18. A negation for "$x<-6$" (without using a slash sign) would be "$x \geq -6$."

19. A negation for "$q \geq 5$" would be "$q<5$."

20. A negation for "$r \leq 19$" would be "$r>19$."

23. A translation of "$\sim b$" is "I'm not getting better."

24. A translation of "$\sim d$" is "My parrot is not dead."

25. A translation of "$\sim b \vee d$" is "I'm not getting better or my parrot is dead."

26. A translation of "$b \wedge \sim d$" is "I'm getting better and my parrot is not dead."

27. A translation of "$\sim(b \wedge \sim d)$" is "It is not the case that both I'm getting better and my parrot is not dead."

28. A translation of "$\sim(b \vee d)$" is "It is not the case that either I'm getting better or my parrot is dead."

29. If q is false, then $(p \wedge \sim q) \wedge q$ is false, since both parts of the conjunction must be true for the compound statement to be true.

30. If q is true, then $q \vee (q \wedge \sim p)$ is true, since only one part of the disjunction statement must be true for the compound statement to be true.

31. If the conjunction $p \wedge q$ is true, then both p and q must be true. Thus, q must be true.

32. If $p \vee q$ is false, and p is false, then q must also be false. Observe that both parts of the disjunction must be false for a disjunction to be false.

33. If $\sim (p \vee q)$ is true, then $p \vee q$ must be false, since a statement and its negation have opposite truth values. In order for the disjunction $p \vee q$ to be false, both component statements must be false. Thus, p and q are both false.

34. If $\sim (p \wedge q)$ is false, then both p and q must be true. This will assure that the conjunction itself is true making its negation false.

35. Since p is false, $\sim p$ is true, since a statement and its negation have opposite truth values.

36. Since $q = \text{T}$,

$$\begin{aligned} \sim q &= \sim \text{T} \\ &= \text{F}. \end{aligned}$$

Thus, $\sim q$ is false.

37. Since p is false and q is true, we may consider the statement $p \vee q$ as

$$\text{F} \vee \text{T},$$

which is true by the *or* truth table. That is, $p \vee q$ is true.

38. Since p is false and q is true, we may consider the "and" statement as

$$\begin{gathered} \text{F} \wedge \text{T} \\ \text{F}, \end{gathered}$$

by the logical definition of an "and" statement. That is, $p \wedge q$ is false.

39. Since p is false and q is true, we may consider $p \vee \sim q$ as

$$\begin{gathered} \text{F} \vee \sim \text{T} \\ \text{F} \vee \text{F} \\ \text{F}. \end{gathered}$$

That is, $p \vee \sim q$ is false.

40. With the given truth values for p and q we may consider $\sim p \wedge q$ as

$$\begin{gathered} \sim \text{F} \wedge \text{T} \\ \text{T} \wedge \text{T} \\ \text{T}, \end{gathered}$$

by the logical definition of "$\wedge$". Thus, the compound statement is true.

41. With the given truth values for p and q, we may consider $\sim p \vee \sim q$ as

$$\begin{gathered} \sim \text{F} \vee \sim \text{T} \\ \text{T} \vee \text{F} \\ \text{T}. \end{gathered}$$

Thus, $\sim p \vee \sim q$ is true.

42. Replacing p and q with the given truth values, we have

$$\begin{gathered} \text{F} \wedge \sim \text{T} \\ \text{F} \wedge \text{F} \\ \text{F}. \end{gathered}$$

Thus the compound statement $p \wedge \sim q$ is false.

43. Replacing p and q with the given truth values, we have

$$\begin{gathered} \sim (\text{F} \wedge \sim \text{T}) \\ \sim (\text{F} \wedge \text{F}) \\ \sim \text{F} \\ \text{T}. \end{gathered}$$

Thus, the compound statement $\sim (p \wedge \sim q)$ is true.

44. Replacing p and q with the given truth values, we have

$$\begin{gathered} \sim (\sim \text{F} \vee \sim \text{T}) \\ \sim (\text{T} \vee \text{F}) \\ \sim \text{T} \\ \text{F}. \end{gathered}$$

Thus, the statement $\sim (\sim p \vee \sim q)$ is false.

45. Replacing p and q with the given truth values, we have

$$\begin{gathered} \sim [\sim \text{F} \wedge (\sim \text{T} \vee \text{F})] \\ \sim [\text{T} \wedge (\text{F} \vee \text{F})] \\ \sim [\text{T} \wedge \text{F}] \\ \sim \text{F} \\ \text{T}. \end{gathered}$$

Thus, the compound statement $\sim [\sim p \wedge (\sim q \vee p)]$ is true.

46. Replacing p and q with the given truth values, we have

$$\begin{array}{c} \sim[(\sim\text{F} \wedge \sim\text{T}) \vee \sim\text{T}] \\ \sim[(\text{T} \wedge \text{F}) \vee \text{F}] \\ \sim[\text{F} \vee \text{F}] \\ \sim\text{F} \\ \text{T}. \end{array}$$

Thus, the statement $\sim[(\sim p \wedge \sim q) \vee \sim q]$ is true.

47. The statement $3 \geq 1$ is a disjunction since it means "$3 > 1$" or "$3 = 1$."

48. The statement "$6 \geq 2$" is true because $6 > 2$. The statement "$6 \geq 6$" is true because $6 = 6$.

49. Replacing $p, q,$ and r with the given truth values, we have

$$\begin{array}{c} (\text{T} \wedge \text{F}) \vee \sim\text{F} \\ \text{F} \vee \text{T} \\ \text{T}. \end{array}$$

Thus, the compound statement $(p \wedge r) \vee \sim q$ is true.

50. Replacing p, q, and r with the given truth values, we have

$$\begin{array}{c} (\text{F} \vee \sim\text{F}) \wedge \text{T} \\ (\text{F} \vee \text{T}) \wedge \text{T} \\ \text{T} \wedge \text{T} \\ \text{T}. \end{array}$$

Thus, the statement $(q \vee \sim r) \wedge p$ is true.

51. Replacing $p, q,$ and r with the given truth values, we have

$$\begin{array}{c} \text{T} \wedge (\text{F} \vee \text{F}) \\ \text{T} \wedge \text{F} \\ \text{F}. \end{array}$$

Thus, the compound statement $p \wedge (q \vee r)$ is false.

52. Replacing p, q and r with the given truth values, we have

$$\begin{array}{c} (\sim\text{T} \wedge \text{F}) \vee \sim\text{F} \\ (\text{F} \wedge \text{F}) \vee \text{T} \\ \text{F} \vee \text{T} \\ \text{T}. \end{array}$$

Thus, the statement $(\sim p \wedge q) \vee \sim r$ is true.

53. Replacing $p, q,$ and r with the given truth values, we have

$$\begin{array}{c} \sim(\text{T} \wedge \text{F}) \wedge (\text{F} \vee \sim\text{F}) \\ \sim\text{F} \wedge (\text{F} \vee \text{T}) \\ \text{T} \wedge \text{T} \\ \text{T}. \end{array}$$

Thus, the compound statement $\sim(p \wedge q) \wedge (r \vee \sim q)$ is true.

54. Replacing p, q and r with the given truth values, we have

$$\begin{array}{c} (\sim\text{T} \wedge \sim\text{F}) \vee (\sim\text{F} \wedge \text{F}) \\ (\text{F} \wedge \text{T}) \vee (\text{T} \wedge \text{F}) \\ \text{F} \vee \text{F} \\ \text{F}. \end{array}$$

Thus, the statement $(\sim p \wedge \sim q) \vee (\sim r \wedge q)$ is false.

55. Replacing $p, q,$ and r with the given truth values, we have

$$\begin{array}{c} \sim[(\sim\text{T} \wedge \text{F}) \vee \text{F}] \\ \sim[(\text{F} \wedge \text{F}) \vee \text{F}] \\ \sim[\text{F} \vee \text{F}] \\ \sim\text{F} \\ \text{T}. \end{array}$$

Thus, the compound statement $\sim[(p \wedge q) \vee r]$ is true.

56. Replacing p, q and r with the given truth values, we have

$$\begin{array}{l} \sim[\text{F} \vee (\sim\text{F} \wedge \sim\text{T})] \\ \sim[\text{F} \vee (\text{T} \wedge \text{F})] \\ \sim[\text{F} \vee \text{F}] \\ \quad\sim\text{F} \\ \quad\text{T}. \end{array}$$

Thus, the statement $\sim[r \vee (\sim q \wedge \sim p)]$ is true.

57. Since p is false and r is true, we have

$$\begin{array}{c} \text{F} \wedge \text{T} \\ \text{F}. \end{array}$$

The compound statement $p \wedge r$ is false.

58. Since p and q are false, we have

$$\begin{array}{c} \text{F} \vee \sim\text{F} \\ \text{F} \vee \text{T} \\ \text{T}. \end{array}$$

The statement $p \vee \sim q$ is true.

59. Since q is false and r is true, we have

$$\begin{array}{c} \sim\text{F} \vee \sim\text{T} \\ \text{T} \vee \text{F} \\ \text{T}. \end{array}$$

The compound statement $\sim q \vee \sim r$ is true.

60. Since p is false and r is true, we have

$$\begin{gathered}\sim\text{F} \wedge \sim\text{T}\\ \text{T} \wedge \text{F}\\ \text{F}.\end{gathered}$$

The statement $\sim p \wedge \sim r$ is false.

61. Since p and q are false and r is true, we have

$$\begin{gathered}(\text{F} \wedge \text{F}) \vee \text{T}\\ \text{F} \vee \text{T}\\ \text{T}.\end{gathered}$$

The compound statement $(p \wedge q) \vee r$ is true.

62. Since p and q are false and r is true, we have

$$\begin{gathered}\sim\text{F} \vee (\sim\text{T} \vee \sim\text{F})\\ \text{T} \vee (\text{F} \vee \text{T})\\ \text{T} \vee \text{T}\\ \text{T}.\end{gathered}$$

The statement $\sim p \vee (\sim r \vee \sim q)$ is true.

63. Since p and q are false and r is true, we have

$$\begin{gathered}(\sim\text{T} \wedge \text{F}) \vee \sim\text{F}\\ (\text{F} \wedge \text{F}) \vee \text{T}\\ \text{F} \vee \text{T}\\ \text{T}.\end{gathered}$$

The compound statement $(\sim r \wedge q) \vee \sim p$ is true.

64. Since p and q are false and r is true, we have

$$\begin{gathered}\sim(\text{F} \vee \sim\text{F}) \vee \sim\text{T}\\ \sim(\text{F} \vee \text{T}) \vee \text{F}\\ \sim\text{T} \vee \text{F}\\ \text{F} \vee \text{F}\\ \text{F}.\end{gathered}$$

The statement $\sim(p \vee \sim q) \vee \sim r$ is false.

65. **a**, **c**, and **d** are declarative sentences that are true or false and are therefore statements.

b is a command, not a declarative sentence, and is therefore not a statement.

66. **a** is a compound statement, formed using "All payments must be sent to the payment address shown on your billing statement" and "[all payments] must include the remittance coupon from your billing statement."

c and **d** are simple statements, not compound ones.

67. The negation is formed by adding "not": "We may not charge a fee of $35 in each billing period the New Balance on your statement exceeds your credit line."

68. **b**, **c**, and **d** are declarative sentences that are true or false and are therefore statements.

a is a command, not a declarative sentence, and is therefore not a statement.

69. **c** is a compound statement, formed using "Tax rates are lower for a head of household than for a person filing as single" and "the standard deduction is higher."

d is a compound statement, formed by negating the statement "You reduce the exemptions because of the shorter tax table."

b is a simple statement, not a compound one.

70. The negation is formed by removing "not": "You reduce the exemptions because of the shorter tax table."

71. $p \wedge q$, where p is the statement "Tax rates are lower for a head of household than for a person filing as single" and q is the statement "the standard deduction is higher."

72. **(a)** This is a question, not a declarative sentence, and therefore not a statement.

(b), (c), (d), (e) There are declarative sentences that are true or false and therefore statements.

73. **(a)** This is a question, not a declarative sentence, and therefore not a statement.

(b), (d) These are compound statements that are conjunctions.

(c) This is a compound statement in the "If ... then" form.

(e) This is a simple statement.

74. The negation of "You may find that exercise helps you cope with stress" is "You may not find that exercise helps you cope with stress."

75. **(a), (b)** These are commands, not declarative sentences, and therefore not statements.

(c), (d), (e) These are declarative sentences that are true or false and therefore statements.

76. **(a), (b)** These are commands, not declarative sentences, and therefore not statements.

(c) This is a compound statement, formed using the statements "The court won't do it for you" and "Hiring an attorney is usually not cost-effective given the small amount of money involved."

(d) This is a compound statement, formed using the statements "You can't marry," "You're at least 18 years old," and "You have the permission of your parents or guardian."

(e) This is a simple statement, not a compound one.

77. One choice: "Most legal problems are not matters of civil law."

80. "New England won the Super Bowl but Tom Brady is not the best quarterback" may be symbolized as $n \wedge \sim b$.

81. "New England did not win the Super Bowl or Tom Brady is not the best quarterback" may be symbolized as $\sim n \vee \sim b$.

82. "New England did not win the Super Bowl or Tom Brady is the best quarterback" may be symbolized as $\sim n \vee b$.

83. "New England did not win the Super Bowl but Tom Brady is the best quarterback" may be symbolized as $\sim n \wedge b$.

84. "Neither did New England win the Super Bowl nor is Tom Brady the best quarterback" may be symbolized as $\sim n \wedge \sim b$ or $\sim(n \vee b)$.

85. "Either New England won the Super Bowl or Tom Brady is the best quarterback" and it is not the case that both New England won the Super Bowl and Tom Brady is the best quarterback" may be symbolized as $(n \vee b) \wedge [\sim(n \wedge b)]$.

86. Assume that n is true and that b is true. Under these conditions, the statements in Exercises 80-85 have the following truth values.

80. $n \wedge \sim b$: False because n is true and $\sim b$ is false.
81. $\sim n \vee \sim b$: False, because $\sim n$ is false and $\sim b$ is false.
82. $\sim n \vee b$: True, because $\sim n$ is false and b is true.
83. $\sim n \wedge b$: False, because $\sim n$ is false and b is true.
84. $\sim n \wedge b$: False, because $\sim n$ is false and $\sim b$ is false.
85. $(n \vee b) \wedge [\sim(n \vee b)]$: False, since $(n \vee b)$ is true but $[\sim(n \wedge b)]$ is false.

Therefore, the answer is 82 is a true statement.

87. Assume that n is false and that b is false. Under these conditions, the statements in Exercises 80-85 have the following truth values.

80. $n \wedge \sim b$: False, because n is false and $\sim b$ is true.
81. $\sim n \vee \sim b$: True, because $\sim n$ is true and $\sim b$ is true.
82. $\sim n \vee b$: True, because $\sim n$ is true and $\sim b$ is false.
83. $\sim n \wedge b$: False, because $\sim n$ is true and b is false.
84. $\sim n \wedge \sim b$: True, because $\sim n$ is true and $\sim b$ is true.
85. $(n \vee b) \wedge [\sim(n \wedge b)]$: False, since $(n \vee b)$ is false but $[\sim(n \wedge b)]$ is true.

Therefore, the answer is 81, 82, and 84 are true statements.

6.2 Truth Tables and Equivalent Statements

1. Since there are two simple statements (p and r), we have $2^2 = 4$ rows in the truth table.

2. Since there are three simple statements (p, q, and r), we have $2^3 = 8$ rows in the truth table.

3. Since there are four simple statements (p, q, r, and s), we have $2^4 = 16$ rows in the truth table.

4. Since there are five simple statements (p, q, r, s, and t), we have $2^5 = 32$ rows in the truth table.

5. Since there are seven simple statements (p, q, r, s, t, u, and v), we have $2^7 = 128$ rows in the truth table.

6. Since there are eight simple statements (p, q, r, s, m, n, u, and v), we have $2^8 = 256$ rows in the truth table.

7. If the truth table for a certain compound statement has 64 rows, then there must be six distinct component statements since $2^6 = 64$.

8. It is not possible for a truth table of a compound statement to have exactly 48 rows, because 48 is not a whole number power of 2.

9. $\sim p \wedge q$

p	q	$\sim p$	$\sim p \wedge q$
T	T	F	F
T	F	F	F
F	T	T	T
F	F	T	F

10. $\sim p \vee \sim q$

p	q	$\sim p$	$\sim q$	$\sim p \vee \sim q$
T	T	F	F	F
T	F	F	T	T
F	T	T	F	T
F	F	T	T	T

11. $\sim(p \wedge q)$

p	q	$p \wedge q$	$\sim(p \wedge q)$
T	T	T	F
T	F	F	T
F	T	F	T
F	F	F	T

12. $p \vee \sim q$

p	q	$\sim q$	$p \vee \sim q$
T	T	F	T
T	F	T	T
F	T	F	F
F	F	T	T

13. $(q \vee \sim p) \vee \sim q$

p	q	$\sim p$	$\sim q$	$q \vee \sim p$	$(q \vee \sim p) \vee \sim q$
T	T	F	F	T	T
T	F	F	T	F	T
F	T	T	F	T	T
F	F	T	T	T	T

14. $(p \wedge \sim q) \wedge p$

p	q	$\sim q$	$p \wedge \sim q$	$(p \wedge \sim q) \wedge p$
T	T	F	F	F
T	F	T	T	T
F	T	F	F	F
F	F	T	F	F

In Exercises 15–24 to save space we are using the alternative method, filling in columns in the order indicated by the numbers. Observe that columns with the same number are combined (by the logical definition of the connective) to get the next numbered column. Note that this is different from the way the numbered columns are used in the textbook. Remember that the last column (highest numbered column) completed yields the truth values for the complete compound statement. Be sure to align truth values under the appropriate logical connective or simple statement.

15. $\sim q \wedge (\sim p \vee q)$

p	q	$\sim q$	$\wedge$	$(\sim p$	$\vee$	$q)$
T	T	F	F	F	T	T
T	F	T	F	F	F	F
F	T	F	F	T	T	T
F	F	T	T	T	T	F
		1	4	2	3	2

16. $\sim p \vee (\sim q \wedge \sim p)$

p	q	$\sim p$	$\vee$	$(\sim q$	$\wedge$	$\sim p)$
T	T	F	F	F	F	F
T	F	F	F	T	F	F
F	T	T	T	F	F	T
F	F	T	T	T	T	T
		1	4	2	3	2

17. $(p \vee \sim q) \wedge (p \wedge q)$

p	q	$(p$	$\vee$	$\sim q)$	$\wedge$	$(p$	$\wedge$	$q)$
T	T	T	T	F	T	T	T	T
T	F	T	T	T	F	T	F	F
F	T	F	F	F	F	F	F	T
F	F	F	T	T	F	F	F	F
		1	2	1	5	3	4	3

18. $(\sim p \wedge \sim q) \vee (\sim p \vee q)$

p	q	$(\sim p$	$\wedge$	$\sim q)$	$\vee$	$(\sim p$	$\vee$	$q)$
T	T	F	F	F	T	F	T	T
T	F	F	F	T	F	F	F	F
F	T	T	F	F	T	T	T	T
F	F	T	T	T	T	T	T	F
		1	2	1	5	3	4	3

19. $(\sim p \wedge q) \wedge r$

p	q	r	$(\sim p$	$\wedge$	$q)$	$\wedge$	r
T	T	T	F	F	T	F	T
T	T	F	F	F	T	F	F
T	F	T	F	F	F	F	T
T	F	F	F	F	F	F	F
F	T	T	T	T	T	T	T
F	T	F	T	T	T	F	F
F	F	T	T	F	F	F	T
F	F	F	T	F	F	F	F
			1	2	1	4	3

20. $r \vee (p \wedge \sim q)$

p	q	r	r	$\vee$	$(p$	$\wedge$	$\sim q)$
T	T	T	T	T	T	F	F
T	T	F	F	F	T	F	F
T	F	T	T	T	T	T	T
T	F	F	F	T	T	T	T
F	T	T	T	T	F	F	F
F	T	F	F	F	F	F	F
F	F	T	T	T	F	F	T
F	F	F	F	F	F	F	T
			1	4	2	3	2

21. $(\sim p \wedge \sim q) \vee (\sim r \vee \sim p)$

p	q	r	$(\sim p$	$\wedge$	$\sim q)$	$\vee$	$(\sim r$	$\vee$	$\sim p)$
T	T	T	F	F	F	F	F	F	F
T	T	F	F	F	F	T	T	T	F
T	F	T	F	F	T	F	F	F	F
T	F	F	F	F	T	T	T	T	F
F	T	T	T	F	F	T	F	T	T
F	T	F	T	F	F	T	T	T	T
F	F	T	T	T	T	T	F	T	T
F	F	F	T	T	T	T	T	T	T
			1	2	1	5	3	4	3

22. $(\sim r \vee \sim p) \wedge (\sim p \vee \sim q)$

p	q	r	$(\sim r$	$\vee$	$\sim p)$	$\wedge$	$(\sim p$	$\vee$	$\sim q)$
T	T	T	F	F	F	F	F	F	F
T	T	F	T	T	F	F	F	F	F
T	F	T	F	F	F	F	F	T	T
T	F	F	T	T	F	T	F	T	T
F	T	T	F	T	T	T	T	T	F
F	T	F	T	T	T	T	T	T	F
F	F	T	F	T	T	T	T	T	T
F	F	F	T	T	T	T	T	T	T
			1	2	1	5	3	4	3

23. $\sim(\sim p \wedge \sim q) \vee (\sim r \vee \sim s)$

p	q	r	s	$\sim$	$(\sim p$	$\wedge$	$\sim q)$	$\vee$	$(\sim r$	$\vee$	$\sim s)$
T	T	T	T	T	F	F	F	T	F	F	F
T	T	T	F	T	F	F	F	T	F	T	T
T	T	F	T	T	F	F	F	T	T	T	F
T	T	F	F	T	F	F	F	T	T	T	T
T	F	T	T	T	F	F	T	T	F	F	F
T	F	T	F	T	F	F	T	T	F	T	T
T	F	F	T	T	F	F	T	T	T	T	F
T	F	F	F	T	F	F	T	T	T	T	T
F	T	T	T	T	T	F	F	T	F	F	F
F	T	T	F	T	T	F	F	T	F	T	T
F	T	F	T	T	T	F	F	T	T	T	F
F	T	F	F	T	T	F	F	T	T	T	T
F	F	T	T	F	T	T	T	F	F	F	F
F	F	T	F	F	T	T	T	T	F	T	T
F	F	F	T	F	T	T	T	T	T	T	F
F	F	F	F	F	T	T	T	T	T	T	T
				3	1	2	1	6	4	5	4

24. $(\sim r \vee s) \wedge (\sim p \wedge q)$

p	q	r	s	$(\sim r$	$\vee$	$s)$	$\wedge$	$(\sim p$	$\wedge$	$q)$
T	T	T	T	F	T	T	F	F	F	T
T	T	T	F	F	F	F	F	F	F	T
T	T	F	T	T	T	T	F	F	F	T
T	T	F	F	T	T	F	F	F	F	T
T	F	T	T	F	T	T	F	F	F	F
T	F	T	F	F	F	F	F	F	F	F
T	F	F	T	T	T	T	F	F	F	F
T	F	F	F	T	T	F	F	F	F	F
F	T	T	T	F	T	T	T	T	T	T
F	T	T	F	F	F	F	F	T	T	T
F	T	F	T	T	T	T	T	T	T	T
F	T	F	F	T	T	F	T	T	T	T
F	F	T	T	F	T	T	F	T	F	F
F	F	T	F	F	F	F	F	T	F	F
F	F	F	T	T	T	T	F	T	F	F
F	F	F	F	T	T	F	F	T	F	F
				1	2	1	5	3	4	3

25. "It's summertime and the living is easy" has the symbolic form $p \wedge q$. The negation, $\sim(p \wedge q)$, is equivalent, by one of DeMorgan's laws, to $\sim p \vee \sim q$. The corresponding word statement is "It's not summertime, or the living is not easy."

26. "Rachel Reeve was elected president and Joanne Ha was elected treasurer" has the symbolic form $p \wedge q$. The negation, $\sim(\sim p \wedge q)$, is equivalent, by one of De Morgan's laws, to $\sim p \vee \sim q$. The corresponding word statement is "Rachel Reeve was not elected president or Joanne Ha was not elected treasurer."

27. "Either the door was unlocked or the thief broke a window" has the symbolic form $p \vee q$. The negation, $\sim(p \vee q)$, is equivalent, by one of DeMorgan's laws, to $\sim p \wedge \sim q$. The corresponding word statement is "The door was locked and the thief didn't break a window."

28. "Sue brings the wrong book or she forgets the notes" has the symbolic form $p \vee q$. The negation, $\sim(p \vee q)$, is equivalent, by one of De Morgan's laws, to $\sim p \wedge \sim q$. The corresponding word statement is "Sue doesn't bring the wrong book and she doesn't forget the notes."

29. "I'm ready to go, but Emily Portwood isn't" has the symbolic form $p \wedge \sim q$. (The connective "but" is logically equivalent to "and.") The negation, $\sim(p \wedge \sim q)$, is equivalent, by one of DeMorgan's laws, to $\sim p \vee q$. The corresponding word statement is "I'm not ready to go, or Emily Portwood is."

30. "You may say I'm a dreamer, but I'm not the only one" has the symbolic form $p \wedge \sim q$. (Note that the connective "but" is logically equivalent to "and.") The negation, $\sim(p \wedge \sim q)$, is equivalent, by DeMorgan's laws, to $\sim p \vee q$. The corresponding word statement is "You may not say I'm a dreamer, or I am the only one."

31. "$12 > 4$ or $8 = 9$" has the symbolic form $p \vee q$. The negation, $\sim(p \vee q)$, is equivalent, by one of DeMorgan's laws, to $\sim p \wedge \sim q$. The corresponding statement is "$12 \leq 4$ and $8 \neq 9$." (Note that the inequality "$\leq$" is logically equivalent to "$\not>$.")

32. "$2 + 3 = 5$ and $12 + 13 = 15$" has the symbolic form $p \wedge q$. The negation, $\sim(p \wedge q)$, is equivalent, by one of De Morgan's laws, to $\sim p \vee \sim q$. The corresponding statement is "$2+3 \neq 5$ or $12+13 \neq 15$."

33. "Larry or Moe is out sick today" has the symbolic form $p \vee q$. The negation, $\sim(p \vee q)$, is equivalent, by one of De Morgan's laws, to $\sim p \wedge \sim q$. The corresponding word statement is "Neither Larry nor Moe is out sick today."

34. "Jack and Jill went up the hill" has the symbolic form $p \wedge q$. The negation, $\sim(p \wedge q)$, is equivalent, by one of DeMorgan's laws, to $\sim p \vee \sim q$. The corresponding word statement is "Either Jack or Jill didn't go up the hill."

35. $p \veebar q$

p	q	$p \veebar q$
T	T	F
T	F	T
F	T	T
F	F	F

Observe that it is only the first line in the truth table that changes for "exclusive disjunction" since the component statements can not both be true at the same time.

36. "$3 + 1 = 4 \veebar 2 + 5 = 7$" is <u>false</u> since both component statements are true.

37. "$3 + 1 = 4 \veebar 2 + 5 = 9$" is <u>true</u> since the first component statement is true and the second is false.

38. "$3 + 1 = 7 \veebar 2 + 5 = 7$" is <u>true</u> since the first component statement is false and the second is true.

39. Store the truth values of the statements p, q, and s as P, Q, and S, respectively.

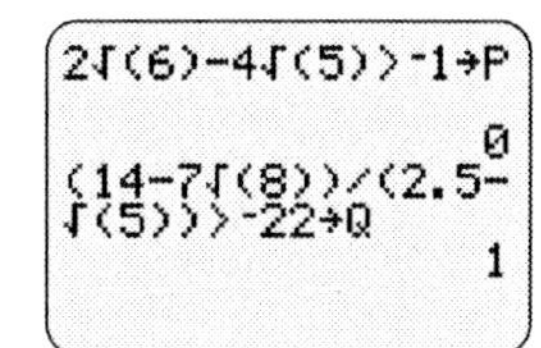

Use the stored values of P, Q, and S to find the truth values of each of the compound statements.

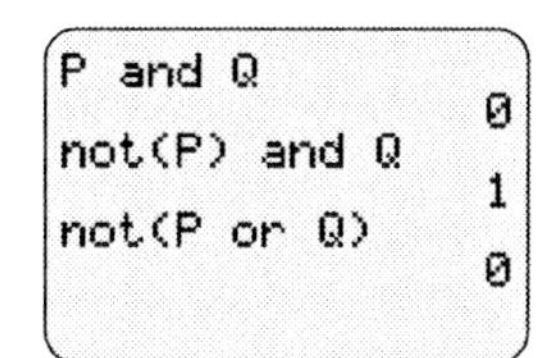

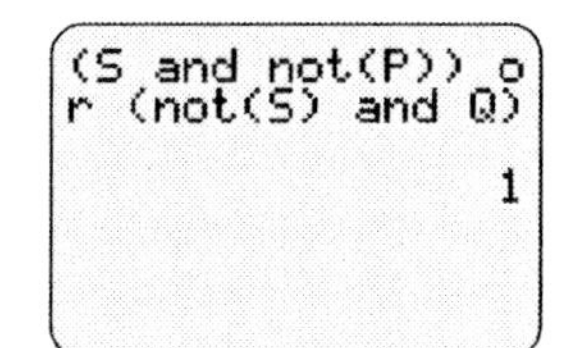

(a) P and Q returns 0, meaning $p \wedge q$ is false.

(b) not (P) and Q returns 1, meaning $\sim p \wedge q$ is true.

(c) not (P or Q) returns 0, meaning $\sim(p \vee q)$ is false.

(d) (S and not (P)) or (not (S) and Q) returns 1, meaning $(s \wedge \sim p) \vee (\sim s \wedge q)$ is true.

40. This statement is of the form $p \wedge q$. Its negation is equivalent to $\sim p \vee \sim q$ by one of DeMorgan's laws. A translation for the negation is "The plan need not clearly state that its purpose is to provide qualifying tax-free benefits, or a specific payment schedule need not be provided for different types of injuries.

42. This statement is of the form $p \wedge q$. Its negation is equivalent to $\sim p \vee \sim q$ by one of DeMorgan's laws. A translation for the negation is "This warranty does not give you specific legal rights or you may not have other rights, which vary from state to state."

43. Letting s represent "You will be completely satisfied," r represent "We will refund your money," and q represent "We will ask you questions," the guarantee translates into symbols as $s \vee (r \wedge \sim q)$. The truth table follows.

s	r	q	s	$\vee$	$(r$	$\wedge$	$\sim q)$
T	T	T	T	T	T	F	F
T	T	F	T	T	T	T	T
T	F	T	T	T	F	F	F
T	F	F	T	T	F	F	T
F	T	T	F	F	T	F	F
F	T	F	F	T	T	T	T
F	F	T	F	F	F	F	F
F	F	F	F	F	F	F	T
		1	1	4	2	3	2

The guarantee would be false in the three cases indicated as "F" in the column labeled "6." These would be if you are not completely satisfied, and they either don't refund your money or they ask you questions.

44. **(a)** p: Tissue samples may be taken from almost anywhere in the body.
q: The procedure used depends on the site.
The statement is $p \wedge q$. The negation is $\sim p \vee \sim q$.
Negation: Either tissue samples may not be taken from almost anywhere in the body or the procedure need does not depend on the site.

(b) p: The procedure can be carried out quickly in the doctor's office.
q: It is not painful.

The statement is of the form $p \wedge q$. The negation is $\sim p \vee \sim q$.
Negation: The procedure cannot be carried out quickly in the doctor's office, or it is painful.

(c) p: Fluid samples may be examined for infection.
q: The cells in the fluid may be separated and examined to detect other abnormalities,

The statement is of the form $p \vee q$. The negation is $\sim p \wedge \sim q$.
Negation: Fluid samples may not be examined for infection, and the cells in the fluid may not be separated and examined to detect other abnormalities.

45. p: The Pennsylvania Fish and Boat Commission is sensitive to the needs of the physically challenged.
q: The Pennsylvania Fish and Boat Commission works to make our facilities accessible.
The statement is $p \wedge q$. The negation is $\sim p \vee \sim q$.
Negation: Either the Pennsylvania Fish and Boat Commission is not sensitive to the needs of the physically challenged or it does not work to make our facilities accessible.

46. Inclusive, since the "and" case is allowed.

47. p: The court won't do it for you.
q: Hiring an attorney is usually not cost effective.
The statement is $p \wedge q$. The negation is $\sim p \vee \sim q$.
Negation: Either the court will do it for you or hiring an attorney is often cost effective.

48. Letting p represent "Liberty without learning is always in peril" and q represent "Learning without liberty is always in vain," the quote translates symbolically as $p \wedge q$. Its negation is equivalent by DeMorgan's laws to $\sim p \vee \sim q$. A translation for the negation is "Liberty without learning is not always in peril, or learning without liberty is not always in vain."

49. Letting c represent "I will cut taxes," e represent "I will eliminate the deficit," and r represent "I will run for reelection," the guarantee translates into symbols as $(c \wedge e) \vee \sim r$. The truth table follows.

c	e	r	$(c$	$\wedge$	$e)$	$\vee$	$\sim r$
T	T	T	T	T	T	T	F
T	T	F	T	T	T	T	T
T	F	T	T	F	F	F	F
T	F	F	T	F	F	T	T
F	T	T	F	F	T	F	F
F	T	F	F	F	T	T	T
F	F	T	F	F	F	F	F
F	F	F	F	F	F	T	T
			1	2	1	4	3

The promise would be false in the three cases indicated as "F" in the column labeled "6." These would be if the senator runs for reelection and either doesn't cut taxes or doesn't eliminate the deficit.

50. p: You could reroll the die again for your Large Straight.
q: You could set aside the 2 Twos and roll for your Twos or for 3 of a Kind.
The statement is $p \vee q$.
Its negation is $\sim p \wedge \sim q$.
Negation: You cannot reroll the die again for your Large Straight and you cannot set aside the 2 Twos and roll for your Twos or for 3 of a Kind.

51. Since only one sign is true and the sign on Door 2 is true, the sign on Door 1 must be false. Thus, either the lady is not behind Door 1 or the tiger is not behind Door 2. Since the lady and the tiger are not behind the same door, the lady must be behind Door 2 and the tiger behind Door 1.

6.3 The Conditional and Circuits

1. The statement "If the antecedent of a conditional statement is false, the conditional statement is true" is true, since a false antecedent will always yield a true conditional statement.

2. The statement "If the consequent of a conditional statement is true, the conditional statement is true" is true, since a true consequent is always associated with a true conditional statement (i.e., it doesn't matter what the truth value of the antecedent is, if the consequent itself is true).

3. The statement "If q is true, then $(p \wedge q) \rightarrow q$ is true" is true, since with a true consequent the conditional statement is always true (even though the antecedent may be false)."

4. The statement "If p is true, then $\sim p \rightarrow (q \vee r)$ is true" is true since the antecedent, $\sim p$, is false.

5. "Given that $\sim p$ is true and q is false, the conditional $p \rightarrow q$ is true" is a true statement since the antecedent, p, must be false.

6. "Given that $\sim p$ is false and q is false, the conditional $p \rightarrow q$ is true" is a false statement since the antecedent, p, must be true, so that $p \rightarrow q$ is false.

9. "$F \rightarrow (4 \neq 7)$" is a true statement, since a false antecedent always yields a conditional statement which is true.

10. "$(6 \geq 6) \rightarrow F$" is a false statement, since the antecedent is true and the consequent is false.

11. "$(4 = 11 - 7) \rightarrow (8 > 0)$" is true since the antecedent and the consequent are both true.

12. "$(4^2 \neq 16) \rightarrow (4 - 4 = 8)$" is a true statement, since a false antecedent always yields a true conditional statement.

13. $d \rightarrow (e \wedge s)$ expressed in words becomes "If she dances tonight, then I'm leaving early and he sings loudly."

14. $(d \wedge s) \rightarrow e$ expressed in words, becomes "If she dances tonight and he sings loudly, then I'm leaving early."

15. $\sim s \rightarrow (d \vee \sim e)$ expressed in words becomes "If he doesn't sing loudly, then she dances tonight or I'm not leaving early."

16. $(\sim d \vee \sim e) \rightarrow \sim s$ expressed in words becomes "If she doesn't dance tonight or I'm not leaving early, then he doesn't sing loudly."

17. The statement "My dog ate my homework, or if I receive a failing grade then I'll run for governor" can be symbolized as $d \vee (f \rightarrow g)$.

18. The statement "I'll run for governor, and if I receive a failing grade then my dog did not eat my homework" can be symbolized as $g \wedge (f \rightarrow \sim d)$.

19. The statement "I'll run for governor if I don't receive a failing grade" can be symbolized as $\sim f \rightarrow g$.

20. The statement "I won't receive a failing grade if my dog didn't eat my homework" can be symbolized as $\sim d \rightarrow \sim f$.

21. Replacing r and q with the given truth values, we have

$$\begin{gathered}\sim \mathrm{F} \rightarrow \mathrm{T} \\ \mathrm{T} \rightarrow \mathrm{T} \\ \mathrm{T}.\end{gathered}$$

Thus, the statement $\sim r \rightarrow q$ is true.

22. Replacing p and r with the given truth values, we have

$$\begin{gathered}\sim \mathrm{F} \rightarrow \sim \mathrm{F} \\ \mathrm{T} \rightarrow \mathrm{T} \\ \mathrm{T}.\end{gathered}$$

Thus, the statement $\sim p \rightarrow \sim r$ is true.

23. Replacing r and p with the given truth values, we have

$$\begin{gathered}\sim \mathrm{F} \rightarrow \mathrm{F} \\ \mathrm{T} \rightarrow \mathrm{F} \\ \mathrm{F}.\end{gathered}$$

Thus, the statement $\sim r \rightarrow p$ is false.

24. Replacing q and r with the given truth values, we have

$$\begin{gathered}\sim \mathrm{T} \rightarrow \mathrm{F} \\ \mathrm{F} \rightarrow \mathrm{F} \\ \mathrm{T}.\end{gathered}$$

Thus, the statement $\sim q \rightarrow r$ is true.

25. Replacing p, q, and r with the given truth values, we have

$$\begin{gathered}\sim \mathrm{F} \rightarrow (\mathrm{T} \wedge \mathrm{F}) \\ \mathrm{T} \rightarrow \mathrm{F} \\ \mathrm{F}.\end{gathered}$$

Thus, the statement $\sim p \rightarrow (q \wedge r)$ is false.

26. Replacing r and p with the given truth values, we have

$$\begin{gathered}(\sim \mathrm{F} \vee \mathrm{F}) \rightarrow \mathrm{F} \\ (\mathrm{T} \vee \mathrm{F}) \rightarrow \mathrm{F} \\ \mathrm{T} \rightarrow \mathrm{F} \\ \mathrm{F}.\end{gathered}$$

Thus, the statement $(\sim r \vee p) \rightarrow p$ is false.

27. Replacing p, q, and r with the given truth values, we have

$$\begin{gathered}\sim \mathrm{T} \rightarrow (\mathrm{F} \wedge \mathrm{F}) \\ \mathrm{F} \rightarrow \mathrm{F} \\ \mathrm{T}.\end{gathered}$$

Thus, the statement $\sim q \rightarrow (p \wedge r)$ is true.

28. Replacing p, q, and r with the given truth values, we have

$$\begin{gathered}(\sim \mathrm{F} \wedge \sim \mathrm{T}) \rightarrow (\mathrm{F} \wedge \sim \mathrm{F}) \\ (\mathrm{T} \wedge \mathrm{F}) \rightarrow (\mathrm{F} \wedge \mathrm{T}) \\ \mathrm{F} \rightarrow \mathrm{F} \\ \mathrm{T}.\end{gathered}$$

Thus, the statement $(\sim p \wedge \sim q) \rightarrow (p \wedge \sim r)$ is true.

29. Replacing p, q, and r with the given truth values, we have

$$\begin{gathered}(\sim \mathrm{F} \rightarrow \sim \mathrm{T}) \rightarrow (\sim \mathrm{F} \wedge \sim \mathrm{F}) \\ (\mathrm{T} \rightarrow \mathrm{F}) \rightarrow (\mathrm{T} \wedge \mathrm{T}) \\ \mathrm{F} \rightarrow \mathrm{T} \\ \mathrm{T}.\end{gathered}$$

Thus, the statement $(p \rightarrow \sim q) \rightarrow (\sim p \wedge \sim r)$ is true.

30. Replacing p, q, and r with the given truth values, we have

$$\begin{gathered}(\mathrm{F} \rightarrow \sim \mathrm{T}) \wedge (\mathrm{F} \rightarrow \mathrm{F}) \\ (\mathrm{F} \rightarrow \mathrm{F}) \wedge \mathrm{T} \\ \mathrm{T} \wedge \mathrm{T} \\ \mathrm{T}.\end{gathered}$$

Thus, the statement $(p \rightarrow \sim q) \wedge (p \rightarrow r)$ is true.

33. According to Equivalent Statement 8, $p \rightarrow q \equiv \sim p \rightarrow q$. Therefore,

$\sim p \rightarrow q \equiv \sim (\sim p) \vee \sim q$ by Equivalent Statement 8

$\sim (\sim p) \vee \sim q \equiv p \vee \sim q$ by Equivalent Statement 7.

34. $\sim q \rightarrow p$

p	q	$\sim q$	$\rightarrow$	p
T	T	F	T	T
T	F	T	T	T
F	T	F	T	F
F	F	T	F	F
		1	2	1

35. $p \rightarrow \sim q$

p	q	p	$\rightarrow$	$\sim q$
T	T	T	F	F
T	F	T	T	T
F	T	F	T	F
F	F	F	T	T
		1	2	1

36.

p	$(p$	$\vee$	$\sim p)$	$\rightarrow$	p	$\wedge$	$\sim p$
T	T	T	F	F	T	F	F
F	F	T	T	F	F	F	T
	1	2	1	5	3	4	3

Since the statement is always false (The truth values in column 5 are all false.), it is a contradiction.

37. $(\sim q \rightarrow \sim p) \rightarrow \sim q$

p	q	$(\sim q$	$\rightarrow$	$\sim p)$	$\rightarrow$	$\sim q$
T	T	F	T	F	F	F
T	F	T	F	F	T	T
F	T	F	T	T	F	F
F	F	T	T	T	T	T
		1	2	1	4	3

38. $(p \vee q) \rightarrow (q \vee p)$

p	q	$(p$	$\vee$	$q)$	$\rightarrow$	$(q$	$\vee$	$p)$
T	T	T	T	T	T	T	T	T
T	F	T	T	F	T	F	T	T
F	T	F	T	T	T	T	T	F
F	F	F	F	F	T	F	F	F
		1	2	1	5	3	4	3

Since this statement is always true (column 5), it is a tautology.

39.

p	q	$(p$	$\wedge$	$\sim q)$	$\wedge$	$(p$	$\rightarrow$	$q)$
T	T	T	F	F	F	T	T	T
T	F	T	T	T	F	T	F	F
F	T	F	F	F	F	F	T	T
F	F	F	F	T	F	F	T	F
		1	2	1	4	3	4	3

Since this statement is always false (The truth values in column 4 are all false.), it is a contradiction.

40. $(\sim p \rightarrow \sim q) \rightarrow (p \wedge q)$

p	q	$(\sim p$	$\rightarrow$	$\sim q)$	$\rightarrow$	$(p$	$\wedge$	$q)$
T	T	F	T	F	T	T	T	T
T	F	F	T	T	F	T	F	F
F	T	T	F	F	T	F	F	T
F	F	T	T	T	F	F	F	F
		1	2	1	5	3	4	3

41. $r \rightarrow (p \wedge \sim q)$

p	q	r	r	$\rightarrow$	$(p$	$\wedge$	$\sim q)$
T	T	T	T	F	T	F	F
T	T	F	F	T	T	F	F
T	F	T	T	T	T	T	T
T	F	F	F	T	T	T	T
F	T	T	T	F	F	F	F
F	T	F	F	T	F	F	F
F	F	T	T	F	F	F	T
F	F	F	F	T	F	F	T
			1	4	2	3	2

42. $[(r \vee p) \wedge \sim q] \rightarrow p$

p	q	r	$[(r$	$\vee$	$p)$	$\wedge$	$\sim q]$	$\rightarrow$	p
T	T	T	T	T	T	F	F	T	T
T	T	F	F	T	T	F	F	T	T
T	F	T	T	T	T	T	T	T	T
T	F	F	F	T	T	T	T	T	T
F	T	T	T	T	F	F	F	T	F
F	T	F	F	F	F	F	F	T	F
F	F	T	T	T	F	T	T	F	F
F	F	F	F	F	F	F	T	T	F
			1	2	1	4	3	6	5

43. $(\sim r \to s) \vee (p \to \sim q)$

p	q	r	s	$(\sim r$	$\to$	$s)$	$\vee$	$(p$	$\to$	$\sim q)$
T	T	T	T	F	T	T	T	T	F	F
T	T	T	F	F	T	F	T	T	F	F
T	T	F	T	T	T	T	T	T	F	F
T	T	F	F	T	F	F	F	T	F	F
T	F	T	T	F	T	T	T	T	T	T
T	F	T	F	F	T	F	T	T	T	T
T	F	F	T	T	T	T	T	T	T	T
T	F	F	F	T	F	F	T	T	T	T
F	T	T	T	F	T	T	T	F	T	F
F	T	T	F	F	T	F	T	F	T	F
F	T	F	T	T	T	T	T	F	T	F
F	T	F	F	T	F	F	T	F	T	F
F	F	T	T	F	T	T	T	F	T	T
F	F	T	F	F	T	F	T	F	T	T
F	F	F	T	T	T	T	T	F	T	T
F	F	F	F	T	F	F	T	F	T	T
				1	2	1	5	3	4	3

44. $(\sim p \wedge \sim q) \to (\sim r \to \sim s)$

p	q	r	s	$(\sim p$	$\wedge$	$\sim q)$	$\to$	$(\sim r$	$\to$	$\sim s)$
T	T	T	T	F	F	F	T	F	T	F
T	T	T	F	F	F	F	T	F	T	T
T	T	F	T	F	F	F	T	T	F	F
T	T	F	F	F	F	F	T	T	T	T
T	F	T	T	F	F	T	T	F	T	F
T	F	T	F	F	F	T	T	F	T	T
T	F	F	T	F	F	T	T	T	F	F
T	F	F	F	F	F	T	T	T	T	T
F	T	T	T	T	F	F	T	F	T	F
F	T	T	F	T	F	F	T	F	T	T
F	T	F	T	T	F	F	T	T	F	F
F	T	F	F	T	F	F	T	T	T	T
F	F	T	T	T	T	T	T	F	T	F
F	F	T	F	T	T	T	T	F	T	T
F	F	F	T	T	T	T	F	T	F	F
F	F	F	F	T	T	T	T	T	T	T
				1	2	1	5	3	4	3

45. The statement is not a tautology if at least one F appears in the final column of a truth table, since a tautology requires all T's in the final column.

46. Let p represent "your eyes are bad" and q represent "your whole body will be full of darkness." The statement has the form $p \to q$. In words, the equivalent form $\sim p \vee q$ becomes "Your eyes are not bad or your whole body will be full of darkness."

47. Let p represent "they can see me now" and q represent "they'd never believe it." The statement has the form $p \to q$. In words, the equivalent form $\sim p \vee q$ becomes "They cannot see me now or they'd never believe it."

48. Let p represent "I have the money" and q represent "I'd buy that car." The statement has the form $p \to q$. In words, the equivalent form $\sim p \vee q$ becomes "I don't have the money or I'd buy that car."

49. Let p represent "I am you" and q represent "I would watch out." The statement has the form $p \to q$. In words, the equivalent form $\sim p \vee q$ becomes "I am not you or I would watch out."

50. "If you build it, he will come" has the form $p \to q$. The negation has the form $p \wedge \sim q$, which translates as "You build it and he won't come."

51. "If I can make it there, I'll make it anywhere" has the form $p \to q$. The negation has the form $p \wedge \sim q$, which translates as "I can make it there and I won't make it anywhere."

52. "If you don't love me, I won't be happy" has the form $\sim p \to \sim q$. The negation has the form $\sim p \wedge q$, which translates as "You don't love me and I will be happy."

53. "If he's my brother, then he's not heavy" has the form $p \to \sim q$. The negation has the form $p \wedge q$, which translates as "He's my brother and he's heavy."

54. The statements $p \to q$ and $\sim p \vee q$ are equivalent if they have the same truth tables.

p	q	p	$\to$	q	$\sim p$	$\vee$	q
T	T	T	T	T	F	T	T
T	F	T	F	F	F	F	F
F	T	F	T	T	T	T	T
F	F	F	T	F	T	T	F
		1	2	1	1	2	1

Since the truth values in the final columns for each statement are the same, the statements are equivalent.

55.

p	q	$\sim$	$(p$	$\to$	$q)$	p	$\wedge$	$\sim q$
T	T	F	T	T	T	T	F	F
T	F	T	T	F	F	T	T	T
F	T	F	F	T	T	F	F	F
F	F	F	F	T	F	F	F	T
		3	1	2	1	1	2	1

Since the truth values in the final columns for each statement are the same, the statements are equivalent.

56.

p	q	p	$\to$	q	q	$\to$	p
T	T	T	T	T	T	T	T
T	F	T	F	F	F	T	T
F	T	F	T	T	T	F	F
F	F	F	T	F	F	T	F
		1	2	1	1	2	1

Since the truth values in the final columns for each statement are not the same, the statements are not equivalent.

57.

p	q	q	$\to$	p	$\sim p$	$\to$	$\sim q$
T	T	T	T	T	F	T	F
T	F	F	T	T	F	T	T
F	T	T	F	F	T	F	F
F	F	F	T	F	T	T	T
		1	2	1	1	2	1

Since the truth values in the final columns for each statement are the same, the statements are equivalent.

58.

p	q	p	$\to$	$\sim q$	$\sim p$	$\vee$	$\sim q$
T	T	T	F	F	F	F	F
T	F	T	T	T	F	T	T
F	T	F	T	F	T	T	F
F	F	F	T	T	T	T	T
		1	2	1	1	2	1

Since the truth values in the final columns for each statement are the same, the statements are equivalent.

59.

p	q	p	$\to$	q	$\sim q$	$\to$	$\sim p$
T	T	T	T	T	F	T	F
T	F	T	F	F	T	F	F
F	T	F	T	T	F	T	T
F	F	F	T	F	T	T	T
		1	2	1	1	2	1

Since the truth values in the final columns for each statement are the same, the statements are equivalent.

60.

p	q	p	$\wedge$	$\sim q$	$\sim q$	$\to$	$\sim p$
T	T	T	F	F	F	T	F
T	F	T	T	T	T	F	F
F	T	F	F	F	F	T	T
F	F	F	F	T	T	T	T
		1	2	1	1	2	1

Since the truth values in the final columns for each statement are not the same, the statements are not equivalent. Observe that since they have opposite truth values, each statement is the negation of the other.

61.

p	q	$\sim p$	$\wedge$	q	$\sim p$	$\to$	q
T	T	F	F	T	F	T	T
T	F	F	F	F	F	T	F
F	T	T	T	T	T	T	T
F	F	T	F	F	T	F	F
		1	2	1	1	2	1

Since the truth values in the final columns for each statement are not the same, the statements are not equivalent.

62.

p	q	p	$\wedge$	q	$\sim$	$(p$	$\to$	$\sim q)$
T	T	T	T	T	T	T	F	F
T	F	T	F	F	F	T	T	T
F	T	F	F	T	F	F	T	F
F	F	F	F	F	F	F	T	T
		1	2	1	5	3	4	3

The columns labeled 2 and 5 are identical.

63.

p	q	p	$\vee$	q	$\sim p$	$\to$	q
T	T	T	T	T	F	T	T
T	F	T	T	F	F	T	F
F	T	F	T	T	T	T	T
F	F	F	F	F	T	F	F
		1	2	1	3	4	3

The columns labeled 2 and 4 are identical.

64.

p	q	p	$\vee$	q	q	$\vee$	p
T	T	T	T	T	T	T	T
T	F	T	T	F	F	T	T
F	T	F	T	T	T	T	F
F	F	F	F	F	F	F	F
		1	2	1	3	4	3

The columns labeled 2 and 4 are identical.

65.

p	q	p	$\wedge$	q	q	$\wedge$	p
T	T	T	T	T	T	T	T
T	F	T	F	F	F	F	T
F	T	F	F	T	T	F	F
F	F	F	F	F	F	F	F
		1	2	1	3	4	3

The columns labeled 2 and 4 are identical.

66.

p	q	r	$(p$	$\vee$	$q)$	$\vee$	r	p	$\vee$	$(q$	$\vee$	$r)$
T	T	T	T	T	T	T	T	T	T	T	T	T
T	T	F	T	T	T	T	F	T	T	T	T	F
T	F	T	T	T	F	T	T	T	T	F	T	T
T	F	F	T	T	F	T	F	T	T	F	F	F
F	T	T	F	T	T	T	T	F	T	T	T	T
F	T	F	F	T	T	T	F	F	T	T	T	F
F	F	T	F	F	F	T	T	F	T	F	T	T
F	F	F	F	F	F	F	F	F	F	F	F	F
			1	2	1	4	3	5	8	6	7	6

The columns labeled 4 and 8 are identical.

67.

p	q	r	$(p$	$\wedge$	$q)$	$\wedge$	r	p	$\wedge$	$(q$	$\wedge$	$r)$
T	T	T	T	T	T	T	T	T	T	T	T	T
T	T	F	T	T	T	F	F	T	F	T	F	F
T	F	T	T	F	F	F	T	T	F	F	F	T
T	F	F	T	F	F	F	F	T	F	F	F	F
F	T	T	F	F	T	F	T	F	F	T	T	T
F	T	F	F	F	T	F	F	F	F	T	F	F
F	F	T	F	F	F	F	T	F	F	F	F	T
F	F	F	F	F	F	F	F	F	F	F	F	F
			1	2	1	4	3	5	8	6	7	6

The columns labeled 4 and 8 are identical.

68.

p	q	r	p	$\vee$	$(q$	$\wedge$	$r)$	$(p$	$\vee$	$q)$	$\wedge$	$(p$	$\vee$	$r)$
T	T	T	T	T	T	T	T	T	T	T	T	T	T	T
T	T	F	T	T	T	F	F	T	T	T	T	T	T	F
T	F	T	T	T	F	F	T	T	T	F	T	T	T	T
T	F	F	T	T	F	F	F	T	T	F	T	T	T	F
F	T	T	F	T	T	T	T	F	T	T	T	F	T	T
F	T	F	F	F	T	F	F	F	T	T	F	F	F	F
F	F	T	F	F	F	F	T	F	F	F	F	F	T	T
F	F	F	F	F	F	F	F	F	F	F	F	F	F	F
			1	4	2	3	2	5	6	5	9	7	8	7

The columns labeled 4 and 9 are identical.

69.

p	q	r	p	$\wedge$	$(q$	$\vee$	$r)$	$(p$	$\wedge$	$q)$	$\vee$	$(p$	$\wedge$	$r)$
T	T	T	T	T	T	T	T	T	T	T	T	T	T	T
T	T	F	T	T	T	T	F	T	T	T	T	T	F	F
T	F	T	T	T	F	T	T	T	F	F	T	T	T	T
T	F	F	T	F	F	F	F	T	F	F	F	T	F	F
F	T	T	F	F	T	T	T	F	F	T	F	F	F	T
F	T	F	F	F	T	T	F	F	F	T	F	F	F	F
F	F	T	F	F	F	T	T	F	F	F	F	F	F	T
F	F	F	F	F	F	F	F	F	F	F	F	F	F	F
			1	4	2	3	2	5	6	5	9	7	8	7

The columns labeled 4 and 9 are identical.

70.

p	q	$(p$	$\wedge$	$q)$	$\vee$	p
T	T	T	T	T	T	T
T	F	T	F	F	T	T
F	T	F	F	T	F	F
F	F	F	F	F	F	F
		1	2	1	4	3

The p column and the column labeled 4 are identical.

71.

p	q	$(p$	$\vee$	$q)$	$\wedge$	p
T	T	T	T	T	T	T
T	F	T	T	F	T	T
F	T	F	T	T	F	F
F	F	F	F	F	F	F
		1	2	1	4	3

The p column and the column labeled 4 are identical.

72. In the diagram, two series circuits are shown, which correspond to $p \wedge q$ and $p \wedge \sim q$. These circuits, in turn, form a parallel circuit. Thus, the logical statement is

$$(p \wedge q) \vee (p \wedge \sim q).$$

One pair of equivalent statements listed in the text includes

$$(p \wedge q) \vee (p \wedge \sim q) \equiv p \wedge (q \vee \sim q)$$

Since $(q \vee \sim q)$ is always true, $p \wedge (q \vee \sim q)$ simplifies to

$$p \wedge \mathrm{T} \equiv p.$$

73. In the diagram, a parallel circuit is shown, which corresponds to $r \vee q$. This circuit, in turn, is in series with p. Thus, the logical statement is

$$p \wedge (r \vee q).$$

74. In the diagram, a series circuit is shown, which corresponds to $\sim q \wedge r$. This circuit, in turn, forms a parallel circuit with p. Thus, the logical statement is

$$p \vee (\sim q \wedge r).$$

75. The diagram shows q in parallel with a series circuit consisting of p and the parallel circuit involving q and $\sim p$. Thus, the logical statement is

$$q \vee [p \wedge (q \vee \sim p)].$$

One pair of equivalent statements listed in the text includes

$$p \wedge (q \vee \sim p) \equiv (p \wedge q) \vee (p \wedge \sim p).$$

Since $(p \wedge \sim p)$ is never true, $p \wedge (q \vee \sim p)$ simplifies to

$$(p \wedge q) \vee F \equiv (p \wedge q).$$

Thus,
$$\begin{aligned} q \vee [p \wedge (q \vee \sim p)] &\equiv q \vee (p \wedge q) \\ &\equiv (q \vee p) \wedge (q \wedge q) \\ &\equiv (q \vee p) \wedge q \\ &\equiv q. \end{aligned}$$

76. In the diagram, a parallel circuit corresponds to $p \vee q$. This circuit is parallel to $\sim p$. Thus, the total circuit corresponds to the logical statement

$$(p \vee q) \vee \sim p.$$

This statement in turn, is equivalent to

$$(\sim p \vee p) \vee q.$$

Since $\sim p \vee p$ is always true, we have

$$\mathrm{T} \vee q \equiv \mathrm{T}.$$

77. The diagram shows two parallel circuits, $\sim p \vee q$ and $\sim p \vee \sim q$, which are parallel to each other. Thus, the total circuit can be represented as

$$(\sim p \vee q) \vee (\sim p \vee \sim q).$$

This circuit can be simplified using the following equivalencies.

$$\begin{aligned} (\sim p \vee q) \vee (\sim p \vee \sim q) &\equiv \sim p \vee q \vee \sim p \vee \sim q \\ &\equiv \sim p \vee q \vee \sim q \\ &\equiv \sim p \vee (q \vee \sim q) \\ &\equiv \sim p \vee \mathrm{T} \\ &\equiv \mathrm{T} \end{aligned}$$

78. In the diagram, series circuits corresponding to $p \wedge q$ and $p \wedge p$ form a parallel circuit. This parallel circuit is parallel to the series circuit corresponding to $r \wedge \sim r$. Thus, the logical statement is

$$[(p \wedge q) \vee (p \wedge p)] \vee (r \wedge \sim r).$$

This statement simplifies to p as follows:

$$\begin{aligned} [(p \wedge q) \vee (p \wedge p)] \vee (r \wedge \sim r) &\equiv [(p \wedge q) \vee p] \vee (r \wedge \sim r) \\ &\equiv p \vee (r \wedge \sim r) \\ &\equiv p \vee \mathrm{F} \\ &\equiv p. \end{aligned}$$

79. In the diagram, series circuit $\sim p \wedge \sim q$ is parallel to the parallel circuit $p \vee q$. This entire circuit is in series with the parallel circuit $p \vee q$ and p. The logical statement is

$$\{[(\sim p \wedge \sim q) \vee (p \vee q)] \wedge (p \vee q)\} \wedge p.$$

This statement simplifies to p as follows:

$$\begin{aligned} &\{[(\sim p \wedge \sim q) \vee (p \vee q)] \wedge (p \vee q)\} \wedge p \\ &\equiv \{[(\sim (p \vee q) \vee (p \vee q)] \wedge (p \vee q)\} \wedge p \\ &\equiv [T \wedge (p \vee q)] \wedge p \\ &\equiv (p \vee q) \wedge p \\ &\equiv p. \end{aligned}$$

80. The logical statement $p \wedge (q \vee \sim p)$ can be represented by the following circuit.

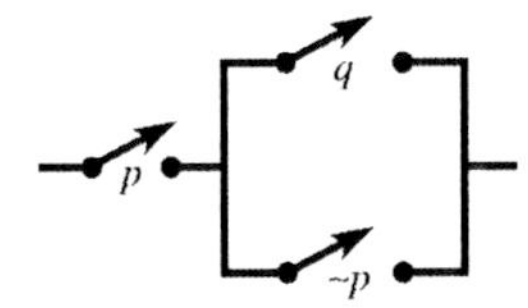

The statement $p \wedge (q \vee \sim p)$ simplifies to $p \wedge q$ as follows:

$$\begin{aligned} p \wedge (q \vee \sim p) &\equiv (p \wedge q) \vee (p \wedge \sim p) \\ &\equiv (p \wedge q) \vee \mathrm{F} \\ &\equiv p \wedge q. \end{aligned}$$

81. The logical statement $(\sim p \wedge \sim q) \wedge \sim r$ can be represented by the following circuit.

82. The logical statement $(p \vee q) \wedge (\sim p \wedge \sim q)$ can be represented by the following circuit.

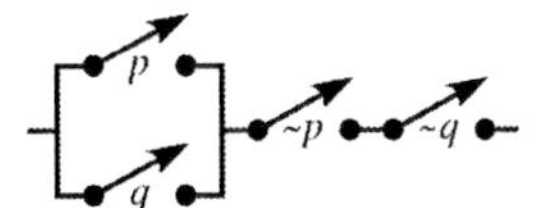

The statement $(p \vee q) \wedge (\sim p \wedge \sim q)$ simplifies to F as follows.

$$\begin{aligned} &(p \vee q) \wedge (\sim p \wedge \sim q) \\ &\equiv [p \wedge (\sim p \wedge \sim q)] \vee [q \wedge (\sim p \wedge \sim q)] \\ &\equiv [(p \wedge \sim p) \wedge \sim q] \vee [q \wedge (\sim q \wedge \sim p)] \\ &\equiv (\mathrm{F} \wedge \sim q) \vee [(q \wedge \sim q) \wedge \sim p] \\ &\equiv \mathrm{F} \vee (\mathrm{F} \wedge \sim p) \\ &\equiv \mathrm{F} \vee \mathrm{F} \\ &\equiv \mathrm{F} \end{aligned}$$

83. The logical statement $(\sim q \wedge \sim p) \vee (\sim p \vee q)$ can be represented by the following circuit.

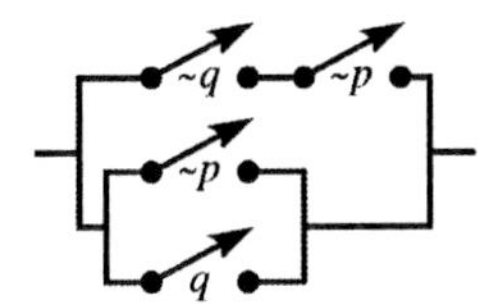

The statement $(\sim q \wedge \sim p) \vee (\sim p \vee q)$ simplifies to $\sim p \vee q$ as follows:

$$\begin{aligned} &(\sim q \wedge \sim p) \vee (\sim p \vee q) \\ &\equiv [\sim q \vee (\sim p \vee q)] \wedge [\sim p \vee (\sim p \vee q)] \\ &\equiv [\sim q \vee \sim p \vee q] \wedge [\sim p \vee \sim p \vee q] \\ &\equiv [(\sim q \vee q) \vee \sim p] \wedge [(\sim p \vee \sim p) \vee q] \\ &\equiv (\mathrm{T} \vee \sim p) \wedge (\sim p \vee q) \\ &\equiv \mathrm{T} \wedge (\sim p \vee q) \\ &\equiv \sim p \vee q. \end{aligned}$$

84. The logical statement $[(p \vee q) \wedge r] \wedge \sim p$ can be represented by the following circuit.

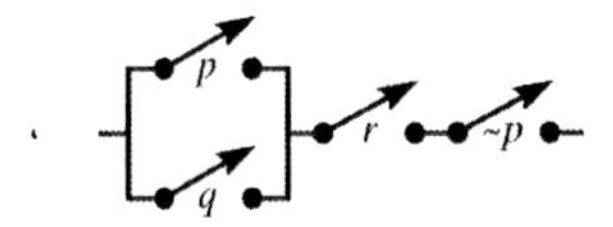

The statement $[(p \vee q) \wedge r] \wedge \sim p$ simplifies to $(r \wedge \sim p) \wedge q$ as follows:

$$\begin{aligned} [(p \vee q) \wedge r] \wedge \sim p &\equiv [(p \wedge r) \vee (q \wedge r)] \wedge \sim p \\ &\equiv [(p \wedge r) \wedge \sim p] \vee [(q \wedge r) \wedge \sim p] \\ &\equiv [p \wedge r \wedge \sim p] \vee [q \wedge r \wedge \sim p] \\ &\equiv [(p \wedge \sim p) \wedge r] \vee [(r \wedge \sim p) \wedge q] \\ &\equiv (\mathrm{F} \wedge r) \vee [(r \wedge \sim p) \wedge q] \\ &\equiv \mathrm{F} \vee [(r \wedge \sim p) \wedge q] \\ &\equiv (r \wedge \sim p) \wedge q \\ &\equiv r \wedge (\sim p \wedge q). \end{aligned}$$

85. The statement $[(\sim p \wedge \sim r) \vee \sim q] \wedge (\sim p \wedge r)$ can be represented by the following circuit.

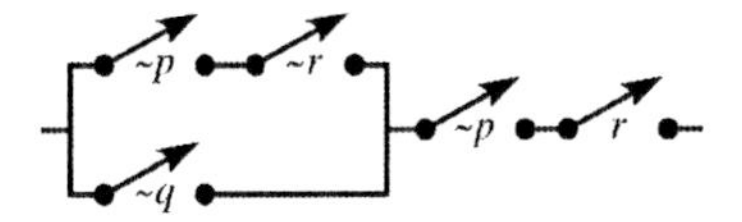

The statement $[(\sim p \wedge \sim r) \vee \sim q] \wedge (\sim p \wedge r)$ simplifies to $(\sim p \wedge r) \wedge \sim q$ in the following manner. Both $[(\sim p \wedge \sim r) \vee \sim q]$ and $(\sim p \wedge r)$ must be true. But if $(\sim p \wedge r)$ is true, then $(\sim p \wedge \sim r)$ is false. If $(\sim p \wedge \sim r)$ is false, then $\sim q$ must be true for the original disjunction to be true. Thus,

$$\begin{aligned} &[(\sim p \wedge \sim r) \vee \sim q] \wedge (\sim p \wedge r) \\ &\equiv (\mathrm{F} \vee \sim q) \wedge (\sim p \wedge r) \\ &\equiv \sim q \wedge (\sim p \wedge r) \\ &\equiv (\sim p \wedge r) \wedge \sim q. \end{aligned}$$

86. The logical statement $\sim q \rightarrow (\sim p \rightarrow q)$ can be represented by the following circuit.

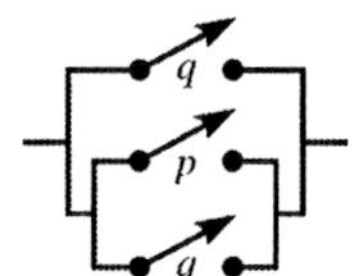

The statement $\sim q \rightarrow (\sim p \rightarrow q)$ simplifies to $p \vee q$ as follows:

$$\begin{aligned}\sim q \rightarrow (\sim p \rightarrow q) &\equiv \sim q \rightarrow (p \vee q)\\ &\equiv q \vee (p \vee q)\\ &\equiv q \vee p \vee q\\ &\equiv p \vee q \vee q\\ &\equiv p \vee (q \vee q)\\ &\equiv p \vee q.\end{aligned}$$

87. The logical statement $\sim p \rightarrow (\sim p \vee \sim q)$ can be represented by the following circuit.

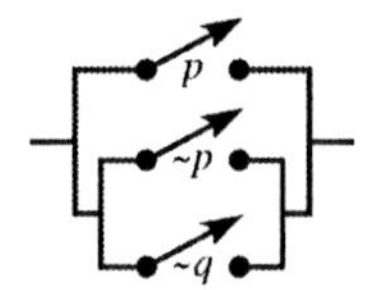

The statement $\sim p \rightarrow (\sim p \vee \sim q)$ simplifies to T as follows:

$$\begin{aligned}\sim p \rightarrow (\sim p \vee \sim q) &\equiv p \vee (\sim p \vee \sim q)\\ &\equiv p \vee \sim p \vee \sim q\\ &\equiv (p \vee \sim p) \vee \sim q\\ &\equiv \text{T} \vee \sim q\\ &\equiv \text{T}.\end{aligned}$$

88. The logical statement $[(p \wedge q) \vee p] \wedge [(p \vee q) \wedge q]$ can be represented by the following circuit..

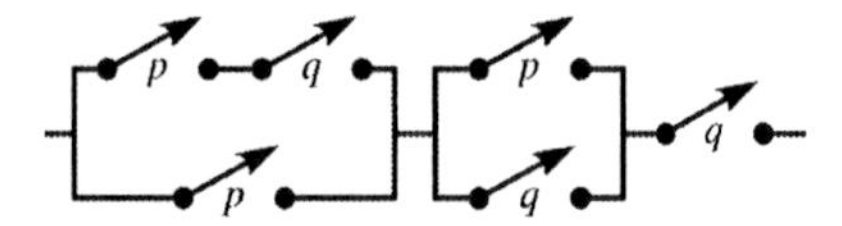

The statement simplifies to $p \wedge q$ as follows:

$$\begin{aligned}[(p \wedge q) \vee p] \wedge [(p \vee q) \wedge q] &\equiv p \wedge [(p \vee q) \wedge q]\\ &\equiv p \wedge q.\end{aligned}$$

89. The logical statement $[(p \wedge q) \vee (p \wedge q)] \vee (p \wedge r)$ can be represented by the following circuit.

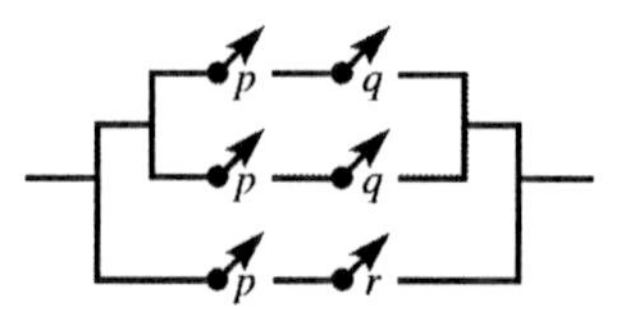

The statement simplifies to $p \wedge (q \vee r)$ as follows:

$$\begin{aligned}[(p \wedge q) \vee (p \wedge q)] \vee (p \wedge r) &\equiv (p \wedge q) \vee (p \wedge r)\\ &\equiv p \wedge (q \vee r).\end{aligned}$$

91. Referring to Figures 10 and 11 of Example 8 in the text:

Cost per year of the circuit in Figure 10
= number of switches × \$0.03 × 24 hrs × 365 days
$= 4 \times 0.03 \times 24 \times 365$
= \$1051.20.

Cost per year of the circuit in Figure 11
= number of switches × \$0.03 × 24 hrs × 365 days
$= 3 \times 0.03 \times 24 \times 365$
= \$788.40

The savings is \$1051.20 − \$788.40 = \$262.80.

92. Each statements has the form $p \rightarrow q$. The equivalent from using *or* is $\sim p \vee q$. The negation is $p \wedge \sim q$.

(a) *Equivalent*: Two or more employers do not provide you with group-term insurance coverage, or you get only one \$50,000 exclusion.

Negation: Two or more employers provide you with group-term insurance coverage, and you do not get only one \$50,000 exclusion.

(b) *Equivalent*: The value of benefits was not less than \$105 in any month, or the unused exclusion cannot be carried over to later months.

Negation: The value of benefits was less than \$105 in any month, and the unused exclusion can be carried over to later months.

(c) *Equivalent*: The plan does not provide for health benefits, or a special rule applies to determine whether the plan is discriminatory.
Negation: The plan provides for health benefits, and a special rule does not apply to determine whether the plan is discriminatory.

93. The form of the statements is $p \rightarrow q$.

An equivalent form is $\sim p \vee q$, which translates as "You are not wheezing persistently or you should see your doctor."

The negation is $p \wedge \sim q$, which translates as "You are wheezing persistently and you should not see your doctor."

94. The form of each statement is $p \rightarrow q$, which is equivalent to $\sim p \vee q$. The negation has the form $p \wedge \sim q$.

(a) Statement: Either you are not married or you can't get married again.
Negation: You are married and you can get married again.
(b) Statement: Your job will cost $500 or less or your contractor is legally required to put it in writing.
Negation: Your job will cost more than $500 and your contractor is not legally required to put it in writing.

(c) Statement: Your application for citizenship is not denied or you can appeal in federal court.
Negation: Your application for citizenship is denied and you cannot appeal in federal court.

6.4 More on the Conditional

Wording may vary in the answers to Exercises 1–28.

1. *The direct statement*: If the exit is ahead, then I don't see it.

(a) *Converse:* If I don't see it, then the exit is ahead.

(b) *Inverse:* If the exit is not ahead, then I see it.

(c) *Contrapositive:* If I see it, then the exit is not ahead.

2. *The direct statement*: If I finish reading this novel, then I'll write a review.

(a) *Converse:* If I write a review, then I finished reading this novel.

(b) *Inverse:* If I don't finish reading this novel, then I won't write a review.

(c) *Contrapositive:* If I don't write a review, then I didn't finish reading this novel.

3. *The direct statement*: If I knew you were coming, I'd have baked a cake.

(a) *Converse:* If I baked a cake, then I knew you were coming.

(b) *Inverse:* If I didn't know you were coming, I wouldn't have baked a cake.

(c) *Contrapositive:* If I didn't bake a cake, then I didn't know you were coming.

4. *The direct statement*: If I'm the bottom, you're the top.

(a) *Converse:* If you're the top, then I'm the bottom.

(b) *Inverse:* If I'm not the bottom, then you're not the top.

(c) *Contrapositive:* If you're not the top, then I'm not the bottom.

5. *It is helpful to reword the given statement.*

The direct statement: If a man is dead, then he doesn't wear plaid.

(a) *Converse:* If a man doesn't wear plaid, then he's dead.

(b) *Inverse:* If a man is not dead, then he wears plaid.

(c) *Contrapositive:* If a man wears plaid, then he's not dead.

6. *It is helpful to reword the given statement.*

The direct statement: If you are a beggar, then you can't be a chooser.

(a) *Converse:* If you can't be a chooser, then you are a beggar.

(b) *Inverse:* If you're not a beggar, then you can be a chooser.

(c) *Contrapositive:* If you can be a chooser, then you are not a beggar.

7. The direct statement: $p \rightarrow \sim q$.

(a) *Converse:* $\sim q \rightarrow p$.

(b) *Inverse:* $\sim p \rightarrow q$.

(c) *Contrapositive:* $q \rightarrow \sim p$.

8. The direct statement: $\sim q \rightarrow \sim p$.

(a) *Converse:* $\sim p \rightarrow \sim q$.

(b) *Inverse:* $q \rightarrow p$.

(c) *Contrapositive:* $p \rightarrow q$.

9. The direct statement: $p \rightarrow (q \vee r)$.

(a) *Converse:* $(q \vee r) \rightarrow p$.

(b) *Inverse:* $\sim p \rightarrow \sim(q \vee r)$ or $\sim p \rightarrow (\sim q \wedge \sim r)$.

(c) *Contrapositive:* $(\sim q \wedge \sim r) \rightarrow \sim p$.

10. The direct statement: $(r \vee \sim q) \rightarrow p$.

(a) *Converse:* $p \rightarrow (r \vee \sim q)$.

(b) *Inverse:* $\sim(r \vee \sim q) \rightarrow \sim p$ or $(\sim r \wedge q) \rightarrow \sim p$.

(c) *Contrapositive:* $\sim p \rightarrow \sim(r \vee \sim q)$ or $\sim p \rightarrow (\sim r \wedge q)$.

13. The statement "Your signature implies that you accept the conditions" becomes "If you sign, then you accept the conditions."

14. The statement "His tardiness implies that he doesn't care" becomes "If he is tardy, then he doesn't care."

15. The statement "You can take this course pass/fail only if you have prior permission" becomes "If you can take this course pass/fail, then you have prior permission."

16. The statement "You can purchase this stock only if you have \$1000" becomes "If you can purchase this stock, then you have \$1000."

17. The statement "You can skate on the pond when the temperature is below 10°" becomes "If the temperature is below 10°, then you can skate on the pond."

18. The statement "The party will be stopped when more than 200 people attend" becomes "If more than 200 people attend, then the party will be stopped."

19. The statement "Eating ten hot dogs is sufficient to make someone sick" becomes "If someone eats ten hot dogs, then he or she will get sick."

20. The statement "Two hours in the desert sun is sufficient to give the typical person a sunburn" becomes "If the typical person spends two hours in the desert sun, then that person will get a sunburn."

21. The statement "A valid passport is necessary for travel to France" becomes "If you travel to France, then you have a valid passport."

22. The statement "Support from the party bosses is necessary to get the nomination" becomes "If someone gets the nomination, then he or she has support from the party bosses."

23. The statement "For a number to have a real square root, it is necessary that it be nonnegative" becomes "If a number has a real square root, then it is nonnegative."

24. The statement "For a number to have a real square root, it is sufficient that it be nonnegative" becomes "If a number is nonnegative, then it has a real square root.

25. The statement "All brides are beautiful" becomes "If someone is a bride, then she is beautiful."

26. The statement "All passengers for Hempstead must change trains at Jamaica station" becomes "If you are a passenger for Hempstead, then you must change trains at Jamaica station."

27. The statement "A number is divisible by 3 if the sum of its digits is divisible by 3" becomes "If the sum of a number's digits is divisible by 3, then it is divisible by 3."

28. The statement "A number is even if its last digit is even" becomes "If a number's last digit is even, then it is even.

29. Option d is the answer since "r is necessary for s" represents the converse, $s \rightarrow r$, of all of the other statements.

33. The statement "$5 = 9 - 4$ if and only if $8 + 2 = 10$" is true, since this is a biconditional composed of two true statements.

34. The statement "$3 + 1 \neq 6$ if and only if $8 \neq 8$" is false since this is a biconditional consisting of a true and a false statement.

35. The statement "$8+7 \neq 15$ if and only if $3 \times 5 \neq 9$" is false, since this is a biconditional consisting of one false statement and one true statement.

36. The statement "$6 \times 2 = 14$ if and only if $9+7 \neq 16$" is true, since this is a biconditional consisting of two false statements.

37. The statement "China is in Asia if and only if Mexico is in Europe" is false, since it is a biconditional consisting of a true statement and a false statement.

38. The statement "The moon is made of green cheese if and only if Hawaii is one of the United States" is false, since it is a biconditional consisting of a false statement and a true statement.

39.

p	q	$(\sim p$	$\wedge$	$q)$	$\leftrightarrow$	$(p$	$\rightarrow$	$q)$
T	T	F	F	T	F	T	T	T
T	F	F	F	F	T	T	F	F
F	T	T	T	T	T	F	T	T
F	F	T	F	F	F	F	T	F
		1	2	1	5	3	4	3

40.

p	q	$(p$	$\leftrightarrow$	$\sim q)$	$\leftrightarrow$	$(\sim p$	$\rightarrow$	$q)$
T	T	T	F	F	F	F	T	T
T	F	T	T	T	F	F	F	F
F	T	F	T	F	T	T	T	T
F	F	F	F	T	F	T	T	F
		1	2	1	5	3	4	3

41. **(a)** "Your employer must tell you if the award qualifies for full or partial tax-free treatment" becomes "If the award qualifies for full or partial tax-free treatment, then your employer must tell you."

(b) "Medical expenses are 'qualified' only if incurred *after* the HSA has been established" becomes "If medical expenses are 'qualified,' then they are incurred *after* the HSA has been established."

(c) "You can avoid this interest deduction limitation if you elect to report the market discount annually as interest income" becomes "If you elect to report the market discount annually as interest income, you can avoid this interest deduction limitation."

42. For the original $p \rightarrow q$, the converse is $q \rightarrow p$, the inverse is $\sim p \rightarrow \sim q$, and the contrapositive is $\sim q \rightarrow \sim p$. For each of the following, the original and the contrapositive are equivalent and the converse and the inverse are equivalent.

(a) *Converse*: If the market discount interest income rule does *not* apply, then the bond was issued before July 19, 1984.
Inverse: If the bond was not issued before July 19, 1984, the market discount interest income rule applies.
Contrapositive: If the market discount interest income rule applies, then the bond was not issued before July 19, 1984,

(b) *Converse*: If the gain is long term, then the bond was held long term.
Inverse: If the bond was not held long term, then the gain is not long term.
Contrapositive: If the gain is not long term, then the bond was not held long term.

(c) *Converse*: If the excess short-term loss is deductible up to the \$3000 capital loss limit, then the net short-term loss exceeds the net long-term gain.
Inverse: If the net short-term loss does not exceed the net long term gain, then the excess short-term loss is not deductible up to the \$3000 capital loss limit.
Contrapositive: If the excess short-term loss is not deductible up to the \$3000 capital loss limit, then the net short-term loss does not exceed net long-term gain.

43. For $p \rightarrow q$, the converse is $q \rightarrow p$, the inverse is $\sim p \rightarrow \sim q$, and the contrapositive is $\sim q \rightarrow \sim p$.

Converse: If you may avoid paying the annual fee billed on this statement, then you close your account within 30 days from the date this statement was mailed.
Inverse: If you do not close your account within 30 days from the date this statement was mailed, you may not avoid paying the annual fee billed on this statement.
Contrapositive: If you may not avoid paying the annual fee billed on this statement, then you do not close your account within 30 days from the date this statement was mailed.

The converse and the inverse are equivalent, and the contrapositive and the original statement are equivalent.

44. The contrapositive of "If you are wheezing persistently, you should see your doctor" is "If you should not see your doctor, then you are not wheezing persistently."

45. **(a)** Let p represent "there are triplets," let q represent "the most persistent stands to gain an extra meal," and let r represent "it may eat at the expense of another." Then the statement can be written as $p \to (q \wedge r)$.

(b) The contrapositive is $\sim(q \wedge r) \to p$, which is equivalent to $(\sim q \vee \sim r) \to p$: If the most persistent does not stand to gain an extra meal or it does not eat at the expense of another, then there are not triplets.

46. For $p \to q$, the converse is $q \to p$, the inverse is $\sim p \to \sim q$, and the contrapositive is $\sim q \to \sim p$.

Converse and inverse are equivalent; original and contrapositive are equivalent.

(a) *Converse*: If you can't get married again, then you are married.
Inverse: If you aren't married, then you can get married again.
Contrapositive: If you can get married again, then you are not married.

(b) *Converse*: If your contractor is legally required to put it in writing, then your job is going to cost more than $500.
Inverse: If your job is not going to cost more than $500, then your contractor is not legally required to put it in writing.
Contrapositive: If your contractor is not legally required to put it in writing, then your job is not going to cost more than $500.

(c) *Converse:* If you can appeal in federal court, then your application for citizenship is denied.
Inverse: If your application for citizenship is not denied, then you cannot appeal in federal court.
Contrapositive: If you cannot appeal in federal court, then your application for citizenship has not been denied.

47. If liberty and equality are not best attained when all persons share alike in the government to the utmost, then they are not, as is thought by some, chiefly to be found in democracy.

48. **(a)** Let d represent "political development in Western Europe will increase" and let a represent "social assimilation is increasing." Then the statement can be written as $d \longleftrightarrow a$. The truth table for this statement is as follows.

d	a	$d \longleftrightarrow a$
T	T	T
T	F	F
F	T	F
F	F	T

(b) If a is true and a is false then $d \longleftrightarrow a$ is false.

49. The statement can be written as

$$(d \to l) \wedge \sim(l \to d)$$

50. If a country has democracy, then it has a high level of education. *Converse*: If a country has a high level of education, then it has democracy. *Inverse*: If a country does not have democracy, then it does not have a high level of education. *Contrapositive*: If a country does not have a high level of education, then it does not have a democracy.

The contrapositive is equivalent to the original.

51. If there is an R.P.F. alliance, there there is a Modéré incumbent. *Converse*: If there is a Modéré incumbent, then there is an R.P.F. alliance. *Inverse*: If there is not an R.P.F. alliance, then there is not a Modéré incumbent. *Contrapositive*: If there is not a Modéré incumbent, then there is not an R.P.F. alliance.
The contrapositive is equivalent to the original.

52. The rule "If a card has a D on one side, then it must have a 3 on the other side" is violated when a card has a D on one side and the number on the other side is not 3. Thus, we only need to turn over cards that have a D or a number other than 3.

D card: This card must be turned over to see whether the rule has been violated. If the number on the other side is 3, the rule has not been violated; however, if the number is not 3, the rule has been violated.

F card: Since the premise of the rule is false for this card, the rule automatically holds. Thus, this card does not need to be turned over.

3 card: Since the conclusion of the rule is true, the rule automatically holds. Thus, this card does not need to be turned over.

7 card: This card must be turned over to see whether the rule has been violated. If the letter is D, then the rule has been violated; however, if the letter on the other side is not D, the rule has not been violated.

53. "Worked on the weekend": Must be turned over to see whether the employee got a day off.
"Did not work on the weekend": Need not be turned over, since it does not describe an employee who worked on the weekend.
"Did get a day off": Need not be turned over, since it cannot describe an employee who worked on the weekend without getting a day off.
"Did not get a day off": Must be turned over to see whether the other side says "worked on the weekend."

54. **(a)** If ...then *form*: If nothing is ventured, then nothing is gained.
Contrapositive: If something is gained, then something is ventured.
Statement using or: Something is ventured or nothing is gained.

(b) If ...then *form*: If something is one of the best things in life, then it is free.
Contrapositive: If something is not free, then it is not one of the best things in life.
Statement using or: Something is not one of the best things in life or it is free.

(c) If ...then *form*: If something is a cloud, then it has a silver lining.
Contrapositive: If something doesn't have a silver lining, then it isn't a cloud.
Statement using or: Something is not a cloud or it doesn't have a silver lining.

56. "p only if q" is equivalent to "if p then q" or "not p or q."

(a) If you can score in this box then the dice include 3 or more of the same number. You cannot score in this box or the dice include 3 or more of the same number.

(b) If you can score in this box, then the dice show any sequence of four numbers. You cannot score in this box or the dice show any sequence of four numbers.

(c) If you can score in this box, then the dice show three of one number and two of another. You cannot score in this box or the dice show three of one number and two of another.

6.5 Analyzing Arguments and Proofs

1. Let p represent "she weighs the same as a duck," q represent "she's made of wood," and r represent "she's a witch." The argument is then represented symbolically by:

$$\begin{array}{l} p \to q \\ \underline{q \to r} \\ p \to r. \end{array}$$

This is the <u>valid</u> argument form Reasoning by Transitivity.

2. Let p represent "love is out of the question," q represent "these lyrics make no sense," and r represent "there's no point to this affection." The argument is then represented symbolically by:

$$\begin{array}{l} p \to q \\ \underline{q \to r} \\ p \to r. \end{array}$$

This is the <u>valid</u> argument form Reasoning by Transitivity.

3. Let p represent "I had a hammer" and q represent "I'd hammer in the morning." The argument is then represented symbolically by:

$$\begin{array}{l} p \to q \\ \underline{p \quad\quad} \\ q. \end{array}$$

This is the <u>valid</u> argument form Modus Ponens.

4. Let p represent "I were a swan" and q represent "I'd be gone." The argument is then represented symbolically by:

$$\begin{array}{l} p \to q \\ \underline{p \quad\quad} \\ q. \end{array}$$

This is the valid argument form Modus Ponens.

5. Let p represent "you want to make trouble" and q represent "the door is that way." The argument is then represented symbolically by:

$$\begin{array}{l} p \to q \\ \underline{q \quad\quad} \\ p. \end{array}$$

Since this is the form Fallacy of the Converse, it is invalid and considered a fallacy.

6. Let p represent "You finish the test" and q represent "you can leave early." The argument is then represented symbolically by:

$$\begin{array}{l} p \to q \\ \underline{q \quad\quad} \\ p. \end{array}$$

Since this is the form Fallacy of the Converse, it is invalid and considered a fallacy.

7. Let p represent "Martin Broudeur plays" and q represent "the opponent gets shut out." The argument is then represented symbolically by:

$$\begin{array}{l} p \to q \\ \underline{\sim q \quad\quad} \\ \sim p. \end{array}$$

This is the valid argument form Modus Tollens.

8. Let p represent "You want to follow along" and q represent "we're on p. 315." The argument is then represented symbolically by:

$$\begin{array}{l} p \to q \\ \underline{\sim q \quad\quad} \\ \sim p. \end{array}$$

This is the valid argument form Modus Tollens.

9. Let p represent "we evolved a race of Isaac Newtons" and q represent "that would not be progress." The argument is then represented symbolically by:

$$\begin{array}{l} p \to q \\ \underline{\sim p \quad\quad} \\ \sim q. \end{array}$$

Note: that since we let q represent "that would not be progress," then $\sim q$ represents "that is progress." Since this is the form Fallacy of the Inverse, it is invalid and considered a fallacy.

10. Let p represent "I have seen farther than others" and q represent " I have stood on the shoulders of giants." The argument is then represented symbolically by:

$$\begin{array}{l} p \to q \\ \underline{\sim p \quad\quad} \\ \sim q. \end{array}$$

Since this is the form Fallacy of the Inverse, it is invalid and considered a fallacy.

11. Let p represent "Something is rotten in the state of Denmark" and q represent "my name isn't Hamlet." The argument is then represented symbolically by:

$$\begin{array}{l} p \vee q \text{ (or } q \vee p) \\ \underline{\sim q \quad\quad} \\ \sim p. \end{array}$$

Since this is the form Disjunctive Syllogism, it is a valid argument.

12. Let p represent "We shall conquer together" and q represent "we shall die together." The argument is then represented symbolically by:

$$\begin{array}{l} p \vee q \text{ (or } q \vee p) \\ \underline{\sim q \quad\quad} \\ p. \end{array}$$

Since this is the form Disjunctive Syllogism, it is a valid argument.

To show validity for the arguments in the following exercises we must show that the conjunction of the premises implies the conclusion. That is, the conditional statement $[P_1 \wedge P_2 \wedge \ldots \wedge P_n] \to C$ *must be a tautology.*

13.
$$\begin{array}{ll} 1.\ p \vee q & \text{T} \\ 2.\ \underline{p \quad\quad} & \text{T} \\ \quad\quad \sim q & \text{F} \end{array}$$

The argument is invalid. When $p = \text{T}$ and $q = \text{T}$, the premises are true but the conclusion is false.

14.
$$\begin{array}{ll} 1.\ p \vee \sim q & \text{T} \\ 2.\ \underline{p \quad\quad} & \text{T} \\ \quad\quad \sim q & \text{F} \end{array}$$

The argument is invalid. When $p = \text{T}$ and $q = \text{T}$, the premises are true but the conclusion is false.

15. 1. $p \to q$ T
2. $q \to p$ T
$p \wedge q$ F

The argument is invalid. When $p =$ F and $q =$ F, the premises are true but the conclusion is false.

16. 1. $\sim p \to q$ T
2. p T
$\sim q$ F

The argument is invalid. When $p =$ T and $q =$ T, the premises are true but the conclusion is false.

17. The argument is valid.

1. $\sim p \to \sim q$ Premise
2. q Premise
3. p 1, 2, Modus Tollens

18. The argument is valid.

1. $p \to \sim q$ Premise
2. q Premise
3. $\sim p$ 1, 2, Modus Tollens

19. The argument is valid.

1. $p \to q$ Premise
2. $\sim q$ Premise
3. $\sim p \to r$ Premise
4. $\sim p$ 1, 2, Modus Tollens
5. r 3, 4, Modus Ponens

20. The argument is valid.

1. $p \vee q$ Premise
2. $\sim p$ Premise
3. $r \to \sim q$ Premise
4. q 1, 2, Disjunctive Syllogism
5. $\sim r$ 3, 4, Modus Tollens

21. The argument is valid.

1. $p \to q$ Premise
2. $q \to r$ Premise
3. $\sim r$ Premise
4. $p \to r$ 1, 2, Transitivity
5. $\sim p$ 3, 4, Modus Tollens

22. The argument is valid.

1. $p \to q$ Premise
2. $r \to \sim q$ Premise
3. $q \to \sim r$ 2, Contrapositive
4. $p \to \sim r$ 1, 3, Transitivity

23. The argument is valid.

1. $p \to q$ Premise
2. $q \to \sim r$ Premise
3. p Premise
4. $r \vee s$ Premise
5. q 1, 3, Modus Ponens
6. $\sim r$ 2, 5, Modus Ponens
7. s 4, 6, Disjunctive Syllogism

24. The argument is valid.

1. $p \to q$ Premise
2. $\sim p \to r$ Premise
3. $s \to \sim q$ Premise
4. $\sim r \to p$ 2, Contrapositive
5. $\sim r \to q$ 1, 4, Transitivity
6. $q \to \sim s$ 3, Contrapositive
7. $\sim r \to \sim s$ 5, 6, Transitivity

25. Make a truth table for the statement $(p \wedge q) \to p$.

p	q	$(p$	$\wedge$	$q)$	$\to$	p
T	T	T	T	T	T	T
T	F	T	F	F	T	T
F	T	F	F	T	T	F
F	F	F	F	F	T	F
		1	2	1	3	2

Since the final column, 3, indicates that the conditional statement that represents the argument is true for all possible truth values of p and q, the statement is a tautology.

26. Make a truth table for the statement $p \to (p \vee q)$.

p	q	p	$\to$	$(p$	$\vee$	$q)$
T	T	T	T	T	T	T
T	F	T	T	T	T	F
F	T	F	T	F	T	T
F	F	F	T	F	F	F
		2	3	1	2	1

27. Make a truth table for the statement $(p \wedge q) \to (p \wedge q)$.

p	q	$(p$	$\wedge$	$q)$	$\to$	$(p$	$\wedge$	$q)$
T	T	T	T	T	T	T	T	T
T	F	T	F	F	T	T	F	F
F	T	F	F	T	T	F	F	T
F	F	F	F	F	T	F	F	F
		1	2	1	3	1	2	1

Since the final column, 3, indicates that the conditional statement that represents the argument is true for all possible truth values of p and q, the statement is a tautology.

29. Let c represent "my computer is working," f represent "the power supply is faulty," and s represent "my stereo works." The argument is then presented symbolically by:

$$\begin{array}{l} c \\ f \to \sim c \\ \underline{\sim f \to s} \\ s. \end{array}$$

The argument is valid.

1.	c	Premise
2.	$f \to \sim c$	Premise
3.	$\sim f \to s$	Premise
4.	$\sim f$	1, 2, Modus Tollens
5.	s	3, 4, Modus Ponens

30. Let. f represent "Fenton runs for senator," h represent "Hoffman runs for governor," and t represent "Tobin runs for congressman." The argument is then represented symbolically by:

$$\begin{array}{l} f \to h \\ \underline{t \to \sim h} \\ t \to \sim f. \end{array}$$

The argument is valid.

1.	$f \to h$	Premise
2.	$t \to \sim h$	Premise
3.	$\sim h \to \sim f$	1, Contrapositive
4.	$t \to \sim f$	2, 3, Transitivity

31. Let s represent "you have strep throat," f represent "you have a fever," and c represent "you have a serious cough." The argument is then represented symbolically by:

$$\begin{array}{l} s \to f \\ c \vee f \\ \underline{\sim c} \\ \sim s. \end{array}$$

The argument is invalid. Suppose s is T, f is T, and c is F. Then the premises are true but the conclusion is false as seen in the table below.

1.	$s \to f$	T
2.	$c \vee f$	T
3.	$\sim c$	T
4.	$\sim s$	F

32. Let u represent "I've got you under my skin," d represent "you are deep in the heart of me," and r represent "you are really a part of me" The argument is then represented symbolically by:

$u \to d$	T
$d \to \sim r$	T
$d \vee r$	T
$u \to r.$	F

The argument is invalid. When $u = \text{T}$, $d = \text{T}$, and $r = \text{F}$, the premises are true but the conclusion is false.

33. Let y represent "the Yankees will be in the World Series," m represent "the Marlins will be in the World Series," and n represent "the National League wins." The argument is then represented symbolically by:

$$\begin{array}{l} y \vee \sim m \\ \sim m \to \sim n \\ \underline{n} \\ y. \end{array}$$

The argument is valid.

1. $y \vee \sim m$	Premise
2. $\sim m \to \sim n$	Premise
3. n	Premise
4. m	2, 3, Modus Tollens
5. y	1,4, Disjunctive Syllogism

34. Let m represent "Matt plays the drums," j represent "Jimmy plays the guitar," and k represent "Karla plays the flute." The argument is then represented symbolically by:

$$\begin{array}{l} m \to j \\ k \vee m \\ \underline{\sim k} \\ j. \end{array}$$

The argument is valid.

1. $m \to j$	Premise
2. $k \vee m$	Premise
3. $\sim k$	Premise
4. m	2, 3, Disjunctive Syllogism
5. j	1, 4, Modus Ponens

35. Let p represent "I am your woman," q represent "you are my man," and r represent "I stop loving you." The argument is then represented symbolically by:

$$\begin{array}{l} (p \wedge q) \rightarrow \sim r \\ \underline{r \qquad\qquad} \\ \sim p \vee \sim q. \end{array}$$

The argument is <u>valid</u>.

1. $(p \wedge q) \rightarrow \sim r$ Premise
2. r Premise
3. $\sim (p \wedge q)$ 1, 2, Modus Tollens
4. $\sim p \vee \sim q$ 3, De Morgan's Law

36. The argument is <u>valid</u>.

Let p represent "my car starts," q represent "the battery is strong," r represent "I got a jump," and s represent "I'm taking the train."
The argument is then represented symbolically by

$$\begin{array}{l} p \rightarrow (q \vee r) \\ p \vee s \\ \underline{\sim q \wedge \sim r \quad} \\ s \end{array}$$

1. $p \rightarrow (q \vee r)$ Premise
2. $p \vee s$ Premise
3. $\sim q \wedge \sim r$ Premise
4. $\sim (q \vee r)$ 3, De Morgan's Law
5. $\sim p$ 1, 4, Modus Tollens
6. s 2, 5, Disjunctive Syllogism

37. We apply reasoning by repeated transitivity to the six premises. A conclusion from this reasoning, which makes the argument valid, is reached by linking the first antecedent to the last consequent. This conclusion is "If I tell you the time, then my life will be miserable."

38. **(a)** $d \rightarrow \sim w$ **(b)** $o \rightarrow w$ or $w \rightarrow \sim o$ **(c)** $p \rightarrow d$ **(d)** $p \rightarrow \sim o$, *Conclusion*: If it is my poultry, then it is not an officer. In Lewis Carroll's words, "My poultry are not officers."

39. **(a)** $s \rightarrow l$ or $\sim l \rightarrow s$ **(b)** $\sim s \rightarrow \sim j$ **(c)** $y \rightarrow \sim l$ **(d)** $y \rightarrow \sim j$, *Conclusion*: If he is your son, then he is not fit to serve on a jury. In Lewis Carroll's words, "None of our sons are fit to serve on a jury."

40. **(a)** $b \rightarrow \sim t$ or $t \rightarrow \sim b$ **(b)** $w \rightarrow c$ **(c)** $\sim b \rightarrow h$ **(d)** $\sim w \rightarrow \sim p$ or $p \rightarrow w$ **(e)** $c \rightarrow t$ **(f)** $p \rightarrow h$, *Conclusion*: If one is a pawnbroker, then one is honest. In Lewis Carroll's words, "No pawnbroker is dishonest."

41. **(a)** $a \rightarrow s$ or $\sim s \rightarrow \sim a$ **(b)** $g \rightarrow i$ **(c)** $i \rightarrow \sim s$ **(d)** $g \rightarrow \sim a$, *Conclusion*: If it is a guinea pig, then it does not appreciate Beethoven. In Lewis Carroll's words, "Guinea pigs never really appreciate Beethoven."

42. **(a)** $d \rightarrow p$ **(b)** $\sim t \rightarrow \sim i$ **(c)** $r \rightarrow \sim f$ or $f \rightarrow \sim r$ **(d)** $o \rightarrow d$ or $\sim d \rightarrow \sim o$ **(e)** $\sim c \rightarrow i$ **(f)** $b \rightarrow s$ **(g)** $p \rightarrow f$ **(h)** $\sim o \rightarrow \sim c$ or $c \rightarrow o$ **(i)** $s \rightarrow \sim t$ or $t \rightarrow \sim s$ **(j)** $b \rightarrow \sim r$, *Conclusion*: If it is written by Brown, then I can't read it. In Lewis Carroll's words, "I cannot read any of Brown's letters."

43. **(a)** $p \rightarrow b$ or $\sim b \rightarrow \sim p$ **(b)** $\sim t \rightarrow \sim l$ **(c)** $o \rightarrow \sim s$ **(d)** $b \rightarrow l$ **(e)** $w \rightarrow p$ **(f)** $\sim s \rightarrow \sim t$ **(g)** $o \rightarrow \sim w$, *Conclusion*: If he is an opium eater, then he doesn'tt wear white gloves. In Lewis Carroll's words, "Opium eaters never wear white kid gloves."

6.6 Analyzing Arguments with Quantifiers

1. Let $b(x)$ represent "x is a book" and $s(x)$ represent "x is a bestseller."

(a) $\exists x[b(x) \wedge s(x)]$

(b) $\forall x[b(x) \rightarrow \sim s(x)]$

(c) No books are bestsellers.

2. Let $d(x)$ represent "x is a dog" and $h(x)$ represent "x will have its day."

(a) $\forall x[d(x) \rightarrow h(x)]$

(b) $\exists x[d(x) \wedge \sim h(x)]$

(c) There is a dog that doesn't have its day.

3. Let $c(x)$ represent "x is a CEO" and $s(x)$ represent "x sleeps well at night."

(a) $\forall x[c(x) \rightarrow \sim s(x)]$

(b) $\exists x[c(x) \wedge s(x)]$

(c) There is a CEO who sleeps well at night.

4. Let $b(x)$ represent "x is a business" and $s(x)$ represent "x is like show business."

(a) $\forall x[b(x) \rightarrow \sim s(x)]$

(b) $\exists x[b(x) \wedge s(x)]$

(c) There is a business like show business.

5. Let $l(x)$ represent "x is a leaf" and $b(x)$ represent "x is brown."

(a) $\forall x[l(x) \rightarrow b(x)]$

(b) $\exists x[l(x) \wedge \sim b(x)]$

(c) There is a leaf that's not brown.

6. Let $d(x)$ represent "x is a day" and $b(x)$ represent "x is better than others."

(a) $\exists x[d(x) \wedge b(x)]$

(b) $\forall x[d(x) \rightarrow \sim b(x)]$

(c) No days are better than others.

7. (a) Let $g(x)$represent "x is a girl" and $f(x)$ represent "x wants to have fun." Let t represent Teri Lovelace. We can represent the argument symbolically as follows.

$$\begin{array}{l} \forall x[g(x) \rightarrow f(x)] \\ \underline{g(t) \qquad\qquad} \\ f(t) \end{array}$$

(b) Draw an Euler diagram where the region representing "girls" must be inside the region representing "people who want to have fun" so that the first premise is true.

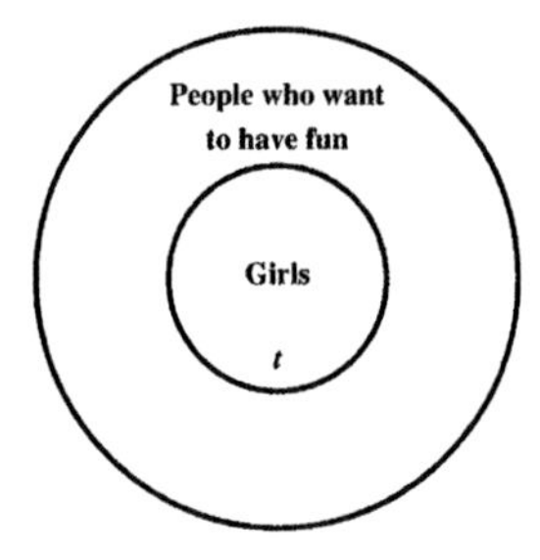

By the second premise, t must lie in the "girls" region. Since this forces the conclusion to be true, the argument is <u>valid</u>.

8. (a) Let $s(x)$ represent "x is a sophomore" and $c(x)$ represent "x has earned at least 60 credits." Let l represent Liliana Molina. We can represent the argument symbolically as follows.

$$\begin{array}{l} \forall x[s(x) \rightarrow c(x)] \\ \underline{s(l) \qquad\qquad} \\ c(l) \end{array}$$

(b) Draw an Euler diagram where the region representing "sophomores" must be inside the region representing "those who have earned at least 60 credits" so that the first premise is true.

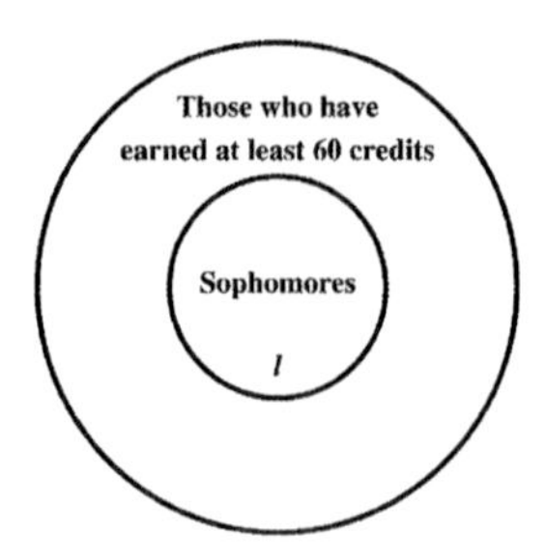

By the second premise, l must lie in the "sophomores" region. Since this forces the conclusion to be true, the argument is <u>valid</u>.

9. (a) Let $p(x)$ represent "x is a professor" and $c(x)$ represent "x is covered with chalk dust." Let o represent Otis Taylor. We can represent the argument symbolically as follows.

$$\begin{array}{l} \forall x[p(x) \rightarrow c(x)] \\ \underline{c(o) \qquad\qquad} \\ p(o) \end{array}$$

(b) Draw an Euler diagram where the region representing "professors" must be inside the region representing "those who are covered with chalk dust" so that the first premise is true.

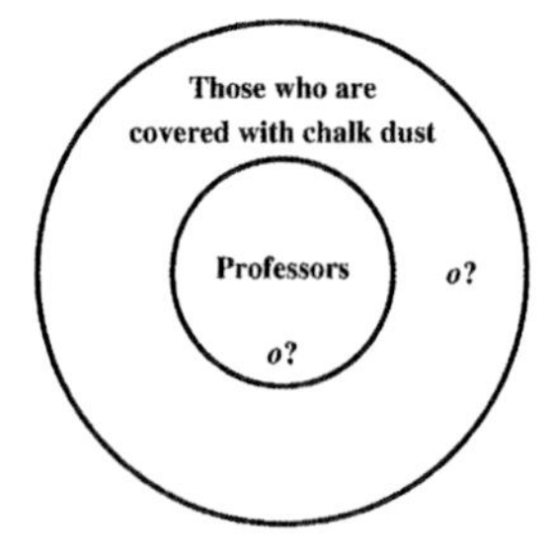

By the second premise, o must lie in the "those who are covered with chalk dust" region. Thus, o could be inside or outside the inner region "professors." Since this allows for a false conclusion (Otis doesn't have to be a professor to be covered with chalk dust), the argument is <u>invalid</u>.

10. **(a)** Let $d(x)$ represent "x is a dinosaur" and $e(x)$ represent "x is extinct." Let o represent the dodo. We can represent the argument symbolically as follows.

$$\begin{array}{l} \forall x[d(x) \rightarrow e(x)] \\ \underline{e(o)} \\ d(o) \end{array}$$

(b) Draw an Euler diagram where the region representing "dinosaurs" must be inside the region representing "extinct things" so that the first premise is true.

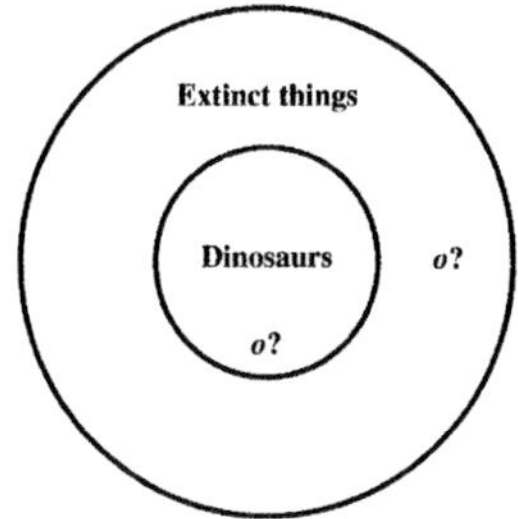

By the second premise, o must lie in the region "extinct things." Thus, o could be inside or outside of the inner region "dinosaurs." Since this allows for a false conclusion (The dodo doesn't have to be a dinosaur to be extinct.), the argument is invalid.

11. **(a)** Let $c(x)$ represent "x is an accountant" and $p(x)$ represent "x uses a spreadsheet." Let n represent Nancy Hart. We can represent the argument symbolically as follows.

$$\begin{array}{l} \forall x[c(x) \rightarrow p(x)] \\ \underline{\sim p(n)} \\ \sim c(n) \end{array}$$

(b) Draw an Euler diagram where the region representing "accountants" must be inside the region representing "those who use spreadsheets" so that the first premise is true.

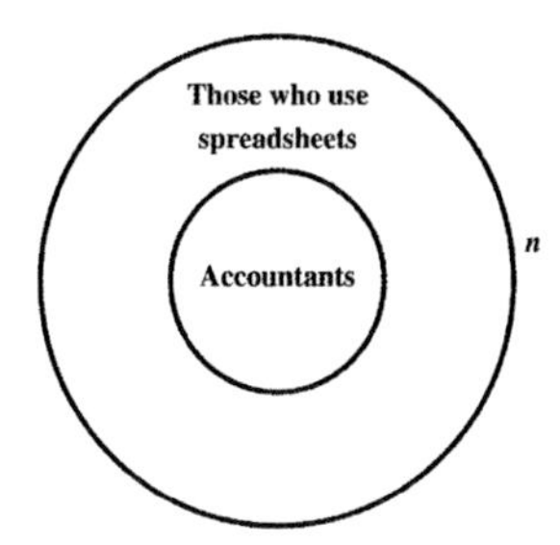

By the second premise, n must lie outside the region representing "those who use spreadsheets." Since this forces the conclusion to be true, the argument is valid.

12. **(a)** Let $f(x)$ represent "x is a fish" and $g(x)$ represent "x has gills." Let w represent a whale. We can represent the argument symbolically as follows.

$$\begin{array}{l} \forall x[f(x) \rightarrow g(x)] \\ \underline{\sim g(w)} \\ \sim f(w) \end{array}$$

(b) Draw an Euler diagram where the region representing "fish" must be inside the region representing "things with gills" so that the first premise is true.

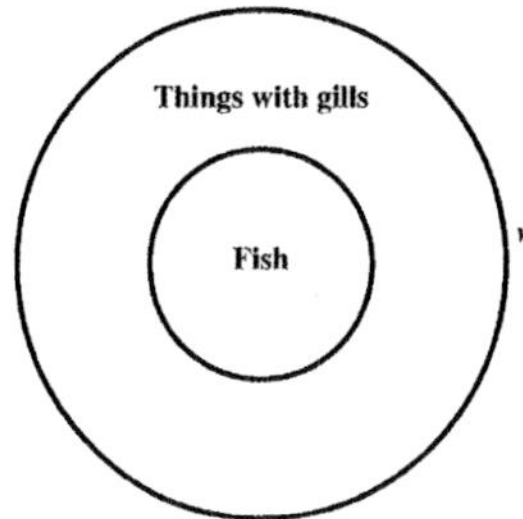

By the second premise, w must lie outside the region representing "things with gills." Since this forces the conclusion to be true, the argument is valid.

13. **(a)** Let $t(x)$ represent "x is turned down for a mortgage," $s(x)$ represent "x has a second income," and $b(x)$ represent "x needs a mortgage broker." We can represent the argument symbolically as follows.

$$\begin{array}{l} \exists x[t(x) \wedge s(x)] \\ \underline{\forall x[t(x) \rightarrow b(x)]} \\ \exists x[s(x) \wedge b(x)] \end{array}$$

(b) Draw an Euler diagram where the region representing "Those who are turned down for a mortgage" intersects the region representing "Those with a 2nd income." This keeps the first premise true.

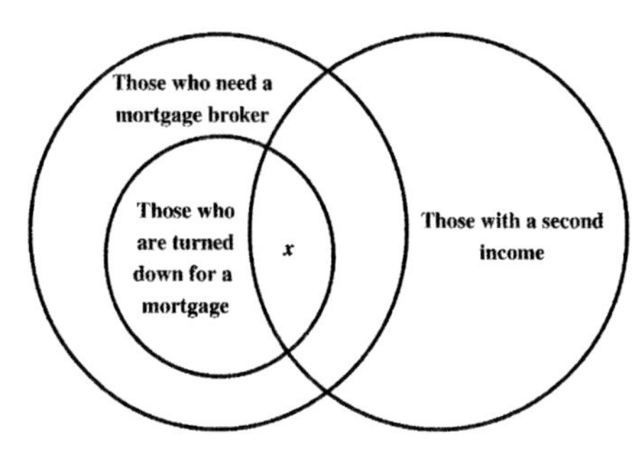

By the second premise the region representing "Those who are turned down for a mortgage" must be inside the region "Those who need a mortgage broker." Since x lies in both regions "These with a 2nd income" and "Those who need a mortgage broker," the conclusion is true and so the argument is valid.

14. **(a)** Let $r(x)$ represent "x is a resident of Minnesota," let $l(x)$ represent "x likes snow," and let $s(x)$ represent "x is a skier." We can represent the argument symbolically as follows.

$$\begin{array}{l} \exists x[r(x) \wedge \sim l(x)] \\ \underline{\forall x[s(x) \rightarrow l(x)]} \\ \exists x[r(x) \wedge \sim s(x)] \end{array}$$

(b) Draw an Euler diagram where the region representing "residents of Minnesota" intersects the regions representing "those who like snow." and "skiers" so that the first premise true.

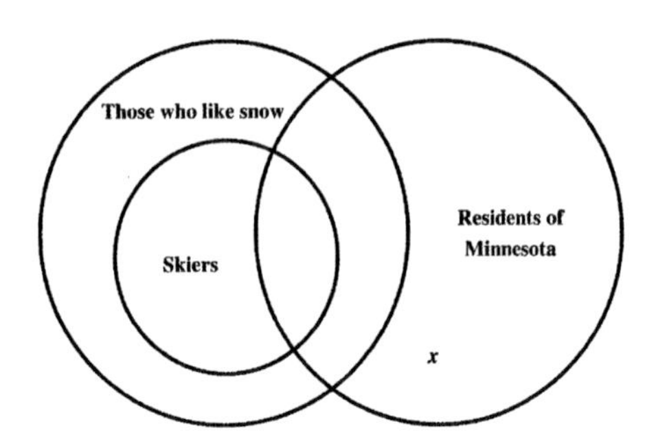

By the second premise the region representing "skiers" must be entirely inside the region representing "those who like snow." Then since x must lie outside the region representing "those who like snow" it must also lie outside "skiers." Hence the conclusion is true and so the argument is valid.

15. **(a)** Let $w(x)$ represent "x wanders" and $l(x)$ represent "x is lost." Let m represent Martha MacDonald We can represent the argument symbolically as follows.

$$\begin{array}{l} \exists x[w(x) \wedge l(x)] \\ \underline{w(m) \qquad\qquad} \\ l(m) \end{array}$$

(b) Draw an Euler diagram where the region representing "those who wander" intersects the region representing "those who are lost." This keeps the first premise true.

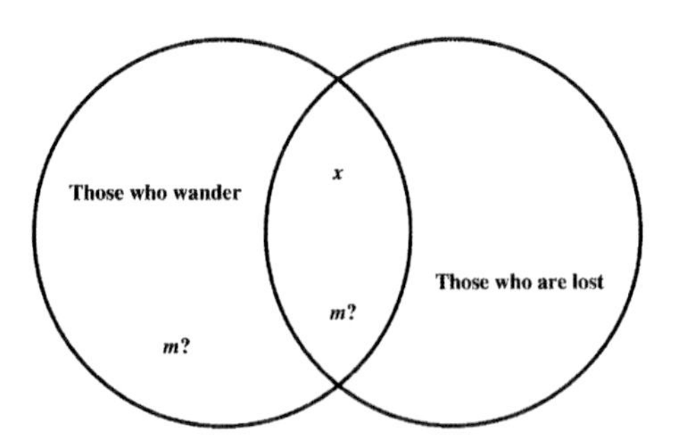

By the second premise, m must lie in the region representing "those who wander." But, m could be inside or outside the region representing "those who are lost." Since this allows for a false conclusion, the argument is invalid.

16. **(a)** Let $o(x)$ represent "x is an old house" and $r(x)$ represent "x is a house with a root cellar." Let m represent my house. We can represent the argument symbolically as follows.

$$\begin{array}{l} \exists x[o(x) \wedge r(x)] \\ \underline{r(m) \qquad\qquad} \\ o(m) \end{array}$$

(b) Draw an Euler diagram where the region representing "old houses" intersects the region representing "houses with root cellars." This keeps the first premise true.

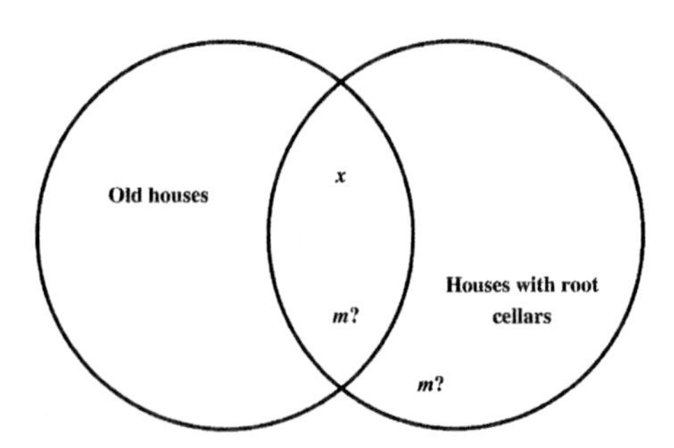

By the second premise, m must lie in the region representing "houses with root cellars." But, m could be inside or outside the region representing "old houses." Since this allows for a false conclusion, the argument is invalid.

17. **(a)** Let $p(x)$ represent "x is a psychologist," $u(x)$ represent "x is a university professor," and $r(x)$ represent "x has a private practice." We can represent the argument symbolically as follows.

$$\begin{array}{l} \exists x[p(x) \wedge u(x)] \\ \exists x[p(x) \wedge r(x)] \\ \hline \exists x[u(x) \wedge r(x)] \end{array}$$

(b) Draw an Euler diagram where the region representing "psychologists" and "university professors" intersect each other to keep the first premise true. Then add a region representing "those with a private practice" intersecting the region "university professors" to keep the second premise true. In the most general case, this region should also intersect the region representing "psychologists."

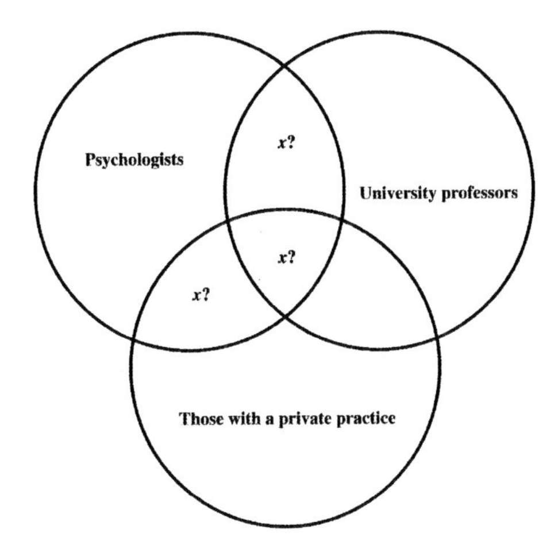

By the first premise, x must lie in the region shared by "psychologists" and "university professors"; by the second premise, x must lie in the region shared by "psychologists" and "those with a private practice." But x may not lie in the region shared by all three regions. Since this diagram shows true premises but a false conclusion, the argument is invalid.

18. **(a)** Let $r(x)$ represent "x is responsible" and $p(x)$ represent "x must pay for this." Let n represent Nola Akala. We can represent the argument symbolically as follows.

$$\begin{array}{l} \exists x[r(x) \wedge p(x)] \\ r(n) \\ \hline p(n) \end{array}$$

(b) Draw an Euler diagram where the region representing "those who are responsible" intersects the region representing "those who will pay for this" to keep the first premise true.

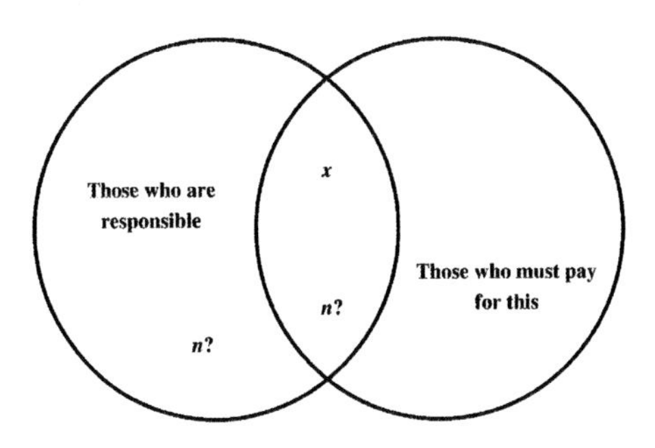

By the second premise, n must lie in the region representing "those who are responsible." But n may or may not lie in the region shared by the region "those who must pay for this." Since the diagram shows true premises but allows a false conclusion, the argument is invalid.

19. **(a)** Let $a(x)$ represent "x is a saint" and $i(x)$ represent "x is a sinner." We can represent the argument symbolically as follows.

$$\begin{array}{l} \forall x[a(x) \wedge i(x)] \\ \exists x[\sim a(x) \\ \hline \exists x[i(x)] \end{array}$$

(b) Draw an Euler diagram where the region representing "saints" intersects the region representing "sinners" to keep the first premise true.

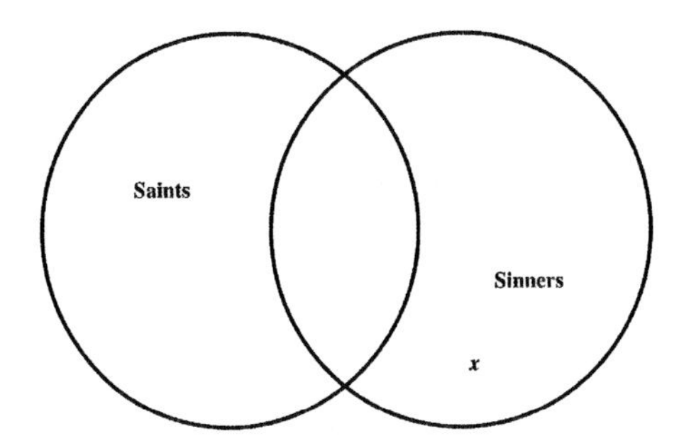

By the second premise, x must lie outside the region representing "saints." But that means x must lie in the part of the "sinners" region not shared by the "saints" region." Hence, the conclusion is true and so the argument is valid.

20. **(a)** Let $f(x)$ represent "x is here for the first time," $w(x)$ represent "we want to make x feel welcome," and $g(x)$ represent "x is here after being gone for awhile." We can represent the argument symbolically as follows.

$$\begin{array}{l} \forall x[f(x) \rightarrow w(x)] \\ \forall x[g(x) \rightarrow w(x)] \\ \underline{\exists x[f(x) \vee g(x)]} \\ \exists x[w(x)] \end{array}$$

(b) Draw an Euler diagram where the region representing "those who are here for the first time" and the region representing "those who are here after being gone for awhile" lie entirely within the region "those whom we want to make feel welcome" to keep the first two premises true.

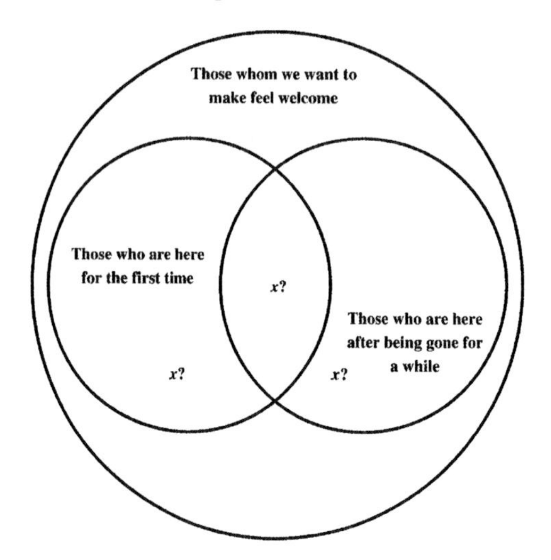

By the third premise, x must lie inside the region representing "those who are here for the first time" or the region representing "those who are here after being gone for awhile"; x may lie in their intersection. In any case, x must lie in the region representing "those whom we want to make feel welcome." Hence, the conclusion is true and so the argument is valid.

21. Interchanging the second premise and the conclusion of Example 4 yields the following argument.

All well-run businesses generate profits.
Monsters, Inc. is a well-run business.
Monsters, Inc. generates profits.

Draw an Euler diagram where the region representing "well-run businesses" must be inside the region representing "things that generate profits" so that the first premise is true.

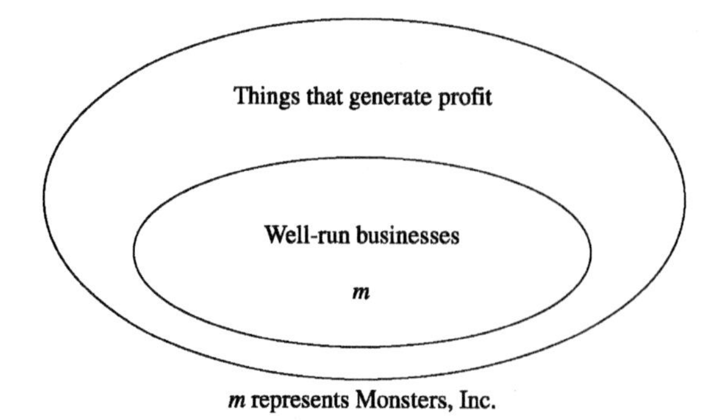

m represents Monsters, Inc.

Let m represent Monsters, Inc. By the second premise, m must lie inside the region representing "well-run businesses." Since this forces the conclusion to be true, the argument is valid, which makes the answer to the question yes.

22. The valid argument of Example 5 is.

All squirrels eat nuts.
All those who eat nuts are healthy.
All who are healthy avoid cigarettes.
―――――――――――――――
All squirrels avoid cigarettes.

Another possible conclusion, which will keep the argument valid, is "All squirrels are healthy." The argument remains valid since the premises diagrammed (Figure 17, in the text) forces this conclusion to be true. (Similarly, "All those who eat nuts avoid cigarettes" is another possible conclusion that is valid.)

23. Since the region representing "major league baseball players" lies entirely inside the region representing "people who earn at least $300,000 a year," a possible first premise is

All major league baseball players earn at least $300,000 a year.

And if r represents Ryan Howard and r is inside the region representing "major league baseball players," then a possible second premise is

Ryan Howard is a major league baseball player.

A valid conclusion drawn from these two premises is that

Ryan Howard earns at least $300,000 a year.

Therefore, a valid argument based on the Euler diagram is as follows.

All major league baseball players earn at least $300,000 a year.
Ryan Howard is a major league baseball player.
―――――――――――――――
Ryan Howard earns at least $300,000 a year.

24. Since the region representing "people who live in California" lies entirely inside the region representing "people who live in the western United States," a possible first premise is

All people who live in California live in the western United States.

And if p represents Phyllis Crittenden and p is outside the region representing "people who live in the western United States," then a possible second premise is

Phyllis Crittenden does not live in the western United States.

A valid conclusion drawn from these two premises is that

Phyllis Crittenden does not live in California.

Therefore, a valid argument based on the Euler diagram is as follows.

All people who live in California live in the western United States.
Phyllis Crittenden does not live in the western United States.
―――――――――――――――
Phyllis Crittenden does not live in California.

25. The following diagram yields true premises. It also forces the conclusion to be true.

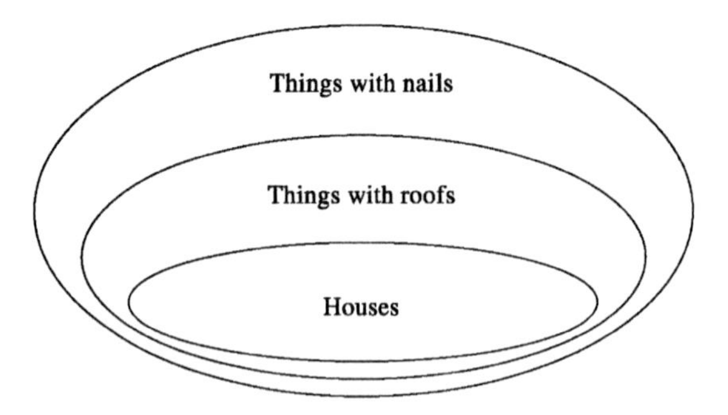

Thus, the argument is valid. Observe that the diagram is the only way to show true premises.

26. The following represents one way to diagram the premises so that they are true but does not lead to a true conclusion.

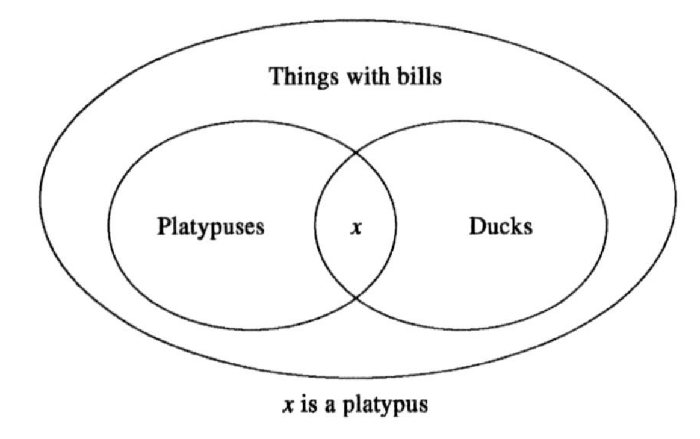

If we let x be a platypus, according to the premises, x could also be a duck. Thus, the argument is invalid.

27. The following represents one way to diagram the premises so that they are true but does not lead to a true conclusion.

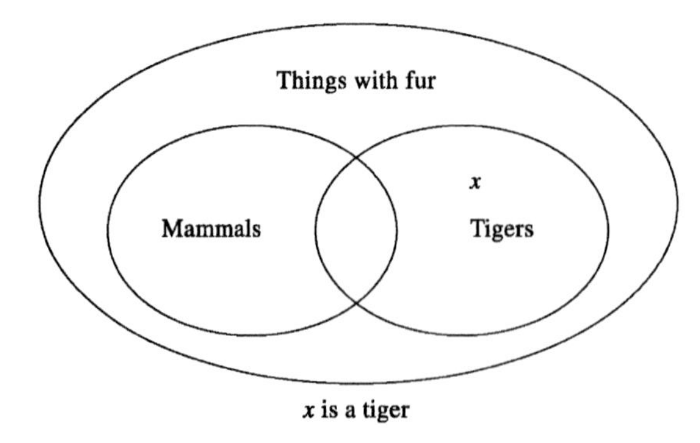

If we let x be a tiger, according to the premises, x could also be a tiger but not a mammal. Thus, the argument is invalid

28. The following Euler diagram yields true premises. It also forces the conclusion to be true.

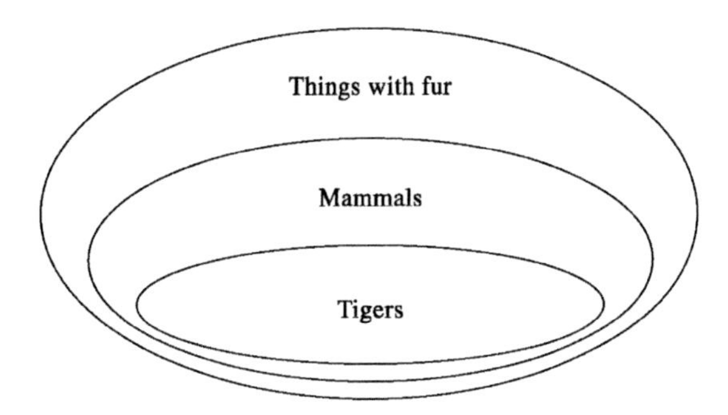

Thus the argument is valid. Observe that the diagram is the only way to show true premises.

29. The following Euler diagram illustrates that the conclusion is not forced to be true.

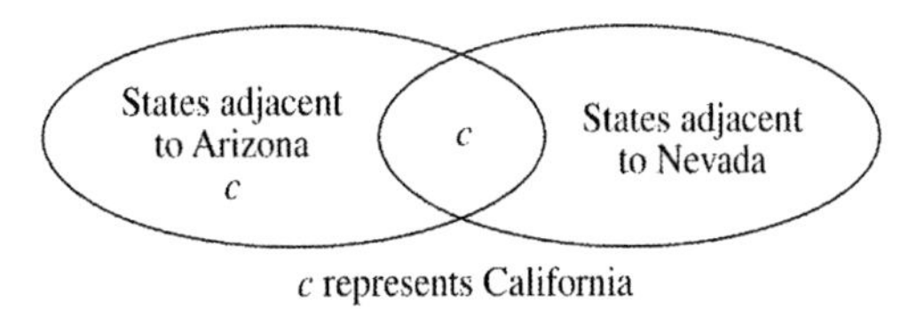

The argument is invalid even though the conclusion is true.

30. The following Euler diagram represents true premises.

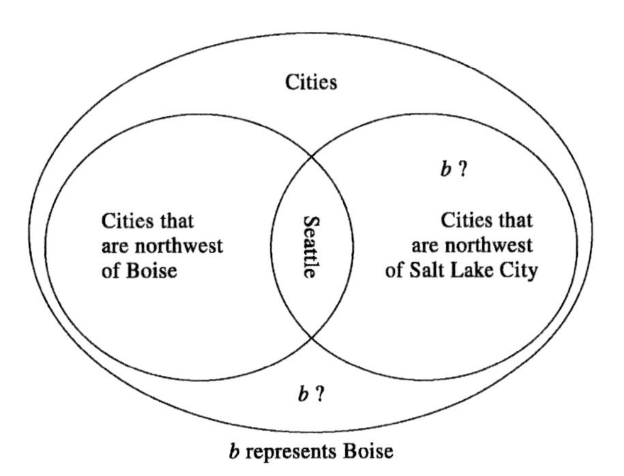

If we let b represent Boise, b must lie outside of the region representing "cities that are northwest of Boise." But b may lie inside or outside of the region representing "cities that are northwest of Salt Lake City." Thus, the argument is invalid.

31. The following Euler diagram represents true premises.

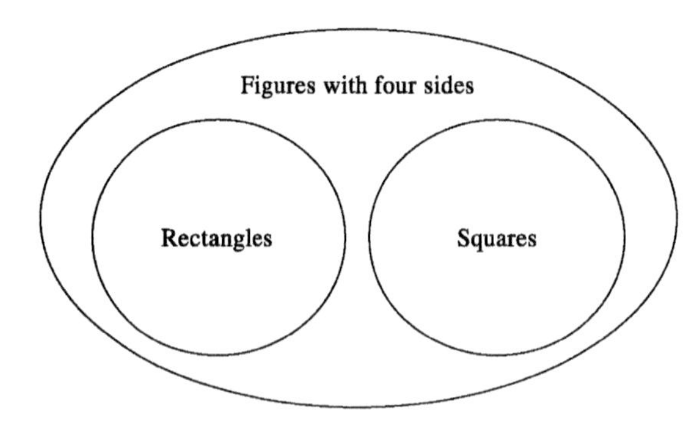

According to the premises, the region representing squares may lie entirely outside of the region representing rectangles. Thus, the argument is <u>invalid</u>, even though the conclusion is true.

32. The following Euler diagram represents the two true premises as being true and we are forced into a true conclusion.

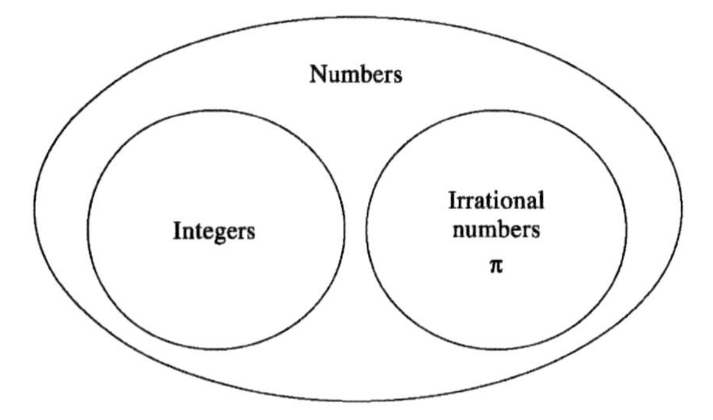

Thus, the argument is <u>valid</u>.

34. We might write the statement "There is no one here who has not done that at one time or another" as "Everyone here has done that at one time or another."

37. **(a)** Let $l(x)$ represent "x is a legislative power herein granted" and $g(x)$ represent "x is vested in a Congress of the United States." We can represent the passage symbolically as follows.

$$\forall x[l(x) \rightarrow g(x)]$$

(b) We make the following argument.

All legislative power herein granted shall be vested in a Congress of the United States.
The power to collect taxes is a legislative power herein granted.

The power to collect taxes shall be vested in a Congress of the United States.

The conclusion is true. Thus, the argument is <u>valid</u>.

(c) Draw an Euler diagram where the region representing "legislative power herein granted" must be inside the region representing "things that are vested in a Congress of the United States" so that the first premise is true. Let c represent "the power to collect taxes." By the second premise, c must lie in the region representing "legislative powers herein granted."

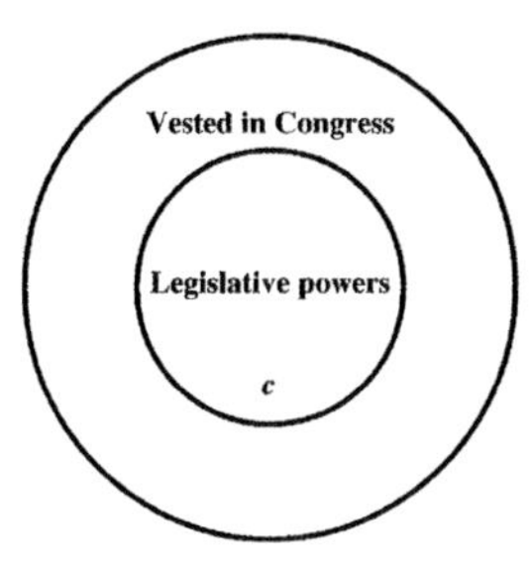

38. (a) Let $r(x)$ represent "x is a Representative,"
$a(x)$ represent "x has attained to the age of twent-five years,"
$c(x)$ represent "x has been seven years a citizen of the United States,"
and $i(x)$ represent "x is an inhabitant of that State in which he shall be chosen."

We can represent the passage symbolically as follows.

$$\forall x\{r(x) \rightarrow [a(x) \wedge c(x) \wedge i(x)]\}$$

(b) We make the following argument.

A Representative shall have attained to the age of twenty-five years.
A Representative shall have been seven years a citizen of the United States.
A Representative shall, when elected, be an inhabitant of that State in which he shall be chosen.
Dennis Hastert is a Representative.

Dennis Hastert shall have attained to the age of twenty-five years, and been seven years a citizen of the United States, and was, when elected, be an inhabitant of that State in which he was chosen.

The conclusion is true. Thus, the argument is valid.

(c) Draw an Euler diagram where the region representing "representative" must be inside the three other regions and the three other regions intersect each other. Let d represent Dennis Hastert. By the fourth premise, d must lie in the region representing "Representative" and, thus, be in all of the regions.

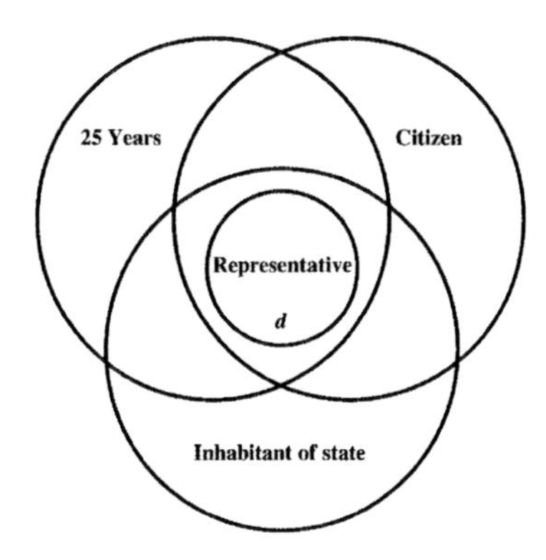

39. **(a)** Let $b(x)$ represent "x is a bill of attainder," $e(x)$ represent "x is an ex post facto law," and $p(x)$ represent "x has been passed." We can represent the passage symbolically as follows.

$$\forall x\{[b(x) \vee e(x)] \rightarrow \sim p(x)\}$$

(b) We make the following argument.

No bill of attainder or ex post facto law shall be passed.
The law forbidding members of the Communist Party to serve as an officer or as an employee of a labor union was a bill of attainder.
―――――――――――――――――――――――――
The law forbidding members of the Communist Party to serve as an officer or as an employee of a labor union shall not be passed.

The conclusion is true. Thus, the argument is valid.

(c) Draw an Euler diagram where the region representing "bill of attainder" and the region representing "ex post facto law" intersect but lie outside of the region representing "bills and laws passed." Let l represent "the law forbidding members of the Communist Party to serve as an officer or as an employee of a labor union." By the second premise, l must lie in the region representing "bill of attainder" and so will lie outside of the region representing "bills and laws passed."

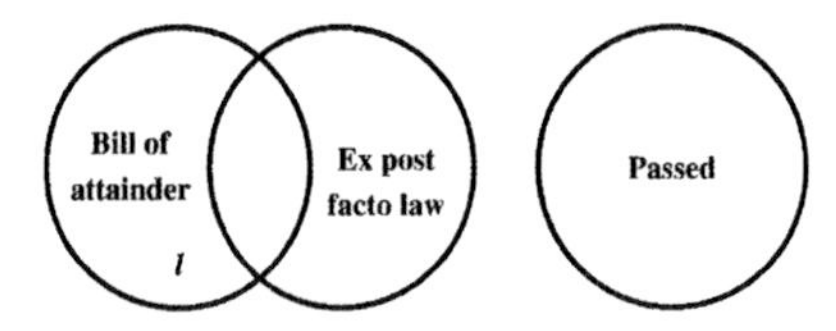

40. **(a)** Let $s(x)$ represent "x is a State,"
$t(x)$ represent "x enters into a treaty,"
$a(x)$ represent "x enters into an alliance,"
and $c(x)$ represent "x "enters into a confederation."

We can represent the passage symbolically as follows.

$$\forall x\{s(x) \rightarrow \sim [t(x) \vee a(x) \vee c(x)]\}$$

(b) We make the following argument.

No State shall enter into any treaty, alliance, or confederation.
Texas is a state.
―――――――――――――――――――――――――
Texas shall not enter into any treaty, alliance, or confederation.

The conclusion is true. Thus, the argument is valid.

(c) Draw an Euler diagram where the region representing "states" must be outside the other three regions and the three other regions intersect. Let t represent Texas. By the second premise, t must lie in the region representing "states" and, thus, must be outside the other three regions.

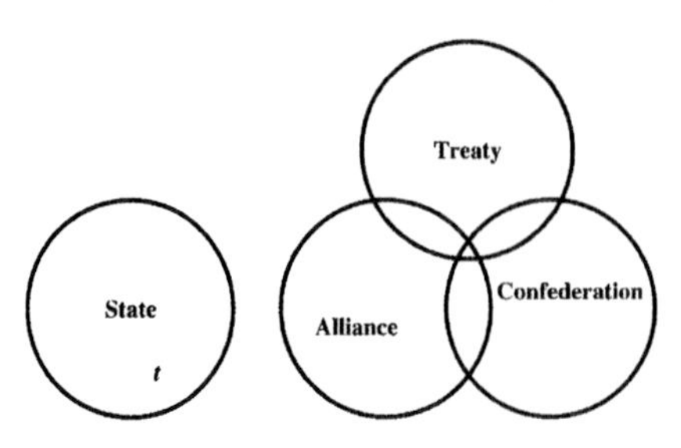

41. **(a)** Since the region corresponding to "Tourette syndrome" is entirely contained inside the region corresponding to "Chronic tics," the conclusion is valid.

(b) Since the region corresponding to "Tourette syndrome" is not entirely contained inside the region corresponding to "OCD," the conclusion is invalid.

(c) Since some of the region corresponding to "Chronic tics" also lies in the region corresponding to "OCD," the conclusion is valid.

(d) Since some of the region corresponding to "OCD" lies outside the region corresponding to "Tourette syndrome," the conclusion is valid.

(e) Since some of the region corresponding to "Chronic tics" lies outside the region corresponding to "Tourette syndrome," the conclusion is invalid.

Thus, the answer is a, c, and d.

42. **(a)** To negate the statement, first negate the quantifier "everyone" by using the quantifier "someone." Then negate the remainder of the statement: "Someone who hears about this will not laugh with me."

(b) To negate the statement, first negate the quantifier "someone" by using the quantifier "no one." Then negate the remainder of the statement: "No one came to destroy your lord the king."

(c) First negate the quantifier "no one" by using the quantifier "there is someone." Then negate the remainder of the statement: "There is someone who does good."

(d) First negate the quantifier "everyone" by using the quantifier "someone." Then negate the remainder of the statement: "Someone is not the friend of one who gives gifts."

(e) To negate the statement, first negate the quantifier "everyone" by using the quantifier "someone." Then negate the remainder of the statement: Someone who quotes proverbs will not quote this proverb about you: "Like mother, like daughter."

In Exercises 43–48, the premises marked A, B, and C are followed by several possible conclusions. Take each conclusions in turn, and check the resulting argument as valid *or* invalid.

A. All kittens are cute animals.
B. All cute animals are admired by animal lovers.
C. Some dangerous animals are admired by animal lovers.

Diagram the first two premises to be true. Then, notice that premise C is correctly represented by Case I, Case II, or Case III in the diagram.

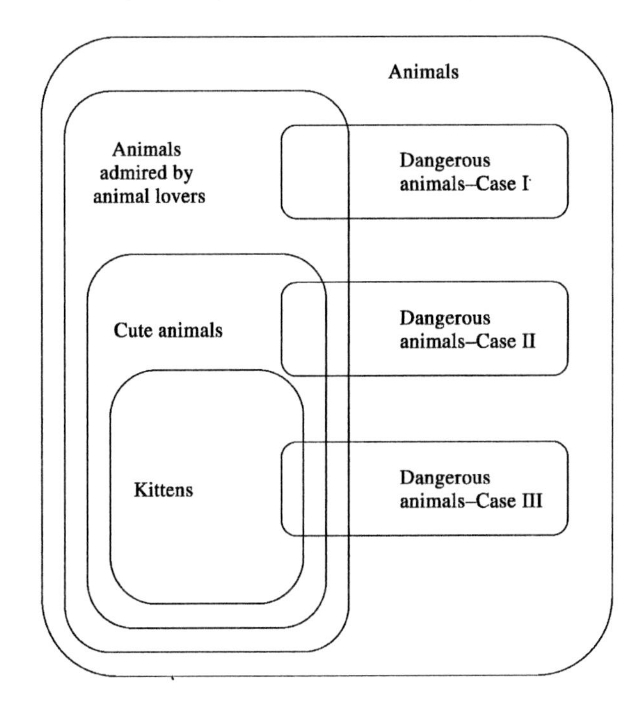

43. We are not forced into the conclusion "Some kittens are dangerous animals" since Case I and Case II represent true premises where this conclusion is false. Thus, the argument is <u>invalid</u>.

44. We are not forced into the conclusion "Some cute animals are dangerous" since Case I represents true premises where this conclusion is false. Thus, the argument is <u>invalid</u>.

45. We are not forced into the conclusion "Some dangerous animals are cute" since Case I represents true premises where this conclusion is false. Thus, the argument is <u>invalid</u>.

46. We are not forced into the conclusion "Kittens are not dangerous animals" since Case III represents true premises where this conclusion is false. Thus, the argument is invalid.

47. The conclusion "All kittens are admired by animal lovers" yields a valid argument since premises A and B force the conclusion to be true.

48. The conclusion "Some things admired by animal lovers are dangerous animals" yields a valid argument since premise C forces the conclusion to be true.

Chapter 6 Review Exercises

1. The negation of "If she doesn't pay me, I won't have enough cash" is "She pays me and I have enough cash."

2. The negation of "I fought the law and the law won" is "I didn't fight the law or the law didn't win.

3. The symbolic form of "He loses the election, but he wins the hearts of the voters" is $l \wedge w$.

4. The symbolic form of "If he wins the hearts of the voters, then he doesn't lose the election" is $w \rightarrow \sim l$.

5. The symbolic form of "He loses the election only if he doesn't win the hearts of the voters" is $l \rightarrow \sim w$.

6. The symbolic form of "He loses the election if and only if he doesn't win the hearts of the voters" is $l \leftrightarrow \sim w$.

7. Writing the symbolic form $\sim l \wedge w$ in words, we get "He doesn't lose the election and he wins the hearts of the voters."

8. Writing the symbolic form $\sim (l \vee \sim w)$ in words, we get "It is not the case that he loses the election or he doesn't win the hearts of the voters."

9. Replacing q and r with the given truth values, we have

$$\sim\text{F} \wedge \sim\text{F}$$
$$\text{T} \wedge \text{T}$$
$$\text{T}$$

The compound statement $\sim q \wedge \sim r$ is true.

10. Replacing $p, q,$ and r with the given truth values, we have

$$\text{F} \vee (\text{T} \wedge \sim\text{F})$$
$$\text{F} \vee (\text{T} \wedge \text{T})$$
$$\text{F} \vee \text{T}$$
$$\text{T}.$$

The statement $r \vee (p \wedge \sim q)$ is true.

11. Replacing r with the given truth value (s not known), we have

$$\text{F} \rightarrow (\text{s} \wedge \text{F})$$
$$\text{T}$$

since a conditional statement with a false antecedent is true.
The compound statement $r \rightarrow (s \vee r)$ is true.

12. Replacing p and q with the given truth values, we have

$$\text{T} \leftrightarrow (\text{T} \rightarrow \text{F})$$
$$\text{T} \leftrightarrow \text{F}$$
$$\text{F}.$$

The statement $p \leftrightarrow (p \rightarrow q)$ is false.

14. The necessary condition for

(a) a conditional statement to be false is that the antecedent must be true and the consequent must be false.

(b) a conjunction to be true is that both component statements must be true.

(c) a disjunction to be false is that both component statements must be false.

15.

p	q	p	$\wedge$	$(\sim p$	$\vee$	$q)$
T	T	T	T	F	T	T
T	F	T	F	F	F	F
F	T	F	F	T	T	T
F	F	F	F	T	T	F
		1	4	2	3	2

The statement is not a tautology.

16.

p	q	$\sim$	$(p$	$\wedge$	$q)$	$\rightarrow$	$(\sim p$	$\vee$	$\sim q)$
T	T	F	T	T	T	T	F	F	F
T	F	T	T	F	F	T	F	T	T
F	T	T	F	F	T	T	T	T	F
F	F	T	F	F	F	T	T	T	T
		3	1	2	1	6	4	5	4

Since the last completed column (6) is all true, the statement is a tautology.

17. "All mathematicians are lovable" can be restated as "If someone is a mathematician, then that person is lovable."

18. "You can have dessert only if you eat your vegetables" can be restated as "If you can have dessert, then you eat your vegatables."

19. "Having at least as many equations as unknowns is necessary for a system to have a unique solution" can be restated as "If a system has a unique solution, then it has a least as many equations as unknowns."

20. "Having a feasible region is sufficient for a linear programming problem to have a minimum" can be restated as "If a linear programming problem has a feasible region, then it has a minimum."

21. *The direct statement*: If the proposed regulations have been approved, then we need to change the way we do business.

(a) *Converse*: If we need to change the way we do business, then the proposed regulations have been approved.

(b) *Inverse*: If the proposed regulations have not been approved, then we do not need to change the way we do business.

(c) *Contrapositive:* If we do not need to change the way we do business, then the proposed regulations have not been approved.

22. *The direct statement*: $(p \vee q) \rightarrow \sim r$

(a) *Converse*: $\sim r \rightarrow (p \vee q)$

(b) *Inverse*: $\sim (p \vee q) \rightarrow \sim (\sim r)$

Using DeMorgan's laws, we can simplify this: $(\sim p \wedge \sim q) \rightarrow r$

(c) *Contrapositive:* $\sim (\sim r) \rightarrow \sim (p \vee q)$

Using DeMorgan's laws, we can simplify this: $r \rightarrow (\sim p \wedge \sim q)$

23. In the diagram, a series circuit corresponding to $p \wedge p$ is followed in series by a parallel circuit represented by $\sim p \vee q$. The logical statement is $(p \wedge p) \wedge (\sim p \vee q)$. This statement is equivalent to $p \wedge q$.

p	q	$(p$	$\wedge$	$p)$	$\wedge$	$(\sim p$	$\vee$	$q)$	p	$\wedge$	q
T	T	T	T	T	T	F	T	T	T	T	T
T	F	T	T	T	F	F	F	F	T	F	F
F	T	F	F	F	F	T	T	T	F	F	T
F	F	F	F	F	F	T	T	F	F	F	F
		1	2	1	6	3	5	4	7	9	8

Columns 6 and 9 are identical.

24. In the diagram, two series circuits represented by $p \wedge p$ and $\sim p \wedge q$ are in parallel. The logical statement is $(p \wedge p) \vee (\sim p \wedge q)$. This statement is equivalent to $p \vee q$.

p	q	$(p$	$\wedge$	$p)$	$\vee$	$(\sim p$	$\wedge$	$q)$	p	$\vee$	q
T	T	T	T	T	T	F	F	T	T	T	T
T	F	T	T	T	T	F	F	F	T	T	F
F	T	F	F	F	T	T	T	T	F	T	T
F	F	F	F	F	F	T	F	F	F	F	F
		1	2	1	6	3	5	4	7	9	8

Columns 6 and 9 are identical.

25. The logical statement $(p \wedge q) \vee (p \wedge p)$ can be represented by the following circuit.

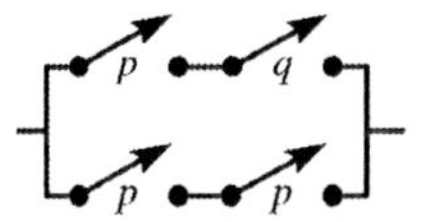

The statement simplifies to p as follows:

$$(p \wedge q) \vee (p \wedge p) = p \wedge (q \wedge p)$$
$$= p$$

26. The logical statement $p \wedge (p \vee q)$ can be represented by the following circuit.

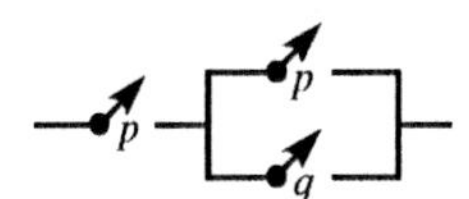

The statement simplifies to $p \wedge (p \vee q)$ simplifies to p by the Absorption Law.

27.

p	q	$(p$	$\veebar$	$q)$	$(p$	$\vee$	$q)$	$\wedge$	$\sim$	$(p$	$\wedge$	$q)$
T	T	T	F	T	T	T	T	F	F	T	T	T
T	F	T	T	F	T	T	F	T	T	T	F	F
F	T	F	T	T	F	T	T	T	T	F	F	T
F	F	F	F	F	F	F	F	F	T	F	F	F
		1	2	1	3	4	3	8	7	5	6	5

The columns labeled 2 and 8 are identical.

28.

p	q	$(p$	$\veebar$	$q)$	$\sim$	$[(p$	$\vee$	$q)$	$\rightarrow$	$(p$	$\wedge$	$q)]$
T	T	T	F	T	F	T	T	T	T	T	T	T
T	F	T	T	F	T	T	T	F	F	T	F	F
F	T	F	T	T	T	F	T	T	F	F	F	T
F	F	F	F	F	F	F	F	F	T	F	F	F
		1	2	1	8	3	4	3	7	5	6	5

The columns labeled 2 and 8 are identical.

29. **(a)** Yes, the statement is true because "this year is 2002" is false and "$1 + 1 = 3$" is false and $\mathrm{F} \rightarrow \mathrm{F}$ is true.

(b) No, the statement was not true in 2002 because then the statement had the value $\mathrm{T} \rightarrow \mathrm{F}$, which is false.

31. Let l represent "you're late one more time" and d represent "you'll be docked." The argument is then presented symbolically as follows.

$$\begin{array}{l} l \rightarrow d \\ \underline{l \qquad} \\ d. \end{array}$$

The argument is valid by Modus Ponens.

32. Let p represent "the company makes a profit" and u represent "the stock goes up." The argument is then presented symbolically as follows.

$$\begin{array}{l} p \rightarrow u \\ \underline{\sim p \qquad} \\ \sim u. \end{array}$$

The argument is invalid by Fallacy of the Inverse.

33. Let l represent "the instructor is late" and w represent "my watch is wrong." The argument is then presented symbolically as follows.

$$\begin{array}{l} l \vee w \\ \underline{\sim w \quad} \\ l. \end{array}$$

The argument is valid by Disjunctive Syllogism.

34. Let l represent "the parent is loving," h represent "the child will be happy," and t represent "the teacher can teach." The argument is then presented symbolically as follows.

$$\begin{array}{l} p \rightarrow h \\ \underline{h \rightarrow t} \\ p \rightarrow t. \end{array}$$

The argument is valid by Reasoning by Transitivity.

35. Let p represent "you play that song one more time" and n represent "I'm going nuts." The argument is then presented symbolically as follows.

$$\begin{array}{l} p \to n \\ \underline{n \qquad} \\ p. \end{array}$$

The argument is invalid by Fallacy of the Converse.

36. Let f represent "it's after five" and c represent "the store is closed." The argument is then presented symbolically as follows.

$$\begin{array}{l} f \to c \\ \underline{\sim c \quad} \\ \sim f. \end{array}$$

The argument is valid by Modus Tollens.

37. Let h represent "we hire a new person," t represent "we'll spend more on training," and r represent "we rewrite the manual." The argument is then presented symbolically as follows.

$$\begin{array}{l} h \to t \\ r \to \sim t \\ \underline{r \qquad\quad} \\ \sim h. \end{array}$$

The argument is valid.

1.	$h \to t$	Premise
2.	$r \to \sim t$	Premise
3.	r	Premise
4.	$\sim t$	2, 3, Modus Ponens
5.	$\sim h$	1, 4, Modus Tollens

38. Let s represent "Smith received enough votes to qualify," j represent "Jones received enough votes to qualify," and e represent "the election was rigged." The argument is then represented symbolically by:

$$\begin{array}{ll} 1. \sim(s \vee j) & \text{T} \\ 2. \ \underline{\ s \to \ e} & \text{T} \\ \quad \sim e. & \text{F} \end{array}$$

The argument is <u>invalid</u>. The premises are true but the conclusion is false when $s = F$, $j = F$, and $e = T$.

39.

$$\begin{array}{ll} 1. \sim p \to \sim q & \text{T} \\ 2. \ \underline{\ q \to \ p} & \text{T} \\ \quad p \vee q & \text{F} \end{array}$$

The argument is <u>invalid</u>. When $p =$ F and $q =$ F, the premises are true but the conclusion is false.

40. The argument is <u>valid</u>.

1.	$p \to q$	Premise
2.	$r \to \sim q$	Premise
3.	$q \to \sim r$	2, Contrapositive
4.	$p \to \sim r$	1, 3, Transitivity

41. Let $d(x)$ represent "x is a dog" and $h(x)$ represent "x goes to heaven."

(a) $\forall x[d(x) \rightarrow h(x)]$

(b) $\exists x[d(x) \wedge \sim h(x)]$

(c) There is a dog that doesn't go to heaven.

42. Let $c(x)$ represent "x is a car" and $m(x)$ represent "x has a manual transmission."

(a) $\exists x[c(x) \wedge m(x)]$

(b) $\forall x[c(x) \rightarrow \sim m(x)]$

(c) All cars don't have manual transmissions. (Or: No car has a manual transmission.)

43. **(a)** Let $f(x)$ represent "x is a member of that fraternity," $w(x)$ represent "x does well academically," and j represent John Cross. We can represent the argument symbolically as follows.

$$\begin{array}{l} \forall x[f(x) \rightarrow w(x)] \\ \underline{f(j) \qquad\qquad\qquad} \\ w(j) \end{array}$$

(b) Because of the first premise, the region representing "members of that fraternity" must be inside the region representing "those who do well academically." And j must be within the region representing "members of that fraternity" because of the second premise. Complete the Euler diagram as follows.

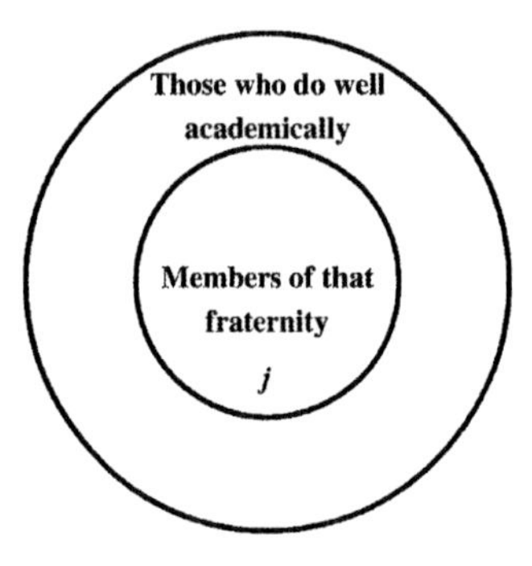

Since, when the premises are diagrammed as being true, we are forced into a true conclusion, the argument is valid.

44. **(a)** Let $f(x)$ represent "x is a member of that fraternity," $w(x)$ represent "x does well academically," and b represent Bill Hoffman. We can represent the argument symbolically as follows.

$$\begin{array}{l} \exists x[f(x) \wedge \sim w(x)] \\ \underline{w(b) \qquad\qquad\qquad} \\ \sim f(b). \end{array}$$

(b) Because of the first premise, part of the region representing "members of that fraternity" must lie outside the region representing "those who do well academically." And, because of the second premise, b must be within the region representing "those who do well academically." But b can lie in the intersection with the region representing "members of that fraternity" or outside of it. (Bill can do well academically and either be a member of the fraternity or not.) Complete the Euler diagram as follows.

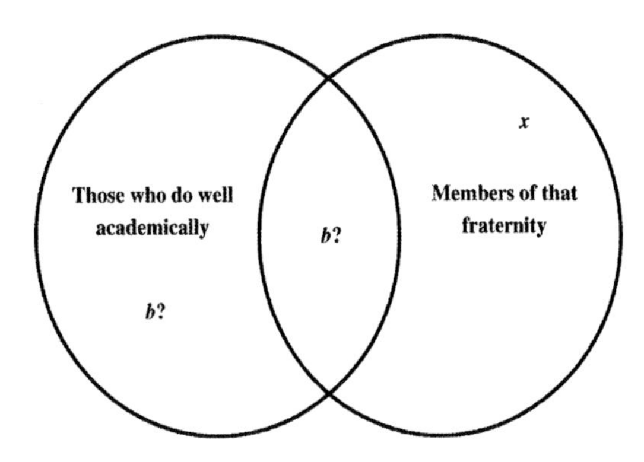

Since, when the premises are diagrammed as being true, we are not forced into a true conclusion, the argument is invalid.

45.

p	q	r	p	$\rightarrow$	$(q$	$\rightarrow$	$r)$	$(p$	$\rightarrow$	$q)$	$\rightarrow$	r
T	T	T	T	T	T	T	T	T	T	T	T	T
T	T	F	T	F	T	F	F	T	T	T	F	F
T	F	T	T	T	F	T	T	T	F	F	T	T
T	F	F	T	T	F	T	F	T	F	F	T	F
F	T	T	F	T	T	T	T	F	T	T	T	T
F	T	F	F	T	T	F	F	F	T	T	F	F
F	F	T	F	T	F	T	T	F	T	F	T	T
F	F	F	F	T	F	T	F	F	T	F	F	F
			1	4	2	3	2	5	6	5	8	7

To determine if the statements are equivalent, compare columns 4 and 8. Since they are not identical, the statements are not equivalent.

46. An equivalent form $a \rightarrow b$ without the conditional is $\sim a \vee b$. Use the first to transform the conditional inside the parentheses and then to transform the conditional outside the parentheses.

(a) $p \rightarrow (q \rightarrow r) \equiv p \rightarrow (\sim q \vee r) \equiv \sim p \vee (\sim q \vee r)$

(b) $(p \rightarrow q) \rightarrow r \equiv (\sim p \vee q) \rightarrow r \equiv \sim(\sim p \vee q) \vee r \equiv (p \wedge \sim q) \vee r$

The last equivalence follows from one of DeMorgan's laws.

47. **(a)**

p	q	$(p$	$\wedge$	$\sim p)$	$\rightarrow$	q
T	T	T	F	F	T	T
T	F	T	F	F	T	F
F	T	F	F	T	T	T
F	F	F	F	T	T	F
		1	2	1	4	3

48. **a**, **b**, and **c** are declarative sentences that are true or false and are therefore statements.

d is a command, not a declarative sentence, and is therefore not a statement.

49. **a**, **b**, and **c** are compound statements.

50. The converse of "If your top tax bracket is 10% or 15%, your capital gain rate is generally 5%" is "If your capital gain rate is generally 5%, then your top tax bracket is 10% or 15%."

51. The contrapositive of "The Schedule D Tax Worksheet in the Schedule D instructions is used only if you have a net 28% rate gain or unrecaptured Section 1250 gain " is "If you do not have a net 28% rate gain or unrecaptured Section 1250 gain, then the Schedule D Tax Worksheet in the Schedule D instructions is not used."

52. *Contrapositive*: If your doctor does not advise you to consider surgery to either widen the arteries or improve the blood flow to the heart, then the angina does not become more severe despite drug treatment.

Or *statement*: The angina does not become more severe despite drug treatment, or your doctor may advise you to consider surgery to either widen the arteries or improve the blood flow to the heart.

53. The negation of $p \wedge q$ is $\sim p \vee \sim q$.

(a) Regulations do not have both costs and benefits or rules that are passed to solve a problem cannot make it worse.

(b) Shooters do not overwhelmingly have problems with alcoholism or they do not have long criminal histories, particularly arrests for violent acts.

(c) They are not disproportionately involved in automobile crashes or they are not much more likely to have their driver's license suspended or revoked.

54. $(w \rightarrow d) \rightarrow v$

55. (a) Since "real things are not things we can deal with," the regions representing "real things" and "things we can deal with" do not intersect. Since "only things we can measure are things we can deal with," the region representing "things we can deal with" should lie entirely within the region representing "things we can measure." And since "only things we can measure are real things," the region representing "real things" should lie entirely within the region representing "things we can measure." The Euler diagram is as follows.

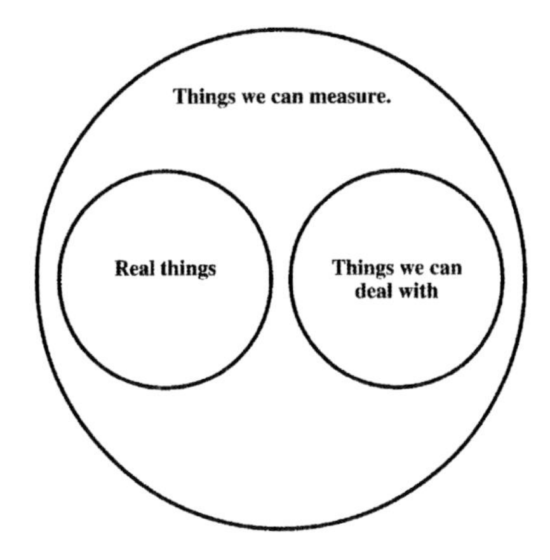

56. (a), (b), (d) These are commands or requests, not declarative sentences and therefore not statements.

(c) This is a declarative sentence that is true or false and therefore a statement.

57. (a), (b), (d) These are not statements.

(c) This is a compound statement, formed using "Someone finally runs out of money" and "The player with the most cash wins this colorful, fast-paced junior version of the world's most popular board game."

58. (a) $\sim s \to g$

(b) $l \to \sim g$

(c) $w \to l \equiv \sim l \sim w$

(d) If the puppy does not lie still, it does not care to do worsted work. In Lewis Carroll's words, "Puppies that will not lie still never care to do worsted work."

59. (a) $h \to o$

(b) $a \to m$

(c) $p \to \sim o \equiv o \to \sim p$

(d) $m \to h$

(e) If the bird is in this aviary, it does not live on mince pies. In Lewis Carroll's words, "No bird in this aviary lives on mince pies."

60. (a) $f \to t \equiv \sim t \to \sim f$

(b) $\sim a \to \sim g \equiv g \to a$

(c) $w \to f$

(d) $t \to \sim g \equiv g \to \sim t$

(e) $d \to w \equiv \sim w \to \sim a$

(f) If the kitten will play with a gorilla, it does not have green eyes. In Lewis Carroll's words, "No kitten with green eyes will play with a gorilla."

61. **(a)** $u \to c$

(b) $p \to r$

(c) $s \to h$

(d) $\sim u \to \sim r \equiv r \to u$

(e) $h \to p$

(f) If the writer is Shakespeare, the writer is clever. In Lewis Carroll's words, "Shakespeare was clever."

Extended Application: Logic Puzzles

Draw charts as indicated and complete using the initial information given. Use "•" for Yes and "x" for No. For any cell that is assigned "•", mark "x" in the appropriate nearby unmarked cells in that row and column.

1. 1. *The one who bicycles in pursuit of fitness drinks Bevé.*
Mark a "•" in the box at the intersection of BEVE and BICYCLING. Then mark "x" in the rest of the cells in the remainder of the BEVE row and the remaining four waters in the BICYCLING column.

2. *Tim enjoys aerobicising every morning before work. Ben is neither the one who drinks Sparkling Creed nor the one who imbibes Bevé.*

Mark a "•" in the box at the intersection of TIM and AEROBICISING. Then mark "x" in the rest of the cells in the remainder of the TIM row and the AEROBICISING column. Also, since Tim aerobicises (and doesn't bicycle), he doesn't drink Bevé; so mark "x" at the intersection of TIM and BEVE. Mark "x" in the cell at the intersection of BEN and SPARKLING CREEK and another at the intersection of BEN and BEVE. Also, since Ben doesn't drink Bevé, mark "x" in the cell at the intersection of BEN and BICYCLING.

3. *Page (who is neither the one who jogs nor the one who walks to keep in shape) drinks Purity. Meg drinks Mountain Clear, but not after jogging.*
Mark "x" in the cell at the intersection of PAGE and JOGGING and another at the intersection of PAGE and WALKING. Then put a "•" in the box at the intersection of PAGE and PURITY and fill the remainder of the PURITY column with "x"s. Also, since Page doesn't drink Bevé, mark "x" in the cell at the intersection of PAGE and BICYCLING.
Mark a "•" in the box at the intersection of MEG and MOUNTAIN CLEAR and fill the remainder of the MOUNTAIN CLEAR column with "x"s. Then mark "x" in the cell intersection of MEG and JOGGING. Also, since Meg doesn't drink Bevé, mark "x" in the cell at the intersection of MEG and BICYCLING.

At this point table should appear as follows.

		EXERCISE					WATER				
		AEROBICISING	BICYCLING	JOGGING	ROLLERBLADING	WALKING	BEVE	CRYSTAL SPRING	MOUNTAIN CLEAR	PURITY	SPARKLING CREEK
EXERCISE	ANNIE	×							×	×	
	BEN	×	×				×		×	×	×
	MEG	×	×	×			×	×	●	×	×
	PAGE	×	×	×		×	×	×	×	●	×
	TIM	●	×	×	×	×	×		×	×	
WATER	BEVE	×	●	×	×	×					
	CRYSTAL SPRING		×								
	MOUNTAIN CLEAR		×								
	PURITY		×								
	SPARKLING CREEK		×								

First, determine who drinks which water.
Mountain Clear, of course, is Meg (3) and Purity is Page (3).
Bevé [bicycling (1) isn't Ben (2), Tim [Aerobicising (2)], Page [Purity (3)], or Meg [Mountain Clear (3)], so it must be Annie.
Sparkling Creek isn't Ben (2) or Annie so it has to be Tim.
Crystal Spring now has to be Ben.

Now, determine each person's choice of exercise.
Tim, of course, is aerobicising (2).
Annie drinks Bevé so she's bicycling (1).
Page isn't aerobicising (2), bicycling (1), jogging or walking (3), so she's rollerblading.
Meg isn't jogging (3) so she's walking and Ben is jogging.

In summary:

Annie, bicycling, Bevé
Ben, jogging, Crystal Spring
Meg, walking, Mountain Clear
Page, rollerblading, Purity
Tim, aerobicising, Sparkling Creek

2. 1. *Dr. Hoo, who is from Yale, will not be lecturing on Thursday. Dr. Zhivago's lecture will be exactly three days after the lecture on chaos theory.*
Mark a "x" in the box the intersection of DR. HOO and THURSDAY.
Then mark "x" at the intersection of DR. ZHIVAGO and CHAOS THEORY.
Also, he or she can't speak on Monday, Tuesday, or Wednesday so mark "x"at the intersection of DR. ZHIVAGO and those days. This also means that the lecture on Chaos Theory can't be given on Wednesday, Thursday, or Friday so mark "x" at the intersection of CHAOS THEORY and those days.

2. *If Dr. Jay is lecturing on Thursday, then the person giving the kinetic energy lecture will appear on Tuesday; otherwise, Dr. Jay will speak on Tuesday, and kinetic energy will be topic of Monday's lecture.*
This set of conditions is difficult to determine at this point, so go on to the next step and return here.

3. *Dr. Know (who is not giving the lecture on quantum mechanics) is not the Harvard physicist who will speak on Monday. The photonics lecture will not be given on either Wednesday or Thursday.*
Mark "x" in the box at the intersection of DR. KNOW and QUANTUM MECHANICS and also at the intersection of DR. KNOW and MONDAY. Also, since Monday's lecture will be given by a Harvard physicist, that can't be Dr. Hoo (who is from Yale); so mark "x" in the cell intersection of DR. HOO and MONDAY. Then mark "x" in the cells at the intersection of PHOTONICS and WEDNESDAY and THURSDAY.

Let's consider the possibilities given in the second set of conditions above. First of all, if Dr. Jay speaks on Thursday, then the Kinetic Energy lecture would be on Tuesday. That means that Chaos Theory couldn't be given on Tuesday, Wednesday, Thursday, or Friday (1) and it can't be placed on Monday so this set of conditions leads to conflicts. Therefore, Dr. Jay speaks Tuesday and the Kinetic Energy lecture will be on Monday.

At this point, the table should appear as follows.

		PHYSICIST					TOPIC				
		DR. DENTON	DR. HOO	DR. JAY	DR. KNOW	DR. ZHIVAGO	CHAOS THEORY	KINETIC ENERGY	MAGNETISM	PHOTONICS	QUANTUM MECHANICS
WEEKDAY	MONDAY		×	×	×	×	×	●	×	×	×
	TUESDAY	×	×	●	×	×		×			
	WEDNESDAY			×		×	×	×		×	
	THURSDAY		×	×			×	×		×	
	FRIDAY			×			×	×			
TOPIC	CHAOS THEORY					×					
	KINETIC ENERGY										
	MAGNETISM										
	PHOTONICS										
	QUANTUM MECHANICS				×						

Determine the days for each of the physicists first.
Chaos Theory is now on Tuesday [It can't be on Monday, Wednesday, Thursday, or Friday (1)]. Condition (1) also puts Dr. Zhivago on Friday.
Dr. Hoo isn't Monday (3), Tuesday (That's Dr. Jay.), Thursday (1), or Friday, so he or she has to be on Wednesday.
Dr. Know can't be Monday, Tuesday, Wednesday, or Friday, so he or she must lecture on Thursday.
And the only day left for Dr. Denton is Monday.

Now determine each speaker's topic.
Since Dr. Denton speaks on Monday, the topic is Kinetic Energy.
Dr. Jay speaks on Tuesday and the topic is Chaos Theory.
That means Friday's topic has to be Photonics given by Dr. Zhivago.
That leaves Quantum Mechanics and Magnetism for Dr. Hoo and Dr. Know. By condition (3), Dr. Know must lecture on Magnetism, leaving Dr. Hoo to speak on Quantum Mechanics.

In summary:

Monday, Dr. Denton, Kinetic Energy
Tuesday, Dr. Jay, Chaos Theory
Wednesday, Dr. Hoo, Quantum Mechanics
Thursday, Dr. Know, Magnetism
Friday, Dr. Zhivago, Photonics

3. 1. *I went to the store where I bought a CD (which isn't where I sought pruning shears) immediately after I visited PJ Nickle but immediately before I went to the shop where I intended to buy a Crockpot.*
Mark "x" in the box at the intersection of CD and PRUNING SHEARS, at the intersection of CD and PJ NICKLE, and also at the intersection of CD and CROCKPOT. Since the author bought the CD after one stop and before another, the store where he or she bought the CD couldn't have been the first or fifth stop, so mark "x" at the intersection of CD and FIRST and another at the intersection of CD and FIFTH. Also, PJ NICKLE can't be the fifth stop nor was the Crockpot purchased at the first stop; so mark "x" at the intersection of PJ NICKLE and FIFTH and another at the intersection of CROCKPOT and FIRST.

2. *I didn't purchase the fondue pot at Costington's. I went into one store intending to buy a Crockpot, but came out with a garden gnome instead. I didn't go to PJ Nickle for a pair of andirons.*
Mark "x" in the box at the intersection of FONDUE POT and COSTINGTON'S. At the intersection of CROCKPOT and GARDEN GNOME, place a "•". Then mark the four remaining cells in the ITEM SOUGHT column with "x" and do the same for the remaining four cells in the ITEM BOUGHT row. Put "x" at the intersection of PJ NICKLE and ANDIRONS.

3. *The store at which I sought a toaster oven (which wasn't the third one I visited) isn't the place I eventually bought a winter coat. Neither Lacy's nor S-Mart was the fourth shop I visited.*
Mark "x" in the box at the intersection of TOASTER OVEN and THIRD and also at the intersection of TOASTER OVEN and WINTER COAT. Mark "x" at the intersection of FOURTH and LACY'S and FOURTH and S-MART.

4. *I went to Costington's immediately after I visited the shop where I sought pruning shears (which wasn't S-Mart) but immediately before I went to the store where I purchased a set of spark plugs.*
Mark "x" in the box at the intersection of COSTINGTON'S and PRUNING SHEARS and also at the intersection of COSTINGTON'S and SPARK PLUGS. Costington's can't be the first stop so mark "x" in the box at the intersection of COSTINGTON'S and FIRST. And the pruning shears can't have been purchased last so mark "x" in the box at the intersection of PRUNING SHEARS and FIFTH. Costington's can't be the last stop so mark "x" in the box at the intersection of COSTINGTON'S and FIFTH. The spark plugs couldn't have been purchased first, so put "x" in the cell at the intersection of SPARK PLUGS and FIRST. Also, mark "x" in the box at the intersection of PRUNING SHEARS and S-MART.

At this point, the table appears as follows.

		STORE					ITEM SOUGHT					ITEM BOUGHT				
		BULLSEYE	COSTINGTON'S	LACY'S	PJ NICKLE	S-MART	ANDIRONS	CROCKPOT	PRUNING SHEARS	SNEAKERS	TOASTER OVEN	CD	FONDUE POT	GARDEN GNOME	SPARK PLUGS	WINTER COAT
ORDER	FIRST		×					×				×			×	
	SECOND							×								
	THIRD										×					
	FOURTH			×	×	×										
	FIFTH		×		×				×			×				
ITEM BOUGHT	CD				×			×	×							
	FONDUE POT		×					×								
	GARDEN GNOME						×	●	×	×	×					
	SPARK PLUGS		×					×								
	WINTER COAT							×			×					
ITEM SOUGHT	ANDIRONS				×											
	CROCKPOT				×											
	PRUNING SHEARS		×			×										
	SNEAKERS															
	TOASTER OVEN															

First, Costington's bought item is not a fondue pot (2) or spark plugs (4). Nor is it the garden gnome [sought Crockpot (2) and immediately after bought CD (1), which would lead to pruning shears (1)] or CD. So it must be the winter coat.

Next, the item bought while seeking the pruning shears isn't the CD (1) or garden gnome (2), nor can it be the winter coat (above). Because of (4), it can't be the spark plugs; that leaves only the fondue pot.

That means that Costington's is the second stop and spark plugs is the bought item on the third stop.

The CD isn't bought on the first or fifth stop (1), nor can it be bought on the second or third stop (above). So it must be bought on the fourth stop.

Because of (1), PJ Nickle is the third stop and the Crockpot is bought on the fifth stop.

The item sought at the third stop (at PJ Nickle) isn't andirons (2) or the toaster oven (3); it has to be sneakers.

The sought item at the fourth stop is the toaster oven and it isn't sought at either Lacy's or S-Mart (3), so it has to be at Bullseye.

The first stop isn't Costington's, PJ Nickle, S-Mart, or Bullseye, so it must be Lacy's. Which means the fifth stop is at S-Mart.

In summary:

First, Lacy's, pruning shears, fondue pot
Second, Costington's, andirons, winter coat
Third, PJ Nickle, sneakers, spark plugs
Fourth, Bullseye, toaster oven, CD
Fifth, S-Mart, Crockpot, garden gnome

4. Edwina can't work on the 41st floor (1) nor can Zed or Trish or Keith (2). So Ogden must work on the 41st floor.
Because of (2), Zed works on the 42nd floor.
Edwina does not work at accounting, nor does Ogden [He works on the 41st floor but Accounting has at least one floor below it (1).], Zed (1), or Trish (2). That leaves Keith and he works on the 45th floor (2).
That means that Edwina works on the 44th floor, which places Nelson & Leopold on the 43rd floor (1).
That leaves Trish to work on the 43rd floor and Glyptic must be on the 41st floor (2). Now, Glyptic isn't the Web-design firm so it must be the literary agent (3) and the Thebes Group is the Web-design firm.
Briarwood, on the 44th floor (1), isn't accounting (which is on the 45th floor); it's real estate.
That means that Watershed Co. is an accounting firm, Nelson & Leopold are a public relations firm, and Zed works for the Thebes Group.

In summary:

Edwina, 44th, Brierwood Ltd., real estate
Keith, 45th, Watershed Co., accounting
Ogden, 41st, Glyptic, literary agency
Trish, 43rd, Nelson & Leopold, public relations
Zed, 42nd, Thebes Group, Web-design

5. The puzzle (genre) game was rated "just okay" so Darren Castles' game was rated "don't bother" (2).
Gilligan's simulation game isn't "don't bother," "just okay," "totally awesome" (3), or "almost perfect" (4), so it must be "pretty cool."
Since Corley's action game (1) isn't "just okay" (2), "totally awesome" (3), "don't bother" or "pretty cool" (above), it must be "almost perfect." So that has to be *Hypnotic Trace* (4).
Ploof rated his or her game "just okay."
The sports game *Pitching Duel* (1) isn't rated "don't bother" (1) so it must be "totally awesome" and was rated by Milton (3).
The racing game *King of the Road* is rated "don't bother."
Fiji [rated by Kourtney (5)] is then either "pretty cool" or just okay." But Gilligan's game is "pretty cool" (above) so *Fiji* must be "just okay." That means that *Idle Hands* is "pretty cool."
Milton isn't Munoz (3); he's Corley. And Chadwick is Munoz.

In summary:

Alise Gilligan, *Idle Hands*, simulation, "pretty cool"
Chadwick Munoz, *Pitching Duel*, sports, "totally awesome"
Darren Castles, *King of the Road*, racing, "don't bother"
Kourtney Ploof, *Fiji*, puzzle, "just okay"
Milton Corley, *Hypnotic Trace*, action, "almost perfect"

Chapter 7

SETS AND PROBABILITY

7.1 Sets

1. $3 \in \{2, 5, 7, 9, 10\}$

The number 3 is not an element of the set, so the statement is false.

2. $6 \in \{-2, 6, 9, 5\}$

Since 6 is an element of the given set, the statement is true.

3. $9 \notin \{2, 1, 5, 8\}$

Since 9 is not an element of the set, the statement is true.

4. $3 \notin \{7, 6, 5, 4\}$

Since 3 is not an element of the given set, the statement is true.

5. $\{2, 5, 8, 9\} = \{2, 5, 9, 8\}$

The sets contain exactly the same elements, so they are equal. The statement is true.

6. $\{3, 7, 12, 14\} = \{3, 7, 12, 14, 0\}$

Two sets are equal only if they contain exactly the same elements. Since 0 is an element of the second set but not the first, the statement is false.

7. {All whole numbers greater than 7 and less than 10} $= \{8, 9\}$

Since 8 and 9 are the only such numbers, the statement is true.

8. $\{x|x$ is an odd integer, $6 \leq x \leq 18\}$
$= \{7, 9, 11, 15, 17\}$

The number 13 should be included in the set so the statement is false.

9. $0 \in \emptyset$

The empty set has no elements. The statement is false.

In Exercises 11-22,

$$\begin{aligned} A &= \{2, 4, 6, 8, 10, 12\}, \\ B &= \{2, 4, 8, 10\}, \\ C &= \{4, 8, 12\}, \\ D &= \{2, 10\}, \\ E &= \{6\}, \\ \text{and } U &= \{2, 4, 6, 8, 10, 12, 14\}. \end{aligned}$$

11. Since every element of A is also an element of U, A is a subset of U, written $A \subseteq U$.

12. Since every element of E is also an element of A, E is a subset of A, written $E \subseteq A$.

13. A contains elements that do not belong to E, namely 2, 4, 8, 10, and 12, so A is not a subset of E, written $A \nsubseteq E$.

14. Since 10 is an element of B but is not an element of C, B is not a subset of C, written $B \nsubseteq C$.

15. The empty set is a subset of every set, so $\emptyset \subseteq A$.

16. Since 0 is an element of $\{0, 2\}$, but is not an element of D, $\{0, 2\} \nsubseteq D$.

17. Every element of D is also an element of B, so D is a subset of B, $D \subseteq B$.

18. Since 2, 6, and 10 are elements of A, but are not elements of C, $A \nsubseteq C$.

19. Since every element of A is also an element of U, and $A \neq U$, $A \boxed{\subset} U$.
Since every element of E is also an element of A, and $E \neq A$, $E \boxed{\subset} A$.
Since every element of A is not also an element of E, $A \boxed{\not\subset} E$.
Since every element of B is not also an element of C, $B \boxed{\not\subset} C$.
Since ϕ is a subset of every set, and $\neq A$, $\phi \boxed{\subset} A$.
Since every element of $\{0, 2\}$ is not also an element of D, $\{0, 2\} \boxed{\not\subset} D$.
Since every element of D is also an element of B, and $D \neq B$, $D \boxed{\subset} B$.
Since every element of A is not also an element of C, $A \boxed{\not\subset} C$.

20. A set with n distinct elements has 2^n subsets. A has $n = 6$ elements, so there are exactly $2^6 = 64$ subsets of A.

21. Since B has 4 elements, it has 2^4 or 16 subsets. There are exactly 16 subsets of B.

22. A set with n distinct elements has 2^n subsets, and C has $n = 3$ elements. Therefore, there are exactly $2^3 = 8$ subsets of C.

23. Since D has 2 elements, it has 2^2 or 4 subsets. There are exactly 4 subsets of D.

25. Since $\{7, 9\}$ is the set of elements belonging to both sets, which is the intersection of the two sets, we write

$$\{5, 7, 9, 19\} \cap \{7, 9, 11, 15\} = \{7, 9\}.$$

26. $\{8, 11, 15\} \cap \{8, 11, 19, 20\} = \{8, 11\}$

$\{8, 11\}$ is the set of all elements belonging to both of the first two sets, so it is the intersection of those sets.

27. Since $\{1\}$ is the set of elements belonging to both sets, we write

$$\{2, 1, 7\} \cap \{1, 5, 9\} = \{1\}.$$

28. $\{6, 12, 14, 16\} \cap \{6, 14, 19\} = \{6, 14\}$

$\{6, 14\}$ is the set of all elements belonging to both of the first two sets, so it is the intersection of those sets.

29. Since $\emptyset$ contains no elements, there are no elements belonging to both sets. Thus, the intersection is the empty set, and we write

$$\{3, 5, 9, 10\} \cap \emptyset = \emptyset.$$

30. $\{3, 5, 9, 10\} \cup \emptyset = \{3, 5, 9, 10\}$

The empty set contains no elements, so the union of any set with the empty set will result in an answer set that is identical to the original set. (On the other hand, $\{3, 5, 9, 10\} \cap \emptyset = \emptyset$.)

31. $\{1, 2, 4\}$ is the set of elements belonging to both sets, and $\{1, 2, 4\}$ is also the set of elements in the first set or in the second set or possibly both. Thus,

$$\{1, 2, 4\} \cap \{1, 2, 4\} = \{1, 2, 4\}$$

and

$$\{1, 2, 4\} \cup \{1, 2, 4\} = \{1, 2, 4\}$$

are both true statements.

32. It is possible for two nonempty sets to have the same intersection and union only if they are equal, as in Exercise 31.

In Exercises 33-41,

$$\begin{aligned} U &= \{1, 2, 3, 4, 5, 6, 7, 8, 9\}, \\ X &= \{2, 4, 6, 8\}, \\ Y &= \{2, 3, 4, 5, 6\}, \\ \text{and} \quad Z &= \{1, 2, 3, 8, 9\}. \end{aligned}$$

33. $X \cap Y$, the intersection of X and Y, is the set of elements belonging to both X and Y. Thus,

$$\begin{aligned} X \cap Y &= \{2, 4, 6, 8\} \cap \{2, 3, 4, 5, 6\} \\ &= \{2, 4, 6\}. \end{aligned}$$

34. $X \cup Y$, the union of X and Y, is the set of all elements belonging to X or Y or both. Thus,

$$X \cup Y = \{2, 3, 4, 5, 6, 8\}.$$

35. X', the complement of X, consists of those elements of U that are not in X. Thus,

$$X' = \{1, 3, 5, 7, 9\}.$$

36. Y', the complement of Y, is the set of all elements of U that do not belong to Y. Thus,

$$Y' = \{1, 7, 8, 9\}.$$

37. From Exercise 35, $X' = \{1, 3, 5, 7, 9\}$; from Exercise 36, $Y' = \{1, 7, 8, 9\}$. There are no elements common to both X' and Y' so

$$X' \cap Y' = \{1, 7, 9\}.$$

38. $$\begin{aligned} X' \cap Z &= \{1, 3, 5, 7, 9\} \cap \{1, 2, 3, 8, 9\} \\ &= \{1, 3, 9\} \end{aligned}$$

39. First find $X \cup Z$.

$$\begin{aligned} X \cup Z &= \{2, 4, 6, 8\} \cup \{1, 2, 3, 8, 9\} \\ &= \{1, 2, 3, 4, 6, 8, 9\} \end{aligned}$$

Now find $Y \cap (X \cup Z)$.

$$\begin{aligned} Y \cap (X \cup Z) &= \{2, 3, 4, 5, 6\} \cap \{1, 2, 3, 4, 6, 8, 9\} \\ &= \{2, 3, 4, 6\} \end{aligned}$$

40. From Exercise 35, $X' = \{1, 3, 5, 7, 9\}$; from Exercise 36, $Y' = \{1, 7, 8, 9\}$.

$$\begin{aligned} X' \cap (Y' \cup Z) &= \{1, 3, 5, 7, 9\} \cap (\{1, 7, 8, 9\} \cup \{1, 2, 3, 8, 9\}) \\ &= \{1, 3, 5, 7, 9\} \cap \{1, 2, 3, 7, 8, 9\} \\ &= \{1, 3, 7, 9\} \end{aligned}$$

41. From Exercise 36, $Y' = \{1, 7, 8, 9\}$; $Z' = \{4, 5, 6, 7\}$.

$$\begin{aligned} (X \cap Y') \cup Z') &= (\{2, 4, 6, 8\} \cup \{1, 7, 8, 9\}) \cup \{4, 5, 6, 7\} \\ &= \{8\} \cup \{4, 5, 6, 7\} \\ &= \{4, 5, 6, 7, 8\} \end{aligned}$$

42. (a) $$\begin{aligned} (A \cap B) \cup (A \cap B') &= (\{3, 6, 9\} \cap \{2, 4, 6, 8\}) \cup (\{3, 6, 9\} \cap \{0, 1, 3, 5, 7, 9, 10\}) \\ &= \{6\} \cup \{3, 9\} \\ &= \{3, 6, 9\} \\ &= A \end{aligned}$$

43. M' consists of all students in U who are not in M, so M' consists of all students in this school not taking this course.

44. $M \cup N$ is the set of all students in this school taking this course or taking accounting.

45. $N \cap P$ is the set of all students in this school taking both accounting and zoology.

46. $N' \cap P'$ is the set of all students in this school not taking accounting and not taking zoology.

47. $A = \{2, 4, 6, 8, 10, 12\}$,
$B = \{2, 4, 8, 10\}$,
$C = \{4, 8, 12\}$,
$D = \{2, 10\}$,
$E = \{6\}$,
$U = \{2, 4, 6, 8, 10, 12, 14\}$

A pair of sets is disjoint if the two sets have no elements in common. The pairs of these sets that are disjoint are B and E, C and E, D and E, and C and D.

48. Disjoint sets have no elements in common. Since each pair of sets has at least one element in common, none of the pairs are disjoint.

49. B' is the set of all stocks with a closing price below \$26 or above \$30. Therefore,

$$B' = \{\text{AT\&T, CocaCola, Office Max Inc., Texas Instruments}\}.$$

50. $A \cap B$ is the set of all stocks with a high price greater than \$34 and a closing price between \$26 and \$30. $A \cap B = \{\text{Dell Inc.}\}$.

51. $(A \cap B)'$ is the set of all stocks that do not have both a high price greater than \$34 and a closing price between \$26 and \$30;

$$(A \cap B)' = \{\text{AT\&T, CocaCola, Disney, Office Max Inc., Texas Instruments}\}.$$

52. $(A \cup C)'$ is the set of all stocks on the list that do not have a high price greater than \$34 or a positive price change.

$$(A \cup C)' = \{\text{AT\&T, Disney}\}.$$

53. $A = \{1, 2, 3, \{3\}, \{1, 4, 7\}\}$

(a) $1 \in A$ is true.

(b) $\{3\} \in A$ is true.

(c) $\{2\} \in A$ is false. $(\{2\} \subseteq A)$

(d) $4 \in A$ is false. $(4 \in \{1, 4, 7\})$

(e) $\{\{3\}\} \subset A$ is true.

(f) $\{1, 4, 7\} \in A$ is true.

(g) $\{1, 4, 7\} \subseteq A$ is false. $(\{1, 4, 7\} \in A)$

54. $B = \{a, b, c, \{d\}, \{e, f\}\}$

(a) $a \in B$ is true.

(b) $\{b, c, d\} \subset B$ is false. $(d \notin B)$

(c) $\{d\} \in B$ is true.

(d) $\{d\} \subseteq B$ is false. $(\{d\} \in B)$

(e) $\{e, f\} \in B$ is true.

(f) $\{a, \{e, f\}\} \subset B$ is true.

(g) $\{e, f\} \subset B$ is false. $(\{e, f\} \in B)$

55. $V \cap J =$ {General Electric Co., ExxonMobil Corp., Citigroup, Inc., Microsoft Corp., Proctor & Gamble}
$\cap$ {Boeing Co., Proctor & Gamble, Yahoo!, Inc., UnitedHealth Group, Microsoft Corp.}
= {MicrosoftCorp., Proctor & Gamble}

56. $V \cap (F \cup T) =$ {General Electric Co., ExxonMobil Corp., Citigroup, Inc., Microsoft Corp., Proctor & Gamble}
$\cap$ ({Nokia Corp., UnitedHealth Group, Schlumberger Ltd., Google Inc., General Electric Co.}
$\cup$ {UnitedHealth Group, General Electric Co., Microsoft Corp., Citigroup, Inc.,
American International Group})
= {General Electric Co., ExxonMobil Corp., Citigroup, Inc., Microsoft Corp., Proctor & Gamble}
$\cap${Nokia Corp., UnitedHealth Group, Schlumberger Ltd., Google Inc., General Electric Co.,
Microsoft Corp., Citigroup, Inc., American International Group}
= {General Electric Co., Citigroup, Inc, Microsoft Corp.}

57. $(J \cup F)' =$ ({Boeing Co., Procter & Gamble, Yahoo!, Inc., UnitedHealth Group, Microsoft Corp.}
$\cup$ {Nokia Corp., UnitedHealth Group, Schlumberger Ltd., Google Inc., General Electric Co.}
= ({Boeing Co., Procter & Gamble, Yahoo!, Inc., UnitedHealth Group, Microsoft Corp.,
Nokia Corp., Schlumberger Ltd., Google Inc., General Electric Co.,})$'$
= {ExxonMobil Corp., Citigroup Inc., American International Group.}

58. $J' \cap T' =$ {Boeing Co., Procter & Gamble, Yahoo!, Inc., UnitedHealth Group, Microsoft Corp.}$'$
$\cap$ {UnitedHealth Group, General Electric Co., Microsoft Corp., Citigroup, Inc.,
American International Group}$'$
= {General Electric Co., ExxonMobil Corp., Citigroup Inc., Nokia Corp., Sclumberger Ltd.,
Google Inc., General Electric Co., UnitedHealth Group, American International Group}
$\cap$ {ExxonMobil Corp., Procter & Gamble, Boeing Co., Yahoo!, Inc., Nokia Corp.,
Sclumberger Ltd., Google Inc.}
= {ExxonMobil Corp., Nokia Corp., Sclumberger Ltd., Google Inc.}

59. $U = \{s, d, c, g, i, m, h\}$ and $O = \{i, m, h, g\}$, so $O' = \{s, d, c\}$.

60. $U = \{s, d, c, g, i, m, h\}$ and $N = \{s, d, c, g\}$, so

$$N' = \{i, m, h\}.$$

61. $N \cap O = \{s, d, c, g\} \cap \{i, m, h, g\} = \{g\}$

62. $N \cup O = \{s, d, c, g\} \cup \{i, m, h, g\} = \{s, d, c, g, i, m, h\} = U$

63. $N \cap O' = \{s, d, c, g\} \cap \{s, d, c\} = \{s, d, c\}$

64. The number of subsets of a set with 51 elements (50 states plus the District of Columbia) is

$$2^{51} \approx 2.522 \times 10^{15}.$$

65. The total number of subsets is $2^4 = 16$. The number of subsets with no elements is 1, and the number of subsets with one element is 4. Therefore, the number of subsets with at least two elements is $16 - (1 + 4)$ or 11.

66. The number of subsets of a set containing 9 elements is $2^9 = 512$.

67. $F = \{$The Disney Channel, Showtime, HBO, Encore$\}$

68. $G = \{$Showtime, HBO$\}$

69. $H = \{$Encore, Starz$\}$

70. $F \cap H = \{$The Disney Channel, Showtime, HBO, Encore$\} \cap \{$Encore, Starz$\} = \{$Encore$\}$

71. $G \cup H = \{$Showtime, HBO$\} \cup \{$Encore, Starz$\} = \{$Showtime, HBO, Encore, Starz$\}$

72. $G' = \{$Showtime, HBO$\}' = \{$The Disney Channel, Encore, Starz$\}$

73. Joe should always first choose the complement of what Dorothy chose. This will leave only two sets to choose from, and Joe will get the last choice.

74. **(a)** $A \cup (B \cap C)'$

$B \cap C$ is the set of states with both a population over 4,000,000 and an area greater than 40,000 square miles. Therefore, $(B \cap C)'$ is the set of states with not both a population over 4,000,000 and an area greater than 40,000 square miles. As a result, $A \cup (B \cap C)'$ is the set of states whose name contains the letter e or who are not both over 4,000,000 in population and over 40,000 square miles in area.

(b)

$$\begin{aligned}(B \cap C)' &= (\{\text{Alabama, Colorado, Florida, Indiana, Kentucky, New Jersey}\} \cap \{\text{Alabama, Alaska,}\\ &\qquad \text{Colorado, Florida, Kentucky, Nebraska}\})'\\ &= \{\text{Alabama, Colorado, Florida, Kentucky}\}'\\ &= \{\text{Alaska, Hawaii, Indiana, Maine, Nebraska, New Jersey}\}\\ A \cup (B \cap C)' &= \{\text{Kentucky, Maine, Nebraska, New Jersey}\} \cup \{\text{Alaska, Hawaii, Indiana, Maine,}\\ &\qquad \text{Nebraska, New Jersey}\}\\ &= \{\text{Alaska, Hawaii, Indiana, Kentucky, Maine, Nebraska, New Jersey}\}\end{aligned}$$

75. **(a)** $(A \cup B)' \cap C$

$A \cup B$ is the set of states whose name contains the letter e or has a population over 4,000,000. Therefore, $(A \cup B)'$ is the set of states who are not among those whose name contains the letter e or has a population over 4,000,000. As a result, $(A \cup B)' \cap C$ is the set of states who are not among those whose name contains the letter e or has a population over 4,000,000 who also have an area over 40,000 miles.

(b)

$$\begin{aligned}(A \cup B)' &= \{(\text{Kentucky, Maine, Nebraska, New Jersey}\} \cup \{\text{Alabama, Colorado, Florida, Indiana,} \\ &\quad \text{Kentucky, New Jersey}\})' \\ &= \{\text{Alabama, Colorado, Florida, Indiana, Kentucky, Maine, Nebraska, New Jersey}\}' \\ &= \{\text{Alaska, Hawaii}\} \\ (A \cup B)' \cap C &= \{\text{Alaska, Hawaii}\} \cap \{\text{Alabama, Alaska, Colorado, Florida, Kentucky, Nebraska}\} \\ &= \{\text{Alaska}\}\end{aligned}$$

7.2 Applications of Venn Diagrams

1. $B \cap A'$ is the set of all elements in B *and* not in A.

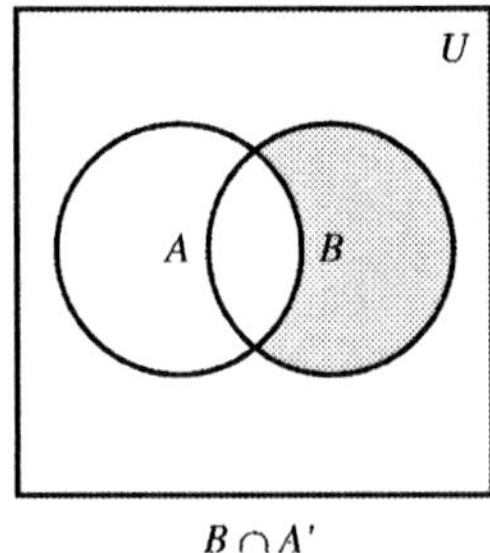

$B \cap A'$

2. $A \cup B'$ is the set of all elements in A *or* not in B, or both.

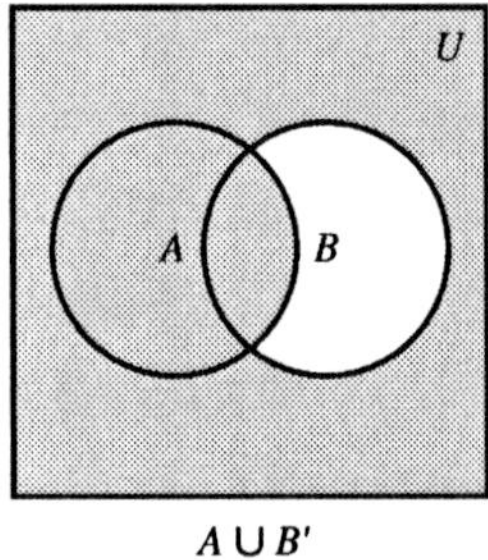

$A \cup B'$

3. $A' \cup B$ is the set of all elements that do not belong to A *or* that do belong to B, or both.

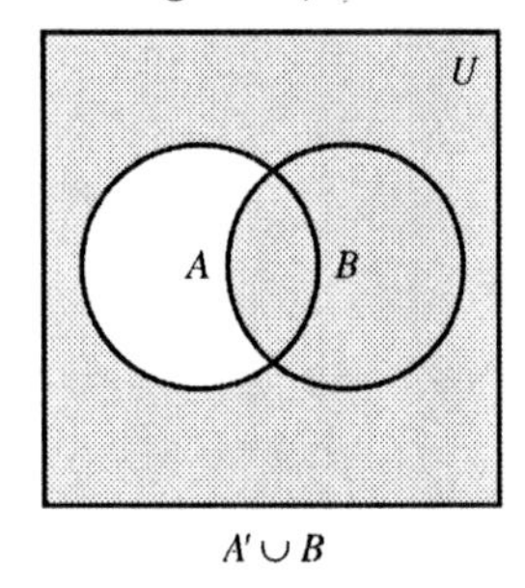

$A' \cup B$

4. $A' \cap B'$ is the set of all elements not in A *and* not in B.

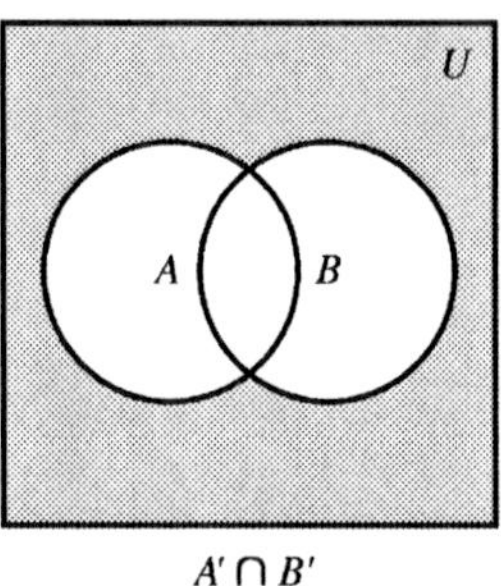

$A' \cap B'$

5. $B' \cup (A' \cap B')$

First find $A' \cap B'$, the set of elements not in A *and* not in B.

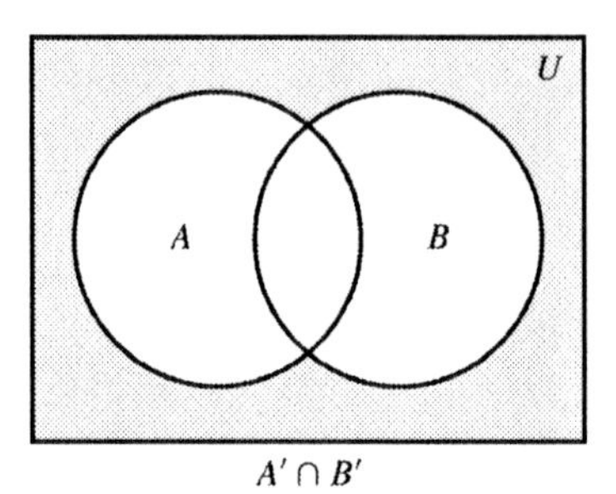

$A' \cap B'$

For the union, we want those elements in B' *or* $(A' \cap B')$, or both.

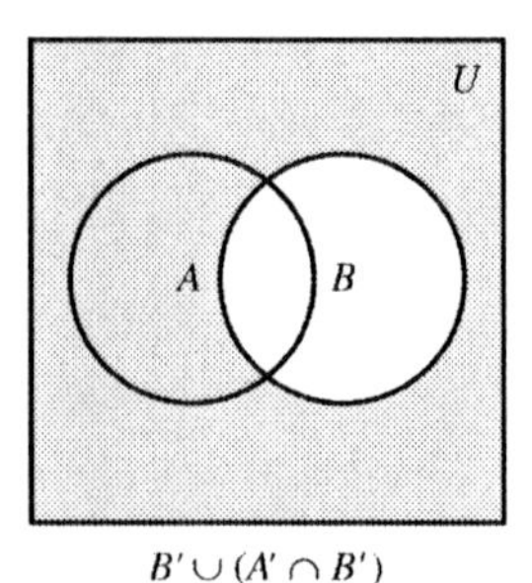

$B' \cup (A' \cap B')$

6. $(A \cap B) \cup B'$

First find $A \cap B$, the set of elements in A *and* in B. Now combine this region with B', the set of all elements not in B. For the union, we want those elements in $A \cap B$ *or* B', or both.

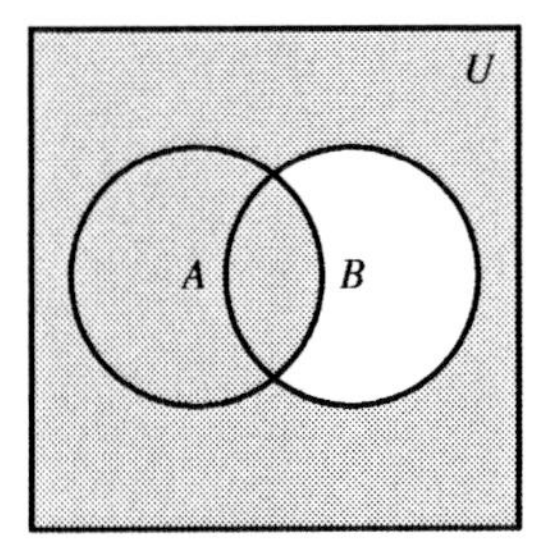

$(A \cap B) \cup B'$

7. U' is the empty set $\emptyset$.

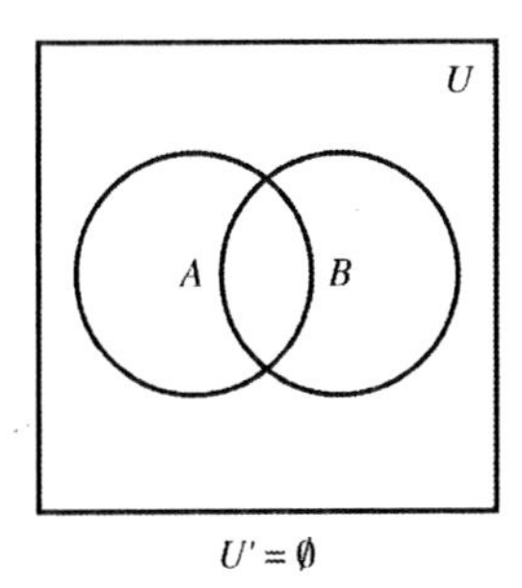

$U' = \emptyset$

8. $\emptyset' = U$, so the entire region is shaded.

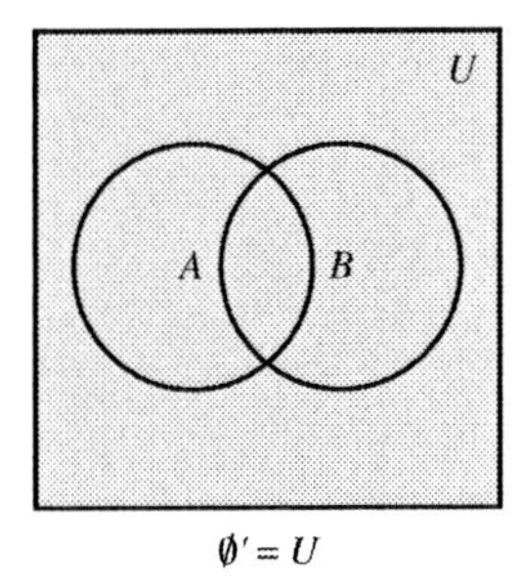

$\emptyset' = U$

9. Three sets divide the universal set into at most 8 regions. (Examples of this situation will be seen in Exercises 11-17.)

11. $(A \cap B) \cap C$

First form the intersection of A with B.

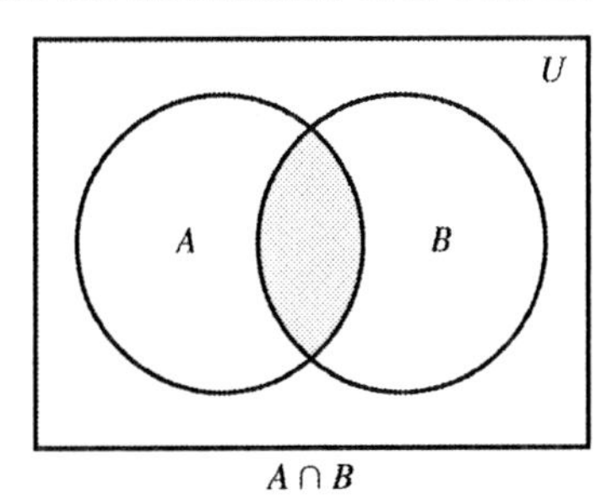

$A \cap B$

Now form the intersection of $A \cap B$ with C. The result will be the set of all elements that belong to all three sets.

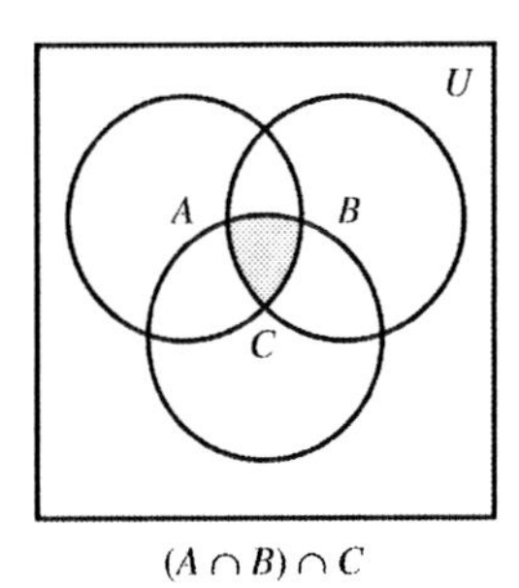

$(A \cap B) \cap C$

12. $(A \cap C') \cup B$

First find $A \cap C'$, the region in A *and* not in C.

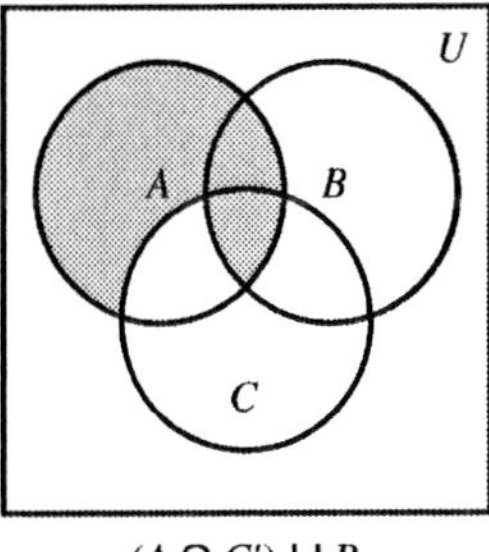

$(A \cap C') \cup B$

For the union, we want the region in $(A \cap C')$ *or* in B, or both.

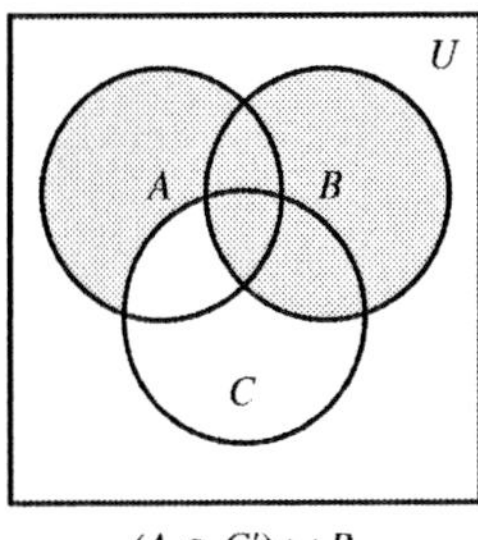

$(A \cap C') \cup B$

13. $A \cap (B \cup C')$

C' is the set of all elements in U that are not elements of C.

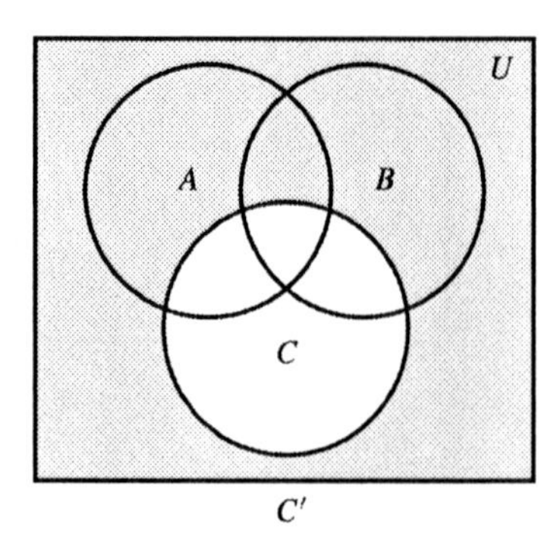

C'

Now form the union of C' with B.

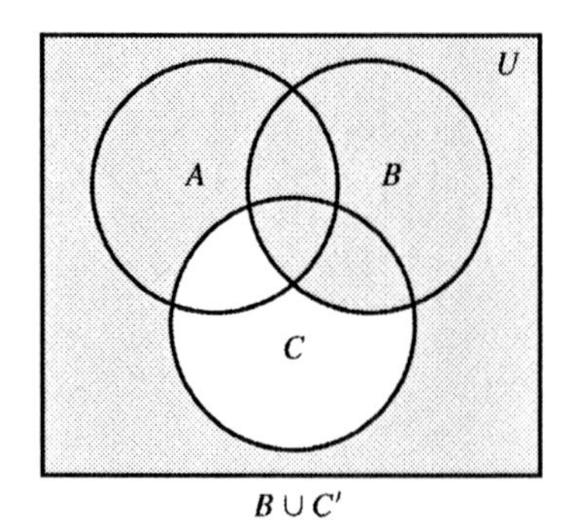

$B \cup C'$

Finally, find the intersection of this region with A.

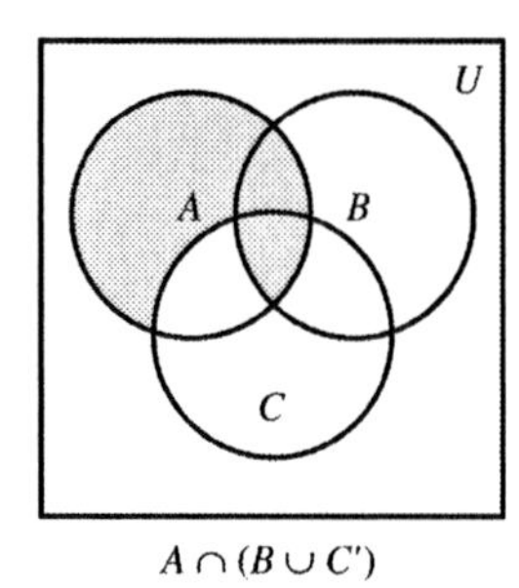

$A \cap (B \cup C')$

14. $A' \cap (B \cap C)$

First find A', the region not in A.

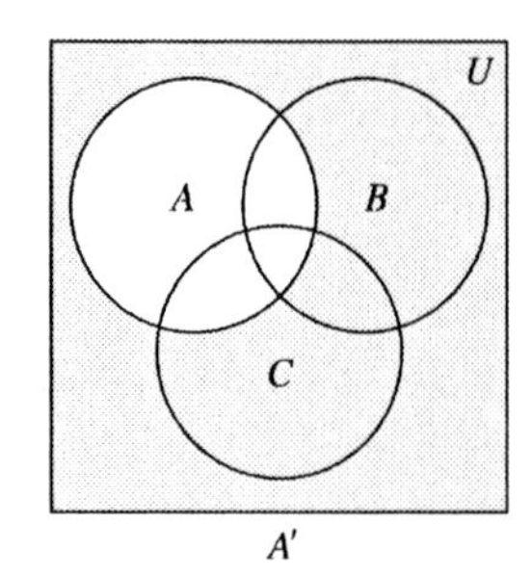

A'

Then find $B \cap C$, the region where B and C overlap.

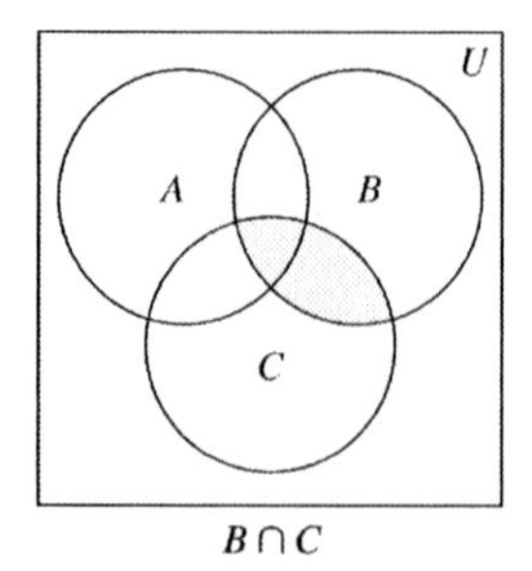

$B \cap C$

Now intersect these regions.

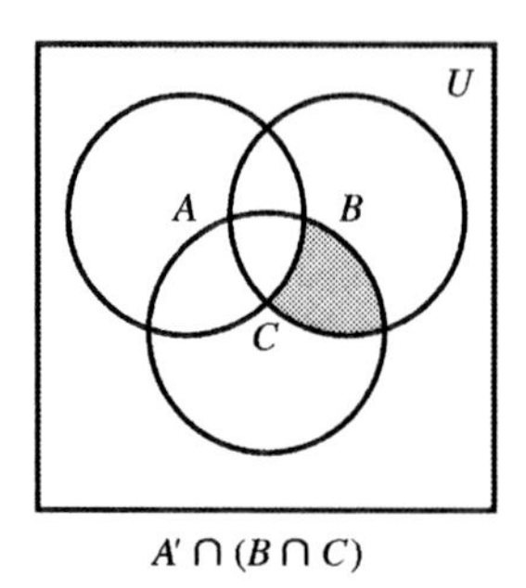

$A' \cap (B \cap C)$

15. $(A' \cap B') \cap C$

$A' \cap B'$ is the region of the universal set not in A *and* not in B.

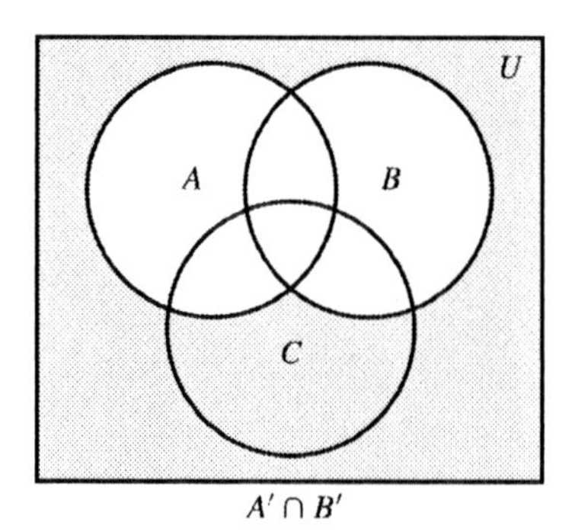

$A' \cap B'$

Now intersect this region with C.

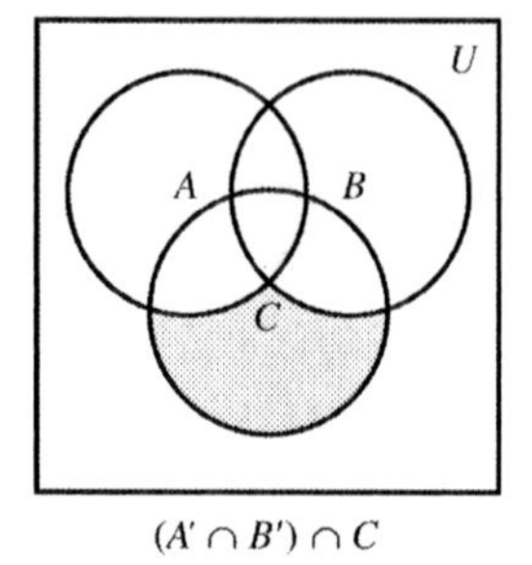

$(A' \cap B') \cap C$

16. $(A \cap B') \cap C$

First find $A \cap B'$, the region in A *and* not in B.

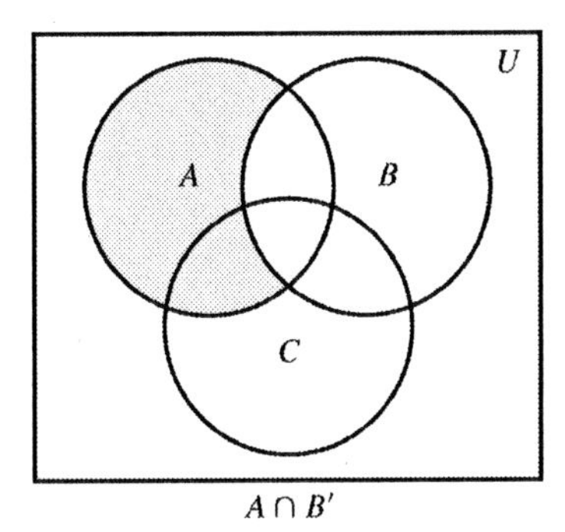

$A \cap B'$

Now intersect this region with C.

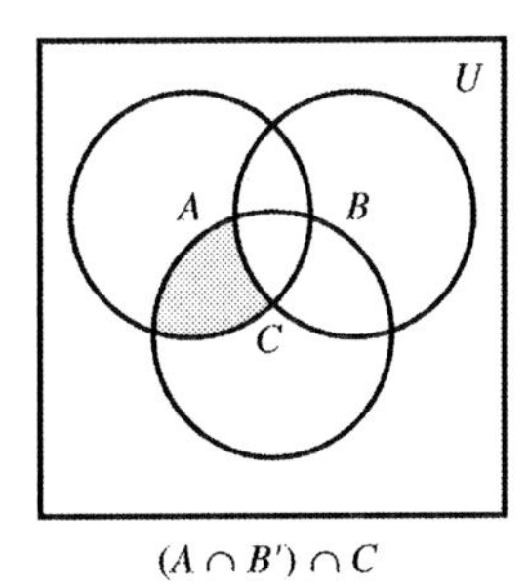

$(A \cap B') \cap C$

17. $(A \cap B') \cup C$

First find $A \cap B'$, the region in A and not in B.

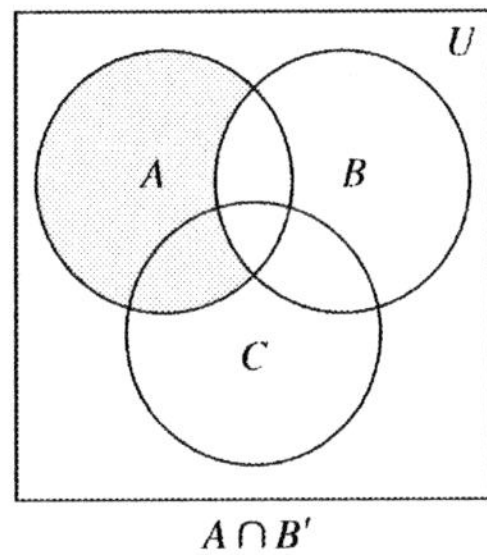

$A \cap B'$

For the union, we want the region in $(A \cap B')$ or in C, or both.

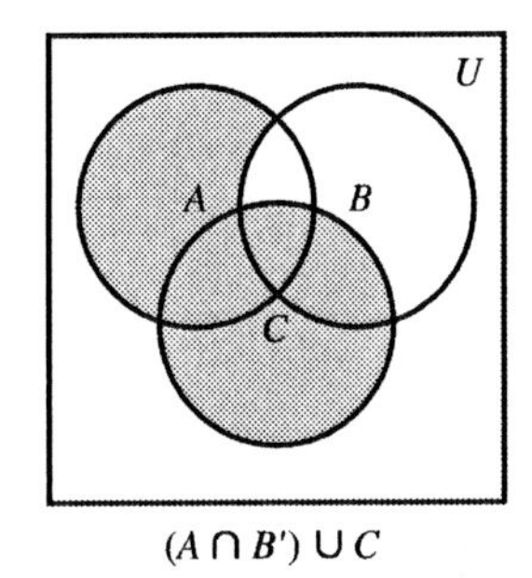

$(A \cap B') \cup C$

18. $A' \cap (B' \cup C)$

First find A'.

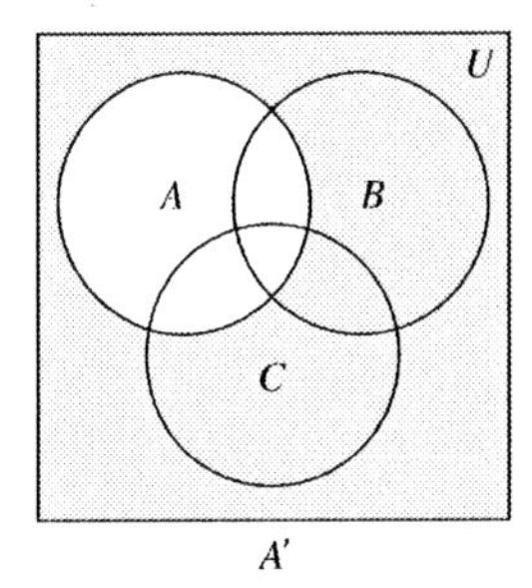

A'

Then find $B' \cup C$, the region not in B *or* in C, or both.

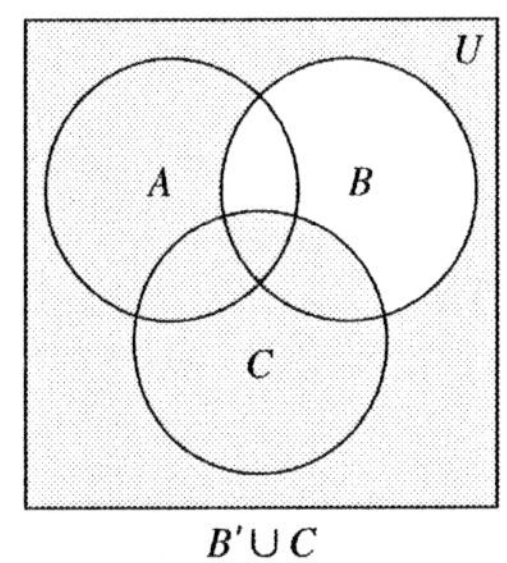

$B' \cup C$

Now intersect these regions.

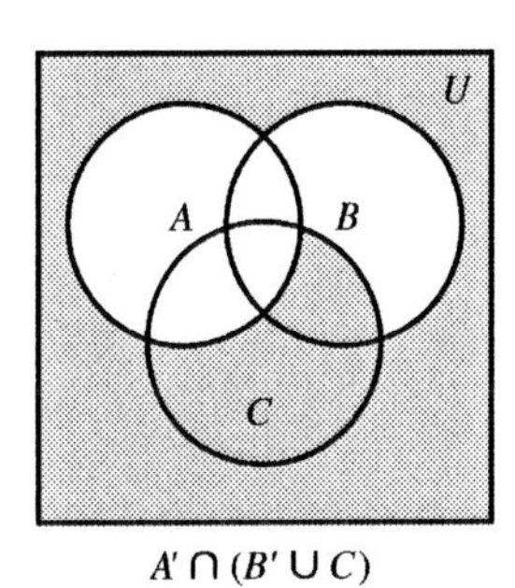

$A' \cap (B' \cup C)$

19. $(A \cup B') \cap C$

First find $A \cup B'$, the region in A or B' or both.

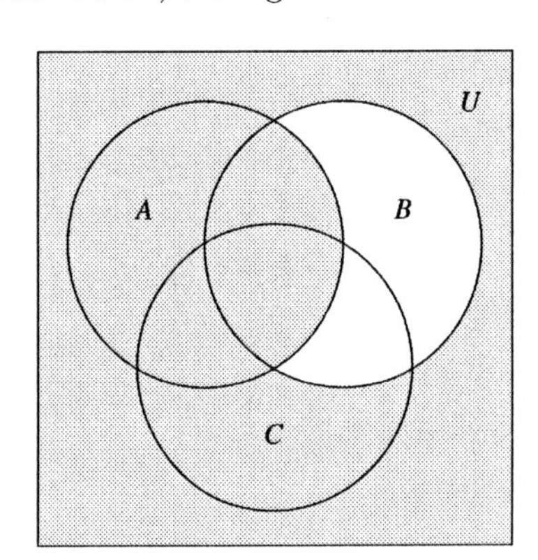

Intersect this with C.

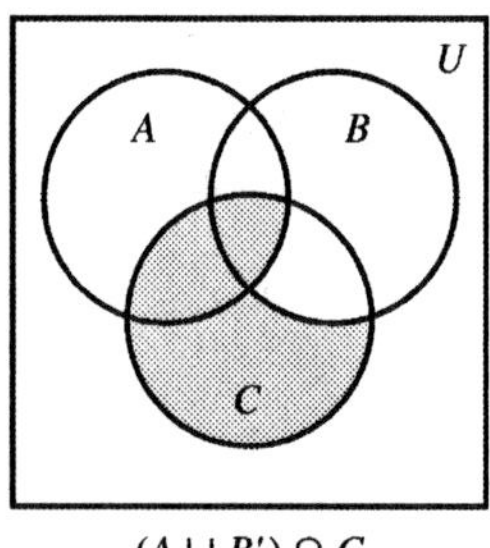

$(A \cup B') \cap C$

20. $A \cup (B' \cap C)$

First find $B' \cap C$, the region in C but not in B.

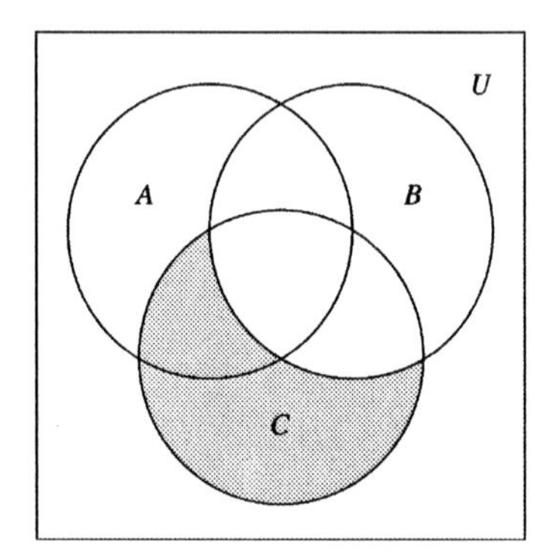

Union this with A.

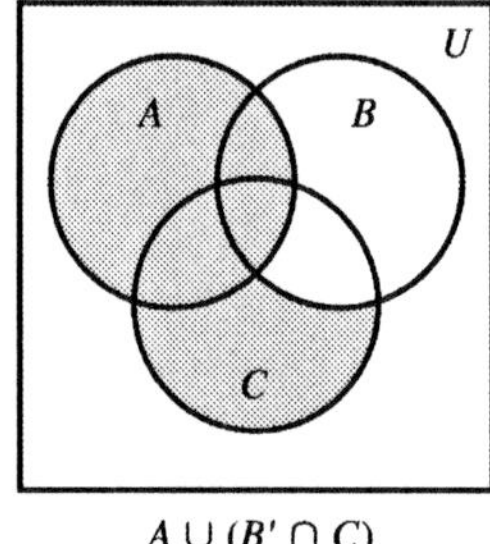

$A \cup (B' \cap C)$

21. $n(A \cup B) = n(A) + n(B) - n(A \cap B)$
$= 5 + 12 - 4$
$= 13$

22. $n(A \cup B) = n(A) + n(B) - n(A \cap B)$
$33 = 15 + 30 - n(A \cap B)$
$33 = 45 - n(A \cap B)$
$n(A \cap B) = 12$

23. $n(A \cup B) = n(A) + n(B) - n(A \cap B)$
$22 = n(A) + 9 - 5$
$22 = n(A) + 4$
$18 = n(A)$

24. $n(A \cup B) = n(A) + n(B) - n(A \cap B)$
$38 = 13 + n(B) - 5$
$38 = 8 + n(B)$
$n(B) = 30$

25. $n(U) = 41$
$n(A) = 16$
$n(A \cap B) = 12$
$n(B') = 20$

First put 12 in $A \cap B$. Since $n(A) = 16$, and 12 are in $A \cap B$, there must be 4 elements in A that are not in $A \cap B$. $n(B') = 20$, so there are 20 not in B. We already have 4 not in B (but in A), so there must be another 16 outside B *and* outside A. So far we have accounted for 32, and $n(U) = 41$, so 9 must be in B but not in any region yet identified. Thus $n(A' \cap B) = 9$.

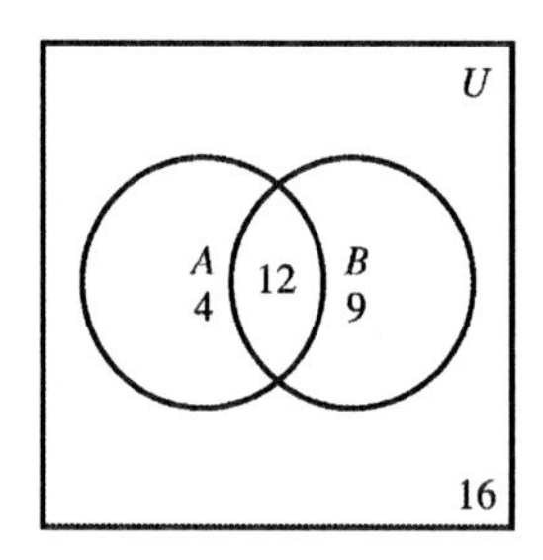

26. $n(A) = 28$
$n(B) = 12$
$n(A \cup B) = 32$
$n(A') = 19$

$n(A \cup B) = n(A) + n(B) - n(A \cap B)$
$32 = 28 + 12 - n(A \cap B)$
$32 = 40 - n(A \cap B)$
$n(A \cap B) = 8$

To fill in the regions, start with $A \cap B$. $n(A) = 28$ and $n(A \cap B) = 8$, so $n(A \cap B') = 20$. $n(B) = 12$ and $n(A \cap B) = 8$, so $n(B \cap A') = 4$. Since $n(A') = 19$, 4 of which are accounted for in $B \cap A'$, 15 elements remain in $A' \cap B'$.

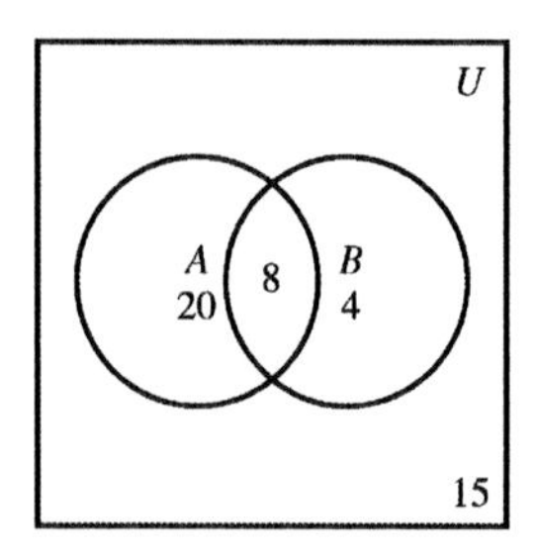

27. $n(A \cup B) = 24$
$n(A \cap B) = 6$
$n(A) = 11$
$n(A' \cup B') = 25$

Start with $n(A \cap B) = 6$. Since $n(A) = 11$, there must be 5 more in A not in B. $n(A \cup B) = 24$; we already have 11, so 13 more must be in B not yet counted. $A' \cup B'$ consists of all the region not in $A \cap B$, where we have 6. So far $5 + 13 = 18$ are in this region, so another $25 - 18 = 7$ must be outside both A and B.

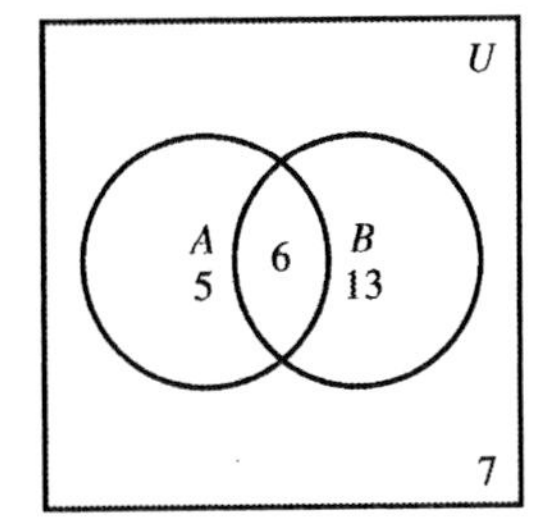

28. $n(A') = 31$
$n(B) = 25$
$n(A' \cup B') = 46$
$n(A \cap B) = 12$

$n(B) = 25$ and $n(A \cap B) = 12$, so $n(B \cap A') = 13$. Since $n(A') = 31$, of which 13 elements are accounted for, 18 elements are in $A' \cap B'$.

$$\begin{aligned} n(A' \cup B') &= n(A') + n(B') - n(A' \cap B') \\ 46 &= 31 + n(B') - 18 \\ 46 &= 13 + n(B') \\ 33 &= n(B') \end{aligned}$$

18 elements are in $A' \cap B'$, so the rest are in $A \cap B'$, and $n(A \cap B') = 15$.

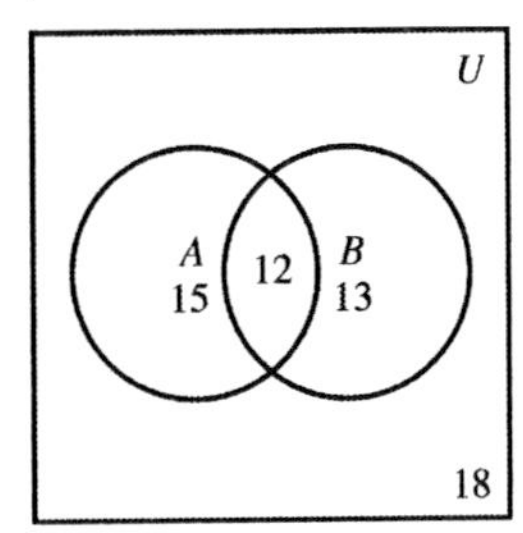

29. $n(A) = 28$
$n(B) = 34$
$n(C) = 25$
$n(A \cap B) = 14$
$n(B \cap C) = 15$
$n(A \cap C) = 11$
$n(A \cap B \cap C) = 9$
$n(U) = 59$

We start with $n(A \cap B \cap C) = 9$. If $n(A \cap B) = 14$, an additional 5 are in $A \cap B$ but not in $A \cap B \cap C$. Similarly, $n(B \cap C) = 15$, so $15 - 9 = 6$ are in $B \cap C$ but not in $A \cap B \cap C$. Also, $n(A \cap C) = 11$, so $11 - 9 = 2$ are in $A \cap C$ but not in $A \cap B \cap C$.

Now we turn our attention to $n(A) = 28$. So far we have $2 + 9 + 5 = 16$ in A; there must be another $28 - 16 = 12$ in A not yet counted. Similarly, $n(B) = 34$; we have $5 + 9 + 6 = 20$ so far, and $34 - 20 = 14$ more must be put in B. For C, $n(C) = 25$; we have $2 + 9 + 6 = 17$ counted so far. Then there must be 8 more in C not yet counted. The count now stands at 56, and $n(U) = 59$, so 3 must be outside the three sets.

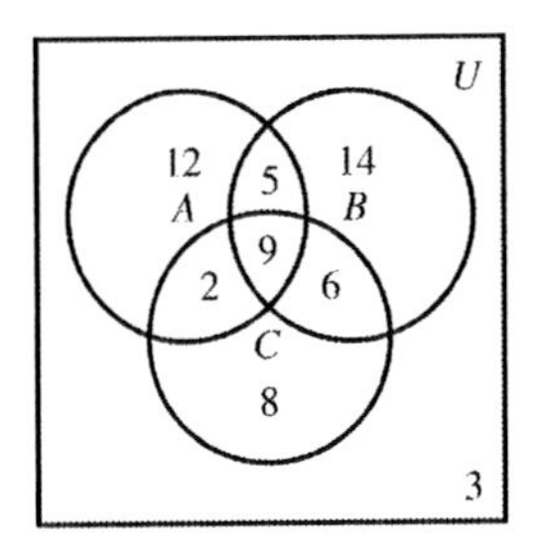

30. $n(A) = 54$
$n(A \cap B) = 22$
$n(A \cup B) = 85$
$n(A \cap B \cap C) = 4$
$n(A \cap C) = 15$
$n(B \cap C) = 16$
$n(C) = 44$
$n(B') = 63$

Start with $A \cap B \cap C$. We have $n(A \cap C) = 15$, of which 4 elements are in $A \cap B \cap C$, so $n(A \cap B' \cap C) = 11$. $n(B \cap C) = 16$, of which 4 elements are in $A \cap B \cap C$, so $n(B \cap C \cap A') = 12$. $n(C) = 44$, so 17 elements are in $C \cap A' \cap B'$. $n(A \cap B) = 22$, so 18 elements are in $A \cap B \cap C'$. $n(A) = 54$, so $54 - 11 - 18 - 4 = 21$ elements are in $A \cap B' \cap C'$.

Now use the union rule.

$$\begin{aligned} n(A \cup B) &= n(A) + n(B) - n(A \cap B) \\ 85 &= 54 + n(B) - 22 \\ 53 &= n(B) \end{aligned}$$

This leaves 19 elements in $B \cap A' \cap C'$. $n(B') = 63$, of which $21 + 11 + 17 = 49$ are accounted for, leaving 14 elements in $A' \cap B' \cap C'$.

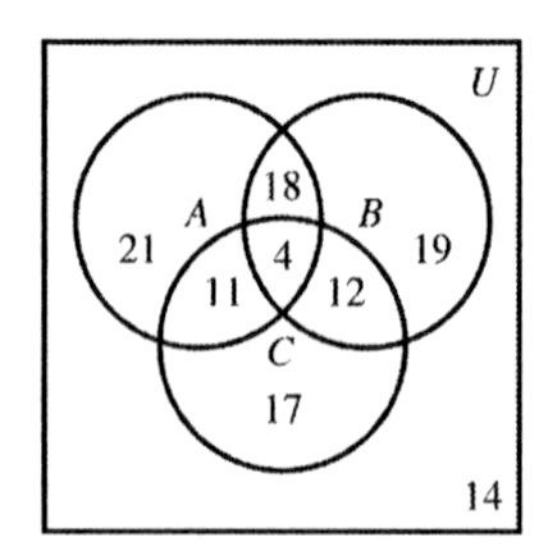

31. $n(A \cap B) = 6$
$n(A \cap B \cap C) = 4$
$n(A \cap C) = 7$
$n(B \cap C) = 4$
$n(A \cap C') = 11$
$n(B \cap C') = 8$
$n(C) = 15$
$n(A' \cap B' \cap C') = 5$

Start with $n(A \cap B) = 6$ and $n(A \cap B \cap C) = 4$ to get $6 - 4 = 2$ in that portion of $A \cap B$ outside of C. From $n(B \cap C) = 4$, there are $4 - 4 = 0$ elements in that portion of $B \cap C$ outside of A. Use $n(A \cap C) = 7$ to get $7 - 4 = 3$ elements in that portion of $A \cap C$ outside of B.
Since $n(A \cap C') = 11$, there are $11 - 2 = 9$ elements in that part of A outside of B and C. Use $n(B \cap C') = 8$ to get $8 - 2 = 6$ elements in that part of B outside of A and C. Since $n(C) = 15$, there are $15 - 3 - 4 - 0 = 8$ elements in C outside of A and B. Finally, 5 must be outside all three sets, since $n(A' \cap B' \cap C') = 5$.

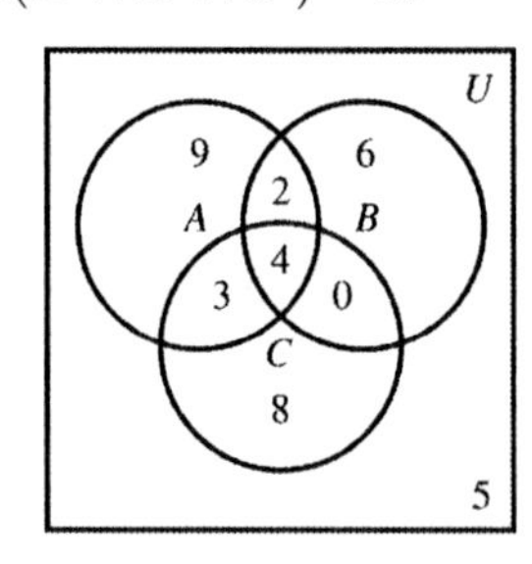

32. $n(A) = 13$
$n(A \cap B \cap C) = 4$
$n(A \cap C) = 6$
$n(A \cap B') = 6$
$n(B \cap C) = 6$
$n(B \cap C') = 11$
$n(B \cup C) = 22$
$n(A' \cap B' \cap C') = 5$

Start with the regions $A \cap B \cap C$ and $A' \cap B' \cap C'$.
$n(B \cap C) = 6$, leaving 2 elements in $B \cap C \cap A'$.
$n(A \cap C) = 6$, leaving 2 elements in $A \cap C \cap B'$.
$n(A \cap B') = 6$, leaving 4 elements in $A \cap B' \cap C'$.
$n(A) = 13$, leaving 3 elements in $A \cap B \cap C'$.
$n(B \cap C') = 11$, leaving 8 elements in $B \cap C' \cap A'$.

Now use the union rule.

$$\begin{aligned} n(B \cup C) &= n(B) + n(C) - n(B \cap C) \\ 22 &= 17 + n(C) - 6 \\ 11 &= n(C) \end{aligned}$$

This leaves 3 elements in $C \cap A' \cap B'$.

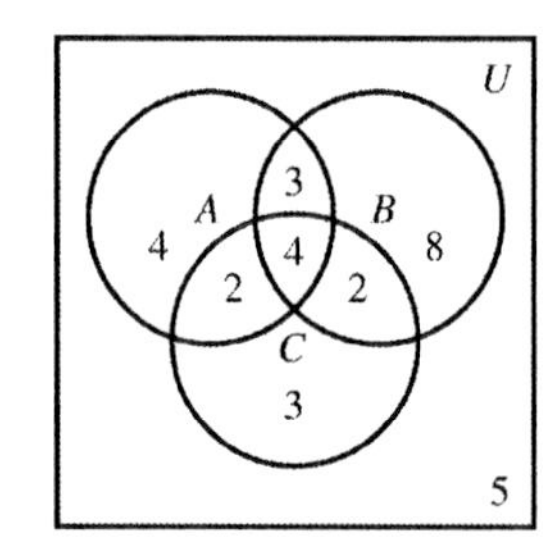

33. $(A \cup B)' = A' \cap B'$

For $(A \cup B)'$, first find $A \cup B$.

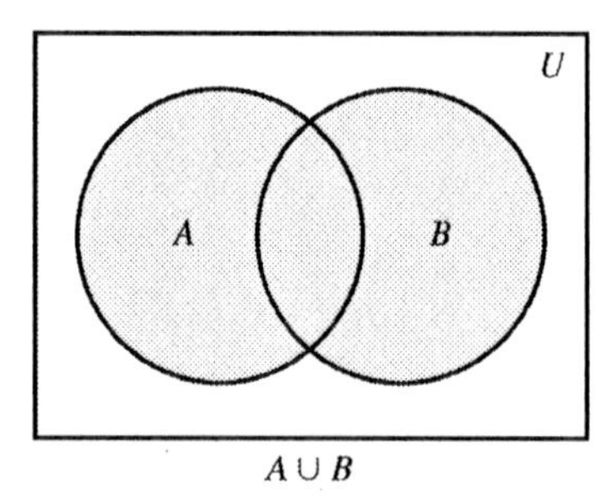

$A \cup B$

Now find $(A \cup B)'$, the region outside $A \cup B$.

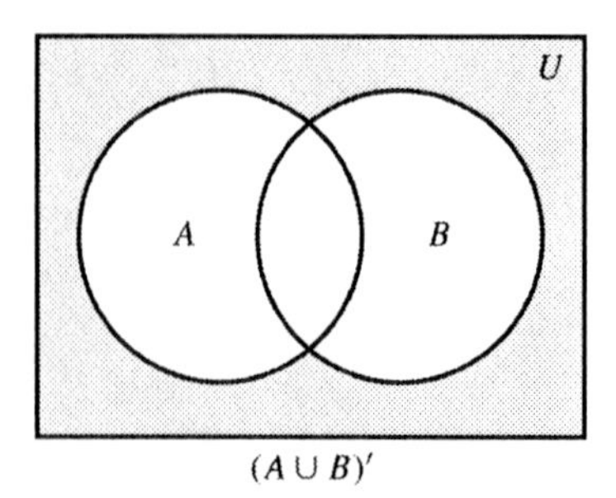

$(A \cup B)'$

For $A' \cap B'$, first find A' and B' individually.

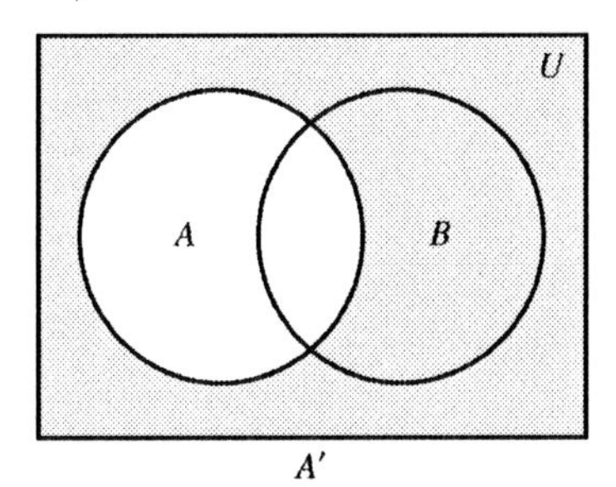

A'

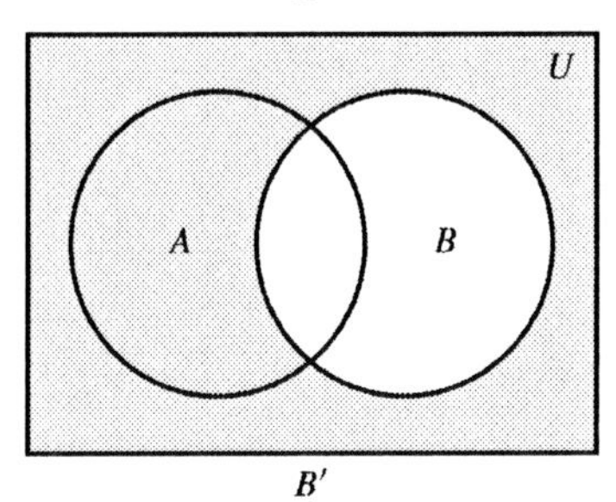

B'

Then $A' \cap B'$ is the region where A' and B' overlap, which is the entire region outside $A \cup B$ (the same result as in the second diagram). Therefore,

$$(A \cup B)' = A' \cap B'.$$

34. $(A \cap B)'$ is the complement of the intersection of A and B; hence it contains all elements not in $A \cap B$.

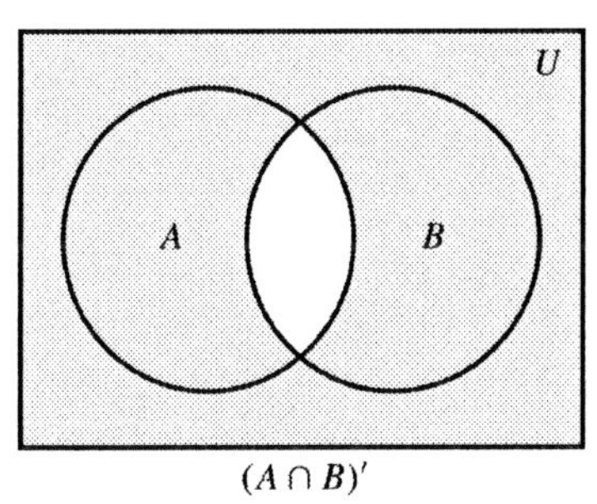

$(A \cap B)'$

$A' \cup B'$ is the union of the complements of A and B; hence it contains any element that is either not in A *or* not in B.

A' is the set of all elements in U that are not in A.

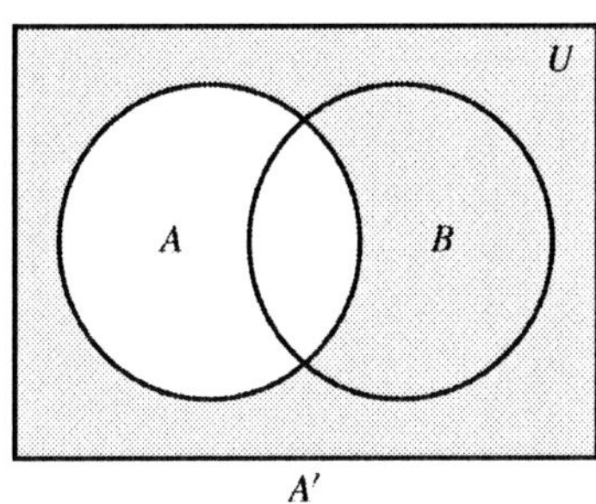

A'

B' is the set of all elements in U that are not in B.

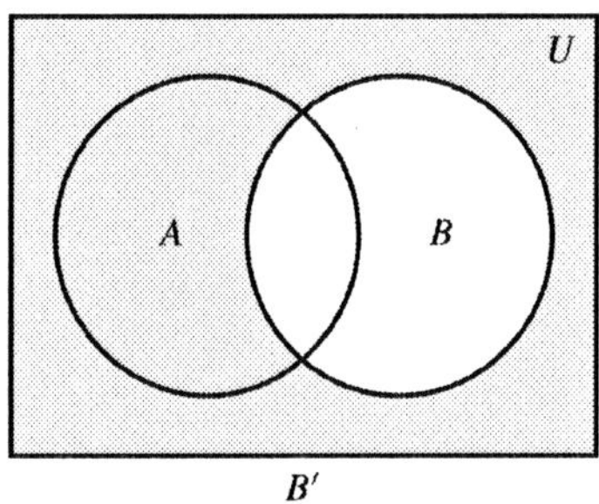

B'

Form the union of A' and B'.

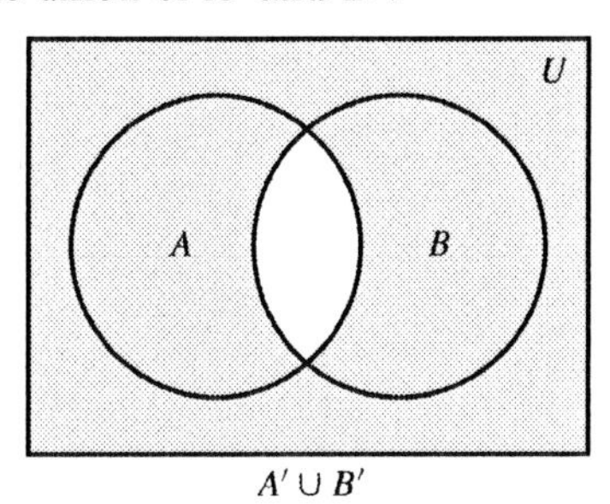

$A' \cup B'$

The Venn diagrams show that

$$(A \cap B)' = A' \cup B',$$

as claimed.

35. $A \cap (B \cup C) = (A \cap B) \cup (A \cap C)$

First find A and $B \cup C$ individually.

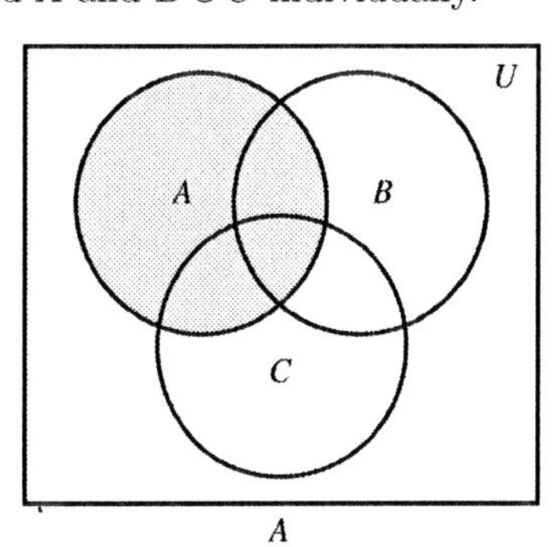

A

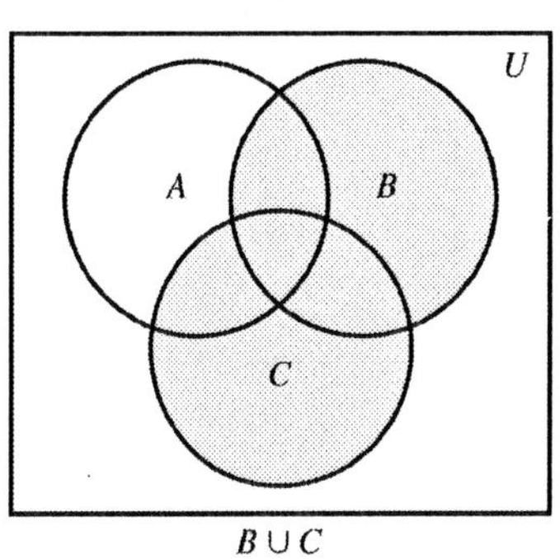

$B \cup C$

Then $A \cap (B \cup C)$ is the region where the above two diagrams overlap.

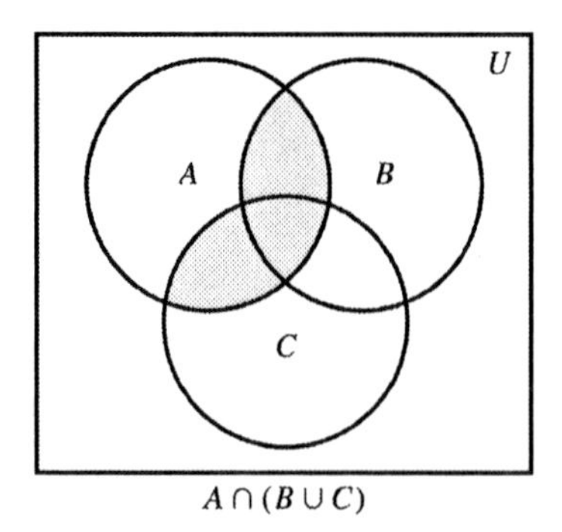

$A \cap (B \cup C)$

Next find $A \cap B$ and $A \cap C$ individually.

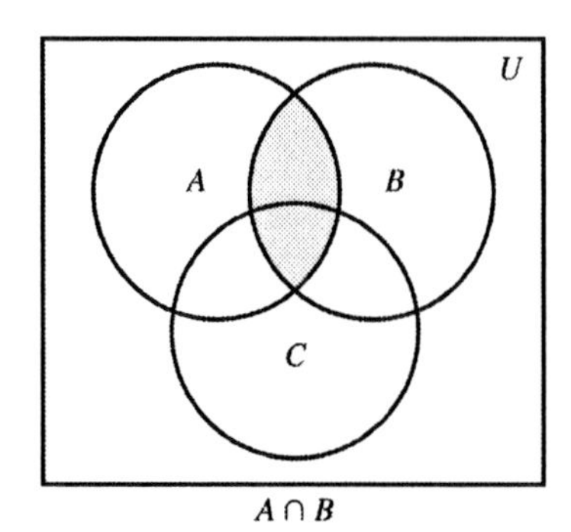

$A \cap B$

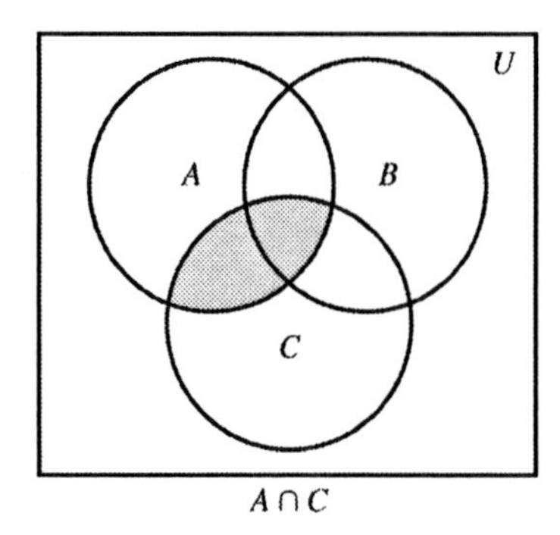

$A \cap C$

Then $(A \cap B) \cup (A \cap C)$ is the union of the above two diagrams.

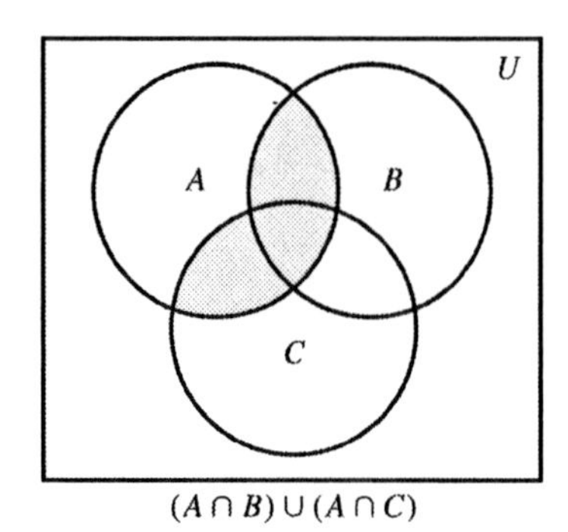

$(A \cap B) \cup (A \cap C)$

The Venn diagram for $A \cap (B \cup C)$ is identical to the Venn diagram for $(A \cap B) \cup (A \cap C)$, so conclude that

$$A \cap (B \cup C) = (A \cap B) \cup (A \cap C).$$

36. $A \cup (B \cap C)$ contains all the elements in A or in both B and C.

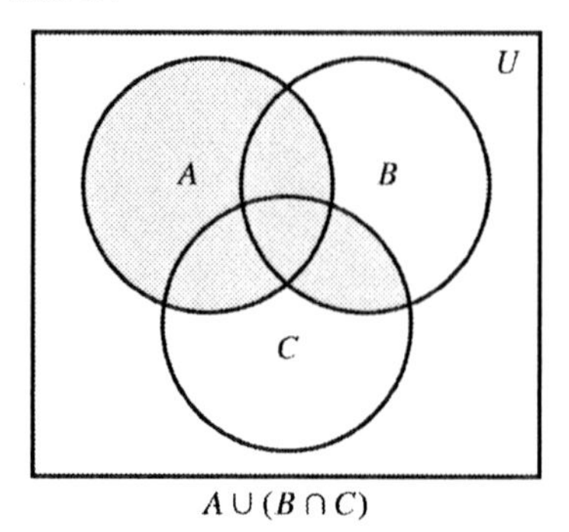

$A \cup (B \cap C)$

$(A \cup B) \cap (A \cup C)$ contains the intersection $A \cup B$ and $A \cup C$.

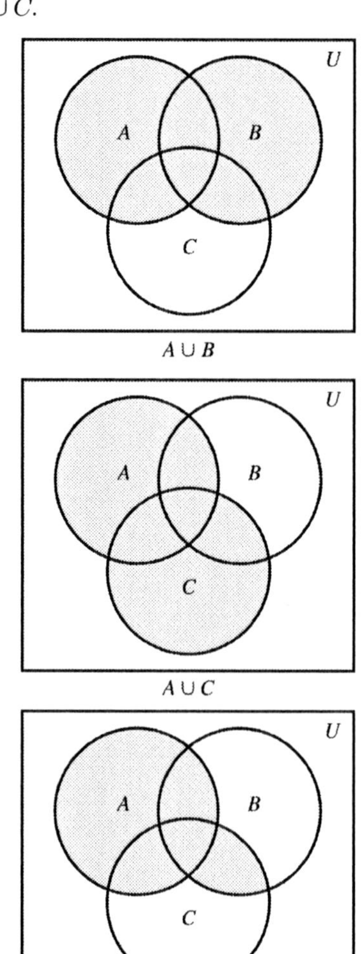

$A \cup B$

$A \cup C$

$(A \cup B) \cap (A \cup C)$

Comparing the Venn diagrams, we see that

$$A \cup (B \cap C) = (A \cup B) \cap (A \cup C),$$

as claimed.

37. Prove

$$\begin{aligned} &n(A \cup B \cup C) \\ &= n(A) + n(B) + n(C) - n(A \cap B) - n(A \cap C) \\ &\quad - n(B \cap C) + n(A \cap B \cap C) \end{aligned}$$

$$\begin{aligned} &n(A \cup B \cup C) \\ &= n[A \cup (B \cup C)] \\ &= n(A) + n(B \cup C) - n[A \cap (B \cup C)] \\ &= n(A) + n(B) + n(C) - n(B \cap C) \\ &\quad - n[(A \cap B) \cup (A \cap C)] \\ &= n(A) + n(B) + n(C) - n(B \cap C) \\ &\quad - \{n(A \cap B) + n(A \cap C) \\ &\quad - n[(A \cap B) \cap (A \cap C)]\} \\ &= n(A) + n(B) + n(C) - n(B \cap C) - n(A \cap B) \\ &\quad - n(A \cap C) + n(A \cap B \cap C) \end{aligned}$$

38. Let M be the set of those who use a microwave oven, E be the set of those who use an electric range, and G be the set of those who use a gas range. We are given the following information.

$n(U) = 140$
$n(M) = 58$
$n(E) = 63$
$n(G) = 58$
$n(M \cap E) = 19$
$n(M \cap G) = 17$
$n(G \cap E) = 4$
$n(M \cap G \cap E) = 1$
$n(M' \cap G' \cap E') = 2$

Since $n(M \cap G \cap E) = 1$, there is 1 element in the region where the three sets overlap.
Since $n(M \cap E) = 19$, there are $19 - 1 = 18$ elements in $M \cap E$ but not in $M \cap G \cap E$.
Since $n(M \cap G) = 17$, there are $17 - 1 = 16$ elements in $M \cap G$ but not in $M \cap G \cap E$.
Since $n(G \cap E) = 4$, there are $4 - 1 = 3$ elements in $G \cap E$ but not in $M \cap G \cap E$.
Now consider $n(M) = 58$. So far we have $16 + 1 + 18 = 35$ in M; there must be another $58 - 35 = 23$ in M not yet counted.
Similarly, $n(E) = 63$; we have $18 + 1 + 3 = 22$ counted so far. There must be $63 - 22 = 41$ more in E not yet counted.
Also, $n(G) = 58$; we have $16 + 1 + 3 = 20$ counted so far. There must be $58 - 20 = 38$ more in G not yet counted.
Lastly, $n(M' \cap G' \cap E') = 2$ indicates that there are 2 elements outside of all three sets.

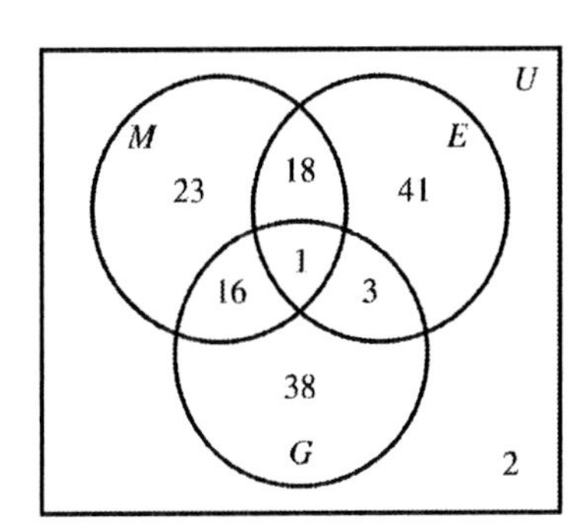

Note that the numbers in the Venn diagram add up to 142 even though $n(U) = 140$. Jeff has made some error, and he should definitely be reassigned.

39. Let A be the set of trucks that carried early peaches, B be the set of trucks that carried late peaches, and C be the set of trucks that carried extra late peaches. We are given the following information.

$n(A) = 34$
$n(B) = 61$
$n(C) = 50$
$n(A \cap B) = 25$
$n(B \cap C) = 30$
$n(A \cap C) = 8$
$n(A \cap B \cap C) = 6$
$n(A' \cap B' \cap C') = 9$

Start with $A \cap B \cap C$.
We know that $n(A \cap B \cap C) = 6$.
Since $n(A \cap B) = 25$, the number in $A \cap B$ but not in C is $25 - 6 = 19$.
Since $n(B \cap C) = 30$, the number in $B \cap C$ but not in A is $30 - 6 = 24$.
Since $n(A \cap C) = 8$, the number in $A \cap C$ but not in B is $8 - 6 = 2$.
Since $n(A) = 34$, the number in A but not in B or C is $34 - (19 + 6 + 2) = 7$.
Since $n(B) = 61$, the number in B but not in A or C is $61 - (19 + 6 + 24) = 12$.
Since $n(C) = 50$, the number in C but not in A or B is $50 - (24 + 6 + 2) = 18$.

Since $n(A' \cap B' \cap C') = 9$, the number outside $A \cup B \cup C$ is 9.

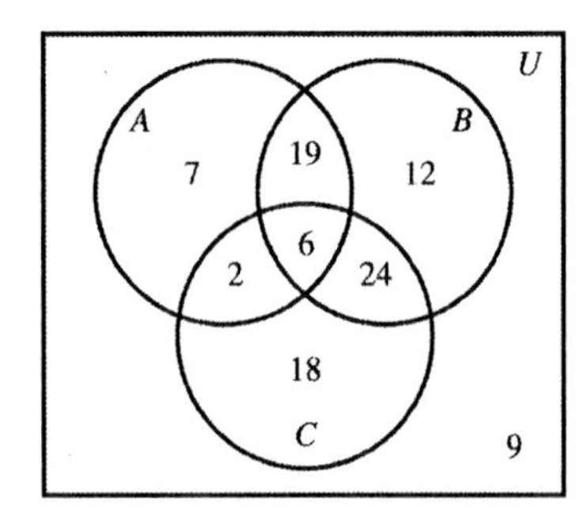

(a) From the Venn diagram, 12 trucks carried only late peaches.

(b) From the Venn diagram, 18 trucks carried only extra late peaches.

(c) From the Venn diagram, 7 + 12 + 18 = 37 trucks carried only one type of peach.

(d) From the Venn diagram, 6 + 2 + 19 + 24 + 7 + 12 + 18 + 9 = 97 trucks went out during the week.

40. **(a)** $n(Y \cap R) = 40$ since 40 is the number in the table where the Y row and the R column meet.

(b) $n(M \cap D) = 30$ since 30 is the number in the table where the M row and the D column meet.

(c) $n(D \cap Y) = 15$ and $n(M) = 80$ since that is the total in the M row. $n(M \cap (D \cap Y)) = 0$ since no person can simultaneously have an age in the range 21-25 *and* have an age in the range 26-35. By the union rule for sets,

$$\begin{aligned} &n(M \cup (D \cap Y)) \\ &\quad = n(M) + n(D \cap Y) - n(M \cap (D \cap Y)) \\ &\quad = 80 + 15 - 0 \\ &\quad = 95. \end{aligned}$$

(d) $Y' \cap (D \cup N)$ consists of all people in the D column or in the N column who are at the same time not in the Y row. Therefore,

$$\begin{aligned} n(Y' \cap (D \cup N)) &= 30 + 50 + 20 + 10 \\ &= 110. \end{aligned}$$

(e) $n(N) = 45$
$n(O) = 70$
$n(O') = 220 - 70 = 150$
$n(O' \cap N) = 15 + 20 = 35$

By the union rule,

$$\begin{aligned} n(O' \cup N) &= n(O') + n(N) - n(O' \cap N) \\ &= 150 + 45 - 35 \\ &= 160. \end{aligned}$$

(f) $M' \cap (R' \cap N')$ consists of all people who are not in the R column and not in the N column and who are at the same time not in the M row. Therefore,

$$n(M' \cap (R' \cap N')) = 15 + 50 = 65.$$

(g) $M \cup (D \cap Y)$ consists of all people age 21–25 who drink diet cola *or* anyone age 26–35.

41. **(a)** $n(Y \cap B) = 2$ since 2 is the number in the table where the Y row and the B column meet.

(b) $\begin{aligned} n(M \cup A) &= n(M) + n(A) - n(M \cap A) \\ &= 33 + 41 - 14 = 60 \end{aligned}$

(c) $n[Y \cap (S \cup B)] = 6 + 2 = 8$

(d) $\begin{aligned} &n[O' \cup (S \cup A)] \\ &\quad = n(O') + n(S \cup A) - n[O' \cap (S \cup A)] \\ &\quad = (23 + 33) + (52 + 41) - (6 + 14 + 15 + 14) \\ &\quad = 100 \end{aligned}$

(e) Since $M' \cup O'$ is the entire set, $(M' \cup O') \cap B = B$. Therefore,

$$n[(M' \cup O') \cap B] = n(B) = 27.$$

(f) $Y \cap (S \cup B)$ is the set of all bank customers who are of age 18-29 and who invest in stocks or bonds.

42. We start with the innermost region, which is the number of professors who invested in stocks and bonds and certificates of deposit (CDs). Since this is our unknown, place an x in this region. If 80 invested in stocks and bonds, then $80 - x$ invested in only stocks and bonds.

If 83 invested in bonds and CDs, then $83 - x$ invested in only bonds and CDs. If 85 invested in stocks and CDs, then $85 - x$ invested in only stocks and CDs. If 111 invested in stocks, then the number who invested in only stocks is:

$$111 - [(80 - x) + (85 - x) + x] = x - 54.$$

If 98 invested in bonds, then the number who invested in only bonds is;

$$98 - [(80 - x) + (83 - x) + x] = x - 65.$$

If 100 invested in CDs, then the number who invested in only CDs is:

$$100 - [(85 - x) + (83 - x) + x] = x - 68.$$

There are 9 who did not invest in any of the three, so place a 9 outside all three circles. Now, the sum of all the regions is 150, so

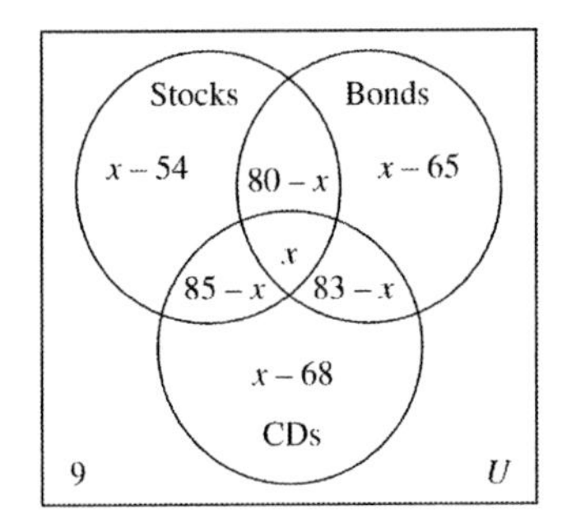

$$\begin{aligned} 150 &= (x - 54) + (80 - x) + (x - 65) + x \\ &\quad + (85 - x) + (83 - x) + (x - 68) + 9 \\ 150 &= 70 + x \\ x &= 80 \end{aligned}$$

80 professors invested in stocks and bonds and certificates of deposits.

43. Let T be the set of all tall pea plants, G be the set of plants with green peas, and S be the set of plants with smooth peas. We are given the following information.

$n(U) = 50$
$n(T) = 22$
$n(G) = 25$
$n(S) = 39$
$n(T \cap G) = 9$
$n(G \cap S) = 20$
$n(T \cap G \cap S) = 6$
$n(T' \cap G' \cap S') = 4$

Start by filling in the Venn Diagram with the numbers for the last two regions, $T \cap G \cap S$ and $T' \cap G' \cap S'$, as shown below. With $n(T \cap G) = 9$, this leaves $n(T \cap G \cap S') = 9 - 6 = 3$. With $n(G \cap S) = 20$, this leaves $n(T' \cap G \cap S) = 20 - 6 = 14$. Since $n(G) = 25$, $n(T' \cap G \cap S') = 25 - 3 - 6 - 14 = 2$. With no other regions that we can calculate, denote by x the number in $T \cap G' \cap S'$. Then $n(T \cap G' \cap S') = 22 - 3 - 6 - x = 13 - x$, and $n(T' \cap G' \cap S) = 39 - 6 - 14 - x = 19 - x$, as shown. Summing the values for all eight regions,

$$\begin{aligned} (13 - x) + 3 + 2 + x + 6 + 14 + (19 - x) + 4 &= 50 \\ 61 - x &= 50 \\ x &= 11 \end{aligned}$$

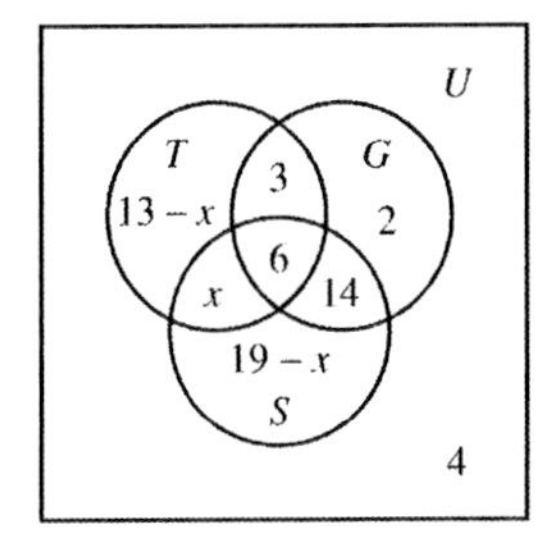

(a) $n(T \cap S) = 11 + 6 = 17$

(b) $n(T \cap G' \cap S') = 13 - x = 13 - 11 = 2$

(c) $n(T' \cap G \cap S) = 14$

44. (a) The blood has the A antigen but is Rh negative and has no B antigen. This blood type is A-negative.

(b) Both A and B antigens are present and the blood is Rh negative. This blood type is AB-negative.

(c) Only the B antigen is present. This blood type is B-negative.

(d) Both A and Rh antigens are present. This is blood type is A-positive.

(e) All antigens are present. This blood type is AB-positive.

(f) Both B and Rh antigens are present. This blood type is B-positive.

(g) Only the Rh antigen is present. This blood type is O-positive.

(h) No antigens at all are present. This blood type is O-negative.

45. First fill in the Venn diagram, starting with the region common to all three sets.

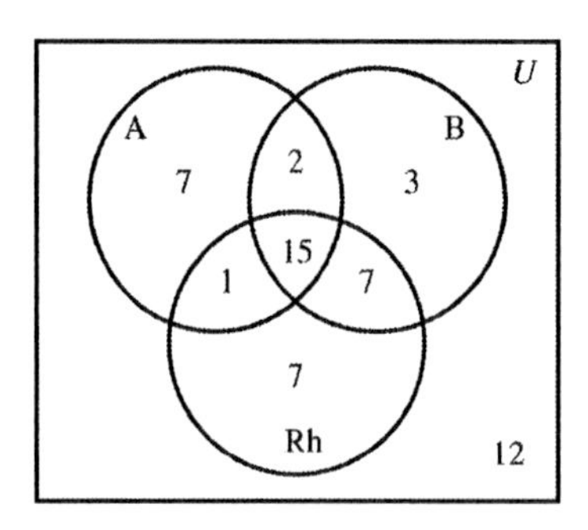

(a) The total of these numbers in the diagram is 54.

(b) $7 + 3 + 7 = 17$ had only one antigen.

(c) $1 + 2 + 7 = 10$ had exactly two antigens.

(d) A person with O-positive blood has only the Rh antigen, so this number is 7.

(e) A person with AB-positive blood has all three antigens, so this number is 15.

(f) A person with B-negative blood has only the B antigen, so this number is 3.

(g) A person with O-negative blood has none of the antigens. There are 12 such people.

(h) A person with A-positive blood has the A and Rh antigens, but not the B-antigen. The number is 1.

46. Extend the table to include totals for each row and each column.

	W	B	I	A	Total
F	1,078,064	143,278	6041	18,941	1,246,324
M	1,025,650	148,022	7106	21,186	1,201,964
Total	2,103,714	291,300	13,147	40,127	2,448,288

(a) $n(F)$ is the total for the first row in the table: $n(F) = 1{,}246{,}324$. Thus, there are 1,246,324 people in the set F.

(b) $n(F \cap (I \cup A))$ is the sum of the entries in the first row in the I and A columns. Therefore, $n(F \cap (I \cup A)) = n(F \cap I) + n(F \cap A) = 24{,}982$. Therefore, there are 24,982 people in the set $F(\cap(I \cup A)$.

(c) $n(M \cup B) = n(M) + n(B) - n(M \cap B) = 1{,}201{,}964 + 291{,}300 - 148{,}022 = 1{,}345{,}242$
There are 1,345,242 people in the set $M \cup B$.

(d) $W' \cup I' \cup A'$ is the universe, since each person is either *not* white, or *not* American Indian, or *not* Asian or Pacific Islander. Thus, there are 2,448,288 people in the set $W' \cup I' \cup A'$.

47. Extend the table to include totals for each row and each column.

	H	F	Total
A	95	34	129
B	41	38	79
C	9	7	16
D	202	150	352
Total	347	229	576

(a) $n(A \cap F)$ is the entry in the table that is in both row A and column F. Thus, there are 34 players in the set $A \cap F$.

(b) Since all players in the set C are either in set H or set F, $C \cap (H \cup F) = C$. Thus, $n(C \cap (H \cup F)) = n(C) = 16$, the total for row C. There are 16 players in the set $C \cap (H \cup F)$.

(c) $n(D \cup F) = n(D) + n(F) - n(D \cap F)$
$= 352 + 229 - 150$
$= 431$

(d) $B' \cap C'$ is the set of players who are both *not* in B and *not* in C. Thus, $B' \cap C' = A \cup D$, and since A and D are disjoints $n(A \cup D) = n(A) + n(D) = 129 + 352 = 481$. There are 481 players in the set $B' \cap C'$.

48. **(a)** $n(A \cup B)$ is the total number of female personnel serving in the Army or the Air Force: $n(A \cup B) = n(A) + n(B) = 147{,}129$. Thus, there are 147,129 women in the set $A \cup B$.

(b) To determine the number in $E \cup (C \cup D)$, it may help to think of $C \cup D$ as a single set to write the first equation.

$$\begin{aligned} n(E \cup (C \cup D)) &= n(E) + n(C \cup D) - n(E \cap (C \cup D)) \\ &= n(E) + n(C) + n(D) - [n(E \cap C) + n(E \cap D)] \\ &= 174{,}929 + 54{,}248 + 10{,}779 - (45{,}415 + 9683) \\ &= 184{,}858 \end{aligned}$$

There are 184,858 people in the set $E \cup (C \cup D)$.

(c) $O' \cap M' = E$, since the enlisted are the only group who are both *not* officers and *not* cadets or midshipmen. Thus, $n(O' \cap M') = n(E) = 174{,}929$. There are 174,929 people in the set $O' \cap M'$.

49. Reading directly from the table, $n(A \cap B) = 110.6$. Thus, there are 110.6 million people in the set $A \cap B$.

50. $n(G \cup B) = n(G) + n(B) - n(G \cap B) = 80.4 + 52.6 - 10.3 = 122.7$

Thus, there are 122.7 million people in the set $G \cup B$.

51. $n(G \cup (C \cap H)) = n(G) + n(C \cap H) = 80.4 + 5.0 = 85.4$

There are 85.4 million people in the set $G \cup (C \cap H)$.

52. The only intersection of the set F and the set $B \cup H$ is the set $F \cap B$. Therefore, $n(F \cap (B \cup H)) = n(F \cap B) = 37.6$. There are 37.6 million people in the set $F \cap (B \cup H)$.

53. $n(H \cup D) = n(H) + n(D) - n(H \cap D) = 53.6 + 19.6 - 2.2 = 71.0$

There are 71.0 million people in the set $H \cup D$.

54. First of all, $A' \cap C' = B \cup D \cup E$ since the only people *not* in set A and *not* in the set C are the people in set B or set D or set E. Second, $G' = F \cup H$, since the only people *not* in the set G are either in the set F or the set H. Thus, the set $G' \cap (A' \cap C')$ consists of people in either F or H and also in B, D, or E. Therefore,

$$\begin{aligned} n(G' \cap (A' \cap C')) &= n(F \cap B) + n(F \cap D) + n(F \cap E) + n(H \cap B) + n(H \cap D) + n(H \cap E) \\ &= 37.6 + 13.1 + 2.2 + 4.7 + 2.2 + 0.3 \\ &= 60.1 \end{aligned}$$

For Exercises 55–58, extend the table to include totals for each row and each column.

	W	B	H	A	Total
N	49,101	11,783	9862	3181	73,927
M	104,689	9279	14,239	5594	133,801
I	11,754	1730	918	418	14,820
D	21,372	4250	2917	607	29,146
Total	186,916	27,042	27,936	9800	251,694

55. $n(N \cap (B \cup H)) = n(N \cap B) + n(N \cap H) = 11{,}783 + 9862 = 21{,}645$

There are 21,645 thousand people in the set $N \cap (B \cup H)$.

56. $n((M \cup I) \cap A = n(M \cap A) + n(I \cap A) = 5594 + 418 = 6012$

There are 6012 thousand people in the set $(M \cup I) \cap A$.

57. First, notice that $A' = W \cup B \cup H$. Therefore, the set $(D \cup W) \cap A'$ is just $D \cup W$ restricted to the sets, W, B, or H. In other words,

$$\begin{aligned} n((D \cup W) \cap A') &= n(D \cap A') + n(W \cap A') - n((D \cap W) \cap A') \\ &= n(D \cap A') + n(W) - n(D \cap W) \\ &= [n(D \cap W) + n(D \cap B) + n(D \cap H)] + n(W) - n(D \cap W) \\ &= n(D \cap B) + n(D \cap H) + n(W) \\ &= 4250 + 2917 + 186{,}916 \\ &= 194{,}083 \end{aligned}$$

There are 194,083 thousand people in the set $(D \cup W) \cap A'$.

58. Notice that $M' = N \cup I \cup D$. Therefore,

$$\begin{aligned} n(M' \cap (B \cup A)) &= n(N \cap B) + n(I \cap B) + n(D \cap B) + n(N \cap A) + n(I \cap A) + (D \cap A) \\ &= 11{,}783 + 1730 + 4250 + 3181 + 418 + 607 \\ &= 21{,}969 \end{aligned}$$

There are 21,969 thousand people in the set $M' \cap (B \cup A)$.

59. Let W be the set of women, C be the set of those who speak Cantonese, and F be the set of those who set off firecrackers. We are given the following information.

$n(W) = 120$
$n(C) = 150$
$n(F) = 170$
$n(W' \cap C) = 108$
$n(W' \cap F') = 100$
$n(W \cap C' \cap F) = 18$
$n(W' \cap C' \cap F') = 78$
$n(W \cap C \cap F) = 30$

Note that

$n(W' \cap C \cap F') = n(W' \cap F') - n(W' \cap C' \cap F') = 100 - 78 = 22.$

Furthermore,

$n(W' \cap C \cap F) = n(W' \cap C) - n(W' \cap C \cap F') = 108 - 22 = 86.$

We now have

$n(W \cap C \cap F') = n(C) - n(W' \cap C \cap F) - n(W \cap C \cap F) - n(W' \cap C \cap F') = 150 - 86 - 30 - 22 = 12.$

With all of the overlaps of W, C, and F determined, we can now compute $n(W \cap C' \cap F') = 60$ and $n(W' \cap C' \cap F) = 36$.

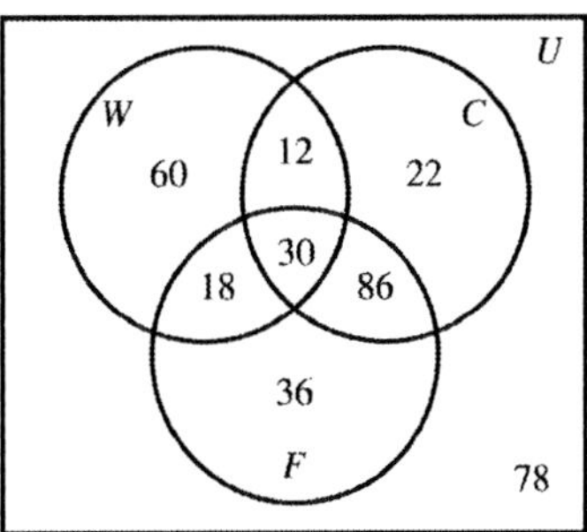

(a) Adding up the disjoint components, we find the total attendance to be

$$60 + 12 + 18 + 30 + 22 + 86 + 36 + 78 = 342.$$

(b) $n(C') = 342 - n(C) = 342 - 150 = 192$

(c) $n(W \cap F') = 60 + 12 = 72$

(d) $n(W' \cap C \cap F) = 86$

60. Let F be the set of people who brought food, C be the set of those who brought costumes, and K be the set of those who brought crafts. We are given the following information.

$n(U) = 75$
$n(F \cap C \cap K) = 15$
$n(F \cap C) = 25$
$n(F) = 42$
$n(C \cap K \cap F') = 6$
$n(K \cap F' \cap C') = 4$
$n(F' \cap C' \cap K') = 10$
$n(C \cap K') = 18$

Start by putting 15 in the Venn diagram for $F \cap C \cap K$, 6 for $C \cap K \cap F'$, 4 for $K \cap F' \cap C'$, and 10 for $F' \cap C' \cap K'$, as shown. With $n(F \cap C) = 25$ this leaves $n(F \cap C' \cap K') = 25 - 15 = 10$.

With no other regions that we can calculate, denote by x the number in $F \cap C \cap K'$. Then $n(C \cap K' \cap F') = 18 - x$, and $n(F \cap C' \cap K') = 42 - 10 - 15 - x = 17 - x$, as shown. Summing the values for all eight regions,

$$\begin{aligned}(17 - x) + x + (18 - x) + 10 + 15 + 6 + 4 + 10 &= 75\\ 80 - x &= 75\\ x &= 5\end{aligned}$$

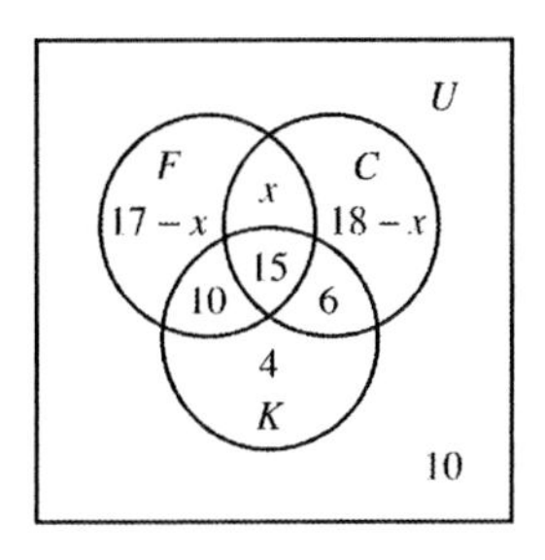

(a) $n(C \cap F) = 15 + x = 15 + 5 = 20$

(b) $n(C) = x + (180 - x) + 15 + 6 = 39$

(c) $n(K \cap C') = 10 + 4 = 14$

(d) $n(K') = (17 - x) + x + (18 - x) + 10 = 12 + 5 + 13 + 10 = 40$

(e) $n(F \cup C) = (17 - x) + x + (18 - x) + 10 + 15 + 6 = 12 + 5 + 13 + 10 + 15 + 6 = 61$

61. Let F be the set of fat chickens (so F' is the set of thin chickens), R be the set of red chickens (so R' is the set of brown chickens), and M be the set of male chickens, or roosters (so M' is the set of female chickens, or hens). We are given the following information.

$n(F \cap R \cap M) = 9$
$n(F' \cap R' \cap M') = 13$
$n(R \cap M) = 15$
$n(F' \cap R) = 11$
$n(R \cap M') = 17$
$n(F) = 56$
$n(M) = 41$
$n(M') = 48$

First, note that $n(M) + n(M') = n(U) = 89$, the total number of chickens.
Since $n(R \cap M) = 15$, $n(F' \cap R \cap M) = 15 - 9 = 6$.
Since $n(F' \cap R) = 11, n(F' \cap R \cap M') = 11 - 6 = 5$.
Since $n(R \cap M') = 17, n(F \cap R \cap M') = 17 - 5 = 12$.
Since $n(M') = 48, n(F \cap R' \cap M') = 48 - (12 + 5 + 13) = 18$.
Since $n(F) = 56, n(F \cap R' \cap M) = 56 - (18 + 12 + 9) = 17$.
And, finally, since $n(M) = 41$, $n(F' \cap R' \cap M) = 41 - (17 + 9 + 6) = 9$.

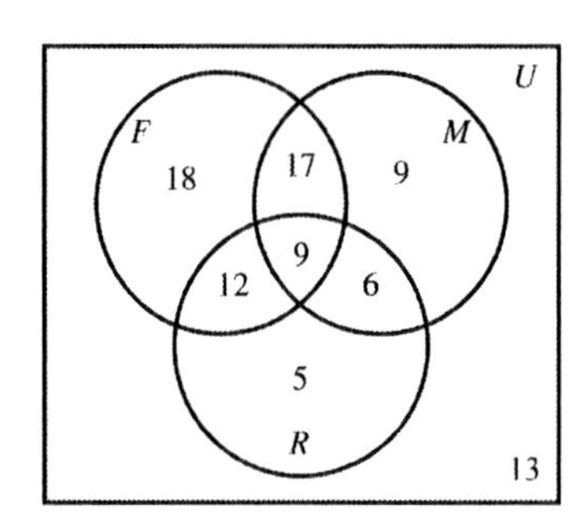

(a) $n(F) = 56$

(b) $n(R) = n(R \cap M) + n(R \cap M') = 15 + 17 = 32$

(c) $n(F \cap M) = n(F \cap R \cap M) + n(F \cap R' \cap M) = 17 + 9 = 26$

(d) $n(F \cap M') = n(F) - n(F \cap M) = 56 - 26 = 30$

(e) $n(F' \cap R') = n(F' \cap R' \cap M) + n(F' \cap R' \cap M') = 9 + 13 = 22$

(f) $n(F \cap R) = n(F \cap R \cap M) + n(F \cap R \cap M') = 9 + 12 = 21$

7.3 Introduction to Probability

3. The sample space is the set of the twelve months, {January, February, March, ..., December}.

4. List the days in April.

$$S = \{1, 2, 3, 4, \ldots, 29, 30\}$$

5. The possible number of points earned could be any whole number from 0 to 80. The sample space is the set

$$\{0, 1, 2, 3, \ \ldots, \ 79, \ 80\}.$$

6. List the possible number of hours of TV watching in a day.

$$S = \{0, 1, 2, 3, \ \ldots, 23, 24\}$$

7. The possible decisions are to go ahead with a new oil shale plant or to cancel it. The sample space is the set {go ahead, cancel}.

8. Let u = up and d = down. There are $2^3 = 8$ possible 3-day outcomes, so

$$S = \{uuu, uud, udu, duu, ddu, dud, udd, ddd\}.$$

9. Let h = heads and t = tails for the coin; the die can display 6 different numbers. There are 12 possible outcomes in the sample space, which is the set

$$\{(h, 1), \ (t, 1), \ (h, 2), \ (t, 2), \ (h, 3), \ (t, 3), \ (h, 4), \ (t, 4), \ (h, 5), \ (t, 5), \ (h, 6), \ (t, 6)\}.$$

10. There are $5 \cdot 5 = 25$ possible outcomes.

$$\begin{aligned} S = \{&(1,1),(1,2),(1,3),(1,4),(1,5),\\ &(2,1),(2,2),(2,3),(2,4),(2,5),\\ &(3,1),(3,2),(3,3),(3,4),(3,5),\\ &(4,1),(4,2),(4,3),(4,4),(4,5),\\ &(5,1),(5,2),(5,3),(5,4),(5,5)\}\end{aligned}$$

13. Use the first letter of each name. The sample space is the set

$$S = \{\text{AB, AC, AD, AE, BC, BD, BE, CD, CE, DE}\}.$$

$n(S) = 10$. Assuming the committee is selected at random, the outcomes are equally likely.

(a) One of the committee members must be Chinn. This event is {AC, BC, CD, CE}.

(b) Alam, Bartolini, and Chinn may be on any committee; Dickson and Ellsberg may not be on the same committee. This event is

$$\{\text{AB, AC, AD, AE, BC, BD, BE, CD, CE}\}.$$

(c) Both Alam and Chinn are on the committee. This event is {AC}.

14. S = {(CA, CO, NJ), (CA, CO, NY), (CA,CO,UT) (CA, NJ, NY), (CA, NJ, UT), (CA, NY, UT), (CO, NJ, NY), (CO, NJ, UT), (CO, NY, UT), (NJ, NY, UT)}

$N(s) = 10$

Assuming the states are chosen at random, the outcomes are equally likely.

(a) Of the states listed, the ones that border an ocean are CA, NJ, and NY. Therefore, the event "all three states border an ocean" is the set {(CA, NJ, NY)}.

(b) The states that border an ocean are CA, NJ, and NY. Therefore, the event "exactly two of the three states border an ocean" is the set {(CA, CO, NJ), (CA, CO, NY), (CA, NJ, UT), (CA, NY, UT), (CO, NJ, NY), (NJ, NY, UT)}.

(c) The states that lie west of the Mississippi River are CA, CO, and UT. Therefore, the event "exactly one of the three states is west of the Mississippi River" is the set {(CA, NJ, NY), (CO, NJ, NY), (NJ, NY, UT)}.

15. Each outcome consists of two of the numbers 1, 2, 3, 4, and 5, without regard for order. For example, let (2, 5) represent the outcome that the slips of paper marked with 2 and 5 are drawn. There are ten equally likely outcomes in this sample space, which is

$$\begin{aligned} S = \{&(1,2), \ (1,3), \ (1,4), \ (1,5), \ (2,3),\\ &(2,4), \ (2,5), \ (3,4), \ (3,5), \ (4,5)\}.\end{aligned}$$

(a) Both numbers in the outcome pair are even. This event is $\{(2, 4)\}$, which is called a simple event since it consists of only one outcome.

(b) One number in the pair is even and the other number is odd. This event is

$$\{(1,2), \ (1,4), (2,3), (2,5), (3,4), (4,5)\}.$$

(c) Each slip of paper has a different number written on it, so it is not possible to draw two slips marked with the same number. This event is $\emptyset$, which is called an impossible event since it contains no outcomes.

16. Let w = wrong; c = correct.

$S = \{www, wwc, wcw, cww, ccw, cwc, wcc, ccc\}$

$n(S) = 8$. The problem states the outcomes are equally likely.

(a) The student gets three answers wrong. This event is written $\{www\}$.

(b) The student gets exactly two answers correct. Since either the first, second, or third answer can be wrong, this can happen in three ways. The event is written $\{ccw, cwc, wcc\}$.

(c) The student gets only the first answer correct. The second and third answers must be wrong. This event is written $\{cww\}$.

17. $S = \{HH, THH, HTH, TTHH, THTH, HTTH, TTTH, TTHT, THTT, HTTT, TTTT\}$

$n(S) = 11$. The outcomes are not equally likely.

(a) The coin is tossed four times. This event is written $\{TTHH, THTH, HTTH, TTTH, TTHT, THTT, HTTT, TTTT\}$.

(b) Exactly two heads are tossed. This event is written $\{HH, THH, HTH, TTHH, THTH, HTTH\}$.

(c) No heads are tossed. This event is written $\{TTTT\}$.

18. There are 4 possibilities for the first choice and 5 for the second choice. The sample space is

$$\begin{aligned} S = \{&(1,1),(1,2),(1,3),(1,4),(1,5),\\ &(2,1),(2,2),(2,3),(2,4),(2,5),\\ &(3,1),(3,2),(3,3),(3,4),(3,5),\\ &(4,1),(4,2),(4,3),(4,4),(4,5)\}. \end{aligned}$$

$n(S) = 20$. Yes, the outcomes are equally likely.

(a) The first choice must be 2 or 4; the second can range from 1 to 5:

$$\begin{aligned} \{&(2,1),(2,2),(2,3),(2,4),(2,5),\\ &(4,1),(4,2),(4,3),(4,4),(4,5)\}. \end{aligned}$$

(b) The first choice can range from 1 to 4; the second must be 2 or 4:

$$\{(1,2),(1,4),(2,2),(2,4),(3,2),(3,4),(4,2),(4,4)\}.$$

(c) The choices must add up to 5:

$$\{(1,4),(2,3),(3,2),(4,1)\}.$$

(d) It is not possible for the sum to be 1: $\emptyset$.

For Exercises 19–24, use the sample space

$$S = \{1,2,3,4,5,6\}.$$

19. "Getting a 2" is the event $E = \{2\}$, so $n(E) = 1$ and $n(S) = 6$.

If all the outcomes in a sample space S are equally likely, then the probability of an event E is

$$P(E) = \frac{n(E)}{n(S)}.$$

In this problem,

$$P(E) = \frac{n(E)}{n(S)} = \frac{1}{6}.$$

20. Let O be the event "getting an odd number."

$$O = \{1,3,5\}$$
$$P(O) = \frac{3}{6} = \frac{1}{2}$$

21. "Getting a number less than 5" is the event $E = \{1,2,3,4\}$, so $n(E) = 4$.

$$P(E) = \frac{4}{6} = \frac{2}{3}.$$

22. Let A be the event "getting a number greater than 2."

$$A = \{3,4,5,6\}$$
$$P(A) = \frac{4}{6} = \frac{2}{3}$$

23. "Getting a 3 or a 4" is the event $E = \{3,4\}$, so $n(E) = 2$.

$$P(E) = \frac{2}{6} = \frac{1}{3}.$$

24. Let B be the event "getting any number except 3."

$$B = \{1,2,4,5,6\}$$
$$P(B) = \frac{5}{6}$$

For Exercises 25–34, the sample space contains all 52 cards in the deck, so $n(S) = 52$.

25. Let E be the event "a 9 is drawn." There are four 9's in the deck, so $n(E) = 4$.

$$P(9) = P(E) = \frac{n(E)}{n(S)} = \frac{4}{52} = \frac{1}{13}$$

26. Let B be the event "drawing a black card." There are 26 black cards in the deck, 13 spades and 13 clubs.

$$n(B) = 26$$
$$P(B) = \frac{26}{52} = \frac{1}{2}$$

27. Let F be the event "a black 9 is drawn." There are two black 9's in the deck, so $n(F) = 2$.

$$P(\text{black } 9) = P(F) = \frac{n(F)}{n(S)} = \frac{2}{52} = \frac{1}{26}$$

28. Let H be the event "a heart is drawn." There are 13 hearts in the deck.

$$n(H) = 13$$
$$P(H) = \frac{13}{52} = \frac{1}{4}$$

29. Let G be the event "a 9 of hearts is drawn." There is only one 9 of hearts in a deck of 52 cards, so $n(G) = 1$.

$$P(9 \text{ of hearts}) = P(G) = \frac{n(G)}{n(S)} = \frac{1}{52}$$

30. Let F be the event "drawing a face card." The face cards are the jack, queen, and king of each of the four suits.

$$n(F) = 12$$
$$P(F) = \frac{12}{52} = \frac{3}{13}$$

31. Let H be the event "a 2 or a queen is drawn." There are four 2's and four queens in the deck, so $n(H) = 8$.

$$P(2 \text{ or queen}) = P(H) = \frac{n(H)}{n(S)} = \frac{8}{52} = \frac{2}{13}$$

32. Let R be the event "drawing a black 7 or a red 8." There are two black 7's and two red 8's.

$$n(R) = 4$$
$$P(R) = \frac{4}{52} = \frac{1}{13}$$

33. Let E be the event "a red card or a ten is drawn." There are 26 red cards and 4 tens in the deck. But 2 tens are red cards and are counted twice. Use the result from the previous section.

$$\begin{aligned} n(E) &= n(\text{red cards}) + \text{n(tens)} - n(\text{red tens}) \\ &= 26 + 4 - 2 \\ &= 28 \end{aligned}$$

Now calculate the probability of E.

$$\begin{aligned} P(\text{red card or ten}) &= \frac{n(E)}{n(S)} \\ &= \frac{28}{52} \\ &= \frac{7}{13} \end{aligned}$$

34. Let E be the event "a spade or a king is drawn." There are 13 spades and 4 kings in the deck. But the king of spades is counted twice. Use the result from the previous section.

$$\begin{aligned} n(E) &= n(\text{spades}) + n(\text{kings}) - n(\text{king of spades}) \\ &= 13 + 4 - 1 \\ &= 16 \end{aligned}$$

Now calculate the probability of E.

$$\begin{aligned} P(\text{spade or king}) &= \frac{n(E)}{n(S)} \\ &= \frac{16}{52} \\ &= \frac{4}{13} \end{aligned}$$

For Exercises 35-40, the sample space consists of all the marbles in the jar. There are $3 + 4 + 5 + 8 = 20$ marbles, so $n(S) = 20$.

35. 3 of the marbles are white, so

$$P(\text{white}) = \frac{3}{20}.$$

36. There are 4 orange marbles.

$$P(\text{orange}) = \frac{4}{20} = \frac{1}{5}$$

37. 5 of the marbles are yellow, so

$$P(\text{yellow}) = \frac{5}{20} = \frac{1}{4}.$$

38. There are 8 black marbles.

$$P(\text{black}) = \frac{8}{20} = \frac{2}{5}$$

39. $3 + 4 + 5 = 12$ of the marbles are not black, so

$$P(\text{not black}) = \frac{12}{20} = \frac{3}{5}.$$

40. There are 9 marbles which are orange or yellow.

$$P(\text{orange or yellow}) = \frac{9}{20}$$

41. The outcomes are not equally likely.

42. Let W_1 be the event "win on the first draw" and W_2 be the event "win on the second draw."
First of all, $P(W_1) = \frac{1}{3}$, a simple choice from three slips of paper.
To determine $P(W_2)$, the first slip of paper is drawn (from the three available) and thrown away. There are two slips left which may be chosen in any way. So $P(W_2) = \frac{1}{3} \cdot \frac{1}{2} = \frac{1}{6}$. Altogether, the probability of winning using this strategy is

$$P(W_1) + P(W_2) = \frac{1}{3} + \frac{1}{6} = \frac{1}{2}.$$

43. E: worker is female
F: worker has worked less than 5 yr
G: worker contributes to a voluntary retirement plan

(a) E' occurs when E does not, so E' is the event "worker is male."

(b) $E \cap F$ occurs when both E and F occur, so $E \cap F$ is the event "worker is female and has worked less than 5 yr."

(c) $E \cup G'$ is the event "worker is female or does not contribute to a voluntary retirement plan."

(d) F' occurs when F does not, so F' is the event "worker has worked 5 yr or more."

(e) $F \cup G$ occurs when F or G occurs or both, so $F \cup G$ is the event "worker has worked less than 5 yr or contributes to a voluntary retirement plan."

(f) $F' \cap G'$ occurs when F does not and G does not, so $F' \cap G'$ is the event "worker has worked 5 yr or more and does not contribute to a voluntary retirement plan."

44. **(a)** $P(\text{Federal government}) = \dfrac{19.191}{32.723} \approx 0.5865$

(b) $P(\text{Industry}) = \dfrac{2.234}{32.723} \approx 0.0683$

(c) $P(\text{Academic institutions}) = \dfrac{6.553}{32.723} \approx 0.2003$

45. **(a)**
$$P(\text{invested in stocks and bonds}) = \frac{80}{150} = \frac{8}{15}$$

(b) $P(\text{invested in stocks and bonds and CDs})$
$$= \frac{80}{150} = \frac{8}{15}$$

46. E: person smokes
F: person has a family history of heart disease
G: person is overweight

(a) G': "person is not overweight."

(b) $F \cap G$: "person has a family history of heart disease and is overweight."

(c) $E \cup G'$: "person smokes or is not overweight."

47. E: person smokes
F: person has a family history of heart disease
G: person is overweight

(a) $E \cup F$ occurs when E or F or both occur, so $E \cup F$ is the event "person smokes or has a family history of heart disease, or both."

(b) $E' \cap F$ occurs when E does not occur and F does occur, so $E' \cap F$ is the event "person does not smoke and has a family history of heart disease."

(c) $F' \cup G'$ is the event "person does not have a family history of heart disease or is not overweight, or both."

48. **(a)** $P(\text{heart disease}) = \dfrac{695{,}754}{2{,}447{,}864} \approx 0.2842$

(b) $P(\text{cancer or heart disease}) = \dfrac{558{,}847 + 695{,}754}{2{,}447{,}864} \approx 0.5125$

(c) $P(\text{not an accident and not diabetes mellitus})$

$$= \frac{695{,}754 + 558{,}847 + 163{,}010 + 125{,}500 + 65{,}984 + 663{,}347}{2{,}447{,}864}$$

≈ 0.9283

49. The total population for 2020 is 322,742, and the total for 2050 is 393,931.

(a) $P(\text{Hispanic in 2020}) = \dfrac{52{,}652}{322{,}742}$

≈ 0.1631

(b) $P(\text{Hispanic in 2050}) = \dfrac{96{,}508}{393{,}931}$

≈ 0.2450

(c) $P(\text{Black in 2020}) = \dfrac{41{,}538}{322{,}742}$

≈ 0.1287

(d) $P(\text{Black in 2050}) = \dfrac{53{,}555}{393{,}931}$

≈ 0.1360

50. **(a)** $P(\text{Corps}) = \dfrac{9188}{91{,}950} \approx 0.0999$

(b) $P(\text{lost in battle}) = \dfrac{22{,}803}{91{,}950} \approx 0.2480$

(c) $P(\text{I Corps lost in battle}) = \dfrac{6059}{12{,}222} \approx 0.4957$

(d) $P(\text{I Corps not lost in battle}) = \dfrac{12{,}222 - 6059}{12{,}222} \approx 0.5043$

$P(\text{II Corps not lost in battle}) = \dfrac{11{,}347 - 4369}{11{,}347} \approx 0.6150$

$P(\text{III Corps not lost in battle}) = \dfrac{10{,}675 - 4211}{10{,}675} \approx 0.6055$

$P(\text{V Corps not lost in battle}) = \dfrac{10{,}907 - 2187}{10{,}907} \approx 0.7995$

$P(\text{VI Corps not lost in battle}) = \dfrac{13{,}596 - 242}{13{,}596} \approx 0.9822$

$P(\text{XI Corps not lost in battle}) = \dfrac{9188 - 3801}{9188} \approx 0.5863$

$P(\text{XII Corps not lost in battle}) = \dfrac{9788 - 1082}{9788} \approx 0.8895$

$P(\text{Calvary not lost in battle}) = \dfrac{11{,}851 - 610}{11{,}851} \approx 0.9485$

$P(\text{Artillery not lost in battle}) = \dfrac{2376 - 242}{2376} \approx 0.8981$

VI Corps had the highest probability of not being lost in battle.

(e) $P(\text{I Corps loss}) = \dfrac{6059}{12{,}222} \approx 0.4957$

$P(\text{II Corps loss}) = \dfrac{4369}{11{,}347} \approx 0.3850$

$P(\text{III Corps loss}) = \dfrac{4211}{10{,}675} \approx 0.3945$

$P(\text{V Corps loss}) = \dfrac{2187}{10{,}907} \approx 0.2005$

$P(\text{VI Corps loss}) = \dfrac{242}{13{,}596} \approx 0.0178$

$P(\text{XI Corps loss}) = \dfrac{3801}{9188} \approx 0.4137$

$P(\text{XII Corps loss}) = \dfrac{1082}{9788} \approx 0.1105$

$P(\text{Calvary loss}) = \dfrac{610}{11{,}851} \approx 0.0515$

$P(\text{Artillery loss}) = \dfrac{242}{2376} \approx 0.1019$

I Corps had the highest probability of loss.

51. (a) $P(\text{III Corps}) = \dfrac{22{,}083}{70{,}076} \approx 0.3151$

(b) $P(\text{lost in battle}) = \dfrac{22{,}557}{70{,}076} \approx 0.3219$

(c) $P(\text{I Corps lost in battle}) = \dfrac{7661}{20{,}706} \approx 0.3670$

(d) $P(\text{I Corps not lost in battle}) = \dfrac{20{,}706 - 7661}{20{,}706} \approx 0.6300$

$P(\text{II Corps not lost in battle}) = \dfrac{20{,}666 - 6603}{20{,}666} \approx 0.6805$

$P(\text{III Corps not lost in battle}) = \dfrac{22{,}083 - 8007}{22{,}083} \approx 0.6374$

$P(\text{Calvary not lost in battle}) = \dfrac{6621 - 286}{6621} \approx 0.9568$

The Calvary had the highest probability of not being lost in battle.

(e) $P(\text{I Corps loss}) = \dfrac{7661}{20{,}706} \approx 0.3700$

$P(\text{II Corps loss}) = \dfrac{6603}{20{,}666} \approx 0.3195$

$P(\text{III Corps loss}) = \dfrac{8007}{22{,}083} \approx 0.3626$

$P(\text{Calvary loss}) = \dfrac{286}{6621} \approx 0.0432$

I Corps had the highest probability of loss.

52. (a) $P(\text{brought costumes and food}) = \dfrac{20}{75} = \dfrac{4}{15}$

(b) $P(\text{brought crafts, but neither food nor costumes}) = \dfrac{4}{75}$

(c) $P(\text{brought food or costumes}) = \dfrac{61}{75}$

53. There were 342 in attendance.

(a) $P(\text{speaks Cantonese}) = \dfrac{150}{342} = \dfrac{25}{57}$

(b) $P(\text{does not speak Cantonese}) = \dfrac{192}{342} = \dfrac{32}{57}$

(c) $P(\text{woman who did not light firecracker})$.

$= \dfrac{72}{342} = \dfrac{4}{19}$

7.4 Basic Concepts of Probability

2. A person can own a dog and own an MP3 player at the same time. No, these events are not mutually exclusive.

3. A person can be from Texas and be a business major at the same time. No, these events are not mutually exclusive.

4. A person can be retired and be over 70 years old at the same time. No, these events are not mutually exclusive.

5. A person cannot be a teenager and be 70 years old at the same time. Yes, these events are mutually exclusive.

6. A person cannot be one of the ten tallest people in the United States and be under 4 feet tall at the same time. Yes, these events are mutually exclusive.

7. A person can be male and be a nurse at the same time. No, these events are not mutually exclusive.

8. When two dice are rolled, there are 36 equally likely outcomes.

(a) Of the 36 ordered pairs, there is only one for which the sum is 2, namely $\{(1,1)\}$. Thus,

$$P(\text{sum is } 2) = \frac{1}{36}.$$

(b) $\{(1,3),(2,2),(3,1)\}$ comprise the ways of getting a sum of 4. Thus,

$$P(\text{sum is } 4) = \frac{3}{36} = \frac{1}{12}.$$

(c) $\{(1,4),(2,3),(3,2),(4,1)\}$ comprise the ways of getting a sum of 5. Thus,

$$P(\text{sum is } 5) = \frac{4}{36} = \frac{1}{9}.$$

(d) $\{(1,5),(2,4),(3,3),(4,2),(5,1)\}$ comprise the ways of getting a sum of 6. Thus,

$$P(\text{sum is } 6) = \frac{5}{36}.$$

9. When the two dice are rolled, there are 36 equally likely outcomes. Let 5-3 represent the outcome "the first die shows a 5 and the second die shows a 3," and so on.

(a) Rolling a sum of 8 occurs when the outcome is 2-6, 3-5, 4-4, 5-3, or 6-2. Therefore, since there are five such outcomes, the probability of this event is

$$P(\text{sum is } 8) = \frac{5}{36}.$$

(b) A sum of 9 occurs when the outcome is 3-6, 4-5, 5-4, or 6-3, so

$$P(\text{sum is } 9) = \frac{4}{36} = \frac{1}{9}.$$

(c) A sum of 10 occurs when the outcome is 4-6, 5-5, or 6-4, so

$$P(\text{sum is } 10) = \frac{3}{36} = \frac{1}{12}.$$

(d) A sum of 13 does not occur in any of the 36 outcomes, so

$$P(\text{sum is } 13) = \frac{0}{36} = 0.$$

10. Again, when two dice are rolled there are 36 equally likely outcomes.

(a) Here, the event is the union of four mutually exclusive events, namely, the sum is 9, the sum is 10, the sum is 11, and the sum is 12. Hence,

$$\begin{aligned} P(\text{sum is 9 or more}) &= P(\text{sum is } 9) + P(\text{sum is } 10) \\ &\quad + P(\text{sum is } 11) + (\text{sum is } 12) \\ &= \frac{4}{36} + \frac{3}{36} + \frac{2}{36} + \frac{1}{36} \\ &= \frac{10}{36} = \frac{5}{18}. \end{aligned}$$

(b) $P(\text{sum is less than } 7)$

$$\begin{aligned} &= P(\text{sum is } 1) + P(\text{sum is } 2) + P(\text{sum is } 3) \\ &\quad + P(\text{sum is } 4) + P(\text{sum is } 5) + P(\text{sum is } 6) \\ &= \frac{0}{36} + \frac{1}{36} + \frac{2}{36} + \frac{3}{36} + \frac{4}{36} + \frac{5}{36} \\ &= \frac{15}{36} \\ &= \frac{5}{12} \end{aligned}$$

(c) $P(\text{sum is between 5 and } 8)$

$$\begin{aligned} &= P(\text{sum is } 6) + P(\text{sum is } 7) \\ &= \frac{5}{36} + \frac{6}{36} \\ &= \frac{11}{36} \end{aligned}$$

11. Again, when two dice are rolled, there are 36 equally likely outcomes.

(a) $P(\text{sum is not more than } 5)$

$$\begin{aligned} &= P(2) + P(3) + P(4) + P(5) \\ &= \frac{1}{36} + \frac{2}{36} + \frac{3}{36} + \frac{4}{36} \\ &= \frac{10}{36} \\ &= \frac{5}{18} \end{aligned}$$

(b) $P(\text{sum is not less than } 8)$

$$\begin{aligned} &= P(8) + P(9) + P(10) + P(11) + P(12) \\ &= \frac{5}{36} + \frac{4}{36} + \frac{3}{36} + \frac{2}{36} + \frac{1}{36} \\ &= \frac{15}{36} \\ &= \frac{5}{12} \end{aligned}$$

(c) $P(\text{sum is between 3 and 7})$

$$= P(4) + P(5) + P(6) = \frac{3}{36} + \frac{4}{36} + \frac{5}{36} = \frac{12}{36} = \frac{1}{3}$$

12. $P(\text{first die is 3 or sum is 8})$

$$= P(\text{first die is 3}) + P(\text{sum is 8}) - P(\text{first die is 3 and sum is 8})$$

$$= \frac{6}{36} + \frac{5}{36} - \frac{1}{36} = \frac{10}{36} = \frac{5}{18}$$

13. $P(\text{second die is 5 or the sum is 10})$

$$= P(\text{second die is 5}) + P(\text{sum is 10}) - P(\text{second die is 5 and sum is 10})$$

$$= \frac{6}{36} + \frac{3}{36} - \frac{1}{36} = \frac{8}{36} = \frac{2}{9}$$

14. (a) The sample space is

3 – 1	3 – 1	3 – 5	3 – 5	3 – 9	3 – 9
3 – 1	3 – 1	3 – 5	3 – 5	3 – 9	3 – 9
4 – 1	4 – 1	4 – 5	4 – 5	4 – 9	4 – 9
4 – 1	4 – 1	4 – 5	4 – 5	4 – 9	4 – 9
8 – 1	8 – 1	8 – 5	8 – 5	8 – 9	8 – 9
8 – 1	8 – 1	8 – 5	8 – 5	8 – 9	8 – 9

where the first number in each pair is the number that appears on A and the second the number that appears on B. B beats A in 20 of 36 possible outcomes. Thus,

$$P(B \text{ beats } A) = \frac{20}{36} = \frac{5}{9}.$$

(b) The sample space is

1 – 2	1 – 2	1 – 6	1 – 6	1 – 7	1 – 7
1 – 2	1 – 2	1 – 6	1 – 6	1 – 7	1 – 7
5 – 2	5 – 2	5 – 6	5 – 6	5 – 7	5 – 7
5 – 2	5 – 2	5 – 6	5 – 6	5 – 7	5 – 7
9 – 2	9 – 2	9 – 6	9 – 6	9 – 7	9 – 7
9 – 2	9 – 2	9 – 6	9 – 6	9 – 7	9 – 7

where the first number in each pair is the number that appears on B and the second the number that appears on C. C beats B in 20 of 36 possible outcomes. Thus,

$$P(C \text{ beats } B) = \frac{20}{36} = \frac{5}{9}.$$

(c) The sample space is

3 – 2	3 – 2	3 – 6	3 – 6	3 – 7	3 – 7
3 – 2	3 – 2	3 – 6	3 – 6	3 – 7	3 – 7
4 – 2	4 – 2	4 – 6	4 – 6	4 – 7	4 – 7
4 – 2	4 – 2	4 – 6	4 – 6	4 – 7	4 – 7
8 – 2	8 – 2	8 – 6	8 – 6	8 – 7	8 – 7
8 – 2	8 – 2	8 – 6	8 – 6	8 – 7	8 – 7

where the first number in each pair is the number that appears on A and the second the number that appears on C. A beats C in 20 of 36 possible outcomes. Thus,

$$P(A \text{ beats } C) = \frac{20}{36} = \frac{5}{9}.$$

15. (a) The events E, "9 is drawn," and F, "10 is drawn," are mutually exclusive, so $P(E \cap F) = 0$.

Using the union rule,

$$P(9 \text{ or } 10) = P(9) + P(10) = \frac{4}{52} + \frac{4}{52} = \frac{8}{52} = \frac{2}{13}.$$

(b) $P(\text{red or } 3) = P(\text{red}) + P(3) - P(\text{red and } 3)$

$$= \frac{26}{52} + \frac{4}{52} - \frac{2}{52} = \frac{28}{52} = \frac{7}{13}$$

(c) Since these events are mutually exclusive,

$$P(9 \text{ or black } 10) = P(9) + P(\text{black } 10) = \frac{4}{52} + \frac{2}{52} = \frac{6}{52} = \frac{3}{26}.$$

(d) $P(\text{heart or black}) = P(\text{heart}) + P(\text{black})$

$$- P(\text{heart and black})$$

$$= \frac{13}{52} + \frac{26}{52} - \frac{0}{52}$$

$$= \frac{39}{52}$$

$$= \frac{3}{4}.$$

(e) $P(\text{face card or diamond})$

$$= P(\text{face card}) + P(\text{diamond})$$

$$- P(\text{face card and diamond})$$

$$= \frac{12}{52} + \frac{13}{52} - \frac{3}{52}$$

$$= \frac{22}{52}$$

$$= \frac{11}{26}$$

16. (a) Less than a 4 would be an ace, a 2, or a 3. There are a total of 12 aces, 2's, and 3's in a deck of 52, so

$$P(\text{ace or 2 or 3}) = \frac{12}{52} = \frac{3}{13}.$$

(b) There are 13 diamonds plus three 7's in other suits, so

$$P(\text{diamond or 7}) = \frac{16}{52} = \frac{4}{13}.$$

Alternatively, using the union rule for probability,

$P(\text{diamond}) + P(7) - P(\text{7 of diamonds})$

$$= \frac{13}{52} + \frac{4}{52} - \frac{1}{52} = \frac{16}{52} = \frac{4}{13}.$$

(c) There are 26 black cards plus 2 red aces, so

$$P(\text{black or ace}) = \frac{28}{52} = \frac{7}{13}.$$

(d) $P(\text{heart or black}) = \frac{13}{52} + \frac{26}{52} = \frac{39}{52} = \frac{3}{4}.$

(e) There are 26 red cards plus 6 black face cards, so

$$P(\text{red or face card}) = \frac{32}{52} = \frac{8}{13}.$$

17. (a) Since these events are mutually exclusive,

$$P(\text{brother or uncle}) = P(\text{brother}) + P(\text{uncle})$$

$$= \frac{2}{13} + \frac{3}{13}$$

$$= \frac{5}{13}.$$

(b) Since these events are mutually exclusive,

$$P(\text{brother or cousin}) = P(\text{brother}) + P(\text{cousin})$$

$$= \frac{2}{13} + \frac{5}{13}$$

$$= \frac{7}{13}.$$

(c) Since these events are mutually exclusive,

$$P(\text{brother or mother}) = P(\text{brother}) + P(\text{mother})$$

$$= \frac{2}{13} + \frac{1}{13}$$

$$= \frac{3}{13}.$$

18. (a) There are 3 uncles plus 5 cousins out of 13, so

$$P(\text{uncle or cousin}) = \frac{8}{13}.$$

(b) There are 3 uncles, 2 brothers, and 5 cousins, for a total of 10 out of 13, so

$$P(\text{male or cousin}) = \frac{10}{13}.$$

(c) There are 2 aunts, 5 cousins, and 1 mother, for a total of 5 out of 10, so

$$P(\text{female or cousin}) = \frac{8}{13}.$$

19. (a) There are 5 possible numbers on the first slip drawn, and for each of these, 4 possible numbers on the second, so the sample space contains $5 \cdot 4 = 20$ ordered pairs. Two of these ordered pairs have a sum of 9: $(4, 5)$ and $(5, 4)$. Thus,

$$P(\text{sum is 9}) = \frac{2}{20} = \frac{1}{10}.$$

(b) The outcomes for which the sum is 5 or less are $(1, 2), (1, 3), (1, 4), (2, 1), (2, 3), (3, 1), (3, 2)$, and $(4, 1)$. Thus,

$$P(\text{sum is 5 or less}) = \frac{8}{20} = \frac{2}{5}.$$

(c) Let A be the event "the first number is 2" and B the event "the sum is 6." Use the union rule.

$$P(A \cup B) = P(A) + P(B) - P(A \cap B)$$

$$= \frac{4}{20} + \frac{4}{20} - \frac{1}{20}$$

$$= \frac{7}{20}$$

20. **(a)** The sample space for this experiment is listed in part (b) below. The only outcomes in which both numbers are even are $(2,4)$ and $(4,2)$, so

$$P(\text{even}) = \frac{2}{20} = \frac{1}{10}.$$

(b) The sample space is

$\{(\underline{1,2}),\ (1,3),\ (\underline{1,4}),\ (\underline{1,5}),\ (\underline{2,1}),\ (\underline{2,3}),\ (\underline{2,4}),\ (\underline{2,5}),\ (3,1),\ (\underline{3,2}),\ (\underline{3,4}),\ (\underline{3,5}),\ (\underline{4,1}),\ (\underline{4,2}),\ (\underline{4,3}),\ (\underline{4,5}),\ (\underline{5,1}),\ (\underline{5,2}),\ (\underline{5,3}),\ (\underline{5,4})\}.$

The 18 underlined pairs are the outcomes in which one number is even or greater than 3, so

$$P(\text{even or } > 3) = \frac{18}{20} = \frac{9}{10}.$$

(c) The sum is 5 in the outcomes $(1,4)$, $(2,3)$, $(3,2)$, and $(4,1)$. The second draw is 2 in the outcomes $(1,2)$, $(3,2)$, $(4,2)$, and $(5,2)$. There are 7 distinct outcomes out of 20, so

$$P(\text{sum is 5 or second number is 2}) = \frac{7}{20}.$$

21. Since $P(E \cap F) = 0.16$, the overlapping region $E \cap F$ is assigned the probability 0.16 in the diagram. Since $P(E) = 0.26$ and $P(E \cap F) = 0.16$, the region in E but not F is given the label 0.10. Similarly, the remaining regions are labeled.

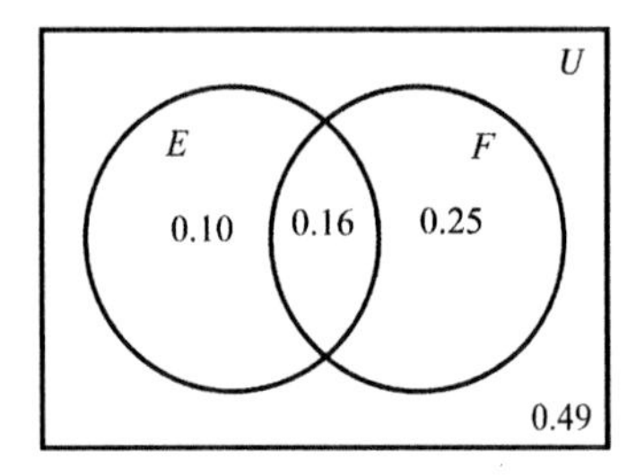

(a) $P(E \cup F) = 0.10 + 0.16 + 0.25$
$= 0.51$

Consequently, the part of U outside $E \cup F$ receives the label

$$1 - 0.51 = 0.49.$$

(b) $P(E' \cap F) = P(\text{in } F \text{ but not in } E)$
$= 0.25$

(c) The region $E \cap F'$ is that part of E which is not in F. Thus,

$$P(E \cap F') = 0.10.$$

(d) $P(E' \cup F') = P(E') + P(F') - P(E' \cap F')$
$= 0.74 + 0.59 - 0.49$
$= 0.84$

22. $P(Z) = 0.42,\ P(Y) = 0.35,\ P(Z \cup Y) = 0.59$

Begin by using the union rule for probability.

$$\begin{aligned} P(Z \cup Y) &= P(Z) + P(Y) - P(Z \cap Y) \\ 0.59 &= 0.42 + 0.35 - P(Z \cap Y) \\ 0.59 &= 0.77 - P(Z \cap Y) \\ -0.18 &= -P(Z \cap Y) \\ 0.18 &= P(Z \cap Y) \end{aligned}$$

This gives the first value to be labeled in the Venn diagram. Then the part of Z outside Y must contain $0.42 - 0.18 = 0.24$, and the part of Y outside Z must contain $0.35 - 0.18 = 0.17$. Observe that $0.24 + 0.18 + 0.17 = 0.59$, which agrees with the given information that $P(Z \cup Y) = 0.59$. The part of U outside both Y and Z must contain $1 - 0.59 = 0.41$.

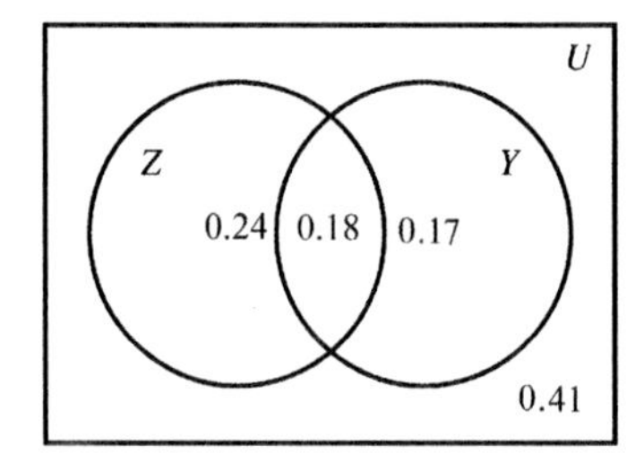

This Venn diagram may now be used to find the following probabilities.

(a) $Z' \cap Y'$ is the event presented by the part of the Venn diagram that is outside Z and outside Y.

$$P(Z' \cap Y') = 0.41$$

(b) $Z' \cup Y'$ is everything outside Z or outside Y or both, which is all of U except $Z \cap Y$.

$$P(Z' \cup Y') = 1 - 0.18 = 0.82$$

(c) $Z' \cup Y$ is everything outside Z or inside Y or both.

$$P(Z' \cup Y) = 0.17 + 0.41 + 0.18 = 0.76$$

(d) $Z \cap Y'$ is everything inside Z and outside Y.

$$P(Z \cap Y') = 0.24$$

24. Let E be the event "a 3 is rolled."

$$P(E) = \frac{1}{6} \text{ and } P(E') = \frac{5}{6}.$$

The odds in favor of rolling a 3 are

$$\frac{P(E)}{P(E')} = \frac{\frac{1}{6}}{\frac{5}{6}} = \frac{1}{5},$$

which is written "1 to 5."

25. Let E be the event "4, 5, or 6 is rolled." Here $E = \{4, 5, 6\}$, so $P(E) = \frac{3}{6} = \frac{1}{2}$, and $P(E') = \frac{1}{2}$. The odds in favor of rolling 4, 5 or 6 are

$$\frac{P(E)}{P(E')} = \frac{\frac{1}{2}}{\frac{1}{2}} = \frac{1}{1}.$$

which is written "1 to 1."

26. Let E be the event "a 2, 3, 4, or 5 is rolled." Here $P(E) = \frac{4}{6} = \frac{2}{3}$ and $P(E') = \frac{1}{3}$. The odds in favor of E are

$$\frac{P(E)}{P(E')} = \frac{\frac{2}{3}}{\frac{1}{3}} = \frac{2}{1},$$

which is written "2 to 1."

27. Let F be the event "some number less than 6 is rolled." Here $F = \{1, 2, 3, 4, 5\}$, so $P(F) = \frac{5}{6}$ and $P(F') = \frac{1}{6}$. The odds in favor of rolling a number less than 2 are

$$\frac{P(F)}{P(F')} = \frac{\frac{5}{6}}{\frac{1}{6}} = \frac{5}{1},$$

which is written "5 to 1."

28. **(a)** Yellow: There are 3 ways to win and 15 ways to lose. The odds in favor of drawing yellow are 3 to 15, or 1 to 5.

(b) Blue: There are 11 ways to win and 7 ways to lose; the odds in favor of drawing blue are 11 to 7.

(c) White: There are 4 ways to win and 14 ways to lose; the odds in favor of drawing white are 4 to 14, or 2 to 7.

29. Let E be the event "draw a white marble." Then $P(E) = \frac{2}{9}$ and $P(E') = \frac{7}{9}$. The odds of not drawing a white marble are

$$\frac{P(E')}{P(E)} = \frac{\frac{7}{9}}{\frac{2}{9}} = \frac{7}{2},$$

which is written "7 to 2."

30. When two dice are rolled, there are 36 equally likely outcomes.

$$\begin{aligned} P(7 \text{ or } 11) &= P(7) + P(11) \\ &= \frac{6}{36} + \frac{2}{36} \\ &= \frac{8}{36} \\ &= \frac{2}{9} \end{aligned}$$

The odds of rolling a 7 or 11 are

$$\frac{P(E)}{P(E')} = \frac{\frac{2}{9}}{1 - \frac{2}{9}} = \frac{\frac{2}{9}}{\frac{7}{9}} = \frac{2}{7},$$

which is written "2 to 7."

31. The statement is not correct.

Assume two dice are rolled.

$$\begin{aligned} P(\text{you win}) &= P(\text{first die is greater than second}) \\ &= \frac{15}{36} \\ &= \frac{5}{12} \end{aligned}$$

$$\begin{aligned} P(\text{other player wins}) &= 1 - P(\text{you win}) \\ &= 1 - \frac{5}{12} \\ &= \frac{7}{12} \end{aligned}$$

33. $P(\text{You will eat out today.}) = \frac{1}{1+2} = \frac{1}{3}$

$P(\text{Bottled water will be tap water.}) = \frac{1}{1+4} = \frac{1}{5}$

$P(\text{Earth will be struck by meteor.}) = \frac{1}{1+9000} = \frac{1}{900}$

$P\,(\text{You will go to Disney World.}) = \frac{1}{1+9} = \frac{1}{10}$

$P(\text{You'll regain weight.}) = \frac{9}{9+10} = \frac{9}{19}$

34. It is possible to establish an exact probability for this event, so this is not an empirical probability.

35. This is empirical; only a survey could determine the probability.

36. It is not possible to establish an exact probability for this event, so this is an empirical probability.

37. This is not empirical; a formula can compute the probability exactly.

38. It is not possible to establish an exact probability for this event, so this is an empirical probability.

39. This is empirical, based on experience and conditions rather than probability theory.

40. The gambler's claim is a mathematical fact, so this is not an empirical probability.

41. This is empirical, based on experience rather than probability theory.

43. Each of the probabilities is between 0 and 1 and the sum of all the probabilities is

$$0.09 + 0.32 + 0.21 + 0.25 + 0.13 = 1,$$

so this assignment is possible.

44. The probability assignment is possible because the probability of each outcome is a number between 0 and 1, and the sum of the probabilities of all the outcomes is

$$0.92 + 0.03 + 0 + 0.02 + 0.03 = 1.$$

45. The sum of the probabilities

$$\frac{1}{3} + \frac{1}{4} + \frac{1}{6} + \frac{1}{8} + \frac{1}{10} = \frac{117}{120} < 1,$$

so this assignment is not possible.

46. The probability assignment is not possible. All of the probabilities are between 0 and 1, but the sum of the probabilities is

$$\frac{1}{5} + \frac{1}{3} + \frac{1}{4} + \frac{1}{5} + \frac{1}{10} = \frac{13}{12}$$

which is greater than 1.

47. This assignment is not possible because one of the probabilities is -0.08, which is not between 0 and 1. A probability cannot be negative.

48. The probability assignment is not possible. One of the probabilities is negative instead of being between 0 and 1, and the sum of the probabilities is not 1.

49. The answers that are given are theoretical. Using the Monte Carlo method with at least 50 repetitions on a graphing calculator should give values close to these.

(a) 0.2778 **(b)** 0.4167

50. The answers that are given are theoretical. Using the Monte Carlo method with at least 50 repetitions on a graphing calculator should give values close to these.

(a) 0.2778 **(b)** 0.4167

51. The answers that are given are theoretical. Using the Monte Carlo method with at least 100 repetitions should give values close to these.

(a) 0.0463 **(b)** 0.2963

52. The answers that are given are theoretical. Using the Monte Carlo method with at least 50 repetitions on a graphing calculator should give values close to these.

(a) 0.15625 **(b)** 0.3125

54. First, notice $(B \cap A') \cup (A \cup B') = U$. As a result,

$$\begin{aligned} P(B \cap A') + (A \cup B') &= P(U) = 1 \\ P(B \cap A') &= 1 - P(A \cup B') \\ &= 1 - 0.9 = 0.1. \end{aligned}$$

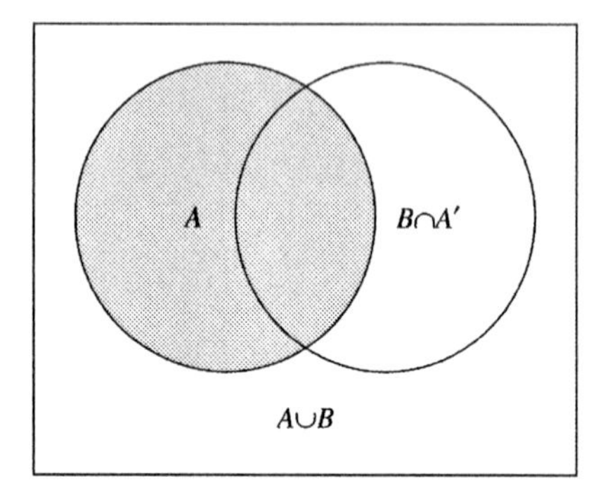

From the Venn diagaram, note that $A \cup B = A \cup (B \cap A')$. Therefore,

$$\begin{aligned} P(A \cup B) &= P(A) + P(B \cap A') \\ 0.7 &= P(A) + 0.1 \\ P(A) &= 0.6. \end{aligned}$$

55. Let C be the event "the calculator has a good case," and let B be the event "the calculator has good batteries."

$$\begin{aligned} &P(C \cap B) \\ &= 1 - P[(C \cap B)'] \\ &= 1 - P(C' \cup B') \\ &= 1 - [P(C') + P(B') - P(C' \cap B')] \\ &= 1 - (0.08 + 0.11 - 0.03) \\ &= 0.84 \end{aligned}$$

Thus, the probability that the calculator has a good case and good batteries is 0.84.

56. **(a)** $$\begin{aligned} P(\$500 \text{ or more}) &= 1 - P(\text{less than } \$500) \\ &= 1 - (0.21 + 0.17) \\ &= 1 - 0.38 \\ &= 0.62 \end{aligned}$$

(b) $$\begin{aligned} P(\text{less than } \$1000) &= 0.21 + 0.17 + 0.16 \\ &= 0.54 \end{aligned}$$

(c) $$\begin{aligned} P(\$500 \text{ to } \$2999) &= 0.16 + 0.15 + 0.12 \\ &= 0.43 \end{aligned}$$

(d) $$\begin{aligned} P(\$3000 \text{ or more}) &= 0.08 + 0.07 + 0.04 \\ &= 0.19 \end{aligned}$$

57. (a) $P(\text{less than } \$25) = 0.02 + 0.05 = 0.07$

(b) $P(\text{more than } \$24.99) = 1 - P(\text{less than } \$25)$
$= 1 - 0.07 = 0.93$

(c) $P(\$50 \text{ to } \$199.99) = P(\$50 - \$74.99)$
$+ P(\$75 - \$99.99)$
$+ P(\$100 - \$199.99)$
$= 0.13 + 0.14 + 0.22 = 0.49$

58. (a) $P(\text{less than } \$350)$
$= 1 - P(\$350 \text{ or more})$
$= 1 - (0.12 + 0.03)$
$= 1 - 0.15$
$= 0.85$

(b) $P(\$75 \text{ or more})$
$= P(\$75 - \$99.99) + P(\$100 - \$199.99)$
$+ P(\$200 - \$349.99) + P(\$350 - \$499.99)$
$+ P(\$500 \text{ or more})$
$= 0.14 + 0.22 + 0.18 + 0.12 + 0.03$
$= 0.69$

(c) $P(\$200 \text{ or more})$
$= P(\$200 - \$349.99) + P(\$350 - \$499.99)$
$+ P(\$500 \text{ or more})$
$= 0.18 + 0.12 + 0.03$
$= 0.33$

59. We are given that $P(\text{profit}) = 0.74$, so

$$P(\text{no profit}) = 1 - 0.74 = 0.26.$$

The odds against the company's making a profit are

$$\frac{P(\text{no profit})}{P(\text{profit})} = \frac{0.26}{0.74} = \frac{13}{37},$$

or 13 to 37.

60. Let S be the event "the person is short," and let O be the event "the person is overweight."

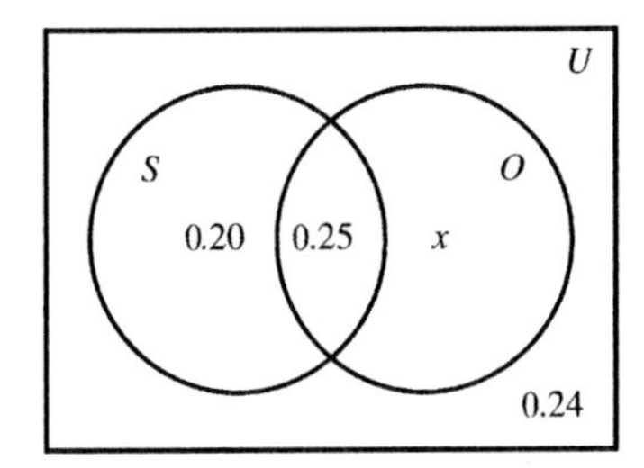

From the Venn diagram,

$$\begin{aligned} 0.20 + 0.25 + x + 0.24 &= 1 \\ 0.69 + x &= 1 \\ x &= 0.31. \end{aligned}$$

The probability that a person is

(a) overweight is $0.25 + 0.31 = 0.56$;

(b) short, but not overweight is 0.20;

(c) tall (not short) and overweight is 0.31.

61. $P(C) = 0.039$, $P(M \cap C) = 0.035$, $P(M \cup C) = 0.491$

Place the given information in a Venn diagram by starting with 0.035 in the intersection of the regions for M and C.

Since $P(C) = 0.039$,

$$0.039 - 0.035 = 0.004$$

goes inside region C, but outside the intersection of C and M. Thus,

$$P(C \cap M') = 0.004.$$

Since $P(M \cup C) = 0.491$,

$$0.491 - 0.035 - 0.004 = 0.452$$

goes inside region M, but outside the intersection of C and M. Thus, $P(M \cap C') = 0.452$. The labeled regions have probability

$$0.452 + 0.035 + 0.004 = 0.491.$$

Since the entire region of the Venn diagram must have probability 1, the region outside M and C, or $M' \cap C'$, has probability

$$1 - 0.491 = 0.509.$$

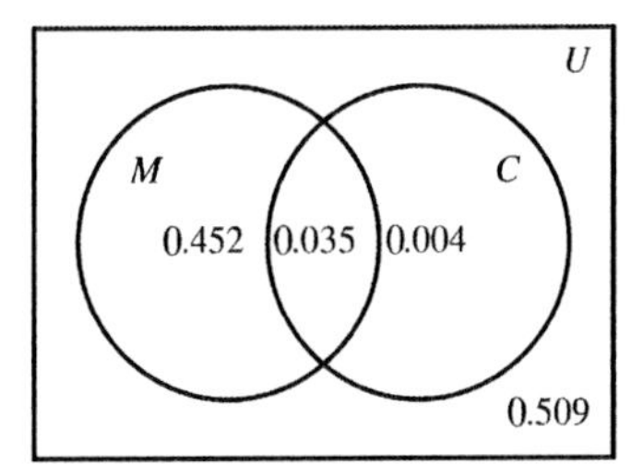

(a) $P(C') = 1 - P(C)$
$= 1 - 0.039$
$= 0.961$

(b) $P(M) = 0.452 + 0.035$
$= 0.487$

(c) $P(M') = 1 - P(M)$
$= 1 - 0.487$
$= 0.513$

(d) $P(M' \cap C') = 0.509$

(e) $P(C \cap M') = 0.004$

(f) $P(C \cup M')$
$$= P(C) + P(M') - P(C \cap M')$$
$$= 0.039 + 0.513 - 0.004$$
$$= 0.548$$

62. (a) Since red is dominant, the event "plant has red flowers"

$$= \{RR, RW, WR\};\ P(\text{red}) = \frac{3}{4}.$$

(b) $P(\text{white}) = 1 - P(\text{red}) = \frac{1}{4}$

63. (a) Now red is no longer dominant, and RW or WR results in pink, so

$$P(\text{red}) = P(RR) = \frac{1}{4}.$$

(b) $P(\text{pink}) = P(RW) + P(WR)$
$$= \frac{1}{4} + \frac{1}{4} = \frac{1}{2}$$

(c) $P(\text{white}) = P(WW) = \frac{1}{4}$

64. (a) $P(\text{no more than 4 good toes})$

$$= 0.77 + 0.13 = 0.90$$

(b) $P(5 \text{ toes}) = 0.13 + 0.10 = 0.23$

65. Let L be the event "visit results in lab work" and R be the event "visit results in referral to specialist." We are given the probability a visit results in neither is 35%, so $P((L \cup R)') = 0.35$. Since $P(L \cup R) = 1 - P((L \cup R)')$, we have

$$P(L \cup R) = 1 - 0.35 = 0.65.$$

We are also given $P(L) = 0.40$ and $P(R) = 0.30$. Using the union rule for probability,

$$P(L \cup R) = P(L) + P(R) - P(L \cap R)$$
$$0.65 = 0.40 + 0.30 - P(L \cap R)$$
$$0.65 = 0.50 - P(L \cap R)$$
$$P(L \cap R) = 0.05$$

The correct answer choice is **a**.

66. Let T be the event "patient visits a physical therapist" and C be the event "patient visits a chiropractor." If 22% of patients visit both a physical therapist and a chiropractor, then $P(T \cap C) = 0.22$. If 12% of patients visit neither, then $P((T \cup C)') = 0.12$. This means

$$P(T \cup C) = 1 - P((T \cup C)') = 1 - 0.12 = 0.88.$$

Let $x = P(T)$. If the probability that a patient visits a chiropractor exceeds by 0.14 the probability that a patient visits a physical therapist, then $P(C) = P(T) + 0.14 = x + 0.14$. Using the union rule for probability, we have

$$P(T \cup C) = P(T) + P(C) - P(T \cap C)$$
$$0.88 = x + (x + 0.14) - 0.22$$
$$0.88 = 2x - 0.08$$
$$0.96 = 2x$$
$$x = 0.48$$

The correct answer choice is **d**.

67. Let $x = P(A \cap B)$,
$y = P(B \cap C)$,
$z = P(A \cap C)$,
and $w = P((A \cup B \cup C)')$.

If an employee must choose exactly two or none of the supplementary coverages A, B, and C, then $P(A \cap B \cap C) = 0$ and the probabilities of the region representing a single choice of coverages A, B, or C are also 0. We can represent the choices and probabilities with the following Venn diagram.

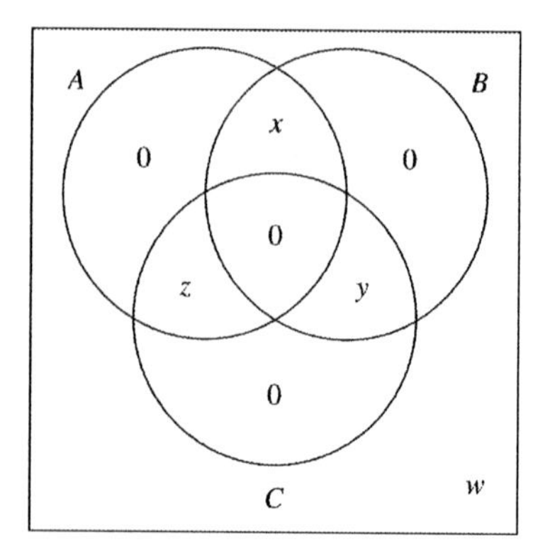

The information given leads to the following system of equations.

$$\begin{aligned} x + y + z + w &= 1 \\ x \quad + z \quad &= \frac{1}{4} \\ x + y \quad\quad &= \frac{1}{3} \\ y + z \quad &= \frac{5}{12} \end{aligned}$$

Using a graphing calculator or computer program, the solution to the system is $x = 1/2, y = 1/4, z = 1/6, w = 1/2$. Since the probability that a randomly chosen employee will choose no supplementary coverage is w, the correct answer choice is c.

68. Gore: $\frac{1}{2+1} = \frac{1}{3}$

Daschle: $\frac{1}{4+1} = \frac{1}{5}$

Kerry: $\frac{1}{4+1} = \frac{1}{5}$

Dodd: $\frac{1}{4+1} = \frac{1}{5}$

Lieberman: $\frac{1}{5+1} = \frac{1}{6}$

Biden: $\frac{1}{5+1} = \frac{1}{6}$

Leahy: $\frac{1}{6+1} = \frac{1}{7}$

Feingold: $\frac{1}{8+1} = \frac{1}{9}$

Edwards: $\frac{1}{9+1} = \frac{1}{10}$

Gephardt: $\frac{1}{15+1} = \frac{1}{16}$

Find the sum of the probabilities.

$$\frac{1}{3} + \frac{1}{5} + \frac{1}{5} + \frac{1}{5} + \frac{1}{6} + \frac{1}{6} + \frac{1}{7} + \frac{1}{9} + \frac{1}{10} + \frac{1}{16}$$

$$= \frac{8483}{5040} \approx 1.68$$

Since the sum of the probabilities of all possible outcomes cannot be greater than 1, there is something wrong with the assignment of odds.

69. Since 55 of the workers were women, $130 - 55 = 75$ were men. Since 3 of the women earned more than \$40,000, $55 - 3 = 52$ of them earned \$40,000 or less. Since 62 of the men earned \$40,000 or less, $75 - 62 = 13$ earned more than \$40,000.
These data for the 130 workers can be summarized in the following table.

	Men	Women
\$40,000 or less	62	52
Over \$40,000	13	3

(a) P(a woman earning \$40,000 or less)

$$= \frac{52}{130} = 0.4$$

(b) P(a man earning more than \$40,000)

$$= \frac{13}{130} = 0.1$$

(c) P(a man or is earning more than \$40,000)

$$= \frac{62 + 13 + 3}{130}$$

$$= \frac{78}{130} = 0.6$$

(d) P(a woman or is earning \$40,000 or less)

$$= \frac{52 + 3 + 62}{130}$$

$$= \frac{117}{130} = 0.9$$

70. Let R be the event "the person buys rock music," and let T be the event "the person is a teenager."

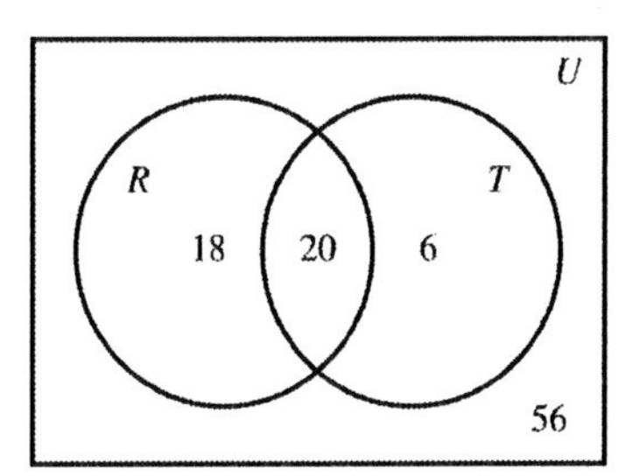

The probability that a person

(a) is a teenager who buys nonrock music is $\frac{6}{100} = 0.06$;

(b) buys rock music or is a teenager is $\frac{18}{100} + \frac{20}{100} + \frac{6}{100} = 0.44$;

(c) is not a teenager is $1 - \frac{26}{100} = 0.74$;

(d) is not a teenager, but buys rock music, is $\frac{18}{100} = 0.18$.

71. Let A be the set of refugees who came to escape abject poverty and B be the set of refugees who came to escape political oppression. Then $P(A) = 0.80$, $P(B) = 0.90$, and $P(A \cap B) = 0.70$.

$$\begin{aligned} P(A \cup B) &= P(A) + P(B) - P(A \cap B) \\ &= 0.80 + 0.90 - 0.70 = 1 \\ P(A' \cap B') &= 1 - P(A \cap B) \\ &= 1 - 1 = 0 \end{aligned}$$

The probability that a refugee in the camp was neither poor nor seeking political asylum is 0.

72. There are 18 people, so $n(S) = 18$.

(a) $P(\text{Chinese})$
$= P(\text{Chinese man}) + P(\text{Chinese woman})$
$= \frac{3}{18} + \frac{4}{18}$
$= \frac{7}{18}$

(b) $P(\text{Korean or woman})$
$= P(\text{Korean}) + P(\text{woman}) - P(\text{Korean woman})$
$= \frac{6}{18} + \frac{11}{18} - \frac{4}{18}$
$= \frac{13}{18}$

(c) $P(\text{man or Vietnamese})$
$= P(\text{man}) + P(\text{Vietnamese}) - P(\text{Vietnamese man})$
$= \frac{7}{18} + \frac{5}{18} - \frac{2}{18}$
$= \frac{10}{18}$
$= \frac{5}{9}$

(d) These events are mutually exclusive, so

$P(\text{Chinese or Vietnamese})$
$= P(\text{Chinese}) + P(\text{Vietnamese})$
$= \frac{7}{18} + \frac{5}{18}$
$= \frac{12}{18}$
$= \frac{2}{3}.$

(e) $P(\text{Korean woman}) = \frac{4}{18} = \frac{2}{9}$

73. The odds of winning are 3 to 2; this means there are 3 ways to win and 2 ways to lose, out of a total of 2 + 3 = 5 ways altogether. Hence, the probability of losing is $\frac{2}{5}$.

74. (a) Divide each entry in the original table by 212,156.

	A	B	C	D
O	0.0580	0.0641	0.0382	0.0052
E	0.2847	0.2802	0.2141	0.0456
M	0.0030	0.0036	0.0034	0

(b) $P(A) = \frac{73{,}343}{212{,}156} \approx 0.3457$

(c) This is the sum of the entries in the "O" row and in the "C" and "D" columns.

$$P(O \cap (C \cup D)) = \frac{8111 + 1096}{212{,}156} \approx 0.0434$$

(d) $P(A \cup B) = P(A) + P(B)$
$= \frac{73{,}343 + 73{,}786}{212{,}156}$
$= \frac{147{,}129}{212{,}156}$
≈ 0.6935

(e) $P(E \cup (C \cup D))$
$= P(E) + P(C \cup D) - P(E \cap (C \cup D))$
$= P(E) + P(C) + P(D) - [P(E \cap C) + P(E \cap D)]$
$\frac{174{,}929 + 54{,}248 + 10{,}779 - (45{,}415 + 9683)}{212{,}156}$
$= \frac{184{,}858}{212{,}156}$
≈ 0.8713

75. (a) $P(\text{somewhat or extremely intolerant of Facists})$
$= P(\text{somewhat intolerant of Fascists}) + P(\text{extremely intolerant of Facists})$
$= \frac{27.1}{100} + \frac{59.5}{100} = \frac{86.6}{100} = 0.866$

(b) $P(\text{completely tolerant of Communists})$
$= P(\text{no intolerance at all of Communists})$
$= \frac{47.8}{100} = 0.478$

76. **(a)** P(at least some intolerance of Fascists)
$= P(\text{not very much}) + P(\text{somewhat})$
$+ P(\text{extremely intolerant of Facists})$

$$= \frac{20.7}{100} + \frac{43.1}{100} + \frac{22.9}{100} = \frac{86.7}{100} = 0.867$$

(b) P(at least some intolerance of Communists)
$= P(\text{not very much}) + P(\text{somewhat})$
$+ P(\text{extremely intolerant of Communists})$

$$= \frac{33.0}{100} + \frac{34.2}{100} + \frac{17.1}{100} = \frac{84.3}{100}$$

$= 0.843$

77. Since the odds are 4 to 7, the probability of rain is

$$\frac{4}{4+7} = \frac{4}{11}.$$

78. **(a)** There are $67 + 25 = 92$ possible judging combinations with Sasha Cohen finishing in first place. The probability of this outcome is, therefore, $92/220 = 23/55$.

(b) There are 67 possible judging combinations with Irina Slutskaya finishing in second place. The probability of this outcome is, therefore, $67/220$.

(c) There are $92 + 67 = 159$ possible judging combinations with Shizuka Arahawa finishing in third place. The probability of this outcome is, therefore, $159/220$.

7.5 Conditional Probability; Independent Events

1. Let A be the event "the number is 2" and B be the event "the number is odd."

The problem seeks the conditional probability $P(A|B)$. Use the definition

$$P(A|B) = \frac{P(A \cap B)}{P(B)}.$$

Here, $P(A \cap B) = 0$ and $P(B) = \frac{1}{2}$. Thus,

$$P(A|B) = \frac{0}{\frac{1}{2}} = 0.$$

2. $$P(4|\text{even}) = \frac{P(4 \cap \text{even})}{P(\text{even})} = \frac{n(4 \cap \text{even})}{n(\text{even})} = \frac{1}{3}$$

3. Let A be the event "the number is even" and B be the event "the number is 6." Then

$$P(A|B) = \frac{P(A \cap B)}{P(B)} = \frac{\frac{1}{6}}{\frac{1}{6}} = 1.$$

4. $P(\text{sum of } 8|\text{greater than } 7)$

$$= \frac{P(8 \cap \text{greater than } 7)}{P(\text{greater than } 7)} = \frac{n(8 \cap \text{greater than } 7)}{n(\text{greater than } 7)} = \frac{5}{15} = \frac{1}{3}$$

5. Let A be the event "sum of 6" and B be the event "double." 6 of the 36 ordered pairs are doubles, so $P(B) = \frac{6}{36} = \frac{1}{6}$. There is only one outcome, 3-3, in $A \cap B$ (that is, a double with a sum of 6), so $P(A \cap B) = \frac{1}{36}$. Thus,

$$P(A|B) = \frac{\frac{1}{36}}{\frac{1}{6}} = \frac{6}{36} = \frac{1}{6}.$$

6. The event of getting a double given that 9 was rolled is impossible; hence,

$$P(\text{double}|\text{sum of } 9) = 0.$$

7. Use a reduced sample space. After the first card drawn is a heart, there remain 51 cards, of which 12 are hearts. Thus,

$$P(\text{heart on 2nd}|\text{heart on 1st}) = \frac{12}{51} = \frac{4}{17}.$$

8. $P(\text{second is black}|\text{first is a spade}) = \frac{25}{51}$, since there are 25 black cards left out of 51 cards. Note that the sample space is reduced from 52 cards to 51 cards after the first card is drawn.

9. Use a reduced sample space. After the first card drawn is a jack, there remain 51 cards, of which 11 are face cards. Thus,

$$P(\text{face card on 2nd}|\text{jack on 1st}) = \frac{11}{51}.$$

10. $P(\text{second is an ace}|\text{first is not an ace}) = \frac{4}{51}$, since there are 4 aces left out of 51 cards.

11. $P(\text{a jack and a 10})$
$$= P(\text{jack followed by 10}) + P(\text{10 followed by jack})$$
$$= \frac{4}{52} \cdot \frac{4}{51} + \frac{4}{52} \cdot \frac{4}{51}$$
$$= \frac{16}{2652} + \frac{16}{2652}$$
$$= \frac{32}{2652} = \frac{8}{663}$$

12. The probability of drawing an ace and then drawing a 4 is
$$\frac{4}{52} \cdot \frac{4}{51} = \frac{4}{663}.$$
The probability of drawing a 4 and then drawing an ace is
$$\frac{4}{52} \cdot \frac{4}{51} = \frac{4}{663}.$$
Since these are mutually exclusive, the probability of drawing an ace and a 4 is
$$\frac{4}{663} + \frac{4}{663} = \frac{8}{663}.$$

13. $P(\text{two black cards})$
$$= P(\text{black on 1st}) \cdot P(\text{black on 2nd}|\text{black on 1st})$$
$$= \frac{26}{52} \cdot \frac{25}{51}$$
$$= \frac{650}{2652} = \frac{25}{102}$$

14. The probability that the first card is a heart is $\frac{13}{52} = \frac{1}{4}$. The probability that the second is a heart, given that the first is a heart, is $\frac{12}{51}$. Thus, the probability that both are hearts is
$$\frac{1}{4} \cdot \frac{12}{51} = \frac{1}{17}.$$

16. Examine a table of all possible outcomes of rolling a red die and rolling a green die (such as Figure 18 in Section 7.4). There are 9 outcomes of the 36 total outcomes that correspond to rolling "red die comes up even and green die comes up even"—in other words, corresponding to $A \cap B$. Therefore,
$$P(A \cap B) = \frac{9}{36} = \frac{1}{4}.$$
We also know that $P(A) = 1/2$ and $P(B) = 1/2$. Since
$$P(A \cap B) = \frac{1}{4} = \frac{1}{2} \cdot \frac{1}{2} = P(A) \cdot P(B),$$
the events A and B are independent.

17. The knowledge that "it rains more than 10 days" affects the knowledge that "it rains more than 15 days." (For instance, if it hasn't rained more than 10 days, it couldn't possibly have rained more than 15 days.) Since $P(D|C) \neq P(D)$, the events are dependent.

18. Notice that $P(F|E) \neq P(F)$: the knowledge that a person lives in Dallas affects the probability that the person lives in Dallas or Houston. Therefore, the events are dependent.

19. First not that $P(G) = 1/7$ and $P(H) = 1/2$. A tree diagram of all the possible outcomes of the experiment would have 14 branches, exactly one of which would correspond to the outcome "today is Tuesday and the coin comes up heads," or $G \cap H$. Therefore, $P(G \cap H) = 1/14$. But notice that
$$P(G \cap H) = \frac{1}{14} = \frac{1}{7} \cdot \frac{1}{2} = P(G) \cdot P(H).$$
Thus, the events are independent.

20. **(a)** The events that correspond to "sum is 7" are $(2,5), (3,4), (4,3)$, and $(5,2)$, where the first number is the number on the first slip of paper and the second number is the number on the second. Of these, only $(3,4)$ corresponds to "first is 3," so
$$P(\text{first is 3}|\text{sum is 7}) = \frac{1}{4}.$$

(b) The events that correspond to "sum is 8" are $(3,5)$ and $(5,3)$. Of these, only $(3,5)$ corresponds to "first is 3," so
$$P(\text{first is 3}|\text{sum is 8}) = \frac{1}{2}.$$

21. **(a)** Given that the first number is 5, there are four possible sums: $5+1=6$, $5+2=7$, $5+3=8$, and $5+4=9$. One of the four possible outcomes corresponds to the sum 8. Therefore,
$$P(\text{sum is 8}|\text{first number is 5}) = \frac{1}{4}.$$

(b) Given that the first number is 4, there are four possible sums: $4+1=5$, $4+2=6$, $4+3=7$, and $4+5=9$. None of these corresponds to the sum 8. Therefore,
$$P(\text{sum is 8}|\text{first number is 4}) = \frac{0}{4} = 0.$$

22. **(a)** Many answers are possible; for example, let B be the event that the first die is a 5. Then

$$P(A \cap B) = P(\text{sum is 7 and first is 5}) = \frac{1}{36}$$

$$P(A) \cdot P(B) = P(\text{sum is 7}) \cdot P(\text{first is 5}) = \frac{6}{36} \cdot \frac{1}{6} = \frac{1}{36}$$

so, $P(A \cap B) = P(A) \cdot P(B)$.

(b) Many answers are possible; for example, let B be the event that at least one die is a 5.

$$P(A \cap B) = P(\text{sum is 7 and at least one is a 5}) = \frac{2}{36}$$

$$P(A) \cdot P(B) = P(\text{sum is 7}) \cdot P(\text{at least one is a 5}) = \frac{6}{36} \cdot \frac{11}{6}$$

so, $P(A \cap B) \neq P(A) \cdot P(B)$.

26. At the first booth, there are three possibilities: shaker 1 has heads and shaker 2 has heads; shaker 1 has tails and shaker 2 has heads; shaker 1 has heads and shaker 2 has tails.
We restrict ourselves to the condition that at least one head has appeared. These three possibilities are equally likely so the probability of two heads is $\frac{1}{3}$.

At the second booth we are given the condition of one head in one shaker. The probability that the second shaker has one head is $\frac{1}{2}$.

Therefore, you stand the best chance at the second booth.

27. **(a)** Let C be the event "the coin comes up heads" and D be the event "6 is rolled on the die." We have

$$P(C) = \frac{1}{2},\ P(D) = \frac{1}{6},\ P(C \cap D) = \frac{1}{12}.$$

So the probability of winning–of the event $C \cap D$–is 1/12.
What is the probability that either the head or the 6 occurred—in other words, what is $P(C \cup D)$? Use the union for probability.

$$\begin{aligned} P(C \cup D) &= P(C) + P(D) - P(C \cap D) \\ &= \frac{1}{2} + \frac{1}{6} - \frac{1}{12} \\ &= \frac{6}{12} + \frac{2}{12} - \frac{1}{12} \\ &= \frac{7}{12} \end{aligned}$$

We want to find the probability of "head and 6 occured" given that "head or 6 occurred"—that is, $P((C \cap D)|(C \cup D))$. Use the formula for the conditional probability.

$$\begin{aligned} P((C \cap D)|(C \cup D)) &= \frac{P((C \cap D)|(C \cup D))}{P(C \cup D)} \\ &= \frac{P(C \cap D)}{P(C \cup D)} \\ &= \frac{\frac{1}{12}}{\frac{7}{12}} \\ &= \frac{1}{7} \end{aligned}$$

The probability of winning the original game with the additional information is now 1/7. On the other hand, the probability of winning the new game, of the event "6 is rolled," is simply $P(D) = 1/6$. Since $1/6 > 1/7$, it is better to switch.

28. No, these events are not independent.

29. For a two-child family, the sample space is

$$M - M \quad M - F \quad F - M \quad F - F.$$

$$P(\text{same sex}) = \frac{2}{4} = \frac{1}{2}$$

$$P(\text{same sex}|\text{at most one male}) = \frac{1}{3}$$

The events are not independent.
For a three-child family, the same space is

$$\begin{matrix} M - M - M & M - M - F & M - F - M & M - F - F \\ F - M - M & F - M - F & F - F - M & F - F - F. \end{matrix}$$

$$P(\text{same sex}) = \frac{2}{8} = \frac{1}{4}$$

$$P(\text{same sex}|\text{at most one male}) = \frac{1}{4}$$

The events are independent.

30. Since A and B are independent events.

$$P(A \cap B) = P(A) \cdot P(B) = \frac{1}{4} \cdot \frac{1}{5} = \frac{1}{20}.$$

Thus,

$$\begin{aligned} P(A \cup B) &= P(A) + P(B) - P(A \cap B) \\ &= \frac{1}{4} + \frac{1}{5} - \frac{1}{20} \\ &= \frac{2}{5}. \end{aligned}$$

31. **(a)** If A and B are mutually exclusive, then

$$\begin{aligned} P(B) &= P(A \cup B) - P(A) \\ &= 0.7 - 0.5 = 0.2 \end{aligned}$$

(b) If A and B are independent, then

$$\frac{P(A \cap B)}{P(B)} = P(A|B) = P(A) = 0.5.$$

Thus,

$$P(A \cap B) = 0.5P(B).$$

Solving

$$P(A \cup B) = P(A) + P(B) - P(A \cap B)$$

for

$$P(A \cap B)$$

and substituting into the previous equations we get

$$\begin{aligned} P(A) + P(B) - P(A \cup B) &= 0.5P(B) \\ 0.5 + P(B) - 0.7 &= 0.5P(B) \\ -0.2 &= -0.5P(B) \\ 0.4 &= P(B). \end{aligned}$$

$P(B) = 0.4$

32. Assume that each box is equally likely to be drawn from and that within each box each marble is equally likely to be drawn. If Laura does not redistribute the marbles, then the probability of winning the Porsche is $\frac{1}{2}$, since the event of a pink marble being drawn is equivalent to the event of choosing the first of the two boxes.

If however, Laura puts 49 of the pink marbles into the second box with the 50 blue marbles, the probability of a pink marble being drawn increases to $\frac{74}{99}$. The probability of the first box being chosen is $\frac{1}{2}$, and the probability of drawing a pink marble from this box is 1. The probability of the second box being chosen is $\frac{1}{2}$, and the probability of drawing a pink marble from this box is $\frac{49}{99}$. Thus, the probability of drawing a pink marble is $\frac{1}{2} \cdot 1 + \frac{1}{2} \cdot \frac{49}{99} = \frac{74}{99}$. Therefore Laura increases her chances of winning.

33. $P(C|D)$ is the probability that a customer cashes a check, given that the customer made a deposit.

$$\begin{aligned} P(C|D) &= \frac{P(C \cap D)}{P(D)} \\ &= \frac{n(C \cap D)}{n(D)} \\ &= \frac{60}{80} \\ &= \frac{3}{4} \end{aligned}$$

34. The probability that a customer cashing a check will fail to make a deposit is

$$P(D'|C) = \frac{n(D' \cap C)}{n(C)} = \frac{30}{90} = \frac{1}{3}.$$

35. $P(C'|D')$ is the probability that a customer does not cash a check, given that the customer did not make a deposit.

$$\begin{aligned} P(C'|D') &= \frac{P(C' \cap D')}{P(D')} \\ &= \frac{n(C' \cap D')}{n(D')} \\ &= \frac{10}{40} \\ &= \frac{1}{4} \end{aligned}$$

36. The probability that a customer making a deposit will not cash a check is

$$P(C'|D) = \frac{n(C' \cap D)}{n(D)} = \frac{20}{80} = \frac{1}{4}.$$

37. $P[(C \cap D)']$ is the probability that a customer does not both cash a check and make a deposit.

$$\begin{aligned} P[(C \cap D)'] &= 1 - P(C \cap D) \\ &= 1 - \frac{60}{120} \\ &= \frac{60}{120} \\ &= \frac{1}{2} \end{aligned}$$

38. **(a)** Since the separate flights are independent, the probability of 4 flights in a row is

$$(0.792)(0.792)(0.792)(0.792) \approx 0.3935.$$

39. Let M represent the event "the main computer fails" and B the event "the backup computer fails." Since these events are assumed to be independent,

$$\begin{aligned} P(M \cap B) &= P(M) \cdot P(B) \\ &= 0.003(0.005) \\ &= 0.000015. \end{aligned}$$

This is the probability that both computers fail, which means that the company will not have computer service. The fraction of the time it will have service is

$$1 - 0.000015 = 0.999985.$$

Independence is a fairly realistic assumption. Situations such as floods or electric surges might cause both computers to fail at the same time.

40. Let W be the event "withdraw cash from ATM" and C be the event "check account balance at ATM."

$$\begin{aligned} P(C \cup W) &= P(C) + P(W) - P(C \cap W) \\ 0.96 &= 0.32 + 0.92 - P(C \cap W) \\ -0.28 &= -P(C \cap W) \\ P(C \cap W) &= 0.28 \end{aligned}$$

$$\begin{aligned} P(W|C) &= \frac{P(C \cap W)}{P(C)} \\ &= \frac{0.28}{0.32} \\ &\approx 0.875 \end{aligned}$$

The probability that she uses an ATM to get cash given that she checked her account balance is 0.875.

41. Since 60% of production comes off assembly line A, $P(A) = 0.60$. Also $P(\text{pass inspection}|A) = 0.95$, so $P(\text{not pass}|A) = 0.05$. Therefore,

$$\begin{aligned} P(A \cap \text{not pass}) &= P(A) \cdot P(\text{not pass}|A) \\ &= 0.60(0.05) \\ &= 0.03. \end{aligned}$$

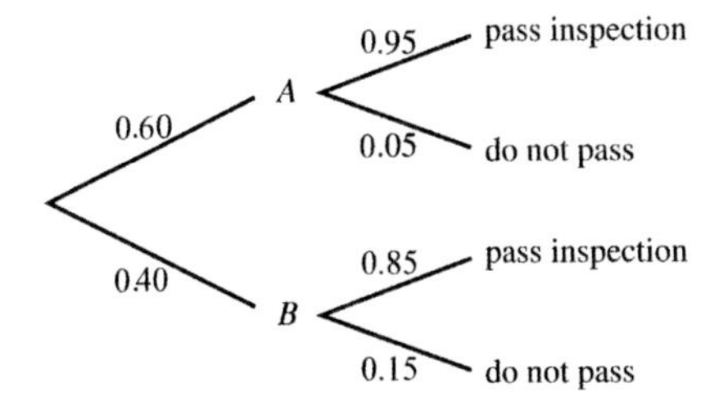

42. Since 40% of the production comes off B, $P(B) = 0.40$. Also, $P(\text{pass}|B) = 0.85$, so $P(\text{not pass}|B) = 0.15$. Therefore,

$$\begin{aligned} P(\text{not pass} \cap B) &= P(B) \cdot P(\text{not pass}|B) \\ &= 0.40(0.15) \\ &= 0.06 \end{aligned}$$

43. $P(\text{bike did not pass inspection})$

$$\begin{aligned} &= 0.60(0.05) + 0.40(0.15) \\ &= 0.03 + 0.06 \\ &= 0.09 \end{aligned}$$

44. The sample space is

$$\{RW, WR, RR, WW\}.$$

The event "red" is $\{RW, WR, RR\}$, and the event "mixed" is $\{RW, WR\}$.

$$\begin{aligned} P(\text{mixed}|\text{red}) &= \frac{n(\text{mixed and red})}{n(\text{red})} \\ &= \frac{2}{3}. \end{aligned}$$

Use the following tree diagram for Exercises 45 through 49

1st child	2nd child	3rd child	Branch	Probability
1/2 B	1/2 B	1/2 B	1	1/8
		1/2 G	2	1/8
	1/2 G	1/2 B	3	1/8
		1/2 G	4	1/8
1/2 G	1/2 B	1/2 B	5	1/8
		1/2 G	6	1/8
	1/2 G	1/2 B	7	1/8
		1/2 G	8	1/8

45. $P(\text{all girls}|\text{first is a girl})$

$$\begin{aligned} &= \frac{P(\text{all girls and first is a girl})}{P(\text{first is a girl})} \\ &= \frac{n(\text{all girls and first is a girl})}{n(\text{first is a girl})} \\ &= \frac{1}{4} \end{aligned}$$

46. $P(3 \text{ girls}|\text{3rd is a girl})$

$$\begin{aligned} &= \frac{P(3 \text{ girls and 3rd is a girl})}{P(\text{3rd is a girl})} \\ &= \frac{\frac{1}{8}}{\frac{1}{2}} \\ &= \frac{1}{4} \end{aligned}$$

47. $P(\text{all girls}|\text{second is a girl})$

$$= \frac{P(\text{all girls and second is a girl})}{P(\text{second is a girl})}$$

$$= \frac{n(\text{all girls and second is a girl})}{n(\text{second is a girl})}$$

$$= \frac{1}{4}$$

48. $P(3 \text{ girls}|\text{at least 2 girls})$

$$= \frac{P(3 \text{ girls and at least 2 girls})}{P(\text{at least 2 girls})}$$

$$= \frac{P(3 \text{ girls})}{P(\text{at least 2 girls})}$$

$$= \frac{P(3 \text{ girls})}{P(2 \text{ girls}) + P(3 \text{ girls})}$$

$$= \frac{\frac{1}{8}}{\frac{3}{8} + \frac{1}{8}}$$

$$= \frac{\frac{1}{8}}{\frac{4}{8}}$$

$$= \frac{1}{4}$$

(Note that

$$P(3 \text{ girls}) = P(GGG) = \frac{1}{2} \cdot \frac{1}{2} \cdot \frac{1}{2} = \frac{1}{8}$$

and

$$P(2 \text{ girls}) = P(GGB) + P(BGG) + P(GBG)$$
$$= \frac{1}{8} + \frac{1}{8} + \frac{1}{8}$$
$$= \frac{3}{8}.)$$

49. $P(\text{all girls}|\text{at least 1 girl})$

$$= \frac{P(\text{all girls and at least 1 girl})}{P(\text{at least 1 girl})}$$

$$= \frac{n(\text{all girls and at least 1 girl})}{n(\text{at least 1 girl})}$$

$$= \frac{1}{7}$$

50. (a) $P(\text{homosexual contact}|\text{male})$

$$= \frac{18{,}203}{28{,}143} \approx 0.6468$$

(b) $P(\text{intervenous drug use}|\text{female})$

$$= \frac{2134}{10{,}410} \approx 0.2050$$

51. By the product rule for independent events, two events are independent if the product of their probabilities is the probability of their intersection.

$$0.75(0.4) = 0.3$$

Therefore, the given events are independent.

52. $P(M) = 0.487$, the total of the M column.

53. $P(C) = 0.039$, the total of the C row.

54. $P(M \cap C) = 0.035$, the entry in the M column and C row.

55. $P(M \cup C) = P(M) + P(C) - P(M \cap C)$
$= 0.487 + 0.039 - 0.035$
$= 0.491$

56. $P(M|C) = \dfrac{P(M \cap C)}{P(C)}$
$= \dfrac{0.035}{0.039}$
≈ 0.897

57. $P(C|M) = \dfrac{P(C \cap M)}{P(M)}$
$= \dfrac{0.035}{0.487}$
≈ 0.072

58. $P(M'|C) = \dfrac{P(M' \cap C)}{P(C)}$
$= \dfrac{0.004}{0.039}$
≈ 0.103

59. By the definition of independent events, C and M are independent if

$$P(C|M) = P(C).$$

From Exercises 44 and 48,

$$P(C) = 0.039$$
$$\text{and} \quad P(C|M) = 0.072.$$

Since $P(C|M) \neq P(C)$, events C and M are not independent, so we say that they are dependent. This means that red-green color blindness does not occur equally among men and women.

60. **(a)** From the table,

$$P(C \cap D) = 0.0008 \text{ and}$$
$$P(C) \cdot P(D) = 0.0400(0.0200) = 0.0008.$$

Since $P(C \cap D) = P(C) \cdot P(D)$, C and D are independent events; color blindness and deafness are independent events.

61. First draw a tree diagram.

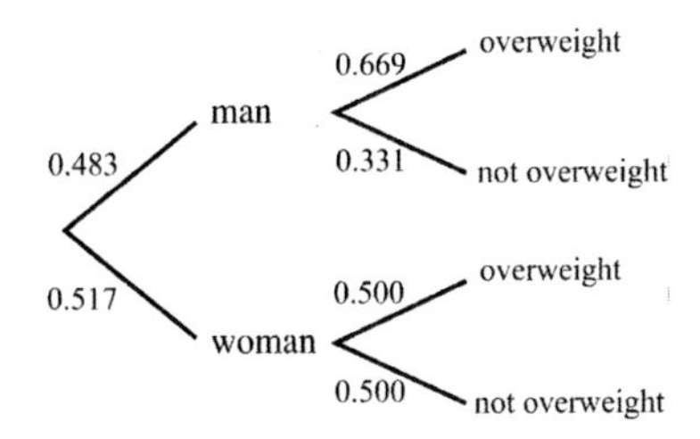

(a) $P(\text{overweight man}) = 0.483(0.669) \approx 0.323$

(b) $P(\text{overweight}) = 0.323 + 0.517(0.500)$
$= 0.323 + 0.25$
≈ 0.582

(c) The two events "man" and "overweight" are independent if

$$P(\text{overweight man}) = P(\text{overweight}) \cdot P(\text{man}).$$

We are given $P(\text{man}) = 0.483$ so that

$$P(\text{overweight}) \cdot P(\text{ man}) = 0.582 \cdot 0.483 \approx 0.281$$

but we found $P(\text{overweight man}) = 0.323$ in part (a). Therefore, the events are not independent.

62. Let E be the event "claim includes emergency rooom charges" and O be "claim includes operating room charges." We wish to find $P(O)$.

We are given that $P(E \cup O) = 0.85$.

If the number of claims that do not include emergency room charges is 25% of the total number of claims, then $P(E') = 0.25$. Therefore,

$$P(E) = 1 - P(E') = 1 - 0.25 = 0.75.$$

If the occurrence of emergency room charges is independent of the occurrence of operating room charges, then $P(E \cap O) = P(E) \cdot P(O)$. Let $x = P(O)$ and use the union rule for probability to find $P(O)$.

$$P(E \cup O) = P(E) + P(O) - P(E \cap O)$$
$$P(E \cup O) = P(E) + P(O) - P(E) \cdot P(O)$$
$$0.85 = 0.75 + x - 0.75 \cdot x$$
$$0.10 = 0.25x$$
$$x = \frac{0.10}{0.25}$$
$$x = 0.40$$

The correct answer is choice **d**.

63. Let H be the event "patient has high blood pressure,"
N be the event "patient has normal blood pressure
L be the event "patient has low blood pressure,"
R be the event "patient has a regular heartbeat,"
and I be the event "patient has an irregular heartbeat.

We wish to determine $P(R \cap L)$.

Statement (i) tells us $P(H) = 0.14$ and statement (ii) tells us $P(L) = 0.22$. Therefore,

$$P(H) + P(N) + P(L) = 1$$
$$0.14 + P(N) + 0.22 = 1$$
$$P(N) = 0.64.$$

Statement (iii) tells us $P(I) = 0.15$. This and statement (iv) lead to

$$P(I \cap H) = \frac{1}{3}P(I) = \frac{1}{3}(0.15) = 0.05.$$

Statement (v) tells us

$$P(N \cap I) = \frac{1}{8}P(N) = \frac{1}{3}(0.64) = 0.08.$$

Make a table and fill in the data just found.

	H	N	L	Totals
R	—	—	—	—
I	0.05	0.08	—	0.15
Totals	0.14	0.64	0.22	1.00

To determine $P(R \cap L)$, we need to find only $P(I \cap L)$.

$$P(I) = P(I \cap H) + P(I \cap N) + P(I \cap L)$$
$$0.15 = 0.05 + 0.08 + P(I \cap L)$$
$$0.15 = 0.13 + P(I \cap L)$$
$$P(I \cap L) = 0.02$$

Now calculate $P(R \cap L)$.

$$P(L) = P(R \cap L) + P(I \cap L)$$
$$0.22 = P(R \cap L) + 0.02$$
$$P(I \cap L) = 0.20$$

The correct answer choice is **e**.

64. **(a)** $P(\text{letter is in drawer 1}) = 0.1$

(b) $P(\text{letter is in drawer 2}|\text{letter is not in drawer 1})$

$$= \frac{0.1}{0.9} \approx 0.1111$$

(c) $P(\text{letter is in drawer 3}|\text{letter is not in drawer 1 or 2})$

$$= \frac{0.1}{0.8} = 0.125$$

(d) $P(\text{letter is in drawer 8}|\text{letter is not in drawers 1 through 7})$

$$= \frac{0.1}{0.3} \approx 0.3333$$

(e) The probability is increasing.

(f) $P(\text{letter is in some drawer}) = 0.8$

(g) $P(\text{letter is in some drawer}|\text{not in drawer 1})$

$$= \frac{0.7}{0.9} \approx 0.7777$$

(h) $P(\text{letter is in some drawer}|\text{not in drawer 1 or 2})$

$$= \frac{0.6}{0.8} = 0.75$$

(i) $P(\text{letter is in some drawer}|\text{not in drawers 1 through 7})$

$$= \frac{0.1}{0.3} \approx 0.3333$$

(j) The probability is decreasing.

65. **(a)** Since only 1 of the 2000 substances results in a marketable drug,

$P(\text{compound survives and becomes marketable})$

$$= \frac{1}{2000} = 0.0005.$$

(b) 1999 out of every 2000 compounds fail to get to market, so the probability of failure is

$$\frac{1999}{2000} = 0.9995.$$

(c) The probability that any one compound does *not* produce a marketable drug is $\frac{1999}{2000}$. If there are "a" compounds and we assume independence,

$$P(\text{none produces a marketable drug}) = \left(\frac{1999}{2000}\right)^a.$$

(d) This is the complement of the event in part (c). The probability that at least one of the drugs will prove marketable is

$$1 - \left(\frac{1999}{2000}\right)^a.$$

(e) For each scientist, $P(\text{none of } c \text{ compounds produces marketable drug})$

$$= \left(\frac{1999}{2000}\right)^c.$$

However, there are N scientists. Thus,

$P(\text{no marketable drug will be discovered in a year})$

$$= \left[\left(\frac{1999}{2000}\right)^c\right]^N$$

$$= \left(\frac{1999}{2000}\right)^{Nc}.$$

(f) This is the complement of the event in part (e), so the probability that at least one marketable drug will be discovered is

$$1 - \left(\frac{1999}{2000}\right)^{Nc},$$

where Nc is the number of drugs tested.

66. $P(A) = \frac{129}{576} = \frac{43}{192}$

67. $P(C|F) = \frac{n(C \cap F)}{n(F)} = \frac{7}{229}$

68. $P(A|H) = \frac{95}{347}$

69. $P(B'|H') = P((A \cup C \cup D)|F)$

$$= \frac{n((A \cup C \cup D) \cap F)}{n(F)}$$

$$= \frac{34 + 7 + 150}{229}$$

$$= \frac{191}{229}$$

70. No, $P(A) \neq P(A|H)$.

71. Draw the tree diagram.

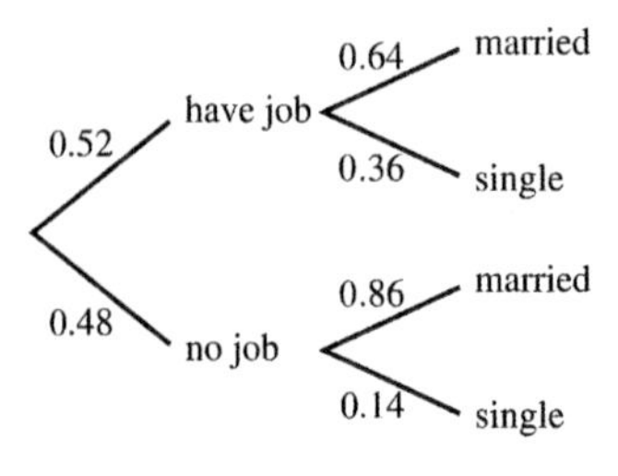

(a) $P(\text{married}) = P(\text{job and married}) + P(\text{no job and married})$
$= 0.52(0.64) + 0.48(0.86) = 0.3328 + 0.4128 = 0.7456$

(b) $P(\text{job and single}) = 0.52(0.36) = 0.1872$

72. **(a)** $P(\text{forecast of rain}|\text{rain}) = \dfrac{66}{80} = 0.825 \approx 83\%$

$P(\text{forecast of no rain}|\text{no rain}) = \dfrac{764}{920} \approx 0.83 \approx 83\%$

(b) $P(\text{rain}|\text{forecast of rain}) = \dfrac{66}{222} \approx 0.2973$

(c) $P(\text{no rain}|\text{forecast of no rain}) = \dfrac{764}{778} \approx 0.9820$

73. **(a)** In this exercise, it is easier to work with complementary events. Let E be the event "at least one of the faults erupts." Then the complementary event E' is "none of the faults erupts," and we can use $P(E) = 1 - P(E')$. Consider the event E': "none of the faults erupts." This means "the first fault does not erupt and the second fault does not erupt and. . .and the seventh fault does not erupt." Letting F_i denote the event "the ith fault erupts," we wish to find

$$P(E') = P(F_1' \cap F_2' \cap F_3' \cap F_4' \cap F_5' \cap F_6' \cap F_7').$$

Since we are assuming the events are independent, we have

$$\begin{aligned} P(E') &= P(F_1' \cap F_2' \cap F_3' \cap F_4' \cap F_5' \cap F_6' \cap F_7') \\ &= P(F_1') \cdot P(F_2') \cdot P(F_3') \cdot P(F_4') \cdot P(F_5') \cdot P(F_6') \cdot P(F_7') \end{aligned}$$

Now use $P(F_i') = 1 - P(F_i)$ and perform the calculations.

$$\begin{aligned} P(E') &= P(F_1') \cdot P(F_2') \cdot P(F_3') \cdot P(F_4') \cdot P(F_5') \cdot P(F_6') \cdot P(F_7') \\ &= (1 - 0.27) \cdot (1 - 0.21) \cdot \ldots \cdot (1 - 0.03) \\ &= (0.73)(0.79)(0.89)(0.90)(0.96)(0.97)(0.97) \\ &\approx 0.42 \end{aligned}$$

Therefore,

$$\begin{aligned} P(E) &= 1 - P(E') \\ &\approx 1 - 0.42 \\ &\approx 0.58. \end{aligned}$$

74. $P(\text{component fails}) = 0.03$

(a) Let n represent the number of these components to be connected in parallel; that is, the component has $n - 1$ backup components.

$P(\text{at least one component works})$

$= 1 - P(\text{no component works})$
$= 1 - P(\text{all } n \text{ components fail})$
$= 1 - (0.03)^n$

If this probability is to be at least 0.999999, then

$$\begin{aligned} 1 - (0.03)^n &\geq 0.999999 \\ -(0.03)^n &\geq -0.000001 \\ (0.03)^n &\leq 0.000001, \end{aligned}$$

and the smallest whole number value of n for which this inequality holds true is $n = 4$. Therefore, $4 - 1 = 3$ backup components must be used.

75. **(a)** $P(\text{second class}) = \dfrac{357}{1316} \approx 0.2713$

(b) $P(\text{surviving}) = \dfrac{499}{1316} \approx 0.3792$

(c) $P(\text{surviving}|\text{first class}) = \dfrac{203}{325} \approx 0.6246$

(d) $P(\text{surviving}|\text{child and third class}) = \dfrac{27}{79} \approx 0.3418$

(e) $P(\text{woman}|\text{first class and survived}) = \dfrac{140}{203} \approx 0.6897$

(f) $P(\text{third class}|\text{man and survived}) = \dfrac{75}{146} \approx 0.5137$

(g) $P(\text{survived}|\text{man}) = \dfrac{146}{805} \approx 0.1814$

$\text{P}(\text{survived}|\text{man and third class}) = \dfrac{75}{462} \approx 0.1623$

No, the events are not independent.

76. The events are probably dependent, and the agent used the product rule for independent events.

77. First draw the tree diagram.

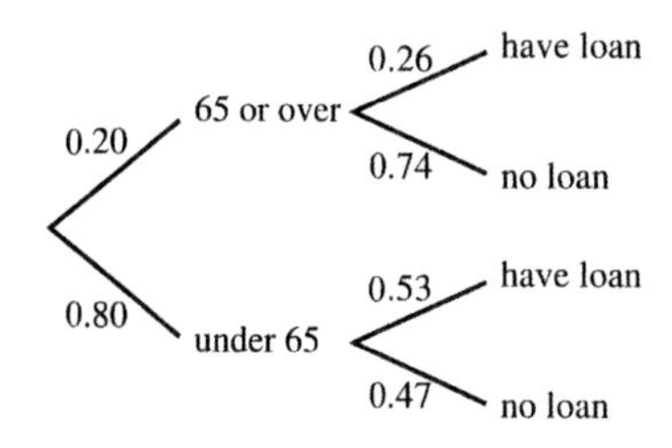

(a) $P(\text{person is 65 or over and has a loan}) = P(\text{65 or over}) \cdot P(\text{has loan}|\text{65 or over}) = 0.20(0.26) = 0.052$

(b) $P(\text{person has a loan}) = P(\text{65 or over and has loan}) + P(\text{under 65 and has loan})$
$= 0.20(0.26) + 0.80(0.53)$
$= 0.052 + 0.424$
$= 0.476$

78.

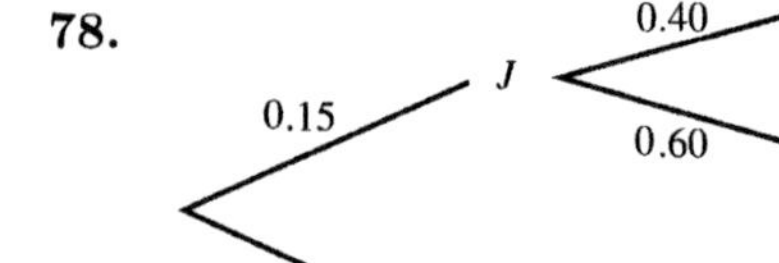

From the tree diagram, we see that the probability that an individual from the community is

(a) a woman jogger is $0.15(0.40) = 0.060$;

(b) not a jogger is 0.85;

(c) a woman is

$$0.15(0.40) + 0.85(0.55) = 0.06 + 0.4675 = 0.5275.$$

(d) The two events "woman" and "jogger" are independent if

$$P(\text{woman jogger}) = P(\text{woman}) \cdot P(\text{jogger}).$$

We are given that $P(\text{jogger}) = 0.15$ so that

$$P(\text{woman}) \cdot P(\text{jogger}) = 0.5275 \cdot 0.15 \approx 0.079$$

but we found $P(\text{woman jogger}) = 0.060$ in part (a). Therefore, the events are not independent.

79.

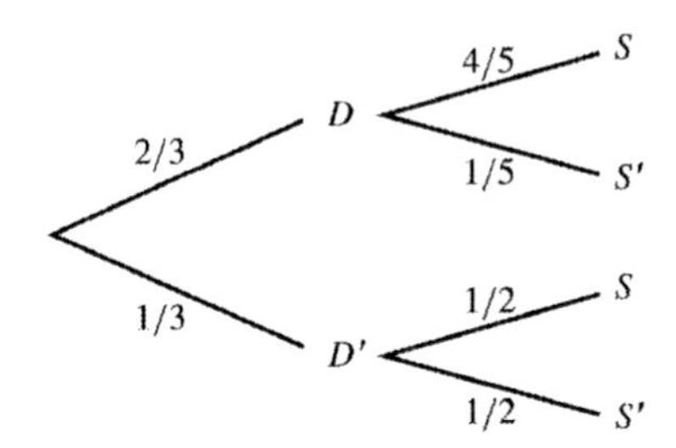

From the tree diagram, we see that the probability that a person

(a) drinks diet soft drinks is

$$\frac{2}{3}\left(\frac{4}{5}\right) + \frac{1}{3}\left(\frac{1}{2}\right) = \frac{8}{15} + \frac{1}{6}$$
$$= \frac{21}{30} = \frac{7}{10};$$

(b) diets, but does not drink diet soft drinks is

$$\frac{2}{3}\left(\frac{1}{5}\right) = \frac{2}{15}.$$

80. First draw the tree diagram.

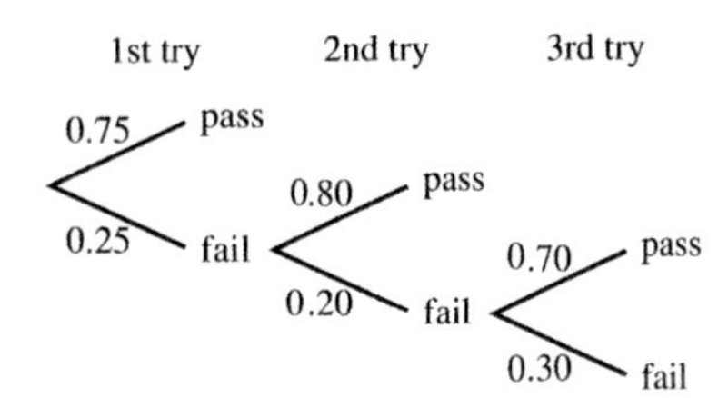

(a) $P(\text{fails both 1st and 2nd tests})$

$= P(\text{fails 1st}) \cdot P(\text{fails 2nd}|\text{fails 1st})$
$= 0.25(0.20)$
$= 0.05$

(b) $P(\text{fails three times in a row})$
$= 0.25(0.20)(0.30)$
$= 0.015$

(c) $P(\text{requires at least 2 tries})$
$= P(\text{does not pass on 1st try})$
$= 0.25$

81. Let F_i be the event "the ith burner fails." The event "all four burners fail" is equivalent to the event "the first burner fails <u>and</u> the second burner fails <u>and</u> the third burner fails <u>and</u> the fourth burner fails"—that is, the event $F_1 \cap F_2 \cap F_3 \cap F_4$. We are told that the burners are independent. Therefore

$$\begin{aligned} P(F_1 \cap F_2 \cap F_3 \cap F_4) &= P(F_1) \cdot P(F_2) \cdot P(F_3) \cdot P(F_4) \\ &= (0.001)(0.001)(0.001)(0.001) \\ &= 0.000000000001 = 10^{-12}. \end{aligned}$$

82. First draw a tree diagram.

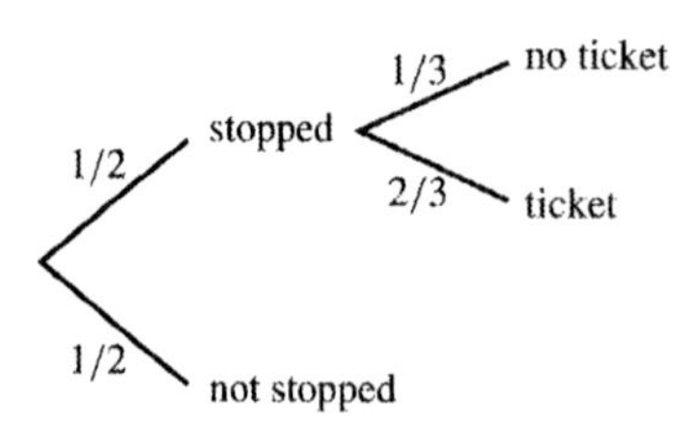

(a) $P(\text{no ticket}) = \frac{1}{2}\left(\frac{1}{3}\right) + \frac{1}{2} = \frac{2}{3}$

(b) $P(\text{no ticket on three consecutive weekends})$

$$= \frac{2}{3} \cdot \frac{2}{3} \cdot \frac{2}{3} = \frac{8}{27}$$

83. $P(\text{luxury car}) = 0.04$ and $P(\text{luxury car}|\text{CPA}) = 0.17$

Use the formal definition of independent events. Since these probabilities are not equal, the events are not independent.

84. Let A be the event "student studies" and B be the event "student gets a good grade." We are told that $P(A) = 0.6$, $P(B) = 0.7$, and $P(A \cap B) = 0.52$.

$$P(A) \cdot P(B) = 0.6(0.7) = 0.42$$

(a) Since $P(A) \cdot P(B)$ is not equal to $P(A \cap B)$, A and B are not independent. Rather, they are dependent events.

(b) Let A be the event "a student studies" and B be the event "the student gets a good grade." Then

$$P(B|A) = \frac{P(B \cap A)}{P(A)} = \frac{0.52}{0.6} \approx 0.87.$$

(c) Let A be the event "a student gets a good grade" and B be the event "the student studied." Then

$$P(B|A) = \frac{P(B \cap A)}{P(A)} = \frac{0.52}{0.7} \approx 0.74.$$

85. (a)

1-point kick after first TD | 2-point conversion after second TD | Outcome

k → 1: r → 2, win; $1 - r$ → 0, lose

$1 - k$ → 0: r → 2, tie; $1 - r$ → 0, lose

From the tree diagram,

$$\begin{aligned} P(\text{win}) &= kr, \\ P(\text{tie}) &= (1-k)r, \\ P(\text{lose}) &= k(1-r) + (1-k)(1-r) \\ &= k - kr + 1 - r - k + kr \\ &= 1 - r. \end{aligned}$$

(b)

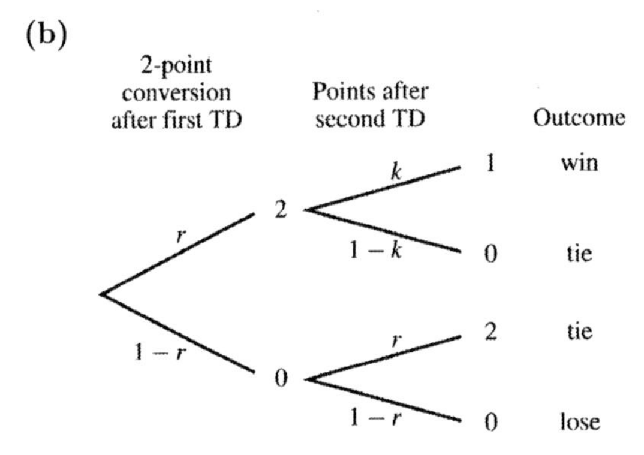

From the tree diagram,

$$\begin{aligned} P(\text{win}) &= rk, \\ P(\text{tie}) &= r(1-k) + (1-r)r \\ &= r - rk + r - r^2 \\ &= 2r - rk - r^2 \\ &= r(2-k-r), \\ P(\text{lose}) &= (1-r)(1-r) \\ &= (1-r)^2. \end{aligned}$$

(c) $P(\text{win})$ is the same under both strategies.

(d) If $r < 1$, $(1-r) > (1-r)^2$. The probability of losing is smaller for the 2-point first strategy.

7.6 Bayes' Theorem

1. Use Bayes' theorem with two possibilities M and M'.

$$\begin{aligned} P(M|N) &= \frac{P(M) \cdot P(N|M)}{P(M) \cdot P(N|M) + P(M') \cdot P(N|M')} \\ &= \frac{0.4(0.3)}{0.4(0.3) + 0.6(0.4)} \\ &= \frac{0.12}{0.12 + 0.24} \\ &= \frac{0.12}{0.36} = \frac{12}{36} = \frac{1}{3} \end{aligned}$$

2. By Bayes' theorem,

$$\begin{aligned} P(M'|N) &= 1 - P(M|N) \\ &= 1 - \frac{P(M) \cdot P(N|M)}{P(M) \cdot P(N|M) + P(M') \cdot P(N|M')} \\ &= 1 - \frac{0.4(0.3)}{0.4(0.3) + 0.6(0.4)} \\ &= 1 - \frac{0.12}{0.12 + 0.24} \\ &= 1 - \frac{1}{3} = \frac{2}{3}. \end{aligned}$$

3. Using Bayes' theorem,

$$\begin{aligned} P(R_1|Q) &= \frac{P(R_1) \cdot P(Q|R_1)}{P(R_1) \cdot P(Q|R_1) + P(R_2) \cdot P(Q|R_2) + P(R_3) \cdot P(Q|R_3)} \\ &= \frac{0.15(0.40)}{(0.15)(0.40) + 0.55(0.20) + 0.30(0.70)} \\ &= \frac{0.06}{0.38} = \frac{6}{38} = \frac{3}{19}. \end{aligned}$$

4. Using Bayes' theorem,

$$\begin{aligned} P(R_2|Q) &= \frac{P(R_2) \cdot P(Q|R_2)}{P(R_1) \cdot P(Q|R_1) + P(R_2) \cdot P(Q|R_2) + P(R_3) \cdot P(Q|R_3)} \\ &= \frac{0.55(0.20)}{(0.15)(0.40) + 0.55(0.20) + 0.30(0.70)} \\ &= \frac{0.11}{0.38} = \frac{11}{38}. \end{aligned}$$

5. Using Bayes' theorem,

$$\begin{aligned} P(R_3|Q) &= \frac{P(R_3) \cdot P(Q|R_3)}{P(R_1) \cdot P(Q|R_1) + P(R_2) \cdot P(Q|R_2) + P(R_3) \cdot P(Q|R_3)} \\ &= \frac{0.30(0.70)}{(0.15)(0.40) + 0.55(0.20) + 0.30(0.70)} \\ &= \frac{0.21}{0.38} = \frac{21}{38}. \end{aligned}$$

6. This is the complement of the event in Exercise 3, so

$$\begin{aligned} P(R_1{}'|Q) &= 1 - P(R_1|Q) \\ &= 1 - \frac{3}{19} = \frac{16}{19}. \end{aligned}$$

7. We first draw the tree diagram and determine the probabilities as indicated below.

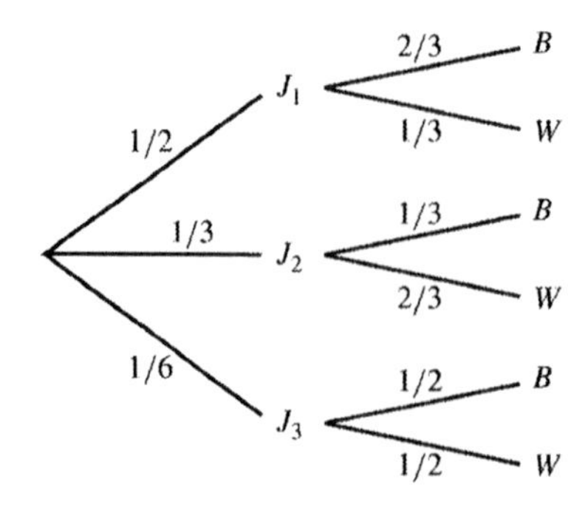

We want to determine the probability that if a white ball is drawn, it came from the second jar. This is $P(J_2|W)$. Use Bayes' theorem.

$$P(J_2|W) = \frac{P(J_2) \cdot P(W|J_2)}{P(J_2) \cdot P(W|J_2) + P(J_1) \cdot P(W|J_1) + P(J_3) \cdot P(W|J_3)} = \frac{\frac{1}{3} \cdot \frac{2}{3}}{\frac{1}{3} \cdot \frac{2}{3} + \frac{1}{2} \cdot \frac{1}{3} + \frac{1}{6} \cdot \frac{1}{2}}$$

$$= \frac{\frac{2}{9}}{\frac{2}{9} + \frac{1}{6} + \frac{1}{12}} = \frac{\frac{2}{9}}{\frac{17}{36}} = \frac{8}{17}$$

8. $$P(J_3|W) = \frac{P(J_3) \cdot P(W|J_3)}{P(J_1)P(W|J_1) + P(J_2)P(W|J_2) + P(J_3)P(W|J_3)} = \frac{\frac{1}{6} \cdot \frac{1}{2}}{\frac{1}{2} \cdot \frac{1}{3} + \frac{1}{3} \cdot \frac{2}{3} + \frac{1}{6} \cdot \frac{1}{2}} = \frac{\frac{1}{12}}{\frac{1}{6} + \frac{2}{9} + \frac{1}{12}} = \frac{3}{17}$$

9. Let G represent "good worker," B represent "bad worker," S represent "pass the test," and F represent "fail the test." The given information if $P(G) = 0.70$, $P(B) = P(G') = 0.30$, $P(S|G) = 0.85$ (and therefore $P(F|G) = 0.15$), and $P(S|B) = 0.35$ (and therefore $P(F|B) = 0.65$). If passing the test is made a requirement for employment, then the percent of the new hires that will turn out to be good workers is

$$P(G|S) = \frac{P(G) \cdot P(S|G)}{P(G) \cdot P(S|G) + P(B) \cdot P(S|B)}$$
$$= \frac{0.70(0.85)}{0.70(0.85) + 0.30(0.35)}$$
$$= \frac{0.595}{0.700}$$
$$= 0.85.$$

85% of new hires become good workers.

10. Let Q be the event "person is qualified" and A be the event "person was approved." Set up a tree diagram.

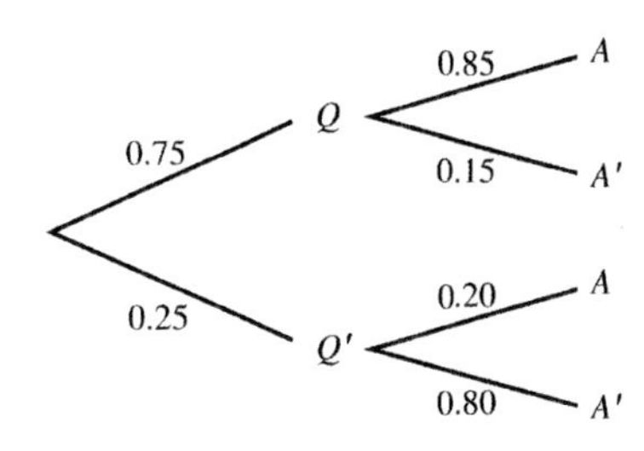

Using Bayes' theorem,

$$P(Q|A) = \frac{P(Q) \cdot P(A|Q)}{P(Q) \cdot P(A|Q) + P(Q') \cdot P(A|Q')}$$
$$= \frac{0.75(0.85)}{0.75(0.85) + 0.25(0.20)}$$
$$= \frac{0.6375}{0.6875} = \frac{6375}{6875}$$
$$= \frac{51}{55} \approx 0.9273$$

11. Let Q represent "qualified" and A represent "approved by the manager." Set up the tree diagram.

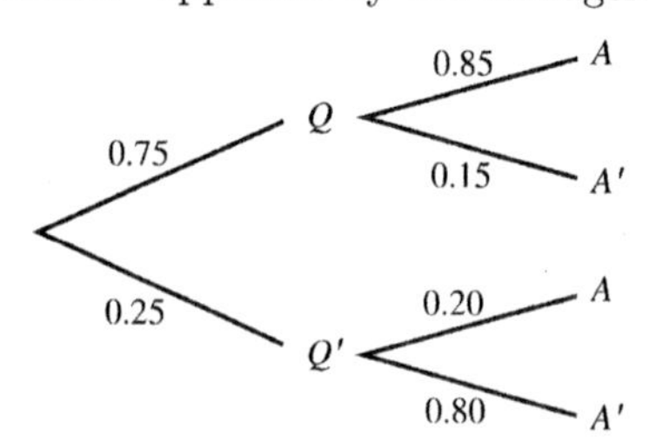

$$P(Q'|A) = \frac{P(Q') \cdot P(A|Q')}{P(Q) \cdot P(A|Q) + P(Q') \cdot P(A|Q')}$$

$$= \frac{0.25(0.20)}{0.75(0.85) + 0.25(0.20)}$$

$$= \frac{0.05}{0.6875} = \frac{4}{55} \approx 0.0727$$

12. Let A be the event "the bag came from supplier A," B be the event "the bag came from supplier B," and D be the event "the bag is damaged." Set up a tree diagram.

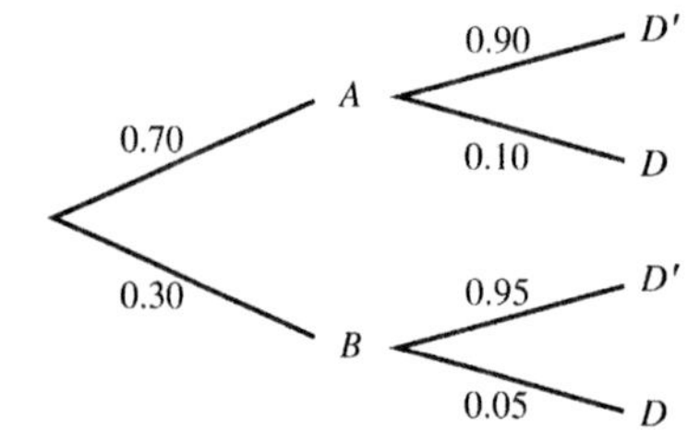

$$P(A|D) = \frac{P(A) \cdot P(D|A)}{P(A) \cdot P(D|A) + P(B) \cdot P(D|B)}$$

$$= \frac{0.70(0.10)}{0.70(0.10) + 0.30(0.05)}$$

$$= \frac{0.070}{0.085} \approx 0.8235$$

13. Let D represent "damaged," A represent "from supplier A, " and B represent "from supplier B." Set up the tree diagram.

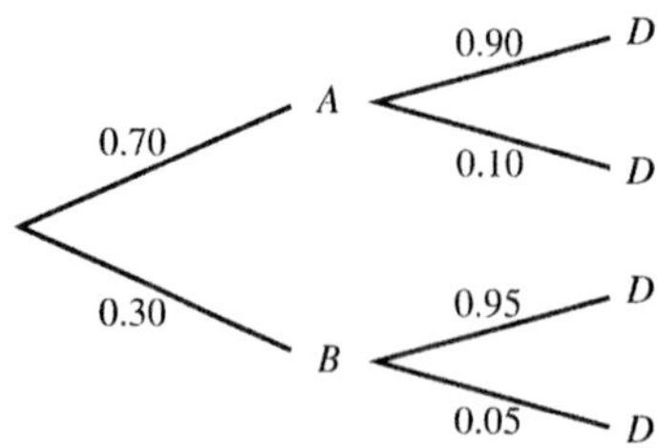

$$P(B|D) = \frac{P(B) \cdot P(D|B)}{P(B) \cdot P(D|B) + P(A) \cdot P(D|A)}$$

$$= \frac{0.30(0.05)}{0.30(0.05) + 0.70(0.10)}$$

$$= \frac{0.015}{0.015 + 0.07}$$

$$= \frac{0.015}{0.085} \approx 0.1765$$

14. Let D be the event "a defective appliance" and A be the event "appliance manufactured by company A." Start with a tree diagram, where the first stage refers to the companies and the second to defective appliances.

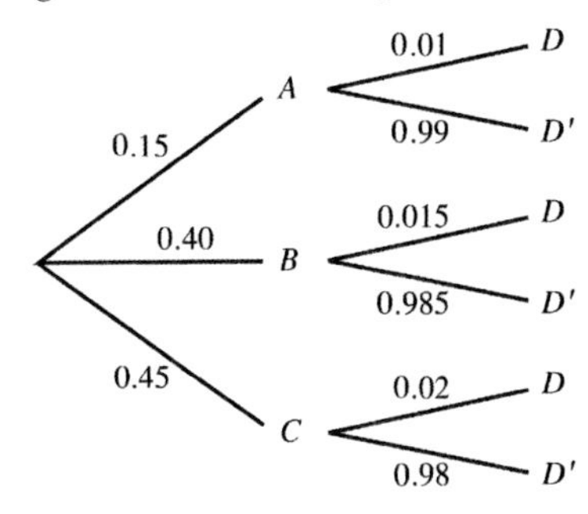

From Bayes' theorem, we have

$$P(A|D) = \frac{P(A) \cdot P(D|A)}{P(A) \cdot P(D|A) + P(B) \cdot P(D|B) + P(C) \cdot P(D|C)}$$

$$= \frac{0.0015}{0.0015 + 0.006 + 0.009} = \frac{0.0015}{0.0165} \approx 0.0909.$$

15. Start with the tree diagram, where the first state refers to the companies and the second to a defective appliance.

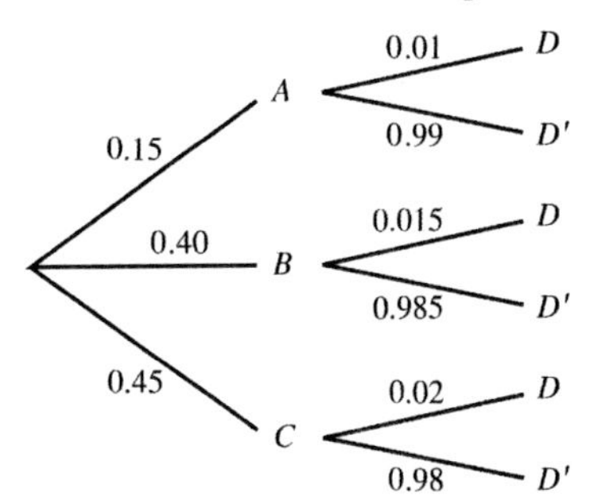

$$P(B|D) = \frac{P(B) \cdot P(D|B)}{P(A) \cdot P(D|A) + P(B) \cdot P(D|B) + P(C) \cdot P(D|C)}$$

$$= \frac{0.40(0.015)}{0.15(0.01) + 0.40(0.015) + 0.45(0.02)} = \frac{0.0060}{0.0165} \approx 0.3636$$

16. Let H be the event "high rating," F_1 be the event "sponsors college game," F_2 be the event "sponsors baseball game," and F_3 be the event "sponsors pro football game." First set up a tree diagram.

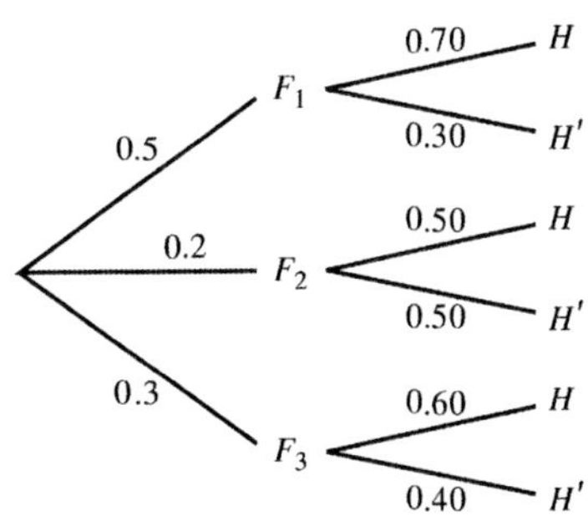

Now use Bayes' theorem.

$$P(F_1|H) = \frac{P(F_1) \cdot P(H|F_1)}{P(F_1)P(H|F_1) + P(F_2)P(H|F_2) + P(F_3)P(H|F_3)}$$

$$= \frac{0.5(0.70)}{0.5(0.70) + 0.2(0.50) + 0.3(0.60)} = \frac{0.35}{0.63} = \frac{5}{9}$$

17. Let H represent "high rating," F_1 represent "sponsors college game," F_2 represent "sponsors baseball game," and F_3 represent "sponsors pro football game."

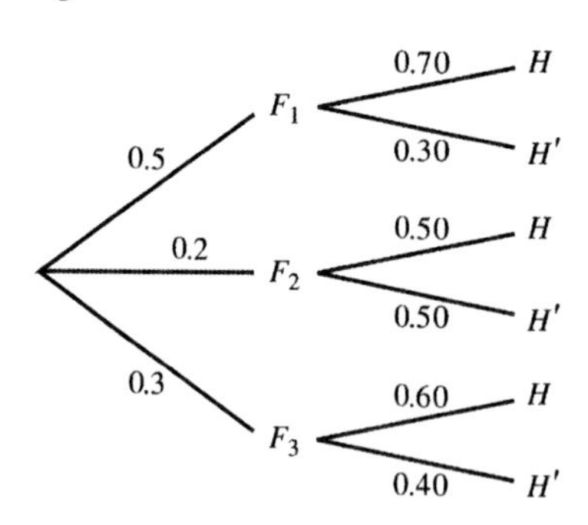

$$\begin{aligned} P(F_3|H) &= \frac{P(F_3)\cdot P(H|F_3)}{P(F_1)\cdot P(H|F_1)+P(F_2)\cdot P(H|F_2)+P(F_3)\cdot P(H|F_3)} \\ &= \frac{0.3(0.60)}{0.5(0.70)+0.2(0.50)+0.3(0.60)} \\ &= \frac{0.18}{0.35+0.10+0.18} \\ &= \frac{0.18}{0.63} = \frac{18}{63} = \frac{2}{7} \end{aligned}$$

18. Let A represent "driver is 16–20,"
B represent "driver is 21–30,"
C represent "driver is 31–65,"
D represent "driver is 66–99,"
and E represent "driver has an accident."

We wish to find $P(A|E)$.

$$\begin{aligned} P(A|E) &= \frac{P(A)\cdot P(E|A)}{P(A)\cdot P(E|A)+P(B)\cdot P(E|B)+P(C)\cdot P(E|C)+P(D)\cdot P(E|D)} \\ &= \frac{0.08(0.06)}{0.08(0.06)+0.15(0.03)+0.49(0.02)+0.28(0.04)} \\ &= \frac{0.0048}{0.0303} \\ &\approx 0.16 \end{aligned}$$

The correct choice is **b**.

19. Using the given information, construct a table similar to the one in the previous exercise.

Category of Policyholder	Portion of Policyholders	Probability of Dying in the Next Year
Standard	0.50	0.010
Preferred	0.40	0.005
Ultra-preferred	0.10	0.001

Let S represent "standard policyholder,"
R represent "preferred policyholder,"
U represent "ultra-preferred policyholder,"
and D represent "policyholder dies in the next year."

We wish to find $P(U|D)$.

$$\begin{aligned} P(U|D) &= \frac{P(U) \cdot P(D|U)}{P(S) \cdot P(D|S) + P(R) \cdot P(D|R) + P(U) \cdot P(D|U)} \\ &= \frac{0.10(0.001)}{0.50(0.010) + 0.40(0.005) + 0.10(0.001)} \\ &= \frac{0.0001}{0.0071} \\ &\approx 0.141 \end{aligned}$$

The correct answer choice is **d**.

20. Let T represent "driver is a teen,"
Y represent "driver is a young adult,"
M represent "driver is in midlife,"
S represent "driver is a senior,"
and C represent "driver has been involved in at least one collision in the past year."

We wish to find $P(Y|C)$.

$$\begin{aligned} P(Y|C) &= \frac{P(Y) \cdot P(C|Y)}{P(T) \cdot P(C|T) + P(Y) \cdot P(C|Y) + P(M) \cdot P(C|M) + P(S) \cdot P(C|S)} \\ &= \frac{0.16(0.08)}{0.08(0.15) + 0.16(0.08) + 0.45(0.04) + 0.31(0.05)} \\ &= \frac{0.0128}{0.0583} \\ &\approx 0.22 \end{aligned}$$

The correct choice is **d**.

21. Let L be the event "the object was shipped by land," A be the event "the object was shipped by air," S be the event "the object was shipped by sea," and E be the event "an error occurred."

$$\begin{aligned} P(L|E) &= \frac{P(L) \cdot P(E|L)}{P(L) \cdot P(E|L) + P(A) \cdot P(E|A) + P(S) \cdot P(E|S)} \\ &= \frac{0.50(0.02)}{0.50(0.02) + 0.40(0.04) + 0.10(0.14)} \\ &= \frac{0.0100}{0.0400} = 0.25 \end{aligned}$$

The correct response is **c**.

22. There are a total of

$$1260 + 700 + 560 + 280 = 2800$$

mortgages being studied at the bank.

(a) $$\begin{aligned} P(5\% \text{ down}|\text{default}) &= \frac{0.05\left(\frac{1260}{2800}\right)}{0.05\left(\frac{1260}{2800}\right) + 0.03\left(\frac{700}{2800}\right) + 0.02\left(\frac{560}{2800}\right) + 0.01\left(\frac{280}{2800}\right)} \\ &= \frac{0.05(0.45)}{0.05(0.45) + 0.03(0.25) + 0.02(0.2) + 0.01(0.1)} \\ &= \frac{0.0225}{0.0225 + 0.0075 + 0.004 + 0.001} = \frac{0.0225}{0.035} \approx 0.643 \end{aligned}$$

(b) A mortgage being paid to maturity is the complement of a mortgage being defaulted.

$$\begin{aligned}P(10\%\text{ down}|\text{paid to maturity}) &= P(10\%\text{ down}|\text{not default})\\ &= \frac{0.97\left(\frac{700}{2800}\right)}{0.95\left(\frac{1260}{2800}\right)+0.97\left(\frac{700}{2800}\right)+0.98\left(\frac{560}{2800}\right)+0.99\left(\frac{280}{2800}\right)}\\ &= \frac{0.97(0.25)}{0.95(0.45)+0.97(0.25)+0.98(0.2)+0.99(0.1)}\\ &= \frac{0.2425}{0.4275+0.2425+0.196+0.099}=\frac{0.2425}{0.965}\approx 0.251\end{aligned}$$

23. Let E represent the event "hemoccult test is positive," and let F represent the event "has colorectal cancer." We are given

$$P(F) = 0.003, P(E|F) = 0.5, \text{ and } P(E|F') = 0.03$$

and we want to find $P(F|E)$. Since $P(F) = 0.003$, $P(F') = 0.997$. Therefore,

$$P(F|E) = \frac{P(F)\cdot P(E|F)}{P(F)\cdot P(E|F) + P(F')\cdot P(E|F')} = \frac{0.003\cdot 0.5}{0.003\cdot 0.5 + 0.997\cdot 0.03} \approx 0.0478.$$

24. Let H be the event "has hepatitis" and T be the event "positive test." First set up a tree diagram.

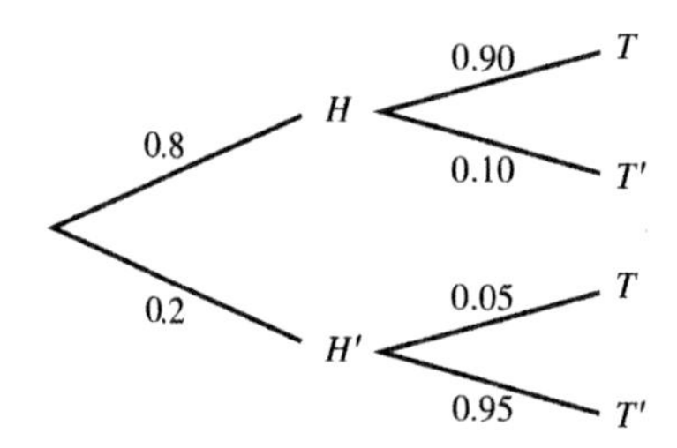

Using Bayes' theorem,

$$P(H|T) = \frac{P(H)\cdot P(T|H)}{P(H)\cdot P(T|H) + P(H')\cdot P(T|H')} = \frac{0.8(0.90)}{0.8(0.90)+0.2(0.05)} = \frac{0.72}{0.73} = \frac{72}{73} \approx 0.9863.$$

25. Draw a tree diagram.

0.54 T^+
0.02 D^+
0.46 T^-
0.06 T^+
0.98 D^-
0.94 T^-

(a) $P(D^+|T^+) = \dfrac{0.02(0.54)}{0.02(0.54)+0.98(0.06)} = \dfrac{0.0108}{0.0696} \approx 0.16$

(b) $P(D^-|T^-) = \dfrac{0.98(0.94)}{0.02(0.46)+0.98(0.94)} = \dfrac{0.9212}{0.9304} \approx 0.99$

(c) $P(D^- \cap T^+) = 0.98(0.06) = 0.0588$
$0.0588(1000) = 58.8$

We would expect about 59 false positives in 1000 examinations.

26. Let H be the event "has HIV" and T be the event "positive test." The problem asks for $P(H|T)$. Using the given values

$$P(H) = \frac{950{,}000}{491{,}000{,}000}$$

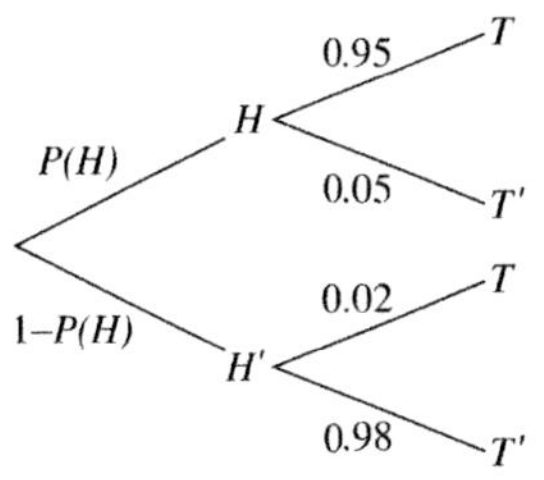

Using Bayes' Theorem,

$$P(H|T) = \frac{P(H)\cdot P(T|H)}{P(H)\cdot P(T|H) + P(H')\cdot P(T|H')} = \frac{\left(\frac{950{,}000}{491{,}000{,}000}\right)(0.95)}{\left(\frac{950{,}000}{491{,}000{,}000}\right)(0.95) + \left(1 - \frac{950{,}000}{491{,}000{,}000}\right)(0.02)} \approx 0.0843$$

27. (a) Let H represent "heavy smoker," L be "light smoker," N be "nonsmoker," and D be "person died." Let $x = P(D|N)$, that is, let x be the probability that a nonsmoker died. Then $P(D|L) = 2x$ and $P(D|H) = 4x$. Create a table.

Level of Smoking	Probability of Level	Probability of Death for Level
H	0.2	$4x$
L	0.3	$2x$
N	0.5	x

We wish to find $P(H|D)$.

$$\begin{aligned} P(H|D) &= \frac{P(H)\cdot P(D|H)}{P(H)\cdot P(D|H) + P(L)\cdot P(D|L) + P(N)\cdot P(D|N)} \\ &= \frac{0.2(4x)}{0.2(4x) + 0.3(2x) + 0.5(x)} \\ &= \frac{0.8x}{1.9x} \\ &\approx 0.42 \end{aligned}$$

The correct answer choice is **d**.

28. Let C represent "patient was critical," S be "patient was serious," T be "patient was stable," and V be "patient survived." We want to find $P(S|V)$.

The problem statement gives probabilities that a patient died in the emergency room, but we are interested in finding the probability that a patient survived. So convert the given probabilities to probabilities that a patient survived by find the probability of the complementary event, using the result

$$P(\text{category of patient}|\text{patient survived}) = 1 \text{ - } P(\text{category of patient}|\text{patient died})$$

and create a table as before.

Category of Patient	Probability of Category	Probability of Survival for Category
C	0.1	0.60
S	0.3	0.90
T	0.6	0.99

$$\begin{aligned} P(S|V) &= \frac{P(S) \cdot P(V|S)}{P(C) \cdot P(V|C) + P(S) \cdot P(V|S) + P(T) \cdot P(V|T)} \\ &= \frac{0.3(0.90)}{0.1(0.60) + 0.3(0.90) + 0.6(0.99)} \\ &= \frac{0.270}{0.924} \\ &\approx 0.29 \end{aligned}$$

The correct answer choice is **b**.

29. Let H represent "person has the disease" and R be "test indicates presence of the disease." We wish to determine $P(H|R)$.

Construct a table as before.

Category of Person	Portion of Population	Probability of Presence of Disease
H	0.01	0.950
H'	0.99	0.005

$$\begin{aligned} P(H|R) &= \frac{P(H) \cdot P(R|H)}{P(H) \cdot P(R|H) + P(H') \cdot P(R|H')} \\ &= \frac{0.01(0.950)}{0.01(0.950) + 0.99(0.005)} \\ &= \frac{0.00950}{0.01445} \\ &\approx 0.657 \end{aligned}$$

The correct answer choice is **b**.

30. Let H represent "male has a circulation problem" and S be "male is a smoker." We wish to determine $P(H|S)$.

Let x be the probability that the male is a smoker and construct a table as before.

Category of Male	Portion of Population	Probability of Being a Smoker
H	0.25	$2x$
H'	0.75	x

$$\begin{aligned} P(H|S) &= \frac{P(H) \cdot P(S|H)}{P(H) \cdot P(S|H) + P(H') \cdot P(S|H')} \\ &= \frac{0.25(2x)}{0.25(2x) + 0.75(x)} \\ &= \frac{0.50x}{1.25x} \\ &\approx \frac{2}{5} \end{aligned}$$

The correct answer choice is **c**.

31. Start with the tree diagram.

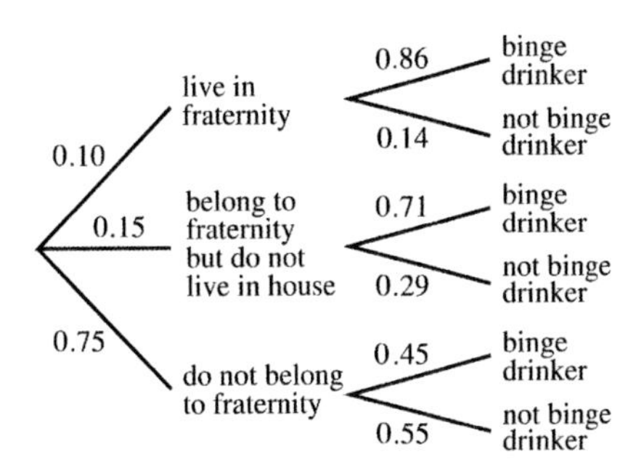

(a) $P(\text{binge drinker}) = 0.10(0.86) + 0.15(0.71) + 0.75(0.45) = 0.53$

(b) $P(\text{lives in fraternity}|\text{binge drinker}) = \dfrac{0.10(0.86)}{0.53} \approx 0.1623$

32. Let M be the event "wife was murdered" and G be the event "husband is guilty." Set up a tree diagram.

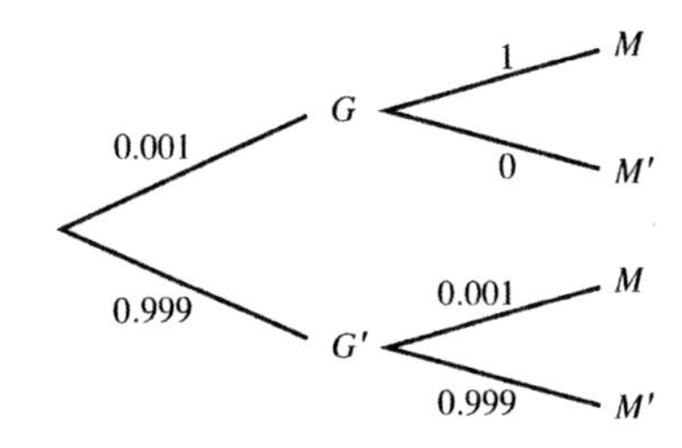

$$P(G|M) = \frac{P(G) \cdot P(M|G)}{P(G) \cdot P(M|G) + P(G') \cdot P(M|G')} = \frac{0.001(1)}{0.001(1) + 0.999(0.001)} \approx 0.500$$

33. $P(\text{between 35 and 44}|\text{never married})$

$$= \frac{0.212(0.195)}{0.135(0.0895) + 0.191(0.434) + 0.212(0.195) + 0.320(0.088) + 0.142(0.074)}$$

$$= \frac{0.041340}{0.283727}$$

$$\approx 0.1457$$

34. The event "has been married" is the complementary event of "never married" and the probabilities are found, for instance, as follows:

$$\begin{aligned} P(\text{has been married}|\text{between 18 and 24}) &= 1 - P(\text{never married}|\text{between 18 and 24}) \\ &= 1 - 0.806 = 0.194. \end{aligned}$$

Therefore,

$P(\text{between 18 and 24}|\text{has been married})$

$$= \frac{0.123(0.194)}{0.123(0.194) + 0.179(0.689) + 0.203(0.868) + 0.316(0.925) + 0.179(0.963)}$$

$$= \frac{0.023862}{0.788074}$$

$$\approx 0.0303$$

35. $P(\text{between 45 and 64}|\text{never married})$

$$= \frac{0.316(0.075)}{0.123(0.806) + 0.179(0.311) + 0.203(0.132) + 0.316(0.075) + 0.179(0.037)}$$

$$= \frac{0.023700}{0.211926}$$

$$\approx 0.1118$$

36. Set up a tree diagram.

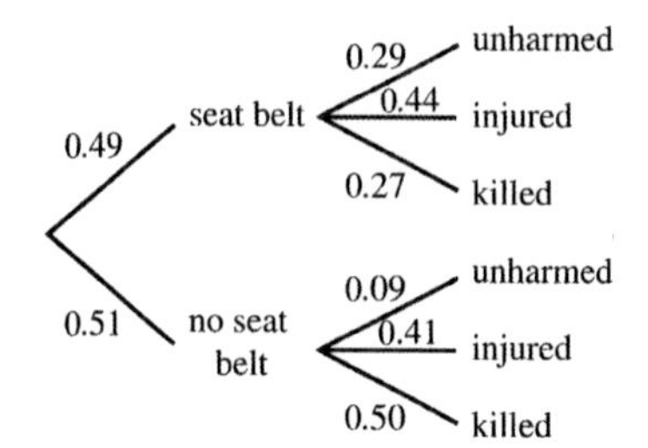

$$P(\text{killed}|\text{wore seat belt}) = \frac{0.49(0.27)}{0.49(0.27) + 0.51(0.50)} \approx 0.3416$$

37. Draw a tree diagram.

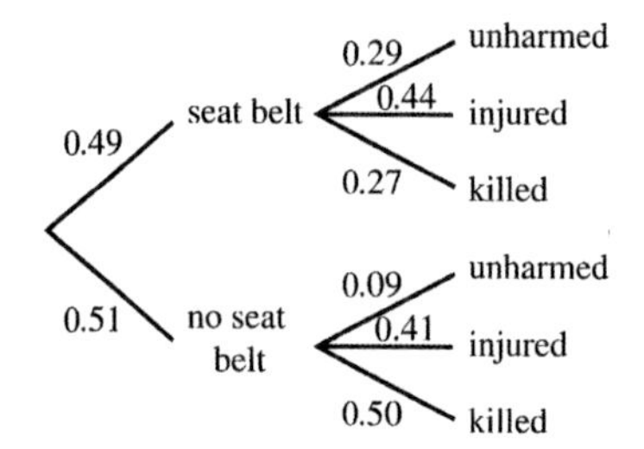

$$P(\text{not wearing seat belt}|\text{unharmed}) = \frac{0.51(0.09)}{0.49(0.29) + 0.51(0.09)} \approx 0.2441$$

38. $P(1997|\text{accident}) = \frac{0.16(0.05)}{0.16(0.05) + 0.18(0.02) + 0.20(0.03)}$

$$= \frac{0.0080}{0.0176}$$

$$\approx 0.45$$

The correct answer choice is **d.**

39.

Category	Proportion of Population	Probability of Being Picked Up
Has terrorist ties	$\frac{1}{1{,}000{,}000}$	0.99
Does not have terrorists ties	$\frac{999{,}999}{1{,}000{,}000}$	0.01

$$P(\text{Has terrorist ties}|\text{Picked up}) = \frac{\frac{1}{1{,}000{,}000}(0.99)}{\frac{1}{1{,}000{,}000}(0.99) + \frac{999{,}999}{1{,}000{,}000}(0.01)}$$

$$= \frac{\frac{1}{1{,}000{,}000}(0.99)}{\frac{1}{1{,}000{,}000}(0.99) + \frac{999{,}999}{1{,}000{,}000}(0.01)} \cdot \frac{1{,}000{,}000}{1{,}000{,}000}$$

$$= \frac{0.99}{10{,}000.98}$$

$$\approx 9.9 \times 10^{-5}$$

Chapter 7 Review Exercises

1. $9 \in \{8, 4, -3, -9, 6\}$

Since 9 is not an element of the set, this statement is false.

2. $4 \notin \{3, 9, 7\}$

Since 4 is not an element of the given set, the statement is true.

3. $2 \notin \{0, 1, 2, 3, 4\}$

Since 2 is an element of the set, this statement is false.

4. $0 \in \{0, 1, 2, 3, 4\}$

Since 0 is an element of the given set, the statement is true.

5. $\{3, 4, 5\} \subseteq \{2, 3, 4, 5, 6\}$

Every element of $\{3, 4, 5\}$ is an element of $\{2, 3, 4, 5, 6\}$, so this statement is true.

6. $\{1, 2, 5, 8\} \subseteq \{1, 2, 5, 10, 11\}$

Since 8 is an element of the first set but not of the second set, the first set cannot be a subset of the second. The statement is false.

7. $\{3, 6, 9, 10\} \subseteq \{3, 9, 11, 13\}$

10 is an element of $\{3, 6, 9, 10\}$, but 10 is not an element of $\{3, 9, 11, 13\}$. Therefore, $\{3, 6, 9, 10\}$ is not a subset of $\{3, 9, 11, 13\}$. The statement is false.

8. $\emptyset \subseteq \{1\}$

The empty set is a subset of every set, so the statement is true.

9. $\{2, 8\} \not\subseteq \{2, 4, 6, 8\}$

Since both 2 and 8 are elements of $\{2, 4, 6, 8\}$, $\{2, 8\}$ is a subset of $\{2, 4, 6, 8\}$. This statement is false.

10. $0 \subseteq \emptyset$

The empty set contains no elements and has no subsets except itself. Therefore, the statement is false.

In Exercises 11–20,

$$U = \{\text{a, b, c, d, e, f, g, h}\},$$
$$K = \{\text{c, d, e, f, h}\},$$
$$\text{and} \quad R = \{\text{a, c, d, g}\}.$$

11. K has 5 elements, so it has $2^5 = 32$ subsets.

12. $n(R) = 4$, so R has $2^4 = 16$ subsets.

13. K' (the complement of K) is the set of all elements of U that do *not* belong to K.

$$K' = \{\text{a, b, g}\}$$

14. $R' = \{\text{b, e, h}\}$ since these elements are in U but not in R.

15. $K \cap R$ (the intersection of K and R) is the set of all elements belonging to both set K and set R.

$$K \cap R = \{\text{c, d}\}$$

16. $K \cup R = \{\text{a, c, d, e, f, g, h}\}$ since these elements are in K or R, or both.

17. $(K \cap R)' = \{\text{a, b, e, f, g, h}\}$ since these elements are in U but not in $K \cap R$. (See Exercise 15.)

18. $(K \cup R)' = \{\text{b}\}$ since this element is in U but not in $K \cup R$. (*See* Exercise 16.)

19. $\emptyset' = U$

20. $U' = \emptyset$, which is always true.

21. $A \cap C$ is the set of all female employees in the K.O. Brown Company who are in the accounting department.

22. $B \cap D$ is the set of all sales employees who have MBA degrees.

23. $A \cup D$ is the set of all employees in the K.O. Brown Company who are in the accounting department *or* have MBA degrees.

24. $A' \cap D$ is the set of all employees with MBA degrees who are not in the accounting department.

25. $B' \cap C'$ is the set of all male employees who are not in the sales department.

26. $(B \cup C)'$ is the set of all employees who are not either in the sales department or female, that is, all male employees not in the sales department.

27. $A \cup B'$ is the set of all elements which belong to A or do not belong to B, or both.

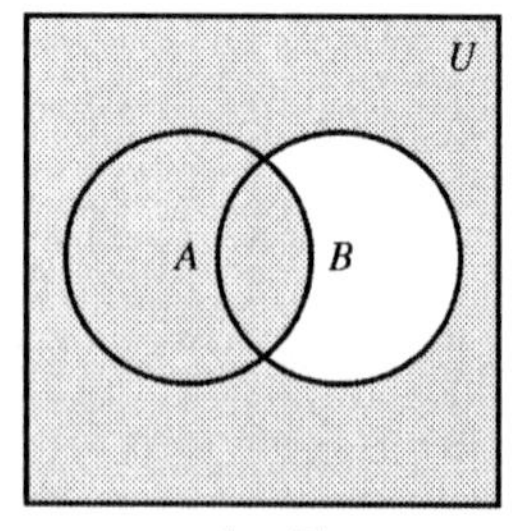

$A \cup B'$

28. $A' \cap B$ contains all elements in B and not in A.

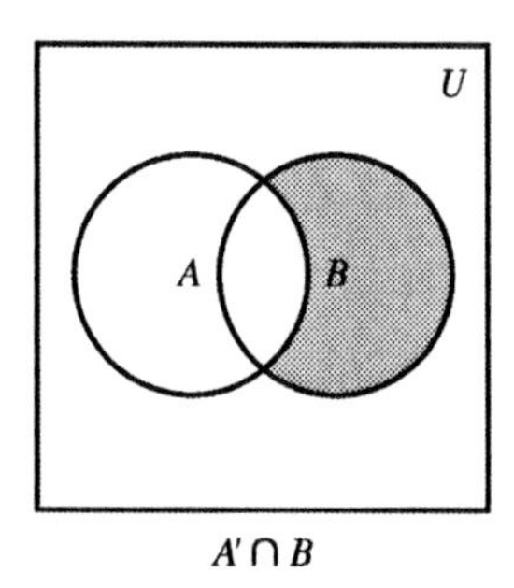

$A' \cap B$

29. $(A \cap B) \cup C$

First find $A \cap B$.

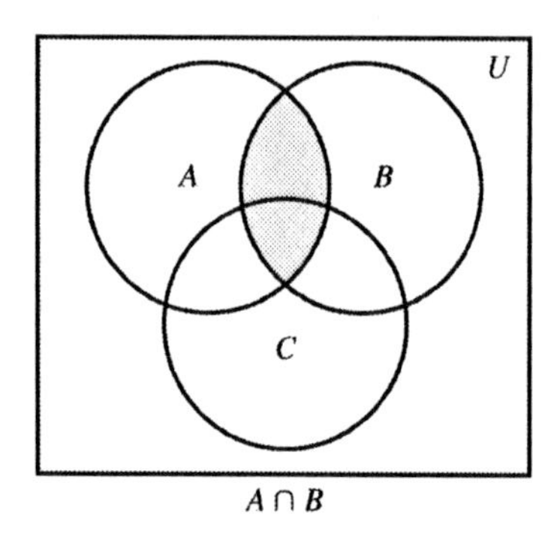

$A \cap B$

Now find the union of this region with C.

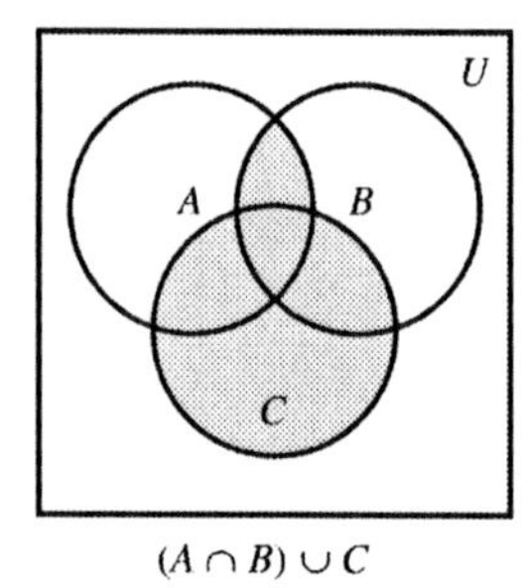

$(A \cap B) \cup C$

30. $(A \cup B)' \cap C$ includes those elements in C and not in either A or B.

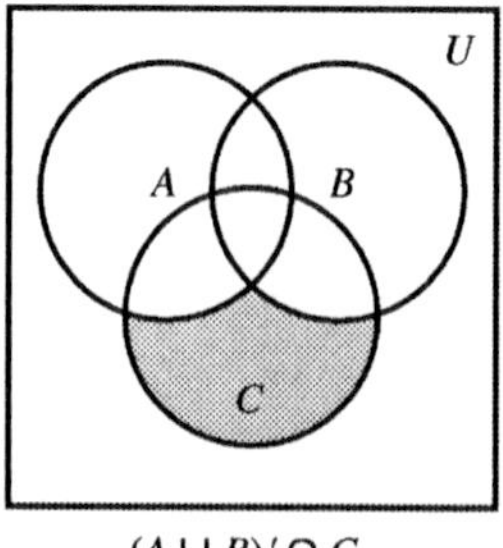

$(A \cup B)' \cap C$

31. The sample space for rolling a die is

$$S = \{1, 2, 3, 4, 5, 6\}.$$

32. $S = \{\text{ace}, 2, 3, 4, 5, 6, 7, 8, 9, 10, \text{J}, \text{Q}, \text{K}\}$

33. The sample space of the possible weights is

$$S = \{0, 0.5, 1, 1.5, 2, \ldots, 299.5, 300\}.$$

34. There are 16 possibilities.

$$S = \{HHHH, HHHT, HHTH, HTHH, THHH, HHTT, HTHT, HTTH, THHT, TTHH, THTH, HTTT, THTT, TTHT, TTTH, TTTT\}$$

35. The sample space consists of all ordered pairs (a, b) where a can be 3, 5, 7, 9, or 11, and b is either R (red) or G(green). Thus,

$$S = \{(3,\text{R}), (3,\text{G}), (5,\text{R}), (5,\text{G}), (7,\text{R}), (7,\text{G}), (9,\text{R}), (9,\text{G}), (11,\text{R}), (11,\text{G})\}.$$

36. Let R = red and G = green.

$$E = \{(7, R), (7, G), (9, R), (9, G), (11, R), (11, G)\}$$

37. The event F that the second ball is green is

$$F = \{(3,\text{G}), (5,\text{G}), (7,\text{G}), (9,\text{G}), (11,\text{G})\}.$$

38. The outcomes are not equally likely since there are more red than green balls. For example, $(7, R)$ is twice as likely as $(7, G)$.

39. There are 13 hearts out of 52 cards in a deck. Thus,

$$P(\text{heart}) = \frac{13}{52} = \frac{1}{4}.$$

40. There are 2 red queens out of 52 cards, so

$$P(\text{red queen}) = \frac{2}{52} = \frac{1}{26}.$$

41. There are 3 face cards in each suit (jack, queen, and king) and there are 4 suits, so there are $3 \cdot 4 = 12$ face cards out of the 52 cards. Thus,

$$P(\text{face card}) = \frac{12}{52} = \frac{3}{13}.$$

42. There are 26 black cards plus 6 red face cards, so

$$P(\text{black or a face card}) = \frac{32}{52} = \frac{8}{13}.$$

43. There are 4 queens of which 2 are red, so

$$\begin{aligned} P(\text{red}|\text{queen}) &= \frac{n(\text{red and queen})}{n(\text{queen})} \\ &= \frac{2}{4} = \frac{1}{2}. \end{aligned}$$

44. There are 12 face cards, of which 4 are jacks, so

$$P(\text{jack}|\text{face card}) = \frac{4}{12} = \frac{1}{3}.$$

45. There are 4 kings of which all 4 are face cards. Thus,

$$\begin{aligned} P(\text{face card}|\text{king}) &= \frac{n(\text{face card and king})}{n(\text{king})} \\ &= \frac{4}{4} = 1. \end{aligned}$$

50. Independent events are never mutually exclusive. If A and B are nonempty and independent, then

$$P(A \cap B) = P(A) \cdot P(B).$$

For mutually exclusive events, $P(A \cap B) = 0$, which would mean $P(A) = 0$ or $P(B) = 0$. This is impossible.

51. Marilyn vos Savant's answer is that the contestant should switch doors. To understand why, recall that the puzzle begins with the contestant choosing door 1 and then the host opening door 3 to reveal a goat. When the host opens door 3 and shows the goat, that does not affect the probability of the car being behind door 1; the contestant had a $\frac{1}{3}$ probability of being correct to begin with, and he still has a $\frac{1}{3}$ probability after the host opens door 3.

The contestant knew that the host would open another door regardless of what was behind door 1, so opening either other door gives no new information about door 1. The probability of the car being behind door 1 is still $\frac{1}{3}$; with the goat behind door 3, the only other place the car could be is behind door 2, so the probability that the car is behind door 2 is now $\frac{2}{3}$. By switching to door 2, the contestant can double his chances of winning the car.

52. Let C be the event "a club is drawn." There are 13 clubs in the deck, so $n(C) = 13$, $P(C) = \frac{13}{52} = \frac{1}{4}$, and $P(C') = 1 - P(C) = \frac{3}{4}$. The odds in favor of drawing a club are

$$\frac{P(C)}{P(C')} = \frac{\frac{1}{4}}{\frac{3}{4}} = \frac{1}{3},$$

which is written "1 to 3."

53. Let E represent the event "draw a black jack." $P(E) = \frac{2}{52} = \frac{1}{26}$ and then $P(E') = \frac{25}{26}$. The odds in favor of drawing a black jack are

$$\frac{P(E)}{P(E')} = \frac{\frac{1}{26}}{\frac{25}{26}} = \frac{1}{25},$$

or 1 to 25.

54. Let R be the event "a red face card is drawn" and Q be the event "a queen is drawn." Use the union rule for probability to find $P(R \cup Q)$.

$$\begin{aligned} P(R \cup Q) &= P(R) + P(Q) - P(R \cap Q) \\ &= \frac{6}{52} + \frac{4}{52} - \frac{2}{52} \\ &= \frac{8}{52} = \frac{2}{13} \end{aligned}$$

$$\begin{aligned} P(R \cup Q)' &= 1 - P(R \cup Q) \\ &= 1 - \frac{2}{13} = \frac{11}{13} \end{aligned}$$

The odds in favor of drawing a red face card or a queen are

$$\frac{P(R \cup Q)}{P(R \cup Q)'} = \frac{\frac{2}{13}}{\frac{11}{13}} = \frac{2}{11},$$

which is written "2 to 11."

55. The sum is 8 for each of the 5 outcomes 2-6, 3-5, 4-4, 5-3, and 6-2. There are 36 outcomes in all in the sample space.

$$P(\text{sum is } 8) = \frac{5}{36}$$

56. A sum of 0 is impossible, so

$$P(\text{sum is } 0) = 0.$$

57. $P(\text{sum is at least } 10)$
$= P(\text{sum is } 10) + P(\text{sum is } 11) + P(\text{sum is } 12)$

$$= \frac{3}{36} + \frac{2}{36} + \frac{1}{36}$$
$$= \frac{6}{36} = \frac{1}{6}$$

58. $P(\text{sum is no more than } 5)$

$$= P(2) + P(3) + P(4) + P(5)$$
$$= \frac{1}{36} + \frac{2}{36} + \frac{3}{36} + \frac{4}{36}$$
$$= \frac{10}{36} = \frac{5}{18}$$

59. The sum can be 9 or 11. $P(\text{sum is } 9) = \frac{4}{36}$ and $P(\text{sum is } 11) = \frac{2}{36}$.

$P(\text{sum is odd number greater than } 8)$

$$= \frac{4}{36} + \frac{2}{36}$$
$$= \frac{6}{36} = \frac{1}{6}$$

60. A roll greater than 10 means 11 or 12. There are 3 ways to get 11 or 12, 2 for 11 and 1 for 12. Hence,

$$P(12|\text{sum greater than } 10) = \frac{1}{3}.$$

61. Consider the reduced sample space of the 11 outcomes in which at least one die is a four. Of these, 2 have a sum of 7, 3-4 and 4-3. Therefore,

$P(\text{sum is } 7|\text{at least one die is a } 4)$

$$= \frac{2}{11}.$$

62. For $P(\text{at least } 9|\text{one die is a } 5)$, the sample space is reduced to

$$\{(5,1), (5,2), (5,3), (5,4), (5,5), (5,6), (1,5), (2,5), (3,5), (4,5), (6,5)\}.$$

Of these 11 outcomes, 5 give a sum of 9 or more, so

$$P(\text{at least } 9|\text{at least one die is } 5) = \frac{5}{11}.$$

63. $P(E) = 0.51,\ P(F) = 0.37,\ P(E \cap F) = 0.22$

(a)
$$\begin{aligned} P(E \cup F) &= P(E) + P(F) - P(E \cap F) \\ &= 0.51 + 0.37 - 0.22 \\ &= 0.66 \end{aligned}$$

(b) Draw a Venn diagram.

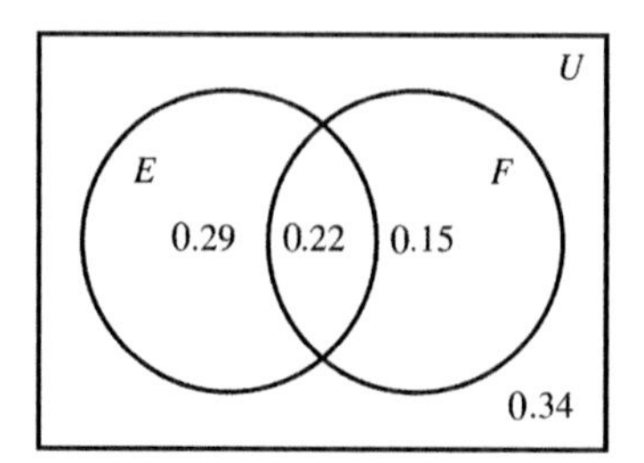

$E \cap F'$ is the portion of the diagram that is inside E and outside F.

$$P(E \cap F') = 0.29$$

(c) $E' \cup F$ is outside E or inside F, or both.

$$P(E' \cup F) = 0.22 + 0.15 + 0.34 = 0.71.$$

(d) $E' \cap F'$ is outside E and outside F.

$$P(E' \cap F') = 0.34$$

64. First make a tree diagram. Let A represent "box A" and K represent "black ball."

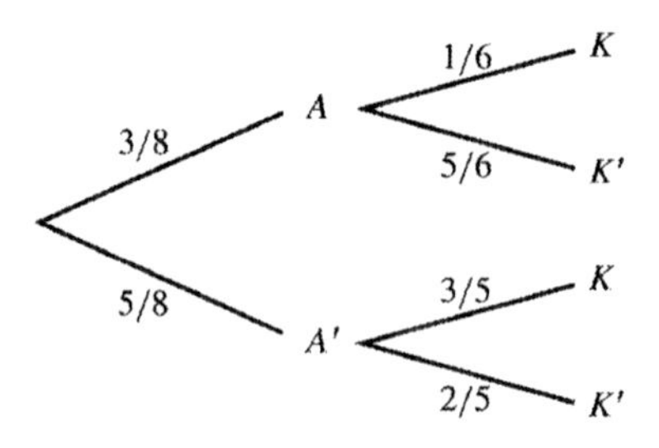

Use Bayes' theorem.

$$\begin{aligned} P(A|K) &= \frac{P(A) \cdot P(K|A)}{P(A) \cdot P(K|A) + P(A') \cdot P(K|A')} \\ &= \frac{\frac{3}{8} \cdot \frac{1}{6}}{\frac{3}{8} \cdot \frac{1}{6} + \frac{5}{8} \cdot \frac{3}{5}} \\ &= \frac{\frac{1}{16}}{\frac{7}{16}} = \frac{1}{7} \end{aligned}$$

65. The probability that the ball came from box B, given that it is red, is

$$P(B|\text{red})$$
$$= \frac{P(B)\cdot P(\text{red}|B)}{P(B)\cdot P(\text{red}|B) + P(A)\cdot P(\text{red}|A)}$$
$$= \frac{\frac{5}{8}\left(\frac{2}{5}\right)}{\frac{5}{8}\left(\frac{2}{5}\right)+\frac{3}{8}\left(\frac{5}{6}\right)}$$
$$= \frac{4}{9}.$$

66. Let Mrepresent "first urn," N represent "second urn," R represent "red ball," and B represent "blue ball." Let x be the number of blue balls in the second urn. The probability that both balls drawn are the same color is

$$P(R|M)\cdot P(R|N) + P(B|M)\cdot P(B|N)$$
$$= \frac{4}{10}\cdot\frac{16}{x+16} + \frac{6}{10}\cdot\frac{x}{x+16}$$
$$= \frac{6x+64}{10(x+16)}$$
$$= \frac{3x+32}{5(x+16)}.$$

Now set this expression equal to 0.44 and solve for x.

$$\frac{3x+32}{5(x+16)} = 0.44$$
$$3x+32 = 2.2x+35.2$$
$$0.8x = 3.2$$
$$x = 4$$

The correct answer choice is **a**.

67. First make a tree diagram letting C represent "a competent shop" and R represent "an appliance is repaired correctly."

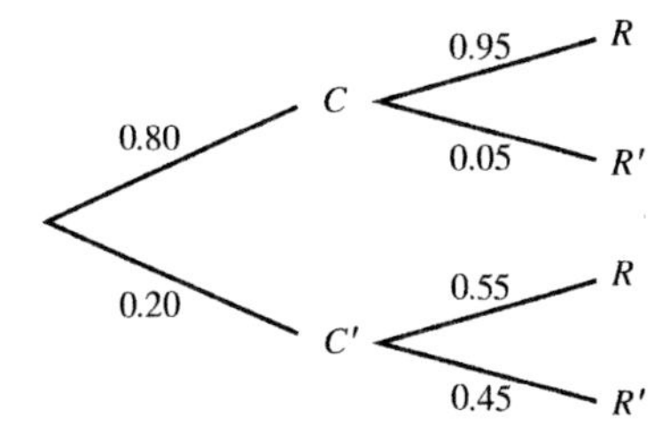

To obtain $P(C|R)$, use Bayes' theorem.

$$P(C|R) = \frac{P(C)\cdot P(R|C)}{P(C)\cdot P(R|C) + P(C')\cdot P(R|C')}$$
$$= \frac{0.80(0.95)}{0.80(0.95)+0.20(0.55)}$$
$$= \frac{0.76}{0.87} \approx 0.8736$$

68. Let C represent "competent shop" and R represent "able to repair appliance." Draw a tree diagram and label the given information.

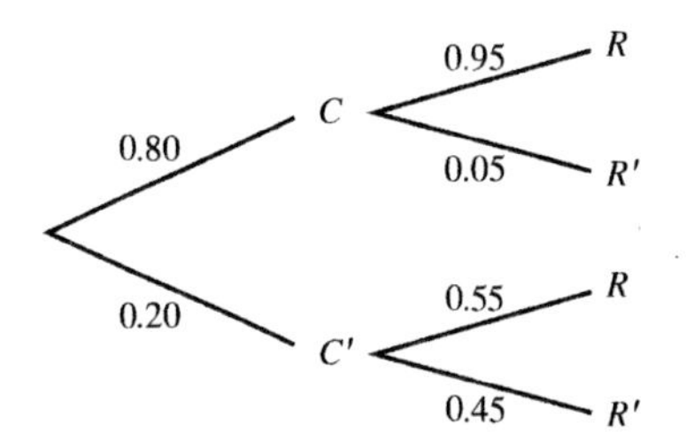

The probability that an appliance that was repaired correctly was repaired by an incompetent shop is

$$P(C'|R) = \frac{P(C'\cap R)}{P(R)}$$
$$= \frac{P(C')\cdot P(R|C')}{P(C)\cdot P(R|C) + P(C')\cdot P(R|C')}$$
$$= \frac{0.20(0.55)}{0.80(0.95)+0.20(0.55)}$$
$$= \frac{0.11}{0.76+0.11} = \frac{0.11}{0.87} = \frac{11}{87}$$
$$\approx 0.1264.$$

69. Refer to the tree diagram for Exercise 67. Use Bayes' theorem.

$$P(C|R') = \frac{P(C)\cdot P(R'|C)}{P(C)\cdot P(R'|C) + P(C')\cdot P(R'|C')}$$
$$= \frac{0.80(0.05)}{0.80(0.05)+0.20(0.45)}$$
$$= \frac{0.04}{0.13} \approx 0.3077$$

70. See the tree diagram in Exercise 67. The probability that an appliance that was repaired incorrectly was repaired by an incompetent shop is

$$P(C'|R') = \frac{P(C'\cap R')}{P(R')}$$
$$= \frac{0.20(0.45)}{0.20(0.45)+0.80(0.05)}$$
$$= \frac{0.09}{0.13} = \frac{9}{13} \approx 0.6923.$$

71. To find $P(R)$, use

$$P(R) = P(C)\cdot P(R|C) + P(C')\cdot P(R|C')$$
$$= 0.80(0.95)+0.20(0.55) = 0.87.$$

72. The events C and R are independent if

$$P(C|R) = P(C).$$

From Exercise 67, $P(C|R) = 0.8736$; $P(C) = 0.80$ was given. Therefore, the events are not independent.

73. (a) "A customer buys neither machine" may be written $(E \cup F)'$ or $E' \cap F'$.

(b) "A customer buys at least one of the machines" is written $E \cup F$.

74. (a) $P(\text{no more than 3 defects})$

$$\begin{aligned} &= P(0) + P(1) + P(2) + P(3) \\ &= 0.34 + 0.26 + 0.18 + 0.12 \\ &= 0.90 \end{aligned}$$

(b) $P(\text{at least 3 defects})$

$$\begin{aligned} &= P(3) + P(4) + P(5) \\ &= 0.12 + 0.07 + 0.03 \\ &= 0.22 \end{aligned}$$

75. Use Bayes' theorem to find the required probabilities.

(a) Let D be the event "item is defective" and E_k be the event "item came from supplier k," $k = 1, 2, 3, 4$.

$$\begin{aligned} P(D) &= P(E_1) \cdot P(D|E_1) + P(E_2) \cdot P(D|E_2) \\ &\quad + P(E_3) \cdot P(D|E_3) + P(E_4) \cdot P(D|E_4) \\ &= 0.17(0.01) + 0.39(0.02) + 0.35(0.05) \\ &\quad + 0.09(0.03) \\ &= 0.0297 \end{aligned}$$

(b) Find $P(E_4|D)$. Using Bayes' theorem, the numerator is

$$P(E_4) \cdot P(D|E_4) = 0.09(0.03) = 0.0027.$$

The denominator is $P(E_1) \cdot P(D|E_1) + P(E_2) \cdot P(D|E_2) + P(E_3) \cdot P(D|E_3) + P(E_4) \cdot P(D|E_4)$, which, from part (a), equals 0.0297.

Therefore,

$$P(E_4|D) = \frac{0.0027}{0.0297} \approx 0.0909.$$

(c) Find $P(E_2|D)$. Using Bayes' theorem with the same denominator as in part (a),

$$\begin{aligned} P(E_2|D) &= \frac{P(E_2) \cdot P(D|E_2)}{0.0418} \\ &= \frac{0.39(0.02)}{0.0297} \\ &= \frac{0.0078}{0.0297} \\ &\approx 0.2626. \end{aligned}$$

(d) Since $P(D) = 0.0297$ and $P(D|E_4) = 0.03$,

$$P(D) \neq P(D|E_4)$$

Therefore, the events are not independent.

76. (a)

Car Type	Satisfied	Not Satisfied	Totals
New	300	100	400
Used	450	150	600
Totals	750	250	1000

(b) 1000 buyers were surveyed.

(c) 300 bought a new car and were satisfied.

(d) 250 were not satisfied.

(e) 600 bought used cars.

(f) 150 who were not satisfied had bought a used car.

(g) The event is "those who purchased a used car given that the buyer is not satisfied."

(h) $P(\text{used car}|\text{not satisfied})$

$$\begin{aligned} &= \frac{n(\text{used car and not satisfied})}{n(\text{not satisfied})} \\ &= \frac{150}{250} = \frac{3}{5} \end{aligned}$$

(i) $P(\text{not satisfied}|\text{used car})$

$$\begin{aligned} &= \frac{n(\text{used car and not satisfied})}{n(\text{buyers of used cars})} \\ &= \frac{150}{600} = \frac{1}{4} \end{aligned}$$

(k) The events "car is new" and "customer is satisfied" are independent if

$$\begin{aligned} &P(\text{car is new and customer is satisfied}) \\ &\quad = P(\text{car is new}) \\ &\quad\quad \cdot P(\text{customer is satisfied}). \end{aligned}$$

From the table, we have

$$\begin{aligned} &P(\text{car is new}) \cdot P(\text{customer is satisfied}) \\ &\quad = \frac{400}{1000} \cdot \frac{750}{1000} = \frac{3}{10} \end{aligned}$$

and

$$\begin{aligned} &P(\text{car is new and customer is satisfied}) \\ &\quad = \frac{300}{1000} = \frac{3}{10} \end{aligned}$$

Therefore, the events are independent.

77. Let E represent "customer insures exactly one car" and S represent "customer insures a sports car." Let x be the probability that a customer who insures exactly one car insures a sports car, or $P(S|E)$. Make a tree diagram.

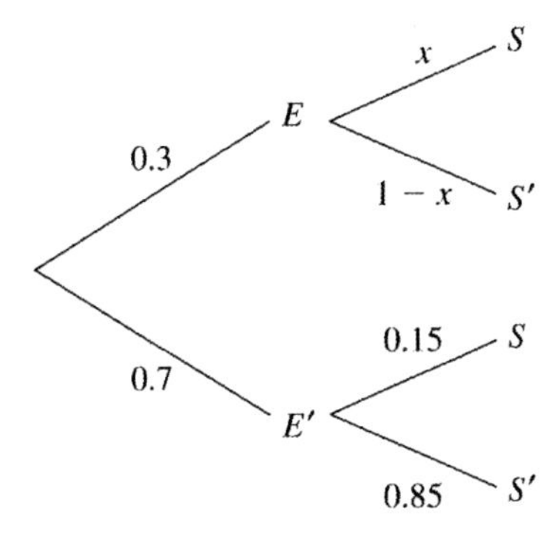

We are told that 20% of the customers insure a sports car, or $P(S) = 0.20$.

$$\begin{aligned} P(S) &= P(E) \cdot P(S|E) + P(E') \cdot P(S|E') \\ 0.20 &= 0.30(x) + 0.70(0.15) \\ 0.20 &= 0.3x + 0.105 \\ 0.3x &= 0.095 \\ x &\approx 0.316666667 \end{aligned}$$

Therefore, the probability that a customer insures a car other than a sports car is

$$\begin{aligned} P(S') &= 1 - P(S) \\ &\approx 1 - 0.316666667 \\ &= 0.683333333. \end{aligned}$$

Finally, the probability that a randomly selected customer insures exactly one car and that car is not a sports car is

$$\begin{aligned} P(E \cap S') &= P(E) \cdot P(S') \\ &\approx 0.3 \cdot 0.683333333 \\ &\approx 0.21. \end{aligned}$$

The correct answer choice is **b**.

78. Let Y represent the set of young policyholders, M represent the set of male policyholders, and W represent the set of married policyholders

We want to find the number of young (Y), female (M'), and sincle (W') policyholders, or $n(Y \cap M' \cap W')$.

We are given the following information.

$$\begin{aligned} n(Y) &= 3000 \\ n(M) &= 4600 \\ n(W) &= 7000 \\ n(Y \cap M) &= 1320 \\ n(M \cap W) &= 3010 \\ n(Y \cap W) &= 1400 \\ n(Y \cap M \cap W) &= 600 \end{aligned}$$

Use a Venn diagram and enter the information as it is found.

Begin with $n(Y \cap M \cap W) = 600$.

Since $n(Y \cap W) = 1400$, the number in $Y \cap W$ but not in M, or $n(Y \cap M' \cap W)$, is $1400 - 600 = 800$.

Since $n(Y \cap M) = 1320$,
$$n(Y \cap M \cap W') = 1320 - 600 = 720.$$

Since $n(Y) = 3000$,
$$\begin{aligned} n(Y \cap M' \cap W') &= 3000 - 600 - 720 - 800 \\ &= 880. \end{aligned}$$

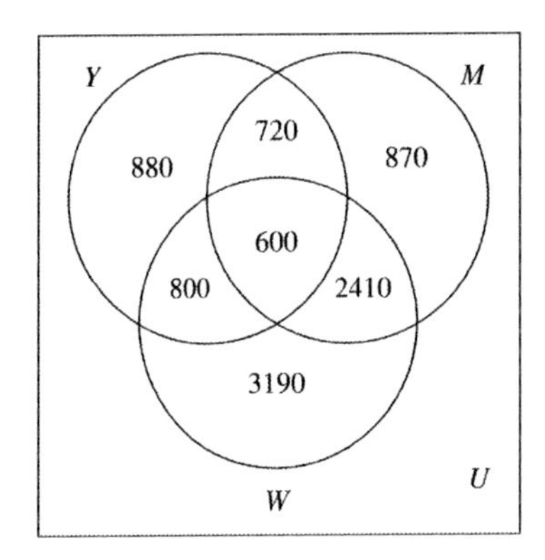

So the correct answer choice is **d**.

79. Let C represent "the automobile owner purchases collision coverage" and D represent "the automobile owner purchases disability coverage." We want to find $P(C' \cap D') = P[(C \cup D)'] = 1 - P(C \cup D)$. We are given that $P(C) = 2 \cdot P(D)$ and that $P(C \cap D) = 0.15$. Let $x = P(D)$.

$$\begin{aligned} P(C \cap D) &= P(C) \cdot P(D) \\ 0.15 &= 2x \cdot x \\ 0.075 &= x^2 \\ x &= \sqrt{0.075} \\ x &\approx 0.2739 \end{aligned}$$

So $P(D) = x \approx 0.27$ and $P(C) = 2x \approx 0.55$. Using the union rule for probability,

$$\begin{aligned} P(C \cup D) &= P(C) + P(D) - P(C \cap D) \\ &= 0.55 + 0.27 - 0.15 \\ &= 0.67. \end{aligned}$$

Finally, $P(C' \cap D') = 1 - 0.67 = 0.33$. The correct answer choice is **b**.

80. Let A represent "the policyholder has auto policy,"
H represent "the policyholder has homeowners policy,"
and R represent "the policyholder will renew."

We want to find $P(R|A \cup H)$, the probability, or percentage, of policyholders who will renew at least one policy. We are given $P(A) = 0.65, P(H) = 0.50$, and $P(A \cap H) = 0.15$. Complete a Venn diagram.

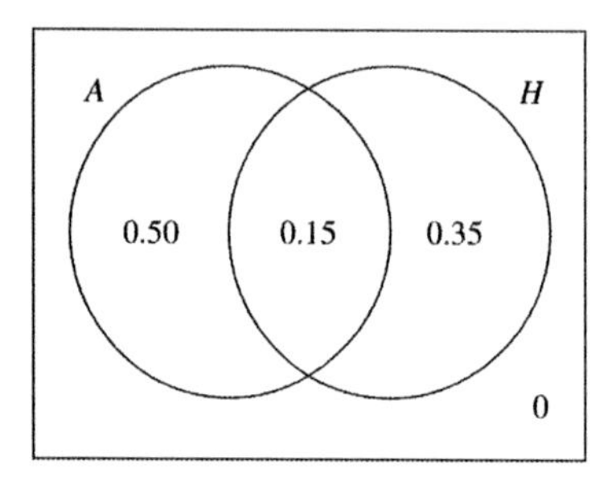

We are also told "40% of policyholders who have only an auto policy will renew," so $P(R|A \cap H') = 0.40$. We are similarly given $P(R|H) = 0.60$ and $P(R|A \cap H) = 0.80$. Using the Venn diagram as a guide, we have

$$\begin{aligned} P(R|A \cup H) &= P(A \cap H')P(R|A \cap H') + P(H \cap A')P(R|H \cap A') + P(A \cap H)P(R|A \cap H) \\ &= 0.50(0.40) + 0.35(0.60) + 0.15(0.80) \\ &= 0.53. \end{aligned}$$

The correct answer choice is **d**.

81. (a)

	N_2	T_2
N_1	N_1N_2	N_1T_2
T_1	T_1N_2	T_1T_2

Since the four combinations are equally likely, each has probability $\frac{1}{4}$.

(b) $P(\text{two trait cells}) = P(T_1T_2) = \frac{1}{4}$

(c) $P(\text{one normal cell and one trait cell}) = P(N_1T_2) + P(T_1N_2) = \frac{1}{4} + \frac{1}{4} = \frac{1}{2}$

(d) $P(\text{not a carrier and does not have the disease}) = P(N_1N_2) = \frac{1}{4}$

82. Let $P(E)$ be the probability the random donor has blood type E.

(a) $P(O^+) + P(O^-) = 0.38 + 0.08 = 0.46$, or 46%

(b) $P(A^+) + P(A^-) + P(O^+) + P(O^-) = 0.32 + 0.07 + 0.38 + 0.08 = 0.85$, or 85%

(c) $P(B^+) + P(B^-) + P(O^+) + P(O^-) = 0.09 + 0.02 + 0.38 + 0.08 = 0.57$, or 57%

(d) $P(A^-) + P(O^-) = 0.07 + 0.08 = 0.15$, or 15%

(e) $P(B^-) + P(O^-) = 0.02 + 0.08 = 0.10$, or 10%

(f) $P(AB^-) + P(A^-) + P(B^-) + P(O^-) = 0.01 + 0.07 + 0.02 + 0.08 = 0.18$, or 18%

83. Let D represent "man died from causes related to heart desease" and E represent "at least one parent suffered from heart disease." We want to find $P(D|E')$. We are given that $n(U) = 937, n(D) = 210, n(E) = 312$, and $n(U \cap E) = 102$. Construct a table and calculate the missing information.

	E	E'	Totals
D	102	108	210
D'	210	517	727
Totals	312	625	937

Therefore,

$$P(D|E') = \frac{P(D \cap E')}{P(E')} = \frac{\frac{108}{937}}{\frac{625}{937}} = \frac{108}{625} \approx 0.173.$$

The correct answer choice is **b**.

84. We want to find $P(A' \cap B' \cap C''|A')$. Use a Venn diagram, fill in the information given, and use the diagram to help determine the missing values.

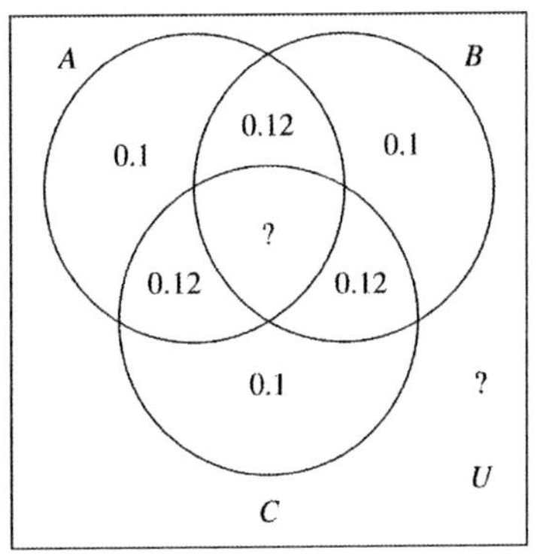

To determine $P(A \cap B \cap C)$, we are told that "The probability that a woman has all three risk factors, given that she has A and B, is 1/3." Therefore, $P(A \cap B \cap C|A \cap B) = 1/3$. Let $x = P(A \cap B)$; then, using the diagram as a guide,

$$\begin{aligned} P(A \cap B \cap C) + P(A \cap B \cap C') &= P(A \cap B) \\ \frac{1}{3}x + 0.12 &= x \\ 0.12 &= \frac{2}{3}x \\ x &= 0.18 \end{aligned}$$

So, $P(A \cap B \cap C) = (1/3)(0.16) = 0.06$. By DeMorgan's laws, we have

$$A' \cap B' \cap C' = (A \cup B \cup C)'$$

so that

$$\begin{aligned} P(A' \cap B' \cap C') &= P[(A \cup B \cup C)'] = 1 - P(A \cup B \cup C) \\ &= 1 - [3(0.10) + 3(0.12) + 0.06] = 0.28. \end{aligned}$$

Therefore,

$$P(A' \cap B' \cap C'|A') = \frac{P(A' \cap B' \cap C' \cap A')}{P(A')} = \frac{P(A' \cap B' \cap C')}{P(A')} = \frac{0.28}{0.6} \approx 0.467.$$

The correct answer choice is **c**.

85. Let B represent "the person voted for Bush,"
K represent "the person voted for Kerry,"
O represent "the person voted for another candidate,"
and M represent "the person was male."

Use a tree diagram and fill in the missing information.

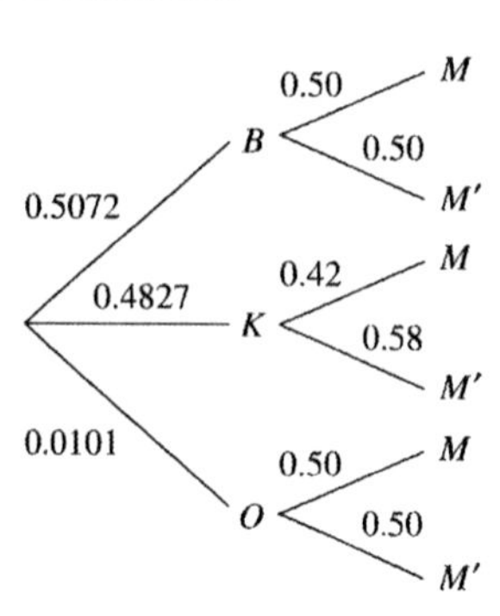

(a) $P(M) = P(B) \cdot P(M|B) + P(K) \cdot P(M|K) + P(O) \cdot P(M|O)$
$= 0.5072(0.50) + 0.4827(0.42) + 0.0101(0.50)$
≈ 0.4614

About 46.14% of the voters were male.

(b) $P(B|M) = \dfrac{P(B) \cdot P(M|B)}{P(B) \cdot P(M|B) + P(K) \cdot P(M|K) + P(O) \cdot P(M|O)}$
$= \dfrac{P(B) \cdot P(M|B)}{P(M)} \approx \dfrac{0.5072(0.50)}{0.4614} \approx 0.5497$

(c) First, note that $P(\text{female}) = P(M') = 1 - P(M) = 1 - 0.4614 = 0.5386$. Therefore,

$$P(B|M') = \frac{P(B) \cdot P(M'|B)}{P(M')} \approx \frac{0.5072(0.50)}{0.5386} \approx 0.4708.$$

86. Let C be the set of viewers who watch situation comedies,
G be the set of viewers who watch game shows,
and M be the set of viewers who watch movies.

We are given the following information.

$$\begin{aligned} n(C) &= 20 \\ n(G) &= 19 \\ n(M) &= 27 \\ n(M \cap G') &= 19 \\ n(C \cap G') &= 15 \\ n(C \cap M) &= 10 \\ n(C \cap G \cap M) &= 3 \\ n(C' \cap G' \cap M') &= 7 \end{aligned}$$

Start with $C \cap G \cap M$: $n(C \cap G \cap M) = 3$.
Since $n(C \cap M) = 10$, the number of people who watched comedies and movies but not game shows, or $n(C \cap G' \cap M)$, is $10 - 3 = 7$.
Since $n(M \cap G') = 19$, $n(C' \cap G' \cap M) = 19 - 7 = 12$.
Since $n(M) = 27$, $n(C' \cap G \cap M) = 27 - 3 - 7 - 12 = 5$.
Since $n(C \cap G') = 15$, $n(C \cap G' \cap M') = 15 - 7 = 8$.

Since $n(C) = 20$, $n(C \cap G \cap M') = 20 - 8 - 3 - 7 = 2$.
Finally, since $n(G) = 19$, $n(C' \cap G \cap M') = 19 - 2 - 3 - 5 = 9$.

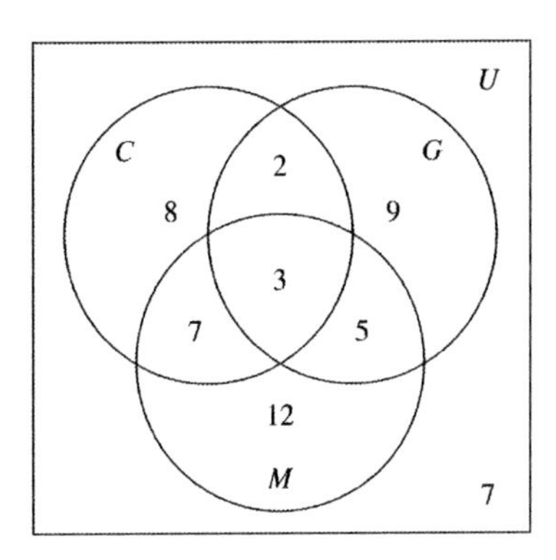

(a) $n(U) = 8 + 2 + 9 + 7 + 3 + 5 + 12 + 7 = 53$

(b) $n(C \cap G' \cap M) = 7$

(c) $n(C' \cap G' \cap M) = 12$

(d) $n(M') = n(U) - n(M) = 53 - 27 = 26$

87. **(a)** $P(\text{answer yes}) = P(\text{answer } B) \cdot P(\text{answer yes}|\text{answer } B) + P(\text{answer } A) \cdot P(\text{answer yes}|\text{answer } A)$

Divide by $P(\text{answer } B)$.

$$\frac{P(\text{answer yes})}{P(\text{answer } B)} = P(\text{answer yes}|\text{answer } B) + \frac{P(\text{answer } A) \cdot P(\text{answer yes}|\text{answer } A)}{P(\text{answer } B)}$$

Solve for $P(\text{answer yes}|\text{answer } B)$.

$$P(\text{answer yes}|\text{answer } B) = \frac{P(\text{answer yes}) - P(\text{answer } A) \cdot P(\text{answer yes}|\text{ answer } A)}{P(\text{answer } B)}$$

(b) Using the formula from part (a),

$$\frac{0.6 - \frac{1}{2}\left(\frac{1}{2}\right)}{\frac{1}{2}} = \frac{7}{10}.$$

88. Let C be the event "the culprit penny is chosen." Then

$$P(C|HHH) = \frac{P(C \cap HHH)}{P(HHH)}.$$

These heads will result two different ways. The culprit coin is chosen $\frac{1}{3}$ of the time and the probability of a head on any one flip is $\frac{3}{4}$: $P(C \cap HHH) = \frac{1}{3}\left(\frac{3}{4}\right)^3 \approx 0.1406$. If a fair (innocent) coin is chosen, the probability of a head on any one flip is $\frac{1}{2}$: $P(C'|HHH) = \frac{2}{3}\left(\frac{1}{2}\right)^3 \approx 0.0833$. Therefore,

$$P(C|HHH) = \frac{P(C \cap HHH)}{P(HHH)} = \frac{P(C \cap HHH)}{P(C \cap HHH) + P(C' \cap HHH)} \approx \frac{0.1406}{0.1406 + 0.0833} \approx 0.6279$$

89. In calculating the probability of two babies in a family would die of SIDS is $(1/8543)^2$, he assumed that the events that either infant died of SIDS are independent. There may be a genetic factor, in which case the events are dependent.

90. $P(\text{earthquake}) = \frac{9}{9+1} = \frac{9}{10} = 0.90$

91. **(a)** $P(\text{making a 1st down with } n \text{ yards to go}) = \frac{\text{number of successes}}{\text{number of trials}}$

n	Trials	Successes	Probability of Making First Down with n Yards to Go
1	543	388	$\frac{388}{543} \approx 0.7145$
2	327	186	$\frac{186}{327} \approx 0.5688$
3	356	146	$\frac{146}{356} \approx 0.4101$
4	302	97	$\frac{97}{302} \approx 0.3212$
5	336	91	$\frac{91}{336} \approx 0.2708$

92. Let W be the set of western states,
S be the set of small states, and
E be the set of early states.

We are given the following information.

$$\begin{aligned} n(W) &= 22 \\ n(S) &= 22 \\ n(E) &= 26 \\ n(W' \cap S' \cap E') &= 9 \\ n(W \cap S) &= 13 \\ n(S \cap E) &= 10 \\ n(W \cap S \cap E) &= 5 \end{aligned}$$

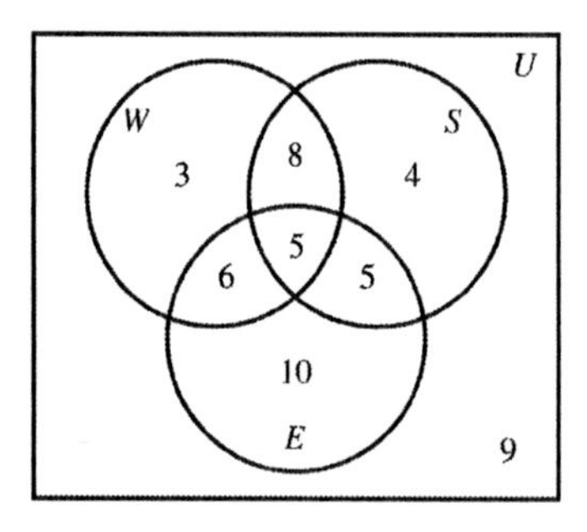

First, put 5 in $W \cap S \cap E$ and 9 in $W' \cap S' \cap E'$.

Complete $S \cap E$ with 5 for a total of 10.
Complete $W \cap S$ with 8 for a total of 13.
Complete S with 4 for a total of 22.

To complete the rest of the diagram requires solving some equations. Let the incomplete region of $W \cap E$ be x, the incomplete region of E be y, and the incomplete region of W be z. Then, using the given values and the fact that $n(U) = 50$,

$$\begin{aligned} x + y \qquad &= 16 \\ x \qquad + z &= 9 \\ x + y + z &= 19. \end{aligned}$$

The solution to the system is $x = 6, y = 10$, and $z = 3$.

Complete $W \cap E$ with 6 for a total of 9.
Complete E with 10 for a total of 26.
Complete W with 3 for a total of 22.

(a) $n(W \cap S' \cap E') = 3$

(b) $n(W' \cap S') = n((W \cup S)') = 19$

93. Let L be the set of songs about love,
P be the set of songs about prison,
and T be the set of songs about trucks.

We are given the following information.

$$\begin{aligned} n(L \cap P \cap T) &= 12 \\ n(L \cap P) &= 13 \\ n(L) &= 28 \\ n(L \cap T) &= 18 \\ n(L' \cap P) &= 5 \\ n(P) &= 18 \\ n(P \cap T) &= 15 \\ n(P' \cap T) &= 16 \end{aligned}$$

Start with $L \cap P \cap T$: $n(L \cap P \cap T) = 12$.
Since $n(L \cap P) = 13$, $n(L \cap P \cap T') = 1$.
Since $n(L \cap T) = 18$, $n(L \cap P' \cap T) = 6$.
Since $n(L) = 28$, $n(L \cap P' \cap T') = 28 - 12 - 1 - 6 = 9$.
Since $n(P \cap T) = 15$, $n(L' \cap P \cap T) = 3$.
Since $n(P) = 18$, $n(L' \cap P \cap T') = 18 - 1 - 12 - 3 = 2$.
Since $n(P' \cap T) = 16$, $n(L' \cap P' \cap T) = 16 - 6 = 10$.
Finally, $n(L' \cap P' \cap T') = 8$.

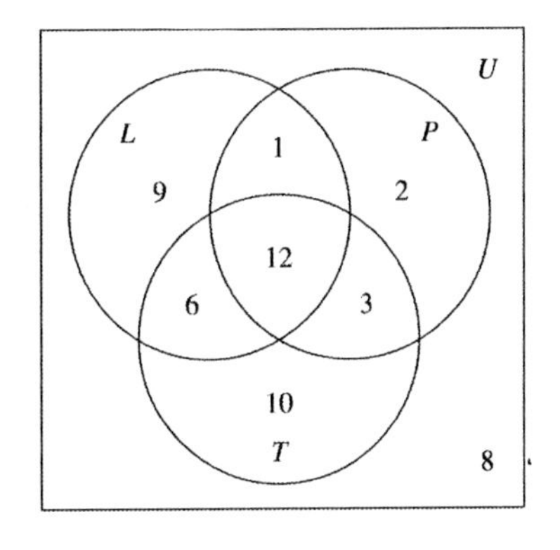

(a) $n(U) = 9 + 1 + 2 + 6 + 12 + 3 + 10 + 8 = 51$

(b) $n(T) = 6 + 12 + 3 + 10 = 31$

(c) $n(P) = 1 + 2 + 12 + 3 = 18$

(d) $n(T \cap P) = 12 + 3 = 15$

(e) $n(P') = n(U) - n(P) = 51 - 18 = 33$

(f) $n(L') = n(U) - n(L) = 51 - 28 = 23$

94. Let R be "a red side is facing up" and
RR be "the 2-sided red card is chosen."

If a red side is facing up, we want to find $P(RR|R)$ since the other possibility would be a green side is facing down.

$$P(RR|R) = \frac{P(RR)}{P(R)} = \frac{\frac{1}{3}}{\frac{1}{2}} = \frac{2}{3}$$

No, the bet is not a good bet.

95. **(a)** $P(\text{double miss}) = 0.05(0.05) = 0.0025$

(b) $P(\text{specific silo destroyed}) = 1 - P(\text{double miss}) = 1 - 0.0025 = 0.9975$

(c) $P(\text{all ten destroyed}) = (0.9975)^{10} \approx 0.9753$

(d) $P(\text{at least one survived})$
$= 1 - P(\text{none survived}) = 1 - P(\text{all ten destroyed})$
$= 1 - 0.9753 = 0.0247$ or 2.47%

This does not agree with the quote of a 5% chance that at least one would survive.

(e) The events that each of the two bombs hit their targets are assumed to be independent. The events that each silo is destroyed are assumed to be independent.

96. Let G be the set of people who watched gymnastics,
B be the set of people who watched baseball,
and S be the set of people who watched soccer.

We want to find $P(G' \cap B' \cap S')$ or, by DeMorgan's laws, $P[(G \cup B \cup S)']$
We are given the following information.

$$\begin{aligned} P(G) &= 0.28 \\ P(B) &= 0.29 \\ P(S) &= 0.19 \\ P(G \cap B) &= 0.14 \\ P(B \cap S) &= 0.12 \\ P(G \cap S) &= 0.10 \\ P(G \cap B \cap S) &= 0.08 \end{aligned}$$

Start with $P(G \cap B \cap S) = 0.08$ and work from the inside out.
Since $P(G \cap S) = 0.10$, $P(G \cap B' \cap S) = 0.02$
Since $P(B \cap S) = 0.12$, $P(G' \cap B \cap S) = 0.04$
Since $P(G \cap B) = 0.14$, $P(G \cap B \cap S') = 0.06$.
Since $P(S) = 0.19$, $P(G' \cap B' \cap S) = 0.19 - 0.14 = 0.05$.
Since $P(B) = 0.29$, $P(G' \cap B \cap S') = 0.29 - 0.18 = 0.11$.
Since $P(G) = 0.28$, $P(G \cap B' \cap S') = 0.28 - 0.16 = 0.12$.

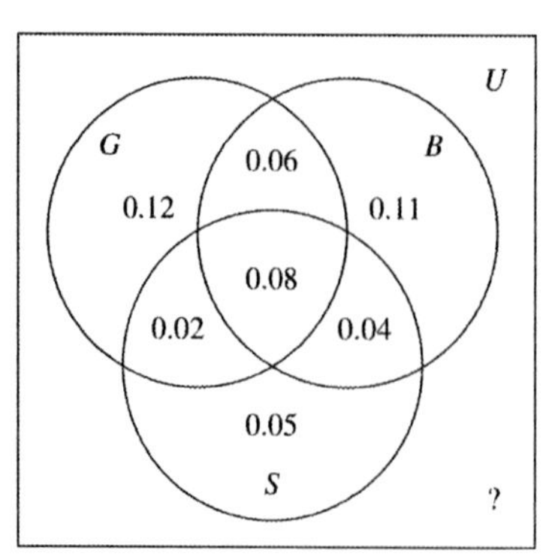

Therefore,

$$\begin{aligned} P(G' \cap B' \cap S) &= P[(G \cup B \cup S)'] \\ &= 1 - P(G \cup B \cup S) \\ &= 1 - (0.12 + 0.06 + 0.11 + 0.02 + 0.08 + 0.04 + 0.05) = 0.52. \\ P(G' \cap B' \cap S) &= 1 - (0.12 + 0.06 + 0.11 + 0.02 + 0.08 + 0.04 + 0.05) = 0.52. \end{aligned}$$

The correct answer choice is **d**.

Extended Application: Medical Diagnosis

1. Using Bayes' theorem,

$$\begin{aligned} P(H_2|C_1) &= \frac{P(C_1|H_2) \cdot P(H_2)}{P(C_1|H_1)P(H_1) + P(C_1|H_2)P(H_2) + P(C_1|H_3)P(H_3)} \\ &= \frac{0.4(0.15)}{0.9(0.8) + 0.4(0.15) + 0.1(0.05)} = \frac{0.06}{0.785} \approx 0.076. \end{aligned}$$

2. Using Bayes' theorem,

$$\begin{aligned} P(H_1|C_2) &= \frac{P(C_2|H_1) \cdot P(H_1)}{P(C_2|H_1)P(H_1) + P(C_2|H_2)P(H_2) + P(C_2|H_3)P(H_3)} \\ &= \frac{0.2(0.8)}{0.2(0.8) + 0.8(0.15) + 0.3(0.05)} = \frac{0.16}{0.295} \approx 0.542. \end{aligned}$$

3. Using Bayes' theorem,

$$\begin{aligned} P(H_3|C_2) &= \frac{P(C_2|H_3) \cdot P(H_3)}{P(C_2|H_1)P(H_1) + P(C_2|H_2)P(H_2) + P(C_2|H_3)P(H_3)} \\ &= \frac{0.3(0.05)}{0.2(0.8) + 0.8(0.15) + 0.3(0.05)} = \frac{0.015}{0.295} \approx 0.051. \end{aligned}$$

Chapter 8

COUNTING PRINCIPLES; FURTHER PROBABILITY TOPICS

8.1 The Multiplication Principle; Permutations

1. $6! = 6 \cdot 5 \cdot 4 \cdot 3 \cdot 2 \cdot 1 = 720$

2. $7! = 7 \cdot 6 \cdot 5 \cdot 4 \cdot 3 \cdot 2 \cdot 1 = 5040$

3. $$\begin{aligned} 15! &= 15 \cdot 14 \cdot 13 \cdot 12 \cdot 11 \cdot 10 \cdot 9 \cdot 8 \cdot 7 \\ &\quad \cdot 6 \cdot 5 \cdot 4 \cdot 3 \cdot 2 \cdot 1 \\ &\approx 1.308 \cdot 10^{12} \end{aligned}$$

4. $$\begin{aligned} 16! &= 16 \cdot 15 \cdot 14 \cdot 13 \cdot 12 \cdot 11 \cdot 10 \\ &\quad \cdot 9 \cdot 8 \cdot 7 \cdot 6 \cdot 5 \cdot 4 \cdot 3 \cdot 2 \cdot 1 \\ &\approx 2.092 \cdot 10^{13} \end{aligned}$$

5. $$\begin{aligned} P(13,2) &= \frac{13!}{(13-2)!} = \frac{13!}{11!} \\ &= \frac{13 \cdot 12 \cdot 11!}{11!} \\ &= 156 \end{aligned}$$

6. $$\begin{aligned} P(12,3) &= \frac{12!}{(12-3)!} = \frac{12!}{9!} \\ &= \frac{12 \cdot 11 \cdot 10 \cdot 9!}{9!} \\ &= 1320 \end{aligned}$$

7. $$\begin{aligned} P(38,17) &= \frac{38!}{(38-17)!} = \frac{38!}{21!} \\ &\approx 1.024 \cdot 10^{25} \end{aligned}$$

8. $$\begin{aligned} P(33,19) &= \frac{33!}{(33-19)!} = \frac{33!}{14!} \\ &\approx 9.960 \cdot 10^{25} \end{aligned}$$

9. $P(n,0) = \dfrac{n!}{(n-0)!} = \dfrac{n!}{n!} = 1$

10. $P(n,n) = \dfrac{n!}{(n-n)!} = \dfrac{n!}{0!} = \dfrac{n!}{1} = n!$

11. $P(n,1) = \dfrac{n!}{(n-1)!} = \dfrac{n(n-1)!}{(n-1)!} = n$

12. $$\begin{aligned} P(n,n-1) &= \frac{n!}{[n-(n-1)]!} = \frac{n!}{(n-n+1)!} \\ &= \frac{n!}{1!} = n! \end{aligned}$$

13. By the multiplication principle, there will be $6 \cdot 3 \cdot 2 = 36$ different home types available.

14. By the multiplication principle, there will be

$$3 \cdot 8 \cdot 7 = 168$$

different meals possible.

15. There are 4 choices for the first name and 5 choices for the middle name, so, by the multiplication principle, there are $4 \cdot 5 = 20$ possible arrangements.

16. The number of ways to choose a slate of 3 officers is

$$\begin{aligned} P(16,3) &= \frac{16!}{(16-3)!} = \frac{16!}{13!} \\ &= \frac{16 \cdot 15 \cdot 14 \cdot 13!}{13!} \\ &= 3360. \end{aligned}$$

18. There is exactly one 3-letter subset of the letters A, B, and C, namely A, B, and C.

19. In Example 7, there are only 3 unordered 2-letter subsets of letters A, B, and C. They are AB, AC, and BC.

20. **(a)** initial

This word contains 3 i's, 1 n, 1 t, 1 a, and 1 ℓ. Use the formula for distinguishable permutations with $n = 7$, $n_1 = 3$, $n_2 = 1$, $n_3 = 1$, $n_4 = 1$, and $n_5 = 1$.

$$\begin{aligned} \frac{n!}{n_1! n_2! n_3! n_4! n_5!} &= \frac{7!}{3!1!1!1!1!} \\ &= \frac{7 \cdot 6 \cdot 5 \cdot 4 \cdot 3!}{3!} \\ &= 840 \end{aligned}$$

There are 840 distinguishable permutations of the letters.

(b) little

Use the formula for distinguishable permutations with $n = 6$, $n_1 = 2$, $n_2 = 1$, $n_3 = 2$, and $n_4 = 1$.

$$\frac{6!}{2!1!2!1!} = \frac{6!}{2!2!} = \frac{6 \cdot 5 \cdot 4 \cdot 3 \cdot 2 \cdot 1}{2 \cdot 1 \cdot 2 \cdot 1} = 180$$

There are 180 distinguishable permutations.

(c) decreed

Use the formula for distinguishable permutations with $n = 7$, $n_1 = 2$, $n_2 = 3$, $n_3 = 1$, and $n_4 = 1$.

$$\frac{7!}{2!3!1!1!} = \frac{7!}{2!3!} = \frac{7 \cdot 6 \cdot 5 \cdot 4 \cdot 3!}{2 \cdot 1 \cdot 3!} = 420$$

There are 420 distinguishable permutations.

21. Use the formula for distinguishable permutations. The number of different "words" is

$$\frac{n!}{n_1!n_2!n_3!n_4!} = \frac{13!}{5!4!2!2!} = 540,540.$$

22. **(a)** The 9 books can be arranged in

$$P(9,9) = 9! = 362,880 \text{ ways.}$$

(b) The blue books can be arranged in 4! ways, the green books can be arranged in 3! ways, and the red books can be arranged in 2! ways. There are 3! ways to choose the order of the 3 groups of books. Therefore, using the multiplication principle, the number of possible arrangements is

$$4!3!2!3! = 24 \cdot 6 \cdot 2 \cdot 6 = 1728.$$

(c) Use the formula for distinguishable permutations with $n = 9$, $n_1 = 4$, $n_2 = 3$, and $n_3 = 2$. The number of distinguishable arrangements is

$$\frac{9!}{4!3!2!} = \frac{9 \cdot 8 \cdot 7 \cdot 6 \cdot 5 \cdot 4!}{4! \cdot 6 \cdot 2} = 1260.$$

(d) There are 4 choices for the blue book, 3 for the green book, and 2 for the red book. The total number of arrangements is

$$4 \cdot 3 \cdot 2 = 24.$$

(e) From part (d) there are 24 ways to select a blue, red, and green book if the order does not matter. There 3! ways to choose the order. Using the multiplication principle, the number of possible ways is

$$24 \cdot 3! = 24 \cdot 6 = 144.$$

23. **(a)** Since there are 14 distinguishable objects to be arranged, use permutations. The number of arrangements is

$$P(14,14) = 14! = 87,178,291,000 \text{ or } 8.7178291 \times 10^{10}.$$

(b) There are 3! ways to arrange the pyramids among themselves, 4! ways to arrange the cubes, and 7! ways to arrange the spheres. We must also consider the number of ways to arrange the order of the three groups of shapes. This can be done in 3! ways. Using the multiplication principle, the number of arrangements is

$$3!4!7!3! = 6 \cdot 24 \cdot 5040 \cdot 6 = 4,354,560.$$

(c) In this case, all of the objects that are the same shape are indistinguishable. Use the formula for distinguishable permutations. The number of distinguishable arrangements is

$$\frac{n!}{n_1!n_2!n_3!} = \frac{14!}{3!4!7!} = 120,120.$$

(d) There are 3 choices for the pyramid, 4 for the cube, and 7 for the sphere. The total number of ways is

$$3 \cdot 4 \cdot 7 = 84.$$

(e) From part (d) there are 84 ways if the order does not matter. There are 3! ways to choose the order. Using the multiplication principle, the number of possible ways is

$$84 \cdot 3! = 84 \cdot 6 = 504.$$

24. $P(4,4) = \dfrac{4!}{(4-4)!} = \dfrac{4!}{0!}$

If $0! = 0$, then $P(4,4)$ would be undefined.

25. $10! = 10 \cdot 9!$

To find the value of 10!, multiply the value of 9! by 10.

26.
$$\begin{aligned} 451! &= 451 \cdot 450! \\ &\approx 451 \cdot 1.7333687 \times 10^{1000} \\ &\approx 781.7493 \times 10^{1000} \\ &= 7.817493 \times 10^{1002} \end{aligned}$$

27. **(a)** The number 13! has 2 factors of five so there must be 2 ending zeros in the answer.

(b) The number 27! has 6 factors of five (one each in 5, 10, 15, and 20 and two factors in 25), so there must be 6 ending zeros in the answer.

(c) The number 75! has $15 + 3 = 18$ factors of five (one each in 5, 10,..., 75 and two factors each in 25, 50, and 75), so there must be 18 ending zeros in the answer.

28. **(a)** Since 12! has two 5s, there are two ending zeros in the answer to 12!. Thus, $12! \neq 479{,}001{,}610$.

(b) Since 23! has four 5s, there are four ending zeros in the answer to 23!. Thus, $23! \neq 25{,}852{,}016{,}740{,}000{,}000{,}000{,}000$.

(c) Since 15! has three 5s, there are three ending zeros in the answer to 15!. Thus, $15! \neq 1{,}307{,}643{,}680{,}000$.

(d) Since 14! has two 5s, there are two ending zeros in the answer to 14!. Using a calculator, 14! is approximated at 8.71782912E10. Since the last two digits are zero, $14! = 87{,}178{,}291{,}200$.

29. Use the multiplication principle. There are

$$8 \cdot 7 \cdot 4 \cdot 5 = 1120$$

varieties of automobile available.

30. 5 of the 12 drugs can be administered in

$$\begin{aligned} P(12,5) &= \frac{12!}{(12-5)!} = \frac{12!}{7!} \\ &= \frac{12 \cdot 11 \cdot 10 \cdot 9 \cdot 8 \cdot 7!}{7!} \\ &= 95{,}040 \end{aligned}$$

different sequences.

31. If each species were to be assigned 3 initials, since there are 26 different letters in the alphabet, there could be $26^3 = 17,576$ different 3-letter designations. This would not be enough. If 4 initials were used, the biologist could represent $26^4 = 456,976$ different species, which is more than enough. Therefore, the biologist should use at least 4 initials.

32. 7 of 11 monkeys can be arranged in

$$\begin{aligned} P(11,7) &= \frac{11!}{(11-7)!} = \frac{11!}{4!} \\ &= \frac{11 \cdot 10 \cdot 9 \cdot 8 \cdot 7 \cdot 6 \cdot 5 \cdot 4!}{4!} \\ &= 1{,}663{,}200 \end{aligned}$$

different ways.

33. The number of ways to seat the people is

$$\begin{aligned} P(6,6) &= \frac{6!}{0!} = \frac{6!}{1} \\ &= 6 \cdot 5 \cdot 4 \cdot 3 \cdot 2 \cdot 1 \\ &= 720. \end{aligned}$$

34. A ballot would consist of a list of the 3 candidates for office 1 and a list of the 6 candidates for office 2. The number of ways to list candidates for office 1 is $P(3,3) = 3! = 6$. The number of ways to list candidates for office 2 is $P(6,6) = 6! = 720$. There are two ways to choose which office goes first. By the multiplication principle, the number of different ballots is

$$6 \cdot 720 \cdot 2 = 8640.$$

35. The number of ways to arrange a schedule of 3 classes is

$$\begin{aligned} P(6,3) &= \frac{6!}{(6-3)!} = \frac{6!}{3!} \\ &= \frac{6 \cdot 5 \cdot 4 \cdot 3!}{3!} \\ &= 120. \end{aligned}$$

36. Pick any 4 of the 375 nonmathematical courses. The number of possible schedules is

$$\begin{aligned} P(375,4) &= \frac{375!}{(375-4)!} = \frac{375!}{371!} \\ &= \frac{375 \cdot 374 \cdot 373 \cdot 372 \cdot 371!}{371!} \\ &= 1.946 \times 10^{10}. \end{aligned}$$

37. The number of possible batting orders is

$$\begin{aligned} P(19,9) &= \frac{19!}{(19-9)!} = \frac{19!}{10!} \\ &= 33{,}522{,}128{,}640 \\ &\approx 3.352 \times 10^{10}. \end{aligned}$$

38. The number of ways to select the 4 officers is

$$\begin{aligned} P(35,4) &= \frac{35!}{(35-4)!} = \frac{35!}{31!} \\ &= \frac{35 \cdot 34 \cdot 33 \cdot 32 \cdot 31!}{31!} \\ &= 1{,}256{,}640. \end{aligned}$$

39. (a) The number of ways 5 works can be arranged is

$$P(5,5) = 5! = 120.$$

(b) If one of the 2 overtures must be chosen first, followed by arrangements of the 4 remaining pieces, then

$$P(2,1) \cdot P(4,4) = 2 \cdot 24 = 48$$

is the number of ways the program can be arranged.

40. (a) Pick one of the 5 traditional numbers followed by an arrangement of the remaining total of 7. The program can be arranged in

$$P(5,1) \cdot P(7,7) = 5 \cdot 7! = 25,200$$

different ways.

(b) Pick one of the 3 original Cajun compositions to play last, preceded by an arrangement of the remaining total of 7. This program can be arranged in

$$P(7,7) \cdot P(3,1) = 7! \cdot 3 = 15,120$$

different ways.

41. By the multiplication principle, a person could schedule the evening of television viewing in

$$8 \cdot 5 \cdot 7 = 280$$

different ways.

42. (a) There are 4 tasks to be performed in selecting 4 letters for the call letters. The first task may be done in 2 ways, the second in 25, the third in 24, and the fourth in 23. By the multiplication principle, there will be

$$2 \cdot 25 \cdot 24 \cdot 23 = 27{,}600$$

different call letter names possible.

(b) With repeats possible, there will be

$$2 \cdot 26 \cdot 26 \cdot 26 = 2 \cdot 26^3 \quad \text{or} \quad 35,152$$

call letter names possible.

(c) To start with W or K, make no repeats, and end in R, there will be

$$2 \cdot 24 \cdot 23 \cdot 1 = 1104$$

possible call letter names.

43. (a) There are 5 odd digits: 1, 3, 5, 7, and 9. There are 7 decisions to be made, one for each digit; there are 5 choices for each digit. Thus, $5^7 = 78,125$ phone numbers are possible.

(b) The first digit has 9 possibilities, since 0 is not allowed; the middle 5 digits each have 10 choices; the last digit must be 0. Thus, there are

$$9 \cdot 10^5 \cdot 1 = 900,000$$

possible phone numbers.

(c) Solve as in part (b), except that the last *two* digits must be 0; therefore there are

$$9 \cdot 10^4 \cdot 1 \cdot 1 = 90,000$$

possible phone numbers.

(d) There are no choices for the first three digits; thus,

$$1^3 \cdot 10^4 = 10,000$$

phone numbers are possible.

(e) The first digit cannot be 0; in the absence of repetitions there are 9 choices for the second digit, and the choices decrease by one for each subsequent digit. The result is

$$9 \cdot 9 \cdot 8 \cdot 7 \cdot 6 \cdot 5 \cdot 4 = 544,320$$

phone numbers.

44. (a) Our number system has ten digits, which are 1 through 9 and 0.

There are 3 tasks to be performed in selecting 3 digits for the area code. The first task may be done in 8 ways, the second in 2, and the third in 10. By the multiplication principle, there will be

$$8 \cdot 2 \cdot 10 = 160$$

different area codes possible.

There are 7 tasks to be performed in selecting 7 digits for the telephone number. The first task may be done in 8 ways, and the other 6 tasks may each be done in 10 ways. By the multiplication principle, there will be

$$8 \cdot 10^6 = 8{,}000{,}000$$

different telephone numbers possible within each area code.

(b) Some numbers, such as 911, 800, and 900, are reserved for special purposes and are therefore unavailable for use as area codes.

45. There are 8 choices for the first digit, since it cannot be 0 or 1. Since restrictions are eliminated for the second digit, there are 10 possibilities for each of the second and third digits. Thus, the total number of area codes would be

$$8 \cdot 10 \cdot 10 = 800.$$

46. **(a)** There were

$$26^3 \cdot 10^3 = 17{,}576{,}000$$

license plates possible that had 3 letters followed by 3 digits.

(b) There were

$$10^3 \cdot 26^3 = 17{,}576{,}000$$

new license plates possible when plates were also issued having 3 digits followed by 3 letters.

(c) There were

$$26 \cdot 10^3 \cdot 26^3 = 456{,}976{,}000$$

new license plates possible when plates were also issued having 1 letter followed by 3 digits and then 3 letters.

47. Since a social security number has 9 digits with no restrictions, there are

$$10^9 = 1,000,000,000 \text{ (1 billion)}$$

different social security numbers. Yes, this is enough for every one of the 281 million people in the United States to have a social security number.

48. If there are no restrictions on the digits used, there would be

$$10^5 = 100{,}000$$

different 5-digit zip codes possible.

If the first digit is not allowed to be 0, there would be

$$9 \cdot 10^4 = 90{,}000$$

zip codes possible.

49. Since a zip code has nine digits with no restrictions, there are

$$10^9 = 1{,}000{,}000{,}000$$

different 9-digit zip codes.

50. There are 3 possible identical shapes on each card.
There are 3 possible shapes for the identical shapes.
There are 3 possible colors.
There are 3 possible styles.
Therefore, the total number of cards is
$3 \cdot 3 \cdot 3 \cdot 3 = 81.$

51. Since a 20-sided die is rolled 12 times, the number of possible games is

$$20^{12} \quad \text{or} \quad 4.096 \cdot 10^{15} \text{ games.}$$

52. There are 3 possible answers for the first question and 2 possible answers for each of the 19 other questions. The number of possible objects is

$$3 \cdot 2^{19} = 1{,}572{,}864.$$

20 questions are not enough.

53. **(a)** The number of different circuits is $P(9,9)$ since we do not count the city he is starting in.

$$P(9,9) = 9! = 362,880$$

is the number of different circuits.

(b) He must check half of the circuits since, for each circuit, there is a corresponding one in the reverse order. Therefore,

$$\frac{1}{2}(362,880) = 181,440$$

circuits should be checked.

(c) No, it would not be feasible.

54. **(a)** Since the starting seat is not counted, the number of arrangements is

$$P(19,19) = 19! \approx 1.216451 \times 10^{17}.$$

(b) Since the starting bead is not counted and the necklace can be flipped, the number of arrangements is

$$\frac{P(14,14)}{2} = \frac{14!}{2} = 43{,}589{,}145{,}600.$$

8.2 Combinations

2. To evaluate $\binom{8}{3}$, use the formula

$$\binom{n}{r} = \frac{n!}{(n-r)!r!}$$

with $n = 8$ and $r = 3$.

$$\binom{8}{3} = \frac{8!}{(8-3)!3!} = \frac{8!}{5!3!} = \frac{8 \cdot 7 \cdot 6 \cdot 5!}{5! \cdot 3 \cdot 2 \cdot 1} = 56$$

3. $$\binom{12}{5} = \frac{12!}{(12-5)!5!} = \frac{12!}{7!5!} = \frac{12 \cdot 11 \cdot 10 \cdot 9 \cdot 8 \cdot 7!}{7! \cdot 5 \cdot 4 \cdot 3 \cdot 2 \cdot 1} = 792$$

4. To evaluate $\binom{44}{20}$, use the formula

$$\binom{n}{r} = \frac{n!}{(n-r)!r!}$$

with $n = 44$ and $r = 20$.

$$\binom{44}{20} = \frac{44!}{(44-20)!20!} = \frac{44!}{24!20!} = 1.761 \cdot 10^{12}$$

5. $$\binom{40}{18} = \frac{40!}{(40-18)!18!} = \frac{40!}{22!18!} \approx 1.134 \cdot 10^{11}$$

6. $$\binom{n}{0} = \frac{n!}{(n-0)!0!} = \frac{n!}{n! \cdot 1} = 1$$

7. $$\binom{n}{n} = \frac{n!}{(n-n)!n!} = \frac{n!}{0!n!} = \frac{n!}{1 \cdot n!} = 1$$

8. $$\binom{n}{1} = \frac{n!}{(n-1)!1!} = \frac{n(n-1)!}{(n-1)! \cdot 1} = n$$

9. $$\binom{n}{n-1} = \frac{n!}{[n-(n-1)]!(n-1)!} = \frac{n!}{(n-n+1)!(n-1)!} = \frac{n(n-1)!}{1!(n-1)!} = n$$

10. There are 13 clubs, from which 6 are to be chosen. The number of ways in which a hand of 6 clubs can be chosen is

$$\binom{13}{6} = \frac{13!}{7!6!} = 1716.$$

11. **(a)** There are

$$\binom{5}{2} = \frac{5!}{3!2!} = \frac{5 \cdot 4 \cdot 3!}{3! \cdot 2 \cdot 1} = 10$$

different 2-card combinations possible.

(b) The 10 possible hands are

$$\{1,2\}, \{2,3\}, \{3,4\}, \{4,5\}, \{1,3\},$$
$$\{2,4\}, \{3,5\}, \{1,4\}, \{2,5\}, \{1,5\}.$$

Of these, 7 contain a card numbered less than 3.

12. **(a)** The number of ways to select a committee of 4 from a club with 31 members is

$$\binom{31}{4} = 31,465.$$

(b) If the committee must have at least 1 member and at most 3 members, it must have 1, 2, or 3 members. The number of committees is

$$\binom{31}{1} + \binom{31}{2} + \binom{31}{3} = 31 + 465 + 4495 = 4991.$$

13. Choose 2 letters from {L, M, N}; order is important.

(a)

There are 9 ways to choose 2 letters if repetition is allowed.

(b)

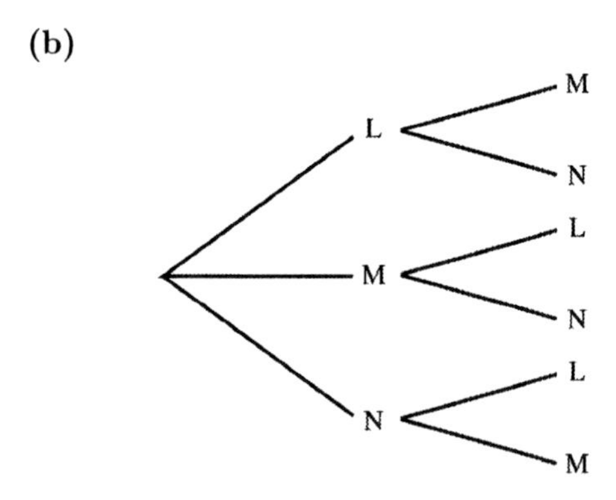

There are 6 ways to choose 2 letters if no repeats are allowed.

(c) The number of 3 elements taken 2 at a time is

$$\binom{3}{2} = \frac{3!}{1!2!} = 3.$$

This answer differs from both parts (a) and (b).

14. **(a)** With repetition permitted, the tree diagram shows 16 different pairs.

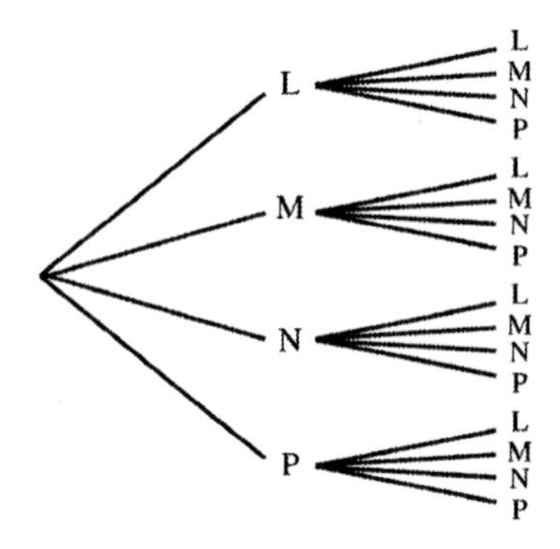

(b) If repetition is not permitted, one branch is missing from each of the clusters of second branches, for a total of 12 different pairs.

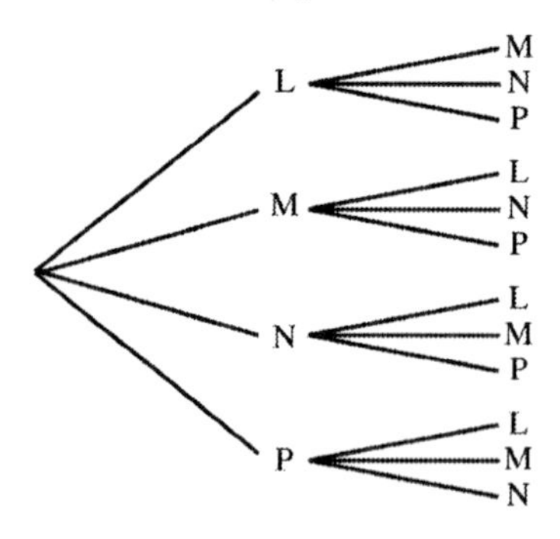

(c) Find the number of combinations of 4 elements taken 2 at a time.

$$\binom{4}{2} = 6$$

No repetitions are allowed, so the answer cannot equal that for part (a). However, since order does not matter, our answer is only half of the answer for part (b). For example, LM and ML are distinct in (b) but not in (c). Thus, the answer differs from both (a) and (b).

17. Order does not matter in choosing members of a committee, so use combinations rather than permutations.

(a) The number of committees whose members are all men is

$$\binom{9}{5} = \frac{9!}{4!5!} = \frac{9 \cdot 8 \cdot 7 \cdot 6 \cdot 5!}{4 \cdot 3 \cdot 2 \cdot 1 \cdot 5!} = 126.$$

(b) The number of committees whose members are all women is

$$\binom{11}{5} = \frac{11!}{6!5!} = \frac{11 \cdot 10 \cdot 9 \cdot 8 \cdot 7 \cdot 6!}{6! \cdot 5 \cdot 4 \cdot 3 \cdot 2 \cdot 1} = 462.$$

(c) The 3 men can be chosen in

$$\binom{9}{3} = \frac{9!}{6!3!} = \frac{9 \cdot 8 \cdot 7 \cdot 6!}{6! \cdot 3 \cdot 2 \cdot 1} = 84 \text{ ways.}$$

The 2 women can be chosen in

$$\binom{11}{2} = \frac{11!}{9!2!} = \frac{11 \cdot 10 \cdot 9!}{9! \cdot 2 \cdot 1} = 55 \text{ ways.}$$

Using the multiplication principle, a committee of 3 men and 2 women can be chosen in

$$84 \cdot 55 = 4620 \text{ ways.}$$

18. Since order is not important, the answers are combinations.

(a) If there are at least 4 women, there will be either 4 women and 1 man or 5 women and no men. The number of such committees is

$$\binom{11}{4}\binom{9}{1}+\binom{11}{5}\binom{9}{0}=2970+462$$
$$=3432.$$

(b) If there are no more than 2 men, there will be either no men and 5 women, 1 man and 4 women, or 2 men and 3 women. The number of such committees is

$$\binom{9}{0}\binom{11}{5}+\binom{9}{1}\binom{11}{4}+\binom{9}{2}\binom{11}{3}$$
$$=462+2970+5940$$
$$=9372.$$

19. Order is important, so use permutations. The number of ways in which the children can find seats is

$$P(12,11)=\frac{12!}{(12-11)!}=\frac{12!}{1!}$$
$$=12!$$
$$=479{,}001{,}600.$$

20. Order does not matter, so use combinations.

(a) The 3 students who will take part in the course can be chosen in

$$\binom{14}{3}=\frac{14!}{11!3!}=\frac{14\cdot 13\cdot 12\cdot 11!}{11!\cdot 3\cdot 2\cdot 1}=364 \text{ ways.}$$

(b) The 9 students who will not take part in the course can be chosen in

$$\binom{14}{9}=\frac{14!}{3!11!}=364 \text{ ways.}$$

21. Since order does not matter, the answers are combinations.

(a) $\binom{16}{2}=\frac{16!}{14!2!}=\frac{16\cdot 15\cdot 14!}{14!\cdot 2\cdot 1}=120$

120 samples of 2 marbles can be drawn.

(b) $\binom{16}{4}=1820$

1820 samples of 4 marbles can be drawn.

(c) Since there are 9 blue marbles in the bag, the number of samples containing 2 blue marbles is

$$\binom{9}{2}=36.$$

22. Since order does not matter, use combinations.

(a) There are

$$\binom{26}{3}=2600$$

possible samples of 3 apples.

(b) There are

$$\binom{7}{3}=35$$

possible samples of 3 rotten apples.

(c) There are

$$\binom{7}{1}\binom{19}{2}=1197$$

possible samples with exactly 1 rotten apple.

23. Since order does not matter, use combinations.

(a) $\binom{5}{3}=\frac{5!}{2!3!}=\frac{5\cdot 4\cdot 3!}{2\cdot 1\cdot 3!}=10$

There are 10 possible samples with all black jelly beans.

(b) There is only 1 red jelly bean, so there are no samples in which all 3 are red.

(c) $\binom{3}{3}=1$

There is 1 sample with all yellow.

(d) $\binom{5}{2}\binom{1}{1}=10\cdot 1=10$

There are 10 samples with 2 black and 1 red.

(e) $\binom{5}{2}\binom{3}{1}=10\cdot 3=30$

There are 30 samples with 2 black and 1 yellow.

(f) $\binom{3}{2}\binom{5}{1}=3\cdot 5=15$

There are 15 samples with 2 yellow and 1 black.

(g) There is only 1 red jelly bean, so there are no samples containing 2 red jelly beans.

24. Since order is important, use a permutation. The plants can be arranged in

$$P(9,5)=9\cdot 8\cdot 7\cdot 6\cdot 5=15{,}120$$

different ways.

25. Show that $\binom{n}{r} = \binom{n}{n-r}$.

Work with each side of the equation separately.

$$\binom{n}{r} = \frac{n!}{r!(n-r)!}$$

$$\binom{n}{n-r} = \frac{n!}{(n-r)![n-(n-r)]!} = \frac{n!}{(n-r)!r!}$$

Since both results are the same, we have shown that

$$\binom{n}{r} = \binom{n}{n-r}.$$

26. Use combinations since order does not matter.

(a) First consider how many pairs of circles there are. This number is

$$\binom{6}{2} = \frac{6!}{2!4!} = 15.$$

Each pair intersects in two points. The total number of intersection points is $2 \cdot 15 = 30$.

(b) The number of pairs of circles is

$$\binom{n}{2} = \frac{n!}{(n-2)!2!} = \frac{n(n-1)(n-2)!}{(n-2)! \cdot 2} = \frac{1}{2}n(n-1).$$

Each pair intersects in two points. The total number of points is

$$2 \cdot \frac{1}{2}n(n-1) = n(n-1).$$

27. There are 7 digits. The number of cases with the same number of dots on both sides is $\binom{7}{1} = 7$. The number of cases with a different number of dots on each side is $\binom{7}{2} = \frac{7!}{5!2!} = 21$. The total number of dominoes that can be formed is $\binom{7}{1} + \binom{7}{2} = 7 + 21 = 28$.

28. Since order is important, use permutations. (Each secretary is being assigned to a manager, which is essentially the same as putting them in numbered slots.) The secretaries can be selected in

$$P(8,3) = 8 \cdot 7 \cdot 6 = 336$$

different ways.

29. Order is important in arranging a schedule, so use permutations.

(a) $P(6,6) = \frac{6!}{0!} = 6! = 720$

She can arrange her schedule in 720 ways if she calls on all 6 prospects.

(b) $P(6,4) = \frac{6!}{2!} = 360$

She can arrange her schedule in 360 ways if she calls on only 4 of the 6 prospects.

30. Since order is not important, use combinations.

(a) Since 3 workers are to be chosen from a group of 9, the number of possible delegations is

$$\binom{9}{3} = 84.$$

(b) Since a particular worker must be in the delegation, the first person can only be chosen in 1 way. The two others must be selected from the 8 workers who are not the worker who must be included. The number of different delegations is

$$1 \cdot \binom{8}{2} = 28.$$

(c) We must count those delegations with exactly 1 woman (1 woman and 2 men), those with exactly 2 women (2 woman and 1 man), and those with 3 women. The number of delegations including at least 1 woman is

$$\binom{4}{1}\binom{5}{2} + \binom{4}{2}\binom{5}{1} + \binom{4}{3} = 4 \cdot 10 + 6 \cdot 5 + 4 = 74.$$

31. There are 2 types of meat and 6 types of extras. Order does not matter here, so use combinations.

(a) There are $\binom{2}{1}$ ways to choose one type of meat and $\binom{6}{3}$ ways to choose exactly three extras. By the multiplication principle, there are

$$\binom{2}{1}\binom{6}{3} = 2 \cdot 20 = 40$$

different ways to order a hamburger with exactly three extras.

(b) There are

$$\binom{6}{3} = 20$$

different ways to choose exactly three extras.

(c) "At least five extras" means "5 extras or 6 extras." There are $\binom{6}{5}$ different ways to choose exactly 5 extras and $\binom{6}{6}$ ways to choose exactly 6 extras, so there are

$$\binom{6}{5} + \binom{6}{6} = 6 + 1 = 7$$

different ways to choose at least five extras.

32. Since order is not important, use combinations.

$$\binom{50}{5} = \frac{50!}{45!5!} = 2{,}118{,}760$$

33. Select 8 of the 16 smokers and 8 of the 22 nonsmokers; order does not matter in the group, so use combinations. There are

$$\binom{16}{8}\binom{22}{8} = 4{,}115{,}439{,}900$$

different ways to select the study group.

34. Since the plants are selected at random, that is, order does not matter, the answers are combinations.

(a) She is selecting 4 plants out of 11 plants. The number of ways in which this can be done is

$$\binom{11}{4} = 330.$$

(b) She is selecting 2 of the 6 wheat plants and 2 of the 5 other plants. The number of ways in which this can be done is

$$\binom{6}{2}\binom{5}{2} = 150.$$

35. Order does not matter in choosing a delegation, so use combinations. This committee has $5 + 4 = 9$ members.

(a) There are

$$\binom{9}{3} = \frac{9!}{6!3!} = \frac{9 \cdot 8 \cdot 7 \cdot 6!}{6! \cdot 3 \cdot 2 \cdot 1} = 84 \text{ possible delegations.}$$

(b) To have all Democrats, the number of possible delegations is

$$\binom{5}{3} = 10.$$

(c) To have 2 Democrats and 1 Republican, the number of possible delegations is

$$\binom{5}{2}\binom{4}{1} = 10 \cdot 4 = 40.$$

(d) We have previously calculated that there are 84 possible delegations, of which 10 consist of all Democrats. Those 10 delegations are the only ones with no Republicans, so the remaining $84 - 10 = 74$ delegations include at least one Republican.

36. Since order is important, use permutations.

$$P(10, 4) = \frac{10!}{(10 - 4)!} = \frac{10!}{6!} = 5040$$

different committees are possible.

37. Order does not matter in choosing the panel, so use combinations.

$$\binom{45}{3} = \frac{45!}{42!3!} = \frac{45 \cdot 44 \cdot 43 \cdot 42!}{3 \cdot 2 \cdot 1 \cdot 42!} = 14{,}190$$

The publisher was wrong. There are 14,190 possible three judge panels.

38. Since order does not matter, use combinations.

$$\binom{52}{13} = \frac{52!}{(52 - 13)!13!} = \frac{52!}{39!13!} = 635{,}013{,}559{,}600$$

39. Since the cards are chosen at random, that is, order does not matter, the answers are combinations.

(a) There are 4 queens and 48 cards that are not queens. The total number of hands is

$$\binom{4}{4}\binom{48}{1} = 1 \cdot 48 = 48.$$

(b) Since there are 12 face cards (3 in each suit), there are 40 nonface cards. The number of ways to choose no face cards (all 5 nonface cards) is

$$\binom{40}{5} = \frac{40!}{35!5!} = 658{,}008.$$

(c) If there are exactly 2 face cards, there will be 3 nonface cards. The number of ways in which the face cards can be chosen is $\binom{12}{2}$, while the number of ways in which the nonface cards can be chosen is $\binom{40}{3}$. Using the multiplication principle, the number of ways to get this result is

$$\binom{12}{2}\binom{40}{3} = 66 \cdot 9880 = 652{,}080.$$

(d) If there are at least 2 face cards, there must be either 2 face cards and 3 nonface cards, 3 face cards and 2 nonface cards, 4 face cards and 1 nonface card, or 5 face cards. Use the multiplication principle as in part (c) to find the number of ways to obtain each of these possibilities. Then add these numbers. The total number of ways to get at least 2 face cards is

$$\binom{12}{2}\binom{40}{3} + \binom{12}{3}\binom{40}{2} + \binom{12}{4}\binom{40}{1} + \binom{12}{5}$$
$$= 66 \cdot 9880 + 220 \cdot 780 + 495 \cdot 40 + 792$$
$$= 652{,}080 + 171{,}600 + 19{,}800 + 792$$
$$= 844{,}272.$$

(e) The number of ways to choose 1 heart is $\binom{13}{1}$, the number of ways to choose 2 diamonds is $\binom{13}{2}$, and the number of ways to choose 2 clubs is $\binom{13}{2}$. Using the multiplication principle, the number of ways to get this result is

$$\binom{13}{1}\binom{13}{2}\binom{13}{2} = 13 \cdot 78 \cdot 78 = 79{,}092.$$

40. (a) List the possibilities for each suit.

5, 6, 7, 8, 9; 5, 6, 7, 8, 10; 5, 6, 7, 9, 10;
5, 6, 8, 9, 10; 5, 7, 8, 9, 10; 6, 7, 8, 9, 10

There are 6 possibilities for each suit and there are 4 suits, so there are $4 \cdot 6 = 24$ possibilities.

(b) There are 6 cards of each suit from 5 to 10. Select 5 of the 6 cards. There are

$$4 \cdot \binom{6}{5} = 4 \cdot 6 = 24 \text{ possibilities.}$$

41. Since order does not matter, use combinations.

2 good hitters: $\binom{5}{2}\binom{4}{1} = 10 \cdot 4 = 40$

3 good hitters: $\binom{5}{3}\binom{4}{0} = 10 \cdot 1 = 10$

The total number of ways is $40 + 10 = 50$.

42. Since the hitters are being chosen at random, that is, order does not matter, the answers are combinations.

(a) The coach will choose 2 of the 6 good hitters and 1 of the 8 poor hitters. Using the multiplication principle, this can be done in

$$\binom{6}{2}\binom{8}{1} = 120 \text{ ways.}$$

(b) The coach will choose 3 of the 6 good hitters. This can be done in

$$\binom{6}{3} = 20 \text{ ways.}$$

(c) The coach must choose either 2 good hitters and 1 poor hitter or 3 good hitters. Add the results from parts (a) and (b). This can be done in

$$\binom{6}{2}\binom{8}{1} + \binom{6}{3} = 140 \text{ ways.}$$

43. Since order does not matter, use combinations.

(a) There are

$$\binom{20}{5} = 15{,}504$$

different ways to select 5 of the orchids.

(b) If 2 special orchids must be included in the show, that leaves 18 orchids from which the other 3 orchids for the show must be chosen. This can be done in

$$\binom{18}{3} = 816$$

different ways.

44. There are no restrictions as to whether the scoops have to be different flavors.

(a) The number of different double-scoop cones will be

$$31 \cdot 31 = 961.$$

(b) The number of different triple-scoop cones will be

$$31 \cdot 31 \cdot 31 = 31^3 = 29{,}791.$$

(c) There are

$$\binom{31}{2} = \frac{31!}{29!2!} = 465$$

ways to make double-scoop cones with two different flavors. In addition, there would be 31 ways to make double-scoop cones with the same flavors. Therefore,

$$465 + 31 = 496$$

double-scoop cones can be made if order doesn't matter.

45. In the lottery, 6 different numbers are to be chosen from the 99 numbers.

(a) There are

$$\binom{99}{6} = \frac{99!}{93!6!} = 1{,}120{,}529{,}256$$

different ways to choose 6 numbers if order is not important.

(b) There are

$$P(99, 6) = \frac{99!}{93!} = 806{,}781{,}064{,}320$$

different ways to choose 6 numbers if order matters.

46. Since order is not important, use combinations. To pick 5 of the 6 winning numbers, we must also pick 1 of the 93 losing numbers. Therefore, the number of ways to pick 5 of the 6 winning numbers is

$$\binom{6}{5}\binom{93}{1} = 6 \cdot 93 = 558.$$

47. **(a)** There can be 5, 4, 3, 2, 1, or no toppings. The total number of possibilities for the first pizza is

$$\binom{11}{5} + \binom{11}{4} + \binom{11}{3} + \binom{11}{2} + \binom{11}{1} + \binom{11}{0}$$
$$= 462 + 330 + 165 + 55 + 11 + 1$$
$$= 1024.$$

The total number of possibilities for the toppings on two pizzas is

$$1024 \cdot 1024 = 1{,}048{,}576.$$

(b) In part (a), we found that if the order of the two pizzas matters, there are

$$1024^2 = 1{,}048{,}576$$

possibilities. If we had a list of all of these possibilities and if the order of the pizzas doesn't matter, we must eliminate all of the possibilities that involve the same two pizzas. There are 1024 such items on the list, one of each of the possibilities for one pizza. Therefore, the number of items on the list that have a duplicate is

$$1{,}048{,}576 - 1024 = 1{,}047{,}552.$$

To eliminate duplicates, we eliminate the second listing of each of these, that is,

$$\frac{1{,}047{,}552}{2} = 523{,}776.$$

Subtracting this from the number of possibilities on the list, we see that if the order of the two pizzas doesn't matter, the number of possibilities is

$$1{,}048{,}576 - 523{,}776 = 524{,}800.$$

48. **(a)** A pizza can have 3, 2, 1, or no toppings. The number of possibilities is

$$\binom{17}{3} + \binom{17}{2} + \binom{17}{1} + \binom{17}{0} = 680 + 136 + 17 + 1$$
$$= 834.$$

There are also four speciality pizzas, so the number of different pizzas is 834 + 4 = 838.

(b) The number of 4forAll Pizza possibilities if all four pizzas are different is

$$\binom{838}{4} = 20{,}400{,}978{,}015.$$

The number of 4forAll Pizza possibilities if there are three different pizzas (2 pizzas are same and the other 2 are different) is

$$838 \cdot \binom{837}{2} = 838 \cdot 349{,}866 = 293{,}187{,}708.$$

The number of 4forAll Pizza possibilities if there are two different pizzas (3 pizzas are same or 2 pizzas and 2 pizzas are same) is

$$838 \cdot 837 + \binom{838}{2} = 701{,}406 + 350{,}703 = 1{,}052{,}109.$$

The number of 4forAll Pizza possibilities if all four are the same is 838. The total number of 4forAll Pizza possibilities is

$$\begin{aligned}&20{,}400{,}978{,}015 + 293{,}187{,}708\\&+ 1{,}052{,}109 + 838\\&= 20{,}695{,}218{,}670\end{aligned}$$

(c) Using the described method, there would be 837 vertical lines and 4 X's or 841 objects, so the total number is

$$\binom{841}{4} = 20{,}695{,}218{,}670.$$

49. (a) $$\binom{8}{1}+\binom{8}{2}+\binom{8}{3}+\binom{8}{4}+\binom{8}{5}+\binom{8}{6}+\binom{8}{7}+\binom{8}{8}$$
$$= 8 + 28 + 56 + 70 + 56 + 28 + 8 + 1 = 255$$

There are 255 breakfasts that can be made.

(b) She has 2 choices. For the first choice she has 4 items. For the second choice she has 4 items.

$$4 \cdot 4 = 16$$

She can make 16 breakfasts.

(c) She has $\binom{4}{2}$ choices of cereal mix and $\binom{4}{3}$ choices of add-in mix. Her total number of choices is

$$\binom{4}{2}\binom{4}{3} = 6 \cdot 4 = 24.$$

(d) He has

$$\binom{4}{1}+\binom{4}{2}+\binom{4}{3}+\binom{4}{4} = 4+6+4+1 = 15$$

choices of cereal mix and

$$\binom{4}{1}+\binom{4}{2}+\binom{4}{3}+\binom{4}{4} = 4+6+4+1 = 15$$

choices of add-in mix. His total number of breakfasts is

$$15 \cdot 15 = 225.$$

(e) $$\binom{7}{0}+\binom{7}{1}+\binom{7}{2}+\binom{7}{3}+\binom{7}{4}+\binom{7}{5}+\binom{7}{6}+\binom{7}{7}$$
$$= 1 + 7 + 21 + 35 + 35 + 21 + 7 + 1 = 128$$

She has 128 different cereals.

50. Consider the first conference with five teams in each of the three divisions. The three winners from the three divisions can result in $5 \cdot 5 \cdot 5$, or 5^3, ways. Then, of the remaining $15 - 3 = 12$ teams, the three wild card teams can be chosen in $12 \cdot 11 \cdot 10$ ways. And since the order of the teams is not relevant, there are $\frac{5^3 \cdot 12 \cdot 11 \cdot 10}{6}$ ways to choose the teams from the first conference.

In the second conference, the situation is the same with the single exception being that one division has six, not five, teams. Therefore, there are $6 \cdot 5 \cdot 5 = 6 \cdot 5^2$ ways to choose the three division winners and $13 \cdot 12 \cdot 11$ ways to choose the wild card teams. Therefore, there are $\frac{6 \cdot 5^2 \cdot 13 \cdot 12 \cdot 11}{6}$ ways to choose the six teams from the second conference.

Finally, the number of ways the six teams can be selected from the first conference and the six teams can be selected from the second conference is

$$\frac{5^3 \cdot 12 \cdot 11 \cdot 10}{6} \cdot \frac{6 \cdot 5^2 \cdot 13 \cdot 12 \cdot 11}{6} = 1{,}179{,}750{,}000.$$

51. (a) The number of ways the names can be arranged is

$$18! \approx 6.402 \times 10^{15}.$$

(b) 4 lines consist of a 3 syllable name repeated, followed by a 2 syllable name and then a 4 syllable name. Including order, the number of arrangements is

$$\begin{aligned}&10 \cdot 4 \cdot 4 \cdot 9 \cdot 3 \cdot 3 \cdot 8 \cdot 2 \cdot 2 \cdot 7 \cdot 1 \cdot 1\\&= 2{,}903{,}040.\end{aligned}$$

2 lines consist of a 3 syllable name repeated, followed by two more 3 syllable names. Including order, the number of arrangements is

$$6 \cdot 5 \cdot 4 \cdot 3 \cdot 2 \cdot 1 = 720.$$

The number of ways the similar 4 lines can be arranged among the 6 total lines is

$$\binom{6}{4} = 15.$$

The number of arrangements that fit the pattern is

$$2{,}903{,}040 \cdot 720 \cdot 15 \approx 3.135 \times 10^{10}.$$

52. **(a)** The number of ways to form the two committees assuming the nominating committee is formed first is

$$\binom{19}{7}\binom{12}{5} = 39{,}907{,}296.$$

(b) The number of ways to form the two committees assuming the public relations committee is formed first is

$$\binom{19}{5}\binom{14}{7} = 39{,}907{,}296.$$

(c) The number of indistinguishable ways can be thought of as first choosing the 7 places occupied by the red shirts out of 19 possible places in the line up and then choosing the 5 places occupied by yellow shirts out of the remaining 12 places. The number of ways is

$$\binom{19}{7}\binom{12}{5} = 39{,}907{,}296.$$

This is the same calculation as in part (a).

53. **(a)** The number of different committees possible is

$$\binom{5}{2} + \binom{5}{3} + \binom{5}{4} + \binom{5}{5} = 10 + 10 + 5 + 1 = 26.$$

(b) The total number of subsets is

$$2^5 = 32.$$

The number of different committees possible is

$$2^5 - \binom{5}{1} - \binom{5}{0} = 32 - 5 - 1 = 26.$$

54. **(a)** The number of ways the judges can be selected is

$$\binom{12}{9} = 220.$$

(b) The number of different sets of scores is

$$\binom{12}{9}\binom{12}{9} = 220^2 = 48{,}400.$$

8.3 Probability Applications of Counting Principles

1. There are $\binom{11}{3}$ samples of 3 apples.

$$\binom{11}{3} = \frac{11 \cdot 10 \cdot 9}{3 \cdot 2 \cdot 1} = 165$$

There are $\binom{7}{3}$ samples of 3 red apples.

$$\binom{7}{3} = \frac{7 \cdot 6 \cdot 5}{3 \cdot 2 \cdot 1} = 35$$

Thus,

$$P(\text{all red apples}) = \frac{35}{165} = \frac{7}{33}.$$

2. There are $\binom{11}{3} = 165$ ways to select 3 of the 11 apples, while there are $\binom{4}{3} = 4$ ways to select 3 yellow ones. Hence,

$$P(3 \text{ yellow}) = \frac{\binom{4}{3}}{\binom{11}{3}} = \frac{4}{165}.$$

3. There are $\binom{4}{2}$ samples of 2 yellow apples.

$$\binom{4}{2} = \frac{4 \cdot 3}{2 \cdot 1} = 6$$

There are $\binom{7}{1} = 7$ samples of 1 red apple. Thus, there are $6 \cdot 7 = 42$ samples of 3 in which 2 are yellow and 1 red. Thus,

$$P(2 \text{ yellow and } 1 \text{ red apple}) = \frac{42}{165} = \frac{14}{55}.$$

4. "More red than yellow" means 2 or 3 red. There are $\binom{7}{2}$ ways to choose 2 red apples and $\binom{4}{1}$ ways to pick a yellow; hence, there are $\binom{7}{2}\binom{4}{1} = 84$ ways to choose 2 red. Since there are $\binom{7}{3} = 35$ ways to pick 3 red, we have $84 + 35 = 119$ ways to have more red than yellow. Therefore,

$$P(\text{more red}) = \frac{119}{\binom{11}{3}} = \frac{119}{165}.$$

5. The number of 2-card hands is

$$\binom{52}{2} = \frac{52 \cdot 51}{2 \cdot 1} = 1326.$$

6. There are $\binom{4}{2} = 6$ ways to pick 2 aces out of $\binom{52}{2}$ ways to pick 2 cards; hence,

$$P(2 \text{ aces}) = \frac{\binom{4}{2}}{\binom{52}{2}} = \frac{6}{1326} = \frac{1}{221} \approx 0.0045.$$

7. There are $\binom{52}{2} = 1326$ different 2-card hands. The number of 2-card hands with exactly one ace is

$$\binom{4}{1}\binom{48}{2} = 4 \cdot 48 = 192.$$

The number of 2-card hands with two aces is

$$\binom{4}{2} = 6.$$

Thus there are 198 hands with at least one ace. Therefore,

$$P(\text{the 2-card hand contains an ace})$$
$$= \frac{198}{1326} = \frac{33}{221} \approx 0.149.$$

8. There are $\binom{13}{2} = 78$ ways to pick 2 spades; hence,

$$P(2 \text{ spades}) = \frac{78}{1326} = \frac{1}{17} \approx 0.059.$$

9. There are $\binom{52}{2} = 1326$ different 2-card hands. There are $\binom{13}{2} = 78$ ways to get a 2-card hand where both cards are of a single named suit, but there are 4 suits to choose from. Thus,

$$P(\text{two cards of same suit})$$
$$= \frac{4 \cdot \binom{13}{2}}{\binom{52}{2}} = \frac{312}{1326} = \frac{52}{221} \approx 0.235.$$

10. There are $\binom{12}{2} = 66$ ways to pick 2 face cards; hence,

$$P(2 \text{ face cards}) = \frac{66}{1326} = \frac{11}{221} \approx 0.0498.$$

11. There are $\binom{52}{2} = 1326$ different 2-card hands. There are 12 face cards in a deck, so there are 40 cards that are not face cards. Thus,

$$P(\text{no face cards})$$
$$= \frac{\binom{40}{2}}{\binom{52}{2}} = \frac{780}{1326} = \frac{130}{221} \approx 0.588.$$

12. Ace, 2, 3, 4, 5, 6, 7, and 8 are the cards in each suit that are "not higher than 8," for a total of 32, so

$$P(\text{no card higher than 8})$$
$$= \frac{\binom{32}{2}}{\binom{52}{2}} = \frac{496}{1326} = \frac{248}{663} \approx 0.374.$$

13. There are 26 choices for each slip pulled out, and there are 5 slips pulled out, so there are

$$26^5 = 11{,}881{,}376$$

different "words" that can be formed from the letters. If the "word" must be "chuck," there is only one choice for each of the 5 letters (the first slip must contain a "c," the second an "h," and so on). Thus,

$$P(\text{word is "chuck"})$$
$$= \frac{1^5}{26^5} = \left(\frac{1}{26}\right)^5 \approx 8.417 \times 10^{-8}.$$

14. Only the first letter is specified; the other 4 can be any letter. The probability of starting with the letter p is

$$\frac{1}{26} \approx 0.038.$$

15. There are $26^5 = 11{,}881{,}376$ different "words" that can be formed. If the "word" is to have no repetition of letters, then there are 26 choices for the first letter, but only 25 choices for the second (since the letters must all be different), 24 choices for the third, and so on. Thus,

$$P(\text{all different letters})$$
$$= \frac{26 \cdot 25 \cdot 24 \cdot 23 \cdot 22}{26^5}$$
$$= \frac{1 \cdot 25 \cdot 24 \cdot 23 \cdot 22}{26^4}$$
$$= \frac{303{,}600}{456{,}976}$$
$$= \frac{18{,}975}{28{,}561} \approx 0.664.$$

16. There are 26^5 possible 5-letter "words," and 23^5 "words" that do not contain x, y, or z. Hence,

$$P(\text{no x, y, or z})$$
$$= \frac{23^5}{26^5} = \frac{6{,}436{,}343}{11{,}881{,}376} \approx 0.5417.$$

19. $P(\text{at least 2 presidents have the same birthday})$
$= 1 - P(\text{no 2 presidents have the same birthday})$

The number of ways that 42 people can have the same or different birthdays is $(365)^{42}$. The number of ways that 42 people can have all different birthdays is the number of permutations of 365 things taken 42 at a time or $P(365, 42)$. Thus,

$P(\text{at least 2 presidents have the same birthday})$

$$= 1 - \frac{P(365, 42)}{365^{42}}.$$

(Be careful to realize that the symbol P is sometimes used to indicate permutations and sometimes used to indicate probability; in this solution, the symbol is used both ways.)

20. Using the result from Example 6, the probability that at least 2 people in a group of n people have the same birthday is

$$1 - \frac{P(365, n)}{(365)^n}.$$

Therefore, the probability that at least 2 of the 100 U.S. Senators have the same birthday is

$$1 - \frac{P(365, 100)}{(365)^{100}}.$$

21. Since there are 435 members of the House of Representatives, and there are only 365 days in a year, it is a certain event that at least 2 people will have the same birthday. Thus,

$P(\text{at least 2 members have the same birthday}) = 1.$

22. There are $\binom{n}{2}$ ways to pick which pair is to have the same birthday. One member of the pair has 365 choices of a birthday, the other only 1. The other $n-2$ people have 364, 363, 362, etc., choices. Thus, the probability is

$$\binom{n}{2} \cdot \frac{P(365, n-1)}{(365)^n}.$$

23. Each of the 4 people can choose to get off at any one of the 7 floors, so there are 7^4 ways the four people can leave the elevator. The number of ways the people can leave at different floors is the number of permutations of 7 things (floors) taken 4 at a time or

$$P(7, 4) = 7 \cdot 6 \cdot 5 \cdot 4 = 840.$$

The probability that no 2 passengers leave at the same floor is

$$\frac{P(7, 4)}{7^4} = \frac{840}{2401} \approx 0.3499.$$

Thus, the probability that at least 2 passengers leave at the same floor is

$$1 - 0.3499 = 0.6501.$$

(Note the similarity of this problem and the "birthday problem.")

24. Let $x =$ the total number of balls. Since the probability of picking 5 balls which all are blue is $\frac{1}{2}$, we can see that $x > 5$. (If $x = 5$, the probability would be 1.) Let's look at the number of blue balls needed. If there were 6 blue balls, $\binom{6}{5} = 6$ and $\binom{x}{5} = 12$, since the probability is $\frac{1}{2}$. Since x must be larger than the number of blue balls, $x \geq 7$. But since $\binom{7}{5} = 21$,

$$\binom{x}{5} \geq 21 \neq 12.$$

If there were 7 blue balls, $\binom{7}{5} = 21$ and $\binom{x}{5} = 42$. Since $x \geq 8$,

$$\binom{x}{5} \geq 56 \neq 42.$$

If there were 8 blue balls, $\binom{8}{5} = 56$ and $\binom{x}{5} = 112$. Since $x \geq 9$,

$$\binom{x}{5} \geq 126 \neq 112.$$

If there were 9 blue balls, $\binom{9}{5} = 126$ and $\binom{x}{5} = 252$. Since $x \geq 10$, $\binom{x}{5} \geq 252$, and x must be 10.

Therefore, there were 10 balls, 9 of them blue,

$$P(\text{all 5 blue}) = \frac{\binom{9}{5}}{\binom{10}{5}} = \frac{1}{2}.$$

25. $P(\text{at least one \$100-bill})$

$$= P(1 \text{ \$100-bill}) + P(2 \text{ \$100-bills})$$
$$= \frac{\binom{2}{1}\binom{4}{1}}{\binom{6}{2}} + \frac{\binom{2}{2}\binom{4}{0}}{\binom{6}{2}}$$
$$= \frac{8}{15} + \frac{1}{15}$$
$$= \frac{9}{15} = \frac{3}{5}$$

$$P(\text{no \$100-bill}) = \frac{\binom{2}{0}\binom{4}{2}}{\binom{6}{2}} = \frac{6}{15} = \frac{2}{5}$$

It is more likely to get at least one \$100-bill.

26. $P(\text{matched pair})$

$$= P(\text{2 black or 2 brown or 2 blue})$$
$$= P(\text{2 black}) + P(\text{2 brown}) + P(\text{2 blue})$$
$$= \frac{\binom{9}{2}}{\binom{17}{2}} + \frac{\binom{6}{2}}{\binom{17}{2}} + \frac{\binom{2}{2}}{\binom{17}{2}}$$
$$= \frac{36}{136} + \frac{15}{136} + \frac{1}{136}$$
$$= \frac{52}{136} = \frac{13}{34}$$

27. The number of orders of the three types of birds is $P(3,3)$. The number of arrangements of the crows is $P(3,3)$, of the bluejays is $P(4,4)$, and of the starlings is $P(5,5)$. The total number of arrangements of all the birds is $P(12,12)$.

$P(\text{all birds of same type are sitting together})$

$$= \frac{P(3,3) \cdot P(3,3) \cdot P(4,4) \cdot P(5,5)}{P(12,12)}$$
$$\approx 2.165 \times 10^{-4}$$

28. There are 6 letters so the number of possible spellings (counting duplicates) is $6! = 720$. Since the letter l is repeated 2 times and the letter t is repeated 2 times, the spelling little will occur $2!2! = 4$ times. The probability that little will be spelled is $\frac{4}{720} = \frac{1}{180}$.

29. There are 11 letters so the number of possible spellings (counting duplicates) is $11! = 39{,}916{,}800$. Since the letter i is repeated 4 times, the letter s is repeated 4 times, and the letter p is repeated 2 times, the spelling Mississippi will occur $4!4!2! = 1152$ times. The probability that Mississippi will be spelled is

$$\frac{1152}{39{,}916{,}800} \approx 0.0000289.$$

30. There are 11 ways to choose 1 typewriter from the shipment of 11. Since 2 of the 11 are defective, there are 9 ways to choose 1 nondefective typewriter. Thus,

$$P(\text{1 drawn from the 11 is not defective}) = \frac{9}{11}.$$

31. There are $\binom{9}{2}$ possible ways to choose 2 nondefective typewriters out of the $\binom{11}{2}$ possible ways of choosing any 2. Thus,

$$P(\text{no defective}) = \frac{\binom{9}{2}}{\binom{11}{2}} = \frac{36}{55}.$$

32. There are $\binom{11}{3}$ ways to choose 3 typewriters.

$$\binom{11}{3} = \frac{11!}{3!8!} = \frac{11 \cdot 10 \cdot 9}{3 \cdot 2 \cdot 1} = 165$$

There are $\binom{9}{3}$ ways to choose 3 nondefective typewriters.

$$\binom{9}{3} = \frac{9!}{3!6!} = \frac{9 \cdot 8 \cdot 7}{3 \cdot 2 \cdot 1} = 84$$

Thus,

$P(\text{3 drawn from the 9 are nondefective})$

$$= \frac{84}{165} = \frac{28}{55}.$$

33. There are $\binom{9}{4}$ possible ways to choose 4 nondefective typewriters out of the $\binom{11}{4}$ possible ways of choosing any 4. Thus,

$$P(\text{no defective}) = \frac{\binom{9}{4}}{\binom{11}{4}} = \frac{126}{330} = \frac{21}{55}.$$

34. There are $\binom{12}{4} = 495$ different ways to choose 4 engines for testing from the crate of 12. A crate will not be shipped if any one of the 4 in the sample is defective. If there are 2 defectives in the crate, then there are $\binom{10}{4} = 210$ ways of choosing a sample with no defectives. Thus,

$P(\text{shipping a crate with 2 defectives})$

$$= \frac{210}{495} = \frac{14}{33} \approx 0.424.$$

35. There are $\binom{12}{5} = 792$ ways to pick a sample of 5. It will be shipped if all 5 are good. There are $\binom{10}{5} = 252$ ways to pick 5 good ones, so

$$P(\text{all good}) = \frac{252}{792} = \frac{7}{22} \approx 0.318.$$

36. There are $P(5,5)$ different orders of the names. Only one of these would be in alphabetical order. Therefore, $P(5,5) - 1$ are not in alphabetical order. Thus,

$P(\text{not in alphabetical order})$

$$= \frac{P(5,5) - 1}{P(5,5)} = \frac{120 - 1}{120} = \frac{119}{120}.$$

37. There are 20 people in all, so the number of possible 5-person committees is $\binom{20}{5} = 15,504$. Thus, in parts (a)-(g), $n(S) = 15,504$.

(a) There are $\binom{10}{3}$ ways to choose the 3 men and $\binom{10}{2}$ ways to choose the 2 women. Thus,

P(3 men and 2 women)

$$= \frac{\binom{10}{3}\binom{10}{2}}{\binom{20}{5}} = \frac{120 \cdot 45}{15,504} = \frac{225}{646} \approx 0.348.$$

(b) There are $\binom{6}{3}$ ways to choose the 3 Miwoks and $\binom{9}{2}$ ways to choose the 2 Pomos. Thus,

P(exactly 3 Miwoks and 2 Pomos)

$$= \frac{\binom{6}{3}\binom{9}{2}}{\binom{20}{5}} = \frac{20 \cdot 36}{15{,}504} = \frac{15}{323} \approx 0.046.$$

(c) Choose 2 of the 6 Miwoks, 2 of the 5 Hoopas, and 1 of the 9 Pomos. Thus,

P(2 Miwoks, 2 Hoopas, and a Pomo)

$$= \frac{\binom{6}{2}\binom{5}{2}\binom{9}{1}}{\binom{20}{5}} = \frac{15 \cdot 10 \cdot 9}{15{,}504} = \frac{225}{2584} \approx 0.087.$$

(d) There cannot be 2 Miwoks, 2 Hoopas, and 2 Pomos, since only 5 people are to be selected. Thus,

P(2 Miwoks, 2 Hoopas, and 2 Pomos) $= 0$.

(e) Since there are more women then men, there must be 3, 4, or 5 women.

P(more women than men)

$$= \frac{\binom{10}{3}\binom{10}{2} + \binom{10}{4}\binom{10}{1} + \binom{10}{5}\binom{10}{0}}{\binom{20}{5}}$$

$$= \frac{7752}{15{,}504} = \frac{1}{2}$$

(f) Choose 3 of 5 Hoopas and any 2 of the 15 non-Hoopas.

P(exactly 3 Hoopas)

$$= \frac{\binom{5}{3}\binom{15}{2}}{\binom{20}{5}} = \frac{175}{2584} \approx 0.068$$

(g) There can be 2 to 5 Pomos, the rest chosen from the 11 nonPomos.

P(at least 2 Pomos)

$$= \frac{\binom{9}{2}\binom{11}{3} + \binom{9}{3}\binom{11}{2} + \binom{9}{4}\binom{11}{1} + \binom{9}{5}\binom{11}{0}}{\binom{20}{5}}$$

$$= \frac{503}{646} \approx 0.779$$

38. (a) $P(\text{first person}) = \dfrac{5}{40} = \dfrac{1}{8}$

(b) $P(\text{last person}) = \dfrac{5(39!)}{40!}$

$$= \frac{5(39!)}{40(39!)}$$

$$= \frac{5}{40} = \frac{1}{8}$$

(c) No, everybody has the same chance.

39. There are $\binom{52}{5}$ different 5-card poker hands. There are 4 royal flushes, one for each suit. Thus,

P(royal flush)

$$= \frac{4}{\binom{52}{5}} = \frac{4}{2{,}598{,}960} = \frac{1}{649{,}740}$$

$$\approx 1.539 \times 10^{-6}.$$

40. A flush could start with an ace, 2, 3, 4, ..., 7, 8, or 9. This gives 9 choices in each of 4 suits, so there are 36 choices in all. Thus,

$$P(\text{straight flush}) = \frac{36}{\binom{52}{5}} = \frac{36}{2{,}598{,}960}$$

$$\approx 0.00001385$$

$$= 1.385 \cdot 10^{-5}.$$

41. The four of a kind can be chosen in 13 ways and then is matched with 1 of the remaining 48 cards to make a 5-card hand containing four of a kind. Thus, there are $13 \cdot 48 = 624$ poker hands with four of a kind. It follows that

P(four of a kind)

$$= \frac{624}{\binom{52}{5}} = \frac{624}{2{,}598{,}960} = \frac{1}{4165}$$

$$\approx 2.401 \times 10^{-4}.$$

42. A straight could start with an ace, 2, 3, 4, 5, 6, 7, 8, 9, or 10 as the low card, giving 40 choices. For each succeeding card, only the suit may be chosen. Thus, the number of straights is

$$40 \cdot 4^4 = 10{,}240.$$

But this also counts the straight flushes, of which there are 36 (see Exercise 37), and the 4 royal flushes. There are thus 10,200 straights that are not also flushes, so

$$P(\text{straight}) = \frac{10{,}200}{2{,}598{,}960} \approx 0.0039.$$

43. There are 13 different values with 4 cards of each value. The total number of possible three of a kind is then $13 \cdot \binom{4}{3}$. The other 2 cards must be chosen from the remaining 48 cards of different value. However, these 2 cards must be different. Thus, for the last 2 cards, there are 48 cards to choose from, but the cards must not have the same value. The number of possibilities for the last 2 cards is $\binom{48}{2} - 12 \cdot \binom{4}{2}$, and

$$P(\text{three of a kind}) = \frac{13 \cdot \binom{4}{3}\left[\binom{48}{2} - 12 \cdot \binom{4}{2}\right]}{\binom{52}{5}}$$

$$\approx 0.0211.$$

44. There are 13 different values of cards and 4 cards of each value. Choose 2 values out of the 13 for the values of the pairs. The number of ways to select the 2 values is $\binom{13}{2}$. The number of ways to select a pair for each value is $\binom{4}{2}$. There are $52 - 8 = 44$ cards that are neither of these 2 values, so the number of ways to select the fifth card is $\binom{44}{1}$. Thus,

$$P(\text{two pairs}) = \frac{\binom{13}{2}\binom{4}{2}\binom{4}{2}\binom{44}{1}}{\binom{52}{5}}$$

$$= \frac{123{,}552}{2{,}598{,}960} \approx 0.0475.$$

45. There are 13 different values with 4 cards of each value. The total number of possible pairs is $13 \cdot \binom{4}{2}$. The remaining 3 cards must be chosen from the 48 cards of different value. However, among these 3 we cannot have 3 of a kind nor can we have 2 of a kind.

$$P(\text{one pair})$$

$$= \frac{13 \cdot \binom{4}{2}\left[\binom{48}{3} - 12 \cdot \binom{4}{3} - 12\binom{4}{2} \cdot \binom{44}{1}\right]}{\binom{52}{5}}$$

$$\approx 0.4226$$

46. There are $\binom{52}{13}$ different 13-card bridge hands. Since there are only 13 hearts, there is exactly one way to get a bridge hand containing only hearts. Thus,

$$P(\text{only hearts}) = \frac{1}{\binom{52}{13}} \approx 1.575 \cdot 10^{-12}.$$

47. The hand can have exactly 3 aces or 4 aces. There are $\binom{4}{3} = 4$ ways to pick exactly 3 aces, and there are $\binom{48}{10}$ ways to pick the other 10 cards. Also, there is only $\binom{4}{4} = 1$ way to pick 4 aces, and there are $\binom{48}{9}$ ways to pick the other 9 cards. Hence,

$$P(3 \text{ aces}) = \frac{\binom{4}{3}\binom{48}{10} + \binom{4}{4}\binom{48}{9}}{\binom{52}{13}} \approx 0.0438.$$

48. There are $\binom{4}{2}$ ways to obain 2 aces, $\binom{4}{2}$ ways to obtain 2 kings, and $\binom{44}{9}$ ways to obtain the remaining 9 cards. Thus,

$$\text{P(exactly 2 aces and exactly 2 kings)}$$

$$= \frac{\binom{4}{2}\binom{4}{2}\binom{44}{9}}{\binom{52}{13}} \approx 0.0402.$$

49. The number of ways of choosing 3 suits is $P(4, 3)$. The number of ways of choosing 6 of one suit is $\binom{13}{6}$, 4 of another is $\binom{13}{4}$, and 3 of another is $\binom{13}{3}$. Thus,

$$P(6 \text{ of one suit, 4 of another, and 3 of another})$$

$$= \frac{P(4,3)\binom{13}{6}\binom{13}{4}\binom{13}{3}}{\binom{52}{13}}$$

$$\approx 0.0133.$$

Order is important in this problem because 6 spades, 4 hearts, and 3 clubs would be different than 6 hearts, 4 clubs, and 3 spades.

50. There are 21 books, so the number of selections of any 6 books is

$$\binom{21}{6} = 54{,}264.$$

(a) The probability that the selection consisted of 3 Hughes and 3 Morrison books is

$$\frac{\binom{9}{3}\binom{7}{3}}{\binom{21}{6}} = \frac{85 \cdot 35}{54{,}264} = \frac{2940}{54{,}264} \approx 0.0542.$$

(b) A selection containing exactly 4 Baldwin books will contain 2 of the 16 books by the other authors, so the probability is

$$\frac{\binom{5}{4}\binom{16}{2}}{\binom{21}{6}} = \frac{5 \cdot 120}{54{,}264} = \frac{600}{54{,}264} \approx 0.0111.$$

(c) The probability of a selection consisting of 2 Hughes, 3 Baldwin, and 1 Morrison book is

$$\frac{\binom{9}{2}\binom{5}{3}\binom{7}{1}}{\binom{21}{6}} = \frac{36 \cdot 10 \cdot 7}{54{,}264} = \frac{2520}{54{,}264} \approx 0.0464.$$

(d) A selection consisting of at least 4 Hughes books may contain 4, 5, or 6 Hughes books, with any remaining books by the other authors. Therefore, the probability is

$$\frac{\binom{9}{4}\binom{12}{2}+\binom{9}{5}\binom{12}{1}+\binom{9}{6}\binom{12}{0}}{\binom{21}{6}}$$

$$=\frac{126\cdot 66+126\cdot 12+84}{54{,}264}$$

$$=\frac{8316+1512+84}{54{,}264}$$

$$=\frac{9912}{54{,}264}\approx 0.1827.$$

(e) Since there are 9 Hughes books and 5 Baldwin books, there are 14 books written by males. The probability of a selection with exactly 4 books written by males is

$$\frac{\binom{14}{4}\binom{7}{2}}{\binom{21}{6}}=\frac{1001\cdot 21}{54{,}264}=\frac{21{,}021}{54{,}264}\approx 0.3874.$$

(f) A selection with no more than 2 books written by Baldwin may contain 0, 1, or 2 books by Baldwin, with the remaining books by the other authors. Therefore, the probability is

$$\frac{\binom{5}{0}\binom{16}{6}+\binom{5}{1}\binom{16}{5}+\binom{5}{2}\binom{16}{4}}{\binom{21}{6}}$$

$$=\frac{8008+5\cdot 4368+10\cdot 1820}{54{,}264}$$

$$=\frac{8008+21,840+18,200}{54{,}264}$$

$$=\frac{48{,}048}{54{,}264}\approx 0.8854.$$

51. There are $\binom{99}{6}=1{,}120{,}529{,}256$ different ways to pick 6 numbers from 1 to 99, but there is only 1 way to win; the 6 numbers you pick must exactly match the 6 winning numbers, without regard to order. Thus,

$P(\text{win the big prize})$

$$=\frac{1}{1{,}120{,}529{,}256}\approx 8.924\times 10^{-10}.$$

52. To find the probability of picking 5 of the 6 lottery numbers correctly, we must recall that the total number of ways to pick the 6 lottery numbers is $\binom{99}{6}=1{,}120{,}529{,}256$. To pick 5 of the 6 winning numbers, we must also pick 1 of the 93 losing numbers. Therefore, the number of ways of picking 5 of the 6 winning numbers is

$$\binom{6}{5}\binom{93}{1}=558.$$

Thus, the probability of picking 5 of the 6 numbers correctly is

$$\frac{\binom{6}{5}\binom{93}{1}}{\binom{99}{6}}\approx 4.980\cdot 10^{-7}.$$

53. Let A be the event of drawing four royal flushes in a row all in spades, and B be the event of meeting four strangers all with the same birthday. Then,

$$P(A)=\left[\frac{1}{\binom{52}{5}}\right]^4.$$

For four people, the number of possible birthdays is 365^4. Of these there are 365 which are the same (that is, all birthdays January 1 or January 2 or January 3, etc.).

$$P(B)=\frac{365}{365^4}=\frac{1}{365^3}$$

Therefore,

$$P(A\cap B)=\left[\frac{1}{\binom{52}{5}}\right]^4\frac{1}{365^3}\approx 4.507\times 10^{-34}.$$

No, this probability is much smaller than that of winning the lottery.

54. The probability of picking six numbers out of 49 is

$$P(6\text{ out of }49)=\frac{1}{\binom{49}{6}}=\frac{1}{13{,}983{,}816}$$

The probability of picking five numbers out of 52 is

$$P(5\text{ out of }52)=\frac{1}{\binom{52}{5}}=\frac{1}{2{,}598{,}960}$$

The odds of winning the lottery when picking five out of 52 is higher.

55. (a) The number of ways to select 5 numbers between 1 and 55 is $\binom{55}{5}=3{,}478{,}761$ and there are 42 ways to select the bonus number.

$$P(\text{winning jackpot})=\frac{1}{3{,}478{,}761\cdot 42}$$

$$=\frac{1}{146{,}107{,}962}$$

(b) The number of selections you would make over 138 years is

$$138 \cdot 365 \cdot 24 \cdot 60 = 72{,}582{,}480.$$

The probability that none of the selections win is

$$\left(\frac{146{,}107{,}961}{146{,}107{,}962}\right)^{72{,}482{,}480} \approx 0.6085.$$

Therefore, the probability of winning is $1 - 0.6085 = 0.3915$.

56. (a) The number of ways to select 6 numbers between 1 and 49 is $\binom{49}{6} = 13{,}983{,}816$. The number of ways to select 3 of the 6 numbers, while not selecting the bonus number is

$$\binom{6}{3}\binom{42}{3} = 20 \cdot 11{,}480 = 229{,}600.$$

The probability of winning fifth prize is

$$\frac{229{,}600}{13{,}983{,}816} \approx 0.01642.$$

(b) The number of ways to select 2 of the 6 numbers plus the bonus number is

$$\binom{6}{2}\binom{1}{1}\binom{42}{3} = 15 \cdot 1 \cdot 11{,}480 = 172{,}200.$$

The probability of winning sixth prize is

$$\frac{172{,}200}{13{,}983{,}816} \approx 0.01231.$$

57. P(saying "Math class is tough.")

$$= \frac{\binom{1}{1}\binom{269}{3}}{\binom{270}{4}} \approx 0.0148$$

No, it is not correct. The correct figure is 1.48%.

58. (a) There were 28 games played in the season, since the numbers in the "Won" column have a sum of 28 (and the numbers in the "Lost" column have a sum of 28).

(b) Assuming no ties, each of the 28 games had 2 possible outcomes; either Team A won and Team B lost, or else Team A lost and Team B won. By the multiplication principle, this means that there were

$$2^{28} = 268{,}435{,}456$$

different outcomes possible.

(c) Any one of the 8 teams could have been the one that won all of its games, any one of the remaining 7 teams could have been the one that won all but one of its games, and so on, until there is only one team left, and it is the one that lost all of its games. By the multiplication principle, this means that there were

$$8! = 8 \cdot 7 \cdot 6 \cdot 5 \cdot 4 \cdot 3 \cdot 2 \cdot 1 = 40{,}320$$

different "perfect progressions" possible.

(d) Thus,

P("perfect progression" in an 8-team league)

$$= \frac{8!}{2^{28}} \approx 0.0001502 = 1.502 \cdot 10^{-4}.$$

(e) If there are n teams in the league, then the "Won" column will begin with $n-1$, followed by $n-2$, then $n-3$, and so on down to 0. It can be shown that the sum of these n numbers is $\frac{n(n-1)}{2}$, so there are $2^{n(n-1)/2}$ different win/lose progressions possible. The n teams can be ordered in $n!$ different ways, so there are $n!$ different "perfect progressions" possible. Thus,

P("perfect progression" in an n-team league)

$$= \frac{n!}{2^{n(n-1)/2}}.$$

59. (a) There are only 4 ways to win in just 4 calls: the 2 diagonals, the center column, and the center row. There are $\binom{75}{4}$ combinations of 4 numbers that can occur. The probability that a person will win bingo after just 4 numbers are called is $\frac{4}{\binom{75}{4}} \approx 3.291 \times 10^{-6}$.

(b) There is only 1 way to get an L. It can occur in as few as 9 calls. There are $\binom{75}{9}$ combinations of 9 numbers that can occur in 9 calls is $\frac{1}{\binom{75}{9}} \approx 7.962 \times 10^{-12}$.

(c) There is only 1 way to get an X-out. It can ocur in as few as 8 calls. There are $\binom{75}{8}$ combinations of 8 numbers that can occur. The probability that an X-out occurs in 8 calls is $\frac{1}{\binom{75}{8}} \approx 5.927 \times 10^{-11}$.

(d) Four columns contain a permutation of 15 numbers taken 5 at a time. One column contains a permutation of 15 numbers taken 4 at a time. The number of distinct cards is $P(15,5)^4 \cdot P(15,4) \approx 5.524 \times 10^{26}$.

8.4 Binomial Probability

1. This is a Bernoulli trial problem with $P(\text{success}) = P(\text{girl}) = \frac{1}{2}$. The probability of exactly x successes in n trials is

$$\binom{n}{x} p^x (1-p)^{n-x},$$

where p is the probability of success in a single trial. We have $n = 5$, $x = 2$, and $p = \frac{1}{2}$. Note that

$$1 - p = 1 - \frac{1}{2} = \frac{1}{2}.$$

$$P(\text{exactly 2 girls and 3 boys}) = \binom{5}{2}\left(\frac{1}{2}\right)^2\left(\frac{1}{2}\right)^3 = \frac{10}{32} = \frac{5}{16} \approx 0.313$$

2. This is a Bernoulli trial problem with $P(\text{success}) = P(\text{girl}) = \frac{1}{2}$. The probability of exactly x successes in n trials is

$$\binom{n}{x} p^x (1-p)^{n-x},$$

where p is the probability of success in a single trial. Here $n = 5$, $x = 3$, and $p = \frac{1}{2}$.

$P(\text{exactly 3 girls and 2 boys})$

$$= \binom{5}{3}\left(\frac{1}{2}\right)^3\left(\frac{1}{2}\right)^2 = 10\left(\frac{1}{32}\right) = \frac{5}{16} \approx 0.313$$

3. We have $n = 5$, $x = 0$, $p = \frac{1}{2}$, and $1 - p = \frac{1}{2}$.

$$P(\text{no girls}) = \binom{5}{0}\left(\frac{1}{2}\right)^0\left(\frac{1}{2}\right)^5 = \frac{1}{32} \approx 0.031$$

4. We have $n = 5$, $x = 0$ is the number of boys, and $p = \frac{1}{2}$ is the probability of having a boy.

$$P(\text{no boys}) = \binom{5}{0}\left(\frac{1}{2}\right)^0\left(\frac{1}{2}\right)^5 = \frac{1}{32} \approx 0.031$$

5. "At least 4 girls" means either 4 or 5 girls.

$P(\text{at least 4 girls})$

$$= \binom{5}{4}\left(\frac{1}{2}\right)^4\left(\frac{1}{2}\right)^1 + \binom{5}{5}\left(\frac{1}{2}\right)^5\left(\frac{1}{2}\right)^0$$

$$= \frac{5}{32} + \frac{1}{32} = \frac{6}{32} = \frac{3}{16} \approx 0.188$$

6. We have 3, 4, or 5 boys, so

$P(\text{at least 3 boys})$

$$= \binom{5}{3}\left(\frac{1}{2}\right)^3\left(\frac{1}{2}\right)^2 + \binom{5}{4}\left(\frac{1}{2}\right)^4\left(\frac{1}{2}\right)^1 + \binom{5}{5}\left(\frac{1}{2}\right)^5\left(\frac{1}{2}\right)^0$$

$$= \frac{10}{32} + \frac{5}{32} + \frac{1}{32} = \frac{16}{32} = \frac{1}{2}.$$

7. $P(\text{no more than 3 boys})$
$= 1 - P(\text{at least 4 boys})$
$= 1 - P(\text{4 boys or 5 boys})$
$= 1 - [P(\text{4 boys}) + P(\text{5 boys})]$

$$= 1 - \left(\frac{5}{32} + \frac{1}{32}\right)$$

$$= 1 - \frac{6}{32}$$

$$= 1 - \frac{3}{16} = \frac{13}{16} \approx 0.813$$

8. $P(\text{no more than 4 girls})$
$= 1 - P(\text{5 girls})$

$$= 1 - \binom{5}{5}\left(\frac{1}{2}\right)^5\left(\frac{1}{2}\right)^0$$

$$= 1 - \frac{1}{32} = \frac{31}{32} \approx 0.969$$

9. On one roll, $P(1) = \frac{1}{6}$. We have $n = 12$, $x = 12$, and $p = \frac{1}{6}$. Note that $1 - p = \frac{5}{6}$. Thus,

$$P(\text{exactly 12 ones}) = \binom{12}{12}\left(\frac{1}{6}\right)^{12}\left(\frac{5}{6}\right)^0 \approx 4.594 \times 10^{-10}.$$

10. We have $n = 12$, $x = 6$, and $p = \frac{1}{6}$, so

$$P(\text{exactly 6 ones}) = \binom{12}{6}\left(\frac{1}{6}\right)^6\left(\frac{5}{6}\right)^6 \approx 0.0066.$$

11. $P(\text{exactly 1 one}) = \binom{12}{1}\left(\frac{1}{6}\right)^1\left(\frac{5}{6}\right)^{11} \approx 0.2692$

12. We have $n = 12$, $x = 2$, and $p = \frac{1}{6}$, so

$$P(\text{exactly 2 ones}) = \binom{12}{2}\left(\frac{1}{6}\right)^2\left(\frac{5}{6}\right)^{10} \approx 0.2961.$$

13. "No more than 3 ones" means 0, 1, 2, or 3 ones. Thus,

$$\begin{aligned}&P(\text{no more than 3 ones})\\&= P(0 \text{ ones}) + P(1 \text{ one}) + P(2 \text{ ones})\\&\quad + P(3 \text{ ones})\\&= \binom{12}{0}\left(\frac{1}{6}\right)^0\left(\frac{5}{6}\right)^{12} + \binom{12}{1}\left(\frac{1}{6}\right)^1\left(\frac{5}{6}\right)^{11}\\&\quad + \binom{12}{2}\left(\frac{1}{6}\right)^2\left(\frac{5}{6}\right)^{10} + \binom{12}{3}\left(\frac{1}{6}\right)^3\left(\frac{5}{6}\right)^{9}\\&\approx 0.8748.\end{aligned}$$

14. "No more than 1 one" means 0 one or 1 one. Thus,

$$\begin{aligned}&P(\text{no more than 1 one})\\&= P(0 \text{ one}) + P(1 \text{ one})\\&= \binom{12}{0}\left(\frac{1}{6}\right)^0\left(\frac{5}{6}\right)^{12} + \binom{12}{1}\left(\frac{1}{6}\right)^1\left(\frac{5}{6}\right)^{11}\\&\approx 0.3813.\end{aligned}$$

15. Each time the coin is tossed, $P(\text{head}) = \frac{1}{2}$. We have $n = 6$, $x = 6$, $p = \frac{1}{2}$, and $1 - p = \frac{1}{2}$. Thus,

$$\begin{aligned}P(\text{all heads}) &= \binom{6}{6}\left(\frac{1}{2}\right)^6\left(\frac{1}{2}\right)^0\\&= \frac{1}{64} \approx 0.016.\end{aligned}$$

16. We have $n = 6$, $x = 3$, and $p = \frac{1}{2}$, so

$$\begin{aligned}P(\text{exactly 3 heads}) &= \binom{6}{3}\left(\frac{1}{2}\right)^3\left(\frac{1}{2}\right)^3\\&= \frac{20}{64} = \frac{5}{16}\\&\approx 0.313.\end{aligned}$$

17. $$\begin{aligned}&P(\text{no more than 3 heads})\\&= P(0 \text{ heads}) + P(1 \text{ head}) + P(2 \text{ heads})\\&\quad + P(3 \text{ heads})\\&= \binom{6}{0}\left(\frac{1}{2}\right)^0\left(\frac{1}{2}\right)^6 + \binom{6}{1}\left(\frac{1}{2}\right)^1\left(\frac{1}{2}\right)^5\\&\quad + \binom{6}{2}\left(\frac{1}{2}\right)^2\left(\frac{1}{2}\right)^4 + \binom{6}{3}\left(\frac{1}{2}\right)^3\left(\frac{1}{2}\right)^3\\&= \frac{42}{64} = \frac{21}{32} \approx 0.656\end{aligned}$$

18. $$\begin{aligned}&P(\text{at least 3 heads})\\&= P(3 \text{ heads}) + P(4 \text{ heads})\\&\quad + P(5 \text{ heads}) + P(6 \text{ heads})\\&= \binom{6}{3}\left(\frac{1}{2}\right)^3\left(\frac{1}{2}\right)^3 + \binom{6}{4}\left(\frac{1}{2}\right)^4\left(\frac{1}{2}\right)^2\\&\quad + \binom{6}{5}\left(\frac{1}{2}\right)^5\left(\frac{1}{2}\right)^1 + \binom{6}{6}\left(\frac{1}{2}\right)^6\left(\frac{1}{2}\right)^0\\&= \frac{20}{64} + \frac{15}{64} + \frac{6}{64} + \frac{1}{64}\\&= \frac{42}{64} = \frac{21}{32} \approx 0.656\end{aligned}$$

21. $$\begin{aligned}&\binom{n}{r} + \binom{n}{r+1}\\&= \frac{n!}{r!(n-r)!} + \frac{n!}{(r+1)![n-(r+1)]!}\\&= \frac{n!(r+1)}{r!(r+1)(n-r)!}\\&\quad + \frac{n!(n-r)}{(r+1)![n-(r+1)]!(n-r)}\\&= \frac{rn! + n!}{(r+1)!(n-r)!} + \frac{n(n!) - rn!}{(r+1)!(n-r)!}\\&= \frac{rn! + n! + n(n!) - rn!}{(r+1)!(n-r)!}\\&= \frac{n!(n+1)}{(r+1)!(n-r)!}\\&= \frac{(n+1)!}{(r+1)![(n+1)-(r+1)]!}\\&= \binom{n+1}{r+1}\end{aligned}$$

22. Since these two crib deaths cannot be assumed to be independent events, the use of binomial probabilities is not applicable and thus the probabilities that are computed are not correct.

23. Since the potential callers are not likely to have birthdates that are distributed evenly throughout the twentieth century, the use of binomial probabilities is not applicable and thus, the probabilities that are computed are not correct.

24. We define a success to be the event that a customer overpays. In this situation, $n = 15$, $x = 3$, $p = \frac{1}{10}$, and $1 - p = \frac{9}{10}$.

$$\begin{aligned}&P(\text{customer overpays on 3 items})\\&= \binom{15}{3}\left(\frac{1}{10}\right)^3\left(\frac{9}{10}\right)^{12}\\&\approx 0.1285\end{aligned}$$

25. We define a success to be the event that a customer overpays. In this situation, $n = 15$, $x = 0$, $p = \frac{1}{10}$, and $1 - p = \frac{9}{10}$.

P(customer does not overpay for any item)

$$= \binom{15}{0}\left(\frac{1}{10}\right)^0\left(\frac{9}{10}\right)^{15}$$
$$\approx 0.2059$$

26. As in Exercise 24, we define a success to be the event that a customer overpays. In this situation, $n = 15$; $x = 1, 2, 3, \ldots, 15$; $p = \frac{1}{10}$; and $1 - p = \frac{9}{10}$.

P(customer overpays on at least one item)
$= 1 - P$(customer overpays on no items)

$$= 1 - \binom{15}{0}\left(\frac{1}{10}\right)^0\left(\frac{9}{10}\right)^{15}$$
$$\approx 0.7941$$

27. In Exercise 25, we defined a success to be the event that a customer overpays. In this situation, $n = 15$; $x = 2, 3, 4, \ldots, 15$; $p = \frac{1}{10}$; and $1 - p = \frac{9}{10}$.

P(a customer overpays on at least 2 items)
$= 1 - P$(a customer overpays on 0 or 1 item)

$$= 1 - \binom{15}{0}\left(\frac{1}{10}\right)^0\left(\frac{9}{10}\right)^{15} - \binom{15}{1}\left(\frac{1}{10}\right)^1\left(\frac{9}{10}\right)^{14}$$
$$\approx 0.4510$$

28. Again, we define a success to be the event that a customer overpays. In this situation, $n = 15$; $x = 0$, 1, or 2; $p = \frac{1}{10}$; and $1 - p = \frac{9}{10}$.

P(customer overpays on at most 2 items)

$$= \binom{15}{0}\left(\frac{1}{10}\right)^0\left(\frac{9}{10}\right)^{15} + \binom{15}{1}\left(\frac{1}{10}\right)^1\left(\frac{9}{10}\right)^{14}$$
$$+ \binom{15}{2}\left(\frac{1}{10}\right)^2\left(\frac{9}{10}\right)^{13}$$
$$\approx 0.8159$$

29. $n = 20, x = 6, p = 0.256$

$$P(6) = \binom{20}{6}(0.256)^6(0.744)^{14}$$
$$\approx 0.1737$$

30. $n = 20,\ x = 9, p = 0.256$

$$P(6) = \binom{20}{9}(0.256)^9(0.744)^{11}$$
$$\approx 0.0307$$

31. $n = 20, p = 0.256$

P(at least 4)

$$= 1 - \binom{20}{0}(0.256)^0(0.744)^{20} - \binom{20}{1}(0.256)^1(0.744)^{19}$$
$$- \binom{20}{2}(0.256)^2(0.744)^{18} - \binom{20}{3}(0.256)^3(0.744)^{17}$$
$$\approx 0.7925$$

32. $n = 20,\ p = 0.256$

P(at most 5)

$$= \binom{20}{0}(0.256)^0(0.744)^{20} + \binom{20}{1}(0.256)^1(0.744)^{19}$$
$$+ \binom{20}{2}(0.256)^2(0.744)^{18} + \binom{20}{3}(0.256)^3(0.744)^{17}$$
$$+ \binom{20}{4}(0.256)^4(0.744)^{16} + \binom{20}{5}(0.256)^5(0.744)^{15}$$
$$\approx 0.5928$$

33. We have $n = 6$, $x = 2$, $p = \frac{1}{5}$, and $1 - p = \frac{4}{5}$. Thus,

$$P(\text{exactly 2 correct}) = \binom{6}{2}\left(\frac{1}{5}\right)^2\left(\frac{4}{5}\right)^4 \approx 0.2458.$$

34. $n = 6,\ p = \frac{1}{5},\ x = 0$

$$P(\text{0 correct}) = \binom{6}{0}\left(\frac{1}{5}\right)^0\left(\frac{4}{5}\right)^6$$
$$= \frac{4096}{15,625}$$
$$\approx 0.2621$$

35. We have

P(at least 4 correct)
$= P$(4 correct) $+ P$(5 correct) $+ P$(6 correct)

$$= \binom{6}{4}\left(\frac{1}{5}\right)^4\left(\frac{4}{5}\right)^2 + \binom{6}{5}\left(\frac{1}{5}\right)^5\left(\frac{4}{5}\right)^1$$
$$+ \binom{6}{6}\left(\frac{1}{5}\right)^6\left(\frac{4}{5}\right)^0$$
$$\approx 0.0170.$$

36. "No more than 3 correct answers" means 0, 1, 2, or 3 correct answers.

$$\begin{aligned} &P(\text{no more than 3 correct}) \\ &= P(0 \text{ correct}) + P(1 \text{ correct}) \\ &\quad + P(2 \text{ correct}) + P(3 \text{ correct}) \\ &= \binom{6}{0}\left(\frac{1}{5}\right)^0\left(\frac{4}{5}\right)^6 + \binom{6}{1}\left(\frac{1}{5}\right)^1\left(\frac{4}{5}\right)^5 \\ &\quad + \binom{6}{2}\left(\frac{1}{5}\right)^2\left(\frac{4}{5}\right)^4 + \binom{6}{3}\left(\frac{1}{5}\right)^3\left(\frac{4}{5}\right)^3 \\ &\approx 0.9830 \end{aligned}$$

37. $n = 20,\ p = 0.05,\ x = 0$

$$P(0 \text{ defective transistors}) = \binom{20}{0}(0.05)^0(0.95)^{20} \approx 0.3585$$

38. We have $n = 20,\ p = 0.05$, and $1-p = 0.95$. Thus,

$$\begin{aligned} &P(\text{at most 2 defective transistors}) \\ &= P(\text{none defective}) + P(\text{one defective}) \\ &\quad + P(\text{two defective}) \\ &= \binom{20}{0}(0.05)^0(0.95)^{20} + \binom{20}{1}(0.05)^1(0.95)^{19} \\ &\quad + \binom{20}{2}(0.05)^2(0.95)^{18} \\ &\approx 0.9245. \end{aligned}$$

39. Let success mean producing a defective item. Then we have $n = 75,\ p = 0.05$, and $1 - p = 0.95$.

(a) If there are exactly 5 defective items, then $x = 5$. Thus,

$$P(\text{exactly 5 defective}) = \binom{75}{5}(0.05)^5(0.95)^{70} \approx 0.1488.$$

(b) If there are no defective items, then $x = 0$. Thus,

$$P(\text{none defective}) = \binom{75}{0}(0.05)^0(0.95)^{75} \approx 0.0213.$$

(c) If there is at least 1 defective item, then we are interested in $x \geq 1$. We have

$$\begin{aligned} P(\text{at least one defective}) &= 1 - P(x = 0) \\ &\approx 1 - 0.021 \\ &= 0.9787. \end{aligned}$$

40. $n = 58,\ p = 0.7$

(a) The probability that all 58 people like the product is

$$P(\text{all } 58) = \binom{58}{58}(0.7)^{58}(0.3)^0 \approx 1.037 \times 10^{-9}.$$

(b) The probability that from 28 to 30 people (inclusive) like the product is

$$\begin{aligned} &P(\text{exactly } 28) + P(\text{exactly } 29) + P(\text{exactly } 30) \\ &= \binom{58}{28}(0.7)^{28}(0.3)^{30} + \binom{58}{29}(0.7)^{29}(0.3)^{29} \\ &\quad + \binom{58}{30}(0.7)^{30}(0.3)^{28} \\ &\approx 0.0024. \end{aligned}$$

41. **(a)** Since 80% of the "good nuts" are good, 20% of the "good nuts" are bad. Let's let success represent "getting a bad nut." Then 0.2 is the probability of success in a single trial. The probability of 8 successes in 20 trials is

$$\binom{20}{8}(0.2)^8(1-0.2)^{20-8} = \binom{20}{8}(0.2)^8(0.8)^{12} \approx 0.0222$$

(b) Since 60% of the "blowouts" are good, 40% of the "blowouts" are bad. Let's let success represent "getting a bad nut." Then 0.4 is the probability of success in a single trial. The probability of 8 successes in 20 trials is

$$\binom{20}{8}(0.4)^8(1-0.4)^{20-8} = \binom{20}{8}(0.4)^8(0.6)^{12} \approx 0.1797$$

(c) The probability that the nuts are "blowouts" is

$$\frac{\text{Probability of "Blowouts" having 8 bad nuts out of 20}}{\text{Probability of "Good Nuts" or "Blowouts" having 8 bad nuts out of 20}}$$

$$= \frac{0.3\left[\binom{20}{8}(0.4)^8(0.6)^{12}\right]}{0.7\left[\binom{20}{8}(0.2)^8(0.8)^{12}\right] + 0.3\left[\binom{20}{8}(0.4)^8(0.6)^{12}\right]} \approx 0.7766.$$

42. $n = 20, p = 0.05$

$$P(\text{fewer than } 3)$$
$$= P(0) + P(1) + P(2)$$
$$= \binom{20}{0}(0.05)^0(0.95)^{20} + \binom{20}{1}(0.05)^1(0.95)^{19}$$
$$+ \binom{20}{2}(0.05)^2(0.95)^{18}$$
$$\approx 0.9245$$

The answer is **e**.

43. $n = 15, p = 0.85$

$$P(\text{all } 15) = \binom{15}{15}(0.85)^{15}(0.15)^0 \approx 0.0874$$

44. $n = 15, p = 0.85$

$$P(\text{none}) = \binom{15}{0}(0.85)^0(0.15)^{15} \approx 4.379 \times 10^{-13}$$

45. $n = 15, p = 0.85$

$$P(\text{not all}) = 1 - P(\text{all } 15)$$
$$= 1 - \binom{15}{15}(0.85)^{15}(0.15)^0$$
$$\approx 0.9126$$

46. $n = 15, p = 0.85$

$$P(\text{more than half})$$
$$= P(8) + P(9) + P(10) + P(11) + P(12)$$
$$+ P(13) + P(14) + P(15)$$
$$= \binom{15}{8}(0.85)^8(0.15)^7 + \binom{15}{9}(0.85)^9(0.15)^6$$
$$+ \binom{15}{10}(0.85)^{10}(0.15)^5 + \binom{15}{11}(0.85)^{11}(0.15)^4$$
$$+ \binom{15}{12}(0.85)^{12}(0.15)^3 + \binom{15}{13}(0.85)^{13}(0.15)^2$$
$$+ \binom{15}{14}(0.85)^{14}(0.15)^1 + \binom{15}{15}(0.85)^{15}(0.15)^0$$
$$\approx 0.9994$$

47. $n = 100,\ p = 0.012,\ x = 2$

$$P(\text{exactly 2 sets of twins})$$
$$= \binom{100}{2}(0.012)^2(0.988)^{98} \approx 0.2183$$

48. We have $n = 100,\ p = 0.012$, and $1 - p = 0.988$. Thus,

$$P(\text{at most 2 sets})$$
$$= P(x = 0) + P(x = 1) + P(x = 2)$$
$$= \binom{100}{0}(0.012)^0(0.988)^{100} + \binom{100}{1}(0.012)^1(0.988)^{99}$$
$$+ \binom{100}{2}(0.012)^2(0.988)^{98}$$
$$= (0.012)^0(0.988)^{100} + 100(0.012)^1(0.988)^{99}$$
$$+ 4950(0.012)^2(0.988)^{98} \approx 0.8805.$$

49. We have $n = 10{,}000$, $p = 2.5 \cdot 10^{-7} = 0.00000025$, and $1 - p = 0.99999975$. Thus,

$$P(\text{at least 1 mutation occurs})$$
$$= 1 - P(\text{none occurs})$$
$$= 1 - \binom{10{,}000}{0} p^0(1-p)^{10{,}000}$$
$$= 1 - (0.99999975)^{10{,}000}$$
$$\approx 0.0025.$$

50. We define a success to be the event that an inoculated person gets the flu. In this situation, $n = 83,\ p = 0.2$, and $1 - p = 0.8$.

(a) $P(10 \text{ successes}) = \binom{83}{10}(0.2)^{10}(0.8)^{73}$

$$\approx 0.0210$$

(b) $P(\text{no more than 4 succeses})$

$$= P(0 \text{ successes}) + P(1 \text{ success})$$
$$+ P(2 \text{ successes}) + P(3 \text{ successes})$$
$$+ P(4 \text{ successes})$$
$$= \binom{83}{0}(0.2)^0(0.8)^{83} + \binom{83}{1}(0.2)^1(0.8)^{82}$$
$$+ \binom{83}{2}(0.2)^2(0.8)^{81} + \binom{83}{3}(0.2)^3(0.8)^{80}$$
$$+ \binom{83}{4}(0.2)^4(0.83)^{79}$$
$$\approx 8.004 \times 10^{-5}$$

(c) $P(\text{none of the inoculated people get the flu})$

$$= P(\text{no successes})$$
$$= \binom{83}{0}(0.2)^0(0.8)^{83} \approx 9.046 \times 10^{-9}$$

51. $n = 53,\ p = 0.042$

(a) The probability that exactly 5 men are color-blind is

$$P(5) = \binom{53}{5}(0.042)^5(0.958)^{48} \approx 0.0478.$$

(b) The probability that no more than 5 men are color-blind is

$$\begin{aligned} P(\text{no more than 5 men are color-blind}) &= \binom{53}{0}(0.042)^0(0.958)^{53} + \binom{53}{1}(0.042)^1(0.958)^{52} \\ &+ \binom{53}{2}(0.042)^2(0.958)^{51} + \binom{53}{3}(0.042)^3(0.958)^{50} \\ &+ \binom{53}{4}(0.042)^4(0.958)^{49} + \binom{53}{5}(0.042)^5(0.958)^{48} \\ &\approx 0.9767. \end{aligned}$$

(c) The probability that at least 1 man is color-blind is

$$1 - P(0 \text{ men are color-blind}) = 1 - \binom{53}{0}(0.042)^0(0.958)^{53} \approx 0.8971.$$

52. (a) $P(10 \text{ or more}) = 1 - P(\text{less than } 10) = 1 - [P(0) + P(1) + P(2) + \ldots + P(9)]$

$$\begin{aligned} &= 1 - \left[\binom{100}{0}(0.073)^0(0.927)^{100} + \binom{100}{1}(0.073)^1(0.927)^{99} \right. \\ &+ \binom{100}{2}(0.073)^2(0.927)^{98} + \binom{100}{3}(0.073)^3(0.927)^{97} \\ &+ \binom{100}{4}(0.073)^4(0.927)^{96} + \binom{100}{5}(0.073)^5(0.927)^{95} \\ &+ \binom{100}{6}(0.073)^6(0.927)^{94} + \binom{100}{7}(0.073)^7(0.927)^{93} \\ &\left. + \binom{100}{8}(0.073)^8(0.927)^{92} + \binom{100}{9}(0.073)^9(0.927)^{91}\right] \\ &\approx 1 - [0.00051 + 0.00402 + 0.01567 + 0.04031 + 0.07698 + 0.11639 + 0.14512 \\ &\quad + 0.15346 + 0.14049 + 0.11309] \\ &= 1 - 0.80604 = 0.19396 \end{aligned}$$

The probability that 10 or more will experience nausea/vomiting is about 0.1940.

(b) $P(10 \text{ or more}) = 1 - P(\text{less than } 10) = 1 - [P(0) + P(1) + P(2) + \ldots + P(9)]$

$$\begin{aligned} &= 1 - \left[\binom{100}{0}(0.071)^0(0.929)^{100} + \binom{100}{1}(0.071)^1(0.929)^{99} \right. \\ &+ \binom{100}{2}(0.071)^2(0.929)^{98} + \binom{100}{3}(0.071)^3(0.929)^{97} \\ &+ \binom{100}{4}(0.071)^4(0.929)^{96} + \binom{100}{5}(0.071)^5(0.929)^{95} \\ &+ \binom{100}{6}(0.071)^6(0.929)^{94} + \binom{100}{7}(0.071)^7(0.929)^{93} \\ &\left. + \binom{100}{8}(0.071)^8(0.929)^{92} + \binom{100}{9}(0.071)^9(0.929)^{91}\right] \\ &= 1 - 0.82765 = 0.17235 \end{aligned}$$

The probability that 10 or more will experience nausea/vomiting is about 0.1724.

53. **(a)** Since the probability of a particular band matching is 1 in 4 or $\frac{1}{4}$, the probability that 5 bands match is $\left(\frac{1}{4}\right)^5 = \frac{1}{1024}$ or 1 chance in 1024.

(b) The probability that 20 bands match is

$\left(\frac{1}{4}\right)^{20} \approx \frac{1}{1.1 \times 10^{12}}$ or about 1 chance in 1.1×10^{12}.

(c) If 20 bands are compared, the probability that 16 or more bands match is

$$\begin{aligned}
&P(\text{at least } 16)\\
&= P(16) + P(17) + P(18) + P(19) + P(20)\\
&= \binom{20}{16}\left(\frac{1}{4}\right)^{16}\left(\frac{3}{4}\right)^{4} + \binom{20}{17}\left(\frac{1}{4}\right)^{17}\left(\frac{3}{4}\right)^{3}\\
&\quad + \binom{20}{18}\left(\frac{1}{4}\right)^{18}\left(\frac{3}{4}\right)^{2} + \binom{20}{19}\left(\frac{1}{4}\right)^{19}\left(\frac{3}{4}\right)^{1}\\
&\quad + \binom{20}{20}\left(\frac{1}{4}\right)^{20}\left(\frac{3}{4}\right)^{0}\\
&= 4845\left(\frac{1}{4}\right)^{16}\left(\frac{3}{4}\right)^{4} + 1140\left(\frac{1}{4}\right)^{17}\left(\frac{3}{4}\right)^{3}\\
&\quad + 190\left(\frac{1}{4}\right)^{18}\left(\frac{3}{4}\right)^{2} + 20\left(\frac{1}{4}\right)^{19}\left(\frac{3}{4}\right)^{1}\\
&\quad + \left(\frac{1}{4}\right)^{20} \cdot 1\\
&= \left(\frac{1}{4}\right)^{16}\left[4845\left(\frac{81}{256}\right) + 1140\left(\frac{1}{4}\right)\left(\frac{27}{64}\right)\right.\\
&\quad \left. + 190\left(\frac{1}{16}\right)\left(\frac{9}{16}\right) + 20\left(\frac{1}{64}\right)\left(\frac{3}{4}\right) + \frac{1}{256}\right]\\
&= \left(\frac{1}{4}\right)^{16}\left(\frac{392{,}445 + 30{,}780 + 1710 + 60 + 1}{256}\right)\\
&= \frac{424{,}996}{4^{20}}\\
&= \frac{1}{\frac{4^{20}}{424{,}996}}\\
&\approx \frac{1}{2{,}587{,}110}
\end{aligned}$$

or about 1 chance in 2.587×10^6.

54. **(a)** $n = 4, p = 0.25$

$$\begin{aligned}
P(\text{at least } 1) &= 1 - P(\text{none})\\
&= 1 - \binom{4}{0}(0.25)^0(0.75)^4\\
&\approx 0.6836
\end{aligned}$$

(b) $n = 3, p = 0.25$

$$\begin{aligned}
P(\text{at least } 1) &= 1 - P(\text{none})\\
&= 1 - \binom{3}{0}(0.25)^0(0.75)^3\\
&\approx 0.5781
\end{aligned}$$

(c) The assumption of independence is likely not justified because the bacteria would be present in groups of eggs from the same source.

55. $n = 4800, p = 0.001$

$$\begin{aligned}
&P(\text{more than } 1)\\
&= 1 - P(1) - P(0)\\
&= 1 - \binom{4800}{1}(0.001)^1(0.999)^{4799}\\
&\quad - \binom{4800}{0}(0.001)^0(0.999)^{4800}\\
&\approx 0.9523
\end{aligned}$$

56. First, find the probability that one out of 30 vials is ineffective, given that the shipment came from company X.
$n = 30, p = 0.1, x = 1$

$$\begin{aligned}
P(1) &= \binom{30}{1}(0.1)^1(0.9)^{29}\\
&\approx 0.1413
\end{aligned}$$

Next, find the probability that one out of 30 vials is ineffective, given that the shipment came from company Y.
$n = 30, p = 0.02, x = 1$

$$\begin{aligned}
P(1) &= \binom{30}{1}(0.02)^1(0.98)^{29}\\
&\approx 0.3340
\end{aligned}$$

Use Bayes' Theorem to find the probability that shipment came from company X. Let A be the event that the shipment came from company X and B be the event that one vial out of thirty is ineffective.

$$P(A) = \frac{1}{5} = 0.2$$

$$P(B) \approx \frac{1}{5}(0.1413) + \frac{4}{5}(0.3340) \approx 0.2955$$

$$P(B|A) \approx 0.1413$$

$$P(A|B) = \frac{P(B|A)P(A)}{P(B)} \approx \frac{0.1413 \cdot 0.2}{0.2955} \approx 0.10$$

The answer is a.

57. First, find the probability that one group of ten has at least 9 participants complete the study. $n = 10, p = 0.8,$

$$P(\text{at least 9 complete}) = P(9) + P(10) = \binom{10}{9}(0.8)^9(0.2)^1 + \binom{10}{10}(0.8)^{10}(0.2)^0 \approx 0.3758$$

The probability that 2 or more drop out in one group is $1 - 0.3758 = 0.6242$. Thus, the probability that at least 9 participants complete the study in one of the two groups, but not in both groups, is $(0.3758)(0.6242) + (0.6242)(0.3758) \approx 0.469$. The answer is e.

58. We define a success to be the event that a woman would prefer to work part-time rather than full-time. In this situation, $n = 10$; $x = 3, 4, 5, \ldots, 10$; $p = 0.33$; and $1 - p = 0.67$.

$$\begin{aligned}
&P(\text{at least 3}) \\
&= 1 - P(x = 0,\ 1, \text{ or } 2) \\
&= 1 - [P(x = 0) + P(x = 1) + P(x = 2)] \\
&= 1 - P(x = 0) - P(x = 1) - P(x = 2) \\
&= 1 - \binom{10}{0}(0.33)^0(0.67)^{10} - \binom{10}{1}(0.33)^1(0.67)^9 \\
&\quad - \binom{10}{2}(0.33)^2(0.67)^8 \\
&\approx 0.6930
\end{aligned}$$

59. $n = 12, x = 7, p = 0.83$

$$P(7) = \binom{12}{7}(0.83)^7(0.17)^5 \approx 0.0305$$

60. $n = 12, x = 9, p = 0.83$

$$P(9) = \binom{12}{9}(0.83)^9(0.17)^3 \approx 0.2021$$

61. $n = 12, p = 0.83$

$$\begin{aligned}
&P(\text{at least 9}) \\
&= P(9) + P(10) + P(11) + P(12) \\
&= \binom{12}{9}(0.83)^9(0.17)^3 + \binom{12}{10}(0.83)^{10}(0.17)^2 \\
&\quad + \binom{12}{11}(0.83)^{11}(0.17)^1 + \binom{12}{12}(0.83)^{12}(0.17)^0 \\
&\approx 0.8676
\end{aligned}$$

62. $n = 12,\ p = 0.83$

$$\begin{aligned}
&P(\text{at most 9}) \\
&= P(\text{at least 10}) \\
&= 1 - P(10) - P(11) - P(12) \\
&= 1 - \binom{12}{10}(0.83)^{10}(0.17)^2 + \binom{12}{11}(0.83)^{11}(0.17)^1 \\
&\quad + \binom{12}{12}(0.83)^{12}(0.17)^0 \\
&\approx 0.3344
\end{aligned}$$

63. $n = 10,\ p = 0.33,\ 1 - p = 0.67$

(a) The probability that exactly 2 belong to an ethnic minority is

$$\binom{10}{2}(0.33)^2(0.67)^8 \approx 0.1990.$$

(b) The probability that 3 or fewer belong to an ethnic minority is

$$\binom{10}{0}(0.33)^0(0.67)^{10} + \binom{10}{1}(0.33)^1(0.67)^9 + \binom{10}{2}(0.33)^2(0.67)^8 + \binom{10}{3}(0.33)^3(0.67)^7 \approx 0.5684.$$

(c) The probability that one person does not belong to an ethnic minority is 0.67. The probability that exactly 5 do not belong to an ethnic minority is

$$\binom{10}{5}(0.67)^5(0.33)^5 \approx 0.1332.$$

(d) The probability that 6 or more do not belong to an ethnic minority is

$$\binom{10}{6}(0.67)^6(0.33)^4 + \binom{10}{7}(0.67)^7(0.33)^3 + \binom{10}{8}(0.67)^8(0.33)^2 + \binom{10}{9}(0.67)^9(0.33)^1 + \binom{10}{10}(0.67)^{10}(0.33)^0$$

$$\approx 0.7936.$$

64. (a) No, the results only indicated that 84% of college students believe they need to cheat to get ahead in the world today. It says nothing about whether or not they cheat.

(b)
$$\begin{aligned}
P(90 \text{ or more}) &= P(90) + P(91) + \ldots + P(100) \\
&= \binom{100}{90}(0.84)^{90}(0.16)^{10} + \binom{100}{91}(0.84)^{91}(0.16)^{9} \\
&= \binom{100}{92}(0.84)^{92}(0.16)^{8} + \binom{100}{93}(0.84)^{93}(0.16)^{7} \\
&= \binom{100}{94}(0.84)^{94}(0.16)^{6} + \binom{100}{95}(0.84)^{95}(0.16)^{5} \\
&= \binom{100}{96}(0.84)^{96}(0.16)^{4} + \binom{100}{97}(0.84)^{97}(0.16)^{3} \\
&= \binom{100}{98}(0.84)^{98}(0.16)^{2} + \binom{100}{99}(0.84)^{99}(0.16)^{1} \\
&= \binom{100}{100}(0.84)^{100}(0.16)^{0} \\
&\approx 0.02915 + 0.01682 + 0.00864 + 0.00390 + 0.00152 + 0.00051 + 0.00014 \\
&\quad + 0.00003 + 0 + 0 + 0 \\
&= 0.06071
\end{aligned}$$

The probability that 90 or more will answer affirmatively to the question is about 0.0607.

65. (a) The probability that less than 15 will graduate from high school by age 19 is

$$\begin{aligned}
P(\text{less than } 15) &= P(0) + P(1) + P(2) + P(3) + \ldots + P(14) \\
&= \binom{40}{0}(0.152)^0(0.848)^{40} + \binom{40}{1}(0.152)^1(0.848)^{39} + \binom{40}{2}(0.152)^2(0.848)^{38} \\
&\quad + \binom{40}{3}(0.152)^3(0.848)^{37} + \binom{40}{4}(0.152)^4(0.848)^{36} + \binom{40}{5}(0.152)^5(0.848)^{35} \\
&\quad + \binom{40}{6}(0.152)^6(0.848)^{34} + \binom{40}{7}(0.152)^7(0.848)^{33} + \binom{40}{8}(0.152)^8(0.848)^{32} \\
&\quad + \binom{40}{9}(0.152)^9(0.848)^{31} + \binom{40}{10}(0.152)^{10}(0.848)^{30} + \binom{40}{11}(0.152)^{11}(0.848)^{29} \\
&\quad + \binom{40}{12}(0.152)^{12}(0.848)^{28} + \binom{40}{13}(0.152)^{13}(0.848)^{27} + \binom{40}{14}(0.152)^{14}(0.848)^{26} \\
&\approx 0.00137 + 0.00980 + 0.03426 + 0.07779 + 0.12898 \\
&\quad + 0.16646 + 0.17405 + 0.15153 + 0.11204 + 0.07140 \\
&\quad + 0.03968 + 0.01940 + 0.00840 + 0.00324 + 0.00112 \\
&\approx 0.9995
\end{aligned}$$

66. **(a)** $n = 1613, p = \dfrac{1174}{644{,}066}$

$$\begin{aligned} P(\text{at least } 9) &= 1 - P(\text{at most } 8) \\ &= 1 - \text{binomcdf}(1613, 1174/644066, 8) \\ &\approx 0.0033 \end{aligned}$$

(b) $n = 7146, p = \dfrac{1174}{644{,}066}$

$$\begin{aligned} P(\text{at least } 28) &= 1 - P(\text{at most } 27) \\ &= 1 - \text{binomcdf}(7146, 1174/644066, 27) \\ &\approx 2.076 \times 10^{-4} \end{aligned}$$

(c) $n = 7146, p = \dfrac{1174}{644{,}066}$

$$\begin{aligned} P(\text{at most } 54) &= \text{binomcdf}(62572, 1174/644066, 54) \\ &\approx 2.799 \times 10^{-10} \end{aligned}$$

67. **(a)** Suppose the National League wins the series in four games. Then they must win all four games and $P = \binom{4}{4}(0.5)^4(0.5)^0 = 0.0625$. Since the probability that the American League wins the series in four games is equally likely, the probability the series lasts four games is $2(0.0625) = 0.125$.

Suppose the National League wins the series in five games. Then they must win exactly three of the previous four games and $P = \binom{4}{3}(0.5)^3(0.5)^1 \cdot (0.5) = 0.125$. Since the probability that the American League wins the series in five games is equally likely, the probability the series lasts five games is $2(0.125) = 0.25$. Suppose the National League wins the series in six games. Then they must win exactly three of the previous five games and $P = \binom{5}{3}(0.5)^3(0.5)^2 \cdot (0.5) = 0.15625$. Since the probability that the American League wins the series in six games is equally likely, the probability the series lasts six games is $2(0.15625) = 0.3125$. Suppose the National League wins the series in seven games. Then they must win exactly three of the previous six games and $P = \binom{6}{3}(0.5)^3(0.5)^3 \cdot (0.5) = 0.15625$.Since the probability that the American League wins the series in seven games is equally likely, the probability the series last seven games is $2(0.15625) = 0.3125$.

(b) Suppose the better team wins the series in four games. Then they must win all four games and $P = \binom{4}{4}(0.73)^4(0.27)^0 \approx 0.2840$. Suppose the other team wins the series in four games. Then they must win all four games and
$P = \binom{4}{4}(0.27)^4(0.73)^0 \approx 0.0053$. The probability the series lasts four games is the sum of two probabilities, 0.2893.
Suppose the better team wins the series in five games. Then they must win exactly three of the previous four games and $P = \binom{4}{3}(0.73)^3(0.27)^1 \cdot (0.73) \approx 0.3067$. Suppose the other team wins the series in five games. Then they must win exactly three of the previous four games and $P = \binom{4}{3}(0.27)^3(0.73)^1 \cdot (0.27) \approx 0.0155$. The probability the series lasts five games is the sum of the two probabilities, 0.3222.
Suppose the better team wins the series in six games. Then they must win exactly three of the previous five games and $P = \binom{5}{3}(0.73)^3(0.27)^2 \cdot (0.73) \approx 0.2070$. Suppose the other team wins the series in six games. Then they must win exactly three of the previous five games and $P = \binom{5}{3}(0.27)^3(0.73)^2 \cdot (0.27) \approx 0.0283$. The probability the series lasts six games is the sum of the two probabilities, 0.2353.
Suppose the better team wins the series in seven games. Then they must win exactly three of the previous six games and $P = \binom{6}{3}(0.73)^3(0.27)^3 \cdot (0.73) \approx 0.1118$. Suppose the other team wins the series in seven games. Then they must win exactly three of the previous six games and $P = \binom{6}{3}(0.27)^3(0.73)^3 \cdot (0.27) \approx 0.0413$. The probability the series lasts seven games is the sum of the two probabilties, 0.1531.

8.5 Probability Distributions; Expected Value

1. Let x denote the number of heads observed. Then x can take on 0, 1, 2, 3, or 4 as values. The probabilities are as follows.

$$P(x = 0) = \binom{4}{0}\left(\frac{1}{2}\right)^0\left(\frac{1}{2}\right)^4 = \frac{1}{16}$$

$$P(x = 1) = \binom{4}{1}\left(\frac{1}{2}\right)^1\left(\frac{1}{2}\right)^3 = \frac{4}{16} = \frac{1}{4}$$

$$P(x = 2) = \binom{4}{2}\left(\frac{1}{2}\right)^2\left(\frac{1}{2}\right)^2 = \frac{6}{16} = \frac{3}{8}$$

$$P(x = 3) = \binom{4}{3}\left(\frac{1}{2}\right)^3\left(\frac{1}{2}\right)^1 = \frac{4}{16} = \frac{1}{4}$$

$$P(x = 4) = \binom{4}{4}\left(\frac{1}{2}\right)^4\left(\frac{1}{2}\right)^0 = \frac{1}{16}$$

Therefore, the probability distribution is as follows.

Number of Heads	0	1	2	3	4
Probability	$\frac{1}{16}$	$\frac{1}{4}$	$\frac{3}{8}$	$\frac{1}{4}$	$\frac{1}{16}$

2. There are 36 outcomes. We count the number of ways each sum can be obtained, and then divide by 36 to get each probability.

Number of Points	2	3	4	5	6	7	8	9	10	11	12
Ways to Get This Total	1	2	3	4	5	6	5	4	3	2	1
Probability	$\frac{1}{36}$	$\frac{1}{18}$	$\frac{1}{12}$	$\frac{1}{9}$	$\frac{5}{36}$	$\frac{1}{6}$	$\frac{5}{36}$	$\frac{1}{9}$	$\frac{1}{12}$	$\frac{1}{18}$	$\frac{1}{36}$

3. Let x denote the number of aces drawn. Then x can take on values 0, 1, 2, or 3. The probabilities are as follows.

$$P(x=0)=\binom{3}{0}\left(\frac{48}{52}\right)\left(\frac{47}{51}\right)\left(\frac{46}{50}\right)\approx 0.7826$$

$$P(x=1)=\binom{3}{1}\left(\frac{4}{52}\right)\left(\frac{48}{51}\right)\left(\frac{47}{50}\right)\approx 0.2042$$

$$P(x=2)=\binom{3}{2}\left(\frac{4}{52}\right)\left(\frac{3}{51}\right)\left(\frac{48}{50}\right)\approx 0.0130$$

$$P(x=3)=\binom{3}{3}\left(\frac{4}{52}\right)\left(\frac{3}{51}\right)\left(\frac{2}{50}\right)\approx 0.0002$$

Therefore, the probability distribution is as follows.

Number of Aces	0	1	2	3
Probability	0.7826	0.2042	0.0130	0.0002

4. Use combinations to find the probabilities of drawing 0, 1, and 2 black balls.

$$P(0)=\frac{\binom{2}{0}\binom{4}{2}}{\binom{6}{2}}=\frac{6}{15}=\frac{2}{5}$$

$$P(1)=\frac{\binom{2}{1}\binom{4}{1}}{\binom{6}{2}}=\frac{8}{15}$$

$$P(2)=\frac{\binom{2}{2}\binom{4}{0}}{\binom{6}{2}}=\frac{1}{15}$$

Number of Black Balls	0	1	2
Probability	$\frac{2}{5}$	$\frac{8}{15}$	$\frac{1}{15}$

5. Use the probabilities that were calculated in Exercise 1. Draw a histogram with 5 rectangles, corresponding to $x=0$, $x=1$, $x=2$, $x=3$, and $x=4$. $P(x\le 2)$ corresponds to

$$P(x=0)+P(x=1)+P(x=2),$$

so shade the first 3 rectangles in the histogram.

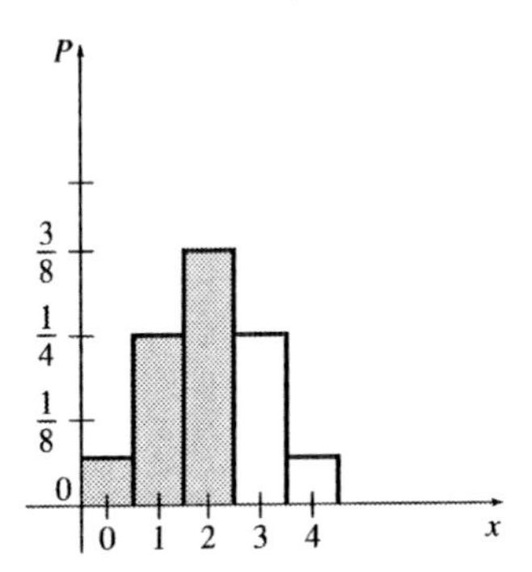

6. $P(x\ge 11)$

Use the probabilities that were calculated in Exercise 2, and shade the regions corresponding to $x=11$ and $x=12$.

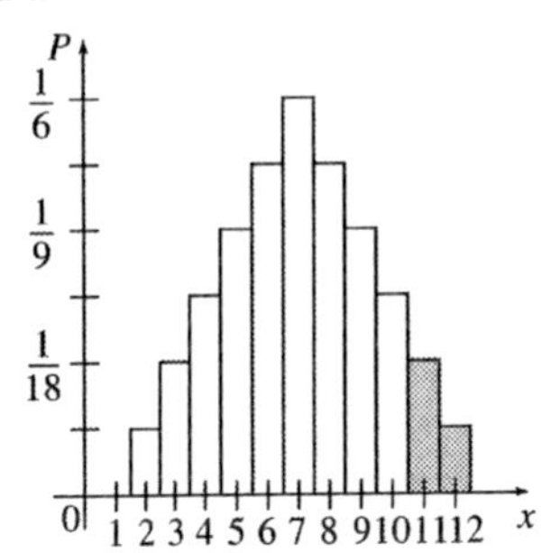

7. Use the probabilities that were calculated in Exercise 3. Draw a histogram with 4 rectangles, corresponding to $x=0$, $x=1$, $x=2$, and $x=3$. $P(\text{at least one ace})=P(x\ge 1)$ corresponds to

$$P(x=1)+P(x=2)+P(x=3),$$

so shade the last 3 rectangles.

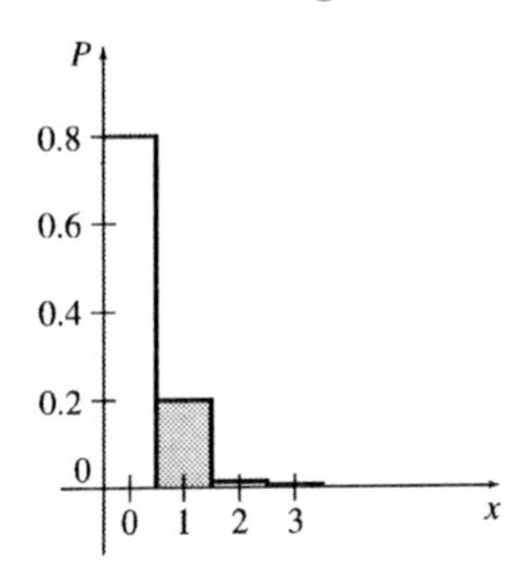

8. P(at least one black ball)

Use the probabilities that were calculated in Exercise 4, and shade the regions corresponding to $x = 1$ and $x = 2$.

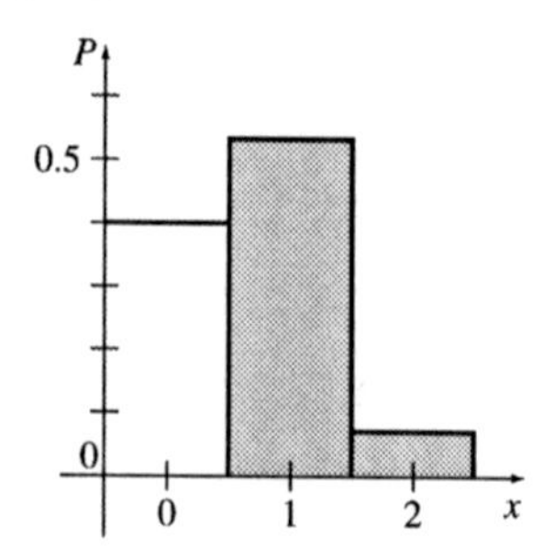

9. $E(x) = 2(0.1) + 3(0.4) + 4(0.3) + 5(0.2)$
$= 3.6$

10. $E(y) = 4(0.4) + 6(0.4) + 8(0.05) + 10(0.15)$
$= 5.9$

11. $E(z) = 9(0.14) + 12(0.22) + 15(0.38) + 18(0.19) + 21(0.07)$
$= 14.49$

12. $E(x) = 30(0.31) + 32(0.29) + 36(0.26) + 38(0.09) + 44(0.05)$
$= 33.56$

13. It is possible (but not necessary) to begin by writing the histogram's data as a probability distribution, which would look as follows.

x	1	2	3	4
$P(x)$	0.2	0.3	0.1	0.4

The expected value of x is

$$E(x) = 1(0.2) + 2(0.3) + 3(0.1) + 4(0.4) = 2.7.$$

14. $P(2) = 0.2,\ P(4) = 0.3,\ P(6) = 0.2,$
$P(8) = 0.1$, and $P(10) = 0.2$.

$$E(x) = 2(0.2) + 4(0.3) + 6(0.2) + 8(0.1) + 10(0.2) = 5.6$$

15. The expected value of x is

$$E(x) = 6(0.1) + 12(0.2) + 18(0.4) + 24(0.2) + 30(0.1) = 18.$$

16. Notice that the probability of all values is 0.2.

$$E(x) = 0.2(10 + 20 + 30 + 40 + 50) = 0.2(150) = 30$$

17. Using the data from Example 4, the expected winnings for Mary are

$$E(x) = -1.2\left(\frac{1}{4}\right) + 1.2\left(\frac{1}{4}\right) + 1.2\left(\frac{1}{4}\right) + (-1.2)\left(\frac{1}{4}\right) = 0.$$

Yes, it is still a fair game if Mary tosses and Donna calls.

18.

	Possible Results	
Result of toss	H	H
Call	H	T
Caller wins?	Yes	No
Probability	$\frac{1}{2}$	$\frac{1}{2}$

(a) Yes, this is still a fair game, since the probability of Donna matching is still $\frac{1}{2}$.

(b) If Donna calls heads, her expected gain (since she will match with probability = 1) is

$$1(1.20) = \$1.20.$$

(c) If Donna calls tails, her expected gain (since she will lose with probability = 1) is

$$1(-1.20¢) = -\$1.20.$$

19. (a)

Number of Yellow Marbles	Probability
0	$\frac{\binom{3}{0}\binom{4}{3}}{\binom{7}{3}} = \frac{4}{35}$
1	$\frac{\binom{3}{1}\binom{4}{2}}{\binom{7}{3}} = \frac{18}{35}$
2	$\frac{\binom{3}{2}\binom{4}{1}}{\binom{7}{3}} = \frac{12}{35}$
3	$\frac{\binom{3}{3}\binom{4}{0}}{\binom{7}{3}} = \frac{1}{35}$

Draw a histogram with four rectangles corresponding to $x = 0$, 1, 2, and 3.

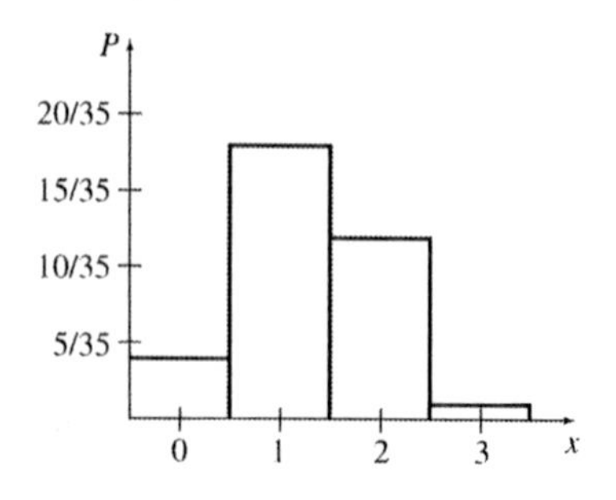

(b) Expected number of yellow marbles

$$= 0\left(\frac{4}{35}\right) + 1\left(\frac{18}{35}\right) + 2\left(\frac{12}{35}\right) + 3\left(\frac{1}{35}\right)$$

$$= \frac{45}{35} = \frac{9}{7} \approx 1.286$$

20. (a) Use combinations to set up the probability distribution. In each case, there are 5 rotten apples and 20 good apples to pick from. There are a total of $\binom{25}{2}$ ways to choose any two apples.

Number of Rotten Apples	0	1	2
Probability	$\frac{\binom{5}{0}\binom{20}{2}}{\binom{25}{2}}$	$\frac{\binom{5}{1}\binom{20}{1}}{\binom{25}{2}}$	$\frac{\binom{5}{2}\binom{20}{0}}{\binom{25}{2}}$
Simplified	$\frac{190}{300}$	$\frac{100}{300}$	$\frac{10}{300}$

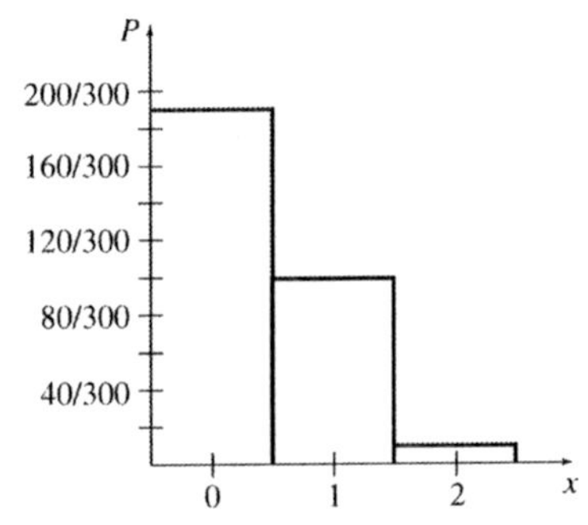

(b) We therefore have

$$E(x) = 0\left(\frac{190}{300}\right) + 1\left(\frac{100}{300}\right) + 2\left(\frac{10}{300}\right)$$

$$= \frac{120}{300} = 0.4.$$

21. (a) Let x be the number of times 1 is rolled. Since the probability of getting a 1 on any single roll is $\frac{1}{6}$, the probability of any other outcome is $\frac{5}{6}$. Use combinations since the order of outcomes is not important.

$$P(x=0) = \binom{4}{0}\left(\frac{1}{6}\right)^0\left(\frac{5}{6}\right)^4 = \frac{625}{1296}$$

$$P(x=1) = \binom{4}{1}\left(\frac{1}{6}\right)^1\left(\frac{5}{6}\right)^3 = \frac{125}{324}$$

$$P(x=2) = \binom{4}{2}\left(\frac{1}{6}\right)^2\left(\frac{5}{6}\right)^2 = \frac{25}{216}$$

$$P(x=3) = \binom{4}{3}\left(\frac{1}{6}\right)^3\left(\frac{5}{6}\right)^1 = \frac{5}{324}$$

$$P(x=4) = \binom{4}{4}\left(\frac{1}{6}\right)^4\left(\frac{5}{6}\right)^0 = \frac{1}{1296}$$

x	0	1	2	3	4
$P(x)$	$\frac{625}{1296}$	$\frac{125}{324}$	$\frac{25}{216}$	$\frac{5}{324}$	$\frac{1}{1296}$

(b) $E(x) = 0\left(\frac{625}{1296}\right) + 1\left(\frac{125}{324}\right) + 2\left(\frac{25}{216}\right)$

$$+ 3\left(\frac{5}{324}\right) + 4\left(\frac{1}{1296}\right)$$

$$= \frac{2}{3}$$

22. The probability that the delegation contains no liberals and 3 conservatives is

$$\frac{\binom{5}{0}\binom{6}{3}}{\binom{11}{3}} = \frac{1 \cdot 6}{11} = \frac{20}{165}.$$

Similarly, use combinations to calculate the remaining probabilities for the probability distribution.

(a) Let x represent the number of liberals on the delegation. The probability distribution of x is as follows.

x	0	1	2	3
$P(x)$	$\frac{20}{165}$	$\frac{75}{165}$	$\frac{60}{165}$	$\frac{10}{165}$

The expected value is

$$E(x) = 0\left(\frac{20}{165}\right) + 1\left(\frac{75}{165}\right) + 2\left(\frac{60}{165}\right) + 3\left(\frac{10}{165}\right)$$

$$= \frac{225}{165} = \frac{15}{11} \approx 1.3636 \text{ liberals.}$$

(b) Let y represent the number of conservatives on the committee. The probability distribution of y is as follows.

y	0	1	2	3
$P(y)$	$\frac{10}{165}$	$\frac{60}{165}$	$\frac{75}{165}$	$\frac{20}{165}$

The expected value is

$$E(y) = 0\left(\frac{10}{165}\right) + 1\left(\frac{60}{165}\right) + 2\left(\frac{75}{165}\right) + 3\left(\frac{20}{165}\right)$$

$$= \frac{270}{165} = \frac{18}{11} \approx 1.6364 \text{ conservatives.}$$

23. Set up the probability distribution.

Number of Women	0	1	2
Probability	$\frac{\binom{3}{0}\binom{5}{2}}{\binom{8}{2}}$	$\frac{\binom{3}{1}\binom{5}{1}}{\binom{8}{2}}$	$\frac{\binom{3}{2}\binom{5}{0}}{\binom{8}{2}}$
Simplified	$\frac{5}{14}$	$\frac{15}{28}$	$\frac{3}{28}$

$$E(x) = 0\left(\frac{5}{14}\right) + 1\left(\frac{15}{28}\right) + 2\left(\frac{3}{28}\right)$$
$$= \frac{21}{28} = \frac{3}{4} = 0.75$$

24. Let x represent the number of junior members on the committee. Use combinations to find the probability of 0, 1, 2, 3, and 4 junior members.

$$\binom{30}{4} = 27{,}405\ ;\ \binom{10}{0}\binom{20}{4} = 4845;$$
$$\binom{10}{1}\binom{20}{3} = 11{,}400; \binom{10}{2}\binom{20}{2} = 8550;$$
$$\binom{10}{3}\binom{20}{1} = 2400; \binom{10}{4}\binom{20}{0} = 210$$

The probability distribution of x is as follows.

x	0	1	2	3	4
$P(x)$	$\frac{323}{1827}$	$\frac{760}{1827}$	$\frac{190}{609}$	$\frac{160}{1827}$	$\frac{2}{261}$

$$E(x) = 0\left(\frac{323}{1827}\right) + 1\left(\frac{760}{1827}\right) + 2\left(\frac{190}{609}\right)$$
$$+ 3\left(\frac{160}{1827}\right) + 4\left(\frac{2}{261}\right)$$
$$= \frac{4}{3}.$$

The expected number of junior members is $1\frac{1}{3}$.

25. Set up the probability distribution as in Exercise 20.

Number of Diamonds	0	1	2
Probability	$\frac{\binom{13}{0}\binom{39}{2}}{\binom{52}{2}}$	$\frac{\binom{13}{1}\binom{39}{1}}{\binom{52}{2}}$	$\frac{\binom{13}{2}\binom{39}{0}}{\binom{52}{2}}$
Simplified	$\frac{741}{1326}$	$\frac{507}{1326}$	$\frac{78}{1326}$

$$E(x) = 0\left(\frac{741}{1326}\right) + 1\left(\frac{507}{1326}\right) + 2\left(\frac{78}{1326}\right)$$
$$= \frac{663}{1326} = \frac{1}{2}$$

26. The probability of drawing 2 diamonds is

$$\frac{\binom{13}{2}}{\binom{52}{2}} = \frac{78}{1326},$$

and the probability of not drawing 2 diamonds is

$$1 - \frac{78}{1326} = \frac{1248}{1326}.$$

Let x represent your net winnings. Then the expected value of the game is

$$E(x) = 4.5\left(\frac{78}{1326}\right) + (-0.5)\left(\frac{1248}{1326}\right)$$
$$= -\frac{273}{1326} \approx -\$0.21 \quad \text{or} \quad -21¢.$$

No, the game is not fair since your expected winnings are not zero.

29. (a) First list the possible sums, 5, 6, 7, 8, and 9, and find the probabilities for each. The total possible number of results are $4 \cdot 3 = 12$. There are two ways to draw a sum of 5 (2 then 3, and 3 then 2). The probability of 5 is $\frac{2}{12} = \frac{1}{6}$. There are two ways to draw a sum of 6 (2 then 4, and 4 then 2). The probability of 6 is $\frac{2}{12} = \frac{1}{6}$. There are four ways to draw a sum of 7 (2 then 5, 3 then 4, 4 then 3, and 5 then 2). The probability of 7 is $\frac{4}{12} = \frac{1}{3}$. There are two ways to draw a sum of 8 (3 then 5, and 5 then 3). The probability of 7 is $\frac{2}{12} = \frac{1}{6}$. There are two ways to draw a sum of 9 (4 then 5, and 5 then 4). The probability of 9 is $\frac{2}{12} = \frac{1}{6}$. The distribution is as follows.

Sum	5	6	7	8	9
Probability	$\frac{1}{6}$	$\frac{1}{6}$	$\frac{1}{3}$	$\frac{1}{6}$	$\frac{1}{6}$

(b)

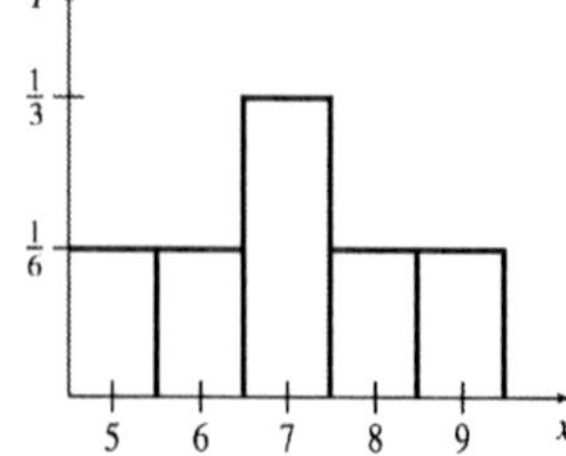

(c) The probability that the sum is even is $\frac{1}{6} + \frac{1}{6} = \frac{1}{3}$. Thus the odds are 1 to 2.

(d) $E(x) = \frac{1}{6}(5) + \frac{1}{6}(6) + \frac{1}{3}(7) + \frac{1}{6}(8) + \frac{1}{6}(9) = 7$

30. The expected value is

$$\begin{aligned} E(x) &= 0(0.02) + 1(0.06) + 2(0.16) + 3(0.25) \\ &\quad + 4(0.32) + 5(0.13) + 6(0.06) \\ &= 3.42 \text{ complaints per day.} \end{aligned}$$

31. We first compute the amount of money the company can expect to pay out for each kind of policy. The sum of these amounts will be the total amount the company can expect to pay out. For a single \$100,000 policy, we have the following probability distribution.

	Pay	Don't Pay
Outcome	\$100,000	\$100,000
Probability	0.0012	0.9998

$$\begin{aligned} E(\text{payoff}) &= 100{,}000(0.0012) + 0(0.9998) \\ &= \$120 \end{aligned}$$

For all 100 such policies, the company can expect to pay out

$$100(120) = \$12,000.$$

For a single \$50,000 policy,

$$\begin{aligned} E(\text{payoff}) &= 50,000(0.0012) + 0(0.9998) \\ &= \$60. \end{aligned}$$

For all 500 such policies, the company can expect to pay out

$$500(60) = \$30{,}000.$$

Similarly, for all 1000 policies of \$10,000, the company can expect to pay out

$$1000(12) = \$12,000.$$

Thus, the total amount the company can expect to pay out is

$$\$12{,}000 + \$30{,}000 + \$12{,}000 = \$54{,}000.$$

32.

Account Number	Expected Value	Exist. Vol. + Exp. Value	Class
1	\$2500	\$17,500	C
2	------	\$40,000	C
3	\$2000	\$22,000	C
4	\$1000	\$51,000	B
5	\$25,000	\$30,000	C
6	\$60,000	\$60,000	A
7	\$16,000	\$46,000	B

33. **(a)** Expected number of good nuts in 50 "blow outs" is

$$E(x) = 50(0.60) = 30.$$

(b) Since 80% of the "good nuts" are good, 20% are bad. Expected number of bad nuts in 50 "good nuts" is

$$E(x) = 50(0.20) = 10.$$

34. Let x represent the benefit amount.

x	4000	3000	2000
$P(x)$	0.4	$0.6 \cdot 0.4 = 0.24$	$0.6^2 \cdot 0.4 = 0.144$

x	1000	0
$P(x)$	$0.6^3 \cdot 0.4 = 0.0864$	$1 - 0.8704 = 0.1296$

$$\begin{aligned} E(x) &= 4000(0.4) + 3000(0.24) + 2000(0.144) \\ &\quad + 1000(0.0864) + 0(0.1296) \\ &= 2694.4 \end{aligned}$$

The answer is **e**.

35. The tour operator earns \$1050 if 1 or more tourists do not show up. The tour operator earns \$950 if all tourists show up. The probability that all tourists show up is $(0.98)^{21} \approx 0.6543$. The expected revenue is $1050(0.3457) + 950(0.6543) = 984.57$

The answer is **e**.

36. Let x represent the number of offspring. We have the following probability distribution.

x	0	1	2	3	4
$P(x)$	0.29	0.23	0.18	0.16	0.14

$$\begin{aligned} E(x) &= 0(0.29) + 1(0.23) + 2(0.18) + 3(0.16) + 4(0.14) \\ &= 1.63 \end{aligned}$$

37. **(a)** Expected cost of Amoxicillin:

$$\begin{aligned} E(x) &= 0.75(\$59.30) + 0.25(\$96.15) \\ &= \$68.51 \end{aligned}$$

Expected cost of Cefaclor:

$$\begin{aligned} E(x) &= 0.90(\$69.15) + 0.10(\$106.00) \\ &= \$72.84 \end{aligned}$$

(b) Amoxicillin should be used to minimize total expected cost.

38. Calculate the probability and payment for the number of days of hospitalization.

X	1	2	3	4	5
$P(x)$	$\frac{5}{15}=\frac{1}{3}$	$\frac{4}{15}$	$\frac{3}{15}=\frac{1}{5}$	$\frac{2}{15}$	$\frac{1}{15}$
Payment	\$100	\$200	\$300	\$325	\$350

Expected payment is

$$100\left(\frac{1}{3}\right)+200\left(\frac{4}{15}\right)+300\left(\frac{1}{5}\right)+325\left(\frac{2}{15}\right)+350\left(\frac{1}{15}\right)$$
$$\approx 213.$$

The answer is **d**.

39. $E(x) = 250(0.152) = 38$

We would expect 38 low-birth-weight babies to graduate from high school.

40. Expected number of a group of 500 college students that say they need to cheat is

$$E(x) = 500(0.84) = 420.$$

41. **(a)** Using binomial probability, $n = 48, x = 0$, $p = 0.0976$.

$$P(0) = \binom{48}{0}(0.0976)^0(0.9024)^{48} \approx 0.007230$$

(b) Using combinations, the probability is

$$\frac{\binom{74}{48}}{\binom{82}{48}} \approx 5.094 \times 10^{-4}.$$

(c) Using binomial probability, $n = 6, x = 5$, $p = 0.1$.

$$P(0) = \binom{6}{5}(0.1)^5(0.9)^1 + (0.1)^6 = 5.5 \times 10^{-5}$$

(d) Using binomial probability, $n = 6, p = 0.1$.

$$P(\text{at least } 2) = 1 - \binom{6}{0}(0.1)^0(0.9)^6 - \binom{6}{1}(0.1)^1(0.9)^5$$
$$\approx 0.1143$$

42. **(a)** Let x represent the amount of damage in millions of dollars. For seeding, the expected value is

$$\begin{aligned}E(x) &= 0.038(335.8) + 0.143(191.1) + 0.392(100)\\ &\quad + 0.255(46.7) + 0.172(16.3)\\ &\approx \$94.0 \text{ million.}\end{aligned}$$

For not seeding, the expected value is

$$\begin{aligned}E(x) &= 0.054(335.8) + 0.206(191.1) + 0.480(100)\\ &\quad + 0.206(46.7) + 0.054(16.3)\\ &\approx \$116.0 \text{ million.}\end{aligned}$$

(b) Seed, since the total expected damage is less with that option.

43. **(a)** We define a success to be a cat sitting in the chair with Kimberly. For this situation, $n = 4$; $x = 0, 1, 2, 3,$ or 4; $p = 0.3$; and $1-p = 0.7$.

Number of Cats	Probability
0	$\binom{4}{0}(0.3)^0(0.7)^4 = 0.2401$
1	$\binom{4}{1}(0.3)^1(0.7)^3 = 0.4116$
2	$\binom{4}{2}(0.3)^2(0.7)^2 = 0.2646$
3	$\binom{4}{3}(0.3)^3(0.7)^1 = 0.0756$
4	$\binom{4}{4}(0.3)^4(0.7)^0 = 0.0081$

(b) Expected number of cats

$$\begin{aligned}&= 0(0.2401) + 1(0.4116) + 2(0.2646)\\ &\quad + 3(0.0756) + 4(0.0081)\\ &= 1.2\end{aligned}$$

(c) Expected number of cats

$$= np = 4(0.3) = 1.2$$

44. **(a)** We define a success to be the event that a letter was delivered the next day. In this situation, $n = 10$; $x = 0, 1, 2, 3, \ldots, 10$; $p = 0.83$, and $1 - p = 0.17$.

Number of Letters Delivered the Next Day	Probability
0	$\binom{10}{0}(0.83)^0(0.17)^{10} \approx 0.0000$
1	$\binom{10}{1}(0.83)^1(0.17)^9 \approx 0.0000$
2	$\binom{10}{2}(0.83)^2(0.17)^8 \approx 0.0000$
3	$\binom{10}{3}(0.83)^3(0.17)^7 \approx 0.0003$
4	$\binom{10}{4}(0.83)^4(0.17)^6 \approx 0.0024$
5	$\binom{10}{5}(0.83)^5(0.17)^5 \approx 0.0141$
6	$\binom{10}{6}(0.83)^6(0.17)^4 \approx 0.0573$
7	$\binom{10}{7}(0.83)^7(0.17)^3 \approx 0.1600$
8	$\binom{10}{8}(0.83)^8(0.17)^2 \approx 0.2929$
9	$\binom{10}{9}(0.83)^9(0.17)^1 \approx 0.3178$
10	$\binom{10}{10}(0.83)^{10}(0.17)^0 \approx 0.1552$

(b) $P(4 \text{ or fewer letters would be delivered})$

$$= P(x = 0) + P(x = 1) + P(x = 2) + P(x = 3) + P(x = 4) \approx 0.0027$$

(d) Expected number of letters delivered next day

$$\approx 0(0.0000) + 1(0.0000) + 2(0.0000) + 3(0.0003) + 4(0.0024) + 5(0.0141) + 6(0.0573) + 7(0.1600) + 8(0.2929) + 9(0.3178) + 10(0.1552) \approx 8.3$$

45. Below is the probability distribution of x, which stands for the person's payback.

x	\$398	\$78	−\$2
$P(x)$	$\frac{1}{500} = 0.002$	$\frac{3}{500} = 0.006$	$\frac{497}{500} = 0.994$

The expected value of the person's winnings is

$$E(x) = 398(0.002) + 78(0.006) + (-2)(0.994) \approx -\$0.72 \text{ or } -72¢.$$

Since the expected value of the payback is not 0, this is not a fair game.

46. Reduce each price by the 50¢ cost of the ra- e ticket, and multiply by the corresponding probability.

$$E(x) = 999.50\left(\frac{1}{10{,}000}\right) + 299.50\left(\frac{2}{10{,}000}\right) + 9.50\left(\frac{20}{10{,}000}\right) + (-0.50)\left(\frac{9977}{10{,}000}\right)$$

$$= \frac{-3200}{10{,}000} = -\$0.32 \text{ or } -32¢$$

No, this is not a fair game. In a fair game the expected value is 0.

47. There are 13 possible outcomes for each suit. That would make $13^4 = 28{,}561$ total possible outcomes. In one case, you win \$5000 (minus the \$1 cost to play the game). In the other 28,560 cases, you lose your dollar.

$$E(x) = 4999\left(\frac{1}{28{,}561}\right) + (-1)\left(\frac{28{,}560}{28{,}561}\right) = -82¢$$

48. The probability of getting exactly 3 of the 4 selections correct and winning this game is

$$\binom{4}{3}\left(\frac{1}{13}\right)^3\left(\frac{12}{13}\right)^1 \approx 0.001681.$$

The probability of losing is 0.998319. If you win, your payback is \$199. Otherwise, you lose \$1 (win −\$1). If x represents your payback, then the expected value is

$$E(x) = 199(0.001681) + (-1)(0.998319) = 0.334519 - 0.998319 = -0.6638 \approx -\$0.66 \text{ or } -66¢.$$

49. There are $18 + 20 = 38$ possible outcomes. In 18 cases you win a dollar and in 20 you lose a dollar; hence,

$$E(x) = 1\left(\frac{18}{38}\right) + (-1)\left(\frac{20}{38}\right) = -\frac{1}{19}, \text{ or about } -5.3¢.$$

50. In this form of roulette,

$$P(\text{even}) = \frac{18}{37} \text{ and } P(\text{noneven}) = \frac{19}{37}.$$

If an even number comes up, you win \$1. Otherwise, you lose \$1 (win −\$1). If x represents your payback, then the expected value is

$$E(x) = 1\left(\frac{18}{37}\right) + (-1)\left(\frac{19}{37}\right) = -\frac{1}{37} \approx -\$0.027 \text{ or } -2.7¢.$$

51. You have one chance in a thousand of winning \$500 on a \$1 bet for a net return of \$499. In the 999 other outcomes, you lose your dollar.

$$E(x) = 499\left(\frac{1}{1000}\right) + (-1)\left(\frac{999}{1000}\right)$$
$$= \frac{-500}{1000} = -50¢$$

52. In this form of the game Keno,

$$P(\text{your number comes up}) = \frac{20}{80} = \frac{1}{4}$$

and

$$P(\text{your number doesn't come up}) = \frac{60}{80} = \frac{3}{4}.$$

If your number comes up, you win \$2.20. Otherwise, you lose \$1 (win −\$1). If x represents your payback, then the expected value is

$$E(x) = 2.20\left(\frac{1}{4}\right) - 1\left(\frac{3}{4}\right)$$
$$= 0.55 - 0.75 = -\$0.20 \quad \text{or} \quad -20¢.$$

53. Let x represent the payback. The probability distribution is as follows.

x	$P(x)$
100,000	$\frac{1}{2{,}000{,}000}$
40,000	$\frac{2}{2{,}000{,}000}$
10,000	$\frac{2}{2{,}000{,}000}$
0	$\frac{1{,}999{,}995}{2{,}000{,}000}$

The expected value is

$$E(x) = 100,000\left(\frac{1}{2{,}000{,}000}\right) + 40{,}000\left(\frac{2}{2{,}000{,}000}\right)$$
$$+ 10{,}000\left(\frac{2}{2{,}000{,}000}\right) + 0\left(\frac{1,999,995}{2{,}000{,}000}\right)$$
$$= 0.05 + 0.04 + 0.01 + 0$$
$$= \$0.10 = 10¢.$$

Since the expected payback is 10¢ and if entering the contest costs 50¢, then it would not be worth it to enter.

54. At any one restaurant, your expected winnings are

$$E(x) = 100{,}000\left(\frac{1}{176{,}402{,}500}\right) + 25{,}000\left(\frac{1}{39{,}200{,}556}\right)$$
$$+ 5000\left(\frac{1}{17{,}640{,}250}\right) + 1000\left(\frac{1}{1{,}568{,}022}\right)$$
$$+ 100\left(\frac{1}{288{,}244}\right) + 5\left(\frac{1}{7056}\right) + 1\left(\frac{1}{588}\right)$$
$$= 0.00488.$$

Going to 25 restaurants gives you expected earnings of 25(0.00488) = 0.122. Since you spent \$1, you lose 87.8¢ on the average, so your expected value is −87.8¢.

55. **(a)** The possible scores are 0, 2, 3, 4, 5, 6. Each score has a probability of $\frac{1}{6}$.

$$E(x) = 0\left(\frac{1}{6}\right) + 2\left(\frac{1}{6}\right) + 3\left(\frac{1}{6}\right) + 4\left(\frac{1}{6}\right)$$
$$+ 5\left(\frac{1}{6}\right) + 6\left(\frac{1}{6}\right)$$
$$= \frac{1}{6}(20) = \frac{10}{3}$$

(b) The possible scores are

0 which has a probability of $\frac{11}{36}$,

4 which has a probability of $\frac{1}{36}$,

5 which has a probability of $\frac{2}{36}$,

6 which has a probability of $\frac{3}{36}$,

7 which has a probability of $\frac{4}{36}$,

8 which has a probability of $\frac{5}{36}$,

9 which has a probability of $\frac{4}{36}$,

10 which has a probability of $\frac{3}{36}$,

11 which has a probability of $\frac{2}{36}$,

12 which has a probability of $\frac{1}{36}$.

$$E(x) = 0\left(\frac{11}{36}\right) + 4\left(\frac{1}{36}\right) + 5\left(\frac{2}{36}\right) + 6\left(\frac{3}{36}\right)$$
$$+ 7\left(\frac{4}{36}\right) + 8\left(\frac{5}{36}\right) + 9\left(\frac{4}{36}\right)$$
$$+ 10\left(\frac{3}{36}\right) + 11\left(\frac{2}{36}\right) + 12\left(\frac{1}{36}\right)$$
$$= \frac{4}{36} + \frac{10}{36} + \frac{18}{36} + \frac{28}{36} + \frac{40}{36} + \frac{36}{36}$$
$$+ \frac{30}{36} + \frac{22}{36} + \frac{12}{36} = \frac{200}{36} = \frac{50}{9}$$

(c) If a single die does not result in a score of zero, the possible scores are 2, 3, 4, 5, 6 with each of these having a probability of $\frac{1}{5}$.

$$\begin{aligned} E(x) &= 2\left(\frac{1}{5}\right) + 3\left(\frac{1}{5}\right) + 4\left(\frac{1}{5}\right) \\ &\quad + 5\left(\frac{1}{5}\right) + 6\left(\frac{1}{5}\right) \\ &= \frac{1}{5}(20) \\ &= 4 \end{aligned}$$

Thus, if a player rolls n dice the expected average score is

$$n \cdot E(x) = n \cdot 4 = 4n.$$

(d) If a player rolls n dice, a nonzero score will occur whenever each die rolls a number other than 1. For each die, there are 5 possibilities so the possible scoring ways for n dice is 5^n. When rolling die there are 6 possibilities so the possible outcomes for n die is 6^n. The probability of rolling a scoring set of die is $\frac{5^n}{6^n}$; thus, the expected value of the player's score when rolling n dice is $E(x) = \frac{5^n(4n)}{6^n}$.

56. **(a)** Expected value of a two-point conversion:

$$E(x) = 2(0.37) = 0.74$$

Expected value of an extra-point kick:

$$E(x) = 1(0.94) = 0.94$$

(b) Since the expected value of an extra-point kick is greater than the expected value of a two-point conversion, the extra-point kick will maximize the number of points scored over the long run.

57. **(a)** Let x be the number of hits. Since the probability of getting a hit on any one time at bat is 0.335, the probability of not getting a hit is 0.765. Use combinations since the order of hits is not important.

$$P(x=0) = \binom{4}{0}(0.335)^0(0.765)^4 \approx 0.1956$$

$$P(x=1) = \binom{4}{1}(0.335)^1(0.765)^3 \approx 0.3941$$

$$P(x=2) = \binom{4}{2}(0.335)^2(0.765)^2 \approx 0.2978$$

$$P(x=3) = \binom{4}{3}(0.335)^3(0.765)^1 \approx 0.1000$$

$$P(x=4) = \binom{4}{4}(0.335)^4(0.765)^0 \approx 0.0126$$

x	0	1	2	3	4
$P(x)$	0.1956	0.3941	0.2978	0.1000	0.0126

(b)
$$\begin{aligned} E(x) &= 0(0.1956) + 1(0.3941) + 2(0.2978) \\ &\quad + 3(0.1000) + 4(0.0126) \\ &\approx 1.34 \end{aligned}$$

Chapter 8 Review Exercises

1. 6 shuttle vans can line up at the airport in

$$P(6,6) = 6! = 720$$

different ways.

2. Since order makes a difference, use permutations.

$$\begin{aligned} P(6,3) &= \frac{6!}{(6-3)!} = \frac{6!}{3!} \\ &= 6 \cdot 5 \cdot 4 = 120 \end{aligned}$$

There are 120 variations in first-, second- and third-place finishes.

3. 3 oranges can be taken from a bag of 12 in

$$\binom{12}{3} = \frac{12!}{9!3!} = \frac{12 \cdot 11 \cdot 10}{3 \cdot 2 \cdot 1} = 220$$

different ways.

4. **(a)** The sample will include 1 of the 2 rotten oranges and 2 of the 10 good oranges. Using the multiplication principle, this can be done in

$$\binom{2}{1}\binom{10}{2} = 2 \cdot 45 = 90 \text{ ways.}$$

(b) The sample will include both of the 2 rotten oranges and 1 of the 10 good oranges. This can be done in

$$\binom{2}{2}\binom{10}{1} = 1 \cdot 10 = 10 \text{ ways.}$$

(c) The sample will include 0 of the 2 rotten oranges and 3 of the 10 good oranges. This can be done in

$$\binom{2}{0}\binom{10}{3} = 1 \cdot 120 = 120 \text{ ways.}$$

(d) If the sample contains at most 2 rotten oranges, it must contain 0, 1, or 2 rotten oranges. Adding the results from parts (a), (b), and (c), this can be done in

$$90 + 10 + 120 = 220 \text{ ways.}$$

5. 2 pictures from a group of 5 different pictures can be arranged in

$$P(5,2) = 5 \cdot 4 = 20$$

different ways.

6. Since a certain picture must be first, the number of ways to arrange the pictures is

$$1 \cdot 4 \cdot 3 \cdot 2 \cdot 1 = 24.$$

7. (a) There are 2! ways to arrange the landscapes, 3! ways to arrange the puppies, and 2 choices whether landscapes or puppies come first. Thus, the pictures can be arranged in

$$2!3! \cdot 2 = 24$$

different ways.

(b) The pictures must be arranged puppy, landscape, puppy, landscape, puppy. Arrange the puppies in 3! or 6 ways. Arrange the landscapes in 2! or 2 ways. In this scheme, the pictures can be arranged in $6 \cdot 2 = 12$ different ways.

8. (a) The order within each list is not important. Use combinations and the multiplication principle. The choice of three items from column A can be made in $\binom{8}{3}$ ways, and the choice of two from column B can be made in $\binom{6}{2}$ ways. Thus, the number of possible dinners is

$$\binom{8}{3}\binom{6}{2} = 56 \cdot 15 = 840.$$

(b) There are

$$\binom{8}{0} + \binom{8}{1} + \binom{8}{2} + \binom{8}{3}$$

ways to pick up to 3 items from column A. Likewise, there are

$$\binom{6}{0} + \binom{6}{1} + \binom{6}{2}$$

ways to pick up to 2 items from column B. We use the multiplication principle to obtain

$$\left[\binom{8}{0} + \binom{8}{1} + \binom{8}{2} + \binom{8}{3}\right]\left[\binom{6}{0} + \binom{6}{1} + \binom{6}{2}\right]$$
$$= (1 + 8 + 28 + 56)(1 + 6 + 15)$$
$$= 93(22)$$
$$= 2046.$$

Since we are assuming that the diner will order at least one item, subtract 1 to exclude the dinner that would contain no items. Thus, the number of possible dinners is 2045.

9. (a) There are $7 \cdot 5 \cdot 4 = 140$ different groups of 3 representatives possible.

(b) $7 \cdot 5 \cdot 4 = 140$ is the number of groups with 3 representatives. For 2 representatives, the number of groups is

$$7 \cdot 5 + 7 \cdot 4 + 5 \cdot 4 = 83.$$

For 1 representative, the number of groups is

$$7 + 5 + 4 = 16.$$

The total number of these groups is

$$140 + 83 + 16 = 239$$

groups.

12. There are $\binom{13}{3}$ ways to choose the 3 balls and $\binom{4}{3}$ ways to get all black balls. Thus,

$$P(\text{all black}) = \frac{\binom{4}{3}}{\binom{13}{3}} = \frac{4}{286} = \frac{2}{143} \approx 0.0140.$$

13. It is impossible to draw 3 blue balls, since there are only 2 blue balls in the basket; hence,

$$P(\text{all blue balls}) = 0.$$

14. There are $\binom{4}{2}$ ways to get 2 black balls and $\binom{7}{1}$ ways to get 1 green ball. Thus,

$P(\text{2 black and 1 green})$

$$= \frac{\binom{4}{2}\binom{7}{1}}{\binom{11}{3}} = \frac{6 \cdot 7}{286} = \frac{42}{286} = \frac{21}{143} \approx 0.1469.$$

15. $P(\text{exactly 2 black balls})$

$$= \frac{\binom{4}{2}\binom{9}{1}}{\binom{13}{3}} = \frac{54}{286} = \frac{27}{143} \approx 0.1888$$

16. There are $\binom{2}{1}$ ways to get 1 blue ball and $\binom{11}{2}$ ways to get 2 nonblue balls. Thus,

$P(\text{exactly 1 blue})$

$$= \frac{\binom{2}{1}\binom{11}{2}}{\binom{13}{3}} = \frac{2 \cdot 55}{286} = \frac{110}{286} = \frac{5}{13} \approx 0.3846.$$

17. $P(\text{2 green balls and 1 blue ball})$

$$= \frac{\binom{7}{2}\binom{2}{1}}{\binom{13}{3}} = \frac{42}{286} = \frac{21}{143} \approx 0.1469$$

18. This is a Bernoulli trial problem with $P(\text{success}) = P(\text{girl}) = \frac{1}{2}$. Here, $n = 6$, $p = \frac{1}{2}$, and $x = 3$.

$P(\text{exactly 3 girls})$

$$= \binom{6}{3}\left(\frac{1}{2}\right)^3\left(\frac{1}{2}\right)^3$$

$$= \frac{20}{64} = \frac{5}{16}$$

$$\approx 0.313$$

19. Let x represent the number of girls. We have $n = 6$, $x = 6$, $p = \frac{1}{2}$, and $1 - p = \frac{1}{2}$, so

$$P(\text{all girls}) = \binom{6}{6}\left(\frac{1}{2}\right)^6\left(\frac{1}{2}\right)^0 = \frac{1}{64} \approx 0.016.$$

20. $P(\text{at least 4 girls})$

$$= P(4 \text{ girls}) + P(5 \text{ girls}) + P(6 \text{ girls})$$

$$= \binom{6}{4}\left(\frac{1}{2}\right)^4\left(\frac{1}{2}\right)^2 + \binom{6}{5}\left(\frac{1}{2}\right)^5\left(\frac{1}{2}\right)^1$$

$$+ \binom{6}{6}\left(\frac{1}{2}\right)^6\left(\frac{1}{2}\right)^0$$

$$= \frac{22}{64} = \frac{11}{32}$$

$$\approx 0.344$$

21. Let x represent the number of boys, and then $p = \frac{1}{2}$ and $1 - p = \frac{1}{2}$. We have

$P(\text{no more than 2 boys})$

$$= P(x \le 2)$$

$$= P(x = 0) + P(x = 1) + P(x = 2)$$

$$= \binom{6}{0}\left(\frac{1}{2}\right)^0\left(\frac{1}{2}\right)^6 + \binom{6}{1}\left(\frac{1}{2}\right)^1\left(\frac{1}{2}\right)^5$$

$$+ \binom{6}{2}\left(\frac{1}{2}\right)^2\left(\frac{1}{2}\right)^4$$

$$= \frac{11}{32} \approx 0.344.$$

22. $P(\text{both red})$

$$= \frac{\binom{26}{2}}{\binom{52}{2}} = \frac{325}{1326} = \frac{25}{102} \approx 0.245$$

23. $P(2 \text{ spades}) = \dfrac{\binom{13}{2}}{\binom{52}{2}} = \dfrac{78}{1326} = \dfrac{1}{17} \approx 0.059$

24. $P(\text{at least 1 card is a spade})$

$$= 1 - P(\text{neither is a spade})$$

$$= 1 - \frac{\binom{39}{2}}{\binom{52}{2}} = 1 - \frac{741}{1326}$$

$$= \frac{585}{1326} = \frac{15}{34} \approx 0.441$$

25. $P(\text{exactly 1 face card})$

$$= \frac{\binom{12}{1}\binom{40}{1}}{\binom{52}{2}} = \frac{480}{1326} = \frac{80}{221} \approx 0.3620$$

26. There are 12 face cards and 40 nonface cards in an ordinary deck.

$P(\text{at least 1 face card})$

$$= P(1 \text{ face card}) + P(2 \text{ face cards})$$

$$= \frac{\binom{12}{1}\binom{40}{1}}{\binom{52}{2}} + \frac{\binom{12}{2}}{\binom{52}{2}}$$

$$= \frac{480}{1326} + \frac{66}{1326}$$

$$= \frac{546}{1326} \approx 0.4118$$

27. $P(\text{at most 1 queen})$

$$= P(0 \text{ queens}) + P(1 \text{ queen})$$

$$= \frac{\binom{48}{2}}{\binom{52}{2}} + \frac{\binom{4}{1}\binom{48}{1}}{\binom{52}{2}}$$

$$= \frac{1128}{1326} + \frac{192}{1326}$$

$$= \frac{1320}{1326} = \frac{220}{221} \approx 0.9955$$

28. This is a Bernoulli trial problem.

(a) $P(\text{success}) = P(\text{head}) = \frac{1}{2}$. Hence, $n = 3$ and $p = \frac{1}{2}$.

Number of Heads	Probability
0	$\binom{3}{0}\left(\frac{1}{2}\right)^0\left(\frac{1}{2}\right)^3 = 0.125$
1	$\binom{3}{1}\left(\frac{1}{2}\right)^1\left(\frac{1}{2}\right)^2 = 0.375$
2	$\binom{3}{2}\left(\frac{1}{2}\right)^2\left(\frac{1}{2}\right)^1 = 0.375$
3	$\binom{3}{3}\left(\frac{1}{2}\right)^3\left(\frac{1}{2}\right)^0 = 0.125$

(b)

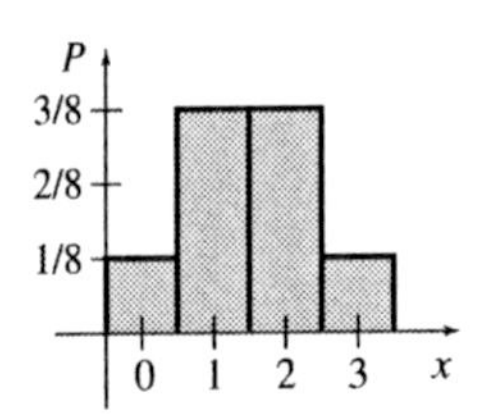

(c) $E(x) = 0(0.125) + 1(0.375) + 2(0.375) + 3(0.125)$
$= 1.5$

29. (a) There are $n = 36$ possible outcomes. Let x represent the sum of the dice, and note that the possible values of x are the whole numbers from 2 to 12. The probability distribution is as follows.

x	2	3	4	5	6
$P(x)$	$\frac{1}{36}$	$\frac{2}{36} = \frac{1}{18}$	$\frac{3}{36} = \frac{1}{12}$	$\frac{4}{36} = \frac{1}{9}$	$\frac{5}{36}$

x	7	8	9	10	11	12
$P(x)$	$\frac{6}{36} = \frac{1}{6}$	$\frac{5}{36}$	$\frac{4}{36} = \frac{1}{9}$	$\frac{3}{36} = \frac{1}{12}$	$\frac{2}{36} = \frac{1}{18}$	$\frac{1}{36}$

(b) The histogram consists of 11 rectangles.

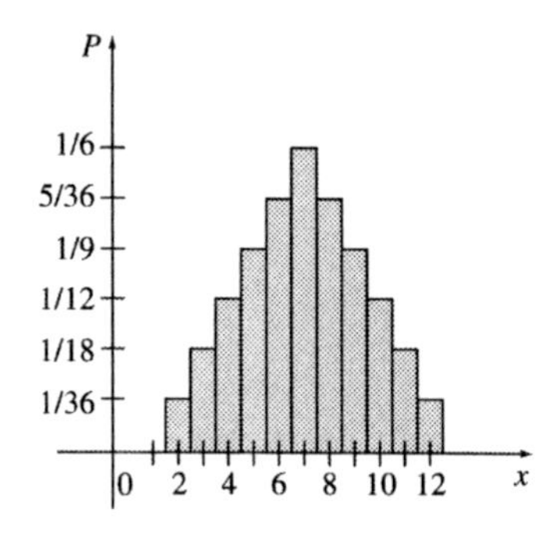

(c) The expected value is

$$\begin{aligned} E(x) &= 2\left(\frac{1}{36}\right) + 3\left(\frac{2}{36}\right) + 4\left(\frac{3}{36}\right) + 5\left(\frac{4}{36}\right) \\ &\quad + 6\left(\frac{5}{36}\right) + 7\left(\frac{6}{36}\right) + 8\left(\frac{5}{36}\right) + 9\left(\frac{4}{36}\right) \\ &\quad + 10\left(\frac{3}{36}\right) + 11\left(\frac{2}{36}\right) + 12\left(\frac{1}{36}\right) \\ &= \frac{252}{36} = 7. \end{aligned}$$

30. The probability that corresponds to the shaded region of the histogram is the total of the shaded areas, that is,

$$1(0.3) + 1(0.2) + 1(0.1) = 0.6.$$

31. The probability that corresponds to the shaded region of the histogram is the total of the shaded areas, that is,

$$1(0.1) + 1(0.3) + 1(0.2) = 0.6.$$

32. The probability of rolling a 6 is $\frac{1}{6}$, and your net winnings would be \$2. The probability of rolling a 5 is $\frac{1}{6}$, and your net winnings would be \$1. The probability of rolling something else is $\frac{4}{6}$, and your net winnings would be $-\$2$. Let x represent your winnings. The expected value is

$$\begin{aligned} E(x) &= 2\left(\frac{1}{6}\right) + 1\left(\frac{1}{6}\right) + (-2)\left(\frac{4}{6}\right) \\ &= -\frac{5}{6} \\ &\approx -\$0.833 \quad \text{or} \quad -83.3¢. \end{aligned}$$

This is not a fair game since the expected value is not 0.

33. Let x represent the number of girls. The probability distribution is as follows.

x	0	1	2	3	4	5
$P(x)$	$\frac{1}{32}$	$\frac{5}{32}$	$\frac{10}{32}$	$\frac{10}{32}$	$\frac{5}{32}$	$\frac{1}{32}$

The expected value is

$$\begin{aligned} E(x) &= 0\left(\frac{1}{32}\right) + 1\left(\frac{5}{32}\right) + 2\left(\frac{10}{32}\right) + 3\left(\frac{10}{32}\right) \\ &\quad + 4\left(\frac{5}{32}\right) + 5\left(\frac{1}{32}\right) \\ &= \frac{80}{32} = 2.5 \text{ girls.} \end{aligned}$$

34. (a)

Number of Aces	Probability
0	$\frac{\binom{4}{0}\binom{48}{3}}{\binom{52}{3}} = \frac{17{,}296}{22{,}100}$
1	$\frac{\binom{4}{1}\binom{48}{2}}{\binom{52}{3}} = \frac{4512}{22{,}100}$
2	$\frac{\binom{4}{2}\binom{48}{1}}{\binom{52}{3}} = \frac{288}{22{,}100}$
3	$\frac{\binom{4}{3}\binom{48}{0}}{\binom{52}{3}} = \frac{4}{22{,}100}$

$$E(x) = 0\left(\frac{17{,}296}{22{,}100}\right) + 1\left(\frac{4512}{22{,}100}\right) + 2\left(\frac{288}{22{,}100}\right) + 3\left(\frac{4}{22{,}100}\right)$$
$$= \frac{5100}{22{,}100} = \frac{51}{221}$$
$$= \frac{3}{13} \approx 0.231$$

(b)

Number of Clubs	Probability
0	$\frac{\binom{13}{0}\binom{39}{3}}{\binom{52}{3}} = \frac{9139}{22{,}100}$
1	$\frac{\binom{13}{1}\binom{39}{2}}{\binom{52}{3}} = \frac{9633}{22{,}100}$
2	$\frac{\binom{13}{2}\binom{39}{1}}{\binom{52}{3}} = \frac{3042}{22{,}100}$
3	$\frac{\binom{13}{3}\binom{39}{0}}{\binom{52}{3}} = \frac{286}{22{,}100}$

$$E(x) = 0\left(\frac{9139}{22{,}100}\right) + 1\left(\frac{9633}{22{,}100}\right) + 2\left(\frac{3042}{22{,}100}\right) + 3\left(\frac{286}{22{,}100}\right)$$
$$= \frac{16{,}575}{22{,}100}$$
$$= \frac{3}{4} = 0.75$$

35. $P(3 \text{ clubs}) = \frac{\binom{13}{3}}{\binom{52}{3}} = \frac{286}{22{,}100} \approx 0.0129$

Thus,

$P(\text{win}) = 0.0129$ and
$P(\text{lose}) = 1 - 0.0129 = 0.9871.$

Let x represent the amount you should pay. Your net winnings are $100 - x$ if you win and $-x$ if you lose. If it is a fair game, your expected winnings will be 0. Thus, $E(x) = 0$ becomes

$$0.0129(100 - x) + 0.9871(-x) = 0$$
$$1.29 - 0.0129x - 0.9871x = 0$$
$$1.29 - x = 0$$
$$x = 1.29.$$

You should pay \$1.29.

36. We define a success to be the event that a student flips heads and is on the committee. In this situation, $n = 6$; $x = 1, 2, 3, 4,$ or 5; $p = \frac{1}{2}$; and $1 - p = \frac{1}{2}$.

$$P(x = 1, 2, 3, 4, \text{ or } 5)$$
$$= 1 - P(x = 6) - P(x = 0)$$
$$= 1 - \binom{6}{6}\left(\frac{1}{2}\right)^6\left(\frac{1}{2}\right)^0 - \binom{6}{0}\left(\frac{1}{2}\right)^0\left(\frac{1}{2}\right)^6$$
$$= 1 - \frac{1}{64} - \frac{1}{64}$$
$$= \frac{62}{64} = \frac{31}{32}$$

37. (a) Given a set with n elements, the number of subsets of size

$$0 \text{ is } \binom{n}{0} = 1,$$
$$1 \text{ is } \binom{n}{1} = n,$$
$$2 \text{ is } \binom{n}{2} = \frac{n(n-1)}{2}, \text{ and}$$
$$n \text{ is } \binom{n}{n} = 1.$$

(b) The total number of subsets is

$$\binom{n}{0} + \binom{n}{1} + \binom{n}{2} + \cdots + \binom{n}{n}.$$

(d) Let $n = 4$.

$$\binom{4}{0} + \binom{4}{1} + \binom{4}{2} + \binom{4}{3} + \binom{4}{4}$$
$$= 1 + 4 + 6 + 4 + 1$$
$$= 16$$
$$= 2^4 = 2^n$$

Let $n = 5$.

$$\binom{5}{0} + \binom{5}{1} + \binom{5}{2} + \binom{5}{3} + \binom{5}{4} + \binom{5}{5}$$
$$= 1 + 5 + 10 + 10 + 5 + 1$$
$$= 32$$
$$= 2^5 = 2^n$$

(e) The sum of the elements in row n of Pascal's triangle is 2^n.

38. (a)

First Card	Second Card	Number of Possibilities for Third Card
1	2	7
1	3	6
1	4	5
1	5	4
1	6	3
1	7	2
1	8	1
2	3	6
2	4	5
2	5	4
2	6	3
2	7	2
2	8	1
3	4	5
3	5	4
3	6	3
3	7	2
3	8	1
4	5	4
4	6	3
4	7	2
4	8	1
5	6	3
5	7	2
5	8	1
6	7	2
6	8	1
7	8	1

The sum of the numbers in the third column is 84.

(b) There are 4 even digits and 5 odd digits.

$$P(\text{all even}) = \frac{\binom{4}{3}\binom{5}{0}}{\binom{9}{3}} = \frac{4}{84} = \frac{1}{21}$$

(c) There are 7 possibilities for three consecutive digits:

$$1, 2, 3$$
$$2, 3, 4$$
$$3, 4, 5$$
$$4, 5, 6$$
$$5, 6, 7$$
$$6, 7, 8$$
$$7, 8, 9.$$

$$P(\text{consecutive integers}) = \frac{7}{\binom{9}{3}} = \frac{7}{84} = \frac{1}{12}$$

(d) Refer to column 3 from part (a). The sum of the numbers when the first card is 4 is $1 + 2 + 3 + 4 = 10$.

$$P(x = 4) = \frac{10}{84} = \frac{5}{42}$$

(e) From part (a), we see that the first card x ranges from 1 to 7. If k is an integer such that $1 \le k \le 7$, the number of possibilities is

$$\begin{aligned} 1 + 2 + \cdots + [9 - (k+1)] \\ &= \frac{[9 - (k+1)][9 - (k+1) + 1]}{2} \\ &= \frac{(8 - k)(9 - k)}{2}. \end{aligned}$$

The probability of $x = k$ is given by

$$\begin{aligned} P(x = k) &= \frac{\frac{(9-k)(8-k)}{2}}{\binom{9}{3}} \\ &= \frac{(9-k)(8-k)}{2} \cdot \frac{1}{84} \\ &= \frac{(9-k)(8-k)}{168}. \end{aligned}$$

The expected value of x is

$$\begin{aligned} E(x) &= 1\left(\frac{8 \cdot 7}{168}\right) + 2\left(\frac{7 \cdot 6}{168}\right) + 3\left(\frac{6 \cdot 5}{168}\right) \\ &\quad + 4\left(\frac{5 \cdot 4}{168}\right) + 5\left(\frac{4 \cdot 3}{168}\right) + 6\left(\frac{3 \cdot 2}{168}\right) \\ &\quad + 7\left(\frac{2 \cdot 1}{168}\right) \\ &= \frac{420}{168} = \frac{5}{2}. \end{aligned}$$

39. $n = 12, x = 0, p = \frac{1}{6}$

$$P(0) = \binom{12}{0}\left(\frac{1}{6}\right)^0\left(\frac{5}{6}\right)^{12} \approx 0.1122$$

40. $n = 12, x = 12, p = \frac{1}{6}$

$$P(12) = \binom{12}{12}\left(\frac{1}{6}\right)^{12}\left(\frac{5}{6}\right)^{0} \approx 4.594 \times 10^{-10}$$

41. $n = 12, x = 10, p = \frac{1}{6}$

$$P(10) = \binom{12}{10}\left(\frac{1}{6}\right)^{10}\left(\frac{5}{6}\right)^{2} \approx 7.580 \times 10^{-7}$$

42. $n = 12, x = 2, p = \frac{1}{6}$

$$P(2) = \binom{12}{2}\left(\frac{1}{6}\right)^2\left(\frac{5}{6}\right)^{10} \approx 0.2961$$

43. $n = 12, p = \frac{1}{6}$

$$\begin{aligned} P(\text{at least } 2) &= 1 - P(\text{at most } 1) \\ &= 1 - P(0) - P(1) \\ &= 1 - \binom{12}{0}\left(\frac{1}{6}\right)^0\left(\frac{5}{6}\right)^{12} \\ &\quad - \binom{12}{1}\left(\frac{1}{6}\right)^1\left(\frac{5}{6}\right)^{11} \\ &\approx 0.6187 \end{aligned}$$

44. $n = 12, p = \frac{1}{6}$

$$\begin{aligned} P(\text{at most } 3) &= P(0) + P(1) + P(2) + P(3) \\ &= \binom{12}{0}\left(\frac{1}{6}\right)^0\left(\frac{5}{6}\right)^{12} \\ &\quad + \binom{12}{1}\left(\frac{1}{6}\right)^1\left(\frac{5}{6}\right)^{11} \\ &\quad + \binom{12}{2}\left(\frac{1}{6}\right)^2\left(\frac{5}{6}\right)^{10} \\ &\quad + \binom{12}{3}\left(\frac{1}{6}\right)^3\left(\frac{5}{6}\right)^{9} \\ &\approx 0.8748 \end{aligned}$$

45. The expected value is $\frac{1}{6}(12) = 2$.

46. $$\begin{aligned} E(x) &= 26,000(0.7) + (-9000)(0.3) \\ &= 15,500 \end{aligned}$$

The expected profit is \$15,500.

47. Observe that for $a+b = 7$, $P(a)P(b) = \left(\frac{1}{2^{a+1}}\right)\left(\frac{1}{2^{b+1}}\right) = \frac{1}{2^{a+b+2}} = \frac{1}{2^9}$. The probability that exactly seven claims will be received during a given two-week period is

$$\begin{aligned} &P(0)P(7) + P(1)P(6) + P(2)P(5) + P(3)P(4) \\ &\quad + P(4)P(3) + P(5)P(2) \\ &\quad + P(6)P(1) + P(7)P(0) \\ &= 8\left(\frac{1}{2^9}\right) = \frac{1}{64}. \end{aligned}$$

The answer is **d**.

48. $P(0) = \frac{1}{2}; P(1) = \frac{1}{6}; P(2) = \frac{1}{12}; P(3) = \frac{1}{20};$
$P(4) = \frac{1}{30}$

The probability of at most 4 claims is

$$\begin{aligned} &P(0) + P(1) + P(2) + P(3) + P(4) \\ &= \frac{1}{2} + \frac{1}{6} + \frac{1}{12} + \frac{1}{20} + \frac{1}{30} \\ &= \frac{5}{6}. \end{aligned}$$

The probability of at least one claim and at most 4 claims is

$$\begin{aligned} &P(0) + P(1) + P(2) + P(3) + P(4) \\ &= \frac{1}{6} + \frac{1}{12} + \frac{1}{20} + \frac{1}{30} \\ &= \frac{1}{3}. \end{aligned}$$

The probability of at least one claim given that there have been at most 4 claims is

$$\frac{\frac{1}{3}}{\frac{5}{6}} = \frac{2}{5}.$$

The answer is **b**.

49. Denote by S the event that a product is successful.
Denote by U the event that a product is unsuccessful.
Denote by Q the event of passing quality control. We must calculate the conditional probabilities $P(S|Q)$ and $P(U|Q)$ using Bayes' Theorem in order to calculate the expected net profit (in millions).

$E = 40P(S|Q) - 15P(U|Q)$.
$P(S) = P(U) = 0.5$
$P(Q|S) = 0.8, P(Q|U) = 0.25$

$$\begin{aligned} P(S|Q) &= \frac{P(S) \cdot P(Q|S)}{P(S) \cdot P(Q|S) + P(U) \cdot P(Q|U)} \\ &= \frac{0.5(0.8)}{0.5(0.8) + 0.5(0.25)} \\ &= \frac{0.4}{0.4 + 0.125} = 0.762 \end{aligned}$$

$$\begin{aligned} P(U|Q) &= \frac{P(U) \cdot P(Q|U)}{P(U) \cdot P(Q|U) + P(S) \cdot P(Q|S)} \\ &= \frac{0.125}{0.525} = 0.238 \end{aligned}$$

Therefore,

$$\begin{aligned} E &= 40P(S|Q) - 15P(U|Q) \\ &= 40(0.762) - 15(0.238) \\ &\approx 27. \end{aligned}$$

So the expected net profit is $27 million, or the correct answer is **e**.

50. If a box is good (probability 0.9) and the merchant samples an excellent piece of fruit from that box (probability 0.80), then he will accept the box and earn a $200 profit on it.

If a box is bad (probability 0.1) and he samples an excellent piece of fruit from the box (probability 0.30), then he will accept the box and earn a −$1000 profit on it.

If the merchant ever samples a nonexcellent piece of fruit, he will not accept the box. In this case he pays nothing and earns nothing, so the profit will be $0.

Let x represent the merchant's earnings. Note that

$$\begin{aligned} 0.9(0.80) &= 0.72, \\ 0.1(0.30) &= 0.03, \\ \text{and } 1 - (0.72 + 0.03) &= 0.25. \end{aligned}$$

The probability distribution is as follows.

x	200	−1000	0
$P(x)$	0.72	0.03	0.25

The expected value when the merchant samples the fruit is

$$\begin{aligned} E(x) &= 200(0.72) + (-1000)(0.03) + 0(0.25) \\ &= 144 - 30 + 0 \\ &= \$114. \end{aligned}$$

We must also consider the case in which the merchant does not sample the fruit. Let x again represent the merchant's earnings. The probability distribution is as follows.

x	200	−1000
$P(x)$	0.9	0.1

The expected value when the merchant does not sample the fruit is

$$\begin{aligned} E(x) &= 200(0.9) + (-1000)(0.1) \\ &= 180 - 100 \\ &= \$80. \end{aligned}$$

Combining these two results, the expected value of the right to sample is $114 − $80 = $34, which corresponds to choice **c**.

51. Let $I(x)$ represent the airline's net income if x people show up.

$$\begin{aligned} I(0) &= 0 \\ I(1) &= 400 \\ I(2) &= 2(400) = 800 \\ I(3) &= 3(400) = 1200 \\ I(4) &= 3(400) - 400 = 800 \\ I(5) &= 3(400) - 2(400) = 400 \\ I(6) &= 3(400) - 3(400) = 0 \end{aligned}$$

Let $P(x)$ represent the probability that x people will show up. Use the binomial probability formula to find the values of $P(x)$.

$$P(0) = \binom{6}{0}(0.6)^0(0.4)^6 = 0.0041$$

$$P(1) = \binom{6}{1}(0.6)^1(0.4)^5 = 0.0369$$

$$P(2) = \binom{6}{2}(0.6)^2(0.4)^4 = 0.1382$$

$$P(3) = \binom{6}{3}(0.6)^3(0.4)^3 = 0.2765$$

$$P(4) = \binom{6}{4}(0.6)^4(0.4)^2 = 0.3110$$

$$P(5) = \binom{6}{5}(0.6)^5(0.4)^1 = 0.1866$$

$$P(6) = \binom{6}{6}(0.6)^6(0.4)^0 = 0.0467$$

(a) $$\begin{aligned} E(I) &= 0(0.0041) + 400(0.0369) + 800(0.1382) \\ &\quad + 1200(0.2765) + 800(0.3110) \\ &\quad + 400(0.1866) + 0(0.0467) \\ &= \$780.56 \end{aligned}$$

(b) $n = 3$

x	0	1	2	3
Income	0	100	200	300
$P(x)$	0.064	0.288	0.432	0.216

$$\begin{aligned} E(I) &= 0(0.064) + 400(0.288) + 800(0.432) \\ &\quad + 1200(0.216) \\ &= \$720 \end{aligned}$$

On the basis of all the calculations, the table given in the exercise is completed as follows.

x	0	1	2	3	4	5	6
Income	0	400	800	1200	800	400	0
$P(x)$	0.004	0.037	0.138	0.276	0.311	0.187	0.047

$n = 4$

x	1	1	2	3	4
Income	0	400	800	1200	800
$P(x)$	0.0256	0.1536	0.3456	0.3456	0.1296

$E(I) = 0(0.0256) + 400(0.1536) + 800(0.3456) + 1200(0.3456) + 800(0.1296) = \$856.32$

$n = 5$

x	0	1	2	3	4	5
Income	0	400	800	1200	800	400
$P(x)$	0.01024	0.0768	0.2304	0.3456	0.2592	0.07776

$E(I) = 0(0.01024) + 400(0.0768) + 800(0.2304) + 1200(0.3456) + 800(0.2592) + 400(0.07776) = \$868.22$

Since $E(I)$ is greatest when $n = 5$, the airlines should book 5 reservations to maximize revenue.

52. **(a)** $P(10 \text{ or more}) = 1 - P(\text{less than } 10) = 1 - [P(0) + P(1) + \ldots + P(9)]$

$$= 1 - \left[\binom{50}{0}(0.23)^0(0.77)^{50} + \binom{50}{1}(0.23)^1(0.77)^{49} + \binom{50}{2}(0.23)^2(0.77)^{48} + \binom{50}{3}(0.23)^3(0.77)^{47} + \binom{50}{4}(0.23)^4(0.77)^{46} + \binom{50}{5}(0.23)^5(0.77)^{45} + \binom{50}{6}(0.23)^6(0.77)^{44} + \binom{50}{7}(0.23)^7(0.77)^{43} + \binom{50}{8}(0.23)^8(0.77)^{42} + \binom{50}{9}(0.23)^9(0.77)^{41}\right]$$

$$\approx 1 - [0 + 0.00003 + 0.00025 + 0.00110 + 0.00387 + 0.01064 + 0.02383 + 0.04474 + 0.07183 + 0.10013]$$

$$= 1 - 0.25614$$

$$= 0.74386$$

or about 0.7439.

(b) The expected number of 50 patients to experience nausea is $E(x) = 50(0.23) = 11.5$ or about 12 patients.

(c) $P(10 \text{ or fewer}) = P(0) + P(1) + P(1) + P(2) + \ldots + P(10)$

$$= \binom{50}{0}(0.1)^0(0.9)^{50} + \binom{50}{1}(0.1)^1(0.9)^{49} + \binom{50}{2}(0.1)^2(0.9)^{48} + \binom{50}{3}(0.1)^3(0.9)^{47} + \binom{50}{4}(0.1)^4(0.9)^{46} + \binom{50}{5}(0.1)^5(0.9)^{45} + \binom{50}{6}(0.1)^6(0.9)^{44} + \binom{50}{7}(0.1)^7(0.9)^{43} + \binom{50}{8}(0.1)^8(0.9)^{42} + \binom{50}{9}(0.1)^9(0.9)^{41} + \binom{50}{10}(0.1)^{10}(0.9)^{40}$$

$$\approx 0.00515 + 0.02863 + 0.07794 + 0.13857 + 0.18090 + 0.18492 + 0.15410 + 0.10763 + 0.06428 + 0.03333 + 0.01518$$

$$= 0.99063$$

or about 0.9906.

(d) The probability that a person experiencing nausea is taking Prozac is

$$\frac{E(\text{people who take Prozac and experience nausea})}{E(\text{people who experience nausea})}$$

$$= \frac{500(0.23)}{500(0.23) + 500(0.10)}$$

$$= \frac{115}{115 + 50}$$

$$= \frac{115}{165}$$

$$\approx 0.6970.$$

53. $P(\text{exactly } 5) = \binom{40}{5}\left(\frac{1}{8}\right)^5\left(\frac{7}{8}\right)^{35}$

≈ 0.1875

The probability that exactly 5 will choose a green piece of paper is about 0.1875.

54. **(a)** Define a success to be the event that an orange M&M is selected. In this situation, $n = 4$; $x = 0, 1, 2, 3$, or 4; $p = 0.2$; and $1 - p = 0.8$.

Number of Orange M&M's	Probability
0	$\binom{4}{0}(0.2)^0(0.8)^4 = 0.4096$
1	$\binom{4}{1}(0.2)^1(0.8)^3 = 0.4096$
2	$\binom{4}{2}(0.2)^2(0.8)^2 = 0.1536$
3	$\binom{4}{3}(0.2)^3(0.8)^1 = 0.0256$
4	$\binom{4}{4}(0.2)^4(0.8)^0 = 0.0016$

(b) Draw a histogram with 5 rectangles.

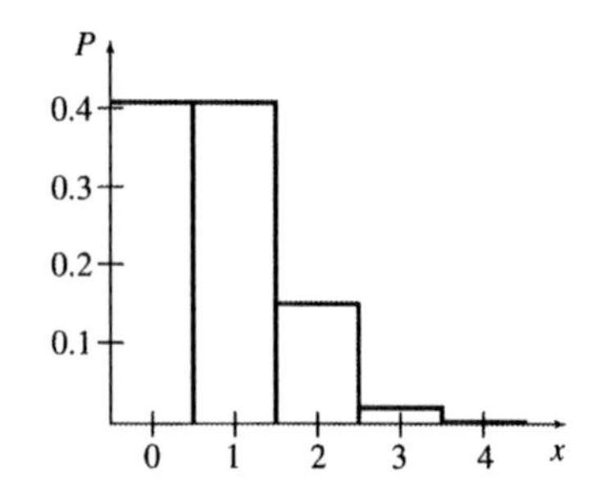

(c) Expected number of orange M&M's $= np = 4(0.2) = 0.8$

55. **(a)** We define a success to be the event that a woman athlete is selected. In this situation, $n = 5$; $x = 0, 1, 2, 3, 4$, or 5; $p = 0.4$; and $1 - p = 0.6$.

Number of Women	Probability
0	$\binom{5}{0}(0.4)^0(0.6)^5 = 0.0778$
1	$\binom{5}{1}(0.4)^1(0.6)^4 = 0.2592$
2	$\binom{5}{2}(0.4)^2(0.6)^3 = 0.3456$
3	$\binom{5}{3}(0.4)^3(0.6)^2 = 0.2304$
4	$\binom{5}{4}(0.4)^4(0.6)^1 = 0.0768$
5	$\binom{5}{5}(0.4)^5(0.6)^0 = 0.01021$

(b) Sketch the histogram with 6 rectangles.

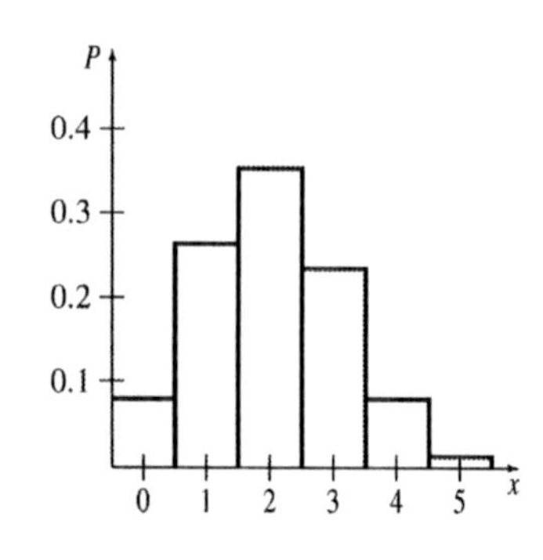

(c) Expected value $= np = 5(0.4) = 2$

56. **(a)**

Number of African-Americans	Probability
0	$\frac{\binom{2}{0}\binom{6}{3}}{\binom{8}{3}} = \frac{20}{56} = \frac{10}{28}$
1	$\frac{\binom{2}{1}\binom{6}{2}}{\binom{8}{3}} = \frac{30}{56} = \frac{15}{28}$
2	$\frac{\binom{2}{2}\binom{6}{1}}{\binom{8}{3}} = \frac{6}{56} = \frac{3}{28}$

(b) Draw a histogram with 3 rectangles.

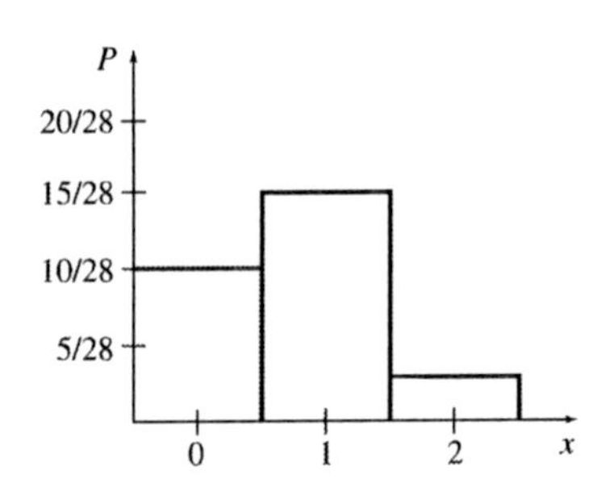

(c) Expected number of African-Americans

$$= 0\left(\frac{10}{28}\right) + 1\left(\frac{15}{28}\right) + 2\left(\frac{3}{28}\right)$$

$$= \frac{21}{28} = \frac{3}{4}$$

57. (a)

Number Who Did Not Do Homework	Probability
0	$\frac{\binom{3}{0}\binom{7}{5}}{\binom{10}{5}} = \frac{21}{252} = \frac{1}{12}$
1	$\frac{\binom{3}{1}\binom{7}{4}}{\binom{10}{5}} = \frac{105}{252} = \frac{5}{12}$
2	$\frac{\binom{3}{2}\binom{7}{3}}{\binom{10}{5}} = \frac{105}{252} = \frac{5}{12}$
3	$\frac{\binom{3}{3}\binom{7}{2}}{\binom{10}{5}} = \frac{21}{252} = \frac{1}{12}$

(b) Draw a histogram with four rectangles.

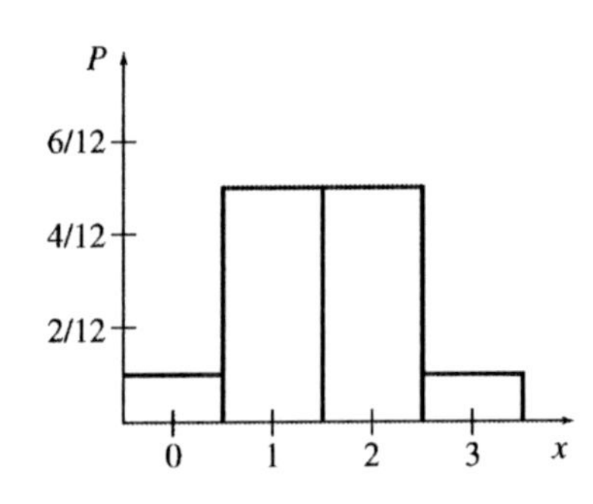

(c) Expected number who did not do homework

$$= 0\left(\frac{1}{12}\right) + 1\left(\frac{5}{12}\right) + 2\left(\frac{5}{12}\right) + 3\left(\frac{1}{12}\right)$$

$$= \frac{18}{12} = \frac{3}{2}$$

58. Let x represent the net winnings for a person who buys one ticket.

x	\$4999	\$999	\$99	−\$1
$P(x)$	$\frac{1}{10{,}000}$	$\frac{2}{10{,}000}$	$\frac{2}{10{,}000}$	$\frac{9995}{10{,}000}$

$$E(x) = \frac{\$4999 + 2(\$999) + 2(\$99) - 9995}{10{,}000}$$

$$= \frac{-\$2800}{10{,}000}$$

$$= -\$0.28 \quad \text{or} \quad -28¢$$

59. It costs $2(0.41 + 0.04) = 0.90$ to play the game.

x	\$1999.18	−\$0.90
$P(x)$	$\frac{1}{8000}$	$\frac{7999}{8000}$

$$E(x) = \$1999.18\left(\frac{1}{8000}\right) - \$0.90\left(\frac{7999}{8000}\right)$$

$$= -\$0.65$$

60. (a) After a specific number is chosen, each of the 10,000 numbers (0000 to 9999) has an equally likely chance of being chosen. Therefore, the probability that the same specific number is chosen again is $\frac{1}{10{,}000}$.

(b) The probability that any specific number is chosen is $\frac{1}{10{,}000}$. Since the selections are independent, the probability that any specific number, in this case 3199, is chosen twice in one day is $\left(\frac{1}{10{,}000}\right)^2 = \frac{1}{100{,}000{,}000}$.

61. If the game was played 365 times a year for 26 years, it was played 9490 times. About $\frac{1}{1000}$ of those times, any one outcome–specifically, 000–would result. So, 000 would result $\frac{1}{1000}(9490) = 9.49$, or about 9.5 times.

62. **(a)** First, we assume 4 numbers are picked. You win if 2, 3, or 4 numbers match.

$$\begin{aligned} P(\text{win}) &= \frac{\binom{20}{2}\binom{60}{2}+\binom{20}{3}\binom{60}{1}+\binom{20}{4}\binom{60}{0}}{\binom{20}{0}\binom{60}{4}+\binom{20}{1}\binom{60}{3}+\binom{20}{2}\binom{60}{2}+\binom{20}{3}\binom{60}{1}+\binom{20}{4}\binom{60}{0}} \\ &= \frac{409{,}545}{1{,}581{,}580} \\ &\approx \frac{1}{3.86} \end{aligned}$$

Next, we assume 5 numbers are picked. You win if 3, 4, or 5 numbers match.

$$\begin{aligned} &P(\text{win}) \\ &= \frac{\binom{20}{3}\binom{60}{2}+\binom{20}{4}\binom{60}{1}+\binom{20}{5}\binom{60}{0}}{\binom{20}{0}\binom{60}{5}+\binom{20}{1}\binom{60}{4}+\binom{20}{2}\binom{60}{3}+\binom{20}{3}\binom{60}{2}+\binom{20}{4}\binom{60}{1}+\binom{20}{5}\binom{60}{0}} \\ &= \frac{2{,}324{,}004}{24{,}040{,}016} \\ &\approx \frac{1}{10.34} \end{aligned}$$

(b) Expected value when you pick 4

$$\begin{aligned} &= 1\cdot\frac{\binom{20}{2}\binom{60}{2}}{1{,}581{,}580}+5\cdot\frac{\binom{20}{3}\binom{60}{1}}{1{,}581{,}580}+55\cdot\frac{\binom{20}{4}\binom{60}{0}}{1{,}581{,}580} \\ &\quad - 1(1) \\ &\approx -\$0.4026. \end{aligned}$$

Expected value when you pick 5

$$\begin{aligned} &= 2\cdot\frac{\binom{20}{3}\binom{60}{2}}{24{,}040{,}016}+20\cdot\frac{\binom{20}{4}\binom{60}{1}}{24{,}040{,}016} \\ &\quad + 300\cdot\frac{\binom{20}{5}\binom{60}{0}}{24{,}040{,}016} - 1(1) \\ &\approx -\$0.3968. \end{aligned}$$

63. **(a)** (i) When 5 socks are selected, we could get 1 matching pair and 3 odd socks or 2 matching pairs and 1 odd sock.

First consider 1 matching pair and 3 odd socks. The number of ways this could be done is

$$\binom{10}{1}\left[\binom{18}{3}-\binom{9}{1}\binom{16}{1}\right] = 6720.$$

$\binom{10}{1}$ gives the number of ways for 1 pair, while $\left[\binom{18}{3}-\binom{9}{1}\binom{16}{1}\right]$ gives the number of ways for the remaining 3 socks from the 18 socks left. We must subtract the number of ways the last 3 socks could contain a pair from the 9 pairs remaining.

Next consider 2 matching pairs and 1 odd sock. The number of ways this could be done is

$$\binom{10}{2}\binom{16}{1} = 720.$$

$\binom{10}{2}$ gives the number of ways for 2 pairs, while $\binom{16}{1}$ gives the number of ways for the 1 odd sock.

The total number of ways is

$$6720 + 720 = 7440.$$

Then

$$P(\text{matching pair}) = \frac{7440}{\binom{20}{5}} \approx 0.4799.$$

(ii) When 6 socks are selected, we could get 3 matching pairs and no odd socks or 2 matching pairs and 2 odd socks or 1 matching pair and 4 odd socks. The number of ways of obtaining 3 matching pairs is $\binom{10}{3} = 120$. The number of ways of obtaining 2 matching pairs and 2 odd socks is

$$\binom{10}{2}\left[\binom{16}{2}-\binom{8}{1}\right] = 5040.$$

The 2 odd socks must come from the 16 socks remaining but cannot be one of the 8 remaining pairs.

The number of ways of obtaining 1 matching pair and 4 odd socks is

$$\binom{10}{1}\left[\binom{18}{4}-\binom{9}{2}-\binom{9}{1}\left[\binom{16}{2}-8\right]\right] = 20{,}160.$$

The 4 odd socks must come from the 18 socks remaining but can be 2 pairs and cannot be 1 pair and 2 odd socks.

The total number of ways is

$$120 + 5040 + 20{,}160 = 25{,}320.$$

Thus,

$$P(\text{matching pair}) = \frac{25{,}320}{\binom{20}{6}} \approx 0.6533.$$

(c) Suppose 6 socks are lost at random. The worst case is they are 6 odd socks. The best case is they are 3 matching pairs.

First find the number of ways of selecting 6 odd socks. This is

$$\binom{10}{6}\binom{2}{1}\binom{2}{1}\binom{2}{1}\binom{2}{1}\binom{2}{1}\binom{2}{1} = 13{,}440.$$

The $\binom{10}{6}$ gives the number of ways of choosing 6 different socks from the 10 pairs. But with each pair, $\binom{2}{1}$ gives the number of ways of selecting 1 sock. Then

$$P(\text{6 odd socks}) = \frac{13,440}{\binom{20}{6}} \approx 0.3467.$$

Next find the number of ways of selecting three matching pairs. This is $\binom{10}{3} = 120$. Then

$$P(\text{3 matching pairs}) = \frac{120}{\binom{20}{6}} \approx 0.003096.$$

64. **(a)**
$$\begin{aligned} P(\text{5 or more}) &= P(5) + P(6) + P(7) + P(8) + P(9) \\ &= 0.0040 + 0.0018 + 0.0007 + 0.0003 + 0.0001 \\ &= 0.0069 \end{aligned}$$

(b) $P(\text{less than 2}) = P(0) + P(1) = 0.7345 + 0.1489 = 0.8834$

(c) The expected number of runs is

$$\begin{aligned} E(x) &= 0(0.7345) + 1(0.1489) + 2(0.0653) + 3(0.0306) + 4(0.0137) + 5(0.0040) + 6(0.0018) \\ &\quad + 7(0.0007) + 8(0.0003) + 9(0.0001) \\ &= 0.4651 \end{aligned}$$

66. There are $\binom{92}{9}$ possible hands.

(a) There are $\binom{10}{9} = 10$ ways to choose 9 of the 10 suits. There are $\binom{9}{1} = 9$ ways to choose a card from each suit. The probability is

$$\frac{10 \cdot 9^9}{\binom{92}{9}} \approx 0.004459.$$

(b) There are $\binom{10}{1} = 10$ ways to choose one suit and $\binom{9}{7} = 36$ ways to choose 7 of the 9 remaining suits. There are $\binom{9}{2} = 36$ ways to choose a pair from one suit and $\binom{9}{1} = 9$ ways to choose a card from each of the 7 suits. The probability is

$$\frac{10 \cdot 36 \cdot 36 \cdot 9^7}{\binom{92}{9}} \approx 0.07135.$$

(c) There are $\binom{10}{2} = 45$ ways to choose two suits and $\binom{8}{5} = 56$ ways to choose 5 of the 8 remaining suits. There are $\binom{9}{2} = 36$ ways to choose a pair from each of the two suits and $\binom{9}{1} = 9$ ways to choose a card from each of the 5 other suits. The probability is

$$\frac{45 \cdot 56 \cdot 36^2 \cdot 9^5}{\binom{92}{9}} \approx 0.2220.$$

Extended Application: Optimal Inventory For a Service Truck

1. (a) $C(M_0) = NL[1-(1-p_1)(1-p_2)(1-p_3)] = 3(54)[1-(0.91)(0.76)(0.83)] = \$69.01$

   (b) $C(M_2) = H_2 + NL[1-(1-p_1)(1-p_3)] = 40 + 3(54)[1-(0.91)(0.83)] = \$79.64$

   (c) $C(M_3) = H_3 + NL[1-(1-p_1)(1-p_2)] = 9 + 3(54)[1-(0.91)(0.76)] = \$58.96$

   (d) $C(M_{12}) = H_1 + H_2 + NL[1-(1-p_3)] = 15 + 40 + 3(54)[1-0.83] = \$82.54$

   (e) $C(M_{13}) = H_1 + H_3 + NL[1-(1-p_2)] = 15 + 9 + 3(54)[1-0.76] = \$62.88$

   (f) $C(M_{123}) = H_1 + H_2 + H_3 + NL[1-1] = 15 + 40 + 9 = \$64.00$

2. Policy M_3, stocking only part 3 on the truck, leads to the lowest expected cost.

3. It is not necessary for the probabilities to add up to 1 because it is possible that no parts will be needed. That is, the events of needing parts 1, 2, and 3 are not the only events in the sample space.

4. For 3 different parts we have 8 different policies: 1 with no parts, 3 with 1 part, 3 with 2 parts, and 1 with 3 parts. The number of different policies, $8 = 2^3$, is the number of subsets of a set containing 3 distinct elements. If there are n different parts, the number of policies is the number of subsets of a set containing n distinct elements which is 2^n.

Chapter 9

STATISTICS

9.1 Frequency Distributions; Measures of Central Tendency

1. **(a)-(b)** Since 0-24 is to be the first interval and there are 25 numbers between 0 and 24 inclusive, we will let all six intervals be of size 25. The other five intervals are 25-49, 50-74, 75-99, 100-124, and 125-149. Making a tally of how many data values lie in each interval leads to the following frequency distribution.

Interval	Frequency
0-24	4
25-49	8
50-74	5
75-99	10
100-124	4
125-149	5

(c) Draw the histogram. It consists of 6 bars of equal width having heights as determined by the frequency of each interval. See the histogram in part (d).

(d) To construct the frequency polygon, join consecutive midpoints of the tops of the histogram bars with line segments.

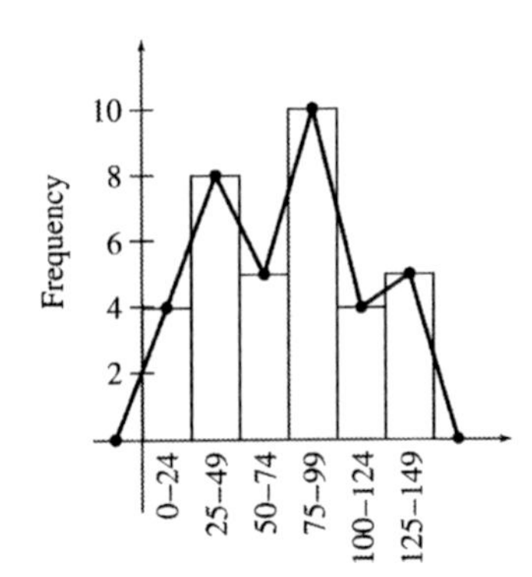

2. **(a)-(b)** Use seven intervals, beginning with 30-39 and ending with 90-99. Making a tally of how many data values lie in each interval leads to the following frequency distribution.

Interval	Frequency
30-39	1
40-49	6
50-59	13
60-69	22
70-79	17
80-89	13
90-99	8

(c)-(d) The histogram consists of 7 bars of equal width having heights as determined by the frequency of each interval.

For the frequency polygon, join consecutive midpoints of the tops of the histogram bars with straight line segments.

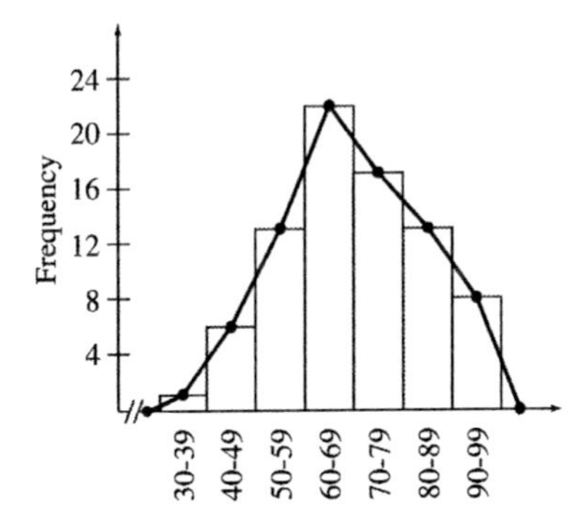

3. **(a)-(b)** There are eight intervals starting with 0-19. Making a tally of how many data values lie in each interval leads to the following frequency distribution.

Interval	Frequency
0-19	4
20-39	5
40-59	4
60-79	5
80-99	9
100-119	3
120-139	4
140-159	2

(c) Draw the histogram. It consists of 8 rectangles of equal width having heights as determined by the frequency of each interval. See the histogram in part (d).

(d) To construct the frequency polygon, join consecutive midpoints of the tops of the histogram bars with line segments.

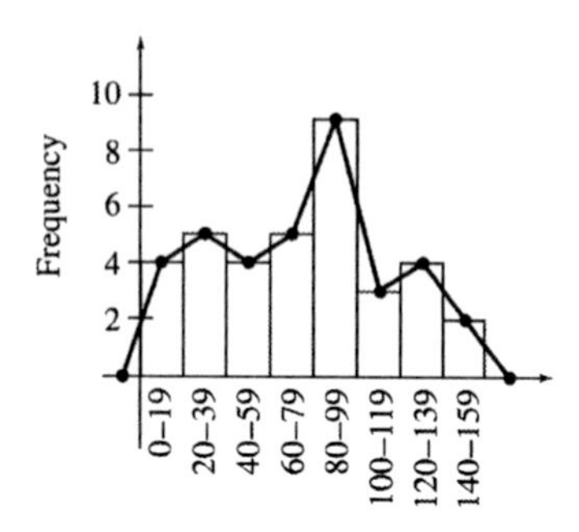

4. (a)-(b)

Interval	Frequency
39-48	6
49-58	13
59-68	20
69-78	19
79-88	13
89-98	9

(c)-(d)

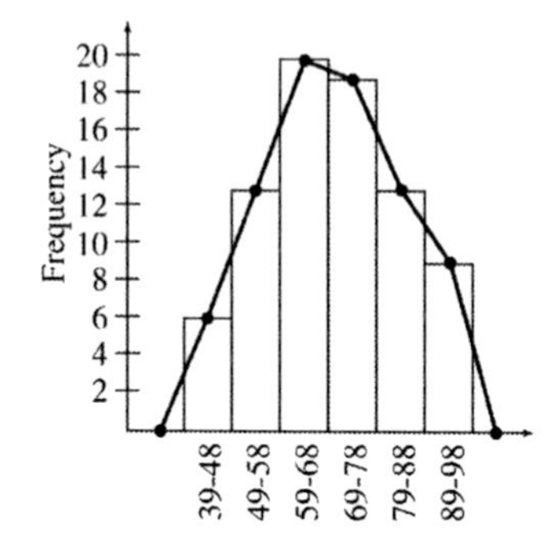

7. $\bar{x} = \frac{\sum x}{n}$
$= \frac{8 + 10 + 16 + 21 + 25}{5}$
$= \frac{80}{5} = 16$

8. $\bar{x} = \frac{\sum x}{n}$
$= \frac{67 + 89 + 75 + 86 + 100 + 93}{6}$
$= \frac{510}{6} = 85$

9. $\sum x = 30{,}200 + 23{,}700 + 33{,}320 + 29{,}410 + 24{,}600 + 27{,}750 + 27{,}300 + 32{,}680 = 228{,}960$

The mean of the 8 numbers is

$$\bar{x} = \frac{\sum x}{n} = \frac{228{,}960}{8} = 28{,}620.$$

10. $\sum x = 38{,}500 + 39{,}720 + 42{,}183 + 21{,}982 + 43{,}250 = 185{,}635$

The mean of the 5 numbers is

$$\bar{x} = \frac{\sum x}{n} = \frac{185{,}635}{5} = 37{,}127.$$

11. $\sum x = 9.4 + 11.3 + 10.5 + 7.4 + 9.1 + 8.4 + 9.7 + 5.2 + 1.1 + 4.7 = 76.8$

The mean of the 10 numbers is

$$\bar{x} = \frac{\sum x}{n} = \frac{76.8}{10} = 7.68.$$

12. $\sum x = 15.3 + 27.2 + 14.8 + 16.5 + 31.8 + 40.1 + 18.9 + 28.4 + 26.3 + 35.3 = 254.6$

The mean of the 10 numbers is

$$\bar{x} = \frac{\sum x}{n} = \frac{254.6}{10} = 25.46.$$

13. Add to the frequency distribution a new column, "Value × Frequency."

Value	Frequency	Value × Frequency
4	6	$4 \cdot 6 =$ 24
6	1	$6 \cdot 1 =$ 6
9	3	$9 \cdot 3 =$ 27
15	2	$15 \cdot 2 =$ 30
Totals:	12	87

The mean is

$$\bar{x} = \frac{\sum xf}{n} = \frac{87}{12} = 7.25.$$

14.

Value	Frequency	Value × Frequency
9	3	$9 \cdot 3 =$ 27
12	5	$12 \cdot 5 =$ 60
15	1	$15 \cdot 1 =$ 15
18	1	$18 \cdot 1 =$ 18
Totals:	10	120

$$\bar{x} = \frac{120}{10} = 12$$

15. 27, 35, 39, 42, 47, 51, 54

The numbers are already arranged in numerical order, from smallest to largest. The median is the middle number, 42.

16. $596, 604, 612, 683, 719$

The median is the middle number, in this case, 612.

17. 100, 114, 125, 135, 150, 172

The median is the mean of the two middle numbers, which is

$$\frac{125+135}{2} = \frac{260}{2} = 130.$$

18. $359, 831, 904, 615, 211, 279, 505$

First, arrange the numbers in numerical order, from smallest to largest.

$211, 279, 359, 505, 615, 831, 904$

The median is the middle number, 505.

19. Arrange the numbers in numerical order, from smallest to largest.

$$3.4, 9.1, 27.6, 28.4, 29.8, 32.1, 47.6, 59.8$$

There are eight numbers here; the median is the mean of the two middle numbers, which is

$$\frac{28.4+29.8}{2} = \frac{58.2}{2} = 29.1.$$

20. 0.2, 1.4, 0.6, 0.2, 2.5, 1.9, 0.8, 1.5

First arrange the numbers in numerical order, from smallest to largest.

0.2, 0.2, 0.6, 0.8, 1.4, 1.5, 1.9, 2.5

Since there are an even number of entries, the median is the mean of the two middle numbers.

$$\text{median} = \frac{0.8+1.4}{2} = 1.1.$$

21. Using a graphing calculator, $\bar{x} \approx 73.861$ and the median is 80.5.

22. Using a graphing calculator, $\bar{x} = 69.475$ and the median is 69.

23. 4, 9, 8, 6, 9, 2, 1, 3

The mode is the number that occurs most often. Here, the mode is 9.

24. $16, 15, 13, 15, 14, 13, 11, 15, 14$

The mode is the most frequent entry. In this case the mode is 15, which occurs 3 times.

25. $55, 62, 62, 71, 62, 55, 73, 55, 71$

The mode is the number that occurs most often. Here, there are two modes, 55 and 62, since they both appear three times.

26. $158, 162, 165, 162, 165, 157, 163$

The mode is the most frequent entry. In this case there are two modes, 162 and 165, each of which occurs twice.

27. 6.8, 6.3, 6.3, 6.9, 6.7, 6.4, 6.1, 6.0

The mode is 6.3.

28. $22.35, 14.90, 17.85, 15.46, 14.91, 17.85, 21.35$

The mode is the most frequent entry. In this case the mode is 17.85, which occurs twice.

31.

Interval	Midpoint, x	Frequency, f	Product, xf
0-24	12	4	48
25-49	37	8	296
50-74	62	5	310
75-99	87	10	870
100-124	112	4	448
125-149	137	5	685
Totals:		36	2657

The mean of this collection of grouped data is

$$\bar{x} = \frac{\sum xf}{n} = \frac{2657}{36} \approx 73.8.$$

The interval 75-99 contains the most data values, 10, so it is the modal class.

32.

Interval	Midpoint, x	Frequency, f	Product, xf
30-39	34.5	1	34.5
40-49	44.5	6	267
50-59	54.5	13	708.5
60-69	64.5	22	1419
70-79	74.5	17	1266.5
80-89	84.5	13	1098.5
90-99	94.5	8	756
Totals:		80	5550

Use the formula for the mean of a grouped frequency distribution.

$$\overline{x} = \frac{\sum xf}{n} = \frac{5550}{80} \approx 69.4$$

The modal class is the interval containing the most data values. The above table shows that the highest frequency, 22, occurs in the interval 60-69.

34. Find the mean of the numbers in the "Price" column.

$$\overline{x} = \frac{\sum x}{n} = \frac{32.02}{10} = 3.202$$

The mean price per bushel of wheat is \$3.20.
To find the median, list the ten values in the "Price" column from smallest to largest.

2.48, 2.62, 2.65, 2.78, 3.38, 3.40, 3.40, 3.45, 3.56, 4.30

The median is the mean of the two middle entries.

$$\frac{3.38 + 3.40}{2} = 3.39$$

The median price per bushel of wheat is \$3.39.

35. Find the mean of the numbers in the "Production" column.

$$\overline{x} = \frac{\sum x}{n} = \frac{21{,}990}{10} = 2199$$

The mean production is 2199 million bushels.
To find the median, list the ten values in the "Production" column from smallest to largest.

1606, 1947, 2105, 2158, 2228, 2277, 2296, 2345, 2481, 2547

The median is the mean of the two middle entries.

$$\frac{2228 + 2277}{2} = 2252.5$$

The median production is 2252.5 million bushels.

36. **(a)** Find the mean.

$$\overline{x} = \frac{\sum x}{n} = \frac{294{,}827}{15} = 19{,}655.133$$

Since the total pay is given in thousands of dollars, the mean total pay for this group of people is \$19,655.133.

(b) The values are listed in order, so the median is the middle value, 15,612.
The median total pay for this group of people is \$15,612,000.

37. Find the mean for the grouped data.

$$\overline{x} = \frac{\sum xf}{n} = \frac{(10{,}000)(4741) + (30{,}000)(3893) + \ldots + (225{,}000)(58)}{4741 + 3893 + \ldots + 58} = \frac{541{,}265{,}000}{13{,}635} \approx \$39{,}696.74$$

The estimated mean household income for African Americans in 2004 is $39,696.74.

38. (a) Find the mean for the grouped data.

$$\overline{x} = \frac{\sum xf}{n} = \frac{(10{,}000)(15{,}530) + \$30{,}000(18{,}265) + \ldots + 225{,}000(1112)}{15{,}530 + 18{,}265 + \ldots + 1112} = \frac{4{,}785{,}365{,}000}{80{,}006} \approx 59{,}812.58$$

The estimated mean household income for white Americans in 2004 is $59,812.58.

39. (a) Find the mean of the numbers in the "Complaints" column.

$$\overline{x} = \frac{\sum x}{n} = \frac{2639}{12} \approx 219.92$$

The mean number of complaints is 219.92 complaints per airline.
To find the median, list the 12 values in the "Complaints" column from smallest to largest.

28, 49, 61, 69, 83, 93, 211, 227, 378, 403, 457, 580

The median is the mean of the two middle numbers.

$$\text{median} = \frac{93 + 211}{2} = 152.$$

The median number of complaints per airline is 152.

(b) The average found is not meaningful because not all airlines carry the same number of passengers.

(c) Find the mean of the numbers in the "Complaints per 100,000 Passengers Boarding" column.

$$\overline{x} = \frac{\sum x}{n} = \frac{10.08}{12} = 0.84$$

The mean number of complaints per 100,000 passengers boarding is 0.84.

To find the median, list the 12 values in the "Complaints per 100,000 Passengers Boarding" column from smallest to largest.

0.18, 0.32, 0.59, 0.62, 0.73, 0.84, 0.91, 1.00, 1.02, 1.17, 1.32, 1.38

The median is the mean of the two middle numbers.

$$\text{median} = \frac{0.84 + 0.91}{2} = 0.875$$

The median number of complaints per 100,000 passengers boarding is 0.875.

40.

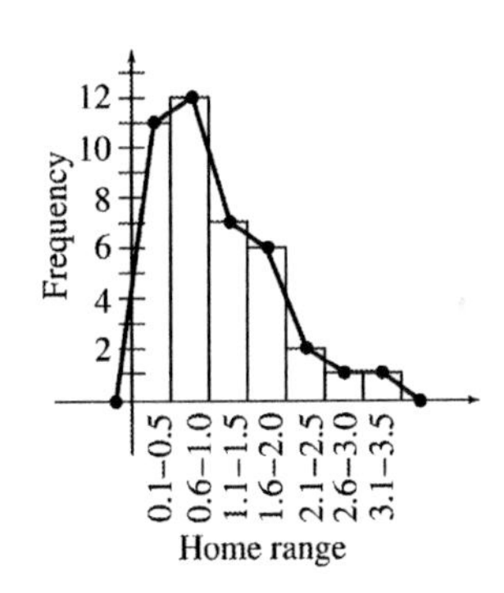

41. Find the mean.

$$\overline{x} = \frac{\sum x}{n} = \frac{16 + 12 + \ldots + 2}{13} = \frac{96}{13} \approx 7.38$$

The mean number of recognized blood types is 7.38.
Find the median.
The values are listed in order.
Since there are 13 values, the median is the seventh value, 7.
The median number of recognized blood types is 7.
The values 7, 5, and 4 each occur the greatest number of times, 2.
The modes are 7, 5, and 4.

42. **(a)** From the histogram, the height of the bar representing 0-9 is 13.4.
Therefore, 13.4% of the population is estimated to be in the 0-9 age group.

(b) From the histogram, the height of the bar representing 60-69 is 7.8.
Therefore, 7.8% of the population is estimated to be in the 60-69 age group.

(c) The tallest bar has a height of 15.
This represents age group 40-49.
Therefore, the age range 40-49 has the largest percent of the population.

43. **(a)** The height of the bar representing age group 20-29 is 12.
Therefore, 12% of the population is estimated to be in the age groups 20-29.

(b) The height of the bar representing age group 70+ is 13.
Therefore, 13% of the population is estimated to be in the age group 70+.

(c) The shortest bar represents age groups 50-59.
Therefore, the age group 50-59 will have the smallest percent of the population.

(d) In Exercise 41, the percentages for various age ranges vary from 7% to 15%, while the estimated percentages for 2025 range from 11% to 13%. So, it seems the U.S. population is becoming uniform for all age groups.

44. **(a)**

Interval	Frequency
0-4	7
5-9	10
10-14	14
15-19	1
20-24	4
25-29	1

(b)

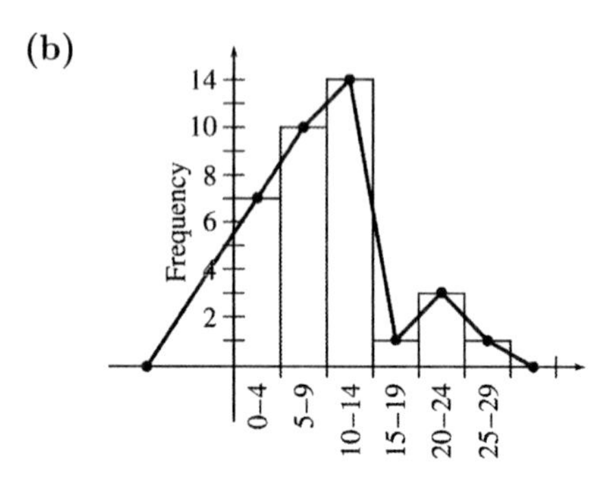

(c) For the original data, $\sum x = 373$, $n = 37$, and

$$\bar{x} = \frac{\sum x}{n} = \frac{373}{37} \approx 10.08.$$

(d)

Interval	Midpoint, x	Frequency, f	Product, xf
0-4	2	7	14
5-9	7	10	70
10-14	12	14	168
15-19	17	1	17
20-24	22	4	88
25-29	27	1	27
Totals:		37	384

The mean of this collection of grouped data is

$$\bar{x} = \frac{\sum xf}{n} = \frac{384}{37} \approx 10.38.$$

(f) Arrange the data in increasing order.

0, 1, 3, 3, 4, 4, 4, 5, 5, 5, 5, 6, 7, 7, 8 ,8,
8, 10, 10, 11, 11, 11, 11,11, 11, 12, 12,
12, 13, 14, 14, 16, 20, 21, 21, 24, 25

There are 37 items. The median is 10.

The item with the greatest frequency is 11, so the mode is 11.

45. **(a)** Find the mean of the numbers in the maximum temperature column.

$$\bar{x} = \frac{\sum x}{n} = \frac{666}{12} = 55.5$$

The mean of the maximum temperatures is 55.5°F. To find the median, list the 12 maximum temperatures from smallest to largest.

$$39, 39, 40, 44, 47, 50, 51, 60, 69, 70, 78, 79$$

The median is the mean of the two middle values.

$$\frac{50+51}{2} = 50.5°\text{F}$$

(b) Find the mean of the numbers in the minimum temperature column.

$$\bar{x} = \frac{\sum x}{n} = \frac{347}{12} \approx 28.9$$

The mean of the minimum temperatures is about 28.9°F.

To find the median, list the 12 minimum temperatures from smallest to largest.

$$16, 18, 20, 21, 24, 26, 31, 32, 37, 37, 42, 43$$

The median is the mean of the two middle values.

$$\frac{26+31}{2} = 28.5°\text{F}$$

46. **(a)**

$$\bar{x} = \frac{\sum x}{n}$$
$$= \frac{35+37+37+37+49+57+64+67+72+77+85}{11}$$
$$= \frac{617}{11} \approx 56.1$$

The mean is 56.1.

(b) The median is 57.

(c) The mode is the most frequent number, which is 37.

47. **(a)** $\dfrac{5{,}700{,}000{,}000 \cdot 1 + 100 \cdot 80{,}000}{1 + 80{,}000}$

$$= \frac{5{,}708{,}000{,}000}{80{,}001}$$
$$\approx 71{,}349$$

The average worth of a citizen of Chukotka is $71,349.

48. **(a)** Counting Gates, there would be 10,001 residents of the town. 10,000 residents have no personal wealth; 1 resident is worth $10,000,000,000.

$$\bar{x} = \frac{10{,}000(0) + 1(10{,}000{,}000{,}000)}{10{,}001}$$

$$\bar{x} = 999{,}900.01$$

The mean wealth is roughly $1 million.

(b) The median is $0 since 0 is the middle value in the list of 10,001 values.

(c) The mode is $0 since it occurs with the greatest frequency.

(d) The median or mode is most representative of the wealth of the town's population.

49. **(a)** Find the mean:

$$\bar{x} = \frac{\sum x}{n} = \frac{96{,}487{,}919}{27} \approx 3{,}573{,}626.63$$

The mean salary is $3,573,627.

Find the median: The values are listed in order. Therefore, the median salary is the middle number, $1,750,000.

Find the mode: The mode is the most frequent entry in the list. Since the values $345,000 and $7,000,000 each occur twice, there are two modes. The modal salaries are $345,000 and $7,000,000.

(b) Since most of the team earned far below the mean salary of $3,573,627 and most of the team earned between the two modes of $345,000 and $7,000,000, the median salary of $1,750,000 best describes this data.

50. $a^0 = 1$ and $a^1 = a$, so the sequence can be written:

$$a^0, a^1, a^2, a^3, \ldots, a^n.$$

There are $n+1$ values and n is even. Therefore, there is an odd number of values. Since there is an odd number of values, the median is the value in the middle position. The middle value is in position $\frac{n-0}{2} = \frac{n}{2}$, which is a whole number since n is even.
The median is equal to $a^{n/2}$, which is choice (c).

9.2 Measures of Variation

1. The standard deviation of a sample of numbers is the square root of the variance of the sample.

2. For every set of numbers, the sum of the deviations from the mean equals zero.

3. The range is the difference of the highest and lowest numbers in the list, or $85 - 52 = 33$.

   To find the standard deviation, first find the mean.

$$\bar{x} = \frac{72 + 61 + 57 + 83 + 52 + 66 + 85}{7} = \frac{476}{7} = 68$$

   To prepare for calculating the standard deviation, construct a table.

x	x^2
72	5184
61	3721
57	3249
83	6889
52	2704
66	4356
85	7225
Total:	33,328

   The variance is

$$s^2 = \frac{\sum x^2 - n\bar{x}^2}{n-1} = \frac{33{,}328 - 7(68)^2}{7-1} = \frac{33{,}328 - 32{,}368}{6} = 160$$

   and the standard deviation is

$$s = \sqrt{160} \approx 12.6.$$

4. $122, 132, 141, 158, 162, 169, 180$

   The range is the difference between the largest and smallest numbers. Here the largest number is 180 and the smallest is 122. The range is

$$180 - 122 = 58.$$

   To find the standard deviation, the first step is to find the mean.

$$\bar{x} = \frac{\sum x}{n} = \frac{122 + 132 + 141 + 158 + 162 + 169 + 180}{7} = \frac{1064}{7} = 152$$

   Now complete the following table.

x	x^2
122	14,884
132	17,424
141	19,881
158	24,964
162	26,244
169	28,561
180	32,400
Total:	164,358

   The total of the second column gives $\sum x^2 = 164{,}358$. The variance is

$$s^2 = \frac{\sum x^2 - n\bar{x}^2}{n-1} = \frac{164{,}358 - 7(152)^2}{7-1} = \frac{164{,}358 - 161{,}728}{6} = \frac{2630}{6} \approx 438.3,$$

   and the standard deviation is

$$s = \sqrt{438.3} \approx 20.9.$$

5. The range is $287 - 241 = 46$. The mean is

$$\bar{x} = \frac{241 + 248 + 251 + 257 + 252 + 287}{6} = 256.$$

x	x^2
241	58,081
248	61,504
251	63,001
257	66,049
252	63,504
287	82,369
Total:	394,508

   The standard deviation is

$$s = \sqrt{\frac{\sum x^2 - n\bar{x}^2}{n-1}} = \sqrt{\frac{394{,}508 - 6(256)^2}{5}} = \sqrt{258.4} \approx 16.1.$$

6. $51, 58, 62, 64, 67, 71, 74, 78, 82, 93$

The range is $93 - 51 = 42$. The mean is

$$\bar{x} = \frac{\sum x}{n} = \frac{700}{10} = 70.$$

x	x^2
51	2601
58	3364
62	3844
64	4096
67	4489
71	5041
74	5476
78	6084
82	6724
93	8649
Total:	50,368

The standard deviation is

$$s = \sqrt{\frac{\sum x^2 - n\bar{x}^2}{n-1}} = \sqrt{\frac{50{,}368 - 10(70)^2}{9}} = \sqrt{152} \approx 12.3.$$

7. The range is $27 - 3 = 24$. The mean is

$$\bar{x} = \frac{\sum x}{n} = \frac{140}{10} = 14.$$

x	x^2
3	9
7	49
4	16
12	144
15	225
18	324
19	361
27	729
24	576
11	121
Total:	2554

The standard deviation is

$$s = \sqrt{\frac{\sum x^2 - n\bar{x}^2}{n-1}} = \sqrt{\frac{2554 - 10(14)^2}{9}} = \sqrt{66} \approx 8.1.$$

8. The range is $57 - 3 = 54$.
The mean is

$$\bar{x} = \frac{\sum x}{n} = \frac{270}{10} = 27.$$

Construct a table.

x	x^2
17	289
57	3249
48	2304
13	169
26	676
3	9
36	1296
21	441
9	81
40	1600
Total:	10,114

The standard deviation is

$$s = \sqrt{\frac{\sum x^2 - n\bar{x}^2}{n-1}} = \sqrt{\frac{10{,}114 - 10(27)^2}{9}} \approx \sqrt{313.78} \approx 17.7.$$

9. Using a graphing calculator, enter the 36 numbers into a list. Using the 1-Var Stats feature of a TI-83/84 Plus calculator, the standard deviation is found to be $Sx \approx 40.04793754$, or 40.05.

10. Using a graphing calculator, enter the 38 numbers into a list. Using the 1-Var Stats feature of a TI-83/84 Plus calculator, the standard deviation is found to be $Sx \approx 6.130921094$, or 6.13.

11. Expand the table to include columns for the midpoint x of each interval for xf, x^2, and fx^2.

Interval	f	x	xf	x^2	fx^2
30-39	4	12	48	144	576
40-49	8	37	296	1369	10,952
50-59	5	62	310	3844	19,220
60-69	10	87	870	7569	75,690
70-79	4	112	448	12,544	50,176
80-89	5	137	685	18,769	93,845
Totals:	36		2657		250,459

The mean of the grouped data is

$$\bar{x} = \frac{\sum xf}{n} = \frac{2657}{36} \approx 73.8.$$

The standard deviation for the grouped data is

$$s = \sqrt{\frac{\sum fx^2 - n\bar{x}^2}{n-1}} = \sqrt{\frac{250{,}459 - 36(73.8)^2}{35}} \approx \sqrt{1554} \approx 39.4.$$

12. Recall that when working with grouped data, x represents the midpoint of each interval. Complete the following table.

Interval	f	x	xf	x^2	fx^2
30-39	1	34.5	34.5	1190.25	1190.25
40-49	6	44.5	267.0	1980.25	11,881.50
50-59	13	54.5	708.5	2970.25	38,613.25
60-69	22	64.5	1419.0	4160.24	91,525.50
70-79	17	74.5	1266.5	5550.25	94,354.25
80-89	13	84.5	1098.5	7140.25	92,823.25
90-99	8	94.5	756.0	8930.25	71,442.00
Totals:	80		5550.0		401,830.00

Use the formulas for grouped frequency distributions to find the mean and then the standard deviation.

$$\bar{x} = \frac{\sum xf}{n} = \frac{5550}{80} = 69.375$$

$$s = \sqrt{\frac{\sum fx^2 - n\bar{x}^2}{n-1}} = \sqrt{\frac{401{,}830 - 80(69.375)^2}{79}} = \sqrt{\frac{16{,}798.75}{79}} \approx \sqrt{212.64} \approx 14.6$$

13. Use $k = 3$ in Chebyshev's theorem.

$$1 - \frac{1}{k^2} = 1 - \frac{1}{3^2} = \frac{8}{9},$$

so at least $\frac{8}{9}$ of the distribution is within 3 standard deviations of the mean.

14. Use $k = 4$ in Chebyshev's theorem.

$$1 - \frac{1}{k^2} = 1 - \frac{1}{4^2} = \frac{15}{16},$$

so at least $\frac{15}{16}$ of the numbers in the data set lie within 4 standard deviations of the mean.

15. Use $k = 5$ in Chebyshev's theorem.

$$1 - \frac{1}{k^2} = 1 - \frac{1}{5^2} = \frac{24}{25},$$

so at least $\frac{24}{25}$ of the distribution is within 5 standard deviations of the mean.

16. We have $36 = 60 - 3 \cdot 8 = \bar{x} - 3s$ and $84 = 60 + 3 \cdot 8 = \bar{x} + 3s$, so Chebyshev's theorem applies with $k = 3$. Hence, at least

$$1 - \frac{1}{k^2} = 1 - \frac{1}{9} = \frac{8}{9}$$

of the numbers lie between 36 and 84.

17. We have $48 = 60 - (3/2) \cdot 8 = \bar{x} - (3/2)s$ and $72 = 60 + (3/2) \cdot 8 = \bar{x} + (3/2)s$, so Chebyshev's theorem applies with $k = 3/2$. Hence, at least

$$1 - \frac{1}{k^2} = 1 - \frac{4}{9} = \frac{5}{9}$$

of the numbers lie between 48 and 72.

18. The answer here is the complement of the answer to Exercise 16. It was found there that at least $8/9$ of the distribution of the numbers are between 36 and 84, so at most $1 - 8/9 = 1/9$ of the numbers are less than 36 or more than 84.

19. The answer here is the complement of the answer to Exercise 17. It was found there that at least $5/9$ of the distribution of the numbers are between 48 and 72, so at most $1 - 5/9 = 4/9$ of the numbers are less than 48 or more than 72.

23. $15, 18, 19, 23, 25, 25, 28, 30, 34, 38$

(a) $$\bar{x} = \frac{1}{10}(15 + 18 + 19 + 23 + 25 + 25 + 28 + 30 + 34 + 38) = \frac{1}{10}(255) = 25.5$$

The mean life of the sample of Brand X batteries is 25.5 hr.

x	x^2
15	225
18	324
19	361
23	529
25	625
25	625
28	784
30	900
34	1156
38	1444
Total:	6973

$$s = \sqrt{\frac{\sum x^2 - n\bar{x}^2}{n-1}}$$
$$= \sqrt{\frac{6973 - 10(25.5)^2}{9}}$$
$$\approx \sqrt{52.28} \approx 7.2$$

The standard deviation of the Brand X lives is 7.2 hr.

(b) Forever Power has a smaller standard deviation (4.1 hr, as opposed to 7.2 hr for Brand X), which indicates a more uniform life.

(c) Forever Power has a higher mean (26.2 hr, as opposed to 25.5 hr for Brand X), which indicates a longer average life.

24. **(a)** $\bar{x} = \frac{\sum x}{n} = \frac{18 + 15 + 7 + 10}{4} = 12.5$

(b) $\bar{x} = \frac{\sum x}{n} = \frac{1 + (-8) + (-5) + 0}{4} = -3.0$

(c)

x	x^2
+18	324
+15	225
+7	49
+10	100
Total:	698

$$s = \sqrt{\frac{\sum x^2 - n\bar{x}^2}{n-1}}$$
$$= \sqrt{\frac{698 - 4(12.5)^2}{3}}$$
$$\approx \sqrt{24.33} \approx 4.9$$

(d)

x	x^2
+1	1
−8	64
−5	25
0	0
Total:	90

$$s = \sqrt{\frac{\sum x^2 - n\bar{x}^2}{n-1}}$$
$$= \sqrt{\frac{90 - 4(-3.0)^2}{3}}$$
$$= \sqrt{18} \approx 4.2$$

(e) $12.5 - (-3) = 15.5$

(f) Low: $15.5 - 7.95 = 7.55$
High: $15.5 + 7.95 = 23.45$

25. **(a)** **(b)**

Sample Number	$\bar{x}$	s
1	$\frac{1}{3}$	2.1
2	2	2.6
3	$-\frac{1}{3}$	1.5
4	0	2.6
5	$\frac{5}{3}$	2.5
6	$\frac{7}{3}$	0.6
7	1	1.0
8	$\frac{4}{3}$	2.1
9	$\frac{7}{3}$	0.6
10	$\frac{2}{3}$	1.2

(c) $\overline{X} = \frac{\sum \bar{x}}{n} \approx \frac{11.3}{10} = 1.13$

(d) $\bar{s} = \frac{\sum s}{n} = \frac{16.8}{10} = 1.68$

(e) The upper control limit for the sample means is

$$\overline{X} + k_1\bar{s} = 1.13 + 1.954(1.68) \approx 4.41.$$

The lower control limit for the sample means is

$$\overline{X} - k_1\bar{s} = 1.13 - 1.954(1.68) \approx -2.15.$$

(f) The upper control limit for the sample standard deviations is

$$k_2\bar{s} = 2.568(1.68) \approx 4.31.$$

The lower control limit for the sample standard deviations is

$$k_3\bar{s} = 0(1.68) = 0.$$

26.

Sample Number	Sample Mean	Sample Standard Deviation
1	0	4.36
2	−0.33	3.21
3	1.00	1.00
4	0.67	4.51
5	0.33	3.21
6	−1.67	3.79

Use the results from Exercise 23(e) and (f). The upper and lower control limits for the standard means are 4.41 and −2.51, while the upper and lower control limits for the sample deviations are 4.31 and 0. The table shows that for the data given in this exercise, all sample means fall within the control limits.

However, two of the sample standard deviations, those for samples 1 and 4, exceed the upper control limit of 4.31. Therefore, the process is out of control.

27. This exercise should be solved using a calculator with a standard deviation key. The answers are $\bar{x} = 1.8158$ mm and $s = 0.4451$ mm.

28. (a) $\overline{x} = \frac{\sum x}{n} = \frac{71.45}{10} = 7.145$

Unemployment is closest to the mean in 1996 when it was 7.24.

(b) Use a graphing calculator to help find the standard deviation.

$$\begin{aligned} s &= \sqrt{\frac{\sum x^2 - n\overline{x}^2}{n-1}} \\ &= \sqrt{\frac{520.7677 - 10(7.145)^2}{10-1}} \\ &\approx \sqrt{1.139717} \approx 1.068 \end{aligned}$$

(c) $\bar{x} + s = 7.145 + 1.068 = 8.213$
$\bar{x} - s = 7.145 - 1.068 = 6.077$

Six of the years (1996, 1997, 1998, 2001, 2004, 2005) fall between these two values, that is, are within 1 standard deviation of the mean.

(d) $\bar{x} + 3s = 7.145 + 3(1.068) = 10.349$
$\bar{x} - 3s = 7.145 - 3(1.068) = 3.941$

All 10 of the years fall between these two values, that is, are within 3 standard deviations of the mean.

29. (a) This exercise should be solved using a calculator with a standard deviation key. The answers are $\bar{x} = 7.3571$ and $s = 0.1326$.

(b) $\bar{x} + 2s = 7.3571 + 2(0.1326) = 7.6223$
$\bar{x} - 2s = 7.3571 - 2(0.1326) = 7.0919$

All the data, or 100%, are within these two values, that is, within 2 standard deviations of the mean.

30. (a) Use a graphing calculator or a spreadsheet to find the variance and standard deviation.

$$\begin{aligned} s^2 &= 14.76 \\ s &= \sqrt{14.76} = 3.84 \end{aligned}$$

(b) $\overline{x} + s = 7.38 + 3.84 = 11.22$
$\overline{x} - s = 7.38 - 3.84 = 3.54$

Ten of the animals have blood types that are within 1 standard deviation of the mean.

31. (a) Find the mean.

$$\overline{x} = \frac{\sum x}{n} = \frac{84 + 91 + \ldots + 164}{7} = \frac{894}{7} = 127.71$$

The mean is 127.71 days.
Find the standard deviation with a graphing calculator or spreadsheet.

$$s = 30.16$$

The standard deviation is 30.16 days.

(b) $\overline{x} + 2s = 127.71 + 2(30.16) = 188.03$
$\overline{x} - 2s = 127.71 - 2(30.16) = 67.39$

All seven of these cancers have doubling times that are within two standard deviations of the mean.

32. (a) Using a graphing calculator, $\overline{x} \approx 128{,}322{,}539.1$. The mean of the domestic box office receipts is $128,322,539. *Bad Boys II,* with domestic box office receipts of $138,540,870, is closest to the mean.

(b) Using a graphing calculator, $s \approx 85{,}260{,}920.52$. The standard deviation of the domestic box office receipts is $85,260,921.

(c) $\overline{x} + s = 128{,}322{,}539 + 85{,}260{,}921 = 213{,}583{,}460$
$\overline{x} - s = 128{,}322{,}539 - 85{,}260{,}921 = 43{,}061{,}618$

10 of the 14 films, or about 71%, have box office receipts within 1 standard deviation of the mean.

$\overline{x} + 2s = 128{,}322{,}539 + 2(85{,}260{,}921) = 298{,}844{,}381$
$\overline{x} - 2s = 128{,}322{,}539 - 2(85{,}260{,}921) = -42{,}199{,}303$

13 of the 14 films, or about 93%, have box office receipts within 2 standard deviations of the mean.

$\overline{x} + 3s = 128{,}322{,}539 + 3(85{,}260{,}921) = 384{,}105{,}302$
$\overline{x} - 3s = 128{,}322{,}539 - 3(85{,}260{,}921) = -127{,}460{,}224$

All of the 14 films, or 100%, have box office receipts within 3 standard deviations of the mean.

33. **(a)** Using a graphing calculator, the standard deviation is $s \approx 4{,}233{,}387$.

(b) The mean is $\overline{x} \approx 3{,}573{,}627$.

$$\overline{x} + 3s = 3{,}573{,}627 + 3(4{,}233{,}387) = 16{,}273{,}788$$
$$\overline{x} - 3s = 3{,}573{,}627 - 3(4{,}233{,}387) = -9{,}126{,}534$$

1 of the 27 players (about 4%), has a salary ($19,331,470) that is beyond 3 standard deviations of the mean.

34. Use a graphing calculator to find values.

(a) $\overline{x} = 2.898$ g
maximum $= 3.8$ g
minimum $= 2.1$ g
$s = 0.374$ g

(b) $\overline{x} = 5.756$ g
maximum $= 6.9$ g
minimum $= 3.3$ g
$s = 0.709$ g

(c) $\overline{x} + 25 = 5.756 + 2(0.709) = 7.174$
$\overline{x} - 25 = 5.756 - 2(0.709) = 4.338$

There are no data values, 0%, of traditional Oreo cookies within 2 standard deviations of the Double Stuf Oreo mean.

(d) There are 46 data values, $\frac{46}{49} \approx 94\%$, of the traditional Oreo cookies (when multiplied by 2) that are within 2 standard deviations of the Double Stuf Oreo mean.

9.3 The Normal Distribution

1. The peak in a normal curve occurs directly above *the mean.*

2. The total area under the normal curve (above the horizontal axis) is 1.

3. For normal distributions where $\mu \neq 0$ or $\sigma \neq 1$, z-scores are found by using the formula

$$z = \frac{x - \mu}{\sigma}.$$

5. Use the table, "Area Under a Normal Curve to the Left of z", in the Appendix. To find the percent of the area under a normal curve between the mean and 1.70 standard deviations from the mean, subtract the table entry for $z = 0$ (representing the mean) from the table entry for $z = 1.7$.

$$0.9554 - 0.5000 = 0.4554$$

Therefore, 45.54% of the area lies between μ and $\mu + 1.7\sigma$.

6. Use the table "Area Under a Normal Curve to the Left of z" in the Appendix. To find the percent of the area under a normal curve between the mean and 0.93 standard deviation from the mean, subtract the table entry for $z = 0$ (representing the mean) from the table entry for $z = 0.93$.

$$0.8238 - 0.5000 = 0.3238$$

Therefore, 32.38% of the area lies between μ and $\mu + 0.93\sigma$.

7. Subtract the table entry for $z = -2.31$ from the table entry for $z = 0$.

$$0.5000 - 0.0104 = 0.4896$$

48.96% of the area lies between μ and $\mu - 2.31\sigma$.

8. Subtract the table entry for $z = -1.45$ from the table entry for $z = 0$.

$$0.5000 - 0.0735 = 0.4265$$

42.65% of the area lies between μ and $\mu - 1.45\sigma$.

9. $P(0.32 \leq z \leq 3.18)$
$= P(z \leq 3.18) - P(z \leq 0.32)$
$=$ (area to the left of 3.18)
$-$(area to the left of 0.32)
$= 0.9993 - 0.6255$
$= 0.3738$ or 37.38%

10. $P(0.99 \leq z \leq 2.37)$
$= P(z \leq 2.37) - P(z \leq 0.99)$
$=$ (area to the left of 2.37)
$-$(area to the left of 0.99)
$= 0.9911 - 0.8389$
$= 0.1522$ or 15.22%

11. $P(-1.83 \leq z \leq -0.91)$
$= P(z \leq -0.91) - P(z \leq -1.83)$
$= 0.1814 - 0.0336$
$= 0.1478$ or 14.78%

12. $P(-3.13 \leq z \leq -2.65)$
$= P(z \leq -2.65) - P(z \leq -3.13)$
$= 0.0040 - 0.0009$
$= 0.0031$ or 0.31%

13. $P(-2.95 \leq z \leq 2.03)$
$= P(z \leq 2.03) - P(z \leq -2.95)$
$= 0.9788 - 0.0016$
$= 0.9772$ or 97.72%

14. $P(-0.15 \leq z \leq 0.23)$
$= P(z \leq 0.23) - P(z \leq -0.15)$
$= 0.5910 - 0.4404$
$= 0.1506$ or 15.06%

15. 5% of the total area is to the left of z.

Use the table backwards. Look in the body of the table for an area of 0.05, and find the corresponding z using the left column and top column of the table.

The closest values to 0.05 in the body of the table are 0.0505, which corresponds to $z = -1.64$, and 0.0495, which corresponds to $z = -1.65$.

16. 1% of the total area is to the left of z.

Use the table backwards, looking for the value closest to 0.0100, and find the corresponding z using the left column and top column of the table.

The closest value to 0.0100 in the body of the table is 0.0099, which corresponds to $z = -2.33$.

17. 10% of the total area is to the right of z.

If 10% of the area is to the right of z, then 90% of the area is to the left of z. The closest value to 0.90 in the body of the table is 0.8997, which corresponds to $z = 1.28$.

18. 25% of the total area is to the right of z.

Having 25% of the area to the right of z means that 75% is to the left. The closest value to 0.75 in the body of the table is 0.7486, which corresponds to $z = 0.67$.

19. For any normal distribution, the value of $P(x \leq \mu)$ is 0.5 since half of the distribution is less than the mean. Similarly, $P(x \geq \mu)$ is 0.5 since half of the distribution is greater than the mean.

20. According to Chebyshev's theorem, the probability that a number will lie within 2 standard deviations of the mean of a probability distribution is at least

$$1 - \frac{1}{2^2} = 1 - \frac{1}{4} = \frac{3}{4} = 0.75.$$

Using the normal distribution, the probability that a number will lie within 2 standard deviations of the mean is 0.9544.
These values are not contradictory, since "at least 0.75" means 0.75 or more. For the normal distribution, the value is more.

21. According to Chebyshev's theorem, the probability that a number will lie within 3 standard deviations of the mean of a probability distribution is at least

$$1 - \frac{1}{3^2} = 1 - \frac{1}{9} = \frac{8}{9} \approx 0.8889.$$

Using the normal distribution, the probability that a number will lie within 3 standard deviations of the mean is 0.9974.

These values are not contradictory since "at least 0.8889" means 0.8889 or more. For the normal distribution, the value is more.

In Exercises 22-28, let x represent the life of a light bulb.

$$\mu = 500, \ \sigma = 100$$

22. At least 500 hr means $x \geq 500$.

$$P(x \geq 500) = 1 - P(x < 500)$$

Find the z-score that corresponds to $x = 500$.

$$z = \frac{500 - 500}{100} = 0$$

$$P(x \geq 500) = P(z \geq 0)$$
$$= 1 - 0.5000 = 0.5000$$

Thus, 10,000(0.5) = 5000 bulbs can be expected to last at least 500 hr.

23. Less than 500 hr

$$z = \frac{x - \mu}{\sigma} = \frac{500 - 500}{100} = 0, \text{ so}$$

$$P(x < 500) = P(z < 0)$$
$$= \text{area to the left of } z = 0$$
$$= 0.5000.$$

Hence, 0.5000(10,000) = 5000 bulbs can be expected to last less than 500 hr.

24. Between 680 and 780 hr

For $x = 680$,

$$z = \frac{680 - 500}{100} = 1.8.$$

For $x = 780$,

$$z = \frac{780 - 500}{100} = 2.8.$$

$$P(680 \leq x \leq 780) = P(1.8 \leq z \leq 2.8)$$
$$= P(z \leq 2.8) - P(z \leq 1.8)$$
$$= 0.9974 - 0.9641$$
$$= 0.0333$$

Thus, 10,000(0.0333) = 333 bulbs can be expected to last between 680 and 780 hr.

25. Between 350 and 550 hr

For $x = 350$,

$$z = \frac{350 - 500}{100} = -1.5,$$

and for $x = 550$,

$$z = \frac{550 - 500}{100} = 0.5.$$

Then

$$\begin{aligned} P(350 < x < 550) &= P(-1.5 < z < 0.5) \\ &= \text{area between } z = -1.5 \\ &\quad \text{and } z = 0.5 \\ &= 0.6915 - 0.0668 \\ &= 0.6247. \end{aligned}$$

Hence, 0.6247(10,000) = 6247 bulbs should last between 350 and 550 hr.

26. Less than 770 hr

For $x = 770$,

$$z = \frac{770 - 500}{100} = 2.7.$$

$P(x < 770) = P(z < 2.7) = 0.9965$

Thus, 10,000(0.9965) = 9965 bulbs can be expected to last less than 770 hr.

27. More than 440 hr

For $x = 440$,

$$z = \frac{440 - 500}{100} = -0.6.$$

Then

$$\begin{aligned} P(x > 440) &= P(z > -0.6) \\ &= \text{area to the right of } z = -0.6 \\ &= 1 - 0.2743 \\ &= 0.7257. \end{aligned}$$

Hence, 0.7257(10,000) = 7257 bulbs should last more than 440 hr.

28. In the standard normal distribution, we must first find the z-values which bound the middle 60%, that is, we must find z_1 and z_2 such that

$$P(z < z_1) = 0.2000 \text{ and } P(z < z_2) = 0.8000.$$

Read backwards in the table, finding the closest values,

$$z_1 = -0.84 \text{ and } z_2 = 0.84.$$

Now find x_1 and x_2.

$$\begin{aligned} \frac{x_1 - 500}{100} &= -0.84 \quad \text{and} \quad & \frac{x_2 - 500}{100} &= 0.84 \\ x_1 - 500 &= -84 & x_2 - 500 &= 84 \\ x_1 &= 416 \quad \text{and} & x_2 &= 584 \end{aligned}$$

Thus, the shortest and longest lengths of life for the middle 60% of the bulbs are 416 hr and 584 hr.

In Exercises 29—32, let x represent the weight of a package.

29. Here, $\mu = 16.5$, $\sigma = 0.5$.

For $x = 16$,

$$z = \frac{16 - 16.5}{0.5} = -1.$$

$P(x < 16) = P(z < -1) = 0.1587$

The fraction of the boxes that are underweight is 0.1587.

30. For $x = 16$, $\mu = 16.5$, and $\sigma = 0.3$,

$$z = \frac{16 - 16.5}{0.3} = -1.67.$$

Hence,

$$\begin{aligned} &P(x < 16) \\ &= P(z < -1.67) \\ &= \text{area to the left of } z = -1.67 \\ &= 0.0475. \end{aligned}$$

The fraction of the boxes that are underweight is 0.048.

31. Here, $\mu = 16.5$, $\sigma = 0.2$.

For $x = 16$,

$$z = \frac{16 - 16.5}{0.2} = -2.5.$$

$P(x < 16) = P(z < -2.5) = 0.0062$

The fraction of the boxes that are underweight is 0.0062.

32. This is the same as Exercise 30 except that $\sigma = 0.1$, so

$$z = \frac{16 - 16.5}{0.1} = -5.$$

Hence,

$$\begin{aligned} &P(x < 16) \\ &= P(z < -5) \\ &= (\text{area to the left of } z = -5) \\ &= 0.0000. \end{aligned}$$

None of the boxes are underweight.

In Exercises 33–38, let x represent the weight of a chicken.

33. More than 1700 g means $x > 1700$.

For $x = 1700$,

$$z = \frac{1700 - 1850}{150} = -1.0.$$

$$\begin{aligned} P(x > 1700) &= 1 - P(x \leq 1700) \\ &= 1 - P(z \leq -1.0) \\ &= 1 - 0.1587 \\ &= 0.8413 \end{aligned}$$

Thus, 84.13% of the chickens will weigh more than 1700 g.

34. Less than 1950 g

For $x = 1950$, we have

$$z = \frac{1950 - 1850}{150} = 0.67.$$

Thus,

$$\begin{aligned} &P(x < 1950) \\ &= P(z < 0.67) \\ &= \text{area to the left of } z = 0.67 \\ &= 0.7486. \end{aligned}$$

Therefore, 74.86% of the chickens will weigh less than 1950 g.

35. Between 1750 and 1900 g means $1750 \leq x \leq 1900$.

For $x = 1750$,

$$z = \frac{1750 - 1850}{150} = -0.67.$$

For $x = 1900$,

$$z = \frac{1900 - 1850}{150} = 0.33.$$

$$\begin{aligned} P(1750 \leq x \leq 1900) &= P(-0.67 \leq z \leq 0.33) \\ &= P(z \leq 0.33) - P(z \leq -0.67) \\ &= 0.6293 - 0.2514 \\ &= 0.3779 \end{aligned}$$

Thus, 37.79% of the chickens will weigh between 1750 and 1900 g.

36. Between 1600 and 2000 g

For $x = 1600$,

$$z = \frac{1600 - 1850}{150} = -1.67,$$

and for $x = 2000$,

$$z = \frac{2000 - 1850}{150} = 1.$$

Thus,

$$\begin{aligned} &P(1600 \leq x \leq 2000) \\ &= P(-1.67 \leq z \leq 1) \\ &= \text{area between } z = -1.67 \text{ and } z = 1 \\ &= 0.8413 - 0.0475 \\ &= 0.7938. \end{aligned}$$

Therefore, 79.38% of the chickens will weigh between 1600 and 2000 g.

37. More than 2100 g or less than 1550 g

$$P(x < 1550 \text{ or } x > 2100) = 1 - P(1550 \leq x \leq 2100).$$

For $x = 1550$,

$$z = \frac{1550 - 1850}{150} = -2.00.$$

For $x = 2100$,

$$z = \frac{2100 - 1850}{150} = 1.67.$$

$$\begin{aligned} &P(x < 1550 \text{ or } x > 2100) \\ &= P(z \leq -2.00) + [1 - P(z \leq 1.67)] \\ &= 0.0228 + (1 - 0.9525) \\ &= 0.0228 + 0.0475 \\ &= 0.0703 \end{aligned}$$

Thus, 7.03% of chickens will weigh more than 2100 g or less than 1550 g.

38. Let $-k$ and k be the two z-values such that the middle 95% of the distribution falls between them.

$$P(z < -k) = 0.0250 \text{ and } P(z < k) = 0.9750.$$

Reading the table backwards, $k = 1.96$. Find the corresponding x-values.

$$\frac{x - 1850}{150} = -1.96 \quad \text{or} \quad \frac{x - 1850}{150} = 1.96$$
$$x - 1850 = -294 \qquad x - 1850 = 294$$
$$x = 1556 \quad \text{or} \quad x = 2144$$

Therefore, the middle 95% of the chickens have weights between 1556 g and 2144 g.

39. Let x represent the bolt diameter.

$$\mu = 0.25, \ \sigma = 0.02$$

First, find the probability that a bolt has a diameter less than or equal to 0.3 in, that is, $P(x \leq 0.3)$. The z-score corresponding to $x = 0.3$ is

$$z = \frac{x - \mu}{\sigma} = \frac{0.3 - 0.25}{0.02} = 2.5.$$

Using the table, find the area to the left of $z = 2.5$. This gives

$$P(x \leq 0.3) = P(z \leq 2.5) = 0.9938.$$

Then

$$\begin{aligned} P(x > 0.3) &= 1 - P(x \leq 0.3) \\ &= 1 - 0.9938 \\ &= 0.0062. \end{aligned}$$

40. Let x represent the number of ounces of milk in a carton.

$$\mu = 32.2, \ \sigma = 1.2$$

Find the z-score for $x = 32$.

$$z = \frac{x - \mu}{\sigma} = \frac{32 - 32.2}{1.2} \approx -0.17$$

$$\begin{aligned} P(x < 32) &= P(z < -0.17) \\ &= \text{ area to the left of } z = -0.17 \\ &= 0.4325 \end{aligned}$$

The probability that a filled carton will contain less than 32 oz is 0.4325.

41. Let x represent the amount of a grocery bill. We are given

$$\mu = 74.50 \text{ and } \sigma = 24.30.$$

The middle 50% of the grocery bills have cutoffs at 25% below the mean and 25% above the mean. At 25% below the mean, the area to the left is 0.2500, which corresponds to about $z = -0.67$. At 25% above the mean, the area to the left is 0.7500, which corresponds to about $z = 0.67$. Find the x-value that corresponds to each z-score.

The largest amount of a grocery bill corresponds to $z = 0.67$.

$$\begin{aligned} \frac{x - 74.50}{24.30} &= 0.67 \\ x - 74.50 &= 16.281 \\ x &\approx 90.78 \end{aligned}$$

The smallest amount of a grocery bill corresponds to $z = -0.67$.

$$\begin{aligned} \frac{x - 74.50}{24.30} &= -0.67 \\ x - 74.50 &= -16.281 \\ x &\approx 58.22 \end{aligned}$$

The middle 50% of customers spend between \$58.22 and \$90.78.

42. Let x represent the weight of an egg (in ounces).

$$\mu = 1.5, \ \sigma = 0.4$$

Find the z-score for $x = 2.2$.

$$z = \frac{x - \mu}{\sigma} = \frac{2.2 - 1.5}{0.4} = 1.75,$$

so

$$\begin{aligned} &P(x > 2.2) \\ &= P(z > 1.75) \\ &= \text{area to the right of } z = 1.75 \\ &= 1 - (\text{area to the left of } z = 1.75) \\ &= 1 - 0.9599 \\ &= 0.0401. \end{aligned}$$

Thus, out of 5 dozen eggs, we expect $0.0401(60) = 2.406$ eggs, or about 2, to be graded extra large.

43. Let x represent the amount of vitamins a person needs. Then

$$\begin{aligned} P(x \leq \mu + 2.5\sigma) &= P(z \leq 2.5) \\ &= 0.9938. \end{aligned}$$

99.38% of the people will receive adequate amounts of vitamins.

44. The Recommended Daily Allowance is

$$\begin{aligned}\mu + 2.5\sigma &= 1200 + 2.5(60)\\ &= 1350 \text{ units.}\end{aligned}$$

45. The Recommended Daily Allowance is

$$\begin{aligned}\mu + 2.5\sigma &= 159 + 2.5(12)\\ &= 189 \text{ units.}\end{aligned}$$

46. The Recommended Daily Allowance is

$$\begin{aligned}\mu + 2.5\sigma &= 1200 + 2.5(92)\\ &= 1430 \text{ units.}\end{aligned}$$

47. Let x represent an individual's blood clotting time (in seconds).

$$\mu = 7.45,\ \sigma = 3.6$$

For $x = 7$,

$$z = \frac{x-\mu}{\sigma} = \frac{7 - 7.45}{3.6} \approx -0.13,$$

and for $x = 8$,

$$z = \frac{8 - 7.45}{3.6} \approx 0.15.$$

Then

$$\begin{aligned}&P(x < 7) + P(x > 8)\\ &\quad = P(z < -0.13) + P(z > 0.15)\\ &\quad = (\text{area to the left of } z = -0.13)\\ &\qquad + (\text{area to the right of } z = 0.15)\\ &\quad = 0.4483 + 0.4404\\ &\quad = 0.8887.\end{aligned}$$

48. Let x represent the length of a fish.

$$\mu = 12.3,\ \sigma = 4.1$$

Find the z-score for $x = 20$.

$$z = \frac{20 - 12.3}{4.1} \approx 1.88$$

$$\begin{aligned}P(x > 20) &= 1 - P(x \le 20)\\ &= 1 - P(z \le 1.88)\\ &= 1 - 0.9699\\ &= 0.0301\end{aligned}$$

49. Let x represent a driving speed.

$$\mu = 52,\ \sigma = 8$$

At the 85th percentile, the area to the left is 0.8500, which corresponds to about $z = 1.04$. Find the x-value that corresponds to this z-score.

$$\begin{aligned}z &= \frac{x-\mu}{\sigma}\\ 1.04 &= \frac{x - 52}{8}\\ 8.32 &= x - 52\\ 60.32 &= x\end{aligned}$$

The 85th percentile speed for this road is 60.32 mph.

50. Let x represent a driving speed.

$$\mu = 30,\ \sigma = 5$$

Read the table backwards. In the body of the table, the closest area to 0.85 is 0.8508, which corresponds to $z = 1.04$. Find the value of x that corresponds to $z = 1.04$.

$$\begin{aligned}z &= \frac{x-\mu}{\sigma}\\ 1.04 &= \frac{x - 30}{5}\\ 5.2 &= x - 30\\ 35.2 &= x\end{aligned}$$

The 85th percentile speed is 35.2 mph.

51. $$\begin{aligned}P\left(x \ge \mu + \frac{3}{2}\sigma\right) &= P(z \ge 1.5)\\ &= 1 - P(z \le 1.5)\\ &= 1 - 0.9332 = 0.0668\end{aligned}$$

Thus, 6.68% of the students receive A's.

52. For a grade of B, we have

$$\frac{1}{2} \le z \le \frac{3}{2}.$$

The area between $z = 0.5$ and $z = 1.5$ is

$$0.9332 - 0.6915 = 0.2417 \text{ or } 24.17\%,$$

which should be the percent of students to receive B's.

53. $P\left(\mu - \frac{1}{2}\sigma \leq x \leq \mu + \frac{1}{2}\sigma\right)$

$$\begin{aligned} &= P(-0.5 \leq z \leq 0.5) \\ &= P(z \leq 0.5) - P(z \leq -0.5) \\ &= 0.6915 - 0.3085 \\ &= 0.383 \end{aligned}$$

Thus, 38.3% of the students receive C's.

54. This system would be more likely to be fair for the freshman psychology class since a large group of students is more likely to produce a normal distribution of total points.

In Exercises 55–58, let x represent a student's test score.

55. Since the top 8% get A's, we want to find the number a for which

$$\begin{aligned} &P(x \geq a) = 0.08, \\ \text{or} \quad &P(x \leq a) = 0.92. \end{aligned}$$

Read the table backwards to find the z-score for an area of 0.92, which is 1.41. Find the value of x that corresponds to $z = 1.41$.

$$\begin{aligned} z &= \frac{x - \mu}{\sigma} \\ 1.41 &= \frac{x - 76}{8} \\ 11.28 &= x - 76 \\ 87.28 &= x \end{aligned}$$

The bottom cutoff score for an A is 87.

56. Since the top 8% of the students get A's and the next 15% get B's, we want to find the number b for which

$$\begin{aligned} &P(x \geq b) = 023 \\ \text{or} \quad &P(x \leq b) = 0.77. \end{aligned}$$

Read the table backwards to find the z-score for an area of 0.77, which is $z = 0.74$. Find the value of x that corresponds to $z = 0.74$.

$$\begin{aligned} z &= \frac{x - \mu}{\sigma} \\ 0.74 &= \frac{x - 76}{8} \\ x &= 81.92 \end{aligned}$$

The bottom cutoff score for a B should be 81.

57. 28% of the students will receive D's and F's, so to find the bottom cutoff score for a C we need to find the number c for which

$$P(x \leq c) = 0.28.$$

Read the table backwards to find the z-score for an area of 0.28, which is -0.58. Find the value of x that corresponds to $z = -0.58$.

$$\begin{aligned} -0.58 &= \frac{x - 76}{8} \\ -4.64 &= x - 76 \\ 71.36 &= x \end{aligned}$$

The bottom cutoff score for a C is 71.

58. Since 8% of the students get F's, the minimum passing score (cutoff for a D) would be the number d for which

$$P(x \leq d) = 0.08.$$

Read the table backwards to find the z-score for an area of 0.08, which is $z = -1.41$. Find the value of x that corresponds to $z = -1.41$.

$$\begin{aligned} z &= \frac{x - \mu}{\sigma} \\ -1.41 &= \frac{x - 76}{8} \\ x &= 64.72 \end{aligned}$$

The bottom cutoff score for a D should be 65.

59. **(a)** The area above the 55th percentile is equal to the area below the 45th percentile.

$$\begin{aligned} 2P(z > 0.55) &= 2[1 - P(z \leq 0.55)] \\ &= 2(1 - 0.7088) \\ &= 2(0.2912) \\ &= 0.5824 \end{aligned}$$

$0.58 = 58\%$

(b) The area above the 60th percentile is equal to the area below the 40th percentile.

$$\begin{aligned} 2P(z > 0.6) &= 2[1 - P(z \leq 0.6)] \\ &= 2(1 - 0.7257) \\ &= 2(0.2743) \\ &= 0.5486 \end{aligned}$$

$0.55 = 55\%$

The probability that the student will be above the 60th percentile or below the 40th percentile is 55%.

60. Let x represent the height of a man.

$$\mu = 69.60,\ \sigma = 3.20$$

For $x = 66.27$,

$$z = \frac{66.27 - 69.60}{3.20} = -1.04.$$

$P(x < 66.27) = P(z < -1.04) = 0.1492$

61. **(a)** $\mu = 93, \sigma = 16$

For $x = 130.5$,

$$z = \frac{130.5 - 93}{16} = 2.34.$$

Then,

$P(x \geq 130.5) = P(z \geq 2.34) = \text{area to the right of } 2.34 = 1 - 0.9904 = 0.0096$

The probability is about 0.01 that a person from this time period would have a lead level of 130.5 ppm or higher. Yes, this provides evidence that Jackson suffered from lead poisioning during this time period.

(b) $\mu = 10, \sigma = 5$

For $x = 130.5$,

$$z = \frac{130.5 - 10}{5} = 24.1.$$

Then,

$P(x \geq 130.5) = P(z \geq 24.1) = \text{area to the right of } 24.1 \approx 0$

The probability is essentially 0 by these standards.
From this we can conclude that Andrew Jackson had lead poisioning.

62. **(a)** $\mu = 6.9, \sigma = 4.6$

Find the z-score for $x = 6.0$.

$$z = \frac{x - \mu}{\sigma} = \frac{6.0 - 6.9}{4.6} \approx -0.20$$

Thus,

$P(x \geq 6.0) = P(z \geq -0.20) = \text{area to the right of } z = -0.20. = 1 - 0.4207 = 0.5793 \approx 0.58$

(c) $\mu = 0.6, \sigma = 0.3$

Find the z-score for $x = 6.0$.

$$z = \frac{6.0 - 0.6}{0.3} = 18$$

Thus,

$P(x \geq 6.0) = P(z \geq 18) = \text{area to the right of } z = 18 \approx 0$

No, the probability is about 0.

63.

	Reference	Models
a. Head size:	$z = \dfrac{55 - 55.3}{2.0} = -0.15$	$z = \dfrac{55 - 50.0}{2.4} = 2.08$
	$P(x \geq 55) = P(z \geq -0.15) = 1 - 0.4404 = 0.5596$	$P(x \geq 55) = P(z \geq 2.08) = 1 - 0.9812 = 0.0188$
b. Neck size:	$z = \dfrac{23.9 - 32.7}{1.4} = -6.29$	$z = \dfrac{23.9 - 31.0}{1.0} = -7.1$
	$P(x \leq 23.9) = P(z \leq -6.29) \approx 0$	$P(x \leq 23.9) = P(z \leq -7.1) \approx 0$
c. Bust size:	$z = \dfrac{82.3 - 90.3}{5.5} = -1.45$	$z = \dfrac{82.3 - 87.4}{3.0} = -1.70$
	$P(x \geq 82.3) = P(z \geq -1.45) = 1 - 0.0735 = 0.9265$	$P(x \geq 82.3) = P(z \geq -1.70) = 1 - 0.0446 = 0.9554$
d. Wrist size:	$z = \dfrac{10.6 - 16.1}{0.8} = -6.88$	$z = \dfrac{10.6 - 15.0}{0.6} = -7.33$
	$P(x \leq 10.6) = P(z \leq -6.88) \approx 0$	$P(x \leq 10.6) = P(z \leq -7.33) \approx 0$
e. Waist size:	$z = \dfrac{40.7 - 69.8}{4.7} = -6.19$	$z = \dfrac{40.7 - 65.7}{3.5} = -7.14$
	$P(x \leq 40.7) = P(z \leq -6.19) \approx 0$	$P(x \leq 40.7) = P(z \leq -7.14) \approx 0$

64.

	Reference	Football
a. head size:	$z = \dfrac{53.0 - 53.7}{2.9} = -0.24$	$z = \dfrac{53.0 - 52.1}{2.3} = 0.39$
	$P(x \geq 53.0) = P(z \geq -0.24) = 1 - 0.4052 = 0.5948$	$P(x \geq 53.0) = P(z \geq 0.39) = 1 - 0.6517 = 0.3483$
b. neck size:	$z = \dfrac{32.1 - 34.2}{1.9} = -1.11$	$z = \dfrac{32.1 - 34.6}{1.8} = -1.39$
	$P(x \leq 32.1) = P(z \leq -1.11) = 0.1335$	$P(x \leq 32.1) = P(z \leq -1.39) = 0.0823$
c. chest size:	$z = \dfrac{75.0 - 91.2}{4.8} = -3.38$	$z = \dfrac{75.0 - 92.3}{3.5} = -4.94$
	$P(x \leq 75.0) = P(z \leq -3.38) = 0.0004$	$P(x \leq 75.0) = P(z \leq -4.94) \approx 0$
d. upper arm size:	$z = \dfrac{27.1 - 28.8}{2.2} = -0.77$	$z = \dfrac{27.1 - 29.9}{1.9} = -1.47$
	$P(x \leq 27.1) = P(z \leq -0.77) = 0.2206$	$P(x \leq 27.1) = P(z \leq -1.47) = 0.0708$
e. waist size:	$z = \dfrac{56.5 - 80.9}{9.8} = -2.49$	$z = \dfrac{56.5 - 75.1}{3.6} = -5.17$
	$P(x \leq 56.5) = P(z \leq -2.49) = 0.0064$	$P(x \leq 56.5) = P(z \leq -5.17) \approx 0$

9.4 Normal Approximation to the Binomial Distribution

1. In order to find the mean and standard deviation of a binomial distribution, you must know the number of trials and the probability of a success on each trial.

2. The normal distribution can be used to approximate a binomial distribution as long as $np \geq 5$ and $n(1-p) \geq 5$.

3. Let x represent the number of heads tossed. For this experiment, $n = 16$, $x = 4$, and $p = \frac{1}{2}$.

(a) $$P(x=4) = \binom{16}{4}\left(\frac{1}{2}\right)^4\left(1-\frac{1}{2}\right)^4 \approx 0.0278$$

(b) $$\mu = np = 16\left(\frac{1}{2}\right) = 8$$

$$\begin{aligned}\sigma &= \sqrt{np(1-p)} \\ &= \sqrt{16\left(\frac{1}{2}\right)\left(\frac{1}{2}\right)} \\ &= \sqrt{4} = 2\end{aligned}$$

For $x = 3.5$,

$$z = \frac{3.5-8}{2} = -2.25.$$

For $x = 4.5$,

$$z = \frac{4.5-8}{2} = -1.75.$$

$$\begin{aligned}&P(z < -1.75) - P(z < -2.25) \\ &= 0.0401 - 0.0122 = 0.0279\end{aligned}$$

4. Let x represent the number of heads tossed. For this experiment, $n = 16, x = 10$, and $p = \frac{1}{2}$.

(a) $$P(x=10) = \binom{16}{10}\left(\frac{1}{2}\right)^{10}\left(1-\frac{1}{2}\right)^6 \approx 0.1222$$

(b) $$\mu = np = 16\left(\frac{1}{2}\right) = 8$$

$$\begin{aligned}\sigma &= \sqrt{np(1-p)} \\ &= \sqrt{16\left(\tfrac{1}{2}\right)\left(\tfrac{1}{2}\right)} \\ &= \sqrt{4} = 2\end{aligned}$$

For $x = 9.5$,

$$z = \frac{9.5-8}{2} = 0.75.$$

For $x = 10.5$,

$$z = \frac{10.5-8}{2} = 1.25.$$

$$\begin{aligned}P(0.75 < z < 1.25) &= P(z < 1.25) - P(z < 0.75) \\ &= 0.8944 - 0.7734 \\ &= 0.1210\end{aligned}$$

5. Let x represent the number of tails tossed. For this experiment, $n = 16$; $x = 13$, 14, 15, or 16; and $p = \frac{1}{2}$.

(a)
$$\begin{aligned}&P(x = 13, 14, 15, \text{ or } 16) \\ &= \binom{16}{13}\left(\frac{1}{2}\right)^{13}\left(1-\frac{1}{2}\right)^3 + \binom{16}{14}\left(\frac{1}{2}\right)^{14}\left(1-\frac{1}{2}\right)^2 \\ &\quad + \binom{16}{15}\left(\frac{1}{2}\right)^{15}\left(1-\frac{1}{2}\right)^1 + \binom{16}{16}\left(\frac{1}{2}\right)^{16}\left(1-\frac{1}{2}\right)^0 \\ &\approx 0.00854 + 0.00183 + 0.00024 + 0.00001 \\ &\approx 0.0106\end{aligned}$$

(b) $$\mu = np = 16\left(\frac{1}{2}\right) = 8$$

$$\sigma = \sqrt{np(1-p)} = \sqrt{16\left(\frac{1}{2}\right)\left(\frac{1}{2}\right)} = \sqrt{4} = 2$$

For $x = 12.5$,

$$z = \frac{12.5-8}{2} = 2.25.$$

$$\begin{aligned}P(z > 2.25) &= 1 - P(z \leq 2.25) \\ &= 1 - 0.9878 \\ &= 0.0122\end{aligned}$$

6. Let x represent the number of tails tossed. For this experiment, $n = 16; x = 0, 1, 2, 3,$ or 4; and $p = \frac{1}{2}$.

(a) $P(x = 0, 1, 2, 3, \text{ or } 4)$

$$= \binom{16}{0}\left(\frac{1}{2}\right)^0\left(1-\frac{1}{2}\right)^{16} + \binom{16}{1}\left(\frac{1}{2}\right)^1\left(1-\frac{1}{2}\right)^{15} + \binom{16}{2}\left(\frac{1}{2}\right)^2\left(1-\frac{1}{2}\right)^{14} + \binom{16}{3}\left(\frac{1}{2}\right)^3\left(1-\frac{1}{2}\right)^{13} + \binom{16}{4}\left(\frac{1}{2}\right)^4\left(1-\frac{1}{2}\right)^{12}$$

$$\approx 0.00001 + 0.00024 + 0.00183 + 0.00854 + 0.02777$$
$$\approx 0.0384$$

(b) $\mu = np = 16\left(\frac{1}{2}\right) = 8$

$$\sigma = \sqrt{np(1-p)} = \sqrt{16\left(\tfrac{1}{2}\right)\left(\tfrac{1}{2}\right)} = \sqrt{4} = 2$$

For $x = 4.5$,

$$z = \frac{4.5 - 8}{2} = -1.75.$$

$P(x < -1.75) = 0.0401$

In Exercises 7–9, let x represent the number of heads tossed. Since $n = 1000$ and $p = \frac{1}{2}$,

$$\mu = np = 1000\left(\frac{1}{2}\right) = 500$$

and

$$\sigma = \sqrt{np(1-p)} = \sqrt{1000\left(\frac{1}{2}\right)\left(\frac{1}{2}\right)} = \sqrt{250} \approx 15.8.$$

7. To find $P(\text{exactly 500 heads})$, find the z-scores for $x = 499.5$ and $x = 500.5$.

For $x = 499.5$,

$$z = \frac{499.5 - 500}{15.8} \approx -0.03.$$

For $x = 500.5$,

$$z = \frac{500.5 - 500}{15.8} \approx 0.03.$$

Using the table,

$$P(\text{exactly 500 heads}) = 0.5120 - 0.4880 = 0.0240.$$

8. Exactly 510 heads corresponds to the area under the normal curve between $x = 509.5$ and $x = 510.5$. The corresponding z-scores are

$$z = \frac{509.5 - 500}{15.8} \approx 0.60$$

and

$$z = \frac{510.5 - 500}{15.8} \approx 0.66.$$

$$\begin{aligned} P(\text{exactly 510 heads}) &= P(509.5 \le x \le 510.5) \\ &= P(0.60 \le z \le 0.66) \\ &= P(z \le 0.66) - P(z \le 0.60) \\ &= 0.7454 - 0.7257 \\ &= 0.0197 \end{aligned}$$

9. Since we want 475 heads or more, we need to find the area to the right of $x = 474.5$. This will be $1-$ (the area to the left of $x = 474.5$). Find the z-score for $x = 474.5$.

$$z = \frac{474.5 - 500}{15.8} \approx -1.61$$

The area to the left of 474.5 is 0.0537, so

$$P(\text{480 heads or more}) = 1 - 0.0537 = 0.9463.$$

10. Let x represent the number of tails tossed.

$n = 1000, p = \frac{1}{2}$

As in Exercise 8, $\mu = 500$ and $\sigma = 15.81$.

Less than 490 tails corresponds to the area under the normal curve to the left of $x = 489.5$. The corresponding z-score is

$$z = \frac{489.5 - 500}{15.81} \approx -0.66.$$

$$\begin{aligned} P(\text{less than 490 tails}) &= P(x \le 489.5) \\ &= P(z \le -0.66) \\ &= 0.2546 \end{aligned}$$

11. Let x represent the number of 5's tossed.

$n = 120,\ p = \frac{1}{6}$

$$\mu = np = 120\left(\frac{1}{6}\right) = 20$$

$$\sigma = \sqrt{np(1-p)} = \sqrt{120\left(\frac{1}{6}\right)\left(\frac{5}{6}\right)} \approx 4.08$$

Since we want the probability of getting exactly twenty 5's, we need to find the area between $x = 19.5$ and $x = 20.5$. Find the corresponding z-scores.

For $x = 19.5$,

$$z = \frac{19.5 - 20}{4.08} \approx -0.12.$$

For $x = 20.5$,

$$z = \frac{20.5 - 20}{4.08} \approx 0.12.$$

Using values from the table,

$$\begin{aligned} P(\text{exactly twenty 5's}) &= 0.5478 - 0.4522 \\ &= 0.0956. \end{aligned}$$

12. Let x represent the number of 6's tossed.

$n = 120, p = \frac{1}{6}$

$$\mu = np = 120\left(\frac{1}{6}\right) = 20$$

$$\sigma = \sqrt{np(1-p)} = \sqrt{120\left(\tfrac{1}{6}\right)\left(\tfrac{5}{6}\right)} \approx 4.08$$

We want the area between $x = 23.5$ and $x = 24.5$. The corresponding z-scores are 0.86 and 1.103.

$$\begin{aligned} &P(\text{exactly twenty-four 6's}) \\ &= P(23.5 \le x \le 24.5) \\ &= P(0.86 \le z \le 1.103) \\ &= P(z \le 1.103) - P(z \le 0.86) \\ &= 0.8643 - 0.8051 \\ &= 0.0592 \end{aligned}$$

13. Let x represent the number of 3's tossed.

$n = 120,\ p = \frac{1}{6}$

$\mu = 20,\ \sigma \approx 4.08$

(These values for μ and σ are calculated in the solution for Exercise 11.)

Since

$$\begin{aligned} &P(\text{more than fifteen 3's}) \\ &\quad = 1 - P(\text{fifteen 3's or less}), \end{aligned}$$

find the z-score for $x = 15.5$.

$$z = \frac{15.5 - 20}{4.08} \approx -1.10$$

From the table, $P(z < -1.10) = 0.1357$.

Thus,

$$\begin{aligned} P(\text{more than fifteen 3's}) &= 1 - 0.1357 \\ &= 0.8643. \end{aligned}$$

14. Let x represent the number of 6's tossed.

$n = 120, p = \frac{1}{6}$

As in Exercise 12, $\mu = 20$ and $\sigma \approx 4.08$.
We want the area to the left of $x = 27.5$. The corresponding z-score is 1.84.

$$\begin{aligned} &P(\text{fewer than twenty-eight 6's}) \\ &= P(x \le 27.5) \\ &= P(z \le 1.84) \\ &= 0.9671 \end{aligned}$$

15. Let x represent the number of times the chosen number appears.

$n = 130;\ x = 26, 27, 28, \ldots, 130;$ and $p = \frac{1}{6}$

$$\mu = np = 130\left(\frac{1}{6}\right) = \frac{65}{3}$$

$$\sigma = \sqrt{np(1-p)} = \sqrt{130\left(\frac{1}{6}\right)\left(\frac{5}{6}\right)} = \frac{5}{6}\sqrt{26}$$

For $x = 25.5$,

$$z = \frac{25.5 - \frac{65}{3}}{\frac{5}{6}\sqrt{26}} \approx 0.90.$$

$$P(z > 0.90) = 1 - P(z \le 0.90) = 1 - 0.8159 = 0.1841$$

16. **(a)** Let x represent the number of heaters that are defective.

$n = 10{,}000,\ p = 0.02$

$\mu = np = 10{,}000(0.02) = 200$
$\sigma = \sqrt{np(1-p)} = \sqrt{10{,}000(0.02)(0.98)} = 14$

To find $P(\text{fewer than } 170)$, find the z-score for $x = 169.5$.

$$z = \frac{169.5 - 200}{14} \approx -2.18$$

$P(\text{fewer than } 170) = 0.0146$

(b) Let x represent the number of heaters that are defective.

$n = 10{,}000,\ p = 0.02,\ \mu = np = 200$

$\sigma = \sqrt{np(1-p)} = \sqrt{10{,}000(0.02)(0.98)} = 14$

We want the area to the right of $x = 222.5$. For $x = 222.5$,

$$z = \frac{222.5 - 200}{14} \approx 1.61.$$

$$\begin{aligned} P(\text{more than 222 defects}) &= P(x \geq 222.5) \\ &= P(z \geq 1.61) \\ &= 1 - P(z \leq 1.61) \\ &= 1 - 0.9463 \\ &= 0.0537 \end{aligned}$$

17. Let x represent the number of defective items.

$n = 75, p = 0.05$

$\mu = np = 75(0.05) = 3.75$
$\sigma = \sqrt{np(1-p)} = \sqrt{75(0.05)(0.95)} = \sqrt{3.5625}$

(a) To find $P(\text{exactly 5 defectives})$, find the z-scores for $x = 4.5$ and $x = 5.5$.

For $x = 4.5$,

$$z = \frac{4.5 - 3.75}{\sqrt{3.5625}} \approx 0.40.$$

For $x = 5.5$,

$$z = \frac{5.5 - 3.75}{\sqrt{3.5625}} \approx 0.93.$$

$$\begin{aligned} P(0.40 < z < 0.93) &= P(z < 0.93) - P(z < 0.40) \\ &= 0.8238 - 0.6554 \\ &= 0.1684 \end{aligned}$$

(b) To find $P(\text{no defectives})$, find the z-scores for $x = -0.5$ and $x = 0.5$.

For $x = -0.5$,

$$z = \frac{-0.5 - 3.75}{\sqrt{3.5625}} \approx -2.25.$$

For $x = 0.5$,

$$z = \frac{0.5 - 3.75}{\sqrt{3.5625}} \approx -1.72.$$

$$\begin{aligned} &P(-2.25 < z < -1.72) \\ &= P(z < -1.72) - P(z < -2.25) \\ &= 0.0427 - 0.0122 \\ &= 0.0305 \end{aligned}$$

(c) To find $P(\text{at least 1 defective})$, find the z-score for $x = 0.5$.

$$z = \frac{0.5 - 3.75}{\sqrt{3.5625}} \approx -1.72$$

$$\begin{aligned} P(z > -1.72) &= 1 - P(z < -1.72) \\ &= 1 - 0.0427 \\ &= 0.9573 \end{aligned}$$

18. Use a calculator or computer to complete this exercise. The answers are given.

(a) $P(\text{all 58 like it}) = 1.04 \times 10^{-9} \approx 0$

(b) $P(\text{exactly 28, 29, or 30 like it}) = 0.0018$

19. Let x represent the number of minimum wage earners who are 16 to 24 years old. $n = 600, p = 0.513, x = 341, 342, \ldots, 600$

$$\begin{aligned} \mu &= np = 600(0.513) = 307.8 \\ \sigma &= \sqrt{np(1-p)} \\ &= \sqrt{600(0.513)(0.487)} \\ &= \sqrt{149.8986} \\ &\approx 12.24 \end{aligned}$$

To find $P(x > 340)$, find the z-score for 340.5.

$$z = \frac{340.5 - 307.8}{12.24} = 2.67$$

$$\begin{aligned} P(z > 2.67) &= 1 - P(z < 2.67) \\ &= 1 - 0.9962 \\ &= 0.0038 \end{aligned}$$

20. Let x be the number of nests escaping predation.

$n = 24, p = 0.3$

$$\mu = np = 24(0.3) = 7.2$$
$$\sigma = \sqrt{np(1-p)} = \sqrt{24(0.3)(0.7)} = \sqrt{5.04} \approx 2.245$$

To find P(at least half escape predation), find the z-score for $x = 11.5$.

$$z = \frac{11.5 - 7.2}{2.245} \approx 1.92$$

$$P(z > 1.92) = 1 - 0.9726 = 0.0274$$

21. (a) Let x represent the number of units an animal consumes.

$n = 120, x = 80, p = 0.6$

$$\mu = np = 120(0.6) = 72$$
$$\sigma = \sqrt{np(1-p)} = \sqrt{120(0.6)(0.4)} = \sqrt{28.8}$$

To find P(80 units consumed), find the z-scores for $x = 79.5$ and $x = 80.5$.

For $x = 79.5$,

$$z = \frac{79.5 - 72}{\sqrt{28.8}} \approx 1.40.$$

For $x = 80.5$,

$$z = \frac{80.5 - 72}{\sqrt{28.8}} \approx 1.58.$$

$$\begin{aligned} P(1.40 < z < 1.58) &= P(z < 1.58) - P(z < 1.40) \\ &= 0.9429 - 0.9192 \\ &= 0.0237 \end{aligned}$$

(b) To find P(at least 70 units), find the z-score for $x = 69.5$.

$$z = \frac{69.5 - 72}{\sqrt{28.8}} \approx -0.47$$

$$\begin{aligned} P(z > -0.47) &= 1 - P(z < -0.47) \\ &= 1 - 0.3192 \\ &= 0.6808 \end{aligned}$$

22. Let x represent the number of hospital patients struck by falling coconuts.

(a) $n = 20; x = 0$ or 1; and $p = 0.025$

$$\begin{aligned} P(x = 0 \text{ or } 1) &= \binom{20}{0}(0.025)^0(0.975)^{20} \\ &\quad + \binom{20}{1}(0.025)^1(0.975)^{19} \\ &\approx 0.60269 + 0.30907 \\ &\approx 0.9118 \end{aligned}$$

(b) $n = 2000; x = 0, 1, 2, \ldots,$ or 70; $p = 0.025$

$$\mu = np = 2000(0.025) = 50$$
$$\sigma = \sqrt{np(1-p)} = \sqrt{2000(0.025)(0.975)} = \sqrt{48.75}$$

To find P(70 or less), find the z-score for $x = 70.5$.

$$z = \frac{70.5 - 50}{\sqrt{48.75}} \approx 2.94$$

$$P(x < 2.94) = 0.9984$$

23. (a) Let x represent the number of people cured.

$n = 25, p = 0.80$

$$\mu = np = 25(0.80) = 20$$
$$\sigma = \sqrt{np(1-p)} = \sqrt{25(0.80)(0.20)} = 2$$

To find

$$P(\text{exactly 20 cured}) = P(19.5 \le x \le 20.5),$$

find the z-scores for $x = 19.5$ and $x = 20.5$.

For $x = 19.5$,

$$z = \frac{19.5 - 20}{2} = -0.25.$$

For $x = 20.5$,

$$z = \frac{20.5 - 20}{2} = 0.25.$$

Using the table,

$$\begin{aligned} P(\text{exactly 20 cured}) &= 0.5987 - 0.4013 \\ &= 0.1974. \end{aligned}$$

(b) Let x represent the number of people who are cured.

$n = 25, p = 0.8$

$$\mu = np = 25(0.8) = 20$$
$$\sigma = \sqrt{np(1-p)} = \sqrt{25(0.8)(0.2)} = \sqrt{4} = 2$$

To find P(all are cured) $= P$(25 are cured), find the z-scores for $x = 24.5$ and $x = 25.5$.

$$z = \frac{24.5 - 20}{2} = 2.25 \qquad z = \frac{25.5 - 20}{2} = 2.75.$$

Using the table,

$$\begin{aligned} P(\text{all are cured}) &= 0.9970 - 0.9878 \\ &= 0.0092. \end{aligned}$$

(c) $$\begin{aligned} P(x = 0) &= \binom{25}{0}(0.80)^0(0.20)^{25} \\ &= (0.20)^{25} \\ &= 3.36 \times 10^{-18} \\ &\approx 0 \end{aligned}$$

(d) From parts a and b, $\mu = 20$ and $\sigma = 2$.

To find $P(12 \text{ or fewer are cured}) = P(x \leq 12)$, find the z-score for $x = 12.5$.

$$z = \frac{12.5 - 20}{2} = -3.75$$

Since the table does not go out to $z = -3.75$, we must extrapolate, that is, read beyond the values in the table.

$$P(x \leq 12) \approx 0.0001$$

24. This exercise should be solved by calculator or computer methods. The answers, which may vary slightly, are

(a) 0.0001,

(b) 0.0002, and

(c) 0.0000.

25. (a) Let x represent the number that are AB−.
$n = 1000$; $x = 10, 11, 12, \ldots, 1000$; $p = 0.006$
$\mu = np = 1000(0.006) = 6$

$$\begin{aligned} \sigma &= \sqrt{np(1-p)} \\ &= \sqrt{1000(0.006)(0.994)} \\ &\approx 2.442 \end{aligned}$$

To find $P(10 \text{ or more})$, find the z-score for $x = 9.5$.

$$z = \frac{9.5 - 6}{2.442} = 1.43$$

$P(z > 1.43) = 1 - 0.9236 = 0.0764$

(b) Let x represent the number that are B−.
$n = 1000$; $x = 20, 21, \ldots, 39, 40$; $p = 0.015$
$\mu = np = 1000(0.015) = 15$

$$\begin{aligned} \sigma &= \sqrt{np(1-p)} \\ &= \sqrt{1000(0.015)(0.985)} \\ &\approx 3.844 \end{aligned}$$

To find $P(\text{between 20 to 40 inclusive})$, find the z-scores for $x = 19.5$ and $x = 40.5$.

$$z = \frac{19.5 - 15}{3.844} = 1.17, z = \frac{40.5 - 15}{3.844} = 6.63$$

$$\begin{aligned} P(1.17 < z < 6.63) &= P(z < 6.63) - P(z < 1.17) \\ &= 1 - 0.8790 \\ &= 0.1210 \end{aligned}$$

(c) $\mu = np = 500(0.015) = 7.5$

$$\begin{aligned} \sigma &= \sqrt{np(1-p)} \\ &= \sqrt{500(0.015)(0.985)} \\ &\approx 2.718 \end{aligned}$$

To find P(15 or more donors being B−), find the z-score for $x = 14.5$.

$$z = \frac{14.5 - 7.5}{2.718} = 2.57$$

$$P(z > 2.57) = 1 - 0.9949 = 0.0051$$

The probability that 15 or more donors are B− is only 0.0051. It is very unlikely that this town has a higher than normal number of donors who are B−.

26. Let x represent the number of motorcyclists injured between 3 p.m. and 6 p.m. $n = 200, p = 0.266, x = 0.1, \ldots, 50$

$$\begin{aligned} \mu &= np = 200(0.266) = 53.2 \\ \sigma &= \sqrt{np(1-p)} \\ &= \sqrt{200(0.266)(0.734)} \\ &= \sqrt{39.0488} \\ &\approx 6.25 \end{aligned}$$

To find $P(x < 51)$, find the z-score for 50.5.

$$z = \frac{50.5 - 53.2}{6.25} = -0.43$$

$$P(z < -0.43) = 0.3336$$

27. $n = 1400, p = 0.55$

$$\begin{aligned} \mu &= np = 1400(0.55) = 770 \\ \sigma &= \sqrt{np(1-p)} = \sqrt{1400(0.55)(0.45)} \approx 18.6 \end{aligned}$$

To find $P(\text{at least 750 people}) = P(x \geq 749.5)$, find the z-score for $x = 749.5$.

$$z = \frac{749.5 - 770}{18.6} \approx -1.10$$

$$\begin{aligned} P(z \geq -1.10) &= 1 - P(z \leq -1.10) \\ &= 1 - 0.1357 \\ &= 0.8643 \end{aligned}$$

28. Let x represent the number of ninth grade students who have tried cigarette smoking. $n = 500, p = 0.487, x = 0, 1, \ldots, 250$

$$\begin{aligned} \mu &= np = 500(0.487) = 243.5 \\ \sigma &= \sqrt{np(1-p)} \\ &= \sqrt{500(0.487)(0.513)} \\ &= \sqrt{124.9155} \\ &\approx 11.18 \end{aligned}$$

To find $P(x < 251)$, find the z-score for 250.5.

$$z = \frac{250.5 - 243.5}{11.18} = 0.63$$

$$P(z < 0.63) = 0.7357$$

29. Let x represent the number of high school students who have carried a weapon. $n = 1200, p = 0.185, x = 201, 202, \ldots, 249$

$$\begin{aligned}\mu &= np = 1200(0.185) = 222\\ \sigma &= \sqrt{np(1-p)}\\ &= \sqrt{1200(0.185)(0.815)}\\ &= \sqrt{180.93}\\ &\approx 13.45\end{aligned}$$

To find $P(200 < x < 250)$, find the z-scores for 200.5 and 249.5.

$$z_1 = \frac{200.5 - 222}{13.45} = -1.60 \qquad z_2 = \frac{249.5 - 222}{13.45} = 2.04$$

$$\begin{aligned}P(-1.60 < z < 2.04) &= P(z < 2.04) - P(z < -1.60)\\ &= 0.9793 - 0.0548\\ &= 0.9245\end{aligned}$$

30. **(a)** The numbers are too large for the calculator to handle.

(b) $n = 5{,}825{,}043,\ p = 0.5$
$\mu = np = 5{,}825{,}043(0.5) = 2{,}912{,}522$

$$\begin{aligned}\sigma &= \sqrt{np(1-p)}\\ &= \sqrt{5{,}825{,}043(0.5)(0.5)}\\ &\approx 1206.8\end{aligned}$$

$$z = \frac{2{,}912{,}253 - 2{,}912{,}522}{1206.8} = -0.22$$

$$z = \frac{2{,}912{,}790 - 2{,}912{,}522}{1206.8} = 0.22$$

$$\begin{aligned}&P(2{,}912{,}253 \le x \le 2{,}912{,}790)\\ &= P(-0.22 \le z \le 0.22)\\ &= P(z \le 0.22) - P(z \le -0.22)\\ &= 0.5871 - 0.4129\\ &= 0.1742\end{aligned}$$

31. Let x represent the number of parents who require homework before TV watching.

$n = 51; x = 0, 1, 2, 3, 4, \text{ or } 5; p = \frac{1}{12}$

$$\mu = np = 51\left(\frac{1}{12}\right) = \frac{17}{4}$$

$$\sigma = \sqrt{np(1-p)} = \sqrt{51\left(\tfrac{1}{12}\right)\left(\tfrac{11}{12}\right)} = \frac{\sqrt{561}}{12}$$

To find $P(5 \text{ or fewer})$, find the z-score for $x = 5.5$.

$$z = \frac{5.5 - \frac{17}{4}}{\frac{\sqrt{561}}{12}} \approx 0.63$$

$$P(z < 0.63) = 0.7357$$

32. Let x represent the number of questions.

$n = 100; x = 60, 61, 62, \ldots, \text{ or } 100; p = \frac{1}{2}$

$$\mu = np = 180\left(\frac{1}{2}\right) = 50$$

$$\begin{aligned}\sigma &= \sqrt{np(1-p)} = \sqrt{100\left(\frac{1}{2}\right)\left(\frac{1}{2}\right)}\\ &= \sqrt{25} = 5\end{aligned}$$

To find $P(60 \text{ or more correct})$, find the z-score for $x = 59.5$.

$$z = \frac{59.5 - 50}{5} = 1.90$$

$$\begin{aligned}P(z > 1.90) &= 1 - P(z \le 1.90)\\ &= 1 - 0.9713\\ &= 0.0287\end{aligned}$$

33. **(a)** $1 - P(x = 0, 1, 2, 3)$

$$\begin{aligned}&= 1 - \left[\binom{156}{0}\left(\frac{1}{3709}\right)^0\left(1 - \frac{1}{3709}\right)^{156}\right.\\ &\quad + \binom{156}{1}\left(\frac{1}{3709}\right)^1\left(1 - \frac{1}{3709}\right)^{155}\\ &\quad + \binom{156}{2}\left(\frac{1}{3709}\right)^2\left(1 - \frac{1}{3709}\right)^{154}\\ &\quad \left.+ \binom{156}{3}\left(\frac{1}{3709}\right)^3\left(1 - \frac{1}{3709}\right)^{153}\right]\\ &= 1.2139 \times 10^{-7}\end{aligned}$$

(b) $n = 156, p = \dfrac{1}{3709}$

$$\begin{aligned}\mu &= np = 156\left(\frac{1}{3709}\right) = 0.042\\ \sigma &= \sqrt{np(1-p)}\\ &= \sqrt{156\left(\tfrac{1}{3709}\right)\left(\tfrac{3708}{3709}\right)}\\ &\approx 0.205\end{aligned}$$

$$\begin{aligned}P(x \ge 4) &= P\left(z \ge \frac{3.5 - 0.042}{0.205}\right)\\ &= P(z \ge 16.9)\\ &\approx 0\end{aligned}$$

(c) $n = 20{,}000, p = \dfrac{1}{3709}$

$$\mu = np = 20{,}000\left(\frac{1}{3709}\right) = 5.39$$

$$\begin{aligned}\sigma &= \sqrt{np(1-p)} \\ &= \sqrt{20{,}000\left(\tfrac{1}{3709}\right)\left(\tfrac{3708}{3709}\right)} \\ &\approx 2.32\end{aligned}$$

$$\begin{aligned}P(x \geq 4) &= P\left(z \geq \frac{3.5 - 5.39}{2.32}\right) \\ &= P(z \geq -0.81) \\ &= 1 - P(z < -0.81) \\ &= 1 - 0.2090 \\ &= 0.7910\end{aligned}$$

Chapter 9 Review Exercises

2. In a grouped frequency distribution, there should be from 6 to 15 intervals.

3. **(a)** Since 450-474 is to be the first interval, let all the intervals be of size 25. The largest data value is 566, so the last interval that will be needed is 550-574. The frequency distribution is as follows.

Interval	Frequency
450-474	5
475-499	6
500-524	5
525-549	2
550-574	2

(b) Draw the histogram. It consists of 5 bars of equal width having heights as determined by the frequency of each interval. See the histogram in part (c).

(c) Construct the frequency polygon by joining consecutive midpoints of the tops of the histogram bars with line segments.

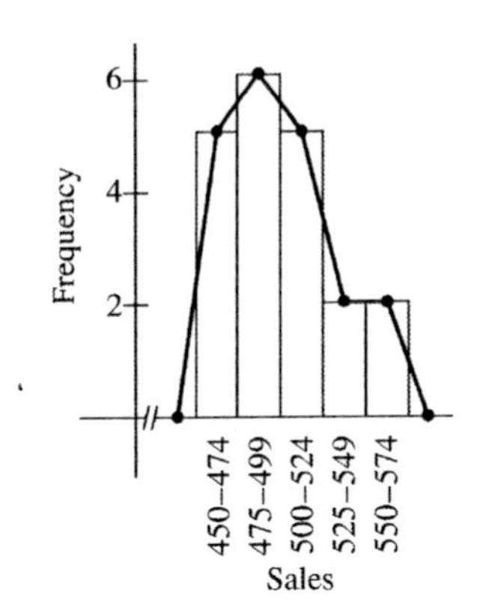

4. **(a)**

Interval	Frequency
9-10	3
11-12	6
13-14	6
15-16	7

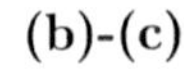

(b)-(c)

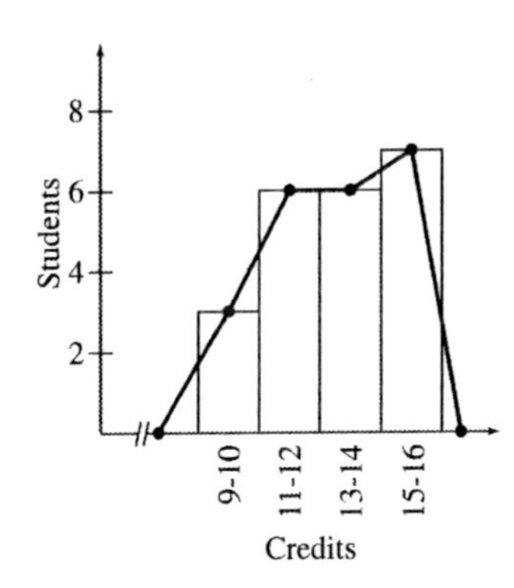

5. $\sum x = 30 + 24 + 34 + 30 + 29 + 28 + 30 + 29$
$= 234$

The mean of the 8 numbers is

$$\bar{x} = \frac{\sum x}{n} = \frac{234}{8} = 29.25.$$

6. $105, 108, 110, 115, 106, 110, 104, 113, 117$

$$\bar{x} = \frac{\sum x}{n} = \frac{988}{9} \approx 109.8$$

7.

Interval	Midpoint, x	Frequency, f	Product, xf
10-19	14.5	6	87
20-29	24.5	12	294
30-39	34.5	14	483
40-49	44.5	10	445
50-59	54.5	8	436
Totals:		50	1745

The mean of this collection of grouped data is

$$\bar{x} = \frac{\sum xf}{n} = \frac{1745}{50} = 34.9.$$

8.

Interval	Midpoint, x	Frequency, f	Product, xf
40-44	42	3	126
45-49	47	6	282
50-54	52	7	364
55-59	57	14	798
60-64	62	3	186
65-69	67	2	134
Totals:		35	1890

Use the formula for the mean of a grouped frequency distribution.

$$\bar{x} = \frac{\sum xf}{n} = \frac{1890}{35} \approx 54$$

10. $12, 17, 21, 23, 27, 27, 34$

The median is the middle number; in this case, it is 23.

The mode is the most frequent number; in this case, it is 27.

11. Arrange the numbers in numerical order, from smallest to largest.

$$35, 36, 36, 38, 38, 42, 44, 48$$

There are 8 numbers here; the median is the mean of the two middle numbers, which is

$$\frac{38+38}{2} = \frac{76}{2} = 38.$$

The mode is the number that occurs most often. Here, there are two modes, 36 and 38, since they both appear twice.

12. The modal class is the interval with the greatest frequency; in this case, the modal class is 30-39.

13. The modal class for the distribution of Exercise 8 is the interval 55-59, since it contains more data values than any of the other intervals.

14. The range of a distribution is the difference between the largest and smallest data items.

16. $22, 27, 31, 35, 41$

The range is the difference between the largest and smallest numbers. For this distribution, the range is

$$41 - 22 = 19.$$

To find the standard deviation, the first step is to find the mean.

$$\begin{aligned}\bar{x} &= \frac{\sum x}{n}\\ &= \frac{22+27+31+35+41}{5}\\ &= \frac{156}{5}\\ &= 31.2\end{aligned}$$

Now complete the following table.

x	x^2
22	484
27	729
31	961
35	1225
41	1681
Total:	5080

$$\begin{aligned}s &= \sqrt{\frac{\sum x^2 - n\bar{x}^2}{n-1}}\\ &= \sqrt{\frac{5080 - 5(31.2)^2}{4}}\\ &= \sqrt{53.2} \approx 7.3\end{aligned}$$

17. The range is $93 - 26 = 67$, the difference of the highest and lowest numbers in the distribution.

The mean is

$$\bar{x} = \frac{\sum x}{n} = \frac{520}{10} = 52.$$

Construct a table with the values of x and x^2.

x	x^2
26	676
43	1849
51	2601
29	841
37	1369
56	3136
29	841
82	6724
74	5476
93	8649
Total:	32,162

The standard deviation is

$$s = \sqrt{\frac{\sum x^2 - n\bar{x}^2}{n-1}} = \sqrt{\frac{32{,}162 - 10(52)^2}{9}} \approx \sqrt{569.1} \approx 23.9.$$

18. Recall that when working with grouped data, x represents the midpoint of each interval. Complete the following table.

Interval	f	x	xf	x^2	fx^2
10-19	6	14.5	87.0	210.25	1261.50
20-29	12	24.5	294.0	600.25	7203.00
30-39	14	34.5	483.0	1190.25	16,663.50
40-49	10	44.5	445.0	1980.25	19,802.50
50-59	8	54.5	436.0	2970.25	23,762.00
Totals:	50		1745.0		68,692.50

Use the formulas for grouped frequency distributions to find the mean and then the standard deviation. (The mean was also calculated in Exercise 7.)

$$\bar{x} = \frac{\sum xf}{n} = \frac{1745}{50} = 34.9$$

$$s = \sqrt{\frac{\sum fx^2 - n\bar{x}^2}{n-1}} = \sqrt{\frac{68{,}692.5 - 50(34.9)^2}{49}} \approx 12.6$$

19. Start with the frequency distribution that was the answer to Exercise 8, and expand the table to include columns for the midpoint x of each interval and for xf, x^2, and fx^2.

Interval	f	x	xf	x^2	fx^2
40-44	3	42	126	1764	5292
45-49	6	47	282	2209	13,254
50-54	7	52	364	2704	18,928
55-59	14	57	798	3249	45,486
60-64	3	62	186	3844	11,532
65-69	2	67	134	4489	8978
Totals:	35		1890		103,470

The mean of the grouped data is

$$\bar{x} = \frac{\sum x}{n} = \frac{1890}{35} = 54.$$

The standard deviation for the grouped data is

$$s = \sqrt{\frac{\sum fx^2 - n\bar{x}^2}{n-1}} = \sqrt{\frac{103{,}470 - 35(54)^2}{34}} \approx \sqrt{41.47} \approx 6.4.$$

21. A skewed distribution has the largest frequency at one end rather than in the middle.

22. Between $z = 0$ and $z = 2.17$

$$P(0 \le z \le 2.17) = 0.9850 - 0.5000 = 0.4850$$

23. To the left of $z = 0.84$

Using the standard normal curve table,

$$P(z < 0.84) = 0.7995.$$

24. Between $z = -2.13$ and $z = 1.11$

$$P(-2.13 \le z \le 1.11) = 0.8665 - 0.0166 = 0.8499$$

25. Between $z = 1.53$ and $z = 2.82$

$$P(1.53 \le z \le 2.82) = P(z \le 2.82) - P(z \le 1.53) = 0.9976 - 0.9370 = 0.0606$$

26. If 7% of the area under the curve is to the right of z, then 93% of the area is to the left of z. Find the value closest to 0.93 in the body of the table, and read the table backwards to find the corresponding z-score, which is $z = 1.48$.

27. The normal distribution is not a good approximation of a binomial distribution that has a value of p close to 0 or 1 because the histogram of such a binomial distribution is skewed and therefore not close to the shape of a normal distribution.

28. **(a)** Let x represent the number of hearts drawn.

$n = 1{,}000{,}000$; $x = 249{,}500, 249{,}501, \ldots, 251{,}000$;

$p = \frac{13}{52} = \frac{1}{4}$

$$\mu = np = 1{,}000{,}000\,(1/4) = 250{,}000$$

$$\sigma = \sqrt{np(1-p)} = \sqrt{1{,}000{,}000\left(\tfrac{1}{4}\right)\left(\tfrac{3}{4}\right)}$$

$$= \sqrt{\frac{3{,}000{,}000}{16}} = \frac{1000\sqrt{3}}{4} = 250\sqrt{3}$$

To find P(between 249,500 and 251,000), find the z-scores for $x = 249{,}499.5$ and $x = 251{,}000.5$.

For $x = 249{,}499.5$,

$$z = \frac{249{,}499.5 - 250{,}000}{250\sqrt{3}} \approx -1.16.$$

For $x = 251{,}000.5$,

$$z = \frac{251{,}000.5 - 250{,}000}{250\sqrt{3}} \approx 2.31.$$

$$\begin{aligned} P(-1.16 < z < 2.31) &= P(2.31) - P(-1.16) \\ &= 0.9896 - 0.1230 \\ &= 0.8666 \end{aligned}$$

29.

Number of Heads, x	Frequency, f	xf	fx^2
0	1	0	0
1	5	5	5
2	7	14	28
3	5	15	45
4	2	8	32
Totals:	20	42	110

(a) $\bar{x} = \dfrac{\sum xf}{n} = \dfrac{42}{20} = 2.1$

$$s = \sqrt{\frac{\sum fx^2 - n\bar{x}^2}{n-1}} = \sqrt{\frac{110 - 20(2.1)^2}{20-1}} \approx 1.07$$

(b) For this binomial experiment,

$$\mu = np = 4\left(\frac{1}{2}\right) = 2,$$

and

$$\sigma = \sqrt{np(1-p)} = \sqrt{4\left(\frac{1}{2}\right)\left(\frac{1}{2}\right)} = \sqrt{1} = 1.$$

(c) The answers to parts (a) and (b) should be close.

30.

Interval	x	Tally	f	xf
1-3	2	𝍸 |	6	12
4-6	5	𝍸	5	25
7-9	8	𝍸 𝍸 |	11	88
10-12	11	𝍸 𝍸 𝍸 𝍸	20	220
13-15	14	𝍸 |	6	84
16-18	17	||	2	34
Totals:			50	463

x	$P(x)$	$x \cdot P(x)$
0	0.001	0.000
1	0.010	0.010
2	0.044	0.088
3	0.117	0.351
4	0.205	0.820
5	0.246	1.230
6	0.205	1.230
7	0.117	0.819
8	0.044	0.352
9	0.010	0.090
10	0.001	0.010
Totals:	1.000	5.000

(a) The mean of the frequency distribution is

$$\bar{x} = \frac{\sum xf}{n} = \frac{463}{50} = 9.26 \approx 9.3.$$

The expected value of the probability distribution is

$$E(x) = \sum(x \cdot P(x)) = 5.$$

(b) The standard deviation of the frequency distribution is

$$s = \sqrt{\frac{\sum fx^2 - n\bar{x}^2}{n-1}}$$

$$= \sqrt{\frac{5027 - 50(9.26)^2}{50-1}} \approx 3.9.$$

The standard deviation of the probability distribution is

$$s = \sqrt{np(1-p)} = \sqrt{10(0.5)(0.5)} \approx 1.58.$$

(c) 95.44% of the area under the normal approximation of the binomial probability distribution will lie between $z = -2$ and $z = 2$.

$$z = -2 \text{ means } -2 = \frac{x-5}{1.58} \quad \text{or} \quad 1.84 = x.$$

$$z = 2 \text{ means } 2 = \frac{x-5}{1.58} \quad \text{or} \quad 8.16 = x.$$

The interval is $1.84 \le x \le 8.16$.

(d) The normal distribution cannot be used to answer probability questions about the frequency distribution because the histogram of the frequency distribution is not close enough to the shape of a normal curve.

31. **(a)** For Stock I,

$$\bar{x} = \frac{11 + (-1) + 14}{3} = 8,$$

so, the mean (average return) is 8%.

$$s = \sqrt{\frac{\sum x^2 - n\bar{x}^2}{n-1}} = \sqrt{\frac{318 - 3(8)^2}{2}} = \sqrt{63} \approx 7.9$$

so the standard deviation is 7.9%.

For Stock II,

$$\bar{x} = \frac{9 + 5 + 10}{3} = 8,$$

so the mean is also 8%.

$$s = \sqrt{\frac{\sum x^2 - n\bar{x}^2}{n-1}} = \sqrt{\frac{206 - 3(8)^2}{2}} = \sqrt{7} \approx 2.6,$$

so the standard deviation is 2.6%.

(b) Both stocks offer an average (mean) return of 8%. The smaller standard deviation for Stock II indicates a more stable return and thus greater security.

32. $$P(x < 32) = P\left(z < \frac{32 - 32.1}{0.1}\right) = P(z < -1) = 0.1587 \text{ or } 15.87\%$$

33. Let x represent the number of overstuffed frankfurters.
$n = 500, p = 0.04, 1 - p = 0.96$

We also need the following results.

$$\mu = np = 500(0.04) = 20$$
$$\sigma = \sqrt{np(1-p)} = \sqrt{500(0.04)(0.96)} = \sqrt{19.2} \approx 4.38$$

(a) P(twenty-five or fewer) or, equivalently, $P(x \le 25)$

First, using the binomial probability formula:

$$P(x \le 25) = \binom{500}{0}(0.04)^0(0.96)^{500} + \binom{500}{1}(0.04)^1(0.96)^{499} + \ldots + \binom{500}{25}(0.04)^{25}(0.96)^{475}$$
$$= (1.4 \times 10^{-9}) + (2.8 \times 10^{-8}) + \ldots + 0.0446 \approx 0.8924$$

(To evaulate the sum, use a calculator or computer program. For example, using a TI-83/84 Plus calculator, enter the following:

sum(seq((500nCrX)(0.04^X)(0.96^(500–X)), X, 0, 25, 1))

The displayed result is 0.8923644609.)

Second, using the normal approximation:

To find $P(x \le 25)$, first find the z-score for 25.5.

$$z = \frac{25.5 - 20}{4.38} \approx 1.26$$
$$P(z < 1.26) = 0.8962$$

(b) $P(\text{exactly twenty-five})$ or $P(x = 25)$

Using the binomial probability formula:

$$P(x = 25) = \binom{500}{25}(0.04)^{25}(0.96)^{475}$$
$$\approx 0.0446$$

Using the normal approximation:

$P(\text{exactly twenty-five})$ corresponds to the area under the normal curve between $x = 24.5$ and $x = 25.5$. The corresponding z-scores are found as follows.

$$z = \frac{24.5 - 20}{4.38} \approx 1.03 \text{ and } z = \frac{25.5 - 20}{4.38} \approx 1.26$$

$$\begin{aligned} P(x = 25) &= P(24.5 < x < 25.5) \\ &= P(1.03 < z < 1.26) \\ &= P(z < 1.26) - P(z < 1.03) \\ &= 0.8962 - 0.8485 \\ &= 0.0477 \end{aligned}$$

(c) $P(\text{at least 30})$, or equivalently, $P(x \geq 30)$

Using the binomial probability formula:

This is the complementary event to "less than 30," which requires fewer calculations. We can use the results from Part (a) to reduce the amount of work even more.

$$\begin{aligned} P(x < 30) &= P(x \leq 25) + P(x = 26) \\ &\quad + P(x = 27) + P(x = 28) \\ &\quad + P(x = 29) \\ &= 0.8924 + \binom{500}{26}(0.04)^{26}(0.96)^{474} \\ &\quad + \cdots + \binom{500}{29}(0.04)^{29}(0.96)^{471} \\ &\approx 0.9804 \end{aligned}$$

Therefore,

$$\begin{aligned} P(x \geq 30) &= 1 - P(x < 30) \\ &= 1 - 0.9804 \\ &= 0.0196. \end{aligned}$$

Using the normal approximation:

Again, use the complementary event. To find $P(x < 30)$, find the z-score for 29.5.

$$z = \frac{29.5 - 20}{4.38} \approx 2.17$$

$$P(z < 2.17) = 0.9850$$

Therefore,

$$\begin{aligned} P(x \geq 30) &= 1 - P(x < 30) \\ &= 1 - 0.9850 \\ &= 0.0150. \end{aligned}$$

34. Let x represent the number of businesses that go bankrupt in their first year.

$n = 50, p = 0.21$

$$\mu = np = 500(0.21) = 10.5$$
$$\sigma = \sqrt{np(1-p)} = \sqrt{50(0.21)(0.79)} \approx 2.88$$

(a) Use the binomial probability formula.

$$P(x = 8) = \binom{50}{8}(0.21)^8(0.79)^{42}$$
$$\approx 0.1019$$

Now use the normal approximation. To find $P(8 \text{ go bankrupt})$, find the z-scores for $x = 7.5$ and $x = 8.5$.

For $x = 7.5$,

$$z = \frac{7.5 - 10.5}{2.88} \approx -1.04.$$

For $x = 8.5$,

$$z = \frac{8.5 - 10.5}{2.88} \approx -0.69.$$

$$\begin{aligned} P(8 \text{ go bankrupt}) &= 0.2451 - 0.1492 \\ &= 0.0959 \end{aligned}$$

(b) Use the binomial probability formula.

$$\begin{aligned} &P(x = 0, 1, \text{ or } 2) \\ &= \binom{50}{0}(0.21)^0(0.79)^{50} + \binom{50}{1}(0.21)^1(0.79)^{49} \\ &\quad + \binom{50}{2}(0.21)^2(0.79)^{48} \\ &\approx 0.00001 + 0.00010 + 0.00066 \\ &\approx 0.0008 \end{aligned}$$

Now use the normal curve approximation. To find $P(x \leq 2)$, find the z-score for $x = 2.5$.

$$z = \frac{2.5 - 10.5}{2.88} \approx -2.78$$

$$P(x \leq 2) = 0.0027$$

35. The table below records the mean and standard deviation for diet A and for diet B.

	$\bar{x}$	s
Diet A	2.7	2.26
Diet B	1.3	0.95

(a) Diet A had the greater mean gain, since the mean for diet A is larger.

(b) Diet B had a more consistent gain, since diet B has a smaller standard deviation.

36. Let x represent the number of flies that are killed.

$n = 1000, x = 980, p = 0.98$

$$\begin{aligned}\mu &= np = 1000(0.98) = 980\\ \sigma &= \sqrt{np(1-p)}\\ &= \sqrt{1000(0.98)(0.02)}\\ &= \sqrt{19.6}\end{aligned}$$

To find $P(\text{exactly } 980)$, find the z-scores for $x = 979.5$ and $x = 980.5$.

For $x = 979.5$,

$$z = \frac{979.5 - 980}{\sqrt{19.6}} \approx -0.11.$$

For $x = 980.5$,

$$z = \frac{980.5 - 980}{\sqrt{19.6}} \approx 0.11.$$

$$\begin{aligned}P(-0.11 < z < 0.11) &= P(z < 0.11) - P(z < -0.11)\\ &= 0.5438 - 0.4562\\ &= 0.0876\end{aligned}$$

37. Let x represent the number of flies that are killed.

$n = 1000;\ x = 0, 1, 2, \ldots, 986;\ p = 0.98$

$\mu = np = 1000(0.98) = 980$

$\sigma = \sqrt{np(1-p)} = \sqrt{1000(0.98)(0.02)} = \sqrt{19.6}$

To find $P(\text{no more than } 986)$, find the z-score for $x = 986.5$.

$$z = \frac{986.5 - 980}{\sqrt{19.6}} \approx 1.47$$

$P(z < 1.47) = 0.9292$

38. Again, let x represent the number of flies that are killed.

$n = 100; x = 975, 976, \ldots, 980; p = 0.98$

As in Exercise 36, $\mu = 980$ and $\sigma = \sqrt{19.6}$. To find $P(\text{at least } 975)$, find the z-score for $x = 974.5$.

$$z = \frac{974.5 - 980}{\sqrt{19.6}} \approx -1.24$$

$$\begin{aligned}P(z > -1.24) &= 1 - P(z < -1.24)\\ &= 1 - 0.1075\\ &= 0.8925\end{aligned}$$

39. Again, let x represent the number of flies that are killed.

$n = 1000;\ x = 973, 974, 975, \ldots, 993;\ p = 0.98$

As in Exercise 37, $\mu = 980$ and $\sigma = \sqrt{19.6}$. To find $P(\text{between 973 and 993})$, find the z-scores for $x = 972.5$ and $x = 993.5$.

For $x = 972.5$,

$$z = \frac{972.5 - 980}{\sqrt{19.6}} \approx -1.69.$$

For $x = 993.5$,

$$z = \frac{993.5 - 980}{\sqrt{19.6}} \approx 3.05.$$

$$\begin{aligned}P(-1.69 \le z \le 3.05) &= P(z \le 3.05) - P(z \le -1.69)\\ &= 0.9989 - 0.0455\\ &= 0.9534\end{aligned}$$

40. At least 50 min/day

$$P(x \ge 50) = 1 - P(x < 50)$$

Find the z-score for $x = 50$.

$$z = \frac{50 - 42}{12} \approx 0.67$$

$$P(x \ge 50) = 1 - 0.7486 = 0.2514,$$

so 25.14% of the residents commute at least 50 min/day.

41. No more than 40 min/day

$\mu = 42,\ \sigma = 12$

Find the z-score for $x = 35$.

$$z = \frac{40 - 42}{12} \approx -0.17$$

$P(x \le 40) = P(z \le -0.17) = 0.4325$

43.25% of the residents commute no more than 40 min/day.

42. Between 32 and 40 min/day

Find the z-scores for $x = 32$ and $x = 40$.

For $x = 32$,

$$z = \frac{32 - 42}{12} \approx -0.83.$$

For $x = 40$,

$$z = \frac{40 - 42}{12} \approx -0.17.$$

$$\begin{aligned} P(32 \le x \le 40) &= 0.4325 - 0.2033 \\ &= 0.2292, \end{aligned}$$

so 22.92% of the residents commute between 32 and 40 min/day.

43. Between 38 and 60 min/day

$\mu = 42,\ \sigma = 12$

Find the z-scores for $x = 38$ and $x = 60$.

For $x = 38$,

$$z = \frac{38 - 42}{12} \approx -0.33.$$

For $x = 60$,

$$z = \frac{60 - 42}{12} = 1.5.$$

$$\begin{aligned} P(38 \le x \le 60) &= P(-0.33 \le z \le 1.5) \\ &= P(z \le 1.5) - P(z \le -0.33) \\ &= 0.9332 - 0.3707 \\ &= 0.5625 \end{aligned}$$

56.25% of the residents commute between 38 and 60 min/day.

44. **(a)** More than 130

$$\begin{aligned} P(x \ge 130) &= P(z \ge 2) \\ &= 1 - 0.9772 \\ &= 0.0228 \end{aligned}$$

About 2.28% of the people will have an IQ above 130.

(b) Less than 85

$$\begin{aligned} P(x < 85) &= P(z < -1) \\ &= 0.1587 \end{aligned}$$

About 15.87% of the people will have an IQ below 85.

(c) Between 85 and 115

$$\begin{aligned} P(85 \le x \le 115) &= P(-1 \le z \le 1) \\ &= 0.8413 - 0.1587 \\ &= 0.6826 \end{aligned}$$

About 68.26% of the people will have an IQ between 85 and 115.

45. **(a)** The mean is found as follows.

$$\overline{x} = \frac{\sum x}{n} = \frac{1647}{12} = 137.25$$

To find the median, arrange the data in order from smallest to largest.

80, 83, 92, 93, 112, 121, 140,
159, 169, 197, 199, 202

Because there are an even number of items, the median is the mean of the two middle entries.

$$\text{median} = \frac{121 + 140}{2} = 130.5$$

Each number occurs only once in the list so there is no mode.

(b) To find the standard deviation, construct a table.

x	x^2
83	6889
93	8649
112	12,544
121	14,641
92	8464
80	6400
140	19,600
159	25,281
169	28,561
197	38,809
199	39,601
202	40,804
Total:	250,243

The standard deviation is

$$\begin{aligned} s &= \sqrt{\frac{\sum x^2 - n\overline{x}^2}{n-1}} \\ &= \sqrt{\frac{250{,}243 - 12(137.25)^2}{12 - 1}} \\ &\approx \sqrt{2199.30} \approx 46.9. \end{aligned}$$

(c) $\overline{x} + s = 137.25 + 46.90 = 184.15$
$\overline{x} - s = 137.25 + 46.90 = 90.35$

Seven of the 12 years fall between these two values. Thus,

$$\frac{7}{12} \approx 0.583 \text{ or } 58.3\%$$

of the data is within one standard deviation of the mean.

(d) $\overline{x} + s = 137.25 + 2(46.90) = 231.05$
$\overline{x} - s = 137.25 - 2(46.90) = 43.45$

All of the data fall between these two values. Thus, 100% of the data is within two standard deviations of the mean.

46. $n = 500, p = 0.555$

$$\mu = np = 500(0.555) = 277.5$$
$$\sigma = \sqrt{np(1-p)} = \sqrt{500(0.555)(0.445)} \approx 11.11$$

$$P(x > 300) = P\left(z > \frac{300.5 - 277.5}{11.11}\right) = P(z > 2.07) = 1 - 0.9808 = 0.0192$$

47. (a) $P(x \geq 35) = P\left(z \geq \frac{35 - 28.0}{5.5}\right)$

$$= P(z \geq 1.27) = 1 - P(z < 1.27) = 1 - 0.8980 = 0.1020$$

(b) $P(x \geq 35) = P\left(z \geq \frac{35 - 32.2}{8.4}\right)$

$$= P(z \geq 0.33) = 1 - P(z < 0.33) = 1 - 0.6293 = 0.3707$$

(d) $P(x \geq 1.4) = P\left(z \geq \frac{1.4 - 1.64}{0.08}\right)$

$$= P(z \geq -3) = 1 - P(z < -3) = 1 - 0.0013 = 0.9987$$

(e) $P(z < -1.5) + P(z > 1.5)$

$$= 2P(z < -1.5) = 2(0.0668) = 0.1336$$

Extended Application: Statistics in the Law-The Castaneda Decision

1. $z = \dfrac{688 - 339}{\sqrt{870 \cdot 0.791 \cdot 0.209}} \approx 29.1$

2. The court used the normal approximation to compute this (tiny) probability.

3. (a) $220(0.791) = 174.02$

The expected number of Mexican-American is 174.

(b) $\sigma = \sqrt{np(1-p)} = \sqrt{220(0.791)(1 - 0.791)} \approx 6.03$

(c) $z = \dfrac{100 - 174}{6.03} \approx -12.3$

The actual number is 12.3 standard deviations from the expected number.

(d) The table only goes to -3.4 standard deviations; a result this far below the mean, or farther, has probability 0.003, so the pool with 100 Mexican-Americans has probability less than 0.003. Using the normal approximations to the binomial distribution, we can show that the true probability is *much* smaller, in fact less than 10^{-30}.

4. (a) $z = \dfrac{6 - \frac{88}{294} \cdot 112}{\sqrt{112 \cdot \frac{88}{294} \cdot \frac{206}{294}}} \approx -5.7$

The expected number is about 6 standard deviations from the actual number.

(b) Yes; The court should have decided this *was* evidence of discrimination.

Chapter 10

MARKOV CHAINS

10.1 Basic Properties of Markov Chains

1. $\begin{bmatrix} \frac{2}{3} & \frac{1}{2} \end{bmatrix}$ could not be a probability vector because the sum of the entries in the row is not equal to 1.

2. $\begin{bmatrix} \frac{1}{2} & 1 \end{bmatrix}$ could not be a probability vector because the sum of the entries is not equal to 1.

3. $\begin{bmatrix} 0 & 1 \end{bmatrix}$ could be a probability vector since it is a matrix of only one row, having nonnegative entries whose sum is 1.

4. $\begin{bmatrix} 0.1 & 0.1 \end{bmatrix}$ could not be a probability vector because the sum of the entries is not equal to 1.

5. $\begin{bmatrix} 0.4 & 0.2 & 0 \end{bmatrix}$ could not be a probability vector because the sum of the entries in the row is not equal to 1.

6. $\begin{bmatrix} \frac{1}{4} & \frac{1}{8} & \frac{5}{8} \end{bmatrix}$ could be a probability vector since it is a matrix of only one row, having nonnegative entries whose sum is 1.

7. $\begin{bmatrix} 0.07 & 0.04 & 0.37 & 0.52 \end{bmatrix}$ could be a probability vector. It is a matrix of only one row, having nonnegative entries whose sum is 1.

8. $\begin{bmatrix} 0.3 & -0.1 & 0.8 \end{bmatrix}$ could not be a probability vector because it has a negative entry.

9. $\begin{bmatrix} 0 & -0.2 & 0.6 & 0.6 \end{bmatrix}$ could not be a probability vector because it has a negative entry.

10. $\begin{bmatrix} 0.6 & 0 \\ 0 & 0.6 \end{bmatrix}$

The entries in each row do not add up to 1, so this could not be a transition matrix.

11. $\begin{bmatrix} \frac{3}{4} & \frac{1}{4} \\ 1 & 0 \end{bmatrix}$

This could be a transition matrix since it is a square matrix, all entries are between 0 and 1, inclusive, and the sum of the entries in each row is 1.

To draw the transition diagram, give names to the two states (such as 1 and 2) and label the probabilities of going from one state to another. In this case,

$$p_{11} = \frac{3}{4}, \qquad p_{12} = \frac{1}{4},$$
$$p_{21} = 1, \quad \text{and} \quad p_{22} = 0.$$

This information is then used to create the following transition diagram.

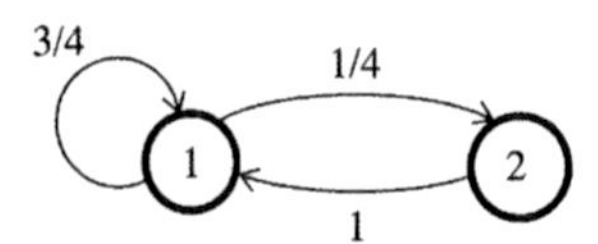

12. $\begin{bmatrix} \frac{1}{3} & \frac{2}{3} \\ \frac{1}{2} & \frac{1}{2} \end{bmatrix}$

This could be a transition matrix since it is a square matrix, all entries are between 0 and 1, inclusive, and the sum of the entries in each row is 1.

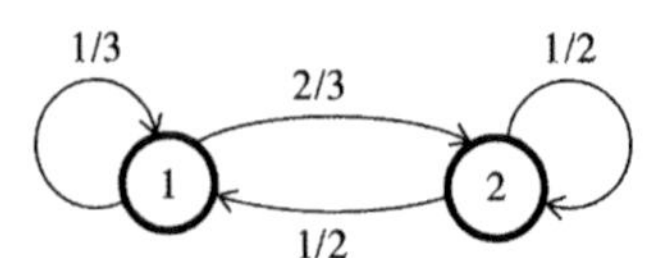

13. $\begin{bmatrix} \frac{1}{4} & \frac{3}{4} & 0 \\ 2 & 0 & 1 \\ 1 & \frac{2}{3} & 3 \end{bmatrix}$

This could not be a transition matrix because it has entries that are greater than 1.

14. $\begin{bmatrix} \frac{1}{3} & \frac{1}{3} & \frac{1}{3} \\ 0 & 1 & 0 \\ \frac{1}{2} & 0 & \frac{1}{2} \end{bmatrix}$

This could be a transition matrix since it meets all the requirements given in the solution for Exercise 12.

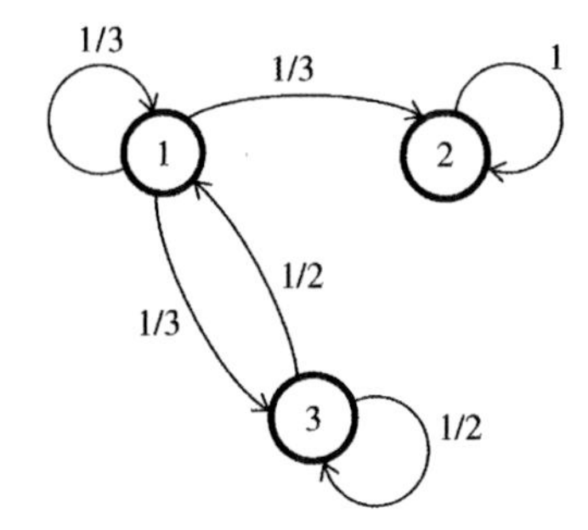

15. $\begin{bmatrix} \frac{1}{3} & \frac{1}{2} & 1 \\ 0 & 1 & 0 \\ \frac{1}{2} & \frac{1}{2} & 1 \end{bmatrix}$

This could not be a transition matrix because the sum of the entries in the first row and in the third row is more than 1.

16. The given diagram is not a transition diagram because the sum of the probabilities from each of the three states is not 1.

17. The transition diagram provides the information

$$p_{\text{AA}} = 0.9,\ p_{\text{AB}} = 0.1,\ p_{\text{AC}} = 0,$$
$$p_{\text{BA}} = 0.1,\ p_{\text{BB}} = 0.7,\ p_{\text{BC}} = 0.2,$$
$$p_{\text{CA}} = 0,\ p_{\text{CB}} = 0.2,\ \text{and } p_{\text{CC}} = 0.8.$$

The transition matrix associated with this diagram is

$$\begin{array}{c} \\ \text{A} \\ \text{B} \\ \text{C} \end{array} \begin{array}{c} \begin{array}{ccc} \text{A} & \text{B} & \text{C} \end{array} \\ \begin{bmatrix} 0.9 & 0.1 & 0 \\ 0.1 & 0.7 & 0.2 \\ 0 & 0.2 & 0.8 \end{bmatrix} \end{array}.$$

18.

$$\begin{array}{c} \\ \text{A} \\ \text{B} \\ \text{C} \end{array} \begin{array}{c} \begin{array}{ccc} \text{A} & \text{B} & \text{C} \end{array} \\ \begin{bmatrix} 0.6 & 0.15 & 0.25 \\ 0.9 & 0.02 & 0.08 \\ 0.35 & 0 & 0.65 \end{bmatrix} \end{array}$$

All entries in this square matrix are between 0 and 1, inclusive, and the sum of the entries in each row is 1, so this is a transition matrix.

19. $A = \begin{bmatrix} 1 & 0 \\ 0.7 & 0.3 \end{bmatrix}$

$$A^2 = \begin{bmatrix} 1 & 0 \\ 0.7 & 0.3 \end{bmatrix} \begin{bmatrix} 1 & 0 \\ 0.7 & 0.3 \end{bmatrix} = \begin{bmatrix} 1 & 0 \\ 0.91 & 0.09 \end{bmatrix}$$

$$A^3 = A \cdot A^2 = \begin{bmatrix} 1 & 0 \\ 0.7 & 0.3 \end{bmatrix} \begin{bmatrix} 1 & 0 \\ 0.91 & 0.09 \end{bmatrix}$$

$$= \begin{bmatrix} 1 & 0 \\ 0.973 & 0.027 \end{bmatrix}$$

The entry in row 1, column 2 of A^3 gives the probability that state 1 changes to state 2 after 3 repetitions of the experiment. The probability is 0.

20. $B = \begin{bmatrix} 0.8 & 0.2 \\ 0 & 1 \end{bmatrix}$

$$B^2 = \begin{bmatrix} 0.8 & 0.2 \\ 0 & 1 \end{bmatrix} \begin{bmatrix} 0.8 & 0.2 \\ 0 & 1 \end{bmatrix} = \begin{bmatrix} 0.64 & 0.36 \\ 0 & 1 \end{bmatrix}$$

$$B^3 = B \cdot B^2 = \begin{bmatrix} 0.8 & 0.2 \\ 0 & 1 \end{bmatrix} \begin{bmatrix} 0.64 & 0.36 \\ 0 & 0 \end{bmatrix}$$

$$= \begin{bmatrix} 0.512 & 0.488 \\ 0 & 1 \end{bmatrix}$$

The entry in row 1, column 2 of B^3 gives the probability that state 1 changes to state 2 after three repetitions of the experiment. This probability is 0.488.

21. $C = \begin{bmatrix} 0.5 & 0.5 \\ 0.72 & 0.28 \end{bmatrix}$

$$C^2 = \begin{bmatrix} 0.5 & 0.5 \\ 0.72 & 0.28 \end{bmatrix} \begin{bmatrix} 0.5 & 0.5 \\ 0.72 & 0.28 \end{bmatrix}$$

$$= \begin{bmatrix} 0.61 & 0.39 \\ 0.5616 & 0.4384 \end{bmatrix}$$

$$C^3 = \begin{bmatrix} 0.5 & 0.5 \\ 0.72 & 0.28 \end{bmatrix} \begin{bmatrix} 0.61 & 0.39 \\ 0.5616 & 0.4384 \end{bmatrix}$$

$$\approx \begin{bmatrix} 0.5858 & 0.4142 \\ 0.5964 & 0.4036 \end{bmatrix}$$

The probability that state 1 changes to state 2 after 3 repetitions is 0.4142, since that is the entry in row 1, column 2 of C^3.

22. $D = \begin{bmatrix} 0.3 & 0.2 & 0.5 \\ 0 & 0 & 1 \\ 0.6 & 0.1 & 0.3 \end{bmatrix}$

$$D^2 = \begin{bmatrix} 0.39 & 0.11 & 0.5 \\ 0.6 & 0.1 & 0.3 \\ 0.36 & 0.15 & 0.49 \end{bmatrix}$$

$$D^3 = D \cdot D^2 = \begin{bmatrix} 0.417 & 0.128 & 0.455 \\ 0.36 & 0.15 & 0.49 \\ 0.402 & 0.121 & 0.477 \end{bmatrix}$$

The probability that state 1 changes to state 2 after three repetitions is 0.128.

23. $E = \begin{bmatrix} 0.8 & 0.1 & 0.1 \\ 0.3 & 0.6 & 0.1 \\ 0 & 1 & 0 \end{bmatrix}$

$$E^2 = \begin{bmatrix} 0.8 & 0.1 & 0.1 \\ 0.3 & 0.6 & 0.1 \\ 0 & 1 & 0 \end{bmatrix} \begin{bmatrix} 0.8 & 0.1 & 0.1 \\ 0.3 & 0.6 & 0.1 \\ 0 & 1 & 0 \end{bmatrix}$$

$$= \begin{bmatrix} 0.67 & 0.24 & 0.09 \\ 0.42 & 0.49 & 0.09 \\ 0.3 & 0.6 & 0.1 \end{bmatrix}$$

$$E^3 = \begin{bmatrix} 0.8 & 0.1 & 0.1 \\ 0.3 & 0.6 & 0.1 \\ 0 & 1 & 0 \end{bmatrix} \begin{bmatrix} 0.67 & 0.24 & 0.09 \\ 0.42 & 0.49 & 0.09 \\ 0.3 & 0.6 & 0.1 \end{bmatrix}$$

$$= \begin{bmatrix} 0.608 & 0.301 & 0.091 \\ 0.483 & 0.426 & 0.091 \\ 0.42 & 0.49 & 0.09 \end{bmatrix}$$

The probability that state 1 changes to state 2 after 3 repetitions is 0.301, since that is the entry in row 1, column 2 of E^3.

24. $F = \begin{bmatrix} 0.01 & 0.9 & 0.09 \\ 0.72 & 0.1 & 0.18 \\ 0.34 & 0 & 0.66 \end{bmatrix}$

$$F^2 = \begin{bmatrix} 0.6787 & 0.099 & 0.2223 \\ 0.1404 & 0.658 & 0.2016 \\ 0.2278 & 0.306 & 0.4662 \end{bmatrix}$$

$$F^3 = \begin{bmatrix} 0.1536 & 0.6207 & 0.2256 \\ 0.5437 & 0.1922 & 0.2641 \\ 0.3811 & 0.2356 & 0.3833 \end{bmatrix}$$

The probability that state 1 changes to state 2 after three repetitions is 0.6207.

25. This exercise should be solved by graphing calculator methods. The first five powers of the transition matrix are

$$A = \begin{bmatrix} 0.1 & 0.2 & 0.2 & 0.3 & 0.2 \\ 0.2 & 0.1 & 0.1 & 0.2 & 0.4 \\ 0.2 & 0.1 & 0.4 & 0.2 & 0.1 \\ 0.3 & 0.1 & 0.1 & 0.2 & 0.3 \\ 0.1 & 0.3 & 0.1 & 0.1 & 0.4 \end{bmatrix},$$

$$A^2 = \begin{bmatrix} 0.2 & 0.15 & 0.17 & 0.19 & 0.29 \\ 0.16 & 0.2 & 0.15 & 0.18 & 0.31 \\ 0.19 & 0.14 & 0.24 & 0.21 & 0.22 \\ 0.16 & 0.19 & 0.16 & 0.2 & 0.29 \\ 0.16 & 0.19 & 0.14 & 0.17 & 0.34 \end{bmatrix},$$

$$A^3 = \begin{bmatrix} 0.17 & 0.178 & 0.171 & 0.191 & 0.29 \\ 0.171 & 0.178 & 0.161 & 0.185 & 0.305 \\ 0.18 & 0.163 & 0.191 & 0.197 & 0.269 \\ 0.175 & 0.174 & 0.164 & 0.187 & 0.3 \\ 0.167 & 0.184 & 0.158 & 0.182 & 0.309 \end{bmatrix},$$

$$A^4 = \begin{bmatrix} 0.1731 & 0.175 & 0.1683 & 0.188 & 0.2956 \\ 0.1709 & 0.1781 & 0.1654 & 0.1866 & 0.299 \\ 0.1748 & 0.1718 & 0.1753 & 0.1911 & 0.287 \\ 0.1712 & 0.1775 & 0.1667 & 0.1875 & 0.2971 \\ 0.1706 & 0.1785 & 0.1641 & 0.1858 & 0.301 \end{bmatrix},$$

and

$$A^5 = \begin{bmatrix} 0.1719 & 0.1764 & 0.1678 & 0.1878 & 0.2961 \\ 0.1717 & 0.1769 & 0.1667 & 0.1872 & 0.2975 \\ 0.1729 & 0.1749 & 0.1701 & 0.1888 & 0.2933 \\ 0.1719 & 0.1765 & 0.1671 & 0.1874 & 0.297 \\ 0.1714 & 0.1773 & 0.1663 & 0.1870 & 0.2981 \end{bmatrix}.$$

The probability that state 2 changes to state 4 after 5 repetitions of the experiment is 0.1872, since that is the entry in row 2, column 4 of A^5.

26. This exercise should be solved by graphing calculator methods. Let A be the given transition matrix. The first power, A^1, is the given matrix. The other powers of the transition matrix are

$$A^2 = \begin{bmatrix} 0.23 & 0.21 & 0.24 & 0.17 & 0.15 \\ 0.26 & 0.18 & 0.26 & 0.16 & 0.14 \\ 0.23 & 0.18 & 0.24 & 0.19 & 0.16 \\ 0.19 & 0.19 & 0.27 & 0.18 & 0.17 \\ 0.17 & 0.20 & 0.26 & 0.19 & 0.18 \end{bmatrix},$$

$$A^3 = \begin{bmatrix} 0.226 & 0.192 & 0.249 & 0.177 & 0.156 \\ 0.222 & 0.196 & 0.252 & 0.174 & 0.156 \\ 0.219 & 0.189 & 0.256 & 0.177 & 0.159 \\ 0.213 & 0.192 & 0.252 & 0.181 & 0.162 \\ 0.213 & 0.189 & 0.252 & 0.183 & 0.163 \end{bmatrix},$$

$$A^4 = \begin{bmatrix} 0.2205 & 0.1916 & 0.2523 & 0.1774 & 0.1582 \\ 0.2206 & 0.1922 & 0.2512 & 0.1778 & 0.1582 \\ 0.2182 & 0.1920 & 0.2525 & 0.1781 & 0.1592 \\ 0.2183 & 0.1909 & 0.2526 & 0.1787 & 0.1595 \\ 0.2176 & 0.1906 & 0.2533 & 0.1787 & 0.1598 \end{bmatrix},$$

$$A^5 = \begin{bmatrix} 0.2193 & 0.1917 & 0.2523 & 0.1780 & 0.1588 \\ 0.2196 & 0.1915 & 0.2523 & 0.1779 & 0.1587 \\ 0.2191 & 0.1915 & 0.2523 & 0.1782 & 0.1590 \\ 0.2188 & 0.1914 & 0.2525 & 0.1782 & 0.1591 \\ 0.2186 & 0.1915 & 0.2525 & 0.1782 & 0.1592 \end{bmatrix}.$$

The probability that state 2 changes to state 4 after 5 repetitions of the experiment is found by looking at the entry in row 2, column 4 of A^5. This probability is 0.1779.

27. (a) We are asked to show that

$$X_0(P^n) = (\cdots(((X_0P)P)P)\cdots P)$$

is true for any natural number n, where the expression on the right side of the equation has a total of n factors of P. This may be proven by mathematical induction on n.

When $n = 1$, the statement becomes $X_0P = (X_0P)$, which is obviously true. When $n = 2$, the statement becomes $X_0(P^2) = (X_0P)P$, or $X_0(PP) = (X_0P)P$, which is true since matrix multiplication is associative. Next, assume the nth statement is true in order to show that the $(n+1)$st statement is true. That is, assume that

$$X_0(P^n) = (\cdots(((X_0P)P)P)\cdots P)$$

is true. Associativity plays a role here also.

$$\begin{aligned} X_0(P^{n+1}) &= X_0(P^n \cdot P) \\ &= (X_0P^n)P \\ &= (\cdots(((X_0P)P)P)\cdots P)P \end{aligned}$$

Conclude that

$$X_0(P^n) = (\cdots(((X_0P)P)P)\cdots P)$$

is true for any natural number n.

28. The given matrix is

$$A = \begin{bmatrix} 0.8 & 0.2 \\ 0.35 & 0.65 \end{bmatrix}.$$

The one-week matrix is just A.

The two-week matrix is

$$A^2 = \begin{bmatrix} 0.71 & 0.29 \\ 0.5075 & 0.4925 \end{bmatrix}.$$

The three-week matrix is

$$A^3 = \begin{bmatrix} 0.6695 & 0.3305 \\ 0.5784 & 0.4216 \end{bmatrix}.$$

The four-week matrix is

$$A^4 = \begin{bmatrix} 0.6513 & .03487 \\ 0.6103 & 0.3897 \end{bmatrix}.$$

(a) The required probability is given by the first row, first column entry in A, 0.8.

(b) Use A^2; the probability is 0.71.

(c) Use A^3; the probability is 0.6695.

(d) Use A^4; the probability is 0.6513.

(e) Use A^2; the required probability is given in row 2, column 1. This probability is 0.5075.

29. The probability vector is $\begin{bmatrix} 0.4 & 0.6 \end{bmatrix}$.

(a) $\begin{bmatrix} 0.4 & 0.6 \end{bmatrix} \begin{bmatrix} 0.8 & 0.2 \\ 0.35 & 0.65 \end{bmatrix} = \begin{bmatrix} 0.53 & 0.47 \end{bmatrix}$

Thus, after 1 wk Johnson has a 53% market share, and NorthClean has a 47% share.

(b) $C^2 = \begin{bmatrix} 0.8 & 0.2 \\ 0.35 & 0.65 \end{bmatrix} \begin{bmatrix} 0.8 & 0.2 \\ 0.35 & 0.65 \end{bmatrix}$

$$= \begin{bmatrix} 0.71 & 0.29 \\ 0.5075 & 0.4925 \end{bmatrix}$$

$$\begin{bmatrix} 0.4 & 0.6 \end{bmatrix} \begin{bmatrix} 0.71 & 0.29 \\ 0.5075 & 0.4925 \end{bmatrix} = \begin{bmatrix} 0.5885 & 0.4115 \end{bmatrix}$$

After 2 wk, Johnson has a 58.85% market share, and NorthClean has a 41.15% share.

(c) $C^3 = \begin{bmatrix} 0.8 & 0.2 \\ 0.35 & 0.65 \end{bmatrix} \begin{bmatrix} 0.71 & 0.29 \\ 0.5075 & 0.4925 \end{bmatrix}$

$$= \begin{bmatrix} 0.6695 & 0.3305 \\ 0.5784 & 0.4216 \end{bmatrix}$$

$$\begin{bmatrix} 0.4 & 0.6 \end{bmatrix} \begin{bmatrix} 0.6695 & 0.3305 \\ 0.5784 & 0.4216 \end{bmatrix} = \begin{bmatrix} 0.6148 & 0.3852 \end{bmatrix}$$

After 3 wk, the shares are 61.48% and 38.52%, respectively.

(d) $C^4 = \begin{bmatrix} 0.8 & 0.2 \\ 0.35 & 0.65 \end{bmatrix} \begin{bmatrix} 0.6695 & 0.3305 \\ 0.5784 & 0.4216 \end{bmatrix}$

$= \begin{bmatrix} 0.6513 & 0.3487 \\ 0.6103 & 0.3897 \end{bmatrix}$

$$\begin{bmatrix} 0.4 & 0.6 \end{bmatrix} \begin{bmatrix} 0.6513 & 0.3487 \\ 0.6103 & 0.3897 \end{bmatrix} = \begin{bmatrix} 0.6267 & 0.3733 \end{bmatrix}$$

After 4 wk, the shares are 62.67% and 37.33%, respectively.

30. The probability of a G_1 becoming a G_2 must be 0.30 so that the row sum is 1. All of the other entries are given directly in the exercise. All of the probabilities are given in the following transition matrix.

$$\begin{array}{c} \\ G_0 \\ G_1 \\ G_2 \end{array} \begin{array}{c} \begin{array}{ccc} G_0 & G_1 & G_2 \end{array} \\ \begin{bmatrix} 0.75 & 0.20 & 0.05 \\ 0 & 0.70 & 0.30 \\ 0 & 0 & 1 \end{bmatrix} \end{array}$$

31. The transition matrix P is

$$\begin{array}{c} \\ G_0 \\ G_1 \\ G_2 \end{array} \begin{array}{c} \begin{array}{ccc} G_0 & G_1 & G_2 \end{array} \\ \begin{bmatrix} 0.75 & 0.20 & 0.05 \\ 0 & 0.70 & 0.30 \\ 0 & 0 & 1 \end{bmatrix} \end{array}.$$

We have 50,000 new policyholders, all in G_0. The probability vector for these people is

$$\begin{array}{ccc} G_0 & G_1 & G_2 \\ [1 & 0 & 0] \end{array}.$$

(a) After 1 year, the distribution of people in each group is

$$\begin{bmatrix} 1 & 0 & 0 \end{bmatrix} \begin{bmatrix} 0.75 & 0.20 & 0.05 \\ 0 & 0.70 & 0.30 \\ 0 & 0 & 1 \end{bmatrix}$$

$$= \begin{bmatrix} 0.75 & 0.20 & 0.05 \end{bmatrix}.$$

There are

$$0.75(50{,}000) = 37{,}500 \text{ people in } G_0$$
$$0.2(50{,}000) = 10{,}000 \text{ people in } G_1$$
$$0.05(50{,}000) = 2500 \text{ people in } G_2.$$

(b) $P^2 = \begin{bmatrix} 0.75 & 0.20 & 0.05 \\ 0 & 0.70 & 0.30 \\ 0 & 0 & 1 \end{bmatrix} \begin{bmatrix} 0.75 & 0.20 & 0.05 \\ 0 & 0.70 & 0.30 \\ 0 & 0 & 1 \end{bmatrix}$

$= \begin{bmatrix} 0.5625 & 0.29 & 0.1475 \\ 0 & 0.49 & 0.51 \\ 0 & 0 & 1 \end{bmatrix}$

After 2 years, the distribution of people in each group is

$$\begin{bmatrix} 1 & 0 & 0 \end{bmatrix} \begin{bmatrix} 0.5625 & 0.29 & 0.1475 \\ 0 & 0.49 & 0.51 \\ 0 & 0 & 1 \end{bmatrix}$$

$$= \begin{bmatrix} 0.5625 & 0.29 & 0.1475 \end{bmatrix}.$$

There are

$$0.5625(50{,}000) = 28{,}125 \text{ people in } G_0$$
$$0.29(50{,}000) = 14{,}500 \text{ people in } G_1$$
$$0.1475(50{,}000) = 7375 \text{ people in } G_2.$$

(c)

$$P^3 = \begin{bmatrix} 0.75 & 0.20 & 0.05 \\ 0 & 0.70 & 0.30 \\ 0 & 0 & 1 \end{bmatrix} \begin{bmatrix} 0.5625 & 0.29 & 0.1475 \\ 0 & 0.49 & 0.51 \\ 0 & 0 & 1 \end{bmatrix}$$

$$\approx \begin{bmatrix} 0.4219 & 0.3155 & 0.2626 \\ 0 & 0.343 & 0.657 \\ 0 & 0 & 1 \end{bmatrix}$$

After 3 years, the distribution of people in each group is

$$\begin{bmatrix} 1 & 0 & 0 \end{bmatrix} \begin{bmatrix} 0.4219 & 0.3155 & 0.2626 \\ 0 & 0.343 & 0.657 \\ 0 & 0 & 1 \end{bmatrix}$$

$$\approx \begin{bmatrix} 0.4219 & 0.3155 & 0.2626 \end{bmatrix}.$$

There are

$$0.4219(50{,}000) = 21{,}094 \text{ people in } G_0$$
$$0.3155(50{,}000) = 15{,}775 \text{ people in } G_1$$
$$0.2626(50{,}000) = 13{,}131 \text{ people in } G_2.$$

(d)

$$P^3 = \begin{bmatrix} 0.75 & 0.20 & 0.05 \\ 0 & 0.70 & 0.30 \\ 0 & 0 & 1 \end{bmatrix} \begin{bmatrix} 0.4219 & 0.3155 & 0.2626 \\ 0 & 0.343 & 0.657 \\ 0 & 0 & 1 \end{bmatrix}$$

$$\approx \begin{bmatrix} 0.3164 & 0.3052 & 0.3784 \\ 0 & 0.2401 & 0.7599 \\ 0 & 0 & 1 \end{bmatrix}$$

After 4 years, the distribution of people in each group is

$$\begin{bmatrix} 1 & 0 & 0 \end{bmatrix} \begin{bmatrix} 0.3164 & 0.3052 & 0.3784 \\ 0 & 0.2401 & 0.7599 \\ 0 & 0 & 1 \end{bmatrix}$$

$$\approx \begin{bmatrix} 0.3164 & 0.3052 & 0.3784 \end{bmatrix}.$$

There are

$$\begin{aligned} 0.3164(50{,}000) &= 15{,}820 \text{ people in } G_0, \\ 0.3052(50{,}000) &= 15{,}261 \text{ people in } G_1, \\ 0.3784(50{,}000) &= 18{,}918 \text{ people in } G_2. \end{aligned}$$

32. The transition matrix P is

$$\begin{array}{c} \\ G_0 \\ G_1 \\ G_2 \end{array} \begin{array}{c} \begin{array}{ccc} G_0 & G_1 & G_2 \end{array} \\ \begin{bmatrix} 0.75 & 0.20 & 0.05 \\ 0.10 & 0.70 & 0.20 \\ 0.10 & 0.30 & 0.60 \end{bmatrix} \end{array}.$$

We have 50,000 new policyholders, all in G_0. The probability vector for these people is

$$X_0 = \begin{array}{c} \begin{array}{ccc} G_0 & G_1 & G_2 \end{array} \\ \begin{bmatrix} 1 & 0 & 0 \end{bmatrix} \end{array}$$

The initial number of people in each group is found by multiplying $50{,}000X_0$.

$$\begin{aligned} 50{,}000X_0 &= 50{,}000[1 \quad 0 \quad 0] \\ &= [50{,}000 \quad 0 \quad 0] \end{aligned}$$

(a) After 1 year, the distribution of people in each group is

$$\begin{bmatrix} 50{,}000 & 0 & 0 \end{bmatrix} P$$

$$= \begin{bmatrix} 50{,}000 & 0 & 0 \end{bmatrix} \begin{bmatrix} 0.75 & 0.20 & 0.05 \\ 0.10 & 0.70 & 0.20 \\ 0.10 & 0.30 & 0.60 \end{bmatrix}$$

$$= \begin{bmatrix} 37{,}500 & 10{,}000 & 2500 \end{bmatrix}$$

There are 37,500 people in G_0, 10,000 people in G_1, and 2500 people in G_2.

(b) After 2 years, the distribution of people in each group is

$$\begin{bmatrix} 37{,}500 & 10{,}000 & 2500 \end{bmatrix} P$$

$$= \begin{bmatrix} 37{,}500 & 10{,}000 & 2500 \end{bmatrix} \begin{bmatrix} 0.75 & 0.20 & 0.05 \\ 0.10 & 0.70 & 0.20 \\ 0.10 & 0.30 & 0.60 \end{bmatrix}$$

$$= \begin{bmatrix} 29{,}375 & 15{,}250 & 5375 \end{bmatrix}.$$

There are 29,375 people in G_0, 15,250 people in G_1, and 5375 people in G_2.

(c) After 3 years, the distribution of people in each group is

$$\begin{bmatrix} 29{,}375 & 15{,}250 & 5375 \end{bmatrix} P$$

$$= \begin{bmatrix} 29{,}375 & 15{,}250 & 5375 \end{bmatrix} \begin{bmatrix} 0.75 & 0.20 & 0.05 \\ 0.10 & 0.70 & 0.20 \\ 0.10 & 0.30 & 0.60 \end{bmatrix}$$

$$\approx \begin{bmatrix} 24{,}094 & 18{,}163 & 7744 \end{bmatrix}.$$

There are 24,094 people in G_0, 18,163 people in G_1, and 7744 people in G_2.

(d)

$$P^2 = \begin{bmatrix} 0.75 & 0.20 & 0.05 \\ 0.10 & 0.70 & 0.20 \\ 0.10 & 0.30 & 0.60 \end{bmatrix} \begin{bmatrix} 0.75 & 0.20 & 0.05 \\ 0.10 & 0.70 & 0.20 \\ 0.10 & 0.30 & 0.60 \end{bmatrix}$$

$$= \begin{bmatrix} 0.5875 & 0.305 & 0.1075 \\ 0.165 & 0.57 & 0.265 \\ 0.165 & 0.41 & 0.425 \end{bmatrix}$$

(e) After two years, a driver in G_0 has a 0.5875 probability of remaining in G_0.

33. $P = \begin{bmatrix} 0.825 & 0.175 & 0 \\ 0.060 & 0.919 & 0.021 \\ 0.049 & 0 & 0.951 \end{bmatrix}$

The initial probability vector is

$$\begin{bmatrix} 0.26 & 0.6 & 0.14 \end{bmatrix}.$$

(a) The share held by each type after 1 yr is given by

$$\begin{bmatrix} 0.26 & 0.6 & 0.14 \end{bmatrix} \begin{bmatrix} 0.825 & 0.175 & 0 \\ 0.060 & 0.919 & 0.021 \\ 0.049 & 0 & 0.951 \end{bmatrix}$$

$$= \begin{bmatrix} 0.2574 & 0.5969 & 0.1457 \end{bmatrix}.$$

(b)

$$P^2 = \begin{bmatrix} 0.825 & 0.175 & 0 \\ 0.060 & 0.919 & 0.021 \\ 0.049 & 0 & 0.951 \end{bmatrix} \begin{bmatrix} 0.825 & 0.175 & 0 \\ 0.060 & 0.919 & 0.021 \\ 0.049 & 0 & 0.951 \end{bmatrix}$$

$$= \begin{bmatrix} 0.691 & 0.305 & 0.004 \\ 0.106 & 0.855 & 0.039 \\ 0.087 & 0.009 & 0.904 \end{bmatrix}$$

The share held by each after 2 yr is

$$\begin{bmatrix} 0.26 & 0.6 & 0.14 \end{bmatrix} \begin{bmatrix} 0.691 & 0.305 & 0.004 \\ 0.106 & 0.855 & 0.039 \\ 0.087 & 0.009 & 0.904 \end{bmatrix}$$

$$= \begin{bmatrix} 0.2553 & 0.5936 & 0.1511 \end{bmatrix}.$$

(c) $P^3 = \begin{bmatrix} 0.825 & 0.175 & 0 \\ 0.060 & 0.919 & 0.021 \\ 0.049 & 0 & 0.951 \end{bmatrix} \begin{bmatrix} 0.691 & 0.305 & 0.004 \\ 0.106 & 0.855 & 0.039 \\ 0.087 & 0.009 & 0.904 \end{bmatrix} = \begin{bmatrix} 0.589 & 0.401 & 0.01 \\ 0.141 & 0.804 & 0.055 \\ 0.117 & 0.023 & 0.860 \end{bmatrix}$

The share held by each after 3 yr is

$$\begin{bmatrix} 0.26 & 0.6 & 0.14 \end{bmatrix} \begin{bmatrix} 0.589 & 0.401 & 0.01 \\ 0.141 & 0.804 & 0.055 \\ 0.117 & 0.023 & 0.860 \end{bmatrix} = \begin{bmatrix} 0.2536 & 0.5902 & 0.1562 \end{bmatrix}.$$

(d) $P^{23} = \begin{bmatrix} 0.825 & 0.175 & 0 \\ 0.060 & 0.919 & 0.021 \\ 0.049 & 0 & 0.951 \end{bmatrix}^{23} \approx \begin{bmatrix} 0.250 & 0.585 & 0.165 \\ 0.247 & 0.565 & 0.189 \\ 0.234 & 0.384 & 0.382 \end{bmatrix}$

The share held by each after 23 yr is

$$\begin{bmatrix} 0.26 & 0.6 & 0.14 \end{bmatrix} \begin{bmatrix} 0.250 & 0.585 & 0.165 \\ 0.247 & 0.565 & 0.189 \\ 0.234 & 0.384 & 0.382 \end{bmatrix} = \begin{bmatrix} 0.2459 & 0.5447 & 0.2095 \end{bmatrix}.$$

34. (a) Let A denote agricultural, U denote urban, and I denote idle. Then the transition matrix P is given by

$$\begin{array}{c} \\ A \\ U \\ I \end{array} \begin{array}{c} \begin{array}{ccc} A & U & I \end{array} \\ \begin{bmatrix} 0.80 & 0.15 & 0.05 \\ 0 & 0.90 & 0.10 \\ 0.10 & 0.20 & 0.70 \end{bmatrix} \end{array}.$$

(b) The initial categories are

$$X_0 = \begin{bmatrix} 0.35 & 0.10 & 0.55 \end{bmatrix}.$$

(c) Multiply by P to obtain the results after 10 yr:

$$X_0P = \begin{bmatrix} 0.335 & 0.2525 & 0.4125 \end{bmatrix}.$$

(d) Multiply again by P to obtain the results after 20 yr:

$$X_0P^2 = \begin{bmatrix} 0.3093 & 0.36 & 0.3308 \end{bmatrix}.$$

(e) The transition matrix for a 20-yr period is

$$P^2 = \begin{bmatrix} 0.645 & 0.265 & 0.09 \\ 0.01 & 0.83 & 0.16 \\ 0.15 & 0.335 & 0.515 \end{bmatrix}.$$

(f) The probability that an idle plot of land is still idle after 20 yr is given by the entry of P^2 in the third row, third column; that is, 0.515.

35. $P = \begin{bmatrix} 0.9216 & 0.0780 & 0.0004 \\ 0.0460 & 0.8959 & 0.0581 \\ 0.0003 & 0.0301 & 0.9696 \end{bmatrix}$

The initial distribution of businesses is given by $A = [2094 \quad 2363 \quad 2378]$.

(a) 1966: After 1 year, the distribution of businesses is

$$AP = [2094 \quad 2363 \quad 2378] \begin{bmatrix} 0.9216 & 0.0780 & 0.0004 \\ 0.0460 & 0.8959 & 0.0581 \\ 0.0003 & 0.0301 & 0.9696 \end{bmatrix} = [2039 \quad 2352 \quad 2444].$$

There will be 2039 small, 2352 medium, and 2444 large businesses.

(b) 1967: After 2 years, the distribution of businesses is

$$[2039\ \ 2352\ \ 2444]P = [2039\ \ 2352\ \ 2444]\begin{bmatrix} 0.9216 & 0.0780 & 0.0004 \\ 0.0460 & 0.8959 & 0.0581 \\ 0.0003 & 0.0301 & 0.9696 \end{bmatrix} = [1988\ \ 2340\ \ 2507].$$

There will be 1988 small, 2340 medium, and 2507 large businesses.

(c) $$P^2 = \begin{bmatrix} 0.9216 & 0.0780 & 0.0004 \\ 0.0460 & 0.8959 & 0.0581 \\ 0.0003 & 0.0301 & 0.9696 \end{bmatrix}\begin{bmatrix} 0.9216 & 0.0780 & 0.004 \\ 0.0460 & 0.8959 & 0.0581 \\ 0.0003 & 0.0301 & 0.9696 \end{bmatrix} = \begin{bmatrix} 0.8529 & 0.1418 & 0.0053 \\ 0.0836 & 0.8080 & 0.1084 \\ 0.0020 & 0.0562 & 0.9419 \end{bmatrix}$$

(d) The probability that a medium business will become a small business after 2 years is 0.0836, or 8.36%.

(e) The probability that a medium business will become a large business after 2 years is 0.1084, or 10.84%.

36. **(a)** If there is no one in line, then after 1 min there will be either 0, 1, or 2 people in line with probabilities $p_{00} = \frac{1}{2}$, $p_{01} = \frac{1}{3}$, and $p_{02} = \frac{1}{6}$. If there is one person in line, then that person will be served and either 0, 1, or 2 new people will join the line, with probabilities $p_{10} = \frac{1}{2}$, $p_{11} = \frac{1}{3}$, and $p_{12} = \frac{1}{6}$. If there are two people in line, then one of them will be served and either 0 or 1 new person will join the line, with probabilities $p_{21} = \frac{1}{2}$ and $p_{22} = \frac{1}{2}$; it is impossible for both people in line to be served, so $p_{20} = 0$. Therefore, the transition matrix is

$$A = \begin{bmatrix} \frac{1}{2} & \frac{1}{3} & \frac{1}{6} \\ \frac{1}{2} & \frac{1}{3} & \frac{1}{6} \\ 0 & \frac{1}{2} & \frac{1}{2} \end{bmatrix}.$$

(b) The transition matrix for a two-minute period is

$$A^2 = \begin{bmatrix} \frac{1}{2} & \frac{1}{3} & \frac{1}{6} \\ \frac{1}{2} & \frac{1}{3} & \frac{1}{6} \\ 0 & \frac{1}{2} & \frac{1}{2} \end{bmatrix}\begin{bmatrix} \frac{1}{2} & \frac{1}{3} & \frac{1}{6} \\ \frac{1}{2} & \frac{1}{3} & \frac{1}{6} \\ 0 & \frac{1}{2} & \frac{1}{2} \end{bmatrix} = \begin{bmatrix} \frac{5}{12} & \frac{13}{36} & \frac{2}{9} \\ \frac{5}{12} & \frac{13}{36} & \frac{2}{9} \\ \frac{1}{4} & \frac{5}{12} & \frac{1}{3} \end{bmatrix}.$$

(c) The probability that a queue with no one in line has two people in line 2 min later is $\frac{2}{9}$, since that is the entry in row 1, column 3 of A^2.

37. **(a)** Since the transition matrix

$$P = \begin{bmatrix} \frac{5}{7} & \frac{2}{7} & 0 & 0 \\ 0 & \frac{1}{2} & \frac{1}{3} & \frac{1}{6} \\ 0 & 0 & \frac{1}{2} & \frac{1}{2} \\ 0 & 0 & \frac{1}{4} & \frac{3}{4} \end{bmatrix}$$

describes the proportional change of rabbits among various immune response classifications from one week to the next, we need to consider the entry in the first row, first column of P^5. Because P has zero entries in rows two through four of column one, the proportion of the rabbits in group 1 that were still in group 1 five weeks later was $\frac{5^5}{7^5} \approx 0.1859$.

(b) Find the product X_0P^4, where $X_0 = [9\ \ 4\ \ 0\ \ 0]$.

$X_0P^4 = [2.34\ \ 2.62\ \ 3.47\ \ 4.56]$, where the entries are approximate. Therefore, after 4 weeks there are approximately 2.34 rabbits in group 1, 2.62 rabbits in group 2, 3.47 in group 3, and 4.56 in group 4.

(c) Using a graphing calculator, when P is raised to a larger and larger power, the entries in the first row, first two columns, and the entries in the second row, first two columns are either zero or positive numbers that are getting smaller—that is, they are approaching zero. This leads to the conclusion that the long-range probability of rabbits in group 1 or 2 staying in group 1 or 2 is zero.

38. (a)

$$\begin{array}{c} \\ \text{Single} \\ \text{Multiple} \end{array} \begin{array}{c} \begin{array}{cc} \text{Single} & \text{Multiple} \end{array} \\ \begin{bmatrix} 0.90 & 0.10 \\ 0.05 & 0.95 \end{bmatrix} \end{array}$$

(b) $\begin{bmatrix} 0.75 & 0.25 \end{bmatrix}$

(c) $\begin{bmatrix} 0.75 & 0.25 \end{bmatrix} \begin{bmatrix} 0.90 & 0.10 \\ 0.05 & 0.95 \end{bmatrix} = \begin{bmatrix} 0.688 & 0.313 \end{bmatrix}$

After 5 yr, 68.8% can be expected to live in single-family dwellings and 31.3% in multiple-family dwellings.

(d) $P^2 = \begin{bmatrix} 0.90 & 0.10 \\ 0.05 & 0.95 \end{bmatrix} \begin{bmatrix} 0.90 & 0.10 \\ 0.05 & 0.95 \end{bmatrix} = \begin{bmatrix} 0.815 & 0.185 \\ 0.0925 & 0.9075 \end{bmatrix}$

$$\begin{bmatrix} 0.75 & 0.25 \end{bmatrix} \begin{bmatrix} 0.815 & 0.185 \\ 0.0925 & 0.9075 \end{bmatrix} = \begin{bmatrix} 0.634 & 0.366 \end{bmatrix}$$

After 10 yr, 63.4% can be expected to live in single-family dwellings and 36.6% in multiple-family dwellings.

(e) The transition matrix for a 10-yr period is given by

$$P^2 = \begin{bmatrix} 0.815 & 0.185 \\ 0.0925 & 0.9075 \end{bmatrix}.$$

(f) The probability that someone living in a single family dwelling is still doing so 10 yr later is given by the entry of P^2 in the first row, first column; that is, 0.815.

39. $P = \begin{bmatrix} 0.71 & 0.19 & 0.03 & 0.07 & 0.00 \\ 0.52 & 0.31 & 0.04 & 0.13 & 0.00 \\ 0.40 & 0.16 & 0.22 & 0.22 & 0.00 \\ 0.34 & 0.19 & 0.09 & 0.37 & 0.01 \\ 0.21 & 0.25 & 0.13 & 0.37 & 0.04 \end{bmatrix}$

The initial probability vector is $X_0 = \begin{bmatrix} 0.2 & 0.2 & 0.2 & 0.2 & 0.2 \end{bmatrix}$.

(a) After 1 year,

$$X_0P = \begin{bmatrix} 0.2 & 0.2 & 0.2 & 0.2 & 0.2 \end{bmatrix} \begin{bmatrix} 0.71 & 0.19 & 0.03 & 0.07 & 0.00 \\ 0.52 & 0.31 & 0.04 & 0.13 & 0.00 \\ 0.40 & 0.16 & 0.22 & 0.22 & 0.00 \\ 0.34 & 0.19 & 0.09 & 0.37 & 0.01 \\ 0.21 & 0.25 & 0.13 & 0.37 & 0.04 \end{bmatrix}$$

$$= \begin{bmatrix} 0.436 & 0.220 & 0.102 & 0.232 & 0.010 \end{bmatrix}$$

The percentage of the population that can be expected in each type of housing after one year are: 43.6% in type I, 22% in type II, 10.2% in type III, 23.2% in type IV, and 1% in type V.

(b) After 2 years,

$$\begin{bmatrix} 0.436 & 0.220 & 0.102 & 0.232 & 0.010 \end{bmatrix} P$$

$$= \begin{bmatrix} 0.436 & 0.220 & 0.102 & 0.232 & 0.010 \end{bmatrix} \begin{bmatrix} 0.71 & 0.19 & 0.03 & 0.07 & 0.00 \\ 0.52 & 0.31 & 0.04 & 0.13 & 0.00 \\ 0.40 & 0.16 & 0.22 & 0.22 & 0.00 \\ 0.34 & 0.19 & 0.09 & 0.37 & 0.01 \\ 0.21 & 0.25 & 0.13 & 0.37 & 0.04 \end{bmatrix}$$

$$\approx \begin{bmatrix} 0.5457 & 0.2139 & 0.0665 & 0.1711 & 0.0027 \end{bmatrix}.$$

The percentage of the population that can be expected in each type of housing after two years are: 54.57% in type I, 21.39% in type II, 6.65% in type III, 17.11% in type IV, and 0.27% in type V.

(c) $$P^2 = \begin{bmatrix} 0.71 & 0.19 & 0.03 & 0.07 & 0.00 \\ 0.52 & 0.31 & 0.04 & 0.13 & 0.00 \\ 0.40 & 0.16 & 0.22 & 0.22 & 0.00 \\ 0.34 & 0.19 & 0.09 & 0.37 & 0.01 \\ 0.21 & 0.25 & 0.13 & 0.37 & 0.04 \end{bmatrix} \begin{bmatrix} 0.71 & 0.19 & 0.03 & 0.07 & 0.00 \\ 0.52 & 0.31 & 0.04 & 0.13 & 0.00 \\ 0.40 & 0.16 & 0.22 & 0.22 & 0.00 \\ 0.34 & 0.19 & 0.09 & 0.37 & 0.01 \\ 0.21 & 0.25 & 0.13 & 0.37 & 0.04 \end{bmatrix}$$

$$= \begin{bmatrix} 0.6387 & 0.2119 & 0.0418 & 0.1069 & 0.0007 \\ 0.5906 & 0.2260 & 0.0485 & 0.1336 & 0.0013 \\ 0.5300 & 0.2026 & 0.0866 & 0.1786 & 0.0022 \\ 0.5041 & 0.2107 & 0.0722 & 0.2089 & 0.0041 \\ 0.4653 & 0.2185 & 0.0834 & 0.2275 & 0.0053 \end{bmatrix}$$

(d) The percent of those living in a commercial area (type V) that can be expected to be living in a middle class family household (type I) after 2 years is 0.4653, or 46.53%.

(e) The percent of those living in a commercial area (type V) that can be expected to be living in an unsound rented multi-family dwelling (type IV) after 2 years is 0.2275, or 22.75%.

40. **(a)** Use L for liberal, C for conservative, and I for independent. The transition matrix P is given by

$$\begin{array}{c} \\ \text{L} \\ \text{C} \\ \text{I} \end{array} \begin{array}{c} \begin{array}{ccc} \text{L} & \text{C} & \text{I} \end{array} \\ \begin{bmatrix} 0.80 & 0.15 & 0.05 \\ 0.20 & 0.70 & 0.10 \\ 0.20 & 0.20 & 0.60 \end{bmatrix} \end{array}.$$

(b) The initial distribution is given by

$$X_0 = \begin{bmatrix} 0.40 & 0.45 & 0.15 \end{bmatrix}.$$

(c) One month later in July,

$$X_0 P = \begin{bmatrix} 0.44 & 0.405 & 0.155 \end{bmatrix},$$

so there will be 44% liberals, 40.5% conservatives, and 15.5% independents.

(d) Two months later in August,

$$X_0 P^2 = (X_0 P) P = \begin{bmatrix} 0.464 & 0.3805 & 0.1555 \end{bmatrix},$$

so there will be 46.4% liberals, 38.05% conservatives, and 15.55% independents.

(e) Three months later in September,

$$X_0P^3 = (X_0P^2)P = \begin{bmatrix} 0.4784 & 0.36705 & 0.15455 \end{bmatrix},$$

so there will be 47.84% liberals, 36.705% conservatives, and 15.455% independents.

(f) Four months later in October,

$$X_0P^4 = (X_0P^3)P = \begin{bmatrix} 0.48704 & 0.359605 & 0.153355 \end{bmatrix},$$

so there will be 48.704% liberals, 35.9605% conservatives, and 15.3355% independents.

(g) The transition matrix for a two-month period is given by

$$P^2 = \begin{bmatrix} 0.80 & 0.15 & 0.05 \\ 0.20 & 0.70 & 0.10 \\ 0.20 & 0.20 & 0.60 \end{bmatrix} \begin{bmatrix} 0.80 & 0.15 & 0.05 \\ 0.20 & 0.70 & 0.10 \\ 0.20 & 0.20 & 0.60 \end{bmatrix} = \begin{bmatrix} 0.68 & 0.235 & 0.085 \\ 0.32 & 0.54 & 0.14 \\ 0.32 & 0.29 & 0.39 \end{bmatrix}$$

41. (a) $\begin{bmatrix} 0.443 & 0.364 & 0.193 \\ 0.277 & 0.436 & 0.287 \\ 0.266 & 0.304 & 0.430 \end{bmatrix} \begin{bmatrix} 0.443 & 0.364 & 0.193 \\ 0.277 & 0.436 & 0.287 \\ 0.266 & 0.304 & 0.430 \end{bmatrix} = \begin{bmatrix} 0.3484 & 0.3786 & 0.2730 \\ 0.3198 & 0.3782 & 0.3020 \\ 0.3164 & 0.3601 & 0.3235 \end{bmatrix}$

(b) The desired probability is found in row 1, column 1. The probability that if England won the last game, England will win the game after the next one is 0.3484.

(c) The desired probability is found in row 2, column 1. The probability that if Australia won the last game, England will win the game after the next one is 0.3198.

10.2 Regular Markov Chains

1. Let $A = \begin{bmatrix} 0.2 & 0.8 \\ 0.9 & 0.1 \end{bmatrix}$.

A is a regular transition matrix since $A^1 = A$ contains all positive entries.

2. Let $A = \begin{bmatrix} 0.28 & 0.72 \\ 0.47 & 0.53 \end{bmatrix}$.

A is a regular transition matrix since $A^1 = A$ contains all positive entries.

3. Let $B = \begin{bmatrix} 1 & 0 \\ 0.65 & 0.35 \end{bmatrix}$.

$$B^2 = \begin{bmatrix} 1 & 0 \\ 0.65 & 0.35 \end{bmatrix} \begin{bmatrix} 1 & 0 \\ 0.65 & 0.35 \end{bmatrix} = \begin{bmatrix} 1 & 0 \\ 0.88 & 0.12 \end{bmatrix}$$

B is not regular since any power of B will have $\begin{bmatrix} 1 & 0 \end{bmatrix}$ as its first row and thus cannot have all positive entries.

4. Let $B = \begin{bmatrix} 0.55 & 0.45 \\ 0 & 1 \end{bmatrix}$.

$$B^2 = \begin{bmatrix} 0.30250 & 0.69750 \\ 0 & 1 \end{bmatrix}$$

$$B^3 = \begin{bmatrix} 0.16638 & 0.83363 \\ 0 & 1 \end{bmatrix}$$

B is not regular since any power of B will have $\begin{bmatrix} 0 & 1 \end{bmatrix}$ as its second row and thus cannot have all positive entries.

5. Let $P = \begin{bmatrix} 0 & 1 & 0 \\ 0.4 & 0.2 & 0.4 \\ 1 & 0 & 0 \end{bmatrix}$.

$$P^2 = \begin{bmatrix} 0 & 1 & 0 \\ 0.4 & 0.2 & 0.4 \\ 1 & 0 & 0 \end{bmatrix} \begin{bmatrix} 0 & 1 & 0 \\ 0.4 & 0.2 & 0.4 \\ 1 & 0 & 0 \end{bmatrix} = \begin{bmatrix} 0.4 & 0.2 & 0.4 \\ 0.48 & 0.44 & 0.08 \\ 0 & 1 & 0 \end{bmatrix}$$

$$P^3 = \begin{bmatrix} 0 & 1 & 0 \\ 0.4 & 0.2 & 0.4 \\ 1 & 0 & 0 \end{bmatrix} \begin{bmatrix} 0.4 & 0.2 & 0.4 \\ 0.48 & 0.44 & 0.08 \\ 0 & 1 & 0 \end{bmatrix} = \begin{bmatrix} 0.48 & 0.44 & 0.08 \\ 0.256 & 0.568 & 0.176 \\ 0.4 & 0.2 & 0.4 \end{bmatrix}$$

P is a regular transition matrix since P^3 contains all positive entries.

6. Let $C = \begin{bmatrix} 0.3 & 0.5 & 0.2 \\ 1 & 0 & 0 \\ 0.5 & 0.1 & 0.4 \end{bmatrix}$.

$$C^2 = \begin{bmatrix} 0.69 & 0.17 & 0.14 \\ 0.3 & 0.5 & 0.2 \\ 0.45 & 0.29 & 0.26 \end{bmatrix}$$

C is a regular transition matrix since C^2 contains all positive entries.

7. Let $P = \begin{bmatrix} \frac{1}{4} & \frac{3}{4} \\ \frac{1}{2} & \frac{1}{2} \end{bmatrix}$, and let V be the probability vector $\begin{bmatrix} v_1 & v_2 \end{bmatrix}$. We want to find V such that

$$VP = V,$$

or $\begin{bmatrix} v_1 & v_2 \end{bmatrix} \begin{bmatrix} \frac{1}{4} & \frac{3}{4} \\ \frac{1}{2} & \frac{1}{2} \end{bmatrix} = \begin{bmatrix} v_1 & v_2 \end{bmatrix}$.

Use matrix multiplication on the left to obtain

$\begin{bmatrix} \frac{1}{4}v_1 + \frac{1}{2}v_2 & \frac{3}{4}v_1 + \frac{1}{2}v_2 \end{bmatrix} = \begin{bmatrix} v_1 & v_2 \end{bmatrix}$.

Set corresponding entries from the two matrices equal to get

$$\frac{1}{4}v_1 + \frac{1}{2}v_2 = v_1$$
$$\frac{3}{4}v_1 + \frac{1}{2}v_2 = v_2.$$

Multiply both equations by 4 to eliminate fractions.

$$v_1 + 2v_2 = 4v_1$$
$$3v_1 + 2v_2 = 4v_2$$

Simplify both equations.

$$-3v_1 + 2v_2 = 0$$
$$3v_1 - 2v_2 = 0$$

This is a dependent system. To find the values of v_1 and v_2, an additional equation is needed. Since $V = \begin{bmatrix} v_1 & v_2 \end{bmatrix}$ is a probability vector,

$$v_1 + v_2 = 1.$$

To find v_1 and v_2, solve the system

$$-3v_1 + 2v_2 = 0 \quad (1)$$
$$v_1 + v_2 = 1. \quad (2)$$

From equation (2), $v_1 = 1 - v_2$. Substitute $1 - v_2$ for v_1 in equation (1) to obtain

$$-3(1 - v_2) + 2v_2 = 0$$
$$-3 + 3v_2 + 2v_2 = 0$$
$$-3 + 5v_2 = 0$$
$$v_2 = \frac{3}{5}.$$

Since $v_1 = 1 - v_2$, $v_1 = \frac{2}{5}$, and the equilibrium vector is

$$V = \begin{bmatrix} \frac{2}{5} & \frac{3}{5} \end{bmatrix}.$$

8. Let $P = \begin{bmatrix} \frac{2}{3} & \frac{1}{3} \\ \frac{1}{8} & \frac{7}{8} \end{bmatrix}$, and let V be the probability vector $\begin{bmatrix} v_1 & v_2 \end{bmatrix}$. We want to find V such that

$$VP = V,$$

or $\begin{bmatrix} v_1 & v_2 \end{bmatrix} \begin{bmatrix} \frac{2}{3} & \frac{1}{3} \\ \frac{1}{8} & \frac{7}{8} \end{bmatrix} = \begin{bmatrix} v_1 & v_2 \end{bmatrix}$.

Use matrix multiplication on the left.

$$\begin{bmatrix} \frac{2}{3}v_1 + \frac{1}{8}v_2 & \frac{1}{3}v_1 + \frac{7}{8}v_2 \end{bmatrix} = \begin{bmatrix} v_1 & v_2 \end{bmatrix}$$

Set corresponding entries from the two matrices equal to get

$$\frac{2}{3}v_1 + \frac{1}{8}v_2 = v_1$$
$$\frac{1}{3}v_1 + \frac{7}{8}v_2 = v_2.$$

Multiply both equations by 24 to eliminate fractions.

$$16v_1 + 3v_2 = 24v_1$$
$$8v_1 + 21v_2 = 24v_2$$

Simplify both equations.

$$-8v_1 + 3v_2 = 0$$
$$8v_1 - 3v_2 = 0$$

These equations are dependent. To find the values of v_1 and v_2, an additional equation is needed. Since $V = \begin{bmatrix} v_1 & v_2 \end{bmatrix}$ is a probability vector

$$v_1 + v_2 = 1.$$

To find v_1 and v_2, solve the system

$$\begin{aligned} -8v_1 + 3v_2 &= 0 \quad (1) \\ v_1 + v_2 &= 1. \quad (2) \end{aligned}$$

From equation (2), $v_1 = 1 - v_2$. Substitute $1 - v_2$ for v_1 in equation (1) to get

$$\begin{aligned} -8(1 - v_2) + 3v_2 &= 0 \\ -8 + 8v_2 + 3v_2 &= 0 \\ 11v_2 &= 8 \\ v_2 &= \tfrac{8}{11} \end{aligned}$$

and $$v_1 = 1 - v_2 = \tfrac{3}{11}.$$

The equilibrium vector is

$$\begin{bmatrix} \frac{3}{11} & \frac{8}{11} \end{bmatrix}.$$

9. Let $P = \begin{bmatrix} 0.4 & 0.6 \\ 0.3 & 0.7 \end{bmatrix}$, and let V be the probability vector $\begin{bmatrix} v_1 & v_2 \end{bmatrix}$. We want to find V such that

$$VP = V$$

$$\begin{bmatrix} v_1 & v_2 \end{bmatrix} \begin{bmatrix} 0.4 & 0.6 \\ 0.3 & 0.7 \end{bmatrix} = \begin{bmatrix} v_1 & v_2 \end{bmatrix}.$$

By matrix multiplication and equality of matrices,

$$\begin{aligned} 0.4v_1 + 0.3v_2 &= v_1 \\ 0.6v_1 + 0.7v_2 &= v_2. \end{aligned}$$

Simplify the equations to get the dependent system

$$\begin{aligned} -0.6v_1 + 0.3v_2 &= 0 \\ 0.6v_1 - 0.3v_2 &= 0. \end{aligned}$$

Since V is a probability vector,

$$v_1 + v_2 = 1.$$

To find v_1 and v_2, solve the system

$$\begin{aligned} 0.6v_1 - 0.3v_2 &= 0 \\ v_1 + v_2 &= 1 \end{aligned}$$

by the substitution method. Observe that $v_2 = 1 - v_1$.

$$\begin{aligned} 0.6v_1 - 0.3(1 - v_1) &= 0 \\ 0.9v_1 - 0.3 &= 0 \\ v_1 &= \frac{0.3}{0.9} = \frac{1}{3} \\ v_2 &= 1 - \frac{1}{3} = \frac{2}{3} \end{aligned}$$

The equilibrium vector is $\begin{bmatrix} \frac{1}{3} & \frac{2}{3} \end{bmatrix}$.

10. Let $P = \begin{bmatrix} 0.1 & 0.9 \\ 0.8 & 0.2 \end{bmatrix}$, and let V be the probability vector $\begin{bmatrix} v_1 & v_2 \end{bmatrix}$. We want to find V such that

$$VP = V$$

$$\begin{bmatrix} v_1 & v_2 \end{bmatrix} \begin{bmatrix} 0.1 & 0.9 \\ 0.8 & 0.2 \end{bmatrix} = \begin{bmatrix} v_1 & v_2 \end{bmatrix}.$$

By matrix multiplication and equality of matrices,

$$\begin{aligned} 0.1v_1 + 0.8v_2 &= v_1 \\ 0.9v_1 + 0.2v_2 &= v_2. \end{aligned}$$

Simplify these equations to get the dependent system

$$\begin{aligned} -0.9v_1 + 0.8v_2 &= 0 \\ 0.9v_1 - 0.8v_2 &= 0. \end{aligned}$$

Since V is a probability vector,

$$v_1 + v_2 = 1.$$

To find v_1 and v_2, solve the system

$$\begin{aligned} 0.9v_1 - 0.8v_2 &= 0 \\ v_1 + v_2 &= 1. \end{aligned}$$

by the substitution method. Observe that $v_2 = 1 - v_1$.

$$\begin{aligned} 0.9v_1 - 0.8(1 - v_1) &= 0 \\ 1.7v_1 - 0.8 &= 0 \\ v_1 &= \frac{0.8}{1.7} = \frac{8}{17} \\ v_2 &= 1 - \frac{8}{17} = \frac{9}{17} \end{aligned}$$

The equilibrium vector is

$$\begin{bmatrix} \frac{8}{17} & \frac{9}{17} \end{bmatrix}.$$

11. Let V be the probability vector $\begin{bmatrix} v_1 & v_2 & v_3 \end{bmatrix}$.

$$VP = V$$

$$\begin{bmatrix} v_1 & v_2 & v_3 \end{bmatrix} \begin{bmatrix} 0.1 & 0.1 & 0.8 \\ 0.4 & 0.3 & 0.3 \\ 0.1 & 0.2 & 0.7 \end{bmatrix} = \begin{bmatrix} v_1 & v_2 & v_3 \end{bmatrix}$$

$$\begin{aligned} 0.1v_1 + 0.4v_2 + 0.1v_3 &= v_1 \\ 0.1v_1 + 0.3v_2 + 0.2v_3 &= v_2 \\ 0.8v_1 + 0.3v_2 + 0.7v_3 &= v_3 \end{aligned}$$

Simplify the equations to get the dependent system

$$\begin{aligned} -0.9v_1 + 0.4v_2 + 0.1v_3 &= 0 \\ 0.1v_1 - 0.7v_2 + 0.2v_3 &= 0 \\ 0.8v_1 + 0.3v_2 - 0.3v_3 &= 0. \end{aligned}$$

Since V is a probability vector,

$$v_1 + v_2 + v_3 = 1.$$

Solving the above system of four equations using the Gauss-Jordan method, we obtain

$$v_1 = \frac{5}{31}, v_2 = \frac{19}{93}, v_3 = \frac{59}{93}.$$

The equilibrium vector is $\begin{bmatrix} \frac{5}{31} & \frac{19}{93} & \frac{59}{93} \end{bmatrix}$.

12. Let V be the probability vector $\begin{bmatrix} v_1 & v_2 & v_3 \end{bmatrix}$.

$$VP = V$$

$$\begin{bmatrix} v_1 & v_2 & v_3 \end{bmatrix} \begin{bmatrix} 0.5 & 0.2 & 0.3 \\ 0.1 & 0.4 & 0.5 \\ 0.3 & 0.1 & 0.6 \end{bmatrix} = \begin{bmatrix} v_1 & v_2 & v_3 \end{bmatrix}$$

$$\begin{aligned} 0.5v_1 + 0.1v_2 + 0.3v_3 &= v_1 \\ 0.2v_1 + 0.4v_2 + 0.1v_3 &= v_2 \\ 0.3v_1 + 0.5v_2 + 0.6v_3 &= v_3 \end{aligned}$$

Simplify the equations to get the dependent system

$$\begin{aligned} -0.5v_1 + 0.1v_2 + 0.3v_3 &= 0 \\ 0.2v_1 - 0.6v_2 + 0.1v_3 &= 0 \\ 0.3v_1 + 0.5v_2 - 0.4v_3 &= 0. \end{aligned}$$

Since V is a probability vector,

$$v_1 + v_2 + v_3 = 1.$$

Solving the above system of four equations using the Gauss-Jordan method, we obtain

$$v_1 = \frac{19}{58}, v_2 = \frac{11}{58}, v_3 = \frac{14}{29}.$$

The equilibrium vector is $\begin{bmatrix} \frac{19}{58} & \frac{11}{58} & \frac{14}{29} \end{bmatrix}$.

13. Let V be the probability vector $\begin{bmatrix} v_1 & v_2 & v_3 \end{bmatrix}$.

$$\begin{bmatrix} v_1 & v_2 & v_3 \end{bmatrix} \begin{bmatrix} 0.25 & 0.35 & 0.4 \\ 0.1 & 0.3 & 0.6 \\ 0.55 & 0.4 & 0.05 \end{bmatrix} = \begin{bmatrix} v_1 & v_2 & v_3 \end{bmatrix}$$

$$\begin{aligned} 0.25v_1 + 0.1v_2 + 0.55v_3 &= v_1 \\ 0.35v_1 + 0.3v_2 + 0.4v_3 &= v_2 \\ 0.4v_1 + 0.6v_2 + 0.05v_3 &= v_3 \end{aligned}$$

Simplify these equations to get the dependent system

$$\begin{aligned} -0.75v_1 + 0.1v_2 + 0.55v_3 &= 0 \\ 0.35v_1 - 0.7v_2 + 0.4v_3 &= 0 \\ 0.4v_1 + 0.6v_2 - 0.95v_3 &= 0. \end{aligned}$$

Since V is a probability vector,

$$v_1 + v_2 + v_3 = 1.$$

Solving this system we obtain

$$v_1 = \frac{170}{563},\ v_2 = \frac{197}{563},\ v_3 = \frac{196}{563}.$$

Thus, the equilibrium vector is

$$\begin{bmatrix} \frac{170}{563} & \frac{197}{563} & \frac{196}{563} \end{bmatrix}.$$

14. Let $P = \begin{bmatrix} 0.16 & 0.28 & 0.56 \\ 0.43 & 0.12 & 0.45 \\ 0.86 & 0.05 & 0.09 \end{bmatrix}$, and

let V be the probability vector $\begin{bmatrix} v_1 & v_2 & v_3 \end{bmatrix}$.

$$\begin{bmatrix} v_1 & v_2 & v_3 \end{bmatrix} \begin{bmatrix} 0.16 & 0.28 & 0.56 \\ 0.43 & 0.12 & 0.45 \\ 0.86 & 0.05 & 0.09 \end{bmatrix} = \begin{bmatrix} v_1 & v_2 & v_3 \end{bmatrix}$$

$$\begin{aligned} 0.16v_1 + 0.43v_2 + 0.86v_3 &= v_1 \\ 0.28v_1 + 0.12v_2 + 0.05v_3 &= v_2 \\ 0.56v_1 + 0.45v_2 + 0.09v_3 &= v_3 \end{aligned}$$

Simplify these equations and also use the equation $v_1 + v_2 + v_3 = 1$ to get the system

$$\begin{aligned} v_1 + v_2 + v_3 &= 1 \\ -0.84v_1 + 0.43v_2 + 0.86v_3 &= 0 \\ 0.28v_1 - 0.88v_2 + 0.05v_3 &= 0 \\ 0.56v_1 + 0.45v_2 - 0.91v_3 &= 0. \end{aligned}$$

Solve this system by the Gauss-Jordan method to obtain $v_1 = \frac{7783}{16{,}799}$, $v_2 = \frac{2828}{16{,}799}$, and $v_3 = \frac{6188}{16{,}799}$. The equilibrium vector is

$$\begin{bmatrix} \frac{7783}{16{,}799} & \frac{2828}{16{,}799} & \frac{6188}{16{,}799} \end{bmatrix}.$$

15. $\begin{bmatrix} v_1 & v_2 & v_3 \end{bmatrix}\begin{bmatrix} 0.75 & 0.20 & 0.05 \\ 0 & 0.70 & 0.30 \\ 0 & 0 & 1 \end{bmatrix} = \begin{bmatrix} v_1 & v_2 & v_3 \end{bmatrix}.$

$$\begin{aligned} 0.75v_1 \qquad\qquad &= v_1 \\ 0.20v_1 + 0.70v_2 \quad &= v_2 \\ 0.05v_1 + 0.30v_2 + v_3 &= v_3. \end{aligned}$$

Simplify the equations to get the dependent system

$$\begin{aligned} -0.25v_1 \qquad\quad &= 0 \\ 0.20v_1 - 0.30v_2 &= 0 \\ 0.05v_1 + 0.30v_2 &= 0. \end{aligned}$$

We also have

$$v_1 + v_2 + v_3 = 1.$$

Solving the system of four equations, we obtain

$$v_1 = 0, v_2 = 0, v_3 = 1.$$

The equilibrium vector is $[0 \;\; 0 \;\; 1]$.

16. Let $P = \begin{bmatrix} 0.75 & 0.20 & 0.05 \\ 0.10 & 0.70 & 0.20 \\ 0.10 & 0.30 & 0.60 \end{bmatrix}$ and let V be the probability vector $\begin{bmatrix} v_1 & v_2 & v_3 \end{bmatrix}$.

$$VP = V$$

$$\begin{bmatrix} v_1 & v_2 & v_3 \end{bmatrix}\begin{bmatrix} 0.75 & 0.20 & 0.05 \\ 0.10 & 0.70 & 0.20 \\ 0.10 & 0.30 & 0.60 \end{bmatrix} = \begin{bmatrix} v_1 & v_2 & v_3 \end{bmatrix}$$

$$\begin{aligned} 0.75v_1 + 0.10v_2 + 0.10v_3 &= v_1 \\ 0.20v_1 + 0.70v_2 + 0.30v_3 &= v_2 \\ 0.05v_1 + 0.20v_2 + 0.60v_3 &= v_3 \end{aligned}$$

Simplify the equations and use the equation $v_1 + v_2 + v_3 = 1$ to get the system

$$\begin{aligned} -0.25v_1 + 0.10v_2 + 0.10v_3 &= 0 \\ 0.20v_1 - 0.30v_2 + 0.30v_3 &= 0 \\ 0.05v_1 + 0.20v \quad - 0.40v_3 &= 0 \\ v_1 + \quad v_2 + \quad v_3 &= 0 \end{aligned}$$

Solve the system using the Gauss-Jordan method to obtain

$$v_1 = \frac{2}{7}, v_2 = \frac{19}{42}, v_3 = \frac{11}{42}.$$

The equilibrium vector is $\begin{bmatrix} \frac{2}{7} & \frac{19}{42} & \frac{11}{42} \end{bmatrix}$.

17. $\begin{bmatrix} v_1 & v_2 & v_3 \end{bmatrix}\begin{bmatrix} 0.825 & 0.175 & 0 \\ 0.060 & 0.919 & 0.021 \\ 0.049 & 0 & 0.951 \end{bmatrix}$

$= \begin{bmatrix} v_1 & v_2 & v_3 \end{bmatrix}$

$$\begin{aligned} 0.825v_1 + 0.060v_2 + 0.049v_3 &= v_1 \\ 0.175v_1 + 0.919v_2 \qquad\qquad &= v_2 \\ 0.021v_2 + 0.951v_3 &= v_3 \end{aligned}$$

Also, $v_1 + v_2 + v_3 = 1$.
Solving this system, we obtain

$$v_1 = \tfrac{81}{331},\ v_2 = \tfrac{175}{331},\ v_3 = \tfrac{75}{331}.$$

The equilibrium vector is

$$\begin{bmatrix} \frac{81}{331} & \frac{175}{331} & \frac{75}{331} \end{bmatrix}.$$

18. $\begin{bmatrix} v_1 & v_2 & v_3 \end{bmatrix}\begin{bmatrix} 0.80 & 0.15 & 0.05 \\ 0 & 0.90 & 0.10 \\ 0.10 & 0.20 & 0.70 \end{bmatrix} = \begin{bmatrix} v_1 & v_2 & v_3 \end{bmatrix}$

$$\begin{aligned} 0.80v_1 \qquad\qquad + 0.10v_3 &= v_1 \\ 0.15v_1 + 0.90v_2 + 0.20v_3 &= v_2 \\ 0.05v_1 + 0.10v_2 + 0.70v_3 &= v_3 \end{aligned}$$

Simplify these equations and also use the equation $v_1 + v_2 + v_3 = 1$ to get the system

$$\begin{aligned} v_1 + \quad v_2 + \quad v_3 &= 1 \\ -0.20v_1 \qquad\quad + 0.10v_3 &= 0 \\ 0.15v_1 - 0.10v_2 + 0.20v_3 &= 0 \\ 0.05v_1 + 0.10v_20 - .30v_3 &= 0. \end{aligned}$$

Solving this system by the Gauss-Jordan method, we obtain $v_1 = \frac{2}{17}$, $v_2 = \frac{11}{17}$, and $v_3 = \frac{4}{17}$. The equilibrium vector is

$$\begin{bmatrix} \frac{2}{17} & \frac{11}{17} & \frac{4}{17} \end{bmatrix}.$$

19. $\begin{bmatrix} v_1 & v_2 & v_3 \end{bmatrix}\begin{bmatrix} 0.80 & 0.15 & 0.05 \\ 0.20 & 0.70 & 0.10 \\ 0.20 & 0.20 & 0.60 \end{bmatrix}$

$= \begin{bmatrix} v_1 & v_2 & v_3 \end{bmatrix}$

$$\begin{aligned} 0.80v_1 + 0.20v_2 + 0.20v_3 &= v_1 \\ 0.15v_1 + 0.70v_2 + 0.20v_3 &= v_2 \\ 0.05v_1 + 0.10v_2 + 0.60v_3 &= v_3 \end{aligned}$$

Solving this system, we obtain

$$v_1 = \tfrac{1}{2},\ v_2 = \tfrac{7}{20},\ v_3 = \tfrac{3}{20}.$$

The equilibrium vector is

$$\begin{bmatrix} \frac{1}{2} & \frac{7}{20} & \frac{3}{20} \end{bmatrix}.$$

20. $\begin{bmatrix} v_1 & v_2 \end{bmatrix} \begin{bmatrix} 0.90 & 0.10 \\ 0.05 & 0.95 \end{bmatrix} = \begin{bmatrix} v_1 & v_2 \end{bmatrix}$

$$\begin{aligned} 0.90v_1 + 0.05v_2 &= v_1 \\ 0.10v_1 + 0.95v_2 &= v_2 \end{aligned}$$

Simplify these equations to obtain the system

$$\begin{aligned} -0.10v_1 + 0.05v_2 &= 0 \\ 0.10v_1 - 0.05v_2 &= 0. \end{aligned}$$

These equations are dependent. Use the substitution method to solve the system

$$\begin{aligned} -0.10v_1 + 0.05v_2 &= 0 \\ v_1 + \quad v_2 &= 1, \end{aligned}$$

obtaining $v_1 = \frac{1}{3}$ and $v_2 = \frac{2}{3}$. The equilibrium vector is

$$\begin{bmatrix} \frac{1}{3} & \frac{2}{3} \end{bmatrix}.$$

21. Let V be the probability vector $\begin{bmatrix} x_1 & x_2 \end{bmatrix}$. We want to find V such that

$$V \begin{bmatrix} p & 1-p \\ 1-q & q \end{bmatrix} = V.$$

The system of equations is

$$\begin{aligned} px_1 + (1-q)x_2 &= x_1 \\ (1-p)x_1 + qx_2 &= x_2. \end{aligned}$$

Collecting like terms and simplifying leads to

$$(p-1)x_1 + (1-q)x_2 = 0,$$

so $$x_1 = \frac{1-q}{1-p}x_2.$$

Substituting this into $x_1 + x_2 = 1$, we obtain

$$\frac{1-q}{1-p}x_2 + x_2 = 1$$

or $$\frac{2-p-q}{1-p}x_2 = 1;$$

therefore,

$$x_2 = \frac{1-p}{2-p-q}$$

and $$x_1 = \frac{1-q}{2-p-q},$$

so $$V = \begin{bmatrix} \frac{1-q}{2-p-q} & \frac{1-p}{2-p-q} \end{bmatrix}.$$

Since $0 < p < 1$ and $0 < q < 1$, the matrix is always regular.

23. Let V be the probability vector $\begin{bmatrix} x_1 & x_2 \end{bmatrix}$.

We have $P = \begin{bmatrix} a_{11} & a_{12} \\ a_{21} & a_{22} \end{bmatrix}$,

where $a_{11} + a_{21} = 1$
and $a_{12} + a_{22} = 1$.

The resulting equations are

$$\begin{aligned} a_{11}x_1 + a_{21}x_2 &= x_1 \\ a_{12}x_1 + a_{22}x_2 &= x_2, \end{aligned}$$

which we simplify to

$$\begin{aligned} (a_{11} - 1)x_1 + a_{21}x_2 &= 0 \\ a_{12}x_1 + (a_{22} - 1)x_2 &= 0. \end{aligned}$$

Hence, $x_1 = \dfrac{a_{21}}{1-a_{11}}x_2 = \dfrac{a_{21}}{a_{21}}x_2 = x_2$,

which we substitute into $x_1 + x_2 = 1$, obtaining

$$\begin{aligned} x_2 + x_2 &= 1 \\ 2x_2 &= 1 \\ x_2 &= \tfrac{1}{2} \end{aligned}$$

and, therefore,

$$x_1 = 1 - \tfrac{1}{2} = \tfrac{1}{2}.$$

The equilibrium vector is

$$\begin{bmatrix} \frac{1}{2} & \frac{1}{2} \end{bmatrix}.$$

24. There are an infinite number of solutions to the system $VK = V$. A few examples would be $(0, 0, 0)$, $(5, 7, 11)$, and $(\frac{5}{11}, \frac{7}{11}, 1)$. In fact, any vector of the form $(\frac{5}{11}x_3, \frac{7}{11}x_3, x_3)$ would be a solution to the system.

25. The transition matrix for the given information is

	Works	Doesn't Work
Works	0.9	0.1
Doesn't Work	0.8	0.2

Let V be the probability vector $\begin{bmatrix} v_1 & v_2 \end{bmatrix}$.

$$\begin{bmatrix} v_1 & v_2 \end{bmatrix} \begin{bmatrix} 0.9 & 0.1 \\ 0.8 & 0.2 \end{bmatrix} = \begin{bmatrix} v_1 & v_2 \end{bmatrix}$$

$$\begin{aligned} 0.9v_1 + 0.8v_2 &= v_1 \\ 0.1v_1 + 0.2v_2 &= v_2 \end{aligned}$$

Simplify these equations to get the dependent system

$$-0.1v_1 + 0.8v_2 = 0$$
$$0.1v_1 - 0.8v_2 = 0.$$

Also, $v_1 + v_2 = 1$, so $v_1 = 1 - v_2$.

$$0.1(1 - v_2) - 0.8v_2 = 0$$
$$0.1 - 0.9v_2 = 0$$

$$v_2 = \frac{1}{9},\ v_1 = \frac{8}{9}$$

The equilibrium vector is

$$\begin{bmatrix} \frac{8}{9} & \frac{1}{9} \end{bmatrix}.$$

The long-range probability that the line will work correctly is $\frac{8}{9}$.

26. $\begin{bmatrix} v_1 & v_2 \end{bmatrix} \begin{bmatrix} 0.95 & 0.05 \\ 0.85 & 0.15 \end{bmatrix} = \begin{bmatrix} v_1 & v_2 \end{bmatrix}$

$$0.95v_1 + 0.85v_2 = v_1$$
$$0.05v_1 + 0.15v_2 = v_2$$

Simplify these equations to obtain the system

$$-0.05v_1 + 0.85v_2 = 0$$
$$0.05v_1 - 0.85v_2 = 0.$$

These equations are dependent. Use the substitution method to solve the system

$$-0.05v_1 + 0.85v_2 = 0$$
$$v_1 + v_2 = 1,$$

obtaining $v_1 = \frac{17}{18}$ and $v_2 = \frac{1}{18}$. The long-run probability that the line will work properly is $\frac{17}{18}$.

27. (a) The transition matrix is

	30-yr	15-yr	Adjustable
30-yr	0.444	0.479	0.077
15-yr	0.150	0.802	0.048
Adjustable	0.463	0.367	0.170

To find the long-range trend, use the system

$$v_1 + v_2 + v_3 = 1$$
$$0.444v_1 + 0.150v_2 + 0.463v_3 = v_1$$
$$0.479v_1 + 0.802v_2 + 0.367v_3 = v_2$$
$$0.077v_1 + 0.048v_2 + 0.170v_3 = v_3.$$

Simplify these equations to obtain the system

$$v_1 + v_2 + v_3 = 1$$
$$-0.556v_1 + 0.150v_2 + 0.463v_3 = 0$$
$$0.479v_1 - 0.198v_2 + 0.367v_3 = 0$$
$$0.077v_1 + 0.048v_2 - 0.830v_3 = 0.$$

Solve this system by the Gauss-Jordan method to obtain $v_1 = 0.240$, $v_2 = 0.697$, and $v_3 = 0.063$.

The long range trend is 24.0% 30-yr fixed-rate, 69.7% 15-yr fixed-rate, and 6.3% adjustable.

28. This exercise should be solved by graphing calculator methods. The solution may vary. The answers are as follows.

(a) $\begin{bmatrix} 0.4 & 0.6 \end{bmatrix}$; $\begin{bmatrix} 0.53 & 0.47 \end{bmatrix}$; $\begin{bmatrix} 0.5885 & 0.4115 \end{bmatrix}$; $\begin{bmatrix} 0.614825 & 0.385175 \end{bmatrix}$; $\begin{bmatrix} 0.626671 & 0.373329 \end{bmatrix}$; $\begin{bmatrix} 0.632002 & 0.367998 \end{bmatrix}$; $\begin{bmatrix} 0.634401 & 0.365599 \end{bmatrix}$; $\begin{bmatrix} 0.635480 & 0.364520 \end{bmatrix}$; $\begin{bmatrix} 0.635966 & 0.364034 \end{bmatrix}$; $\begin{bmatrix} 0.636185 & 0.363815 \end{bmatrix}$

(b) 0.236364; 0.106364; 0.047864; 0.021539; 0.009693; 0.004362; 0.001963; 0.000884; 0.000398; 0.000179

(c) The ratio is roughly 0.45 for each week.

(d) Each week, the difference between the probability vector and the equilibrium vector is slightly less than half of what it was the previous week.

(e) $\begin{bmatrix} 0.75 & 0.25 \end{bmatrix}$; $\begin{bmatrix} 0.6875 & 0.3125 \end{bmatrix}$; $\begin{bmatrix} 0.659375 & 0.340625 \end{bmatrix}$; $\begin{bmatrix} 0.646719 & 0.353281 \end{bmatrix}$; $\begin{bmatrix} 0.641023 & 0.358977 \end{bmatrix}$; $\begin{bmatrix} 0.638461 & 0.361539 \end{bmatrix}$; $\begin{bmatrix} 0.637307 & 0.362693 \end{bmatrix}$; $\begin{bmatrix} 0.636788 & 0.363212 \end{bmatrix}$; $\begin{bmatrix} 0.636555 & 0.363445 \end{bmatrix}$; $\begin{bmatrix} 0.636450 & 0.363550 \end{bmatrix}$;

0.113636; 0.051136; 0.023011; 0.010355; 0.004659; 0.002097; 0.000943; 0.000424; 0.000191; 0.000086

The ratio is roughly 0.45 for each week, which is the same conclusion as before.

29. Let V be the probability vector $\begin{bmatrix} v_1 & v_2 & v_3 \end{bmatrix}$.

$$VP = V$$

$$\begin{bmatrix} v_1 & v_2 & v_3 \end{bmatrix} \begin{bmatrix} 0.9216 & 0.0780 & 0.0004 \\ 0.0460 & 0.8959 & 0.0581 \\ 0.0003 & 0.0301 & 0.9696 \end{bmatrix} = \begin{bmatrix} v_1 & v_2 & v_3 \end{bmatrix}$$

$$\begin{aligned} 0.9216v_1 + 0.0460v_2 + 0.0003v_3 &= v_1 \\ 0.0780v_1 + 0.8959v_2 + 0.0301v_3 &= v_2 \\ 0.0004v_1 + 0.0581v_2 + 0.9696v_3 &= v_3 \end{aligned}$$

Simplify the equations and use the equation $v_1 + v_2 + v_3 = 1$ to get the system

$$\begin{aligned} -0.0784v_1 + 0.0460v_2 + 0.0003v_3 &= 0 \\ 0.0780v_1 - 0.1041v_2 + 0.0301v_3 &= 0 \\ 0.0004v_1 + 0.0581v_2 - 0.0304v_3 &= 0 \\ v_1 + \quad v_2 + \quad v_3 &= 1. \end{aligned}$$

Using a graphing calculator, the solution to the system is

$$v_1 = 0.1691, v_2 = 0.2847, v_3 = 0.5462.$$

This means, if these trends continue, eventually 16.91% of the businesses will be small, 28.47% will be medium, and 54.62% will be large.

30. **(a)** Look at the probability of a region in group 2 moving up to group 3; that is, the entry in the second row, third column of

$$P = \begin{bmatrix} 0.733 & 0.267 & 0 & 0 & 0 \\ 0.278 & 0.555 & 0.167 & 0 & 0 \\ 0.133 & 0.133 & 0.667 & 0 & 0.067 \\ 0 & 0 & 0.412 & 0.294 & 0.294 \\ 0 & 0 & 0 & 0.250 & 0.750 \end{bmatrix},$$

which is 0.167.

(b) Using a graphing calculator, notice that

$$P^3 = \begin{bmatrix} 0.550 & 0.360 & 0.087 & 0 & 0.003 \\ 0.418 & 0.353 & 0.204 & 0.003 & 0.022 \\ 0.281 & 0.232 & 0.352 & 0.029 & 0.107 \\ 0.108 & 0.098 & 0.339 & 0.131 & 0.324 \\ 0.014 & 0.014 & 0.176 & 0.236 & 0.561 \end{bmatrix},$$

where entries are rounded to three decimal places. Look at the entry in the third row, fifth column; it is 0.107.

(c) First, note that all the entries of P^4 are positive, so P is a regular transition matrix. Therefore, there exists a unique equilibrium vector $V = \begin{bmatrix} v_1 & v_2 & v_3 & v_4 & v_5 \end{bmatrix}$ such that $VP = V$. Also, since V is a probability vector, then $v_1 + v_2 + v_3 + v_4 + v_5 = 1$.
Expand the equation

$$\begin{bmatrix} v_1 & v_2 & v_3 & v_4 & v_5 \end{bmatrix} \begin{bmatrix} 0.733 & 0.267 & 0 & 0 & 0 \\ 0.278 & 0.555 & 0.167 & 0 & 0 \\ 0.133 & 0.133 & 0.667 & 0 & 0.067 \\ 0 & 0 & 0.412 & 0.294 & 0.294 \\ 0 & 0 & 0 & 0.250 & 0.750 \end{bmatrix} = \begin{bmatrix} v_1 & v_2 & v_3 & v_4 & v_5 \end{bmatrix}$$

to get

$$\begin{aligned}0.733v_1 + 0.278v_2 + 0.133v_3 &= v_1\\ 0.267v_1 + 0.555v_2 + 0.133v_3 &= v_2\\ 0.167v_2 + 0.667v_3 + 0.412v_4 &= v_3\\ 0.294v_4 + 0.250v_5 &= v_4\\ 0.067v_3 + 0.294v_4 + 0.750v_5 &= v_5,\end{aligned}$$

which along with $v_1 + v_2 + v_3 + v_4 + v_5 = 1$ simplifies to the system

$$\begin{aligned}-0.267v_1 + 0.278v_2 + 0.133v_3 &= 0\\ 0.267v_1 - 0.445v_2 + 0.133v_3 &= 0\\ 0.167v_2 - 0.333v_3 + 0.412v_4 &= 0\\ -0.706v_4 + 0.25v_5 &= 0\\ 0.067v_3 + 0.294v_4 - 0.25v_5 &= 0\\ v_1 + v_2 + v_3 + v_4 + v_5 &= 1.\end{aligned}$$

Use matrices and a graphing calculator to solve this system for V, where entries are rounded to three decimal places.

$$\begin{bmatrix} v_1 & v_2 & v_3 & v_4 & v_5 \end{bmatrix} = \begin{bmatrix} 0.402 & 0.297 & 0.186 & 0.030 & 0.086 \end{bmatrix},$$

so the long-term probabilities are 0.402 for group 1, 0.297 for group 2, 0.186 for group 3, 0.030 for group 4, and 0.086 for group 5.

31. The transition matrix is

$$\begin{array}{c} \\ A \\ B \\ C \end{array}\begin{array}{c} \begin{array}{ccc} A & B & C \end{array} \\ \begin{bmatrix} 0.3 & 0.3 & 0.4 \\ 0.15 & 0.3 & 0.55 \\ 0.3 & 0.6 & 0.1 \end{bmatrix} \end{array}.$$

To find the long-range distribution, use the system

$$\begin{aligned}v_1 + v_2 + v_3 &= 1\\ 0.3v_1 + 0.15v_2 + 0.3v_3 &= v_1\\ 0.3v_1 + 0.3v_2 + 0.6v_3 &= v_2\\ 0.4v_1 + 0.55v_2 + 0.1v_3 &= v_3.\end{aligned}$$

Simplify these equations to obtain the system

$$\begin{aligned}v_1 + v_2 + v_3 &= 1\\ -0.7v_1 + 0.15v_2 + 0.3v_3 &= 0\\ 0.3v_1 - 0.7v_2 + 0.6v_3 &= 0\\ 0.4v_1 + 0.55v_2 - 0.9v_3 &= 0.\end{aligned}$$

Solve this system by the Gauss-Jordan method to obtain $v_1 = \frac{60}{251}$, $v_2 = \frac{102}{251}$, and $v_3 = \frac{89}{251}$. The long-range prediction is

$$\begin{bmatrix} \frac{60}{251} & \frac{102}{251} & \frac{89}{251} \end{bmatrix}.$$

32. **(a)** For the 1967-1979 trends, the transition matrix is

	Poor	Middle Class	A- uent
Poor	0.645	0.355	0
Middle Class	0.062	0.875	0.063
A- uent	0	0.311	0.689

which is a regular transition matrix.
To find the long-range trend, use the system

$$\begin{aligned} v_1 + \quad v_2 + \quad v_3 &= 1 \\ 0.645v_1 + 0.062v_2 \quad &= v_1 \\ 0.355v_1 + 0.875v_2 + 0.311v_3 &= v_2 \\ 0.063v_2 + 0.689v_3 &= v_3. \end{aligned}$$

Simplify these equations to obtain the system

$$\begin{aligned} v_1 + \quad v_2 + \quad v_3 &= 1 \\ -0.355v_1 + 0.062v_2 \quad &= 0 \\ 0.355v_1 - 0.125v_2 + 0.311v_3 &= 0 \\ 0.063v_2 - 0.311v_3 &= 0. \end{aligned}$$

Solve this system by the Gauss-Jordan method to obtain $v_1 = 0.127$, $v_2 = 0.726$, and $v_3 = 0.147$.

The long-range trend is 12.7% poor, 72.6% middle class, and 14.7% a- uent.

(b) For the 1980-1991 trends, the transition matrix is

$$P = \begin{bmatrix} 0.696 & 0.304 & 0 \\ 0.085 & 0.84 & 0.075 \\ 0 & 0.271 & 0.729 \end{bmatrix}, \text{ where rows and columns are labeled as in part (a).}$$

P^2 has only positive entries, so P is regular. The matrix equation $VP = V$, where $V = \begin{bmatrix} v_1 & v_2 & v_3 \end{bmatrix}$, leads to the system of equations

$$\begin{aligned} 0.696v_1 + 0.085v_2 \quad &= v_1 \\ 0.304v_1 + \quad 0.84v_2 + 0.271v_3 &= v_2 \\ 0.075v_2 + 0.729v_3 &= v_3 \\ v_1 + \quad v_2 + \quad v_3 &= 1, \end{aligned}$$

which simplifies to

$$\begin{aligned} -0.304v_1 + 0.085v_2 \quad &= 0 \\ 0.304v_1 - \quad 0.16v_2 + 0.271v_3 &= 0 \\ 0.075v_2 - 0.271v_3 &= 0 \\ v_1 + \quad v_2 + \quad v_3 &= 1. \end{aligned}$$

Solving by the Gauss-Jordan method leads to $v_1 = 0.180$, $v_2 = 0.643$, $v_3 = 0.178$, so the long-range trends are 18.0% poor, 64.3% middle class, and 17.8% a- uent.

33. Let V be the probability vector $\begin{bmatrix} v_1 & v_2 & v_3 & v_4 & v_5 \end{bmatrix}$.

$$VP = V$$

$$\begin{bmatrix} v_1 & v_2 & v_3 & v_4 & v_5 \end{bmatrix} \begin{bmatrix} 0.71 & 0.19 & 0.03 & 0.07 & 0.00 \\ 0.52 & 0.31 & 0.04 & 0.13 & 0.00 \\ 0.40 & 0.16 & 0.22 & 0.22 & 0.00 \\ 0.34 & 0.19 & 0.09 & 0.37 & 0.01 \\ 0.21 & 0.25 & 0.13 & 0.37 & 0.04 \end{bmatrix} = \begin{bmatrix} v_1 & v_2 & v_3 & v_4 & v_5 \end{bmatrix}$$

$$\begin{aligned} 0.71v_1 + 0.52v_2 + 0.40v_3 + 0.34v_4 + 0.21v_5 &= v_1 \\ 0.19v_1 + 0.31v_2 + 0.16v_3 + 0.19v_4 + 0.25v_5 &= v_2 \\ 0.03v_1 + 0.04v_2 + 0.22v_3 + 0.09v_4 + 0.13v_5 &= v_3 \\ 0.07v_1 + 0.13v_2 + 0.22v_3 + 0.37v_4 + 0.37v_5 &= v_4 \\ 0.01v_4 + 0.04v_5 &= v_5 \end{aligned}$$

Simplify the equations and use the equation $v_1 + v_2 + v_3 + v_4 + v_5 = 1$ to get the following system.

$$\begin{aligned} -0.29v_1 + 0.52v_2 + 0.40v_3 + 0.34v_4 + 0.21v_5 &= 0 \\ 0.19v_1 - 0.69v_2 + 0.16v_3 + 0.19v_4 + 0.25v_5 &= 0 \\ 0.03v_1 + 0.04v_2 - 0.78v_3 + 0.09v_4 + 0.13v_5 &= 0 \\ 0.07v_1 + 0.13v_2 + 0.22v_3 - 0.63v_4 + 0.37v_5 &= 0 \\ 0.01v_4 - 0.96v_5 &= 0 \\ v_1 + v_2 + v_3 + v_4 + v_5 &= 1 \end{aligned}$$

Using a graphing calculator, the solution to the system is

$$v_1 = 0.6053, v_2 = 0.2143, v_3 = 0.0494, v_4 = 0.1295, v_5 = 0.0013.$$

This means, if these trends continue, the long-term probabilities of people living in each type of housing are: 0.6053 in type I, 0.2143 in type II, 0.0494 in type III, 0.1295 in type IV, and 0.0013 in type V.

34. (a) Look at the probability in the third row, third column of

$$P = \begin{bmatrix} 0.645 & 0.099 & 0.152 & 0.033 & 0.071 \\ 0.611 & 0.138 & 0.128 & 0.033 & 0.090 \\ 0.514 & 0.067 & 0.271 & 0.030 & 0.118 \\ 0.609 & 0.107 & 0.178 & 0.064 & 0.042 \\ 0.523 & 0.093 & 0.183 & 0.022 & 0.179 \end{bmatrix}$$

which is 0.271.

(b) Use a graphing calculator to find

$$P^2 = \begin{bmatrix} 0.612 & 0.098 & 0.171 & 0.033 & 0.087 \\ 0.611 & 0.100 & 0.168 & 0.033 & 0.088 \\ 0.592 & 0.092 & 0.187 & 0.032 & 0.097 \\ 0.611 & 0.098 & 0.174 & 0.034 & 0.084 \\ 0.595 & 0.096 & 0.178 & 0.031 & 0.100 \end{bmatrix}$$

where entries are rounded to three decimal places. The probability that a criminal's second crime after committing theft is also theft is the entry in the third row, third column of P^2, which is 0.187.

(c) Since all of the entries of P are positive, then P is a regular transition matrix. Therefore, there is a unique equilibrium probability vector $V = \begin{bmatrix} v_1 & v_2 & v_3 & v_4 & v_5 \end{bmatrix}$. The equation $VP = V$ yields the system of equations

$$\begin{aligned}
0.645v_1 + 0.611v_2 + 0.514v_3 + 0.609v_4 + 0.523v_5 &= v_1\\
0.099v_1 + 0.138v_2 + 0.067v_3 + 0.107v_4 + 0.093v_5 &= v_2\\
0.152v_1 + 0.128v_2 + 0.271v_3 + 0.178v_4 + 0.183v_5 &= v_3\\
0.033v_1 + 0.033v_2 + 0.030v_3 + 0.064v_4 + 0.022v_5 &= v_4\\
0.071v_1 + 0.090v_2 + 0.118v_3 + 0.042v_4 + 0.179v_5 &= v_5,
\end{aligned}$$

which along with the equation
$v_1 + v_2 + v_3 + v_4 + v_5 = 1$ simplifies to

$$\begin{aligned}
-0.355v_1 + 0.611v_2 + 0.514v_3 + 0.609v_4 + 0.523v_5 &= 0\\
0.099v_1 - 0.862v_2 + 0.067v_3 + 0.107v_4 + 0.093v_5 &= 0\\
0.152v_1 + 0.128v_2 - 0.729v_3 + 0.178v_4 + 0.183v_5 &= 0\\
0.033v_1 + 0.033v_2 + 0.030v_3 - 0.936v_4 + 0.022v_5 &= 0\\
0.071v_1 + 0.090v_2 + 0.118v_3 + 0.042v_4 - 0.821v_5 &= 0\\
v_1 + \quad v_2 + \quad v_3 + \quad v_4 + \quad v_5 &= 0
\end{aligned}$$

Use matrices and a graphing calculator to solve this system by the Gauss-Jordan method. This yields the solution

$$V = \begin{bmatrix} 0.607 & 0.097 & 0.174 & 0.032 & 0.090 \end{bmatrix},$$

where entries are rounded to three decimal places. Therefore, the long-term probabilities for each type of crime are 0.607 for nonindex, 0.097 for injury, 0.174 for theft, 0.032 for damage, and 0.090 for combination.

35. **(a)** Let H, S, and U represent humanities, science, and undecided, respectively.

$$\begin{array}{c} \\ \text{H} \\ \text{S} \\ \text{U} \end{array} \begin{array}{c} \begin{array}{ccc} \text{H} & \text{S} & \text{U} \end{array} \\ \begin{bmatrix} 0.35 & 0.2 & 0.45 \\ 0.15 & 0.5 & 0.35 \\ 0.5 & 0.3 & 0.2 \end{bmatrix} \end{array}$$

Let $\begin{bmatrix} v_1 & v_2 & v_3 \end{bmatrix}$ be a probability vector. Then

$$\begin{bmatrix} v_1 & v_2 & v_3 \end{bmatrix} \begin{bmatrix} 0.35 & 0.2 & 0.45 \\ 0.15 & 0.5 & 0.35 \\ 0.5 & 0.3 & 0.2 \end{bmatrix} = \begin{bmatrix} v_1 & v_2 & v_3 \end{bmatrix}.$$

We have the system

$$\begin{aligned}
0.35v_1 + 0.15v_2 + 0.5v_3 &= v_1\\
0.2v_1 + \quad 0.5v_2 + 0.3v_3 &= v_2\\
0.45v_1 + 0.35v_2 + 0.2v_3 &= v_3\\
v_1 + \quad v_2 + \quad v_3 &= 1,
\end{aligned}$$

which is equivalent to the system

$$\begin{aligned}
-0.65v_1 + 0.15v_2 + 0.5v_3 &= 0\\
0.2v_1 - \quad 0.5v_2 + 0.3v_3 &= 0\\
0.45v_1 + 0.35v_2 - 0.8v_3 &= 0\\
v_1 + \quad v_2 + \quad v_3 &= 1.
\end{aligned}$$

To solve this system, we use the augmented matrix

$$\left[\begin{array}{ccc|c} -0.65 & 0.15 & 0.5 & 0 \\ 0.2 & -0.5 & 0.3 & 0 \\ 0.45 & 0.35 & -0.8 & 0 \\ 1 & 1 & 1 & 1 \end{array}\right].$$

Solving by the Gauss-Jordan method, we obtain the matrix

$$\left[\begin{array}{ccc|c} 1 & 0 & 0 & \frac{1}{3} \\ 0 & 1 & 0 & \frac{1}{3} \\ 0 & 0 & 1 & \frac{1}{3} \\ 0 & 0 & 0 & 0 \end{array}\right].$$

Thus, $\begin{bmatrix} v_1 & v_2 & v_3 \end{bmatrix} = \begin{bmatrix} \frac{1}{3} & \frac{1}{3} & \frac{1}{3} \end{bmatrix}$.

The long-range prediction is that $\frac{1}{3}$ of the students will end up with each major.

36. The transition matrix is

$$\begin{bmatrix} p & 1-p \\ 1-p & p \end{bmatrix}.$$

The columns sum to $p + (1-p) = 1$, so by Exercise 23 the equilibrium vector is $\begin{bmatrix} \frac{1}{2} & \frac{1}{2} \end{bmatrix}$.

The long-range prediction for the fraction of the people who will hear the decision correctly is $\frac{1}{2}$.

37. **(a)** For

$$P = \begin{bmatrix} 0.065 & 0.585 & 0.34 & 0.01 \\ 0.042 & 0.44 & 0.42 & 0.098 \\ 0.018 & 0.276 & 0.452 & 0.254 \\ 0 & 0.044 & 0.292 & 0.664 \end{bmatrix},$$

since P^2 has only positive entries, P is a regular transition matrix. Therefore, there exists a unique probability vector $V = [v_1 \quad v_2 \quad v_3 \quad v_4]$ such that $VP = V$.
If we expand the matrix equation

$$[v_1 \quad v_2 \quad v_3 \quad v_4] \begin{bmatrix} 0.065 & 0.585 & 0.34 & 0.01 \\ 0.042 & 0.44 & 0.42 & 0.098 \\ 0.018 & 0.276 & 0.452 & 0.254 \\ 0 & 0.044 & 0.292 & 0.664 \end{bmatrix} = [v_1 \quad v_2 \quad v_3 \quad v_4],$$

we get the system of equations

$$\begin{aligned} 0.065v_1 + 0.042v_2 + 0.018v_3 \qquad\qquad &= v_1 \\ 0.585v_1 + 0.44v_2 + 0.276v_3 + 0.044v_4 &= v_2 \\ 0.34v_1 + 0.42v_2 + 0.452v_3 + 0.292v_4 &= v_3 \\ 0.01v_1 + 0.098v_2 + 0.254v_3 + 0.664v_4 &= v_4, \end{aligned}$$

which along with the equation $v_1 + v_2 + v_3 + v_4 = 1$ simplifies to a system of equations, which can be written as the augmented matrix

$$\left[\begin{array}{cccc|c} -0.935 & 0.042 & 0.018 & 0 & 0 \\ 0.585 & -0.56 & 0.276 & 0.044 & 0 \\ 0.34 & 0.42 & -0.548 & 0.292 & 0 \\ 0.01 & 0.098 & 0.254 & -0.336 & 0 \\ 1 & 1 & 1 & 1 & 1 \end{array}\right].$$

Using the Gauss-Jordan method, this reduces to

$$\left[\begin{array}{cccc|c} 1 & 0 & 0 & 0 & 0.0180 \\ 0 & 1 & 0 & 0 & 0.2368 \\ 0 & 0 & 1 & 0 & 0.3847 \\ 0 & 0 & 0 & 1 & 0.3604 \\ 0 & 0 & 0 & 0 & 0 \end{array}\right],$$

where entries in the fifth column are rounded to four decimal places. Therefore, the long-range prediction for the proportion of the students in each group is group 1, 1.80%; group 2, 23.68%; group 3, 38.47%; and group 4, 36.04%.

(b) Since we assume that students in group 4 will remain in group 4, and that everyone begins in group 1, we'll use the transition matrix

$$P = \begin{bmatrix} 0.065 & 0.585 & 0.34 & 0.01 \\ 0.042 & 0.44 & 0.42 & 0.098 \\ 0.018 & 0.276 & 0.452 & 0.254 \\ 0 & 0 & 0 & 1 \end{bmatrix}$$

and the initial probability vector $X_0 = [1 \ \ 0 \ \ 0 \ \ 0]$.
Use a graphing calculator to calculate X_0P^n for increasing powers of n. Since

$$X_0P^7 = [0.012 \ \ 0.140 \ \ 0.170 \ \ 0.678],$$

and

$$X_0P^8 = [0.010 \ \ 0.115 \ \ 0.140 \ \ 0.735],$$

it will require 8 testing periods before 70% or more of the students will have mastered the material.

38. Let F, C, and R represent fair, cloudy, and rainy, respectively, and let $\begin{bmatrix} v_1 & v_2 & v_3 \end{bmatrix}$ be a probability vector. The transition matrix is

$$\begin{array}{c} \\ \text{F} \\ \text{C} \\ \text{R} \end{array} \begin{array}{c} \begin{array}{ccc} \text{F} & \text{C} & \text{R} \end{array} \\ \begin{bmatrix} 0.60 & 0.25 & 0.15 \\ 0.40 & 0.35 & 0.25 \\ 0.35 & 0.40 & 0.25 \end{bmatrix} \end{array},$$

and the resulting system of equations is

$$\begin{aligned} 0.60v_1 + 0.40v_2 + 0.35v_3 &= v_1 \\ 0.25v_1 + 0.35v_2 + 0.40v_3 &= v_2 \\ 0.15v_1 + 0.25v_2 + 0.25v_3 &= v_3. \end{aligned}$$

Also, $v_1 + v_2 + v_3 = 1$.

Solving this system, we obtain

$$v_1 = \tfrac{155}{318}, v_2 = \tfrac{99}{318}, v_3 = \tfrac{32}{159}.$$

The equilibrium vector is

$$\begin{bmatrix} \frac{155}{318} & \frac{99}{318} & \frac{32}{159} \end{bmatrix}.$$

Over the long term, the proportion of days that are expected to be fair, cloudy, and rainy are $\frac{155}{318} \approx 48.7\%$, $\frac{99}{318} \approx 31.1\%$, and $\frac{32}{159} \approx 20.1\%$, respectively.

39. **(a)** Let's consider the possibilities for the 2 boxes. Suppose that you have some balls in box 1 (i balls, state i), and you want to get to state $j = i - 1$. There are n balls totally, and you would have to pick one of the i balls in box 1 and move it to box 2. The probability is

$$\frac{i}{n}. \quad \text{(Case 1)}$$

Suppose that you have at least 1 ball in box 1, but less than n balls, and you want to go to state $j = i + 1$. You would have to pick one of the balls in box 2, and put it in box 1. There are n total balls, and $(n - i)$ balls in box 2. The probability of this is

$$\frac{n-i}{n} = 1 - \frac{i}{n}. \quad \text{(Case 2)}$$

Suppose that box 1 is completely empty (0 balls) or completely full (n balls). To go to state 1 or state $n - 1$ respectively, you have only 1 choice in either case: move a ball from box 2 to box 1, or move a ball from box 1 to box 2 respectively. Since there is only 1 possibility in each case (only one thing that can be done), the probability is

$$\frac{n}{n} = 1. \quad \text{(Case 3)}$$

Since any other case would require you to go from state i to state j where $|i - j| \geq 2$, and you only can move 1 ball (that is, change a state by 1), these cases would be impossible and the probability would be 0. (Case 4).

(b) By the explanation in part (a), all entries will be 0 except those in row 0, column 1 which is 1, the entries where the row = column + 1 which is $\frac{\text{row}}{n}$, and the entries where column = row + 1 which is $1 - \frac{\text{row}}{n}$. Therefore, the transition matrix is

$$\begin{array}{c} \\ 0 \\ 1 \\ 2 \\ \vdots \\ n \end{array} \begin{array}{c} \begin{array}{cccccc} 0 & 1 & 2 & \cdots & n \end{array} \\ \begin{bmatrix} 0 & 1 & 0 & \cdots & 0 \\ \frac{1}{n} & 0 & 1 - \frac{1}{n} & \cdots & 0 \\ 0 & \frac{2}{n} & 0 & \cdots & 0 \\ \vdots & \vdots & \vdots & \vdots & \vdots \\ 0 & 0 & 0 & \cdots & 0 \end{bmatrix} \end{array}.$$

(c) $n = 2$

$p_{00} = 0; p_{10} = \frac{i}{n} = \frac{1}{2}; p_{20} = 0; p_{01} = 1; p_{11} = 0;$
$p_{21} = 1; p_{02} = 0; p_{12} = 1 - \frac{i}{n} = 1 - \frac{1}{2} = \frac{1}{2};$
$p_{22} = 0$

The transition matrix for the case $n = 2$ is

$$\begin{bmatrix} 0 & 1 & 0 \\ \frac{1}{2} & 0 & \frac{1}{2} \\ 0 & 1 & 0 \end{bmatrix}.$$

(d) $A^2 = \begin{bmatrix} \frac{1}{2} & 0 & \frac{1}{2} \\ 0 & 1 & 0 \\ \frac{1}{2} & 0 & \frac{1}{2} \end{bmatrix};$

$A^3 = \begin{bmatrix} 0 & 1 & 0 \\ \frac{1}{2} & 0 & \frac{1}{2} \\ 0 & 1 & 0 \end{bmatrix}; \; A^4 = A^2$

Therefore, the transition matrix is not regular.

(e) $\begin{bmatrix} v_1 & v_2 & v_3 \end{bmatrix} \begin{bmatrix} 0 & 1 & 0 \\ \frac{1}{2} & 0 & \frac{1}{2} \\ 0 & 1 & 0 \end{bmatrix} = \begin{bmatrix} v_1 & v_2 & v_3 \end{bmatrix}$

$$\frac{1}{2}v_2 = v_1$$
$$v_1 + v_3 = v_2$$
$$\frac{1}{2}v_2 = v_3$$

Therefore,

$$\begin{aligned} -v_1 + \tfrac{1}{2}v_2 \qquad &= 0 \\ v_1 - v_2 + v_3 &= 0 \\ \tfrac{1}{2}v_2 - v_3 &= 0 \end{aligned}$$

and $v_1 + v_2 + v_3 = 1.$

Solve this system by the Gauss-Jordan method.

$$\left[\begin{array}{ccc|c} -1 & \frac{1}{2} & 0 & 0 \\ 1 & -1 & 1 & 0 \\ 0 & \frac{1}{2} & -1 & 0 \\ 1 & 1 & 1 & 1 \end{array}\right]$$

$$\left[\begin{array}{ccc|c} 1 & -\frac{1}{2} & 0 & 0 \\ 0 & -\frac{1}{2} & 1 & 0 \\ 0 & \frac{1}{2} & -1 & 0 \\ 0 & \frac{3}{2} & 1 & 1 \end{array}\right]$$

$$\left[\begin{array}{ccc|c} 1 & 0 & -1 & 0 \\ 0 & 1 & -2 & 0 \\ 0 & 0 & 0 & 0 \\ 0 & 0 & 4 & 1 \end{array}\right]$$

$$\left[\begin{array}{ccc|c} 4 & 0 & 0 & 1 \\ 0 & 2 & 0 & 1 \\ 0 & 0 & 4 & 1 \\ 0 & 0 & 0 & 0 \end{array}\right]$$

Therefore,

$$4v_1 = 1; v_1 = \tfrac{1}{4}$$
$$2v_2 = 1; v_2 = \tfrac{1}{2}$$
$$4v_3 = 1; v_3 = \tfrac{1}{4}.$$

The equilibrium vector is

$$\begin{bmatrix} \frac{1}{4} & \frac{1}{2} & \frac{1}{4} \end{bmatrix}.$$

40. The transition matrix is

$$P = \begin{bmatrix} 0.12 & 0.88 \\ 0.54 & 0.46 \end{bmatrix}.$$

Let V be the probability vector $\begin{bmatrix} v_1 & v_2 \end{bmatrix}$.

$$\begin{bmatrix} v_1 & v_2 \end{bmatrix} \begin{bmatrix} 0.12 & 0.88 \\ 0.54 & 0.46 \end{bmatrix} = \begin{bmatrix} v_1 & v_2 \end{bmatrix}$$

$$0.12v_1 + 0.54v_2 = v_1$$
$$0.88v_1 + 0.46v_2 = v_2$$

Simplify these equations to get the dependent system

$$-0.88v_1 + 0.54v_2 = 0$$
$$0.88v_1 - 0.54v_2 = 0.$$

Also, $v_1 + v_2 = 1$.
Solving this system, we obtain

$$v_1 = \frac{27}{71} \text{ and } v_2 = \frac{44}{71},$$

and note that

$$\frac{27}{71} \approx 0.38 = 38\%.$$

About 38% of letters in English text are expected to be vowels.

41. (a) If the guard is at the middle door, he is equally likely to stay there or move to either door, so the second row must have all entries of $\frac{1}{3}$. If he is at the door at either end, he is equally likely to stay put or move to the middle door. Therefore, row 1 must be $\begin{bmatrix} \frac{1}{2} & \frac{1}{2} & 0 \end{bmatrix}$. (Note there is no chance, according to the problem, that the guard will go from door 1 to door 3.) Similarly, row 3 must be $\begin{bmatrix} 0 & \frac{1}{2} & \frac{1}{2} \end{bmatrix}$, since there is no chance that he can go from door 3 to door 1.

(b) $\begin{bmatrix} v_1 & v_2 & v_3 \end{bmatrix} \begin{bmatrix} \frac{1}{2} & \frac{1}{2} & 0 \\ \frac{1}{3} & \frac{1}{3} & \frac{1}{3} \\ 0 & \frac{1}{2} & \frac{1}{2} \end{bmatrix} = \begin{bmatrix} v_1 & v_2 & v_3 \end{bmatrix}$

$$\tfrac{1}{2}v_1 + \tfrac{1}{3}v_2 = v_1$$
$$\tfrac{1}{2}v_1 + \tfrac{1}{3}v_2 + \tfrac{1}{2}v_3 = v_2$$
$$\tfrac{1}{3}v_2 + \tfrac{1}{2}v_3 = v_3$$

Therefore, we have the system

$$\begin{aligned} -\tfrac{1}{2}v_1 + \tfrac{1}{3}v_2 \qquad &= 0 \\ \tfrac{1}{2}v_1 - \tfrac{2}{3}v_2 + \tfrac{1}{2}v_3 &= 0 \\ \tfrac{1}{3}v_2 - \tfrac{1}{2}v_3 &= 0 \\ v_1 + v_2 + v_3 &= 1. \end{aligned}$$

Solve this system by the Gauss-Jordan method to obtain $v_1 = \frac{2}{7}, v_2 = \frac{3}{7}$, and $v_3 = \frac{2}{7}$.

The guard spends $\frac{2}{7}$ of the time in front of the first and third doors and $\frac{3}{7}$ of the time in front of the middle door.

10.3 Absorbing Markov Chains

1.
$$\begin{array}{c} \\ 1 \\ 2 \\ 3 \end{array}\begin{array}{c} \begin{array}{ccc} 1 & 2 & 3 \end{array} \\ \begin{bmatrix} 0.25 & 0.05 & 0.7 \\ 0.35 & 0 & 0.65 \\ 0 & 0 & 1 \end{bmatrix} \end{array}$$

Since $p_{33} = 1$, state 3 is absorbing. There is a probability of 0.7 of going from state 1 to state 3 and a probability of 0.65 of going from state 2 to state 3, so it is possible to go from each nonabsorbing state to the absorbing state. Thus, this is the transition matrix for an absorbing Markov chain.

2.
$$\begin{array}{c} \\ 1 \\ 2 \\ 3 \end{array}\begin{array}{c} \begin{array}{ccc} 1 & 2 & 3 \end{array} \\ \begin{bmatrix} 0.15 & 0.35 & 0.5 \\ 0 & 1 & 0 \\ 0.3 & 0.3 & 0.4 \end{bmatrix} \end{array}$$

Since $p_{22} = 1$, state 2 is absorbing. There is a probability of 0.35 of going from state 1 to state 2 and a probability of 0.3 of going from state 3 to state 2, so it is possible to go from each nonabsorbing state to the absorbing state. Thus, this is the transition matrix of an absorbing Markov chain.

3.
$$\begin{array}{c} \\ 1 \\ 2 \\ 3 \end{array}\begin{array}{c} \begin{array}{ccc} 1 & 2 & 3 \end{array} \\ \begin{bmatrix} 1 & 0 & 0 \\ 0 & 0.25 & 0.75 \\ 0 & 0.85 & 0.15 \end{bmatrix} \end{array}$$

Since $p_{11} = 1$, state 1 is absorbing. Since $p_{21} = 0$ and $p_{31} = 0$, it is not possible to go from either of the nonabsorbing states (state 2 or state 3) to the absorbing state (state 1). Thus, this is not the transition matrix of an absorbing Markov chain.

4.
$$\begin{array}{c} \\ 1 \\ 2 \\ 3 \end{array}\begin{array}{c} \begin{array}{ccc} 1 & 2 & 3 \end{array} \\ \begin{bmatrix} 0.4 & 0 & 0.6 \\ 0 & 1 & 0 \\ 0.5 & 0 & 0.5 \end{bmatrix} \end{array}$$

Since $p_{22} = 1$, state 2 is absorbing. Since $p_{12} = 0$ and $p_{32} = 0$, it is not possible to go from either of the nonabsorbing states (state 1 or state 3) to the absorbing state (state 2). Thus, this is not the transition matrix of an absorbing Markov chain.

5.
$$\begin{array}{c} \\ 1 \\ 2 \\ 3 \\ 4 \end{array}\begin{array}{c} \begin{array}{cccc} 1 & 2 & 3 & 4 \end{array} \\ \begin{bmatrix} 0.2 & 0.5 & 0.1 & 0.2 \\ 0 & 1 & 0 & 0 \\ 0.9 & 0.02 & 0.04 & 0.04 \\ 0 & 0 & 0 & 1 \end{bmatrix} \end{array}$$

Since $p_{22} = 1$ and $p_{44} = 1$, states 2 and 4 are absorbing. It is possible to get from state 1 to states 2 and 4, and from state 3 to states 2 and 4. Thus, this is the transition matrix of an absorbing Markov chain.

6.
$$\begin{array}{c} \\ 1 \\ 2 \\ 3 \\ 4 \end{array}\begin{array}{c} \begin{array}{cccc} 1 & 2 & 3 & 4 \end{array} \\ \begin{bmatrix} 0.32 & 0.41 & 0.16 & 0.11 \\ 0.42 & 0.30 & 0 & 0.28 \\ 0 & 0 & 0 & 1 \\ 1 & 0 & 0 & 0 \end{bmatrix} \end{array}$$

No states are absorbing, so this matrix is not that of an absorbing Markov chain.

7. $$P = \left[\begin{array}{cc|c} 1 & 0 & 0 \\ 0 & 1 & 0 \\ \hline 0.15 & 0.35 & 0.5 \end{array}\right]$$

Here $R = [0.15 \quad 0.35]$ and $Q = [0.5]$.
Find the fundamental matrix F.

$$F = (I_1 - Q)^{-1} = [1 - 0.5]^{-1}$$
$$= [0.5]^{-1} = [\tfrac{1}{0.5}] = [2]$$

The product FR is

$$FR = [2]\,[0.15 \quad 0.35] = [0.3 \quad 0.7].$$

8.
$$\begin{array}{c} \\ 1 \\ 2 \\ 3 \end{array}\begin{array}{c} \begin{array}{ccc} 1 & 2 & 3 \end{array} \\ \begin{bmatrix} 1 & 0 & 0 \\ 0.65 & 0.1 & 0.25 \\ 0 & 0 & 1 \end{bmatrix} \end{array}$$

Rearrange the rows and columns so that absorbing states 1 and 3 come first.

$$\begin{array}{c} \\ 1 \\ 3 \\ 2 \end{array}\begin{array}{c} \begin{array}{ccc} 1 & 3 & 2 \end{array} \\ \left[\begin{array}{cc|c} 1 & 0 & 0 \\ 0 & 1 & 0 \\ \hline 0.65 & 0.25 & 0.1 \end{array}\right] \end{array}$$

Here $R = \begin{bmatrix} 0.65 & 0.25 \end{bmatrix}$ and $Q = [0.1]$. Find the fundamental matrix F.

$$F = (I_1 - Q)^{-1} = \left[\tfrac{9}{10}\right]^{-1} = \left[\tfrac{10}{9}\right]$$

The product matrix FR is

$$FR = \left[\tfrac{10}{9}\right]\left[\tfrac{65}{100} \quad \tfrac{25}{100}\right] = \left[\tfrac{13}{18} \quad \tfrac{5}{18}\right].$$

9.
$$\left[\begin{array}{cc|c} 1 & 0 & 0 \\ 0 & 1 & 0 \\ \hline \frac{1}{2} & \frac{1}{6} & \frac{1}{3} \end{array}\right] = P$$

$$R = \left[\tfrac{1}{2} \quad \tfrac{1}{6}\right],\ Q = \left[\tfrac{1}{3}\right]$$

$$F = (I_1 - Q)^{-1} = \left[1 - \tfrac{1}{3}\right]^{-1} = \left[\tfrac{2}{3}\right]^{-1} = \left[\tfrac{3}{2}\right]$$

$$FR = \left[\tfrac{3}{2}\right]\left[\tfrac{1}{2} \quad \tfrac{1}{6}\right] = \left[\tfrac{3}{4} \quad \tfrac{1}{4}\right]$$

10.
$$\begin{array}{c} \\ 1 \\ 2 \\ 3 \end{array}\begin{array}{c} \begin{array}{ccc} 1 & 2 & 3 \end{array} \\ \begin{bmatrix} 1 & 0 & 0 \\ \frac{5}{8} & \frac{1}{8} & \frac{1}{4} \\ 0 & 0 & 1 \end{bmatrix} \end{array}$$

The rearranged matrix is

$$\begin{array}{c} \\ 1 \\ 3 \\ 2 \end{array}\begin{array}{c} \begin{array}{ccc} 1 & 3 & 2 \end{array} \\ \left[\begin{array}{cc|c} 1 & 0 & 0 \\ 0 & 1 & 0 \\ \hline \frac{5}{8} & \frac{1}{4} & \frac{1}{8} \end{array}\right] \end{array}.$$

Here $R = \left[\tfrac{5}{8} \quad \tfrac{1}{4}\right]$ and $Q = \left[\tfrac{1}{8}\right]$.

Then

$$F = \left[\tfrac{7}{8}\right]^{-1} = \left[\tfrac{8}{7}\right],$$

and

$$FR = \left[\tfrac{8}{7}\right]\left[\tfrac{5}{8} \quad \tfrac{1}{4}\right] = \left[\tfrac{5}{7} \quad \tfrac{2}{7}\right].$$

11.
$$\begin{array}{c} \\ 1 \\ 2 \\ 3 \\ 4 \end{array}\begin{array}{c} \begin{array}{cccc} 1 & 2 & 3 & 4 \end{array} \\ \begin{bmatrix} 1 & 0 & 0 & 0 \\ \frac{1}{3} & 0 & \frac{2}{3} & 0 \\ 0 & 0 & 1 & 0 \\ \frac{1}{4} & \frac{1}{4} & \frac{1}{4} & \frac{1}{4} \end{bmatrix} \end{array} = P$$

Rearrange the rows and columns of P so that the absorbing states come first.

$$\begin{array}{c} \\ 1 \\ 3 \\ 2 \\ 4 \end{array}\begin{array}{c} \begin{array}{cccc} 1 & 3 & 2 & 4 \end{array} \\ \left[\begin{array}{cc|cc} 1 & 0 & 0 & 0 \\ 0 & 1 & 0 & 0 \\ \hline \frac{1}{3} & \frac{2}{3} & 0 & 0 \\ \frac{1}{4} & \frac{1}{4} & \frac{1}{4} & \frac{1}{4} \end{array}\right] \end{array}$$

$$R = \begin{bmatrix} \frac{1}{3} & \frac{2}{3} \\ \frac{1}{4} & \frac{1}{4} \end{bmatrix}; Q = \begin{bmatrix} 0 & 0 \\ \frac{1}{4} & \frac{1}{4} \end{bmatrix}$$

$$F = (I_2 - Q)^{-1} = \left(\begin{bmatrix} 1 & 0 \\ 0 & 1 \end{bmatrix} - \begin{bmatrix} 0 & 0 \\ \frac{1}{4} & \frac{1}{4} \end{bmatrix}\right)^{-1}$$

$$= \begin{bmatrix} 1 & 0 \\ -\frac{1}{4} & \frac{3}{4} \end{bmatrix}^{-1} = \begin{bmatrix} 1 & 0 \\ \frac{1}{3} & \frac{4}{3} \end{bmatrix}$$

$$FR = \begin{bmatrix} 1 & 0 \\ \frac{1}{3} & \frac{4}{3} \end{bmatrix}\begin{bmatrix} \frac{1}{3} & \frac{2}{3} \\ \frac{1}{4} & \frac{1}{4} \end{bmatrix} = \begin{bmatrix} \frac{1}{3} & \frac{2}{3} \\ \frac{4}{9} & \frac{5}{9} \end{bmatrix}$$

12.
$$\begin{array}{c} \\ 1 \\ 2 \\ 3 \\ 4 \end{array}\begin{array}{c} \begin{array}{cccc} 1 & 2 & 3 & 4 \end{array} \\ \begin{bmatrix} \frac{1}{4} & \frac{1}{2} & 0 & \frac{1}{4} \\ 0 & 1 & 0 & 0 \\ 0 & 0 & 1 & 0 \\ \frac{1}{2} & 0 & 0 & \frac{1}{2} \end{bmatrix} \end{array}$$

Note that states 2 and 3 are absorbing states. Rearranging, we obtain

$$\begin{array}{c} \\ 2 \\ 3 \\ 1 \\ 4 \end{array}\begin{array}{c} \begin{array}{cccc} 2 & 3 & 1 & 4 \end{array} \\ \left[\begin{array}{cc|cc} 1 & 0 & 0 & 0 \\ 0 & 1 & 0 & 0 \\ \hline \frac{1}{2} & 0 & \frac{1}{4} & \frac{1}{4} \\ 0 & 0 & \frac{1}{2} & \frac{1}{2} \end{array}\right] \end{array}.$$

Here $R = \begin{bmatrix} \frac{1}{2} & 0 \\ 0 & 0 \end{bmatrix}$ and $Q = \begin{bmatrix} \frac{1}{4} & \frac{1}{4} \\ \frac{1}{2} & \frac{1}{2} \end{bmatrix}$.

Therefore,

$$F = (I_2 - Q)^{-1} = \left(\begin{bmatrix} 1 & 0 \\ 0 & 1 \end{bmatrix} - \begin{bmatrix} \frac{1}{4} & \frac{1}{4} \\ \frac{1}{2} & \frac{1}{2} \end{bmatrix}\right)^{-1}$$

$$= \begin{bmatrix} \frac{3}{4} & -\frac{1}{4} \\ -\frac{1}{2} & \frac{1}{2} \end{bmatrix}^{-1} = \begin{bmatrix} 2 & 1 \\ 2 & 3 \end{bmatrix},$$

and

$$FR = \begin{bmatrix} 2 & 1 \\ 2 & 3 \end{bmatrix} \begin{bmatrix} \frac{1}{2} & 0 \\ 0 & 0 \end{bmatrix} = \begin{bmatrix} 1 & 0 \\ 1 & 0 \end{bmatrix}.$$

13.

$$\begin{array}{c} \\ 1 \\ 2 \\ 3 \\ 4 \\ 5 \end{array} \begin{array}{c} \begin{array}{ccccc} 1 & 2 & 3 & 4 & 5 \end{array} \\ \begin{bmatrix} 1 & 0 & 0 & 0 & 0 \\ 0 & 1 & 0 & 0 & 0 \\ 0.1 & 0.2 & 0.3 & 0.2 & 0.2 \\ 0.3 & 0.5 & 0.1 & 0 & 0.1 \\ 0 & 0 & 0 & 0 & 1 \end{bmatrix} \end{array} = P$$

Rearranging, we obtain the matrix

$$\begin{array}{c} \\ 1 \\ 2 \\ 5 \\ 3 \\ 4 \end{array} \begin{array}{c} \begin{array}{ccccc} 1 & 2 & 3 & 4 & 5 \end{array} \\ \left[\begin{array}{ccc|cc} 1 & 0 & 0 & 0 & 0 \\ 0 & 1 & 0 & 0 & 0 \\ 0 & 0 & 1 & 0 & 0 \\ \hline 0.1 & 0.2 & 0.2 & 0.3 & 0.2 \\ 0.3 & 0.5 & 0.1 & 0.1 & 0 \end{array}\right] \end{array}.$$

$$R = \begin{bmatrix} 0.1 & 0.2 & 0.2 \\ 0.3 & 0.5 & 0.1 \end{bmatrix}; Q = \begin{bmatrix} 0.3 & 0.2 \\ 0.1 & 0 \end{bmatrix}$$

$$F = (I_2 - Q)^{-1} = \left(\begin{bmatrix} 1 & 0 \\ 0 & 1 \end{bmatrix} - \begin{bmatrix} 0.3 & 0.2 \\ 0.1 & 0 \end{bmatrix} \right)^{-1}$$

$$= \begin{bmatrix} 0.7 & -0.2 \\ -0.1 & 1 \end{bmatrix}^{-1} = \begin{bmatrix} \frac{25}{17} & \frac{5}{17} \\ \frac{5}{34} & \frac{35}{34} \end{bmatrix}$$

$$FR = \begin{bmatrix} \frac{25}{17} & \frac{5}{17} \\ \frac{5}{34} & \frac{35}{34} \end{bmatrix} \begin{bmatrix} \frac{1}{10} & \frac{2}{10} & \frac{2}{10} \\ \frac{3}{10} & \frac{5}{10} & \frac{1}{10} \end{bmatrix}$$

$$= \begin{bmatrix} \frac{4}{17} & \frac{15}{34} & \frac{11}{34} \\ \frac{11}{34} & \frac{37}{68} & \frac{9}{68} \end{bmatrix}$$

14.

$$\begin{array}{c} \\ 1 \\ 2 \\ 3 \\ 4 \\ 5 \end{array} \begin{array}{c} \begin{array}{ccccc} 1 & 2 & 3 & 4 & 5 \end{array} \\ \begin{bmatrix} 0.4 & 0.2 & 0.3 & 0 & 0.1 \\ 0 & 1 & 0 & 0 & 0 \\ 0 & 0 & 1 & 0 & 0 \\ 0.1 & 0.5 & 0.1 & 0.1 & 0.2 \\ 0 & 0 & 0 & 0 & 1 \end{bmatrix} \end{array}$$

Observe that states 2, 3, and 5 are absorbing. The rearranged matrix is

$$\begin{array}{c} \\ 2 \\ 3 \\ 5 \\ 1 \\ 4 \end{array} \begin{array}{c} \begin{array}{ccccc} 2 & 3 & 5 & 1 & 4 \end{array} \\ \left[\begin{array}{ccc|cc} 1 & 0 & 0 & 0 & 0 \\ 0 & 1 & 0 & 0 & 0 \\ 0 & 0 & 1 & 0 & 0 \\ \hline 0.2 & 0.3 & 0.1 & 0.4 & 0 \\ 0.5 & 0.1 & 0.2 & 0.1 & 0.1 \end{array}\right] \end{array}.$$

Then

$$F = (I_2 - Q)^{-1} = \begin{bmatrix} \frac{3}{5} & 0 \\ -\frac{1}{10} & \frac{9}{10} \end{bmatrix}^{-1}$$

$$= \begin{bmatrix} \frac{5}{3} & 0 \\ \frac{5}{27} & \frac{10}{9} \end{bmatrix},$$

and

$$FR = \begin{bmatrix} \frac{5}{3} & 0 \\ \frac{5}{27} & \frac{10}{9} \end{bmatrix} \begin{bmatrix} 0.2 & 0.3 & 0.1 \\ 0.5 & 0.1 & 0.2 \end{bmatrix}$$

$$= \begin{bmatrix} \frac{1}{3} & \frac{1}{2} & \frac{1}{6} \\ \frac{16}{27} & \frac{1}{6} & \frac{13}{54} \end{bmatrix}.$$

15. **(a)** The transition matrix is

$$\begin{array}{c} \\ 0 \\ 1 \\ 2 \\ 3 \\ 4 \end{array} \begin{array}{c} \begin{array}{ccccc} 0 & 1 & 2 & 3 & 4 \end{array} \\ \begin{bmatrix} 1 & 0 & 0 & 0 & 0 \\ \frac{1}{2} & 0 & \frac{1}{2} & 0 & 0 \\ 0 & \frac{1}{2} & 0 & \frac{1}{2} & 0 \\ 0 & 0 & \frac{1}{2} & 0 & \frac{1}{2} \\ 0 & 0 & 0 & 0 & 1 \end{bmatrix} \end{array}.$$

(b) Rearranging, we have

$$\begin{array}{c} \\ 0 \\ 4 \\ 1 \\ 2 \\ 3 \end{array} \begin{array}{c} \begin{array}{ccccc} 0 & 4 & 1 & 2 & 3 \end{array} \\ \left[\begin{array}{cc|ccc} 1 & 0 & 0 & 0 & 0 \\ 0 & 1 & 0 & 0 & 0 \\ \hline \frac{1}{2} & 0 & 0 & \frac{1}{2} & 0 \\ 0 & 0 & \frac{1}{2} & 0 & \frac{1}{2} \\ 0 & \frac{1}{2} & 0 & \frac{1}{2} & 0 \end{array}\right] \end{array}.$$

$$R = \begin{bmatrix} \frac{1}{2} & 0 \\ 0 & 0 \\ 0 & \frac{1}{2} \end{bmatrix}; Q \begin{bmatrix} 0 & \frac{1}{2} & 0 \\ \frac{1}{2} & 0 & \frac{1}{2} \\ 0 & \frac{1}{2} & 0 \end{bmatrix}$$

$$F = (I_3 - Q)^{-1} = \left(\begin{bmatrix} 1 & 0 & 0 \\ 0 & 1 & 0 \\ 0 & 0 & 1 \end{bmatrix} - \begin{bmatrix} 0 & \frac{1}{2} & 0 \\ \frac{1}{2} & 0 & \frac{1}{2} \\ 0 & \frac{1}{2} & 0 \end{bmatrix} \right)^{-1}$$

$$= \begin{bmatrix} 1 & -\frac{1}{2} & 0 \\ -\frac{1}{2} & 1 & -\frac{1}{2} \\ 0 & -\frac{1}{2} & 1 \end{bmatrix}^{-1} = \begin{bmatrix} \frac{3}{2} & 1 & \frac{1}{2} \\ 1 & 2 & 1 \\ \frac{1}{2} & 1 & \frac{3}{2} \end{bmatrix}$$

$$FR = \begin{bmatrix} \frac{3}{2} & 1 & \frac{1}{2} \\ 1 & 2 & 1 \\ \frac{1}{2} & 1 & \frac{3}{2} \end{bmatrix} \begin{bmatrix} \frac{1}{2} & 0 \\ 0 & 0 \\ 0 & \frac{1}{2} \end{bmatrix} = \begin{bmatrix} \frac{3}{4} & \frac{1}{4} \\ \frac{1}{2} & \frac{1}{2} \\ \frac{1}{4} & \frac{3}{4} \end{bmatrix}$$

(c) If player A starts with \$1, the probability of ruin for A is $\frac{3}{4}$, since that is the entry in row 1, column 1 of FR. The $\frac{3}{4}$ is the probability that the nonabsorbing state of starting with \$1 will lead to the absorbing state of ruin.

(d) If player A starts with \$3, the probability of ruin for A is $\frac{1}{4}$, since that is the entry in row 3, column 1 of FR.

16. The transition matrix is

$$\begin{array}{c} \\ 0\\1\\2\\3\\4\\5 \end{array}\begin{array}{c} \begin{array}{cccccc} 0 & 1 & 2 & 3 & 4 & 5 \end{array} \\ \begin{bmatrix} 1 & 0 & 0 & 0 & 0 & 0 \\ \frac{3}{5} & 0 & \frac{2}{5} & 0 & 0 & 0 \\ 0 & \frac{3}{5} & 0 & \frac{2}{5} & 0 & 0 \\ 0 & 0 & \frac{3}{5} & 0 & \frac{2}{5} & 0 \\ 0 & 0 & 0 & \frac{3}{5} & 0 & \frac{2}{5} \\ 0 & 0 & 0 & 0 & 0 & 1 \end{bmatrix} \end{array}.$$

States 0 and 5 are absorbing. We arrange to obtain

$$\begin{array}{c} \\ 0\\5\\1\\2\\3\\4 \end{array}\begin{array}{c} \begin{array}{cccccc} 0 & 5 & 1 & 2 & 3 & 4 \end{array} \\ \left[\begin{array}{cc|cccc} 1 & 0 & 0 & 0 & 0 & 0 \\ 0 & 1 & 0 & 0 & 0 & 0 \\ \hline \frac{3}{5} & 0 & 0 & \frac{2}{5} & 0 & 0 \\ 0 & 0 & \frac{3}{5} & 0 & \frac{2}{5} & 0 \\ 0 & 0 & 0 & \frac{3}{5} & 0 & \frac{2}{5} \\ 0 & \frac{2}{5} & 0 & 0 & \frac{3}{5} & 0 \end{array}\right] \end{array}.$$

Then,

$$F = \begin{bmatrix} 1 & -\frac{2}{5} & 0 & 0 \\ -\frac{3}{5} & 1 & -\frac{2}{5} & 0 \\ 0 & -\frac{3}{5} & 1 & -\frac{2}{5} \\ 0 & 0 & -\frac{3}{5} & 1 \end{bmatrix}^{-1}$$

$$= \begin{bmatrix} 1.540284 & 0.9004739 & 0.4739336 & 0.1895735 \\ 1.350711 & 2.251185 & 1.184834 & 0.4739336 \\ 1.066351 & 1.777251 & 2.251185 & 0.9004739 \\ 0.6398104 & 1.066351 & 1.350711 & 1.540284 \end{bmatrix}$$

and

$$FR = \begin{array}{c} \\ 1\\2\\3\\4 \end{array}\begin{array}{c} \begin{array}{cc} 0 & 5 \end{array} \\ \begin{bmatrix} 0.9242 & 0.0758 \\ 0.8104 & 0.1896 \\ 0.6398 & 0.3602 \\ 0.3839 & 0.6161 \end{bmatrix} \end{array}.$$

(a) If B has \$3, then A has \$2 and the probability of ruin is 0.810.

(b) If B has \$1, then A has \$4 and the probability of ruin is 0.384.

17. Use the formulas given in the textbook to calculate r and then x_a if $a = 10, b = 30$, and $p = 0.49$.

$$r = \frac{1-p}{p} = \frac{1-0.49}{0.49} \approx 1.0408$$

The probability that A will be ruined in this situation is

$$x_a = \frac{r^a - r^{a+b}}{1 - r^{a+b}} = \frac{(1.0408)^{10} - (1.0408)^{40}}{1-(1.0408)^{40}}$$
$$\approx 0.8756.$$

18. $p = 0.50$, so

$$r = \frac{1-p}{p} = \frac{1-0.50}{0.50} = 1.$$

Hence,

$$x_a = \frac{b}{a+b} = \frac{30}{10+30} = \frac{30}{40} = \frac{3}{4}.$$

19. $a = 10,\ b = 10$

Complete the chart by using the formulas given in Exercise 17 for r and x_a.

p	r	x_a
0.1	9	0.9999999997
0.2	4	0.99999905
0.3	$\frac{7}{3}$	0.99979
0.4	1.5	0.98295
0.5	1	0.5
0.6	$\frac{2}{3}$	0.017046
0.7	$\frac{3}{7}$	0.000209
0.8	0.25	0.00000095
0.9	$\frac{1}{9}$	0.0000000003

20. To calculate the expected total number of times a Markov chain will visit state j before absorption, regardless of the current state, simply sum the elements in column j of the fundamental matrix.

21. Since every nonabsorbing state leads to the one absorbing state probability 1, every entry in FR should be 1. For example, in the matrix

$$P = \begin{pmatrix} 1 & 0 & 0 \\ 0.5 & 0.5 & 0 \\ 0.5 & 0 & 0.5 \end{pmatrix}$$

the submatrix $Q = \begin{pmatrix} 0.5 & 0 \\ 0 & 0.5 \end{pmatrix}$, the fundamental matrix $F = (I_2 - Q)^{-1} = \begin{pmatrix} 0.5 & 0 \\ 0 & 0.5 \end{pmatrix}^{-1} = \begin{pmatrix} 2 & 0 \\ 0 & 2 \end{pmatrix}$, and the submatrix $R = \begin{pmatrix} 0.5 \\ 0.5 \end{pmatrix}$.

So, the product $FR = \begin{pmatrix} 1 \\ 1 \end{pmatrix}$ is a column matrix of all 1's.

22. This exercise should be solved by graphing calculator methods. The solution may vary. The answers are as follows.

(a) $F = \begin{bmatrix} 1.6667 & 0.6061 \\ 0 & 1.8182 \end{bmatrix}$

$$FR = \begin{bmatrix} 0.1136 & 0.8864 \\ 0.0909 & 0.9091 \end{bmatrix}$$

(b) 0.0909

(c) 0.8864

23. **(a)** Since every living person will eventually end up dead, a safe estimate for the probability of a well person eventually being dead is 1.

(b) To verify the probability in part (a) using the matrix product FR, we first rewrite the transition matrix

$$P = \begin{array}{c} \\ \text{well} \\ \text{ill} \\ \text{dead} \end{array} \begin{array}{c} \begin{array}{ccc} \text{well} & \text{ill} & \text{dead} \end{array} \\ \begin{bmatrix} 0.3 & 0.5 & 0.2 \\ 0 & 0.5 & 0.5 \\ 0 & 0 & 1 \end{bmatrix} \end{array},$$

so that the absorbing state comes first.

$$P = \begin{array}{c} \\ \text{dead} \\ \text{ill} \\ \text{well} \end{array} \begin{array}{c} \begin{array}{ccc} \text{dead} & \text{ill} & \text{well} \end{array} \\ \left[\begin{array}{c|cc} 1 & 0 & 0 \\ \hline 0.5 & 0.5 & 0 \\ 0.2 & 0.5 & 0.3 \end{array}\right] \end{array}, \text{ so}$$

$R = \begin{bmatrix} 0.5 \\ 0.2 \end{bmatrix}$ and

$Q = \begin{bmatrix} 0.5 & 0 \\ 0.5 & 0.3 \end{bmatrix}$. Find the fundamental matrix F.

$$F = (I_2 - Q)^{-1} = \begin{bmatrix} 0.5 & 0 \\ -0.5 & 0.7 \end{bmatrix}^{-1} = \begin{bmatrix} 2 & 0 \\ \frac{10}{7} & \frac{10}{7} \end{bmatrix},$$

so

$FR = \begin{bmatrix} 1 \\ 1 \end{bmatrix}$. Therefore, as k approaches infinity, R approaches FR, Q approaches $\begin{bmatrix} 0 & 0 \\ 0 & 0 \end{bmatrix}$, and P^k approaches

$$P = \begin{array}{c} \\ \text{dead} \\ \text{ill} \\ \text{well} \end{array} \begin{array}{c} \begin{array}{ccc} \text{dead} & \text{ill} & \text{well} \end{array} \\ \left[\begin{array}{c|cc} 1 & 0 & 0 \\ \hline 1 & 0 & 0 \\ 1 & 0 & 0 \end{array}\right] \end{array}.$$

So, this verifies that the probability that all well (and all ill) patients will eventually be dead is 1.

(c) By examining the fundamental matrix F, we see that the expected number of cycles that a well patient will continue to be well before dying is $\frac{10}{7}$, and the expected number of cycles a well person will be ill before dying is $\frac{10}{7}$.

24. **(a)** The transition matrix is

$$\begin{array}{c} \\ 1 \\ 2 \\ 3 \end{array} \begin{array}{c} \begin{array}{ccc} 1 & 2 & 3 \end{array} \\ \begin{bmatrix} 0.05 & 0.15 & 0.8 \\ 0.05 & 0.15 & 0.8 \\ 0 & 0 & 1 \end{bmatrix} \end{array}.$$

Rearranging, we obtain the matrix

$$\begin{array}{c} \\ 3 \\ 1 \\ 2 \end{array} \begin{array}{c} \begin{array}{ccc} 3 & 1 & 2 \end{array} \\ \left[\begin{array}{c|cc} 1 & 0 & 0 \\ \hline 0.8 & 0.05 & 0.15 \\ 0.8 & 0.05 & 0.15 \end{array}\right] \end{array}.$$

$$R = \begin{bmatrix} 0.8 \\ 0.8 \end{bmatrix}; Q = \begin{bmatrix} 0.05 & 0.15 \\ 0.05 & 0.15 \end{bmatrix}$$

(b) $F = [I_2 - Q]^{-1}$

$$= \left(\begin{bmatrix} 1 & 0 \\ 0 & 1 \end{bmatrix} - \begin{bmatrix} 0.05 & 0.15 \\ 0.05 & 0.15 \end{bmatrix}\right)^{-1}$$

$$= \begin{bmatrix} 0.95 & -0.15 \\ -0.05 & 0.85 \end{bmatrix}^{-1}$$

$$= \begin{bmatrix} 1.0625 & 0.1875 \\ 0.0625 & 1.1875 \end{bmatrix}$$

$$FR = \begin{bmatrix} 1.0625 & 0.1875 \\ 0.0625 & 1.1875 \end{bmatrix} \begin{bmatrix} 0.8 \\ 0.8 \end{bmatrix} = \begin{bmatrix} 1 \\ 1 \end{bmatrix}$$

(c) The probability that the disease eventually disappears is 1, since that is the entry in row 2, column 1 of FR.

(d) The expected number of people is 1.25, since that is the sum of the entries in row 2 of F.

25. (a) The transition matrix P is

$$\begin{array}{c} \\ 1 \\ 2 \\ 3 \\ 4 \end{array}\begin{array}{c} \begin{array}{cccc} 1 & 2 & 3 & 4 \end{array} \\ \begin{bmatrix} 0.15 & 0.6 & 0.25 & 0 \\ 0 & 0.15 & 0.25 & 0.6 \\ 0 & 0 & 1 & 0 \\ 0 & 0 & 0 & 1 \end{bmatrix} \end{array}.$$

Note that states 3 and 4 are absorbing. We arrange the matrix to obtain

$$\begin{array}{c} \\ 3 \\ 4 \\ 1 \\ 2 \end{array}\begin{array}{c} \begin{array}{cccc} 3 & 4 & 1 & 2 \end{array} \\ \left[\begin{array}{cc|cc} 1 & 0 & 0 & 0 \\ 0 & 1 & 0 & 0 \\ \hline 0.25 & 0 & 0.15 & 0.6 \\ 0.25 & 0.6 & 0 & 0.15 \end{array}\right] \end{array}.$$

Then

$$F = \begin{bmatrix} 0.85 & -0.6 \\ 0 & 0.85 \end{bmatrix}^{-1} = \begin{bmatrix} \frac{20}{17} & \frac{240}{289} \\ 0 & \frac{20}{17} \end{bmatrix}, \text{ so}$$

$$FR = \begin{array}{c} \\ 1 \\ 2 \end{array}\begin{array}{c} \begin{array}{cc} 3 & 4 \end{array} \\ \begin{bmatrix} \frac{145}{289} & \frac{144}{289} \\ \frac{5}{17} & \frac{12}{17} \end{bmatrix} \end{array}.$$

(b) The probability of a freshman's graduating is the probability of state 1 eventually becoming state 4. From FR we see this probability is $\frac{144}{289}$.

(c) To find the expected number of years that a freshman will be in college before graduating or flunking out, add the entries in row 1 of F to obtain

$$\frac{20}{17} + \frac{240}{289} = \frac{580}{289} \approx 2.007 \text{ yr.}$$

26. (a) The transition matrix is

$$\begin{array}{c} \\ \text{A} \\ \text{LR} \\ \text{SO} \end{array}\begin{array}{c} \begin{array}{ccc} \text{A} & \text{LR} & \text{SO} \end{array} \\ \begin{bmatrix} 0.80 & 0.15 & 0.05 \\ 0.05 & 0.80 & 0.15 \\ 0 & 0 & 1 \end{bmatrix} \end{array}.$$

Rearranging, we obtain the matrix

$$\begin{array}{c} \\ \text{SO} \\ \text{A} \\ \text{LR} \end{array}\begin{array}{c} \begin{array}{ccc} \text{SO} & \text{A} & \text{LR} \end{array} \\ \left[\begin{array}{c|cc} 1 & 0 & 0 \\ \hline 0.05 & 0.80 & 0.15 \\ 0.15 & 0.05 & 0.80 \end{array}\right] \end{array}.$$

$$R = \begin{bmatrix} 0.05 \\ 0.15 \end{bmatrix}; Q = \begin{bmatrix} 0.80 & 0.15 \\ 0.05 & 0.80 \end{bmatrix}$$

$$\begin{aligned} F &= (I_2 - Q)^{-1} \\ &= \left(\begin{bmatrix} 1 & 0 \\ 0 & 1 \end{bmatrix} - \begin{bmatrix} 0.80 & 0.15 \\ 0.05 & 0.80 \end{bmatrix}\right)^{-1} \\ &= \begin{bmatrix} 0.2 & -0.15 \\ -0.05 & 0.2 \end{bmatrix}^{-1} \\ &= \begin{bmatrix} 6.154 & 4.615 \\ 1.538 & 6.154 \end{bmatrix} \end{aligned}$$

$$\begin{aligned} FR &= \begin{bmatrix} 6.154 & 4.615 \\ 1.538 & 6.154 \end{bmatrix}\begin{bmatrix} 0.05 \\ 0.15 \end{bmatrix} \\ &= \begin{bmatrix} 1.000 \\ 1.000 \end{bmatrix} \end{aligned}$$

(b) The probability that a person who commuted by car ends up avoiding the downtown area is 1, since that is the entry in row 1, column 1 of FR.

(c) The expected number of years until a person who commutes by automobile this year ends up avoiding the downtown area is $10.769 \approx 10.77$ yr since that is the sum of the entries in row 1 of F.

27. To answer parts (a), (b), and (c), we need to find the fundamental matrix F associated with the transition matrix

$$P = \begin{array}{c} \\ s \\ n \\ c \\ q \end{array}\begin{array}{c} \begin{array}{cccc} s & n & c & q \end{array} \\ \begin{bmatrix} 0.70 & 0.11 & 0 & 0.19 \\ 0 & 0 & 0.86 & 0.14 \\ 0 & 0 & 0.88 & 0.12 \\ 0 & 0 & 0 & 1 \end{bmatrix} \end{array}$$

First rearrange the rows and columns of P so the absorbing state comes first.

$$\begin{array}{c} \\ q \\ n \\ c \\ s \end{array}\begin{array}{c} \begin{array}{cccc} q & n & c & s \end{array} \\ \left[\begin{array}{c|ccc} 1 & 0 & 0 & 0 \\ \hline 0.14 & 0 & 0.86 & 0 \\ 0.12 & 0 & 0.88 & 0 \\ 0.19 & 0.11 & 0 & 0.70 \end{array}\right] \end{array}$$

Therefore, $Q = \begin{bmatrix} 0 & 0.86 & 0 \\ 0 & 0.88 & 0 \\ 0.11 & 0 & 0.70 \end{bmatrix}$, and so

$$F = (I_3 - Q)^{-1} = \begin{bmatrix} 1 & -0.86 & 0 \\ 0 & 0.12 & 0 \\ -0.11 & 0 & 0.3 \end{bmatrix}^{-1}$$

$$= \begin{array}{c} \\ n \\ c \\ s \end{array} \begin{array}{c} \begin{array}{ccc} n & c & s \end{array} \\ \begin{bmatrix} 1 & \frac{43}{6} & 0 \\ 0 & \frac{25}{3} & 0 \\ \frac{11}{30} & \frac{473}{180} & \frac{10}{3} \end{bmatrix} \end{array}.$$

(a) To find the expected number of years that a student with an interest in teaching will spend as a continuing teacher, look at the entry in row three, column two of F, which is $\frac{473}{180} \approx 2.628$.

(b) To find the expected number of years that a new teacher will spend as a continuing teacher, look at the entry in row one, column two, which is $\frac{43}{6} \approx 7.167$.

(c) To find the expected number of years that a continuing teacher will spend as a continuing teacher, look at the entry in row two, column two, which is $\frac{25}{3} \approx 8.333$.

28. **(a)**

$$\begin{array}{c} \\ 1 \\ 2 \\ 3 \\ 4 \\ 5 \end{array} \begin{array}{c} \begin{array}{ccccc} 1 & 2 & 3 & 4 & 5 \end{array} \\ \begin{bmatrix} 0.4 & 0.3 & 0.2 & 0.1 & 0 \\ 0.2 & 0.1 & 0 & 0.6 & 0.1 \\ 0 & 0 & 1 & 0 & 0 \\ 0.1 & 0.1 & 0.4 & 0.1 & 0.3 \\ 0 & 0 & 0 & 0 & 1 \end{bmatrix} \end{array}$$

is the transition matrix. States 3 and 5 are absorbing. Upon rearranging, we obtain

$$\begin{array}{c} \\ 3 \\ 5 \\ 1 \\ 2 \\ 4 \end{array} \begin{array}{c} \begin{array}{ccccc} 3 & 5 & 1 & 2 & 4 \end{array} \\ \left[\begin{array}{cc|ccc} 1 & 0 & 0 & 0 & 0 \\ 0 & 1 & 0 & 0 & 0 \\ \hline 0.2 & 0 & 0.4 & 0.3 & 0.1 \\ 0 & 0.1 & 0.2 & 0.1 & 0.6 \\ 0.4 & 0.3 & 0.1 & 0.1 & 0.1 \end{array}\right] \end{array}.$$

Then

$$F = \begin{bmatrix} 0.6 & -0.3 & -0.1 \\ -0.2 & 0.9 & -0.6 \\ -0.1 & -0.1 & 0.9 \end{bmatrix}^{-1}$$

$$= \begin{bmatrix} 2.0436 & 0.7629 & 0.7357 \\ 0.6540 & 1.4441 & 1.0354 \\ 0.2997 & 0.2452 & 1.3079 \end{bmatrix},$$

and

$$FR = \begin{array}{c} \\ 1 \\ 2 \\ 4 \end{array} \begin{array}{c} \begin{array}{cc} 3 & 5 \end{array} \\ \begin{bmatrix} 0.703 & 0.297 \\ 0.545 & 0.455 \\ 0.583 & 0.417 \end{bmatrix} \end{array}.$$

The second column of FR gives the probability of ending up in compartment 5 given the initial compartment.

(b) From compartment 1, the probability is 0.297.

(c) From compartment 2, the probability is 0.455.

(d) From compartment 3, the probability is 0 since state 3 is absorbing.

(e) From compartment 4, the probability is 0.417.

(f) To find the expected number of times that a rat in compartment 1 will be in compartment 1 before ending up in compartment 3 or 5, look at the entry in row 1, column 1 of F, $2.0436 \approx 2.04$.

(g) To find the expected number of times that a rat in compartment 4 will be in compartment 4 before ending up in compartment 3 or 5, look at the entry in row 3, column 3 of F, $1.3079 \approx 1.31$.

29. **(a)** If we assume that at each serve the server has a probability of p of winning the next point, then he or she has a probability of $1 - p$ of losing the next point. Consider the first serve. Either the server will win the point (ad in) with a probability of p or lose the point (ad out) with a probability of $1 - p$; the probability of remaining at the current state (deuce) is 0. A similar argument holds for the next serve from any of the three states (ad in, deuce, and ad out). The *loss* and *win* states are absorbing: the server cannot go from either of those states to any other state. Thus, we obtain the given transition matrix from the server's point of view.

(b) If $p = 0.6$, the transition matrix is as follows. (Let the states loss, ad out, deuce, ad in, and win be represented by l, o, d, i, and w, respectively.)

$$P = \begin{array}{c} \\ l \\ o \\ d \\ i \\ w \end{array} \begin{array}{c} \begin{array}{ccccc} l & o & d & i & w \end{array} \\ \begin{bmatrix} 1 & 0 & 0 & 0 & 0 \\ 0.4 & 0 & 0.6 & 0 & 0 \\ 0 & 0.4 & 0 & 0.6 & 0 \\ 0 & 0 & 0.4 & 0 & 0.6 \\ 0 & 0 & 0 & 0 & 1 \end{bmatrix} \end{array}$$

To answer the question, we need to find the fundamental matrix F associated with the transition matrix. The first step is to arrange the rows and columns of P so the absorbing states come first.

$$\begin{array}{c} \\ l \\ w \\ o \\ d \\ i \end{array}\begin{array}{c} \begin{array}{ccccc} l & w & o & d & i \end{array} \\ \left[\begin{array}{cc|ccc} 1 & 0 & 0 & 0 & 0 \\ 0 & 1 & 0 & 0 & 0 \\ \hline 0.4 & 0 & 0 & 0.6 & 0 \\ 0 & 0 & 0.4 & 0 & 0.6 \\ 0 & 0.6 & 0 & 0.4 & 0 \end{array}\right] \end{array}$$

Thus,

$$Q = \begin{array}{c} o \\ d \\ i \end{array}\left[\begin{array}{ccc} 0 & 0.6 & 0 \\ 0.4 & 0 & 0.6 \\ 0 & 0.4 & 0 \end{array}\right] \text{ (columns } o, d, i\text{) and}$$

$$R = \begin{array}{c} o \\ d \\ i \end{array}\left[\begin{array}{cc} 0.4 & 0 \\ 0 & 0 \\ 0 & 0.6 \end{array}\right] \text{ (columns } l, w\text{)}.$$

Now find the fundamental matrix F.

$$F = (I_3 - Q)^{-1}$$

$$= \left[\begin{array}{ccc} 1 & -0.6 & 0 \\ -0.4 & 1 & 0.6 \\ 0 & -0.4 & 1 \end{array}\right]^{-1}$$

$$= \begin{array}{c} o \\ d \\ i \end{array}\left[\begin{array}{ccc} \frac{19}{13} & \frac{15}{13} & \frac{9}{13} \\ \frac{10}{13} & \frac{25}{13} & \frac{15}{13} \\ \frac{4}{13} & \frac{10}{13} & \frac{19}{13} \end{array}\right] \text{ (columns } o, d, i\text{)}$$

To find the probabilities that the server will win when the score is ad out (state o), deuce (state d), and ad in (state i), find FR.

$$FR = \left[\begin{array}{ccc} \frac{19}{13} & \frac{15}{13} & \frac{9}{13} \\ \frac{10}{13} & \frac{25}{13} & \frac{15}{13} \\ \frac{4}{13} & \frac{10}{13} & \frac{19}{13} \end{array}\right]\left[\begin{array}{cc} 0.4 & 0 \\ 0 & 0 \\ 0 & 0.6 \end{array}\right]$$

$$= \begin{array}{c} o \\ d \\ i \end{array}\left[\begin{array}{cc} \frac{38}{65} & \frac{27}{65} \\ \frac{4}{13} & \frac{9}{13} \\ \frac{8}{65} & \frac{57}{65} \end{array}\right] \text{ (columns } l, w\text{)}$$

Therefore, the probability the server will win when the score is ad out (in other words, to move from state o to state w) is $\frac{27}{65} \approx 0.4154$, when the score is deuce (state d to state w) is $\frac{9}{13} \approx 0.6923$, and when the score is ad in (state i to state w) is $\frac{57}{65} \approx 0.8769$.

30. **(a)** Having 0 dollars is an absorbing state and having 7 dollars is an absorbing state, so in the transition matrix, P, the elements $p_{11} = 1$, $p_{88} = 1$, and the remaining entries in rows 1 and 8 are 0. Since for each of the other states the probability is $\frac{1}{2}$ of either gaining or losing a dollar, the transition matrix is

$$P = \begin{array}{c} 0 \\ 1 \\ 2 \\ 3 \\ 4 \\ 5 \\ 6 \\ 7 \end{array}\left[\begin{array}{cccccccc} 1 & 0 & 0 & 0 & 0 & 0 & 0 & 0 \\ \frac{1}{2} & 0 & \frac{1}{2} & 0 & 0 & 0 & 0 & 0 \\ 0 & \frac{1}{2} & 0 & \frac{1}{2} & 0 & 0 & 0 & 0 \\ 0 & 0 & \frac{1}{2} & 0 & \frac{1}{2} & 0 & 0 & 0 \\ 0 & 0 & 0 & \frac{1}{2} & 0 & \frac{1}{2} & 0 & 0 \\ 0 & 0 & 0 & 0 & \frac{1}{2} & 0 & \frac{1}{2} & 0 \\ 0 & 0 & 0 & 0 & 0 & \frac{1}{2} & 0 & \frac{1}{2} \\ 0 & 0 & 0 & 0 & 0 & 0 & 0 & 1 \end{array}\right] \text{ (columns } 0, 1, 2, 3, 4, 5, 6, 7\text{)}.$$

To answer parts (b) and (c), we need to calculate the product matrix FR. To do this, first re-write P so that the absorbing states come first.

$$P = \begin{array}{c} 0 \\ 7 \\ 1 \\ 2 \\ 3 \\ 4 \\ 5 \\ 6 \end{array}\left[\begin{array}{cc|cccccc} 1 & 0 & 0 & 0 & 0 & 0 & 0 & 0 \\ 0 & 1 & 0 & 0 & 0 & 0 & 0 & 0 \\ \hline \frac{1}{2} & 0 & 0 & \frac{1}{2} & 0 & 0 & 0 & 0 \\ 0 & 0 & \frac{1}{2} & 0 & \frac{1}{2} & 0 & 0 & 0 \\ 0 & 0 & 0 & \frac{1}{2} & 0 & \frac{1}{2} & 0 & 0 \\ 0 & 0 & 0 & 0 & \frac{1}{2} & 0 & \frac{1}{2} & 0 \\ 0 & 0 & 0 & 0 & 0 & \frac{1}{2} & 0 & \frac{1}{2} \\ 0 & \frac{1}{2} & 0 & 0 & 0 & 0 & \frac{1}{2} & 0 \end{array}\right] \text{ (columns } 0, 7, 1, 2, 3, 4, 5, 6\text{)},$$

$$\text{so } R = \begin{array}{c} 1 \\ 2 \\ 3 \\ 4 \\ 5 \\ 6 \end{array}\left[\begin{array}{cc} \frac{1}{2} & 0 \\ 0 & 0 \\ 0 & 0 \\ 0 & 0 \\ 0 & 0 \\ 0 & \frac{1}{2} \end{array}\right] \text{ (columns } 0, 7\text{) and}$$

$$Q = \left[\begin{array}{cccccc} 0 & \frac{1}{2} & 0 & 0 & 0 & 0 \\ \frac{1}{2} & 0 & \frac{1}{2} & 0 & 0 & 0 \\ 0 & \frac{1}{2} & 0 & \frac{1}{2} & 0 & 0 \\ 0 & 0 & \frac{1}{2} & 0 & \frac{1}{2} & 0 \\ 0 & 0 & 0 & \frac{1}{2} & 0 & \frac{1}{2} \\ 0 & 0 & 0 & 0 & \frac{1}{2} & 0 \end{array}\right]$$

Therefore,

$$F = (I_6 - Q)^{-1} = \begin{bmatrix} 1 & -\frac{1}{2} & 0 & 0 & 0 & 0 \\ -\frac{1}{2} & 1 & -\frac{1}{2} & 0 & 0 & 0 \\ 0 & -\frac{1}{2} & 1 & -\frac{1}{2} & 0 & 0 \\ 0 & 0 & -\frac{1}{2} & 1 & -\frac{1}{2} & 0 \\ 0 & 0 & 0 & -\frac{1}{2} & 1 & -\frac{1}{2} \\ 0 & 0 & 0 & 0 & -\frac{1}{2} & 1 \end{bmatrix}^{-1} = \begin{bmatrix} \frac{12}{7} & \frac{10}{7} & \frac{8}{7} & \frac{6}{7} & \frac{4}{7} & \frac{2}{7} \\ \frac{10}{7} & \frac{20}{7} & \frac{16}{7} & \frac{12}{7} & \frac{8}{7} & \frac{4}{7} \\ \frac{8}{7} & \frac{16}{7} & \frac{24}{7} & \frac{18}{7} & \frac{12}{7} & \frac{6}{7} \\ \frac{6}{7} & \frac{12}{7} & \frac{18}{7} & \frac{24}{7} & \frac{16}{7} & \frac{8}{7} \\ \frac{4}{7} & \frac{8}{7} & \frac{12}{7} & \frac{16}{7} & \frac{20}{7} & \frac{10}{7} \\ \frac{2}{7} & \frac{4}{7} & \frac{6}{7} & \frac{8}{7} & \frac{10}{7} & \frac{12}{7} \end{bmatrix},$$

$$\text{so } FR = \begin{array}{c} \\ 1 \\ 2 \\ 3 \\ 4 \\ 5 \\ 6 \end{array} \begin{array}{c} \begin{array}{cc} 0 & 7 \end{array} \\ \begin{bmatrix} \frac{6}{7} & \frac{1}{7} \\ \frac{5}{7} & \frac{2}{7} \\ \frac{4}{7} & \frac{3}{7} \\ \frac{3}{7} & \frac{4}{7} \\ \frac{2}{7} & \frac{5}{7} \\ \frac{1}{7} & \frac{6}{7} \end{bmatrix} \end{array}.$$

(b) The probability of ruin for player A if A starts with \$4 is the entry in the fourth row, first column of FR, which is $\frac{3}{7}$.

(c) The probability of ruin for player A if A starts with \$5 is the entry in the fifth row, first column, which is $\frac{2}{7}$.

Chapter 10 Review Exercises

3. $\begin{bmatrix} -0.2 & 1.2 \\ 0.8 & 0.2 \end{bmatrix}$

This could not be a transition matrix because it contains a negative entry.

4. $\begin{bmatrix} 0.4 & 0.6 \\ 1 & 0 \end{bmatrix}$

This could be a transition matrix since it is a square matrix, all entries are between 0 and 1, inclusive, and the sum of the entries in each row is 1.

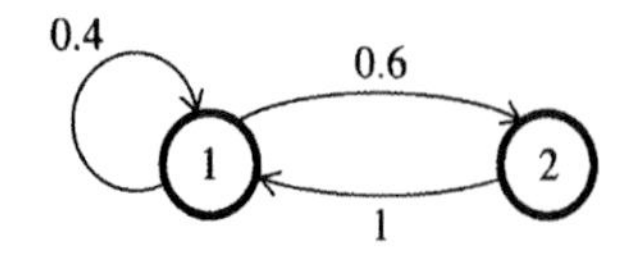

5. $\begin{bmatrix} 0.8 & 0.2 & 0 \\ 0 & 1 & 0 \\ 0.1 & 0.4 & 0.5 \end{bmatrix}$

This could be a transition matrix for the same reasons stated in Exercise 3.

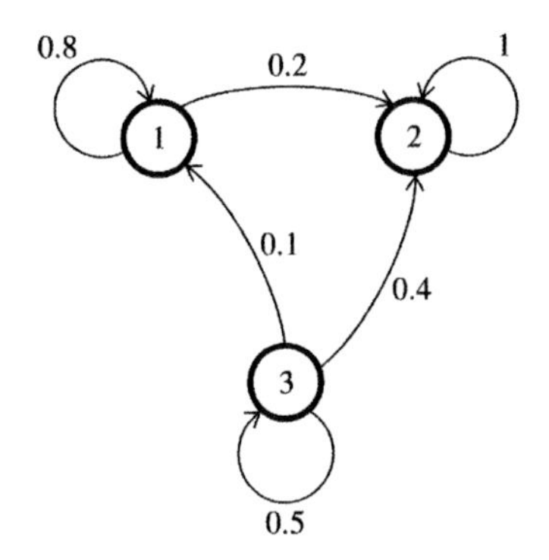

6. $\begin{bmatrix} 0.6 & 0.2 & 0.3 \\ 0.1 & 0.5 & 0.4 \\ 0.3 & 0.3 & 0.4 \end{bmatrix}$

This could not be a transition matrix because the sum of the entries in the first row is not 1.

7. (a) $C = \begin{bmatrix} 0.7 & 0.3 \\ 1 & 0 \end{bmatrix}$

$$C^2 = \begin{bmatrix} 0.7 & 0.3 \\ 1 & 0 \end{bmatrix} \begin{bmatrix} 0.7 & 0.3 \\ 1 & 0 \end{bmatrix} = \begin{bmatrix} 0.79 & 0.21 \\ 0.7 & 0.3 \end{bmatrix}$$

$$C^3 = \begin{bmatrix} 0.7 & 0.3 \\ 1 & 0 \end{bmatrix} \begin{bmatrix} 0.79 & 0.21 \\ 0.7 & 0.3 \end{bmatrix} = \begin{bmatrix} 0.763 & 0.237 \\ 0.79 & 0.21 \end{bmatrix}$$

(b) The probability that state 2 changes to state 1 after three repetitions of the experiment is the entry in row 2, column 1 of C^3, or 0.79.

8. (a) $D = \begin{bmatrix} 0.4 & 0.6 \\ 0.5 & 0.5 \end{bmatrix}$

$$D^2 = \begin{bmatrix} 0.4 & 0.6 \\ 0.5 & 0.5 \end{bmatrix} \begin{bmatrix} 0.4 & 0.6 \\ 0.5 & 0.5 \end{bmatrix} = \begin{bmatrix} 0.46 & 0.54 \\ 0.45 & 0.55 \end{bmatrix}$$

$$D^3 = \begin{bmatrix} 0.4 & 0.6 \\ 0.5 & 0.5 \end{bmatrix} \begin{bmatrix} 0.46 & 0.54 \\ 0.45 & 0.55 \end{bmatrix} = \begin{bmatrix} 0.454 & 0.546 \\ 0.455 & 0.545 \end{bmatrix}$$

(b) The probability that state 2 changes to state 1 after three repetitions of the experiment is the entry in row 2, column 1 of D^3, or 0.455.

9. (a) $E = \begin{bmatrix} 0.2 & 0.5 & 0.3 \\ 0.3 & 0.4 & 0.3 \\ 0 & 1 & 0 \end{bmatrix}$

$$E^2 = \begin{bmatrix} 0.2 & 0.5 & 0.3 \\ 0.3 & 0.4 & 0.3 \\ 0 & 1 & 0 \end{bmatrix} \begin{bmatrix} 0.2 & 0.5 & 0.3 \\ 0.3 & 0.4 & 0.3 \\ 0 & 1 & 0 \end{bmatrix} = \begin{bmatrix} 0.19 & 0.6 & 0.21 \\ 0.18 & 0.61 & 0.21 \\ 0.3 & 0.4 & 0.3 \end{bmatrix}$$

$$E^3 = \begin{bmatrix} 0.2 & 0.5 & 0.3 \\ 0.3 & 0.4 & 0.3 \\ 0 & 1 & 0 \end{bmatrix} \begin{bmatrix} 0.19 & 0.6 & 0.21 \\ 0.18 & 0.61 & 0.21 \\ 0.3 & 0.4 & 0.3 \end{bmatrix} = \begin{bmatrix} 0.218 & 0.545 & 0.237 \\ 0.219 & 0.544 & 0.237 \\ 0.18 & 0.61 & 0.21 \end{bmatrix}$$

(b) The probability that state 2 changes to state 1 after 3 repetitions of the experiment is the entry in row 2, column 1 of E^3, or 0.219.

10. (a) $F = \begin{bmatrix} 0.14 & 0.18 & 0.68 \\ 0.35 & 0.28 & 0.37 \\ 0.71 & 0.22 & 0.07 \end{bmatrix}$

$$F^2 = \begin{bmatrix} 0.14 & 0.18 & 0.68 \\ 0.35 & 0.28 & 0.37 \\ 0.71 & 0.22 & 0.07 \end{bmatrix} \begin{bmatrix} 0.14 & 0.18 & 0.68 \\ 0.35 & 0.28 & 0.37 \\ 0.71 & 0.22 & 0.07 \end{bmatrix} = \begin{bmatrix} 0.5654 & 0.2252 & 0.2094 \\ 0.4097 & 0.2228 & 0.3675 \\ 0.2261 & 0.2048 & 0.5691 \end{bmatrix}$$

$$F^3 = \begin{bmatrix} 0.14 & 0.18 & 0.68 \\ 0.35 & 0.28 & 0.37 \\ 0.71 & 0.22 & 0.07 \end{bmatrix} \begin{bmatrix} 0.5654 & 0.2552 & 0.2094 \\ 0.4097 & 0.2228 & 0.3675 \\ 0.2261 & 0.2048 & 0.5691 \end{bmatrix} \approx \begin{bmatrix} 0.3067 & 0.2109 & 0.4825 \\ 0.3963 & 0.2170 & 0.3868 \\ 0.5074 & 0.2232 & 0.2694 \end{bmatrix}$$

(b) The probability that state 2 changes to state 1 after three repetitions of the experiment is the entry in row 2, column 1 of F^3, or 0.3963.

11. $T^2 = \begin{bmatrix} 0.2 & 0.8 \\ 0.5 & 0.5 \end{bmatrix} \begin{bmatrix} 0.2 & 0.8 \\ 0.5 & 0.5 \end{bmatrix} = \begin{bmatrix} 0.44 & 0.56 \\ 0.35 & 0.65 \end{bmatrix}$

The distribution after two repetitions is

$$DT^2 = \begin{bmatrix} 0.3 & 0.7 \end{bmatrix} \begin{bmatrix} 0.44 & 0.56 \\ 0.35 & 0.65 \end{bmatrix} = \begin{bmatrix} 0.377 & 0.623 \end{bmatrix}.$$

To predict the long-range distribution, let V be the probability vector $\begin{bmatrix} v_1 & v_2 \end{bmatrix}$. We want to find V such that

$$VT = V$$

$$\begin{bmatrix} v_1 & v_2 \end{bmatrix} \begin{bmatrix} 0.2 & 0.8 \\ 0.5 & 0.5 \end{bmatrix} = \begin{bmatrix} v_1 & v_2 \end{bmatrix}.$$

By matrix multiplication and equality of matrices,

$$\begin{aligned} 0.2v_1 + 0.5v_2 &= v_1 \\ 0.8v_1 + 0.5v_2 &= v_2. \end{aligned}$$

Simplify the equations to get the dependent system

$$\begin{aligned} -0.8v_1 + 0.5v_2 &= 0 \\ 0.8v_1 - 0.5v_2 &= 0. \end{aligned}$$

Since V is a probability vector,

$$v_1 + v_2 = 1.$$

To find v_1 and v_2, solve the system

$$\begin{aligned} 0.8v_1 - 0.5v_2 &= 0 \\ v_1 + v_2 &= 1 \end{aligned}$$

by the substitution method. Observe that $v_2 = 1 - v_1$.

$$\begin{aligned} 0.8v_1 - 0.5(1 - v_1) &= 0 \\ 1.3v_1 - 0.5 &= 0 \\ v_1 &= \frac{0.5}{1.3} = \frac{5}{13} \\ v_2 &= 1 - \frac{5}{13} = \frac{8}{13} \end{aligned}$$

The long-range distribution is $\begin{bmatrix} \frac{5}{13} & \frac{8}{13} \end{bmatrix}$.

12. $T^2 = \begin{bmatrix} 0.9 & 0.1 \\ 0.2 & 0.8 \end{bmatrix} \begin{bmatrix} 0.9 & 0.1 \\ 0.2 & 0.8 \end{bmatrix} = \begin{bmatrix} 0.83 & 0.17 \\ 0.34 & 0.66 \end{bmatrix}$

The distribution after two repetitions is

$$DT^2 = \begin{bmatrix} 0.8 & 0.2 \end{bmatrix} \begin{bmatrix} 0.83 & 0.17 \\ 0.34 & 0.66 \end{bmatrix} = \begin{bmatrix} 0.732 & 0.268 \end{bmatrix}.$$

To predict the long-range distribution, let V be the probability vector $\begin{bmatrix} v_1 & v_2 \end{bmatrix}$. We want to find V such that

$$VT = V$$

$$\begin{bmatrix} v_1 & v_2 \end{bmatrix} \begin{bmatrix} 0.9 & 0.1 \\ 0.2 & 0.8 \end{bmatrix} = \begin{bmatrix} v_1 & v_2 \end{bmatrix}.$$

By matrix multiplication and equality of matrices,

$$\begin{aligned} 0.9v_1 + 0.2v_2 &= v_1 \\ 0.1v_1 + 0.8v_2 &= v_2. \end{aligned}$$

Simplify the equations to get the dependent system

$$\begin{aligned} -0.1v_1 + 0.2v_2 &= 0 \\ 0.1v_1 - 0.2v_2 &= 0. \end{aligned}$$

Since V is a probability vector,

$$v_1 + v_2 = 1.$$

To find v_1 and v_2, solve the system

$$\begin{aligned} 0.1v_1 - 0.2v_2 &= 0 \\ v_1 + v_2 &= 1 \end{aligned}$$

by the substitution method. Observe that $v_2 = 1 - v_1$.

$$\begin{aligned} 0.1v_1 - 0.2(1 - v_1) &= 0 \\ 0.3v_1 - 0.2 &= 0 \\ v_1 &= \frac{0.2}{0.3} = \frac{2}{3} \\ v_2 &= 1 - \frac{2}{3} = \frac{1}{3} \end{aligned}$$

The long-range distribution $\begin{bmatrix} \frac{2}{3} & \frac{1}{3} \end{bmatrix}$.

13. $T^2 = \begin{bmatrix} 0.7 & 0.1 & 0.2 \\ 0.3 & 0.3 & 0.4 \\ 0.4 & 0.5 & 0.1 \end{bmatrix}\begin{bmatrix} 0.7 & 0.1 & 0.2 \\ 0.3 & 0.3 & 0.4 \\ 0.4 & 0.5 & 0.1 \end{bmatrix} = \begin{bmatrix} 0.6 & 0.2 & 0.2 \\ 0.46 & 0.32 & 0.22 \\ 0.47 & 0.24 & 0.29 \end{bmatrix}$

The distribution after two repetitions is

$$DT^2 = \begin{bmatrix} 0.2 & 0.4 & 0.4 \end{bmatrix}\begin{bmatrix} 0.6 & 0.2 & 0.2 \\ 0.46 & 0.32 & 0.22 \\ 0.47 & 0.24 & 0.29 \end{bmatrix}$$
$$= \begin{bmatrix} 0.492 & 0.264 & 0.244 \end{bmatrix}.$$

To predict the long-range distribution, let V be the probability vector $\begin{bmatrix} v_1 & v_2 & v_3 \end{bmatrix}$. We want to find V such that

$$VT = V$$

$$\begin{bmatrix} v_1 & v_2 & v_3 \end{bmatrix}\begin{bmatrix} 0.7 & 0.1 & 0.2 \\ 0.3 & 0.3 & 0.4 \\ 0.4 & 0.5 & 0.1 \end{bmatrix} = \begin{bmatrix} v_1 & v_2 & v_3 \end{bmatrix}.$$

By matrix multiplication and equality of matrices,

$$\begin{aligned} 0.7v_1 + 0.3v_2 + 0.4v_3 &= v_1 \\ 0.1v_1 + 0.3v_2 + 0.5v_3 &= v_2 \\ 0.2v_1 + 0.4v_2 + 0.1v_3 &= v_3. \end{aligned}$$

Simplify the equations to get the dependent system

$$\begin{aligned} -0.3v_1 + 0.3v_2 + 0.4v_3 &= 0 \\ 0.1v_1 - 0.7v_2 + 0.5v_3 &= 0 \\ 0.2v_1 + 0.4v_2 - 0.9v_3 &= 0. \end{aligned}$$

Since V is a probability vector,

$$v_1 + v_2 + v_3 = 1.$$

To find v_1 and v_2, solve the system

$$\begin{aligned} -0.3v_1 + 0.3v_2 + 0.4v_3 &= 0 \\ 0.1v_1 - 0.7v_2 + 0.5v_3 &= 0 \\ 0.2v_1 + 0.4v_2 - 0.9v_3 &= 0 \\ v_1 + \quad v_2 + \quad v_3 &= 1 \end{aligned}$$

by the Gauss-Jordan method. The solution is

$$v_1 = \frac{43}{80}, v_2 = \frac{19}{80}, v_3 = \frac{9}{40}.$$

The long-range distribution is $\begin{bmatrix} \frac{43}{80} & \frac{19}{80} & \frac{9}{40} \end{bmatrix}$.

14. $T^2 = \begin{bmatrix} 0.2 & 0.1 & 0.7 \\ 0.1 & 0.1 & 0.8 \\ 0.5 & 0.1 & 0.4 \end{bmatrix} \begin{bmatrix} 0.2 & 0.1 & 0.7 \\ 0.1 & 0.1 & 0.8 \\ 0.5 & 0.1 & 0.4 \end{bmatrix} = \begin{bmatrix} 0.4 & 0.1 & 0.5 \\ 0.43 & 0.10 & 0.47 \\ 0.31 & 0.10 & 0.59 \end{bmatrix}$

The distribution after two repetitions is

$$DT^2 = \begin{bmatrix} 0.1 & 0.1 & 0.8 \end{bmatrix} \begin{bmatrix} 0.4 & 0.1 & 0.5 \\ 0.43 & 0.10 & 0.47 \\ 0.31 & 0.10 & 0.59 \end{bmatrix} = \begin{bmatrix} 0.331 & 0.1 & 0.569 \end{bmatrix}.$$

To predict the long-range distribution, let V be the probability vector $\begin{bmatrix} v_1 & v_2 & v_3 \end{bmatrix}$. We want to find V such that

$$VT = V$$

$$\begin{bmatrix} v_1 & v_2 & v_3 \end{bmatrix} \begin{bmatrix} 0.2 & 0.1 & 0.7 \\ 0.1 & 0.1 & 0.8 \\ 0.5 & 0.1 & 0.4 \end{bmatrix} = \begin{bmatrix} v_1 & v_2 & v_3 \end{bmatrix}.$$

By matrix multiplication and equality of matrices,

$$\begin{aligned} 0.2v_1 + 0.1v_2 + 0.5v_3 &= v_1 \\ 0.1v_1 + 0.1v_2 + 0.1v_3 &= v_2 \\ 0.7v_1 + 0.8v_2 + 0.4v_3 &= v_3. \end{aligned}$$

Simplify the equations to get the dependent system

$$\begin{aligned} -0.8v_1 + 0.1v_2 + 0.5v_3 &= 0 \\ 0.1v_1 - 0.9v_2 + 0.1v_3 &= 0 \\ 0.7v_1 + 0.8v_2 - 0.6v_3 &= 0. \end{aligned}$$

Since V is a probability vector,

$$v_1 + v_2 + v_3 = 1.$$

To find v_1 and v_2, solve the system

$$\begin{aligned} -0.8v_1 + 0.1v_2 + 0.5v_3 &= 0 \\ 0.1v_1 - 0.9v_2 + 0.1v_3 &= 0 \\ 0.7v_1 + 0.8v_2 - 0.6v_3 &= 0 \\ v_1 + \quad v_2 + \quad v_3 &= 1 \end{aligned}$$

by the Gauss-Jordan method. The solution is

$$v_1 = \frac{23}{65}, v_2 = \frac{1}{10}, v_3 = \frac{71}{130}.$$

The long-range distribution is $\begin{bmatrix} \frac{23}{65} & \frac{1}{10} & \frac{71}{130} \end{bmatrix}$.

16. $A = \begin{bmatrix} 0 & 1 \\ 0.2 & 0.8 \end{bmatrix}$

$$\begin{aligned} A^2 &= \begin{bmatrix} 0 & 1 \\ 0.2 & 0.8 \end{bmatrix} \begin{bmatrix} 0 & 1 \\ 0.2 & 0.8 \end{bmatrix} \\ &= \begin{bmatrix} 0.2 & 0.8 \\ 0.16 & 0.84 \end{bmatrix} \end{aligned}$$

A^2 has all positive entries, so A is regular.

17. $A = \begin{bmatrix} 0.4 & 0.2 & 0.4 \\ 0 & 1 & 0 \\ 0.6 & 0.3 & 0.1 \end{bmatrix}$

$$A^2 = \begin{bmatrix} 0.4 & 0.4 & 0.2 \\ 0 & 1 & 0 \\ 0.3 & 0.45 & 0.25 \end{bmatrix}$$

$$A^3 = \begin{bmatrix} 0.28 & 0.54 & 0.18 \\ 0 & 1 & 0 \\ 0.27 & 0.585 & 0.145 \end{bmatrix}$$

Note that the second row will always have zeros; hence, the matrix is not regular.

18. Let $B = \begin{bmatrix} 1 & 0 & 0 \\ 0 & 1 & 0 \\ 0.3 & 0.5 & 0.2 \end{bmatrix}$.

B is not regular since any power of B will have $\begin{bmatrix} 1 & 0 & 0 \end{bmatrix}$ as its first row and thus cannot have all positive entries.

22. $\begin{bmatrix} 0 & 1 & 0 \\ 0.5 & 0.1 & 0.4 \\ 0 & 0 & 1 \end{bmatrix}$

Since $p_{33} = 1$, state 3 is absorbing. Since $p_{23} \neq 0$, it is possible to go from state 2 to the absorbing state. Since $p_{12} = 1$ and $p_{23} = 0.4$, it is possible to go from state 1 to the absorbing state in two steps. This is the transition matrix of an absorbing Markov chain.

23.

$$\begin{array}{c} \\ 1 \\ 2 \\ 3 \end{array} \begin{array}{c} \begin{array}{ccc} 1 & 2 & 3 \end{array} \\ \begin{bmatrix} 0.2 & 0 & 0.8 \\ 0 & 1 & 0 \\ 0.7 & 0 & 0.3 \end{bmatrix} \end{array}$$

Since $p_{22} = 1$, state 2 is absorbing. Since $p_{12} = 0$ and $p_{32} = 0$, it is not possible to go from either of the nonabsorbing states to the absorbing state. Thus, this is not the transition matrix of an absorbing Markov chain.

24. $\begin{bmatrix} 0.5 & 0.1 & 0.1 & 0.3 \\ 0 & 0 & 1 & 0 \\ 1 & 0 & 0 & 0 \\ 0.1 & 0.8 & 0.05 & 0.05 \end{bmatrix}$

There are no absorbing states. Hence, this is not the transition matrix for an absorbing Markov chain.

25.

$$P = \begin{array}{c} \\ 1 \\ 2 \\ 3 \end{array} \begin{array}{c} \begin{array}{ccc} 1 & 2 & 3 \end{array} \\ \begin{bmatrix} 0.2 & 0.45 & 0.35 \\ 0 & 1 & 0 \\ 0 & 0 & 1 \end{bmatrix} \end{array}$$

Arrange the rows and columns of P so the absorbing states come first.

$$\begin{array}{c} \\ 1 \\ 2 \\ 3 \end{array} \begin{array}{c} \begin{array}{ccc} 2 & 3 & 1 \end{array} \\ \left[\begin{array}{cc|c} 1 & 0 & 0 \\ 0 & 1 & 0 \\ \hline 0.45 & 0.35 & 0.2 \end{array}\right] \end{array}.$$

Thus, $Q = [0.2]$. Now find F.

$$\begin{aligned} F &= (I_1 - Q)^{-1} \\ &= ([1] - [0.2])^{-1} \\ &= [0.8]^{-1} = \left[\frac{4}{5}\right]^{-1} \\ &= \left[\frac{5}{4}\right] \end{aligned}$$

$$\begin{aligned} FR &= \left[\frac{5}{4}\right] [0.45 \quad 0.35] \\ &= \left[\frac{5}{4}\right] \left[\frac{9}{20} \quad \frac{7}{20}\right] \\ &= \left[\frac{9}{16} \quad \frac{7}{16}\right] \end{aligned}$$

26.

$$P = \begin{array}{c} \\ 1 \\ 2 \\ 3 \end{array} \begin{array}{c} \begin{array}{ccc} 1 & 2 & 3 \end{array} \\ \begin{bmatrix} 1 & 0 & 0 \\ 0 & 1 & 0 \\ 0.25 & 0.15 & 0.6 \end{bmatrix} \end{array}$$

This matrix does not need to be re-arranged. We have

$$\begin{array}{c} \\ 1 \\ 2 \\ 3 \end{array} \begin{array}{c} \begin{array}{ccc} 1 & 2 & 3 \end{array} \\ \left[\begin{array}{cc|c} 1 & 0 & 0 \\ 0 & 1 & 0 \\ \hline 0.25 & 0.15 & 0.6 \end{array}\right] \end{array}.$$

Thus, $Q = [0.6]$. Now find F.

$$\begin{aligned} F &= (I_1 - Q)^{-1} \\ &= ([1] - [0.6])^{-1} \\ &= [0.4]^{-1} = \left[\frac{2}{5}\right]^{-1} \\ &= \left[\frac{5}{2}\right] \end{aligned}$$

$$FR = \begin{bmatrix} 5 \\ \frac{}{2} \end{bmatrix} [0.25 \quad 0.15]$$
$$= \begin{bmatrix} 5 \\ \frac{}{2} \end{bmatrix} \begin{bmatrix} \frac{1}{4} & \frac{3}{20} \end{bmatrix}$$
$$= \begin{bmatrix} \frac{5}{8} & \frac{3}{8} \end{bmatrix}$$

27.
$$\begin{array}{c} \\ 1 \\ 2 \\ 3 \\ 4 \end{array} \begin{array}{c} \begin{array}{cccc} 1 & 2 & 3 & 4 \end{array} \\ \begin{bmatrix} \frac{1}{5} & \frac{1}{5} & \frac{2}{5} & \frac{1}{5} \\ 0 & 1 & 0 & 0 \\ \frac{1}{2} & \frac{1}{4} & \frac{1}{8} & \frac{1}{8} \\ 0 & 0 & 0 & 1 \end{bmatrix} \end{array} = P$$

Rearranging, we have

$$\begin{array}{c} \\ 2 \\ 4 \\ 1 \\ 3 \end{array} \begin{array}{c} \begin{array}{cccc} 2 & 4 & 1 & 3 \end{array} \\ \left[\begin{array}{cc|cc} 1 & 0 & 0 & 0 \\ 0 & 1 & 0 & 0 \\ \hline \frac{1}{5} & \frac{1}{5} & \frac{1}{5} & \frac{2}{5} \\ \frac{1}{4} & \frac{1}{8} & \frac{1}{2} & \frac{1}{8} \end{array}\right] \end{array}.$$

$$R = \begin{bmatrix} \frac{1}{5} & \frac{1}{5} \\ \frac{1}{4} & \frac{1}{8} \end{bmatrix} \text{ and } Q = \begin{bmatrix} \frac{1}{5} & \frac{2}{5} \\ \frac{1}{2} & \frac{1}{8} \end{bmatrix}$$

$$F = (I_2 - Q)^{-1} = \left(\begin{bmatrix} 1 & 0 \\ 0 & 1 \end{bmatrix} - \begin{bmatrix} \frac{1}{5} & \frac{2}{5} \\ \frac{1}{2} & \frac{1}{8} \end{bmatrix} \right)^{-1}$$
$$= \begin{bmatrix} \frac{4}{5} & -\frac{2}{5} \\ -\frac{1}{2} & \frac{7}{8} \end{bmatrix}^{-1} = \begin{bmatrix} \frac{7}{4} & \frac{4}{5} \\ 1 & \frac{8}{5} \end{bmatrix}$$

$$FR = \begin{bmatrix} \frac{7}{4} & \frac{4}{5} \\ 1 & \frac{8}{5} \end{bmatrix} \begin{bmatrix} \frac{1}{5} & \frac{1}{5} \\ \frac{1}{4} & \frac{1}{8} \end{bmatrix} = \begin{bmatrix} \frac{11}{20} & \frac{9}{20} \\ \frac{3}{5} & \frac{2}{5} \end{bmatrix} \text{ or } \begin{bmatrix} 0.55 & 0.45 \\ 0.6 & 0.4 \end{bmatrix}$$

28.
$$\begin{array}{c} \\ 1 \\ 2 \\ 3 \\ 4 \end{array} \begin{array}{c} \begin{array}{cccc} 1 & 2 & 3 & 4 \end{array} \\ \begin{bmatrix} 0.3 & 0.5 & 0.1 & 0.1 \\ 0.4 & 0.1 & 0.3 & 0.2 \\ 0 & 0 & 1 & 0 \\ 0 & 0 & 0 & 1 \end{bmatrix} \end{array}$$

Rearrange the rows and columns so that absorbing states 3 and 4 come first.

$$\begin{array}{c} \\ 3 \\ 4 \\ 1 \\ 2 \end{array} \begin{array}{c} \begin{array}{cccc} 3 & 4 & 1 & 2 \end{array} \\ \left[\begin{array}{cc|cc} 1 & 0 & 0 & 0 \\ 0 & 1 & 0 & 0 \\ \hline 0.1 & 0.1 & 0.3 & 0.5 \\ 0.3 & 0.2 & 0.4 & 0.1 \end{array}\right] \end{array}$$

We have

$$R = \begin{bmatrix} 0.1 & 0.1 \\ 0.3 & 0.2 \end{bmatrix} \text{ and } Q = \begin{bmatrix} 0.3 & 0.5 \\ 0.4 & 0.1 \end{bmatrix}.$$

$$F = (I_2 - Q)^{-1} = \left(\begin{bmatrix} 1 & 0 \\ 0 & 1 \end{bmatrix} - \begin{bmatrix} 0.3 & 0.5 \\ 0.4 & 0.1 \end{bmatrix} \right)^{-1}$$
$$= \begin{bmatrix} 0.7 & -0.5 \\ -0.4 & 0.9 \end{bmatrix}^{-1} = \begin{bmatrix} 2.0930 & 1.1628 \\ 0.9302 & 1.6279 \end{bmatrix}$$

and

$$FR = \begin{bmatrix} 2.0930 & 1.1628 \\ 0.9302 & 1.6279 \end{bmatrix} \begin{bmatrix} 0.1 & 0.1 \\ 0.3 & 0.2 \end{bmatrix}$$
$$= \begin{bmatrix} 0.5581 & 0.4419 \\ 0.5814 & 0.4186 \end{bmatrix}.$$

29. The initial distribution matrix $D = [\ 0.35 \quad 0.65\ ]$.

(a) The distribution after one campaign is

$$DP = [\ 0.35 \quad 0.65\ ] \begin{bmatrix} 0.8 & 0.2 \\ 0.45 & 0.55 \end{bmatrix}$$
$$= [\ 0.5725 \quad 0.4275\ ].$$

(b) The distribution after three campaigns is

$$DP^3 = [\ 0.35 \quad 0.65\ ] \begin{bmatrix} 0.8 & 0.2 \\ 0.45 & 0.55 \end{bmatrix}^3$$
$$\approx [\ 0.35 \quad 0.65\ ] \begin{bmatrix} 0.7055 & 0.2945 \\ 0.6626 & 0.3374 \end{bmatrix}$$
$$\approx [\ 0.6776 \quad 0.3224\ ].$$

30. Let $P = \begin{bmatrix} 0.8 & 0.2 \\ 0.45 & 0.55 \end{bmatrix}$ and let $V = [v_1 \quad v_2]$, where v_1 is the long-range market share for Dogkins. Solve the equation $VP = V$.

$$[v_1 \quad v_2] \begin{bmatrix} 0.8 & 0.2 \\ 0.45 & 0.55 \end{bmatrix} = [v_1 \quad v_2]$$

$$0.8v_1 + 0.45v_2 = v_1$$
$$0.2v_1 + 0.55v_2 = v_2$$

Simplify the equations to get the dependent system

$$-0.2v_1 + 0.45v_2 = 0$$
$$0.2v_1 - 0.45v_2 = 0.$$

Since V is a probability vector,

$$v_1 + v_2 = 1.$$

To find v_1 and v_2, solve the system using the substitution method.

$$0.2v_1 - 0.45(1 - v_1) = 0$$
$$0.65v_1 - 0.45 = 0$$
$$v_1 = \frac{0.45}{0.65} = \frac{9}{13}$$

The long-range market share for Dogkins is $\frac{9}{13}$.

31. The distribution after 1 mo is

$$\begin{bmatrix} 0.4 & 0.4 & 0.2 \end{bmatrix} \begin{bmatrix} 0.8 & 0.15 & 0.05 \\ 0.25 & 0.55 & 0.2 \\ 0.04 & 0.21 & 0.75 \end{bmatrix} = \begin{bmatrix} 0.428 & 0.322 & 0.25 \end{bmatrix}.$$

32. $X_0 = \begin{bmatrix} 0.4 & 0.4 & 0.2 \end{bmatrix}$

$$A = \begin{bmatrix} 0.8 & 0.15 & 0.05 \\ 0.25 & 0.55 & 0.2 \\ 0.04 & 0.21 & 0.75 \end{bmatrix}$$

$$A^2 = \begin{bmatrix} 0.6795 & 0.213 & 0.1075 \\ 0.3455 & 0.382 & 0.2725 \\ 0.1145 & 0.279 & 0.6065 \end{bmatrix}$$

The distribution after 2 mo is given by

$$X_0A^2 = \begin{bmatrix} 0.4329 & 0.2938 & 0.2733 \end{bmatrix}.$$

33. $$P^2 = \begin{bmatrix} 0.8 & 0.15 & 0.05 \\ 0.25 & 0.55 & 0.2 \\ 0.04 & 0.21 & 0.75 \end{bmatrix} \begin{bmatrix} 0.8 & 0.15 & 0.05 \\ 0.25 & 0.55 & 0.2 \\ 0.04 & 0.21 & 0.75 \end{bmatrix} = \begin{bmatrix} 0.6795 & 0.213 & 0.1075 \\ 0.3455 & 0.382 & 0.2725 \\ 0.1145 & 0.279 & 0.6065 \end{bmatrix}$$

$$P^3 = \begin{bmatrix} 0.8 & 0.15 & 0.05 \\ 0.25 & 0.55 & 0.2 \\ 0.04 & 0.21 & 0.75 \end{bmatrix} \begin{bmatrix} 0.6795 & 0.213 & 0.1075 \\ 0.3455 & 0.382 & 0.2725 \\ 0.1145 & 0.279 & 0.6065 \end{bmatrix} = \begin{bmatrix} 0.60115 & 0.24165 & 0.1572 \\ 0.3828 & 0.31915 & 0.29805 \\ 0.18561 & 0.29799 & 0.5164 \end{bmatrix}$$

The distribution after 3 mo is

$$\begin{bmatrix} 0.4 & 0.4 & 0.2 \end{bmatrix} \begin{bmatrix} 0.60115 & 0.24165 & 0.1572 \\ 0.3828 & 0.31915 & 0.29805 \\ 0.18561 & 0.29799 & 0.5164 \end{bmatrix} = \begin{bmatrix} 0.4307 & 0.2839 & 0.2854 \end{bmatrix}.$$

34. To find the long-range distribution, use the system

$$\begin{aligned} v_1 + v_2 + v_3 &= 1 \\ 0.8v_1 + 0.25v_2 + 0.04v_3 &= v_1 \\ 0.15v_1 + 0.55v_2 + 0.21v_3 &= v_2 \\ 0.05v_1 + 0.2v_2 + 0.75v_3 &= v_3. \end{aligned}$$

Simplify these equations to obtain the system

$$\begin{aligned} v_1 + v_2 + v_3 &= 1 \\ -0.2v_1 + 0.25v_2 + 0.04v_3 &= 0 \\ 0.15v_1 - 0.45v_2 + 0.21v_3 &= 0 \\ 0.05v_1 + 0.2v_2 - 0.25v_3 &= 0. \end{aligned}$$

Solve this system by the Gauss-Jordan method to obtain $v_1 = \frac{47}{114}$, $v_2 = \frac{32}{114}$, and $v_3 = \frac{35}{114}$. The long-range distribution is

$$\begin{bmatrix} \frac{47}{114} & \frac{32}{114} & \frac{35}{114} \end{bmatrix}.$$

35. **(a)** To find the fundamental matrix F associated with the transition matrix

$$\begin{array}{c} \\ 0 \\ 1 \\ 2 \end{array} \begin{array}{c} \begin{array}{ccc} 0 & 1 & 2 \end{array} \\ \left[\begin{array}{c|cc} 1 & 0 & 0 \\ \hline 0.085 & 0.779 & 0.136 \\ 0.017 & 0.017 & 0.966 \end{array}\right] \end{array},$$

first note that $Q = \begin{bmatrix} 0.779 & 0.136 \\ 0.017 & 0.966 \end{bmatrix}$. Therefore,

$$F = (I_2 - Q)^{-1} = \begin{bmatrix} 0.221 & -0.136 \\ -0.017 & 0.034 \end{bmatrix}^{-1} = \begin{array}{c} \\ 1 \\ 2 \end{array} \begin{array}{c} \begin{array}{cc} 1 & 2 \end{array} \\ \begin{bmatrix} 6.536 & 26.144 \\ 3.268 & 42.484 \end{bmatrix} \end{array},$$

where the entries of F are rounded to three decimal places.

(b) For a patient with favorable status, the expected number of 72-hr cycles that the patient will continue to have that status before dying is the entry located in the second row, second column of F, which is 42.484.

(c) For a patient with unfavorable status, the expected number of 72-hr cycles that the patient will have a favorable status before dying is the entry in the first row, second column of F, which is 26.144.

In Exercises 36-45, the original transition matrix is

$$A = \begin{array}{c} \\ \text{T} \\ \text{N} \\ \text{O} \end{array} \begin{array}{c} \begin{array}{ccc} \text{T} & \text{N} & \text{O} \end{array} \\ \begin{bmatrix} 0.3 & 0.5 & 0.2 \\ 0.2 & 0.6 & 0.2 \\ 0.1 & 0.5 & 0.4 \end{bmatrix} \end{array}.$$

36. The probability that a man of normal weight will have a thin son is given by the entry in row 2, column 1 of P, which is 0.2.

37. A grandson is 2 generations down, so we need to look at A^2.

$$A^2 = \begin{array}{c} \\ \text{T} \\ \text{N} \\ \text{O} \end{array} \begin{array}{c} \begin{array}{ccc} \text{T} & \text{N} & \text{O} \end{array} \\ \begin{bmatrix} 0.21 & 0.55 & 0.24 \\ 0.2 & 0.56 & 0.24 \\ 0.17 & 0.55 & 0.28 \end{bmatrix} \end{array}$$

The probability that the grandson of a normal man is thin is given by the entry in row 2, column 1 of A^2. This probability is 0.2.

38. $$P^2 = \begin{bmatrix} 0.3 & 0.5 & 0.2 \\ 0.2 & 0.6 & 0.2 \\ 0.1 & 0.5 & 0.4 \end{bmatrix}\begin{bmatrix} 0.3 & 0.5 & 0.2 \\ 0.2 & 0.6 & 0.2 \\ 0.1 & 0.5 & 0.4 \end{bmatrix} = \begin{bmatrix} 0.21 & 0.55 & 0.24 \\ 0.2 & 0.56 & 0.24 \\ 0.17 & 0.55 & 0.28 \end{bmatrix}$$

$$P^3 = \begin{bmatrix} 0.3 & 0.5 & 0.2 \\ 0.2 & 0.6 & 0.2 \\ 0.1 & 0.5 & 0.4 \end{bmatrix}\begin{bmatrix} 0.21 & 0.55 & 0.24 \\ 0.2 & 0.56 & 0.24 \\ 0.17 & 0.55 & 0.28 \end{bmatrix} = \begin{bmatrix} 0.197 & 0.555 & 0.248 \\ 0.196 & 0.556 & 0.248 \\ 0.189 & 0.555 & 0.256 \end{bmatrix}$$

The probability that a man of normal weight will have a thin great-grandson is given by the entry in row 2, column 1 of P^3, which is 0.196.

39. We can read this probability directly from matrix A. The probability that an overweight man has an overweight son is the entry in row 3, column 3 of A. This probability is 0.4.

40. $$P^2 = \begin{bmatrix} 0.21 & 0.55 & 0.24 \\ 0.2 & 0.56 & 0.24 \\ 0.17 & 0.55 & 0.28 \end{bmatrix}$$

The probability that an overweight man will have an overweight grandson is given by the entry in row 3, column 3 of P^2, which is 0.28.

41. $$A^3 = \begin{array}{c} \\ \text{T} \\ \text{N} \\ \text{O} \end{array} \begin{array}{c} \begin{array}{ccc} \text{T} & \text{N} & \text{O} \end{array} \\ \begin{bmatrix} 0.197 & 0.555 & 0.248 \\ 0.196 & 0.556 & 0.248 \\ 0.189 & 0.555 & 0.256 \end{bmatrix} \end{array}$$

is the transition matrix over 3 generations. The probability of an overweight man having an overweight great-grandson is the entry in row 3, column 3 of A^3. This probability is 0.256.

42. The distribution of men by weight after 1 generation is

$$\begin{bmatrix} 0.2 & 0.55 & 0.25 \end{bmatrix}\begin{bmatrix} 0.3 & 0.5 & 0.2 \\ 0.2 & 0.6 & 0.2 \\ 0.1 & 0.5 & 0.4 \end{bmatrix} = \begin{bmatrix} 0.195 & 0.555 & 0.25 \end{bmatrix}.$$

43. Let $D = \begin{bmatrix} 0.2 & 0.55 & 0.25 \end{bmatrix}$, the initial distribution. From Exercise 37, we have

$$A^2 = \begin{bmatrix} 0.21 & 0.55 & 0.24 \\ 0.2 & 0.56 & 0.24 \\ 0.17 & 0.55 & 0.28 \end{bmatrix}.$$

The distribution after 2 generations is

$$DA^2 = \begin{bmatrix} 0.2 & 0.55 & 0.25 \end{bmatrix}\begin{bmatrix} 0.21 & 0.55 & 0.24 \\ 0.2 & 0.56 & 0.24 \\ 0.17 & 0.55 & 0.28 \end{bmatrix} = \begin{bmatrix} 0.1945 & 0.5555 & 0.25 \end{bmatrix}.$$

44. The distribution of men by weight after 3 generations is

$$\begin{bmatrix} 0.2 & 0.55 & 0.25 \end{bmatrix}\begin{bmatrix} 0.197 & 0.555 & 0.248 \\ 0.196 & 0.556 & 0.248 \\ 0.189 & 0.555 & 0.256 \end{bmatrix} = \begin{bmatrix} 0.1945 & 0.5556 & 0.25 \end{bmatrix}.$$

45. $A = \begin{bmatrix} 0.3 & 0.5 & 0.2 \\ 0.2 & 0.6 & 0.2 \\ 0.1 & 0.5 & 0.4 \end{bmatrix}$

To find the long-term distribution, use the system

$$\begin{aligned} v_1 + \quad v_2 + \quad v_3 &= 1 \\ 0.3v_1 + 0.2v_2 + 0.1v_3 &= v_1 \\ 0.5v_1 + 0.6v_2 + 0.5v_3 &= v_2 \\ 0.2v_1 + 0.2v_2 + 0.4v_3 &= v_3. \end{aligned}$$

Simplify these equations to obtain the system

$$\begin{aligned} v_1 + \quad v_2 + \quad v_3 &= 1 \\ -0.7v_1 + 0.2v_2 + 0.1v_3 &= 0 \\ 0.5v_1 - 0.4v_2 + 0.5v_3 &= 0 \\ 0.2v_1 + 0.2v_2 - 0.6v_3 &= 0. \end{aligned}$$

Solve this system by the Gauss-Jordan method to obtain $v_1 = \frac{7}{36}$, $v_2 = \frac{5}{9}$, and $v_3 = \frac{1}{4}$. The long-range distribution is

$$\begin{bmatrix} \frac{7}{36} & \frac{5}{9} & \frac{1}{4} \end{bmatrix}.$$

46. If the offspring both carry genes AA, then so must their offspring; hence, state 1 ends up in state 1 with probability 1. If the offspring both carry genes a, then so must their offspring; hence, state 6 ends up in state 6 with probability 1. If AA mates with aa, then the offspring will carry genes Aa; hence, state 3 ends up in state 4 with probability 1. If AA mates with Aa, then there are four possible outcomes for a pair of offspring: AA and AA is one of the outcomes, so state 2 ends up in state 1 with probability $\frac{1}{4}$; AA and Aa can happen two ways, so state 2 ends up in state 2 with probability $\frac{2}{4}$ or $\frac{1}{2}$; and Aa and Aa is the last possible outcome, so state 2 ends up in state 4 with probability $\frac{1}{4}$. If Aa mates with Aa, then there are sixteen possible outcomes for a pair of offspring: state 4 ends up in states 1, 2, 3, 4, 5, 6 with respective probabilities $\frac{1}{16}$, $\frac{1}{4}$, $\frac{1}{8}$, $\frac{1}{4}$, $\frac{1}{4}$, and $\frac{1}{16}$. If Aa mates with aa, then there are four possible outcomes for a pair of offspring, corresponding to three of the possible states: state 5 ends up in states 4, 5, 6 with respective probabilities $\frac{1}{4}$, $\frac{1}{2}$, and $\frac{1}{4}$.

This verifies that the transition matrix for this mating experiment is

$$\begin{array}{c} \\ 1 \\ 2 \\ 3 \\ 4 \\ 5 \\ 6 \end{array} \begin{array}{c} \begin{array}{cccccc} 1 & 2 & 3 & 4 & 5 & 6 \end{array} \\ \begin{bmatrix} 1 & 0 & 0 & 0 & 0 & 0 \\ \frac{1}{4} & \frac{1}{2} & 0 & \frac{1}{4} & 0 & 0 \\ 0 & 0 & 0 & 1 & 0 & 0 \\ \frac{1}{16} & \frac{1}{4} & \frac{1}{8} & \frac{1}{4} & \frac{1}{4} & \frac{1}{16} \\ 0 & 0 & 0 & \frac{1}{4} & \frac{1}{2} & \frac{1}{4} \\ 0 & 0 & 0 & 0 & 0 & 1 \end{bmatrix} \end{array}.$$

47. The absorbing states are states 1 and 6 since $a_{11} = 1$ and $a_{66} = 1$.

48. Rearrange the rows and columns of the transition matrix so that the absorbing states come first.

$$\begin{array}{c} \\ 1 \\ 6 \\ 2 \\ 3 \\ 4 \\ 5 \end{array} \begin{array}{c} \begin{array}{cccccc} 1 & 6 & 2 & 3 & 4 & 5 \end{array} \\ \left[\begin{array}{cc|cccc} 1 & 0 & 0 & 0 & 0 & 0 \\ 0 & 1 & 0 & 0 & 0 & 0 \\ \hline \frac{1}{4} & 0 & \frac{1}{2} & 0 & \frac{1}{4} & 0 \\ 0 & 0 & 0 & 0 & 1 & 0 \\ \frac{1}{16} & \frac{1}{16} & \frac{1}{4} & \frac{1}{8} & \frac{1}{4} & \frac{1}{4} \\ 0 & \frac{1}{4} & 0 & 0 & \frac{1}{4} & \frac{1}{2} \end{array}\right] \end{array}$$

From this rearranged matrix, observe that

$$Q = \begin{bmatrix} \frac{1}{2} & 0 & \frac{1}{4} & 0 \\ 0 & 0 & 1 & 0 \\ \frac{1}{4} & \frac{1}{8} & \frac{1}{4} & \frac{1}{4} \\ 0 & 0 & \frac{1}{4} & \frac{1}{2} \end{bmatrix}.$$

49. $F = (I_4 - Q)^{-1}$

$$= \left(\begin{bmatrix} 1 & 0 & 0 & 0 \\ 0 & 1 & 0 & 0 \\ 0 & 0 & 1 & 0 \\ 0 & 0 & 0 & 1 \end{bmatrix} - \begin{bmatrix} \frac{1}{2} & 0 & \frac{1}{4} & 0 \\ 0 & 0 & 1 & 0 \\ \frac{1}{4} & \frac{1}{8} & \frac{1}{4} & \frac{1}{4} \\ 0 & 0 & \frac{1}{4} & \frac{1}{2} \end{bmatrix} \right)^{-1} = \begin{bmatrix} \frac{1}{2} & 0 & -\frac{1}{4} & 0 \\ 0 & 1 & -1 & 0 \\ -\frac{1}{4} & -\frac{1}{8} & \frac{3}{4} & -\frac{1}{4} \\ 0 & 0 & -\frac{1}{4} & \frac{1}{2} \end{bmatrix}^{-1}$$

Use row operations to find this inverse.

$$\left[\begin{array}{cccc|cccc} \frac{1}{2} & 0 & -\frac{1}{4} & 0 & 1 & 0 & 0 & 0 \\ 0 & 1 & -1 & 0 & 0 & 1 & 0 & 0 \\ -\frac{1}{4} & -\frac{1}{8} & \frac{3}{4} & -\frac{1}{4} & 0 & 0 & 1 & 0 \\ 0 & 0 & -\frac{1}{4} & \frac{1}{2} & 0 & 0 & 0 & 1 \end{array}\right]$$

$$\left[\begin{array}{cccc|cccc} 1 & 0 & -\frac{1}{2} & 0 & 2 & 0 & 0 & 0 \\ 0 & 1 & -1 & 0 & 0 & 1 & 0 & 0 \\ 0 & -\frac{1}{8} & \frac{5}{8} & -\frac{1}{4} & \frac{1}{2} & 0 & 1 & 0 \\ 0 & 0 & -\frac{1}{4} & \frac{1}{2} & 0 & 0 & 0 & 1 \end{array}\right]$$

$$\left[\begin{array}{cccc|cccc} 1 & 0 & -\frac{1}{2} & 0 & 2 & 0 & 0 & 0 \\ 0 & 1 & -1 & 0 & 0 & 1 & 0 & 0 \\ 0 & 0 & \frac{1}{2} & -\frac{1}{4} & \frac{1}{2} & \frac{1}{8} & 1 & 0 \\ 0 & 0 & -\frac{1}{4} & \frac{1}{2} & 0 & 0 & 0 & 1 \end{array}\right]$$

$$\left[\begin{array}{cccc|cccc} 1 & 0 & 0 & -\frac{1}{4} & \frac{5}{2} & \frac{1}{8} & 1 & 0 \\ 0 & 1 & 0 & -\frac{1}{2} & 1 & \frac{5}{4} & 2 & 0 \\ 0 & 0 & 1 & -\frac{1}{2} & 1 & \frac{1}{4} & 2 & 0 \\ 0 & 0 & 0 & \frac{3}{8} & \frac{1}{4} & \frac{1}{16} & \frac{1}{2} & 1 \end{array}\right]$$

$$\left[\begin{array}{cccc|cccc} 1 & 0 & 0 & 0 & \frac{8}{3} & \frac{1}{6} & \frac{4}{3} & \frac{2}{3} \\ 0 & 1 & 0 & 0 & \frac{4}{3} & \frac{4}{3} & \frac{8}{3} & \frac{4}{3} \\ 0 & 0 & 1 & 0 & \frac{4}{3} & \frac{1}{3} & \frac{8}{3} & \frac{4}{3} \\ 0 & 0 & 0 & 1 & \frac{2}{3} & \frac{1}{6} & \frac{4}{3} & \frac{8}{3} \end{array}\right]$$

$$F = \begin{bmatrix} \frac{8}{3} & \frac{1}{6} & \frac{4}{3} & \frac{2}{3} \\ \frac{4}{3} & \frac{4}{3} & \frac{8}{3} & \frac{4}{3} \\ \frac{4}{3} & \frac{1}{3} & \frac{8}{3} & \frac{4}{3} \\ \frac{2}{3} & \frac{1}{6} & \frac{4}{3} & \frac{8}{3} \end{bmatrix}$$

$$FR = \begin{bmatrix} \frac{8}{3} & \frac{1}{6} & \frac{4}{3} & \frac{2}{3} \\ \frac{4}{3} & \frac{4}{3} & \frac{8}{3} & \frac{4}{3} \\ \frac{4}{3} & \frac{1}{3} & \frac{8}{3} & \frac{4}{3} \\ \frac{2}{3} & \frac{1}{6} & \frac{4}{3} & \frac{8}{3} \end{bmatrix} \begin{bmatrix} \frac{1}{4} & 0 \\ 0 & 0 \\ \frac{1}{16} & \frac{1}{16} \\ 0 & \frac{1}{4} \end{bmatrix} = \begin{bmatrix} \frac{3}{4} & \frac{1}{4} \\ \frac{1}{2} & \frac{1}{2} \\ \frac{1}{2} & \frac{1}{2} \\ \frac{1}{4} & \frac{3}{4} \end{bmatrix}$$

50. In Exercise 49, it was shown that the fundamental matrix for this absorbing Markov chain is

$$F = \begin{bmatrix} \frac{8}{3} & \frac{1}{6} & \frac{4}{3} & \frac{2}{3} \\ \frac{4}{3} & \frac{4}{3} & \frac{8}{3} & \frac{4}{3} \\ \frac{4}{3} & \frac{1}{3} & \frac{8}{3} & \frac{4}{3} \\ \frac{2}{3} & \frac{1}{6} & \frac{4}{3} & \frac{8}{3} \end{bmatrix}.$$

If Aa mates with Aa (which corresponds to state 4, which in turn corresponds to row 3 of F), $\frac{8}{3}$ pairs of offspring with these genes can be expected before ending up in one of the two absorbing states. This is because $\frac{8}{3}$ is the entry in row 3, column 3 of F.

51. If two parents with the genes Aa are mated, the probability that the recessive gene will eventually disappear is $\frac{1}{2}$. This is found in row 3, column 1 of the matrix FR, because this is the probability of state 4 becoming state 1.

52. **(a)** After the duplication, there are $2n$ genes and n of them are being selected; this can be done in $\binom{2n}{n}$ different ways. Suppose there are i mutant genes before the duplication and j mutant genes in the next generation. After the duplication, there will be $2i$ mutant genes, of which j will be selected; this can be done in $\binom{2i}{j}$ different ways. Also, there are $2n - 2i$ nonmutant genes, of which $n - j$ will be selected; this can be done in $\binom{2n-2i}{n-j}$ different ways.

Therefore, the probability of a generation with i mutant genes being followed by a generation with j mutant genes, which is the transition probability from state i to state j, is

$$p_{ij} = \frac{\binom{2i}{j}\binom{2n-2i}{n-j}}{\binom{2n}{n}}.$$

(b) The absorbing states are state 0 and state n. If a generation has no mutant genes, then after duplication there will still be none, and if a generation consists entirely of mutant genes, its successor will also.

(c) Use

$$p_{ij} = \frac{\binom{2i}{j}\binom{2n-2i}{n-j}}{\binom{2n}{n}}$$

with $n = 3$ and $i = 0, 1, 2, 3$ and $j = 0, 1, 2, 3$ to calculate the entries of the transition matrix. Let $\binom{n}{r} = 0$ when $n < r$.

$$p_{00} = \frac{\binom{0}{0}\binom{6}{3}}{\binom{6}{3}} = 1,\ p_{01} = \frac{\binom{0}{1}\binom{6}{2}}{\binom{6}{3}} = 0, p_{02} = 0,\ p_{03} = 0, p_{10} = \frac{\binom{2}{0}\binom{4}{3}}{\binom{6}{3}} = \frac{1}{5}, p_{11} = \frac{\binom{2}{1}\binom{4}{2}}{\binom{6}{3}} = \frac{3}{5},$$

$$p_{12} = \frac{\binom{2}{2}\binom{4}{1}}{\binom{6}{3}} = \frac{1}{5},\ p_{13} = \frac{\binom{2}{3}\binom{4}{0}}{\binom{6}{3}} = 0, p_{20} = \frac{\binom{4}{0}\binom{2}{3}}{\binom{6}{3}} = 0,\ p_{21} = \frac{\binom{4}{1}\binom{2}{2}}{\binom{6}{3}} = \frac{1}{5}, p_{22} = \frac{\binom{4}{2}\binom{2}{1}}{\binom{6}{3}} = \frac{3}{5},$$

$$p_{23} = \frac{\binom{4}{3}\binom{2}{0}}{\binom{6}{3}} = \frac{1}{5}, p_{30} = \frac{\binom{6}{0}\binom{0}{3}}{\binom{6}{3}} = 0,\ p_{31} = 0,\ p_{32} = 0, p_{33} = \frac{\binom{6}{3}\binom{0}{0}}{\binom{6}{3}} = 1$$

The transition matrix is

$$\begin{array}{c} \\ 0 \\ 1 \\ 2 \\ 3 \end{array}\begin{array}{c} \begin{array}{cccc} 0 & 1 & 2 & 3 \end{array} \\ \begin{bmatrix} 1 & 0 & 0 & 0 \\ \frac{1}{5} & \frac{3}{5} & \frac{1}{5} & 0 \\ 0 & \frac{1}{5} & \frac{3}{5} & \frac{1}{5} \\ 0 & 0 & 0 & 1 \end{bmatrix} \end{array} = P.$$

(d) Rearrange the rows and columns of P.

$$\begin{array}{c} \\ 0 \\ 3 \\ 1 \\ 2 \end{array}\begin{array}{c} \begin{array}{cccc} 0 & 3 & 1 & 2 \end{array} \\ \left[\begin{array}{cc|cc} 1 & 0 & 0 & 0 \\ 0 & 1 & 0 & 0 \\ \hline \frac{1}{5} & 0 & \frac{3}{5} & \frac{1}{5} \\ 0 & \frac{1}{5} & \frac{1}{5} & \frac{3}{5} \end{array}\right] \end{array}$$

$$R = \begin{bmatrix} \frac{1}{5} & 0 \\ 0 & \frac{1}{5} \end{bmatrix},\ Q = \begin{bmatrix} \frac{3}{5} & \frac{1}{5} \\ \frac{1}{5} & \frac{3}{5} \end{bmatrix},$$

$$F = (I_2 - Q)^{-1} = \left(\begin{bmatrix} 1 & 0 \\ 0 & 1 \end{bmatrix} - \begin{bmatrix} \frac{3}{5} & \frac{1}{5} \\ \frac{1}{5} & \frac{3}{5} \end{bmatrix}\right)^{-1} = \begin{bmatrix} \frac{2}{5} & -\frac{1}{5} \\ -\frac{1}{5} & \frac{2}{5} \end{bmatrix}^{-1} = \begin{bmatrix} \frac{10}{3} & \frac{5}{3} \\ \frac{5}{3} & \frac{10}{3} \end{bmatrix}$$

$$FR = \begin{bmatrix} \frac{10}{3} & \frac{5}{3} \\ \frac{5}{3} & \frac{10}{3} \end{bmatrix}\begin{bmatrix} \frac{1}{5} & 0 \\ 0 & \frac{1}{5} \end{bmatrix} = \begin{bmatrix} \frac{2}{3} & \frac{1}{3} \\ \frac{1}{3} & \frac{2}{3} \end{bmatrix}$$

(e) If a set of 3 genes has 1 mutant gene, the probability that the mutant gene will disappear is $\frac{2}{3}$, since that is the entry in row 1, column 1 of FR.

(f) If a set of 3 genes has 1 mutant gene, 5 generations would be expected to have 1 mutant gene before either the mutant genes or the nonmutant genes disappear, since that is the sum of the entries in row 1 of F.

53. Let

$$P = \begin{array}{c} \\ b \\ s \\ m \\ f \\ t \end{array}\begin{array}{c} \begin{array}{ccccc} b & s & m & f & t \end{array} \\ \begin{bmatrix} 0.4225 & 0.241 & 0.1645 & 0.1085 & 0.0635 \\ 0.245 & 0.2625 & 0.205 & 0.169 & 0.1185 \\ 0.153 & 0.191 & 0.25 & 0.233 & 0.173 \\ 0.107 & 0.195 & 0.1965 & 0.229 & 0.2725 \\ 0.073 & 0.11 & 0.184 & 0.26 & 0.373 \end{bmatrix} \end{array}$$

where b, s, m, f, and t represent the states Bottom, Second, Middle, Fourth, and Top, respectively.

(a) To find the probability that the granddaughter (second generation) of someone in the bottom income group (state b) is in the top income group (state t), find P^2 using a graphing calculator.

$$P^2 = \begin{array}{c} \\ b \\ s \\ m \\ f \\ t \end{array} \begin{array}{c} \begin{array}{ccccc} b & s & m & f & t \end{array} \\ \begin{bmatrix} 0.2790 & 0.2246 & 0.1930 & 0.1663 & 0.1371 \\ 0.2259 & 0.2131 & 0.2004 & 0.1882 & 0.1724 \\ 0.1872 & 0.1992 & 0.2044 & 0.2055 & 0.2036 \\ 0.1674 & 0.1891 & 0.2018 & 0.2136 & 0.2279 \\ 0.1410 & 0.1733 & 0.2003 & 0.2259 & 0.2595 \end{bmatrix} \end{array}$$

The probability is 0.1371.

(b) To find the probability that the grandson (second generation) of someone in the top income group (state t) is in the top income group (state t), use P^2 found in part (a). The probability is 0.2595.

(c) Let V be the probability vector $\begin{bmatrix} v_1 & v_2 & v_3 & v_4 & v_5 \end{bmatrix}$ and solve the equation $VP = V$.

$$\begin{bmatrix} v_1 & v_2 & v_3 & v_4 & v_5 \end{bmatrix} \begin{bmatrix} 0.4225 & 0.241 & 0.1645 & 0.1085 & 0.0635 \\ 0.245 & 0.2625 & 0.205 & 0.169 & 0.1185 \\ 0.153 & 0.191 & 0.25 & 0.233 & 0.173 \\ 0.107 & 0.195 & 0.1965 & 0.229 & 0.2725 \\ 0.073 & 0.11 & 0.184 & 0.26 & 0.373 \end{bmatrix} = \begin{bmatrix} v_1 & v_2 & v_3 & v_4 & v_5 \end{bmatrix}$$

$$\begin{aligned} 0.4225v_1 + 0.245v_2 + 0.153v_3 + 0.107v_4 + 0.073v_5 &= v_1 \\ 0.241v_1 + 0.2625v_2 + 0.191v_3 + 0.195v_4 + 0.11v_5 &= v_2 \\ 0.1645v_1 + 0.205v_2 + 0.25v_3 + 0.1965v_4 + 0.184v_5 &= v_3 \\ 0.1085v_1 + 0.169v_2 + 0.233v_3 + 0.229v_4 + 0.26v_5 &= v_4 \\ 0.0635v_1 + 0.1185v_2 + 0.173v_3 + 0.2725v_4 + 0.373v_5 &= v_5 \end{aligned}$$

Simplify the equations and use the equation $v_1 + v_2 + v_3 + v_4 + v_5 = 1$ to get the following system.

$$\begin{aligned} -0.5775v_1 + 0.245v_2 + 0.153v_3 + 0.107v_4 + 0.073v_5 &= 0 \\ 0.241v_1 - 0.7375v_2 + 0.191v_3 + 0.195v_4 + 0.11v_5 &= 0 \\ 0.1645v_1 + 0.205v_2 - 0.75v_3 + 0.1965v_4 + 0.184v_5 &= 0 \\ 0.1085v_1 + 0.169v_2 + 0.233v_3 - 0.771v_4 + 0.26v_5 &= 0 \\ 0.0635v_1 + 0.1185v_2 + 0.173v_3 + 0.2725v_4 - 0.627v_5 &= 0 \\ v_1 + v_2 + v_3 + v_4 + v_5 &= 1 \end{aligned}$$

Using a graphing calculator, the solution to the system is

$$v_1 = 0.2001, v_2 = 0.1999, v_3 = 0.2000, v_4 = 0.1999, v_5 = 0.2001.$$

This means, if the trends given by the transition matrix continue, the probabilities that a person is in each group are: 0.2001 (bottom), 0.1999 (second), 0.2000 (middle), 0.1999 (fourth), and 0.2001 (top).

54. (c) For the transition matrix

$$P = \begin{bmatrix} \frac{17}{32} & \frac{7}{16} & \frac{1}{32} \\ \frac{1}{2} & 0 & \frac{1}{2} \\ 1 & 0 & 0 \end{bmatrix},$$

since P^2 has only positive entries, P is a regular transition matrix. Therefore, there exists a unique equilibrium vector $V = [v_1 \quad v_2 \quad v_3]$ for which
$VP = V$.
This matrix equation expands to give the system of equations

$$\begin{aligned} \frac{17}{32}v_1 + \frac{1}{2}v_2 + v_3 &= v_1 \\ \frac{7}{16}v_1 &= v_2 \\ \frac{1}{32}v_1 + \frac{1}{2}v_2 &= v_3, \end{aligned}$$

which along with the equation $v_1 + v_2 + v_3 = 1$ simplifies to the system of equations

$$\begin{aligned} -15v_1 + 16v_2 + 32v_3 &= 0 \\ 7v_1 - 16v_2 \qquad\quad &= 0 \\ v_1 + 16v_2 - 32v_3 &= 0 \\ v_1 + \quad v_2 + \quad v_3 &= 1. \end{aligned}$$

Using the Gauss-Jordan method to solve this system yields the result $v_1 = \frac{16}{27}, v_2 = \frac{7}{27}, v_3 = \frac{4}{27}$. Therefore, in the long-term a player will be on Jail, the Community Chest, and Go with the probabilities $\frac{16}{27}, \frac{7}{27}$, and $\frac{4}{27}$ respectively.

Extended Application: A Markov Chain Model for Teacher Rentention

1. 0.139; 0.055.

2. They will spend, on average, 13 years in the system.

3. In the transition matrix, the only possible transition from "On Sabbatical" is to "Continuing." This means that every teacher who was on sabbatical in year 1 or year 2 of the study came back to teach the following year. In general, sabbaticals are granted at most every 7 years, on the assumption that the teacher will teach at least one more year, so this outcome is not a surprise. Since in this sample the future of a teacher on sabbatical is exactly like that of a continuing teacher, the only difference in rows 2 and 4 of F is that row 4 is 1 higher in the sabbatical column (we know this teacher will spend at least one year on sabbatical, since he or she is currently on sabbatical). However, if a teacher had died on sabbatical, or become seriously ill in the following year, the transition matrix would show other possible transitions from the sabbatical state, and rows 2 and 4 would look different.

4. The expected number of years spent on sabbatical by a currently active teacher is 0.091, so sabbaticals are rare in this school system.

5. The product FR is

$$F \cdot R = \begin{pmatrix} 0.785 & 0.198 & 0.021 \\ 0.734 & 0.240 & 0.026 \\ 0.933 & 0.060 & 0.007 \\ 0.734 & 0.240 & 0.026 \\ 0.626 & 0.352 & 0.022 \end{pmatrix}$$

	Resigned	Retired	Deceased
New	0.785	0.198	0.021
Continuing	0.734	0.240	0.026
On Leave	0.933	0.060	0.007
On Sabbatical	0.734	0.240	0.026
Ill	0.626	0.352	0.022

(a) 0.933; 0.533

(b) The teacher with at least one year in the system (probability 0.24 versus 0.197 for the new teacher).

(c) 0.021

6. The Markov model assumes the transition probabilities are constant over time. With two sets of transition data, the experimenters could check this by seeing if the transition frequencies for year 1 to year 2 were approximately the same as those for year 2 to 3.

Chapter 11

GAME THEORY

11.1 Strictly Determined Games

For Exercises 1-8, use the following game.

$$\begin{array}{cc} & \quad B \\ & \begin{array}{ccc} 1 & 2 & 3 \end{array} \\ A \begin{array}{c} 1 \\ 2 \\ 3 \end{array} & \begin{bmatrix} 7 & -5 & 0 \\ 3 & -3 & 8 \\ -1 & 5 & 11 \end{bmatrix} \end{array}$$

1. Consider the strategy $(1, 1)$. Player A chooses row 1, and player B chooses column 1. A positive number represents a payoff from B to A. The first row, first column entry is 6, indicating a payoff of \$7 from B to A.

2. The strategy $(1, 2)$ means that player A chooses row 1, and player B chooses column 2. A negative number represents a payoff from A to B. Row 1 and column 2 lead to the number -5, which represents a payoff of \$5 from A to B.

3. Consider the strategy $(2, 2)$. Player A chooses row 2, and player B chooses column 2. A negative number represents a payoff from A to B. The second row, second column entry is -3, indicating a payoff of \$3 from A to B.

4. The strategy $(2, 3)$ means that player A chooses row 2, and player B chooses column 3. A positive number represents a payoff from B to A. Row 2 and column 3 lead to the number 8, which represents a payoff of \$8 from B to A.

5. Consider the strategy $(3, 1)$. Player A chooses row 3, and player B chooses column 1. The third row, first column entry is -1, indicating a payoff of \$1 from A to B.

6. The strategy $(3, 2)$ means that player A chooses row 3 and player B chooses column 2. Row 3 and column 2 lead to the number 5, which represents a payoff of \$5 from B to A.

7. Yes, each entry in column 2 is smaller than the corresponding entry in column 3, so column 2 dominates column 3.

8. Underline the smallest number in each row, and draw a box around the largest number in each column.

$$\begin{bmatrix} \boxed{6} & \underline{-4} & 0 \\ 3 & \underline{-2} & 6 \\ \underline{-1} & \boxed{5} & \boxed{11} \end{bmatrix}$$

There is no number that is both the smallest number in its row and the largest number in its column, so the game has no saddle point.

9. $\begin{bmatrix} 0 & 9 & -3 \\ 3 & -8 & -2 \end{bmatrix}$

Column 3 dominates column 1, so remove column 1 to obtain

$$\begin{bmatrix} 9 & -3 \\ -8 & -2 \end{bmatrix}.$$

10. $\begin{bmatrix} 7 & 6 \\ -2 & -5 \\ 4 & 9 \end{bmatrix}$

Row 1 and row 3 dominate row 2, so remove row 2 to obtain

$$\begin{bmatrix} 7 & 6 \\ 4 & 9 \end{bmatrix}.$$

11. $\begin{bmatrix} 3 & 6 \\ 1 & 4 \\ 4 & -2 \\ -4 & 0 \end{bmatrix}$

Row 1 dominates row 2 and row 4, so remove row 2 and row 4 to obtain

$$\begin{bmatrix} 3 & 6 \\ 4 & -2 \end{bmatrix}.$$

12. $\begin{bmatrix} 2 & -6 & 3 & 1 \\ -2 & 2 & 5 & 4 \\ 1 & -4 & 0 & 2 \end{bmatrix}$

Column 2 dominates columns 3 and 4, so remove column 3 and column 4 to obtain

$$\begin{bmatrix} 2 & -6 \\ -2 & 2 \\ 1 & -4 \end{bmatrix}.$$

13. $\begin{bmatrix} 8 & 12 & -7 \\ -2 & 1 & 4 \end{bmatrix}$

Column 1 dominates column 2, so remove column 2 to obtain

$$\begin{bmatrix} 8 & -7 \\ -2 & 4 \end{bmatrix}.$$

14. $\begin{bmatrix} 6 & 2 \\ -1 & 10 \\ 3 & 5 \end{bmatrix}$

There are no dominated rows or columns, so there are no dominated strategies.

15. $\begin{bmatrix} \underline{-5} & 2 \\ \boxed{5} & \boxed{\underline{4}} \end{bmatrix}$

Underline the smallest number in each row and draw a box around the largest number in each column. The 4 at $(2, 2)$ is the smallest number in its row and the largest number in its column, so the saddle point is 4 at $(2, 2)$. This game is strictly determined and its value is 4.

16. $\begin{bmatrix} 8 & \boxed{\underline{6}} \\ \boxed{12} & \underline{-4} \end{bmatrix}$

Underline the smallest number in each row and draw a box around the largest number in each column. The 6 at $(1, 2)$ is the smallest number in its row and the largest number in its column, so the saddle point is 6 at $(1, 2)$. This game is strictly determined and its value is 6.

17. $\begin{bmatrix} 3 & \underline{-4} & \boxed{1} \\ \boxed{5} & \boxed{3} & \underline{-2} \end{bmatrix}$

Underline the smallest number in each row, and box the largest number in each column; in this matrix, the two categorizations do not overlap. There is no saddle point. This game is not strictly determined.

18. $\begin{bmatrix} -4 & 2 & -3 & \boxed{\underline{-7}} \\ \boxed{4} & \boxed{3} & \boxed{5} & \underline{-9} \end{bmatrix}$

-7 is both the smallest number in its row and the largest number in its column. The saddle point is -7 at the strategy $(1, 4)$; the game has value -7 and is strictly determined.

19. $\begin{bmatrix} \underline{-6} & 2 \\ -1 & \underline{-10} \\ \boxed{\underline{3}} & \boxed{5} \end{bmatrix}$

The 3 at $(3, 1)$ is the smallest number in its row and the largest number in its column, so the saddle point is 3 at $(3, 1)$. This game is strictly determined, and its value is 3.

20. $\begin{bmatrix} 1 & 4 & \underline{-3} & 1 & -1 \\ \boxed{2} & \boxed{5} & \underline{0} & 4 & \boxed{10} \\ 1 & \underline{-3} & \boxed{2} & \boxed{5} & 2 \end{bmatrix}$

There is no number that is both the smallest in its row and the largest in its column. Therefore, there is no saddle point, and the game is not strictly determined.

21. $\begin{bmatrix} 2 & 3 & \boxed{\underline{1}} \\ -1 & \boxed{4} & \underline{-7} \\ 5 & 2 & \underline{0} \\ \boxed{8} & \underline{-4} & -1 \end{bmatrix}$

The 1 at $(1, 3)$ is the smallest number in its row and the largest number in its column, so the saddle point is 1 at $(1, 3)$. This game is strictly determined, and its value is 1.

22. $\begin{bmatrix} \boxed{3} & \boxed{8} & -4 & \underline{-9} \\ -1 & -2 & \boxed{\underline{-3}} & 0 \\ -2 & 6 & \underline{-4} & \boxed{5} \end{bmatrix}$

-3 is both the smallest number in its row and the largest number in its column. The saddle point is -3 at the strategy $(2, 3)$; the game has value -3 and is strictly determined.

23. $\begin{bmatrix} \underline{-6} & 1 & \boxed{4} & \boxed{2} \\ \boxed{9} & \boxed{3} & \underline{-8} & -7 \end{bmatrix}$

There is no saddle point. This game is not strictly determined.

24. $$\begin{bmatrix} \underline{-3} & -2 & \boxed{6} \\ 2 & \boxed{0} & 2 \\ \boxed{5} & -2 & \underline{-4} \end{bmatrix}$$

The entry 0 is both the smallest number in its row and the largest number in its column. The saddle point is 0 at the strategy $(2, 2)$; the game has a value of 0 and is strictly determined.

25. $$\begin{bmatrix} 2 & 3 & 1 \\ -1 & 4 & -7 \\ 5 & 2 & 0 \\ 8 & -4 & -1 \end{bmatrix}$$

(a) Every entry in column 3 is smaller than the corresponding entry in column 1. Thus, column 3 dominates column 1. So, remove column 1 to obtain

$$\begin{bmatrix} 3 & 1 \\ 4 & -7 \\ 2 & 0 \\ -4 & -1 \end{bmatrix}.$$

(b) Every entry in row 1 is greater than the corresponding entries in rows 3 and 4. Thus, row 1 dominates row 3 and row 4. So, remove rows 3 and 4 to obtain

$$\begin{bmatrix} 3 & 1 \\ 4 & -7 \end{bmatrix}.$$

(c) Every entry in column 2 is smaller than the corresponding entry in column 1. Thus, column 2 dominates column 1. So, remove column 1 to obtain

$$\begin{bmatrix} 1 \\ -7 \end{bmatrix}.$$

(d) The entry in row 1 is larger than the entry in row 2. Thus, row 1 dominates row 2. So, remove row 2 to obtain

$$[1].$$

To verify that this is the saddle point, underline the smallest number in each row and box the largest number in each column.

$$\begin{bmatrix} 2 & 3 & \boxed{\underline{1}} \\ -1 & \boxed{4} & \underline{-7} \\ 5 & 2 & \underline{0} \\ \boxed{8} & \underline{-4} & -1 \end{bmatrix}$$

Thus, 1 is the saddle point.

26. $$\begin{bmatrix} 3 & 8 & -4 & -9 \\ -1 & -2 & -3 & 0 \\ -2 & 6 & -4 & 5 \end{bmatrix}$$

(a) Every entry in column 3 is smaller than the corresponding entries in columns 1 and 2. Thus, column 3 dominates column 1 and column 2. So, remove columns 1 and 2 to obtain

$$\begin{bmatrix} -4 & -9 \\ -3 & 0 \\ -4 & 5 \end{bmatrix}.$$

(b) Every entry in row 2 is greater than the corresponding entry in row 1. Thus, row 2 dominates row 1. So, remove row 1 to obtain

$$\begin{bmatrix} -3 & 0 \\ -4 & 5 \end{bmatrix}.$$

(c) Every entry in column 1 is smaller than the corresponding entry in column 2. This, column 1 dominates column 2. So, remove column 2 to obtain

$$\begin{bmatrix} -3 \\ -4 \end{bmatrix}.$$

(d) The entry in row 1 is larger than the entry in row 2. Thus, row 1 dominates row 2. So, remove row 2 to obtain

$$[-3].$$

To verify that this is a saddle point, underline the smallest number in each row and box the largest number in each column.

$$\begin{bmatrix} \boxed{3} & \boxed{8} & -4 & \underline{-9} \\ -1 & -2 & \boxed{\underline{-3}} & 0 \\ -2 & 6 & \underline{-4} & \boxed{5} \end{bmatrix}$$

Thus, -3 is the saddle point.

27. $$\begin{bmatrix} -3 & -2 & 6 \\ 2 & 0 & 2 \\ 5 & -2 & -4 \end{bmatrix}$$

(a) There are no dominated columns.

(b) There are no dominated rows.

28.

$$\begin{array}{l} \\ \text{Repair} \\ \text{No Repair} \end{array} \begin{array}{c} \begin{array}{ccc} 0.01 & 0.10 & 0.20 \end{array} \\ \begin{bmatrix} -\$130 & -\$130 & -\$130 \\ -\ \$25 & -\$200 & -\$500 \end{bmatrix} \end{array}$$

(a) An optimist should make no repairs; minimum cost is \$25.

(b) A pessimist should make repairs; a worst case of \$130 is better than a possible cost of \$500 if no repairs are made.

(c) Find the expected cost of each strategy.

Make repairs:

$$0.7(-130) + 0.2(-130) + 0.1(-130) = \$130$$

Make no repairs:

$$0.7(-25) + 0.2(-200) + 0.1(-500) = -\$107.50$$

He should make no repairs. The expected cost to the company if this strategy is chosen is $-\$107.50$.

29.

$$\begin{array}{r} \\ \text{Stadium} \\ \text{Gym} \\ \text{Both} \end{array} \begin{array}{c} \begin{array}{cc} \text{Rain} & \text{No Rain} \end{array} \\ \begin{bmatrix} -\$1800 & \$2400 \\ \$1500 & \$1500 \\ \$1200 & \$2100 \end{bmatrix} \end{array}$$

(a) If the dean is an optimist, she doesn't think it will rain. \$2400 is the largest possible net profit in that column, so she should set up in the stadium.

(b) If the dean is a pessimist, she thinks it will rain. \$1500 is the largest possible net profit in that column, so she should set up in the gym.

(c) If there is a 0.6 probability of rain, there is a 0.4 probability of no rain. Find the dean's expected profit for each strategy.

$$\begin{aligned} \text{Stadium: } & -\$1800(0.6) + \$2400(0.4) = -\$120 \\ \text{Gym: } & \$1500(0.6) + \$1500(0.4) = \$1500 \\ \text{Both: } & \$1200(0.6) + \$2100(0.4) = \$1560 \end{aligned}$$

She should set up both the stadium and the gym for a maximum profit of \$1560.

30.

$$\begin{array}{r} \\ \text{Repair} \\ \text{No Repair} \end{array} \begin{array}{c} \begin{array}{ccc} 0.01 & 0.10 & 0.20 \end{array} \\ \begin{bmatrix} -\$130 & -\$130 & -\$130 \\ -\$25 & -\$200 & -\$500 \end{bmatrix} \end{array}$$

(a) If the analyst is an optimist, he believes there will be the smallest fraction of defective items; these would occur in the 0.01 column. $-\$25$ is the greater number in that column, so he should choose to make no repairs.

(b) If the analyst is a pessimist, he believes there will be the largest fraction of defective items; these would occur in the 0.20 column. $-\$130$ is the greater number in that column, so he should choose to make repairs.

(c) Find the expected cost to the company for each strategy.

$$\begin{aligned} \text{Repair } & -\$130(0.7) - \$130(0.2) - \$130(0.1) = -\$130 \\ \text{No Repair } & -\$25(0.7) - \$200(0.2) - \$500(0.1) = -\$107.50 \end{aligned}$$

The lower expected cost of \$107.50 to the company occurs when no repairs are made.

31. (a) The payoff matrix is as follows.

$$\begin{array}{l} \\ \text{Market} \\ \text{Don't Market} \end{array} \begin{array}{c} \begin{array}{cc} \text{Better} & \text{Not Better} \end{array} \\ \begin{bmatrix} \$50{,}000 & -\$25{,}000 \\ -\$40{,}000 & -\$10{,}000 \end{bmatrix} \end{array}$$

(b) Find the expected profit under the 2 strategies.

Market product:

$$0.4(50{,}000) + 0.6(-25{,}000) = \$5000$$

Don't market:

$$0.4(-40{,}000) + 0.6(-10{,}000) = -\$22{,}000$$

They should market the product and make a profit of \$5000 since that is better than losing \$22,000.

(c) There are no dominated strategies. There is no saddle point.

32. (a)

$$\begin{array}{l} \\ \text{Overhaul} \\ \text{Don't Overhaul} \end{array} \begin{array}{c} \begin{array}{cc} \text{Fails} & \text{Doesn't Fail} \end{array} \\ \begin{bmatrix} -\$8600 & -\$2600 \\ -\$6000 & \$0 \end{bmatrix} \end{array}$$

(b) Find the expected cost under each strategy.

Overhaul:

$$0.1(-8600) + 0.9(-2600) = -\$3200$$

Don't overhaul:

$$0.55(-6000) + 0.7(0) = -\$3300$$

To minimize his expected costs, the businessman should overhaul the machine before shipping.

(c) Column 1 dominates column 2, and row 2 dominates row 1. The saddle point is $-\$6000$.

33.

		B		
		City 1	City 2	City 3
	City 1	15	−2	6
A	City 2	7	15	9
	City 3	3	−3	15

To get the entries in the above matrix, look, for example, at the entry in row 1, column 2. If merchant A locates in city 1 and merchant B in city 2, then merchant A will get 80% of the business in city 1, 20% in city 2, and 60% in city 3. Taking into account the fraction of the population living in each city, we get

$$0.80(0.30) + 0.20(0.45) + 0.60(0.25) = 0.48.$$

Thus, merchant A gets 48% of the total business. However, this is 2 percentage points below 50%. Hence the entry in row 1, column 2 is -2.

For row 1, column 3, we have

$$0.80(0.30) + 0.20(0.25) + 0.60(0.45) = 0.56,$$

or 56% of the total business for merchant A. However, this is 6 percentage points above 50%.

The remaining entries are found in a similar manner. This game is not strictly determined because there is no saddle point.

34.

		B		
		City 1	City 2	City 3
	City 1	5	−2	6
A	City 2	7	5	9
	City 3	3	−3	5

To get the entries in the above matrix, look, for example, at the entry in row 2, column 1. If merchant A locates in city 2 and merchant B in city 1, then merchant A will get 80% of the business in city 2, 20% in city 3, and 60% in city 1. Taking into account the fraction of the population living in each city, we get

$$0.80(0.45) + 0.20(0.30) + 0.60(0.25) = 0.57.$$

Thus, merchant A gets 57% of the total business. Now 57% is 7 percentage points above 50%, so the entry in row 2, column 1 is $+7$.

Likewise for row 3, column 1, we get

$$0.80(0.25) + 0.20(0.30) + 0.60(0.45) = 0.53 = 53\%,$$

which is 3 percentage points above 50%. The other entries are found in a similar manner. (Note that all diagonal entries are 5 since 55% is 5 percentage points above 50%.)

The 5 at $(2, 2)$ is the smallest entry in its row and the largest in its column, so the saddle point is the 5 at $(2, 2)$. The value of the game is 5.

35.

	Extra Guards to Unoccupied Territory	Extra Guards to Regular Entry Point
On Foot	0.40	0.50
In Vehicle	0.30	0.20

0.40 is the smallest entry in its row and the largest in its column. The saddle point is 0.40 at $(1, 1)$, and the value of the game is 0.40 or 40%.

36. $\begin{bmatrix} -8 & \underline{-10} & 4 \\ 0 & \underline{-12} & 6 \\ \boxed{3} & \boxed{\underline{-7}} & \boxed{8} \end{bmatrix}$

Underline the smallest number in each row, and box the largest number in each column. -7 is the smallest number in its row and the largest number in its column. The saddle point is -7 at $(3, 2)$ and the value of the game is -7.

37. $\begin{bmatrix} 9 & -3 & -4 & 16 \\ 12 & 9 & 6 & 8 \\ -5 & -2 & 3 & 18 \end{bmatrix}$

The saddle point is 6 at $(2, 3)$, and the value of the game is 6.

38. The payoff matrix is as follows.

	Rock	Paper	Scissors
Rock	0	$\underline{-1}$	$\boxed{1}$
Paper	$\boxed{1}$	0	$\underline{-1}$
Scissors	$\underline{-1}$	$\boxed{1}$	0

Underline the smallest number in each row, and box the largest number in each column; in this matrix, the two categorizations do not overlap. The game is not strictly determined since it does not have a saddle point.

39.

		Joann 1	2
John	1	2	−3
	2	−3	4

This payoff matrix has no saddle point, so the game is not strictly determined.

11.2 Mixed Strategies

1. (a) $AMB = \begin{bmatrix} 0.5 & 0.5 \end{bmatrix} \begin{bmatrix} 3 & -4 \\ -5 & 2 \end{bmatrix} \begin{bmatrix} 0.4 \\ 0.6 \end{bmatrix}$

$= \begin{bmatrix} 0.5 & 0.5 \end{bmatrix} \begin{bmatrix} -1.2 \\ -0.8 \end{bmatrix}$

$= [-0.6 - 0.4] = [-1]$

The expected value is -1.

(b) $AMB = \begin{bmatrix} 0.1 & 0.9 \end{bmatrix} \begin{bmatrix} 3 & -4 \\ -5 & 2 \end{bmatrix} \begin{bmatrix} 0.4 \\ 0.6 \end{bmatrix}$

$= \begin{bmatrix} 0.1 & 0.9 \end{bmatrix} \begin{bmatrix} -1.2 \\ -0.8 \end{bmatrix} = [-0.84]$

The expected value is -0.84.

(c) $AMB = \begin{bmatrix} 0.8 & 0.2 \end{bmatrix} \begin{bmatrix} 3 & -4 \\ -5 & 2 \end{bmatrix} \begin{bmatrix} 0.4 \\ 0.6 \end{bmatrix}$

$= \begin{bmatrix} 0.8 & 0.2 \end{bmatrix} \begin{bmatrix} -1.2 \\ -0.8 \end{bmatrix} = [-1.12]$

The expected value is -1.12.

(d) $AMB = \begin{bmatrix} 0.2 & 0.8 \end{bmatrix} \begin{bmatrix} 3 & -4 \\ -5 & 2 \end{bmatrix} \begin{bmatrix} 0.4 \\ 0.6 \end{bmatrix}$

$= \begin{bmatrix} 0.2 & 0.8 \end{bmatrix} \begin{bmatrix} -1.2 \\ -0.8 \end{bmatrix} = [-0.88]$

The expected value is -0.88.

2. (a) $AMB = \begin{bmatrix} 0.1 & 0.4 & 0.5 \end{bmatrix} \begin{bmatrix} 0 & -4 & 1 \\ 3 & 2 & -4 \\ 1 & -1 & 0 \end{bmatrix} \begin{bmatrix} 0.2 \\ 0.4 \\ 0.4 \end{bmatrix}$

$= \begin{bmatrix} 1.7 & -0.1 & -1.5 \end{bmatrix} \begin{bmatrix} 0.2 \\ 0.4 \\ 0.4 \end{bmatrix}$

$= [-0.3]$

The expected value of the game is -0.3.

(b) $AMB = \begin{bmatrix} 0.3 & 0.4 & 0.3 \end{bmatrix} \begin{bmatrix} 0 & -4 & 1 \\ 3 & 2 & -4 \\ 1 & -1 & 0 \end{bmatrix} \begin{bmatrix} 0.8 \\ 0.1 \\ 0.1 \end{bmatrix}$

$= \begin{bmatrix} 1.5 & -0.7 & -1.3 \end{bmatrix} \begin{bmatrix} 0.8 \\ 0.1 \\ 0.1 \end{bmatrix}$

$= [1]$

The expected value of the game is 1.

3. $\begin{bmatrix} 7 & 1 \\ 3 & 4 \end{bmatrix}$

There are no saddle points so the game is not strictly determined, and mixed strategies must be used. Here $a_{11} = 7, a_{12} = 1, a_{21} = 3$, and $a_{22} = 4$. For player A, the optimum strategy is

$$p_1 = \frac{a_{22} - a_{21}}{a_{11} - a_{21} - a_{12} + a_{22}} = \frac{4 - 3}{7 - 3 - 1 + 4} = \frac{1}{7},$$

$$p_2 = 1 - p_1 = 1 - \frac{1}{7} = \frac{6}{7}.$$

For player B, the optimum strategy is

$$q_1 = \frac{a_{22} - a_{12}}{a_{11} - a_{21} - a_{12} + a_{22}} = \frac{4 - 1}{7 - 3 - 1 + 4} = \frac{3}{7},$$

$$q_2 = 1 - q_1 = 1 - \frac{3}{7} = \frac{4}{7}.$$

The value of the game is

$$\frac{a_{11}a_{22} - a_{12}a_{21}}{a_{11} - a_{21} - a_{12} + a_{22}} = \frac{7(4) - 1(3)}{7 - 3 - 1 + 4} = \frac{28 - 3}{7} = \frac{25}{7}.$$

4. $\begin{bmatrix} -4 & 6 \\ 3 & -4 \end{bmatrix}$

This game has no saddle point, so it is not strictly determined and mixed strategies must be used. Here $a_{11} = -4, a_{12} = 6, a_{21} = 3$, and $a_{22} = -4$. To find the optimum strategy for player A, first find p_1.

$$p_1 = \frac{a_{22} - a_{21}}{a_{11} - a_{21} - a_{12} + a_{22}} = \frac{-4 - 3}{-4 - 3 - 6 + (-4)} = \frac{-7}{-17} = \frac{7}{17},$$

$$p_2 = 1 - p_1 = 1 - \frac{7}{17} = \frac{10}{17}$$

Now find the optimum strategy for player B.

$$q_1 = \frac{a_{22} - a_{12}}{a_{11} - a_{21} - a_{12} + a_{22}}$$
$$= \frac{-4 - 6}{-4 - 3 - 6 + (-4)}$$
$$= \frac{-10}{-17} = \frac{10}{17},$$
$$q_2 = 1 - q_1 = 1 - \frac{10}{17}$$
$$= \frac{7}{17}$$

Thus, player A should choose row 1 with probability $\frac{7}{17}$ and row 2 with probability $\frac{10}{17}$. Player B should choose column 1 with probability $\frac{10}{17}$ and column 2 with probability $\frac{7}{17}$. The value of the game is

$$\frac{a_{11}a_{22} - a_{12}a_{21}}{a_{11} - a_{21} - a_{12} + a_{22}} = \frac{-4(-4) - 6(3)}{-4 - 3 - 6 + (-4)}$$
$$= \frac{-2}{-17} = \frac{2}{17}.$$

5. $\begin{bmatrix} -2 & 0 \\ 5 & -4 \end{bmatrix}$

There are no saddle points so the game is not strictly determined, and mixed strategies must be used. Here $a_{11} = -2, a_{12} = 0, a_{21} = 5$, and $a_{22} = -4$. For player A, the optimum strategy is

$$p_1 = \frac{-4 - 5}{-2 - 5 - 0 + (-4)} = \frac{-9}{-11} = \frac{9}{11},$$
$$p_2 = 1 - \frac{9}{11} = \frac{2}{11}.$$

For player B, the optimum strategy is

$$q_1 = \frac{-4 - 0}{-2 - 5 - 0 + (-4)} = \frac{-4}{-11} = \frac{4}{11},$$
$$q_2 = 1 - \frac{4}{11} = \frac{7}{11}.$$

The value of the game is

$$\frac{-2(-4) - 0(5)}{-2 - 5 - 0 + (-4)} = -\frac{8}{11}.$$

6. $\begin{bmatrix} 6 & 3 \\ -1 & 10 \end{bmatrix}$

There are no saddle points. For player A, the optimum strategy is

$$p_1 = \frac{10 - (-1)}{6 - (-1) - 3 + 10} = \frac{11}{14},$$
$$p_2 = 1 - p_1 = \frac{3}{14}.$$

For player B, the optimum strategy is

$$q_1 = \frac{10 - 3}{6 - (-1) - 3 + 10} = \frac{7}{14} = \frac{1}{2},$$
$$q_2 = 1 - q_1 = \frac{1}{2}.$$

The value of the game is

$$\frac{6(10) - 3(-1)}{6 - (-1) - 3 + 10} = \frac{63}{14} = \frac{9}{2}.$$

7. $\begin{bmatrix} 4 & -3 \\ -1 & 9 \end{bmatrix}$

There are no saddle points. For player A, the optimum strategy is

$$p_1 = \frac{9 - (-1)}{4 - (-1) - (-3) + 9} = \frac{10}{17},$$
$$p_2 = 1 - \frac{10}{17} = \frac{7}{17}.$$

For player B, the optimum strategy is

$$q_1 = \frac{9 - (-3)}{4 - (-1) - (-3) + 9} = \frac{12}{17},$$
$$q_2 = 1 - \frac{12}{17} = \frac{5}{17}.$$

The value of the game is

$$\frac{4(9) - (-3)(-1)}{4 - (-1) - (-3) + 9} = \frac{33}{17}.$$

8. $\begin{bmatrix} 0 & 9 \\ 4 & 0 \end{bmatrix}$

There are no saddle points. For player A, the optimum strategy is

$$p_1 = \frac{0 - 4}{0 - 4 - 9 + 0} = \frac{4}{13},$$
$$p_2 = 1 - p_1 = \frac{9}{13}.$$

For player B, the optimum strategy is

$$q_1 = \frac{0 - 9}{0 - 4 - 9 + 0} = \frac{9}{13},$$
$$q_2 = 1 - q_1 = \frac{4}{13}.$$

The value of the game is

$$\frac{0(0) - 9(4)}{0 - 4 - 9 + 0} = \frac{36}{13}.$$

9. $\begin{bmatrix} -1 & 2 \\ \boxed{3} & \boxed{5} \end{bmatrix}$

The game is strictly dominated since it has a saddle point. Thus, pure strategies can be used. The saddle point is at $(2, 1)$ and the value of the game is 3.

10. $\begin{bmatrix} 4 & \frac{1}{5} \\ \frac{2}{3} & -1 \end{bmatrix}$

The game is strictly determined since it has a saddle point. Thus, pure strategies can be used. The value of the game is $\frac{1}{5}$, which is the saddle point and occurs at the strategy $(1, 2)$.

11. $\begin{bmatrix} \frac{8}{3} & -\frac{1}{2} \\ \frac{3}{4} & -\frac{5}{12} \end{bmatrix}$

The game is strictly determined since it has a saddle point at $(2, 2)$. The value of the game is $-\frac{5}{12}$.

12. $\begin{bmatrix} -\frac{1}{2} & \frac{2}{3} \\ \frac{7}{8} & -\frac{3}{4} \end{bmatrix}$

There are no saddle points. For player A, the optimum strategy is

$$p_1 = \frac{-\frac{3}{4} - \frac{7}{8}}{-\frac{1}{2} - \frac{7}{8} - \frac{2}{3} + \left(-\frac{3}{4}\right)} = \frac{-\frac{13}{8}}{-\frac{67}{24}} = \frac{39}{67},$$

$$p_2 = 1 - p_1 = \frac{28}{67}.$$

For player B, the optimum strategy is

$$q_1 = \frac{-\frac{3}{4} - \frac{2}{3}}{-\frac{1}{2} - \frac{7}{8} - \frac{2}{3} + \left(-\frac{3}{4}\right)} = \frac{-\frac{17}{12}}{-\frac{67}{24}} = \frac{34}{67},$$

$$q_2 = 1 - q_1 = \frac{33}{67}.$$

The value of the game is

$$\frac{-\frac{1}{2}\left(-\frac{3}{4}\right) - \frac{2}{3}\left(\frac{7}{8}\right)}{-\frac{1}{2} - \frac{7}{8} - \frac{2}{3} + \left(-\frac{3}{4}\right)} = \frac{-\frac{5}{24}}{-\frac{67}{24}} = \frac{5}{67}.$$

13. $\begin{bmatrix} -2 & \frac{1}{2} \\ 0 & -3 \end{bmatrix}$

There are no saddle points. For player A, the optimum strategy is

$$p_1 = \frac{-3 - 0}{-2 - 0 - \frac{1}{2} + (-3)} = \frac{-3}{\frac{-11}{2}} = \frac{6}{11},$$

$$p_2 = 1 - \frac{6}{11} = \frac{5}{11}.$$

For player B, the optimum strategy is

$$q_1 = \frac{-3 - \frac{1}{2}}{-2 - 0 - \frac{1}{2} + (-3)} = \frac{-\frac{7}{2}}{\frac{-11}{2}} = \frac{7}{11},$$

$$q_2 = 1 - \frac{7}{11} = \frac{4}{11}.$$

The value of the game is

$$\frac{-2(-3) - \frac{1}{2}(0)}{-2 - 0 - \frac{1}{2} + (-3)} = \frac{6}{\frac{-11}{2}} = -\frac{12}{11}.$$

14. $\begin{bmatrix} 8 & 18 \\ -4 & 2 \end{bmatrix}$

The game is strictly determined since there is a saddle point. The value of the game is 8, which is the saddle point and occurs at the strategy $(1, 1)$.

15. $\begin{bmatrix} -4 & 9 \\ 3 & -5 \\ 8 & 7 \end{bmatrix}$

Row 3 dominates row 2, so remove row 2. This gives the matrix

$$\begin{bmatrix} -4 & 9 \\ 8 & 7 \end{bmatrix}.$$

For player A, the optimum strategy is

$$p_1 = \frac{7 - 8}{-4 - 8 - 9 + 7} = \frac{-1}{-14} = \frac{1}{14},$$

$$p_2 = 0 \text{ (row 2 was removed)},$$

$$p_3 = 1 - (p_1 + p_2) = 1 - \frac{1}{14} = \frac{13}{14}.$$

For player B, the optimum strategy is

$$q_1 = \frac{7 - 9}{-4 - 8 - 9 + 7} = \frac{-2}{-14} = \frac{1}{7},$$

$$q_2 = 1 - \frac{1}{7} = \frac{6}{7}.$$

The value of the game is

$$\frac{-4(7) - 9(8)}{-4 - 8 - 9 + 7} = \frac{-100}{-14} = \frac{50}{7}.$$

16. $\begin{bmatrix} 3 & 4 & -1 \\ -2 & 1 & 0 \end{bmatrix}$

Column 1 dominates column 2, so remove column 2. This gives the payoff matrix

$$\begin{bmatrix} 3 & -1 \\ -2 & 0 \end{bmatrix}.$$

For player A, the optimum strategy is

$$p_1 = \frac{0-(-2)}{3-(-2)-(-1)+0} = \frac{1}{3},$$

$$p_2 = 1 - p_1 = \frac{2}{3}.$$

For player B, the optimum strategy is

$$q_1 = \frac{0-(-1)}{3-(-2)-(-1)+0} = \frac{1}{6},$$

$$q_2 = 0 \text{ (column 2 was removed)},$$

$$q_3 = 1-(q_1+q_2) = \frac{5}{6}.$$

The value of the game is

$$\frac{3(0)-(-1)(-2)}{3-(-2)-(-1)+0} = -\frac{1}{3}.$$

17. $\begin{bmatrix} 8 & 6 & 3 \\ -1 & -2 & 4 \end{bmatrix}$

Column 2 dominates column 1, so remove column 1. This gives the matrix

$$\begin{bmatrix} 6 & 3 \\ -2 & 4 \end{bmatrix}.$$

For player A, the optimum strategy is

$$p_1 = \frac{4-(-2)}{6-(-2)-3+4} = \frac{6}{9} = \frac{2}{3},$$

$$p_2 = 1 - \frac{2}{3} = \frac{1}{3}.$$

For player B, the optimum strategy is

$$q_1 = 0 \text{ (column 1 was removed)},$$

$$q_2 = \frac{4-3}{6-(-2)-3+4} = \frac{1}{9},$$

$$q_3 = 1-(q_1+q_2) = 1 - \frac{1}{9} = \frac{8}{9}.$$

The value of the game is

$$\frac{6(4)-3(-2)}{6-(-2)-3+4} = \frac{30}{9} = \frac{10}{3}.$$

18. $\begin{bmatrix} -1 & 6 \\ 8 & 3 \\ -2 & 5 \end{bmatrix}$

Row 1 dominates row 3, so remove row 3. This gives the matrix

$$\begin{bmatrix} -1 & 6 \\ 8 & 3 \end{bmatrix}.$$

For player A, the optimum strategy is

$$p_1 = \frac{3-8}{-1-8-6+3} = \frac{5}{12},$$

$$p_2 = 1 - p_1 = \frac{7}{12},$$

$$p_3 = 0 \text{ (row 3 was removed)}.$$

For player B, the optimum strategy is

$$q_1 = \frac{3-6}{-1-8-6+3} = \frac{1}{4},$$

$$q_2 = 1 - q_1 = \frac{3}{4}.$$

The value of the game is

$$\frac{-1(3)-6(8)}{-1-8-6+3} = \frac{17}{4}.$$

19. $\begin{bmatrix} 9 & -1 & 6 \\ 13 & 11 & 8 \\ 6 & 0 & 9 \end{bmatrix}$

Row 2 dominates row 1, so remove row 1. This gives the matrix

$$\begin{bmatrix} 13 & 11 & 8 \\ 6 & 0 & 9 \end{bmatrix}.$$

Now, column 2 dominates column 1, so remove column 1. This gives the matrix

$$\begin{bmatrix} 11 & 8 \\ 0 & 9 \end{bmatrix}.$$

For player A, the optimum strategy is

$$p_1 = 0 \text{ (row 1 was removed)},$$

$$p_2 = \frac{9-0}{11-0-8+9} = \frac{9}{12} = \frac{3}{4},$$

$$p_3 = 1 - \frac{3}{4} = \frac{1}{4}.$$

For player B, the optimum strategy is

$$q_1 = 0 \text{ (column 1 was removed)},$$

$$q_2 = \frac{9-8}{11-0-8+9} = \frac{1}{12},$$

$$q_3 = 1 - \frac{1}{12} = \frac{11}{12}.$$

The value of the game is

$$\frac{11(9) - 8(0)}{11 - 0 - 8 + 9} = \frac{99}{12} = \frac{33}{4}.$$

20. $\begin{bmatrix} 4 & 8 & -3 \\ 2 & -1 & 1 \\ 7 & 9 & 0 \end{bmatrix}$

Remove row 1 (which is dominated by row 3) and column 1 (which is dominated by column 3). This gives the matrix

$$\begin{bmatrix} -1 & 1 \\ 9 & 0 \end{bmatrix}.$$

For player A, the optimum strategy is

$$p_1 = 0 \text{ (row 1 was removed)},$$

$$p_2 = \frac{0 - 9}{-1 - 9 - 1 + 0} = \frac{9}{11},$$

$$p_3 = 1 - (p_1 + p_2) = \frac{2}{11}.$$

For player B, the optimum strategy is

$$q_1 = 0 \text{ (column 1 was removed)},$$

$$q_2 = \frac{0 - 1}{-1 - 9 - 1 + 0} = \frac{1}{11},$$

$$q_3 = 1 - (q_1 + q_2) = \frac{10}{11}.$$

The value of the game is

$$\frac{-1(0) - 1(9)}{-1 - 9 - 1 + 0} = \frac{9}{11}.$$

21. In a non-strictly-determined game, there is no saddle point. Let

$$M = \begin{bmatrix} a_{11} & a_{12} \\ a_{21} & a_{22} \end{bmatrix}$$

be the payoff matrix of the game. Assume that player B chooses column 1 with probability q_1. The expected value for B, assuming A plays row 1, is E_1, where

$$E_1 = a_{11}q_1 + a_{12}(1 - q_1).$$

The expected value for B if A plays row 2 is E_2, where

$$E_2 = a_{21}q_1 + a_{22}(1 - q_1).$$

The optimum strategy for player B is found by letting $E_1 = E_2$.

$$\begin{aligned} a_{11}q_1 + a_{12}(1 - q_1) &= a_{21}q_1 + a_{22}(1 - q_1) \\ a_{11}q_1 + a_{12} - a_{12}q_1 &= a_{21}q_1 + a_{22} - a_{22}q_1 \\ a_{11}q_1 - a_{21}q_1 - a_{12}q_1 + a_{22}q_1 &= a_{22} - a_{12} \\ q_1(a_{11} - a_{21} - a_{12} + a_{22}) &= a_{22} - a_{12} \\ q_1 &= \frac{a_{22} - a_{12}}{a_{11} - a_{21} - a_{12} + a_{22}} \end{aligned}$$

Since $q_2 = 1 - q_1$,

$$\begin{aligned} q_2 &= 1 - \frac{a_{22} - a_{12}}{a_{11} - a_{21} - a_{12} + a_{22}} \\ &= \frac{a_{11} - a_{21} - a_{12} + a_{22} - (a_{22} - a_{12})}{a_{11} - a_{21} - a_{12} + a_{22}} \\ &= \frac{a_{11} - a_{21}}{a_{11} - a_{21} - a_{21} + a_{22}}. \end{aligned}$$

These are the formulas given in the text for q_1 and q_2.

22. Let the non-strictly-determined game have payoff matrix

$$M = \begin{bmatrix} a_{11} & a_{12} \\ a_{21} & a_{22} \end{bmatrix}.$$

The optimum strategy for player A is $\begin{bmatrix} p_1 & p_2 \end{bmatrix}$, where

$$p_1 = \frac{a_{22} - a_{21}}{a_{11} - a_{21} - a_{12} + a_{22}},$$

$$p_2 = \frac{a_{11} - a_{12}}{a_{11} - a_{21} - a_{12} + a_{22}}.$$

The optimum strategy for player B is $\begin{bmatrix} q_1 \\ q_2 \end{bmatrix}$, where

$$q_1 = \frac{a_{22} - a_{12}}{a_{11} - a_{21} - a_{12} + a_{22}},$$

$$q_2 = \frac{a_{11} - a_{21}}{a_{11} - a_{21} - a_{12} + a_{22}}.$$

The value of the game is AMB.

$$\begin{aligned} AMB &= \begin{bmatrix} p_1 & p_2 \end{bmatrix} \begin{bmatrix} a_{11} & a_{12} \\ a_{21} & a_{22} \end{bmatrix} \begin{bmatrix} q_1 \\ q_2 \end{bmatrix} \\ &= \begin{bmatrix} p_1a_{11} + p_2a_{21} & p_1a_{12} + p_2a_{22} \end{bmatrix} \begin{bmatrix} q_1 \\ q_2 \end{bmatrix} \end{aligned}$$

$$AMB = [p_1a_{11}q_1 + p_2a_{21}q_1 + p_1a_{12}q_2 + p_2a_{22}q_2]$$

Since this is a 1×1 matrix, we will drop the matrix notation.

$$AMB = \frac{a_{22}-a_{21}}{a_{11}-a_{21}-a_{12}+a_{22}} \cdot a_{11} \cdot \frac{a_{22}-a_{12}}{a_{11}-a_{21}-a_{12}+a_{22}}$$
$$+\frac{a_{11}-a_{12}}{a_{11}-a_{21}-a_{12}+a_{22}} \cdot a_{21} \cdot \frac{a_{22}-a_{21}}{a_{11}-a_{21}-a_{12}+a_{22}}$$
$$+\frac{a_{22}-a_{21}}{a_{11}-a_{21}-a_{12}+a_{22}} \cdot a_{12} \cdot \frac{a_{11}-a_{21}}{a_{11}-a_{21}-a_{12}+a_{22}}$$
$$+\frac{a_{11}-a_{12}}{a_{11}-a_{21}-a_{12}+a_{22}} \cdot a_{22} \cdot \frac{a_{11}-a_{21}}{a_{11}-a_{21}-a_{12}+a_{22}}$$
$$= \frac{a_{11}(a_{22}-a_{21})(a_{22}-a_{12})}{(a_{11}-a_{21}-a_{12}+a_{22})^2} + \frac{a_{21}(a_{11}-a_{12})(a_{22}-a_{12})}{(a_{11}-a_{21}-a_{12}+a_{22})^2} + \frac{a_{12}(a_{22}-a_{21})(a_{11}-a_{21})}{(a_{11}-a_{21}-a_{12}+a_{22})^2} + \frac{a_{22}(a_{11}-a_{12})(a_{11}-a_{21})}{(a_{11}-a_{21}-a_{12}+a_{22})^2}$$
$$= \frac{(a_{22}-a_{12})[a_{11}(a_{22}-a_{21})+a_{21}(a_{11}-a_{12})]}{(a_{11}-a_{21}-a_{12}+a_{22})^2} + \frac{(a_{11}-a_{21})[a_{12}(a_{22}-a_{21})+a_{22}(a_{11}-a_{12})]}{(a_{11}-a_{21}-a_{12}+a_{22})^2}$$
$$= \frac{(a_{22}-a_{12})(a_{11}a_{22}-a_{21}a_{12})}{(a_{11}-a_{21}-a_{12}+a_{22})^2} + \frac{(a_{11}-a_{21})(-a_{12}a_{21}+a_{22}a_{11})}{(a_{11}-a_{21}-a_{12}+a_{22})^2}$$
$$= \frac{(a_{11}a_{22}-a_{21}a_{12})(a_{22}-a_{12}+a_{11}-a_{21})}{(a_{11}-a_{21}-a_{12}+a_{22})^2}$$
$$= \frac{a_{11}a_{22}-a_{21}a_{12}}{a_{11}-a_{21}-a_{12}+a_{22}}$$

This is the expression for the value of a non-strictly-determined game that is given in the text.

26. Let

$$M = \begin{bmatrix} a_{11} & a_{12} \\ a_{21} & a_{22} \end{bmatrix}$$

be the payoff matrix of the game.

(a) Let $A = [p_1 \quad p_2]$ be the optimum strategy for player A. Thus,

$$p_1 = \frac{a_{22}-a_{21}}{d} \text{ and } p_2 = \frac{a_{11}-a_{12}}{d}$$

where $d = a_{11} - a_{21} - a_{12} + a_{22}$.

$$AM = [p_1 \quad p_2]\begin{bmatrix} a_{11} & a_{12} \\ a_{21} & a_{22} \end{bmatrix}$$
$$= [p_1a_{11}+p_2a_{21} \quad p_1a_{12}+p_2a_{22}]$$
$$= [g \quad g]$$

Since

$$p_1a_{11}+p_2a_{21}$$
$$= \frac{a_{22}-a_{21}}{d}\cdot a_{11} + \frac{a_{11}-a_{12}}{d}\cdot a_{21}$$
$$= \frac{a_{11}a_{22}-a_{11}a_{21}}{d} + \frac{a_{11}a_{21}-a_{12}a_{21}}{d}$$
$$= \frac{a_{11}a_{22}-a_{11}a_{21}+a_{11}a_{21}-a_{12}a_{21}}{d}$$
$$= \frac{a_{11}a_{22}-a_{12}a_{21}}{d}$$
$$= g$$

and

$$p_1a_{12}+p_2a_{22}$$
$$= \frac{a_{22}-a_{21}}{d}\cdot a_{12} + \frac{a_{11}-a_{12}}{d}\cdot a_{22}$$
$$= \frac{a_{12}a_{22}-a_{12}a_{21}}{d} + \frac{a_{11}a_{22}-a_{12}a_{22}}{d}$$
$$= \frac{a_{12}a_{22}-a_{12}a_{21}+a_{11}a_{22}-a_{12}a_{22}}{d}$$
$$= \frac{a_{11}a_{22}-a_{12}a_{21}}{d}$$
$$= g,$$

then $AM = [g \quad g]$, where g is the value of the game.

(b) Let $B = \begin{bmatrix} q_1 \\ q_2 \end{bmatrix}$ be the optimum strategy for player B. Thus,

$$q_1 = \frac{a_{22}-a_{12}}{d} \text{ and } q_2 = \frac{a_{11}-a_{21}}{d}$$

where $d = a_{11} - a_{21} - a_{12} + a_{22}$.

$$MB = \begin{bmatrix} a_{11} & a_{12} \\ a_{21} & a_{22} \end{bmatrix}\begin{bmatrix} q_1 \\ q_2 \end{bmatrix}$$
$$= \begin{bmatrix} a_{11}q_1 + a_{12}q_2 \\ a_{21}q_1 + a_{22}q_2 \end{bmatrix}$$
$$= \begin{bmatrix} g \\ g \end{bmatrix}$$

Since

$$a_{11}q_1 + a_{12}q_2$$
$$= a_{11}\cdot\frac{a_{22}-a_{12}}{d} + a_{12}\cdot\frac{a_{11}-a_{21}}{d}$$
$$= \frac{a_{11}a_{22}-a_{11}a_{12}}{d} + \frac{a_{11}a_{12}-a_{12}a_{21}}{d}$$
$$= \frac{a_{11}a_{22}-a_{11}a_{12}+a_{11}a_{12}-a_{12}a_{21}}{d}$$
$$= \frac{a_{11}a_{22}-a_{12}a_{21}}{d} = g$$

and

$$\begin{aligned} a_{21}q_1 + a_{22}q_2 &= a_{21} \cdot \frac{a_{22} - a_{12}}{d} + a_{22} \cdot \frac{a_{11} - a_{21}}{d} \\ &= \frac{a_{21}a_{22} - a_{12}a_{21}}{d} + \frac{a_{11}a_{22} - a_{21}a_{22}}{d} \\ &= \frac{a_{21}a_{22} - a_{12}a_{21} + a_{11}a_{22} - a_{21}a_{22}}{d} \\ &= \frac{a_{11}a_{22} - a_{12}a_{21}}{d} = g, \end{aligned}$$

then $MB = \begin{bmatrix} g \\ g \end{bmatrix}$, where g is the value of the game.

27. $\begin{bmatrix} 1 & 2 & 3 \\ 4 & 3 & 1 \end{bmatrix}$

(a)
$$\begin{aligned} E_1 &= 1p_1 + 4(1 - p_1) \\ &= p_1 + 4 - 4p_1 \\ &= 4 - 3p_1 \end{aligned}$$

$$\begin{aligned} E_2 &= 2p_1 + 3(1 - p_1) \\ &= 2p_1 + 3 - 3p_1 \\ &= 3 - p_1 \end{aligned}$$

$$\begin{aligned} E_3 &= 3p_1 + 1(1 - p_1) \\ &= 3p_1 + 1 - p_1 \\ &= 1 + 2p_1 \end{aligned}$$

(b)

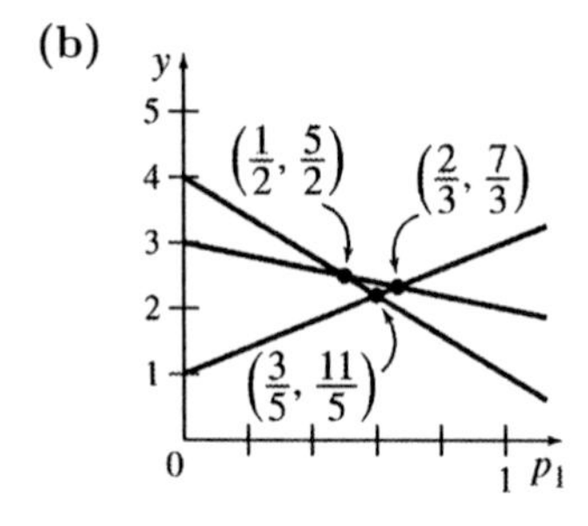

(c) From the graph, $p_1 = \frac{1}{2}$ maximizes the minimum expected value the row player receives.

28. $\begin{bmatrix} -1 & 5 & 1 \\ 3 & 1 & 2 \end{bmatrix}$

(a)
$$\begin{aligned} E_1 &= -1p_1 + 3(1 - p_1) \\ &= -p_1 + 3 - 3p_1 \\ &= 3 - 4p_1 \end{aligned}$$

$$\begin{aligned} E_2 &= 5p_1 + 1(1 - p_1) \\ &= 5p_1 + 1 - p_1 \\ &= 1 + 4p_1 \end{aligned}$$

$$\begin{aligned} E_3 &= 1p_1 + 2(1 - p_1) \\ &= p_1 + 2 - 2p_1 \\ &= 2 - p_1 \end{aligned}$$

(b)

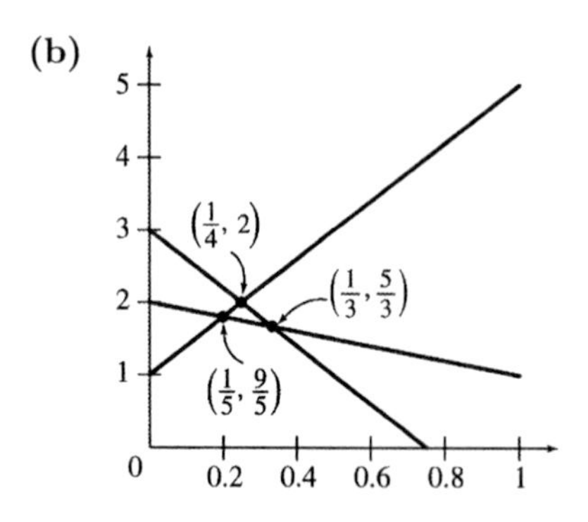

(c) From the graph, $p_1 = \frac{1}{4}$ maximizes the minimum expected value the row player receives.

29. The payoff matrix for this game is

$$\begin{array}{c c} & \begin{matrix} \text{H} & \text{T} \end{matrix} \\ \begin{matrix} \text{H} \\ \text{T} \end{matrix} & \begin{bmatrix} 3 & -2 \\ -2 & 1 \end{bmatrix} \end{array}$$

with $a_{11} = 3, a_{12} = -2, a_{21} = -2, a_{22} = 1$ and

$$\begin{aligned} d &= a_{11} - a_{21} - a_{12} + a_{22} \\ &= 3 - (-2) - (-2) + 1 \\ &= 8. \end{aligned}$$

(a) Your optimum strategy is

$$\text{H: } p_1 = \frac{a_{22} - a_{21}}{d} = \frac{1 - (-2)}{d} = \frac{3}{8}$$

$$\text{T: } p_2 = 1 - p_1 = 1 - \frac{3}{8} = \frac{5}{8}.$$

You should play heads with probability $\frac{3}{8}$ and tails with probability $\frac{5}{8}$.

Your opponent's optimum strategy is

$$\text{H: } q_1 = \frac{a_{22} - a_{12}}{d} = \frac{1 - (-2)}{d} = \frac{3}{8}$$

$$\text{T: } q_2 = 1 - q_1 = 1 - \frac{3}{8} = \frac{5}{8}.$$

Your opponent should also play heads with probability $\frac{3}{8}$ and tails with probability $\frac{5}{8}$.

The value of the game is

$$\begin{aligned} g &= \frac{a_{11}a_{22} - a_{12}a_{21}}{d} \\ &= \frac{(3)(1) - (-2)(-2)}{d} \\ &= \frac{3 - 4}{8} \\ &= -\frac{1}{8}. \end{aligned}$$

(b) If the stranger's strategy is to play twice as many tails as heads, then $q_1 = \frac{1}{3}$ and $q_2 = \frac{2}{3}$. Assume that your strategy is $[p_1 \quad p_2]$ with $p_2 = 1 - p_1$. The expected value of the game is

$$AMB = [p_1 \quad 1-p_1]\begin{bmatrix} 3 & -2 \\ -2 & 1 \end{bmatrix}\begin{bmatrix} \frac{1}{3} \\ \frac{2}{3} \end{bmatrix}$$
$$= [5p_1 - 2 \quad 1 - 3p_1]\begin{bmatrix} \frac{1}{3} \\ \frac{2}{3} \end{bmatrix}$$
$$= \left[-\frac{p_1}{3}\right].$$

Marilyn claims the stranger will win $1 for every six plays, so

$$6\left(-\frac{p_1}{3}\right) = -1$$
$$-2p_1 = -1$$
$$p_1 = \frac{1}{2}.$$

Thus, Marilyn is assuming your strategy is to play heads and tails with probability $\frac{1}{2}$ each.

(c) From part (b), the expected value of the game with the given strategy for your opponent is $-p_1/3$. Since $0 \le p_1 \le 1$, no matter how you choose p_1, $-p_1/3$ will always be nonpositive—i.e., zero or negative. The best you can hope for is an expected value of zero, which will occur when $p_1 = 0$. In other words you should always play tails. The value of the game is then 0.

30.

		Bates	
		T.V.	Radio
Allied	T.V.	1.0	−0.7
	Radio	−0.5	0.6

The optimum strategy for Allied is

$$p_1 = \frac{0.6-(-0.5)}{1-(-0.5)-(-0.7)+0.6} = \frac{1.1}{2.8} = \frac{11}{28},$$
$$p_2 = 1 - \frac{11}{28} = \frac{17}{28}.$$

Allied should use T.V. with probability $\frac{11}{28}$ and radio with probability $\frac{17}{28}$.

The value of the game is

$$\frac{1(0.6)-(-0.7)(-0.5)}{2.8} = \frac{0.25}{2.8} = \frac{5}{56},$$

which represents increased sales of

$$1{,}000{,}000\left(\frac{5}{56}\right) \approx 1{,}000{,}000(0.089286)$$
$$= \$89{,}286.$$

31.

		Competitor's Strategy	
		4.9	4.75
Boeing's Strategy	4.9	2	−4
	4.75	0	2

There is no saddle point. The optimum strategy for pricing is

$$p_1 = \frac{0-2}{-4-2-2+0} = \frac{-2}{-8} = \frac{1}{4},$$
$$p_2 = 1 - p_1 = \frac{3}{4}.$$

(q_1 and q_2 are not of interest here.) This means that Boeing's price strategy should be to aim for the \$4.9 million profit $\frac{1}{4}$ of the time and the \$4.75 million profit $\frac{3}{4}$ of the time. The value is

$$\frac{-4(0)-2(2)}{-4-2-2+0} = \frac{-4}{-8} = \frac{1}{2},$$

which means this strategy will increase Boeing's profit by $\frac{1}{2}$ million dollars.

32. (a)

		Selling during:	
		Rain	Shine
Buying for:	Rain	2500	−1500
	Shine	−1500	3500

(b) The best mixed strategy for Merrill is

$$p_1 = \frac{3500-(-1500)}{2500-(-1500)-(-1500)+3500}$$
$$= \frac{5000}{9000} = \frac{5}{9},$$
$$p_2 = 1 - \frac{5}{9} = \frac{4}{9}.$$

He should invest in rainy day goods $\frac{5}{9}$ of the time and in sunny day goods $\frac{4}{9}$ of the time.

The value of the game is

$$\frac{2500(3500)-(-1500)^2}{9000} = \frac{6{,}500{,}000}{9000} = \frac{6500}{9}$$
$$\approx \$722.22.$$

Thus, his profit is \$722.22.

33. **(a)**

$$\begin{array}{cc} & \textit{Strain} \\ & \begin{array}{cc} 1 & 2 \end{array} \\ \textit{Medicine} \begin{array}{c} 1 \\ 2 \end{array} & \begin{bmatrix} 0.75 & 0.4 \\ 0 & 1 \end{bmatrix} \end{array}$$

(b) There is no saddle point. The optimum strategy for prescribing medicine is

$$p_1 = \frac{1-0}{0.75-0-0.4+1} = \frac{1}{1.35} = \frac{20}{27},$$
$$p_2 = 1 - p_1 = \frac{7}{27}.$$

(q_1 and q_2 are not of interest here.) This means that Dr. Goedeker should prescribe medicine 1 about $\frac{20}{27}$ of the time and medicine 2 about $\frac{7}{27}$ of the time. The result (value) will be

$$\frac{0.75(1)-0.4(0)}{0.75-0-0.4+1} = \frac{0.75}{1.35} = \frac{5}{9},$$

which indicates an effectiveness of 55.56%.

34. The payoff matrix is as follows.

$$\begin{array}{ccc} & & \textit{Jamie} \\ & & \begin{array}{cc} \text{Pounce} & \text{Freeze} \end{array} \\ \textit{Euclid} & \begin{array}{c} \text{Pounce} \\ \text{Freeze} \end{array} & \begin{bmatrix} 3 & 1 \\ -2 & 2 \end{bmatrix} \end{array}$$

The optimum strategy for Euclid is

$$p_1 = \frac{2-(-2)}{3-(-2)-1+2} = \frac{4}{6} = \frac{2}{3},$$
$$p_2 = 1 - \frac{2}{3} = \frac{1}{3}.$$

Euclid should pounce $\frac{2}{3}$ of the time and freeze $\frac{1}{3}$ of the time.

The optimum strategy for Jamie is

$$q_1 = \frac{2-1}{3-(-2)-1+2} = \frac{1}{6},$$
$$q_2 = 1 - \frac{1}{6} = \frac{5}{6}.$$

Jamie should pounce $\frac{1}{6}$ of the time and freeze $\frac{5}{6}$ of the time.

The value of the game is

$$\frac{3(2)-1(-2)}{3-(-2)-1+2} = \frac{8}{6} = \frac{4}{3}.$$

35. **(a)** $\begin{bmatrix} 1 & -1 \\ -1 & 1 \end{bmatrix}$

(b) There is no saddle point. For player A, the optimum strategy is

$$p_1 = \frac{1-(-1)}{1-(-1)-(-1)+1} = \frac{2}{4} = \frac{1}{2},$$
$$p_2 = 1 - p_1 = \frac{1}{2}.$$

For player B, the optimum strategy is

$$q_1 = \frac{1-(-1)}{1-(-1)-(-1)+1} = \frac{2}{4} = \frac{1}{2},$$
$$q_2 = 1 - q_1 = \frac{1}{2}.$$

The value of the game is

$$\frac{1(1)-(-1)(-1)}{1-(-1)-(-1)+1} = \frac{0}{4} = 0,$$

so this is a fair game.

36. **(a)** The payoff matrix is as follows.

$$\begin{array}{ccc} & & \textit{Number of Fingers} \\ & & \text{B } \textit{Shows} \\ & & \begin{array}{cc} 1 & 2 \end{array} \\ \begin{array}{c} \textit{Number of Fingers} \\ \text{A } \textit{Shows} \end{array} & \begin{array}{c} 1 \\ 2 \end{array} & \begin{bmatrix} 2 & -3 \\ -3 & 4 \end{bmatrix} \end{array}$$

(b) For player A, the optimum strategy is

$$p_1 = \frac{4-(-3)}{2-(-3)-(-3)+4} = \frac{7}{12},$$
$$p_2 = 1 - \frac{7}{12} = \frac{5}{12}.$$

For player B, the optimum strategy is

$$q_1 = \frac{4-(-3)}{2-(-3)-(-3)+4} = \frac{7}{12},$$
$$q_2 = 1 - \frac{7}{12} = \frac{5}{12}.$$

This means that each player should show 1 finger $\frac{7}{12}$ of the time and 2 fingers $\frac{5}{12}$ of the time.

The value of the game is

$$\frac{2(4)-(-3)(-3)}{2-(-3)-(-3)+4} = -\frac{1}{12}.$$

37. **(a)** The playoff matrix for the game is

		Number of Fingers 0	2
Number of	0	0	−2
Fingers	2	−2	4

(b) For player A, the optimum strategy is

$$p_1 = \frac{4-(-2)}{0-(-2)-(-2)+4} = \frac{6}{8} = \frac{3}{4},$$

$$p_2 = 1 - p_1 = \frac{1}{4}.$$

For player B, the optimum strategy is

$$q_1 = \frac{4-(-2)}{0-(-2)-(-2)+4} = \frac{6}{8} = \frac{3}{4},$$

$$q_2 = 1 - q_1 = \frac{1}{4}.$$

Both players should choose 0 fingers with probability $\frac{3}{4}$ and 2 fingers with probability $\frac{1}{4}$.

The value of the game is

$$\frac{0(4)-(-2)(-2)}{0-(-2)-(-2)+4} = \frac{-4}{8} = -\frac{1}{2}.$$

11.3 Game Theory and Linear Programming

1. $\begin{bmatrix} 1 & 2 \\ 4 & 1 \end{bmatrix}$

To find the optimum strategy for player A, use the following linear programming problem.

Minimize $w = x + y$
subject to: $x + 4y \geq 1$
$2x + y \geq 1$
with $x \geq 0, y \geq 0.$

Solve this linear programming problem by the graphical method. Sketch the feasible region.

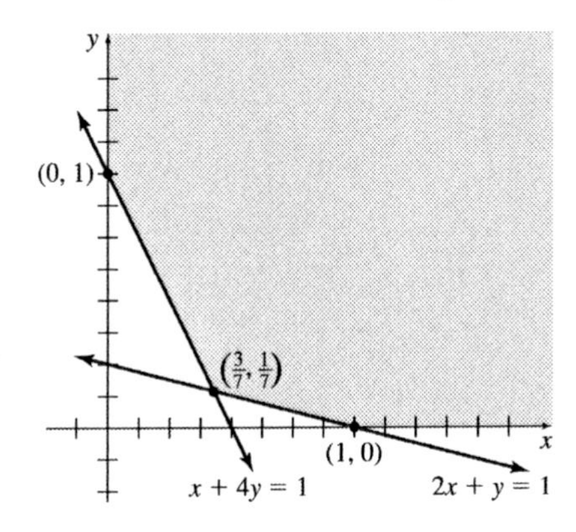

The region is unbounded, with corner points $(0,1)$, $(\frac{3}{7}, \frac{1}{7})$, and $(1,0)$.

Corner Point	Value of $w = x + y$
$(0,1)$	$0 + 1 = 1$
$(\frac{3}{7}, \frac{1}{7})$	$\frac{3}{7} + \frac{1}{7} = \frac{4}{7}$
$(1,0)$	$1 + 0 = 1$

The minimum value is $w = \frac{4}{7}$ at the point where $x = \frac{3}{7}, y = \frac{1}{7}$. Thus, the value of the game is $g = \frac{1}{w} = \frac{7}{4}$, and the optimum strategy for A is

$$p_1 = gx = \frac{7}{4}\left(\frac{3}{7}\right) = \frac{3}{4}, \; p_2 = gy = \frac{7}{4}\left(\frac{1}{7}\right) = \frac{1}{4}.$$

To find the optimum strategy for player B, use the following linear programming problem.

Maximize $z = x + y$
subject to: $x + 2y \leq 1$
$4x + y \leq 1$
with $x \geq 0, y \geq 0.$

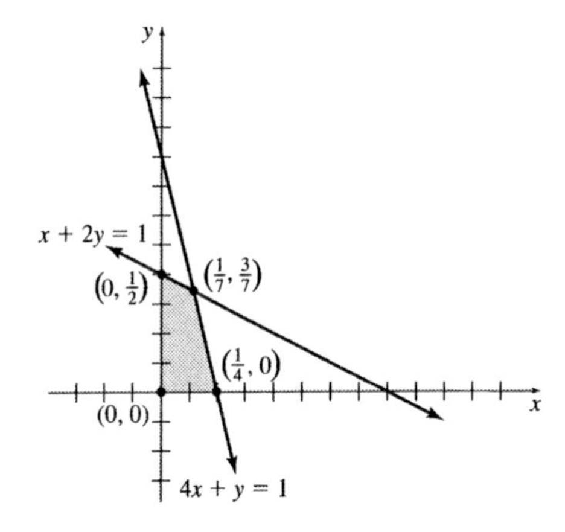

The region is bounded, with corner points $(0, \frac{1}{2})$, $(\frac{1}{7}, \frac{3}{7})$, $(\frac{1}{4}, 0)$, and $(0,0)$.

Corner Point	Value of $z = x + y$
$(0, \frac{1}{2})$	$0 + \frac{1}{2} = \frac{1}{2}$
$(\frac{1}{7}, \frac{3}{7})$	$\frac{1}{7} + \frac{3}{7} = \frac{4}{7}$
$(\frac{1}{4}, 0)$	$\frac{1}{4} + 0 = \frac{1}{4}$
$(0,0)$	$0 + 0 = 0$

The maximum value is $z = \frac{4}{7}$ at the point where $x = \frac{1}{7}, y = \frac{3}{7}$. Thus, the value of the game is $g = \frac{1}{z} = \frac{4}{7}$ (agreeing with our earlier finding), and the optimum strategy for B is

$$q_1 = gx = \frac{7}{4}\left(\frac{1}{7}\right) = \frac{1}{4}, \; q_2 = gy = \frac{7}{4}\left(\frac{3}{7}\right) = \frac{3}{4}.$$

2. $\begin{bmatrix} 6 & 2 \\ 0 & 3 \end{bmatrix}$

To find the optimum strategy for player A, use the following linear programming problem.

$$\begin{array}{ll} \text{Minimize} & w = x + y \\ \text{subject to:} & 6x \geq 1 \\ & 2x + 3y \geq 1 \\ \text{with} & x \geq 0,\ y \geq 0. \end{array}$$

Solve this linear programming problem by the graphical method. Sketch the feasible region.

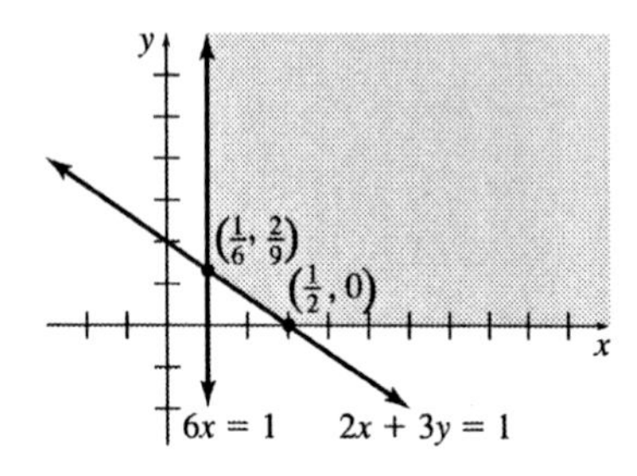

The region is unbounded, with corner points $\left(\frac{1}{6}, \frac{2}{9}\right)$ and $\left(\frac{1}{2}, 0\right)$.

Corner Point	Value of $w = x + y$
$\left(\frac{1}{6}, \frac{2}{9}\right)$	$\frac{1}{6} + \frac{2}{9} = \frac{7}{18}$
$\left(\frac{1}{2}, 0\right)$	$\frac{1}{2} + 0 = \frac{1}{2}$

The minimum value is $w = \frac{7}{18}$ at the point where $x = \frac{1}{6}, y = \frac{2}{9}$. Thus, the value of the game is $g = \frac{1}{w} = \frac{18}{7}$, and the optimum strategy for A is

$$p_1 = gx = \frac{18}{7}\left(\frac{1}{6}\right) = \frac{3}{7}, p_2 = gy = \frac{18}{7}\left(\frac{2}{9}\right) = \frac{4}{7}.$$

To find the optimum strategy for player B, use the following linear programming problem.

$$\begin{array}{ll} \text{Maximize} & z = x + y \\ \text{subject to:} & 6x + 2y \leq 1 \\ & 3y \leq 1 \\ \text{with} & x \geq 0,\ y \geq 0. \end{array}$$

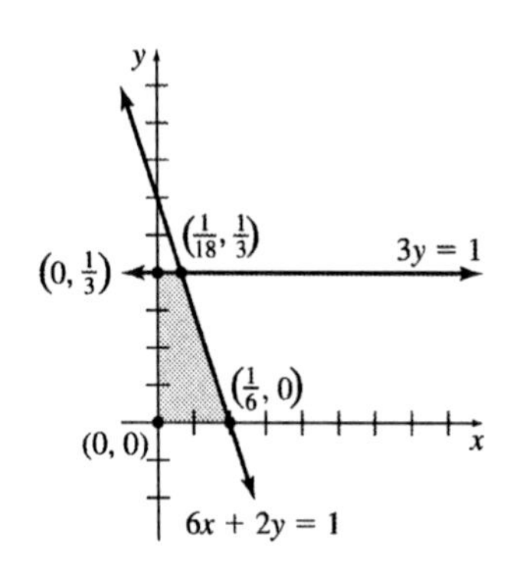

The region is bounded, with corner points $\left(0, \frac{1}{3}\right)$, $\left(\frac{1}{18}, \frac{1}{3}\right)$, $\left(\frac{1}{6}, 0\right)$, and (0,0).

Corner Point	Value of $z = x + y$
$\left(0, \frac{1}{3}\right)$	$\frac{1}{3} + 0 = \frac{1}{3}$
$\left(\frac{1}{18}, \frac{1}{3}\right)$	$\frac{1}{18} + \frac{1}{3} = \frac{7}{18}$
$\left(\frac{1}{6}, 0\right)$	$\frac{1}{6} + 0 = \frac{1}{6}$
$(0, 0)$	$0 + 0 = 0$

The maximum value is $z = \frac{7}{18}$ at the point where $x = \frac{1}{18}, y = \frac{1}{3}$. Thus, the value of the game is $g = \frac{1}{z} = \frac{18}{7}$, (agreeing with our earlier finding), and the optimum strategy for B is

$$q_1 = gx = \frac{18}{7}\left(\frac{1}{18}\right) = \frac{1}{7}, q_2 = gy = \frac{18}{7}\left(\frac{1}{3}\right) = \frac{6}{7}.$$

3. $\begin{bmatrix} 2 & -2 \\ -1 & 6 \end{bmatrix}$

To guarantee that the value of the game is positive, add 2 to each of the entries to eliminate any negative numbers. The 2 will be subtracted later, after the calculations have been performed.

$$\begin{bmatrix} 4 & 0 \\ 1 & 8 \end{bmatrix}$$

To find the optimum strategy for player A, use the following linear programming problem.

$$\begin{array}{ll} \text{Minimize} & w = x + y \\ \text{subject to:} & 4x + y \geq 1 \\ & 8y \geq 1 \\ \text{with} & x \geq 0,\ y \geq 0. \end{array}$$

Solve this linear programming problem by the graphical method. Sketch the feasible region.

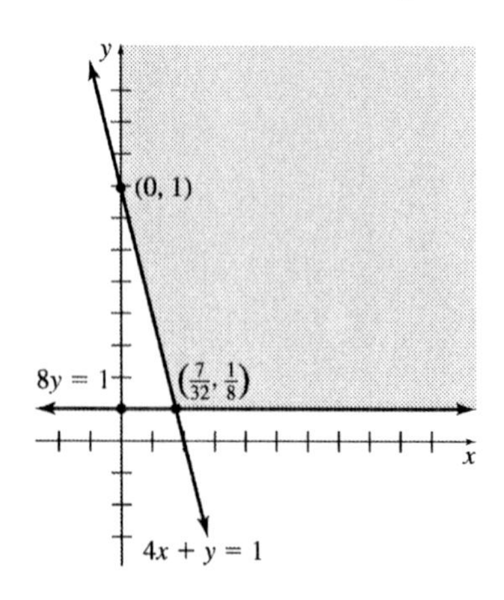

The region is unbounded, with corner points $(0,1)$ and $\left(\frac{7}{32}, \frac{1}{8}\right)$.

Corner Point	Value of $w = x + y$
$(0,1)$	$0 + 1 = 1$
$\left(\frac{7}{32}, \frac{1}{8}\right)$	$\frac{7}{32} + \frac{1}{8} = \frac{11}{32}$

The minimum value is $w = \frac{11}{32}$ at the point where $x = \frac{7}{32}, y = \frac{1}{8}$. Thus, the value of the game is $g = \frac{1}{w} = \frac{32}{11}$, and the optimum strategy for A is

$$p_1 = gx = \frac{32}{11}\left(\frac{7}{32}\right) = \frac{7}{11}, p_2 = gy = \frac{32}{11}\left(\frac{1}{8}\right) = \frac{4}{11}.$$

The value of the game is

$$g - 2 = \frac{32}{11} - 2 = \frac{10}{11}.$$

To find the optimum strategy for player B, use the following linear programming problem.

Maximize $z = x + y$
subject to: $4x \leq 1$
$x + 8y \leq 1$
with $x \geq 0, y \geq 0.$

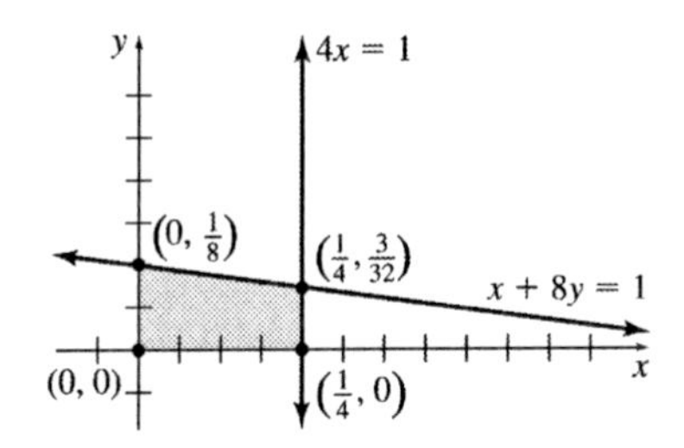

The region is bounded, with corner points $\left(0, \frac{1}{8}\right)$, $\left(\frac{1}{4}, \frac{3}{32}\right)$, $\left(\frac{1}{4}, 0\right)$, and $(0,0)$.

Corner Point	Value of $z = x + y$
$\left(0, \frac{1}{8}\right)$	$0 + \frac{1}{8} = \frac{1}{8}$
$\left(\frac{1}{4}, \frac{3}{32}\right)$	$\frac{1}{4} + \frac{3}{32} = \frac{11}{32}$
$\left(\frac{1}{4}, 0\right)$	$\frac{1}{4} + 0 = \frac{1}{4}$
$(0,0)$	$0 + 0 = 0$

The maximum value is $z = \frac{11}{32}$ at the point where $x = \frac{1}{4}, y = \frac{3}{32}$. Thus, the value of the game is $g = \frac{1}{z} = \frac{32}{11}$ (agreeing with our earlier finding), and the optimum strategy for B is

$$q_1 = gx = \frac{32}{11}\left(\frac{1}{4}\right) = \frac{8}{11}, \ q_2 = gy = \frac{32}{11}\left(\frac{3}{32}\right) = \frac{3}{11}.$$

The value of the game is

$$g - 2 = \frac{32}{11} - 2 = \frac{10}{11}$$

which agrees with the earlier value.

4. $\begin{bmatrix} -1 & 5 \\ 1 & -8 \end{bmatrix}$

To guarantee that the value of the game is positive, add 8 to each of the entries to eliminate any negative numbers. The 8 will be subtracted later, after the calculations have been performed.

$$\begin{bmatrix} 7 & 13 \\ 9 & 0 \end{bmatrix}.$$

To find the optimum strategy for player A, use the following linear programming problem.

Minimize $w = x + y$
subject to: $7x + 9y \geq 1$
$13x \geq 1$
with $x \geq 0, y \geq 0.$

Solve this linear programming problem by the graphical method. Sketch the feasible region.

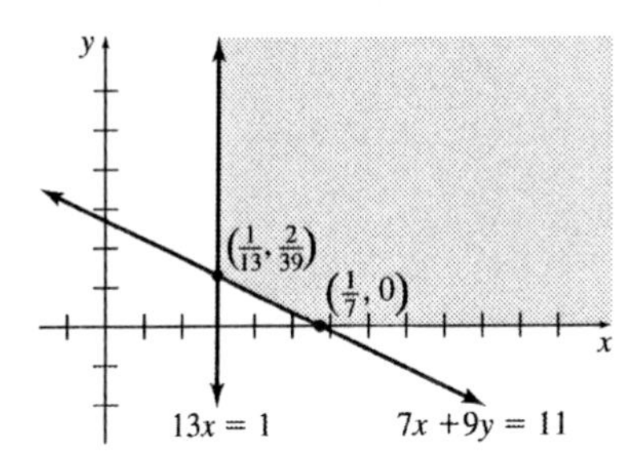

The region is unbounded, with corner points $\left(\frac{1}{13}, \frac{2}{39}\right)$ and $\left(\frac{1}{7}, 0\right)$.

Corner Point	Value of $w = x + y$
$\left(\frac{1}{13}, \frac{2}{39}\right)$	$\frac{1}{13} + \frac{2}{39} = \frac{5}{39}$
$\left(\frac{1}{7}, 0\right)$	$\frac{1}{7} + 0 = \frac{1}{7}$

The minimum value is $w = \frac{5}{39}$ at the point where $x = \frac{1}{13}, y = \frac{2}{39}$. Thus, the value of the game is $g = \frac{1}{w} = \frac{39}{5}$, and the optimum strategy for A is

$$p_1 = gx = \frac{39}{5}\left(\frac{1}{13}\right) = \frac{3}{5}, p_2 = gy = \frac{39}{5}\left(\frac{2}{39}\right) = \frac{2}{5}.$$

The value for the original game is

$$g - 8 = \frac{39}{5} - 8 = -\frac{1}{5}.$$

To find the optimum strategy for player B, use the following linear programming problem.

Maximize $z = x + y$
subject to: $7x + 13y \leq 1$
$9x \leq 1.$
with $x \geq 0,\ y \geq 0.$

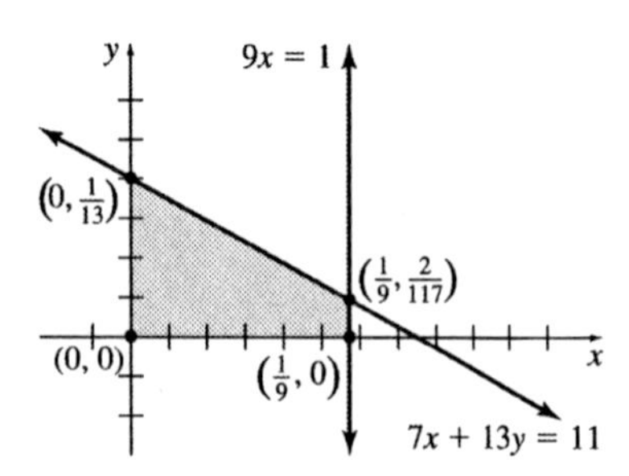

The region is bounded, with corner points $\left(0, \frac{1}{13}\right)$, $\left(\frac{1}{9}, \frac{2}{117}\right)$, $\left(\frac{1}{9}, 0\right)$, and $(0, 0)$.

Corner Point	Value of $z = x + y$
$(0, \frac{1}{13})$	$0 + \frac{1}{13} = \frac{1}{13}$
$(\frac{1}{9}, \frac{2}{117})$	$\frac{1}{9} + \frac{2}{117} = \frac{5}{39}$
$(\frac{1}{9}, 0)$	$\frac{1}{9} + 0 = \frac{1}{9}$
$(0, 0)$	$0 + 0 = 0$

The maximum value is $z = \frac{5}{39}$ at the point where $x = \frac{1}{9}, y = \frac{2}{117}$. Thus, the value of the game is $g = \frac{1}{z} = \frac{39}{5}$ (agreeing with our earlier finding), and the optimum strategy for B is

$$q_1 = gx = \frac{39}{5}\left(\frac{1}{9}\right) = \frac{13}{15}, q_2 = gy = \frac{39}{5}\left(\frac{2}{117}\right) = \frac{2}{15}.$$

The value for the original game is

$$g - 8 = \frac{39}{5} - 8 = -\frac{1}{5}$$

which agrees with the earlier value.

5. $\begin{bmatrix} 7 & -8 \\ -3 & 3 \end{bmatrix}$

Add 8 to each entry to obtain

$$\begin{bmatrix} 15 & 0 \\ 5 & 11 \end{bmatrix}.$$

To find the optimum strategy for player A,

Minimize $w = x + y$
subject to: $15x + 5y \geq 1$
$11y \geq 1$
with $x \geq 0, y \geq 0.$

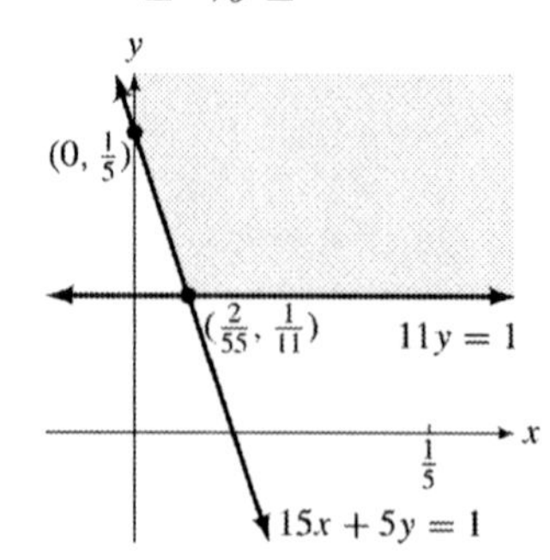

Corner Point	Value of $w = x + y$
$(0, \frac{1}{5})$	$0 + \frac{1}{5} = \frac{1}{5}$
$(\frac{2}{55}, \frac{1}{11})$	$\frac{2}{55} + \frac{1}{11} = \frac{7}{55}$

The minimum value is $w = \frac{7}{55}$ at $(\frac{2}{55}, \frac{1}{11})$. Thus, $g = \frac{1}{w} = \frac{55}{7}$, and the optimum strategy for A is

$$p_1 = gx = \frac{55}{7}\left(\frac{2}{55}\right) = \frac{2}{7},$$

$$p_2 = gy = \frac{55}{7}\left(\frac{1}{11}\right) = \frac{5}{7}.$$

The value of the game is

$$\frac{55}{7} - 8 = -\frac{1}{7}.$$

To find the optimum strategy for player B,

Maximize $z = x + y$
subject to: $15x \leq 1$
$5x + 11y \leq 1$
with $x \geq 0, y \geq 0.$

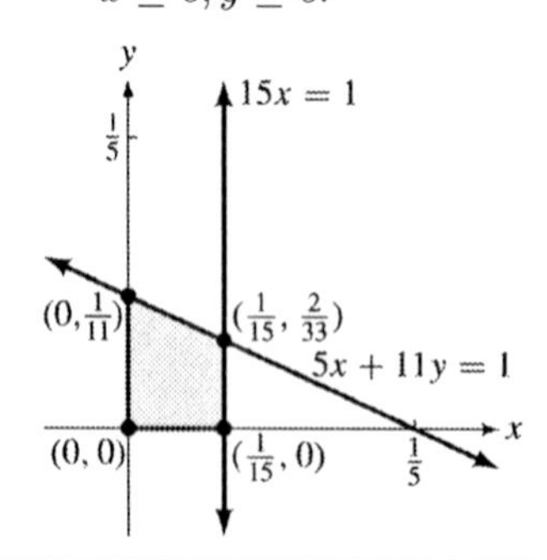

Corner Point	Value of $z = x + y$
$(0, \frac{1}{11})$	$0 + \frac{1}{11} = \frac{1}{11}$
$(\frac{1}{15}, \frac{2}{33})$	$\frac{1}{15} + \frac{2}{33} = \frac{21}{165} = \frac{7}{55}$
$(\frac{1}{15}, 0)$	$\frac{1}{15} + 0 = \frac{1}{15}$
$(0, 0)$	$0 + 0 = 0$

The maximum value is $z = \frac{7}{55}$ at $(\frac{1}{15}, \frac{2}{33})$. The optimum strategy for B is

$$q_1 = gx = \frac{55}{7}\left(\frac{1}{15}\right) = \frac{11}{21},$$

$$q_2 = gy = \frac{55}{7}\left(\frac{2}{33}\right) = \frac{10}{21}.$$

6. $\begin{bmatrix} -4 & 1 \\ 5 & 0 \end{bmatrix}$

To guarantee that the value of the game is positive, we add 4 to all the entries in the matrix to obtain

$$\begin{bmatrix} 0 & 5 \\ 9 & 4 \end{bmatrix}.$$

Let player A choose row 1 with probability p_1 and row 2 with probability p_2. Then

$$\begin{aligned} E_1 &= \quad\quad 9p_2 \\ E_2 &= 5p_1 + 4p_2. \end{aligned}$$

Let g represent the minimum of the expected gains, so that

$$\begin{aligned} E_1 &= \quad\quad 9p_2 \geq g \\ E_2 &= 5p_1 + 4p_2 \geq g. \end{aligned}$$

Dividing by g yields

$$9\left(\frac{p_2}{g}\right) \geq 1$$

$$5\left(\frac{p_1}{g}\right) + 4\left(\frac{p_2}{g}\right) \geq 1.$$

Let $x = \dfrac{p_1}{g}$ and $y = \dfrac{p_2}{g}$.

We have the following linear programming problem:

$$\begin{aligned} &\text{Minimize} && w = x + y \\ &\text{subject to:} && 9y \geq 1 \\ & && 5x + 4y \geq 1 \\ &\text{with} && x \geq 0, y \geq 0. \end{aligned}$$

Graph the feasible region.

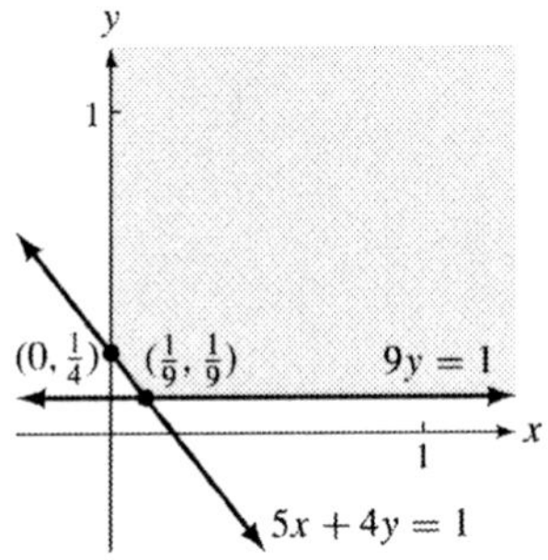

The corner points are $(0, \frac{1}{4})$ and $(\frac{1}{9}, \frac{1}{9})$. The minimum value of $w = x + y$ is $\frac{2}{9}$ at $(\frac{1}{9}, \frac{1}{9})$. Thus, the value of the game is $g = \frac{1}{w} = \frac{9}{2}$. To find the value of the original game, we must subtract 4.

$$\frac{9}{2} - 4 = \frac{9}{2} - \frac{8}{2} = \frac{1}{2}$$

The value of the original game is $\frac{1}{2}$. The optimum strategy for A is

$$p_1 = gx = \frac{9}{2}\left(\frac{1}{9}\right) = \frac{1}{2},$$

$$p_2 = gy = \frac{9}{2}\left(\frac{1}{9}\right) = \frac{1}{2}.$$

Let player B choose column 1 with probability q_1 and column 2 with probability q_2. Then

$$\begin{aligned} E_1 &= \quad\quad 5q_2 \\ E_2 &= 9q_1 + 4q_2. \end{aligned}$$

Let g represent the maximum of the expected gains, so that

$$\begin{aligned} E_1 &= \quad\quad 5q_2 \leq g \\ E_2 &= 9q_1 + 4q_2 \leq g. \end{aligned}$$

Dividing by g yields

$$5\left(\frac{q_2}{g}\right) \leq 1$$

$$9\left(\frac{q_1}{g}\right) + 4\left(\frac{q_2}{g}\right) \leq 1.$$

We have the following linear programming problem:

$$\begin{aligned} &\text{Maximize} && z = x + y \\ &\text{subject to:} && 5y \leq 1 \\ & && 9x + 4y \leq 1 \\ &\text{with} && x \geq 0, y \geq 0. \end{aligned}$$

Graph the feasible region.

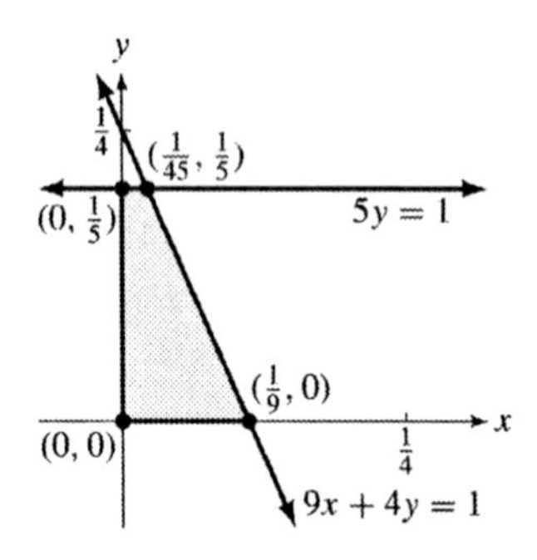

There are four corner points to consider: $(0,0), (0, \frac{1}{5})$, $(\frac{1}{45}, \frac{1}{5})$, and $(\frac{1}{9}, 0)$. The maximum value of $z = x + y$ is $\frac{2}{9}$ at $(\frac{1}{45}, \frac{1}{5})$. As before, the value of the game is $g = \frac{1}{z} = \frac{9}{2}$. The value of the original game again is $\frac{9}{2} - 4 = \frac{1}{2}$. The optimum strategy for B is

$$q_1 = gx = \frac{9}{2}\left(\frac{1}{45}\right) = \frac{1}{10},$$

$$q_2 = gy = \frac{9}{2}\left(\frac{1}{5}\right) = \frac{9}{10}.$$

To summarize, player A should choose row 1 with probability $\frac{1}{2}$ and row 2 with probability $\frac{1}{2}$, while player B should choose column 1 with probability $\frac{1}{10}$ and column 2 with probability $\frac{9}{10}$. When these optimum strategies are used, the value of the game is $\frac{1}{2}$.

7. $\begin{bmatrix} 3 & -4 & 1 \\ 5 & 3 & -2 \end{bmatrix}$

Column 1 is dominated by the other two columns, so remove it.

$$\begin{bmatrix} -4 & 1 \\ 3 & -2 \end{bmatrix}$$

Add 4 to each entry to obtain

$$\begin{bmatrix} 0 & 5 \\ 7 & 2 \end{bmatrix}.$$

The linear programming problem to be solved is as follows.

$$\begin{array}{ll} \text{Maximize} & z = x_2 + x_3 \\ \text{subject to:} & 5x_3 \le 1 \\ & 7x_2 + 2x_3 \le 1 \\ \text{with} & x_2 \ge 0, x_3 \ge 0. \end{array}$$

Use the simplex method to solve the problem. The initial tableau is

$$\begin{array}{c} \\ \\ \\ \end{array}\left[\begin{array}{cccccc|c} x_2 & x_3 & s_1 & s_2 & z & \\ 0 & 5 & 1 & 0 & 0 & 1 \\ \boxed{7} & 2 & 0 & 1 & 0 & 1 \\ \hline -1 & -1 & 0 & 0 & 1 & 0 \end{array}\right].$$

Pivot on the indicated entry.

$$\begin{array}{r} \\ \\ R_2 + 7R_3 \to R_3 \end{array}\left[\begin{array}{ccccc|c} 0 & \boxed{5} & 1 & 0 & 0 & 1 \\ 7 & 2 & 0 & 1 & 0 & 1 \\ \hline 0 & -5 & 0 & 1 & 7 & 1 \end{array}\right]$$

(columns: x_2, x_3, s_1, s_2, z)

Pivot again.

$$\begin{array}{r} \\ -2R_1 + 5R_2 \to R_2 \\ R_1 + R_3 \to R_3 \end{array}\left[\begin{array}{ccccc|c} 0 & 5 & 1 & 0 & 0 & 1 \\ 35 & 0 & -2 & 5 & 0 & 3 \\ \hline 0 & 0 & 1 & 1 & 7 & 2 \end{array}\right]$$

Create a 1 in the columns corresponding to x_2, x_3, and z.

$$\begin{array}{r} \frac{1}{5}R_1 \to R_1 \\ \frac{1}{35}R_2 \to R_2 \\ \frac{1}{7}R_3 \to R_3 \end{array}\left[\begin{array}{ccccc|c} 0 & 1 & \frac{1}{5} & 0 & 0 & \frac{1}{5} \\ 1 & 0 & -\frac{2}{35} & \frac{1}{7} & 0 & \frac{3}{35} \\ \hline 0 & 0 & \frac{1}{7} & \frac{1}{7} & 1 & \frac{2}{7} \end{array}\right]$$

From this final tableau, we have $x_2 = \frac{3}{35}, x_3 = \frac{1}{5}, y_1 = \frac{1}{7}, y_2 = \frac{1}{7}, z = \frac{2}{7}$. Note that $g = \frac{1}{z} = \frac{7}{2}$. The optimum strategy for player A is

$$p_1 = gy_1 = \frac{7}{2}\left(\frac{1}{7}\right) = \frac{1}{2},$$

$$p_2 = gy_2 = \frac{7}{2}\left(\frac{1}{7}\right) = \frac{1}{2}.$$

The optimum strategy for player B is

$$q_1 = 0 \text{ (column 1 was removed)},$$

$$q_2 = gx_2 = \frac{7}{2}\left(\frac{3}{35}\right) = \frac{3}{10},$$

$$q_3 = gx_3 = \frac{7}{2}\left(\frac{1}{5}\right) = \frac{7}{10}.$$

The value of the game is

$$\frac{7}{2} - 4 = -\frac{1}{2}.$$

8. $\begin{bmatrix} -5 & 1 & 4 & 2 \\ 9 & 3 & -8 & -7 \end{bmatrix}$

Because of negative entries, add 8 to all entries. The resulting payoff matrix is

$$\begin{bmatrix} 3 & 9 & 12 & 10 \\ 17 & 11 & 0 & 1 \end{bmatrix}.$$

The linear programming problem to be solved is:

$$\begin{array}{ll} \text{Maximize} & z = x_1 + x_2 + x_3 + x_4 \\ \text{subject to:} & 3x_1 + 9x_2 + 12x_3 + 10x_4 \le 1 \\ & 17x_1 + 11x_2 \qquad\quad + x_4 \le 1. \\ \text{with} & x_1 \ge 0, x_2 \ge 0, x_3 \ge 0, x_4 \ge 0. \end{array}$$

We will solve this problem using the simplex method. The initial tableau is

$$\begin{array}{c} \begin{array}{ccccccc} x_1 & x_2 & x_3 & x_4 & s_1 & s_2 & z \end{array} \\ \left[\begin{array}{ccccccc|c} 3 & 9 & 12 & 10 & 1 & 0 & 0 & 1 \\ \boxed{17} & 11 & 0 & 1 & 0 & 1 & 0 & 1 \\ \hline -1 & -1 & -1 & -1 & 0 & 0 & 1 & 0 \end{array}\right]. \end{array}$$

We arbitrarily choose the first column. The smallest ratio is formed by the 17 in row 2. We make this the pivot and arrive at the following matrix.

$$\begin{array}{r} -3R_2+17R_1 \to R_1 \\ \\ R_2+17R_3 \to R_3 \end{array} \left[\begin{array}{ccccccc|c} 0 & 120 & \boxed{204} & 167 & 17 & -3 & 0 & 14 \\ 17 & 11 & 0 & 1 & 0 & 1 & 0 & 1 \\ \hline 0 & -6 & -17 & -16 & 0 & 1 & 17 & 1 \end{array}\right]$$

(columns: x_1, x_2, x_3, x_4, s_1, s_2, z)

The next pivot is the 204 in row 1, column 3.

$$\begin{array}{r} \\ \\ R_1+12R_3 \to R_3 \end{array} \left[\begin{array}{ccccccc|c} 0 & 120 & 204 & \boxed{167} & 17 & -3 & 0 & 14 \\ 17 & 11 & 0 & 1 & 0 & 1 & 0 & 1 \\ \hline 0 & 48 & 0 & -25 & 17 & 9 & 204 & 26 \end{array}\right]$$

(columns: x_1, x_2, x_3, x_4, s_1, s_2, z)

The next pivot is the 167 in row 1, column 4.

$$\begin{array}{r} \\ -R_1+167R_2 \to R_2 \\ 25R_1+167R_3 \to R_3 \end{array} \left[\begin{array}{ccccccc|c} 0 & 120 & 204 & 167 & 17 & -3 & 0 & 14 \\ 2839 & 1717 & -204 & 0 & -17 & 170 & 0 & 153 \\ \hline 0 & 11{,}016 & 5100 & 0 & 3264 & 1428 & 34{,}068 & 4692 \end{array}\right]$$

(columns: x_1, x_2, x_3, x_4, s_1, s_2, z)

We have arrived at the final tableau. Dividing the bottom row by 34,068 gives a z-value of $\frac{4692}{34{,}068} = \frac{23}{167}$, so $g = \frac{1}{z} = \frac{167}{23}$. The values of y_1 and y_2 are read from the bottom of the columns for the two slack variables after dividing the bottom row by 34,068.

$$y_1 = \frac{3264}{34{,}068} = \frac{16}{167}, y_2 = \frac{1428}{34{,}068} = \frac{7}{167}.$$

We find the values of p_1 and p_2 by multiplying the values of y_1 and y_2 by g.

$$p_1 = gy_1 = \left(\frac{167}{23}\right)\left(\frac{16}{167}\right) = \frac{16}{23}, p_2 = gy_2 = \left(\frac{167}{23}\right)\left(\frac{7}{167}\right) = \frac{7}{23}$$

Next, we find the values of x_1, x_2, x_3, and x_4 by using the first four columns combined with the last column:

$$x_1 = \frac{153}{2839} = \frac{9}{167}, x_2 = 0, x_3 = 0, x_4 = \frac{14}{167}$$

We find the values of q_1, q_2, q_3, and q_4 by multiplying the values of x_1, x_2, x_3, and x_4 by g.

$$q_1 = gx_1\left(\frac{167}{23}\right)\left(\frac{9}{167}\right) = \frac{9}{23},$$

$$q_2 = 0,\ q_3 = 0,$$

$$q_4 = gx_4\left(\frac{167}{23}\right)\left(\frac{14}{167}\right) = \frac{14}{23}$$

Finally, the value of the game is found by subtracting from g the 8 that was added at the beginning, yielding $\frac{167}{23} - 8 = -\frac{17}{23}$.

To summarize, the optimum strategy for player A is $p_1 = \frac{16}{23}$ and $p_2 = \frac{7}{23}$. The optimum strategy for player B is $q_1 = \frac{9}{23}, q_2 = 0, q_3 = 0$, and $q_4 = \frac{14}{23}$. When these strategies are used, the value of the game is $-\frac{17}{23}$.

9. $\begin{bmatrix} -1 & 1 & 4 \\ 3 & -2 & -3 \end{bmatrix}$

Because of negative entries, add 3 to all entries. The resulting payoff matrix is

$$\begin{bmatrix} 2 & 4 & 7 \\ 6 & 1 & 0 \end{bmatrix}.$$

The linear programming problem to be solved is

Maximize $z = x_1 + x_2 + x_3$
subject to: $2x_1 + 4x_2 + 7x_3 \le 1$
$6x_1 + x_2 \le 1$
with $x_1 \ge 0, x_2 \ge 0, x_3 \ge 0$.

We will solve this problem using the simplex method. The initial tableau is

$$\begin{array}{cccccc|c} x_1 & x_2 & x_3 & s_1 & s_2 & z & \\ 2 & 4 & 7 & 1 & 0 & 0 & 1 \\ \boxed{6} & 1 & 0 & 0 & 1 & 0 & 1 \\ \hline -1 & -1 & -1 & 0 & 0 & 1 & 0 \end{array}.$$

We arbitrarily choose the first column. The smallest ratio is formed by the 6 in row 2. We make this the pivot and arrive at the following matrix.

$$\begin{array}{l} \\ -R_2 + 3R_1 \to R_1 \\ \\ R_2 + 6R_3 \to R_3 \end{array} \begin{array}{cccccc|c} x_1 & x_2 & x_3 & s_1 & s_2 & z & \\ 0 & 11 & \boxed{21} & 3 & -1 & 0 & 2 \\ 6 & 1 & 0 & 0 & 1 & 0 & 1 \\ \hline 0 & -5 & -6 & 0 & 1 & 6 & 1 \end{array}$$

The next pivot is the 21 in row 1, column 3.

$$\begin{array}{l} \\ \\ \\ 2R_1 + 7R_3 \to R_3 \end{array} \begin{array}{cccccc|c} x_1 & x_2 & x_3 & s_1 & s_2 & z & \\ 0 & \boxed{11} & 21 & 3 & -1 & 0 & 2 \\ 6 & 1 & 0 & 0 & 1 & 0 & 1 \\ \hline 0 & -13 & 0 & 6 & 5 & 42 & 11 \end{array}$$

The next pivot is the 11 in row 1, column 2.

$$\begin{array}{l} \\ \\ -R_1 + 11R_2 \to R_2 \\ 13R_1 + 11R_3 \to R_3 \end{array} \begin{array}{cccccc|c} x_1 & x_2 & x_3 & s_1 & s_2 & z & \\ 0 & 11 & 21 & 3 & -1 & 0 & 2 \\ 66 & 0 & -21 & -3 & 12 & 0 & 9 \\ \hline 0 & 0 & 273 & 105 & 42 & 462 & 147 \end{array}$$

We have the final tableau. Dividing the bottom row by 462 gives a z-value of $z = \frac{147}{462} = \frac{7}{22}$ so $g = \frac{1}{z} = \frac{22}{7}$. The values of y_1 and y_2 are read from the bottom of the columns for the two slack variables after dividing the entries by 462.

$$y_1 = \frac{105}{462} = \frac{5}{22}, y_2 = \frac{42}{462} = \frac{1}{11}$$

We find the values of p_1 and p_2 by multiplying the values of y_1 and y_2 by g.

$$p_1 = gy_1 = \left(\frac{22}{7}\right)\left(\frac{5}{22}\right) = \frac{5}{7},$$

$$p_2 = gy_2 = \left(\frac{22}{7}\right)\left(\frac{1}{11}\right) = \frac{2}{7}$$

Next, we find the values of x_1, x_2, and x_3 by using the first four columns combined with the last column.

$$x_1 = \frac{9}{66} = \frac{3}{22}, x_2 = \frac{2}{11}, x_3 = 0$$

We find the values of q_1, q_2, and q_3 by multiplying the values of x_1, x_2, and x_3 by g.

$$q_1 = gx_1 = \left(\frac{22}{7}\right)\left(\frac{3}{22}\right) = \frac{3}{7},$$

$$q_2 = \left(\frac{22}{7}\right)\left(\frac{2}{11}\right) = \frac{4}{7}, q_3 = 0$$

Finally, the value of the game is found by subtracting from g the 3 that was added at the beginning, yielding $\frac{22}{7} - 3 = \frac{1}{7}$.

To summarize, the optimum strategy for player A is $p_1 = \frac{5}{7}$ and $p_2 = \frac{2}{7}$. The optimum strategy for player B is $q_1 = \frac{3}{7}, q_2 = \frac{4}{7}$, and $q_3 = 0$. When these strategies are used, the value of the game is $\frac{1}{7}$.

10. $\begin{bmatrix} 1 & 0 \\ -2 & 4 \\ -1 & -1 \end{bmatrix}$

Row 1 dominates row 3. Removing row 3 gives us the following game:

$$\begin{bmatrix} 1 & 0 \\ -2 & 4 \end{bmatrix}.$$

Because of the negative entry, we will add 2 to all entries. The resulting payoff matrix is

$$\begin{bmatrix} 3 & 2 \\ 0 & 6 \end{bmatrix}.$$

The linear programming problem to be solved is:

$$\begin{aligned} &\text{Maximize} && z = x_1 + x_2 \\ &\text{subject to:} && 3x_1 + 2x_2 \le 1 \\ & && 6x_2 \le 1 \\ &\text{with} && x_1 \ge 0, x_2 \ge 0. \end{aligned}$$

The initial tableau is

$$\begin{array}{ccccc|c} x_1 & x_2 & s_1 & s_2 & z & \\ 3 & 2 & 1 & 0 & 0 & 1 \\ 0 & \boxed{6} & 0 & 1 & 0 & 1 \\ \hline -1 & -1 & 0 & 0 & 1 & 0 \end{array}.$$

We arbitrarily choose the second column. The smallest ratio is formed by the 6 in row 2. We make this the first pivot and arrive at the following matrix.

$$\begin{array}{r} \\ -R_2 + 3R_1 \to R_1 \\ \\ R_2 + 6R_3 \to R_3 \end{array} \begin{array}{ccccc|c} x_1 & x_2 & s_1 & s_2 & z & \\ \boxed{9} & 0 & 3 & -1 & 0 & 2 \\ 0 & 6 & 0 & 1 & 0 & 1 \\ \hline -6 & 0 & 0 & 1 & 6 & 1 \end{array}$$

The next pivot is the 9 in row 1, column 1.

$$\begin{array}{r} \\ \\ \\ 2R_1 + 3R_3 \to R_3 \end{array} \begin{array}{ccccc|c} x_1 & x_2 & s_1 & s_2 & z & \\ 9 & 0 & 3 & -1 & 0 & 2 \\ 0 & 6 & 0 & 1 & 0 & 1 \\ \hline 0 & 0 & 6 & 1 & 18 & 7 \end{array}$$

Dividing the bottom row by 18 gives a z-value of $\frac{7}{18}$, so $g = \frac{1}{z} = \frac{18}{7}$. The values of y_1 and y_2 are read from the bottom of the columns for the two slack variables after dividing the bottom row by 18:

$$y_1 = \frac{6}{18} = \frac{1}{3}, y_2 = \frac{1}{18}.$$

We find the values of p_1 and p_2 by multiplying the values of y_1 and y_2 by g:

$$p_1 = \frac{18}{7}\left(\frac{1}{3}\right) = \frac{6}{7},$$

$$p_2 = \frac{18}{7}\left(\frac{1}{18}\right) = \frac{1}{7},$$

$$p_3 = 0 \text{ (row 3 was removed)}.$$

We next find the values of x_1 and x_2 by using the first two columns combined with the last column:

$$x_1 = \frac{2}{9}, x_2 = \frac{1}{6}.$$

We find the values of q_1 and q_2 by multiplying these by g:

$$q_1 = \frac{18}{7}\left(\frac{2}{9}\right) = \frac{4}{7},$$

$$q_2 = \frac{18}{7}\left(\frac{1}{6}\right) = \frac{3}{7}.$$

Finally, the value of the game is found by subtracting from g the 2 that was added at the beginning, yielding $\frac{18}{7} - 2 = \frac{4}{7}$.

To summarize, the optimum strategy for player A is $p_1 = \frac{6}{7}, p_2 = \frac{1}{7}$, and $p_3 = 0$ (since row 3 was removed). The optimum strategy for player B is $q_1 = \frac{4}{7}$ and $q_2 = \frac{3}{7}$. When these strategies are used, the value of the game is $\frac{4}{7}$.

11. $\begin{bmatrix} 1 & 0 & -1 \\ -1 & 0 & 1 \\ 2 & -1 & 2 \end{bmatrix}$

Add 1 to each entry to obtain

$$\begin{bmatrix} 2 & 1 & 0 \\ 0 & 1 & 2 \\ 3 & 0 & 3 \end{bmatrix}.$$

The linear programming problem to be solved is as follows.

$$\begin{aligned} &\text{Maximize} && z = x_1 + x_2 + x_3 \\ &\text{subject to:} && 2x_1 + x_2 \le 1 \\ & && x_2 + 2x_3 \le 1 \\ & && 3x_1 + 3x_3 \le 1 \\ &\text{with} && x_1 \ge 0, x_2 \ge 0, x_3 \ge 0. \end{aligned}$$

The initial tableau is

$$\begin{array}{ccccccc|c} x_1 & x_2 & x_3 & s_1 & s_2 & s_3 & z & \\ 2 & 1 & 0 & 1 & 0 & 0 & 0 & 1 \\ 0 & 1 & 2 & 0 & 1 & 0 & 0 & 1 \\ \boxed{3} & 0 & 3 & 0 & 0 & 1 & 0 & 1 \\ \hline -1 & -1 & -1 & 0 & 0 & 0 & 1 & 0 \end{array}.$$

Pivot on each indicated entry.

$$\begin{array}{r} \\ -2\mathrm{R}_3+3\mathrm{R}_1\rightarrow\mathrm{R}_1 \\ \\ \\ \mathrm{R}_3+3\mathrm{R}_4\rightarrow\mathrm{R}_4 \end{array}
\begin{array}{c} \begin{array}{ccccccc} x_1 & x_2 & x_3 & s_1 & s_2 & s_3 & z \end{array} \\ \left[\begin{array}{ccccccc|c} 0 & \boxed{3} & -6 & 3 & 0 & -2 & 0 & 1 \\ 0 & 1 & 2 & 0 & 1 & 0 & 0 & 1 \\ 3 & 0 & 3 & 0 & 0 & 1 & 0 & 1 \\ \hline 0 & -3 & 0 & 0 & 0 & 1 & 3 & 1 \end{array}\right] \end{array}$$

$$\begin{array}{r} \\ \\ -\mathrm{R}_1+3\mathrm{R}_2\rightarrow\mathrm{R}_2 \\ \\ \mathrm{R}_1+\mathrm{R}_4\rightarrow\mathrm{R}_4 \end{array}
\begin{array}{c} \begin{array}{ccccccc} x_1 & x_2 & x_3 & s_1 & s_2 & s_3 & z \end{array} \\ \left[\begin{array}{ccccccc|c} 0 & 3 & -6 & 3 & 0 & -2 & 0 & 1 \\ 0 & 0 & \boxed{12} & -3 & 3 & 2 & 0 & 2 \\ 3 & 0 & 3 & 0 & 0 & 1 & 0 & 1 \\ \hline 0 & 0 & -6 & 3 & 0 & -1 & 3 & 2 \end{array}\right] \end{array}$$

$$\begin{array}{r} \\ \mathrm{R}_2+2\mathrm{R}_1\rightarrow\mathrm{R}_1 \\ \\ -\mathrm{R}_2+4\mathrm{R}_3\rightarrow\mathrm{R}_3 \\ \mathrm{R}_2+2\mathrm{R}_4\rightarrow\mathrm{R}_4 \end{array}
\begin{array}{c} \begin{array}{ccccccc} x_1 & x_2 & x_3 & s_1 & s_2 & s_3 & z \end{array} \\ \left[\begin{array}{ccccccc|c} 0 & 6 & 0 & 3 & 3 & -2 & 0 & 4 \\ 0 & 0 & 12 & -3 & 3 & 2 & 0 & 2 \\ 12 & 0 & 0 & 3 & -3 & 2 & 0 & 2 \\ \hline 0 & 0 & 0 & 3 & 3 & 0 & 6 & 6 \end{array}\right] \end{array}$$

Create a 1 in the columns corresponding to x_1, x_2, x_3, and z.

$$\begin{array}{r} \\ \frac{1}{6}\mathrm{R}_1\rightarrow\mathrm{R}_1 \\ \frac{1}{12}\mathrm{R}_2\rightarrow\mathrm{R}_2 \\ \frac{1}{12}\mathrm{R}_3\rightarrow\mathrm{R}_3 \\ \frac{1}{6}\mathrm{R}_4\rightarrow\mathrm{R}_4 \end{array}
\begin{array}{c} \begin{array}{ccccccc} x_1 & x_2 & x_3 & s_1 & s_2 & s_3 & z \end{array} \\ \left[\begin{array}{ccccccc|c} 0 & 1 & 0 & \frac{1}{2} & \frac{1}{2} & -\frac{1}{3} & 0 & \frac{2}{3} \\ 0 & 0 & 1 & -\frac{1}{4} & \frac{1}{4} & \frac{1}{6} & 0 & \frac{1}{6} \\ 1 & 0 & 0 & \frac{1}{4} & -\frac{1}{4} & \frac{1}{6} & 0 & \frac{1}{6} \\ \hline 0 & 0 & 0 & \frac{1}{2} & \frac{1}{2} & 0 & 1 & 1 \end{array}\right] \end{array}$$

From this final tableau, we have $x_1 = \frac{1}{6}, x_2 = \frac{2}{3}, x_3 = \frac{1}{6}, y_1 = \frac{1}{2}, y_2 = \frac{1}{2}, y_3 = 0$, and $z = 1$. Note that $g = \frac{1}{z} = 1$. The optimum strategy for player A is

$$p_1 = gy_1 = 1\left(\frac{1}{2}\right) = \frac{1}{2},$$

$$p_2 = gy_2 = 1\left(\frac{1}{2}\right) = \frac{1}{2},$$

$$p_3 = gy_3 = 1(0) = 0.$$

The optimum strategy for player B is

$$q_1 = gx_1 = 1\left(\frac{1}{6}\right) = \frac{1}{6},$$

$$q_2 = gx_2 = 1\left(\frac{2}{3}\right) = \frac{2}{3},$$

$$q_3 = gx_3 = 1\left(\frac{1}{6}\right) = \frac{1}{6}.$$

The value of the game is $1 - 1 = 0$.

12. $\begin{bmatrix} 2 & -1 & 1 \\ 0 & 2 & 3 \\ 4 & 1 & 0 \end{bmatrix}$

Because of the negative entry, we will add 1 to all the entries. The resulting payoff matrix is

$$\begin{bmatrix} 3 & 0 & 2 \\ 1 & 3 & 4 \\ 5 & 2 & 1 \end{bmatrix}.$$

The linear programming problem to be solved is:

$$\begin{array}{ll} \text{Maximize} & z = x_1 + x_2 + x_3 \\ \text{subject to:} & 3x_1 \qquad\quad + 2x_3 \leq 1 \\ & x_1 + 3x_2 + 4x_3 \leq 1 \\ & 5x_1 + 2x_2 + \ x_3 \leq 1 \\ \text{with} & x_1 \geq 0, x_2 \geq 0, x_3 \geq 0. \end{array}$$

The initial tableau is

$$\begin{array}{c} \begin{array}{ccccccc} x_1 & x_2 & x_3 & s_1 & s_2 & s_3 & z \end{array} \\ \left[\begin{array}{ccccccc|c} 3 & 0 & 2 & 1 & 0 & 0 & 0 & 1 \\ 1 & 3 & 4 & 0 & 1 & 0 & 0 & 1 \\ \boxed{5} & 2 & 1 & 0 & 0 & 1 & 0 & 1 \\ \hline -1 & -1 & -1 & 0 & 0 & 0 & 1 & 0 \end{array}\right]. \end{array}$$

We arbitrarily choose the first column. The smallest ratio is formed by the 5 in row 3. We make this the first pivot and arrive at the following matrix.

$$\begin{array}{r} -3R_3 + 5R_1 \rightarrow R_1 \\ -R_3 + 5R_2 \rightarrow R_2 \\ \\ R_3 + 5R_4 \rightarrow R_4 \end{array} \begin{array}{c} \begin{array}{ccccccc} x_1 & x_2 & x_3 & s_1 & s_2 & s_3 & z \end{array} \\ \left[\begin{array}{ccccccc|c} 0 & -6 & 7 & 5 & 0 & -3 & 0 & 2 \\ 0 & 13 & \boxed{19} & 0 & 5 & -1 & 0 & 4 \\ 5 & 2 & 1 & 0 & 0 & 1 & 0 & 1 \\ \hline 0 & -3 & -4 & 0 & 0 & 1 & 5 & 1 \end{array}\right] \end{array}$$

The next pivot is the 19 in row 2, column 3.

$$\begin{array}{r} -7R_2 + 19R_1 \rightarrow R_1 \\ \\ -R_2 + 19R_3 \rightarrow R_3 \\ 4R_2 + 19R_4 \rightarrow R_4 \end{array} \begin{array}{c} \begin{array}{ccccccc} x_1 & x_2 & x_3 & s_1 & s_2 & s_3 & z \end{array} \\ \left[\begin{array}{ccccccc|c} 0 & -205 & 0 & 95 & -35 & -50 & 0 & 10 \\ 0 & \boxed{13} & 19 & 0 & 5 & -1 & 0 & 4 \\ 95 & 25 & 0 & 0 & -5 & 20 & 0 & 15 \\ \hline 0 & -5 & 0 & 0 & 20 & 15 & 95 & 35 \end{array}\right]. \end{array}$$

The next pivot is the 13 in row 2, column 2.

$$\begin{array}{r} 205R_2 + 13R_1 \rightarrow R_1 \\ \\ -25R_2 + 13R_3 \rightarrow R_3 \\ 5R_2 + 13R_4 \rightarrow R_4 \end{array} \begin{array}{c} \begin{array}{ccccccc} x_1 & x_2 & x_3 & s_1 & s_2 & s_3 & z \end{array} \\ \left[\begin{array}{ccccccc|c} 0 & 0 & 3895 & 1235 & 570 & -855 & 0 & 950 \\ 0 & 13 & 19 & 0 & 5 & -1 & 0 & 4 \\ 1235 & 0 & -475 & 0 & -190 & 285 & 0 & 95 \\ \hline 0 & 0 & 95 & 0 & 285 & 190 & 1235 & 475 \end{array}\right] \end{array}$$

Dividing the bottom row by 1235 gives a z-value of $\frac{475}{1235} = \frac{5}{13}$, so $g = \frac{1}{z} = \frac{13}{5}$. The values of y_1, y_2, and y_3 are read from the bottoms of the columns for the three slack variables after multiplying the bottom row by $\frac{1}{1235}$:

$$y_1 = \frac{0}{1235} = 0, y_2 = \frac{285}{1235} = \frac{3}{13}, y_3 = \frac{190}{1235} = \frac{2}{13}.$$

We find the values of p_1, p_2, and p_3 by multiplying the values of y_1, y_2, and y_3 by g:

$$p_1 = \frac{13}{5}(0) = 0, p_2 = \frac{13}{5}\left(\frac{3}{13}\right) = \frac{3}{5}, p_3 = \frac{13}{5}\left(\frac{2}{13}\right) = \frac{2}{5}.$$

We next find the values of x_1, x_2, and x_3 by using the first three columns combined with the last column:

$$x_1 = \frac{95}{1235} = \frac{1}{13}, x_2 = \frac{4}{13}, x_3 = 0.$$

We find the values of q_1, q_2, and q_3 by multiplying the values of x_1, x_2, and x_3 by g:

$$q_1 = \frac{13}{5}\left(\frac{1}{13}\right) = \frac{1}{5}, q_2 = \frac{13}{5}\left(\frac{4}{13}\right) = \frac{4}{5}, q_3 = 0.$$

Finally, the value of the game is found by subtracting from g the 1 that was added at the beginning, yielding $\frac{13}{5} - 1 = \frac{8}{5}$.

To summarize, the optimum strategy for player A is $p_1 = 0, p_2 = \frac{3}{5}$, and $p_3 = \frac{2}{5}$. The optimum strategy for player B is $q_1 = \frac{1}{5}, q_2 = \frac{4}{5}$, and $q_3 = 0$. When these strategies are used, the value of the game is $\frac{8}{5}$.

13. The payoff matrix is as follows.

	Strike	No Strike
Bid \$30,000	−\$5500	\$4500
Bid \$40,000	\$4500	\$0

Add \$5500 to each entry to obtain

$$\begin{bmatrix} 0 & 10{,}000 \\ 10{,}000 & 5500 \end{bmatrix}.$$

To find the optimum strategy for the contractor,

Minimize $w = x + y$

subject to: $10{,}000y \geq 1$

$10{,}000x + 5500y \geq 1$

with $x \geq 0, y \geq 0$.

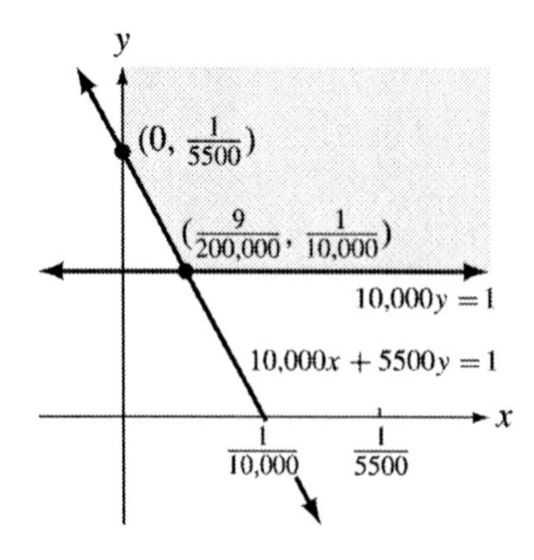

Corner Point	Value of $w = x + y$
$(0, \frac{1}{5500})$	$0 + \frac{1}{5500} = \frac{1}{5500}$
$(\frac{9}{200{,}000}, \frac{1}{10{,}000})$	$\frac{9}{200{,}000} + \frac{1}{10{,}000} = \frac{29}{200{,}000}$

The minimum value is $w = \frac{29}{200{,}000}$ at $\left(\frac{9}{200{,}000}, \frac{1}{10{,}000}\right)$. Thus, $g = \frac{1}{w} = \frac{200{,}000}{29}$, and the optimum strategy for the contractor is

$$p_1 = gx = \frac{200{,}000}{29}\left(\frac{9}{200{,}000}\right) = \frac{9}{29},$$

$$p_2 = gy = \frac{200{,}000}{29}\left(\frac{1}{10{,}000}\right) = \frac{20}{29}.$$

That is, the contractor should bid \$30,000 with probability $\frac{9}{29}$ and \$40,000 with probability $\frac{20}{29}$. The value of the game is

$$\frac{200{,}000}{29} - 5500 \approx \$1396.55.$$

14. $\begin{bmatrix} -1 & -1 & 1 \\ -1 & 0 & 0 \\ 1 & -1 & -1 \\ 1 & 1 & -1 \end{bmatrix}$

Because of the negative entries, we will add 1 to all the entries. The resulting payoff matrix is

$$\begin{bmatrix} 0 & 0 & 2 \\ 0 & 1 & 1 \\ 2 & 0 & 0 \\ 2 & 2 & 0 \end{bmatrix}.$$

The linear programming problem to be solved is:

$$\begin{array}{ll} \text{Maximize} & z = x_1 + x_2 + x_3 \\ \text{subject to:} & 2x_3 \le 1 \\ & x_2 + x_3 \le 1 \\ & 2x_1 \le 1 \\ & 2x_1 + 2x_2 \le 1 \\ \text{with} & x_1 \ge 0, x_2 \ge 0, x_3 \ge 0. \end{array}$$

The initial tableau is

x_1	x_2	x_3	s_1	s_2	s_3	s_4	z	
0	0	2	1	0	0	0	0	1
0	1	1	0	1	0	0	0	1
2	0	0	0	0	1	0	0	1
[2]	2	0	0	0	0	1	0	1
−1	−1	−1	0	0	0	0	1	0

We arbitrarily choose the first column. Both ratios are $\frac{1}{2}$, so we will use the 2 in row 4 as the first pivot. We arrive at the following matrix.

	x_1	x_2	x_3	s_1	s_2	s_3	s_4	z	
	0	0	**[2]**	1	0	0	0	0	1
	0	1	1	0	1	0	0	0	1
$-R_4 + R_3 \to R_3$	0	−2	0	0	0	1	−1	0	0
	2	2	0	0	0	0	1	0	1
$R_4 + 2R_5 \to R_5$	0	0	−2	0	0	0	1	2	1

The next pivot is the 2 in row 1, column 3.

$$\begin{array}{r} \\ \\ -\mathrm{R}_1+2\mathrm{R}_2\rightarrow\mathrm{R}_2 \\ \\ \\ \mathrm{R}_1+\mathrm{R}_5\rightarrow\mathrm{R}_5 \end{array}
\begin{array}{c} \begin{array}{cccccccc} x_1 & x_2 & x_3 & s_1 & s_2 & s_3 & s_4 & z \end{array} \\ \left[\begin{array}{cccccccc|c} 0 & 0 & 2 & 1 & 0 & 0 & 0 & 0 & 1 \\ 0 & 2 & 0 & -1 & 2 & 0 & 0 & 0 & 1 \\ 0 & -2 & 0 & 0 & 0 & 1 & -1 & 0 & 0 \\ 2 & 2 & 0 & 0 & 0 & 0 & 1 & 0 & 1 \\ \hline 0 & 0 & 0 & 1 & 0 & 0 & 1 & 2 & 2 \end{array}\right] \end{array}$$

Dividing the bottom row by 2 gives a z-value of 1, so $g = \frac{1}{z} = 1$. The values of y_1, y_2, y_3, and y_4 are read from the bottom of the columns for the four slack variables after dividing the bottom row by 2:

$$y_1 = \frac{1}{2}, y_2 = 0, y_3 = 0, y_4 = \frac{1}{2}.$$

We find the values of p_1, p_2, p_3, and p_4 by multiplying the values of y_1, y_2, y_3, and y_4 by g:

$$p_1 = 1\left(\frac{1}{2}\right) = \frac{1}{2}, p_2 = 0, p_3 = 0, p_4 = 1\left(\frac{1}{2}\right) = \frac{1}{2}.$$

We next find the values of x_1, x_2, and x_3 by using the first three columns combined with the last column:

$$x_1 = \frac{1}{2}, x_2 = 0, x_3 = \frac{1}{2}.$$

We find the values of q_1, q_2, and q_3 by multiplying the values of x_1, x_2, and x_3 by g:

$$q_1 = 1\left(\frac{1}{2}\right) = \frac{1}{2}, q_2 = 0, q_3 = 1\left(\frac{1}{2}\right) = \frac{1}{2}.$$

Finally, the value of the game is found by subtracting from g the 1 that was added at the beginning, yielding $1 - 1 = 0$.

Thus, labor should use strategies 1 and 4 with probabilities $\frac{1}{2}$ each and should never use strategies 2 or 3. Management should use strategies 1 and 3 with probabilities $\frac{1}{2}$ each and should never use strategy 2. The value of the game is 0.

15. (a) The payoff matrix is as follows.

		OI		
		A	B	C
GI	A	5000	10,000	10,000
	B	8000	4000	8000
	C	6000	6000	3000

Note that $5000 = \frac{1}{2}(10{,}000), 4000 = \frac{1}{2}(8000)$, and $3000 = \frac{1}{2}(6000)$ are the reduced profits for General Items when the two companies run ads in the same city.

(b) The linear programming problem to be solved is as follows.

$$
\begin{array}{ll}
\text{Maximize} & z = x_1 + x_2 + x_3 \\
\text{subject to:} & 5000x_1 + 10{,}000x_2 + 10{,}000x_3 \le 1 \\
& 8000x_1 + 4000x_2 + 8000x_3 \le 1 \\
& 6000x_1 + 6000x_2 + 3000x_3 \le 1 \\
\text{with} & x_1 \ge 0, x_2 \ge 0, x_3 \ge 0.
\end{array}
$$

The initial tableau is

$$
\begin{array}{c}
\begin{array}{ccccccc|c} x_1 & x_2 & x_3 & s_1 & s_2 & s_3 & z & \end{array} \\
\left[\begin{array}{ccccccc|c}
5000 & 10{,}000 & 10{,}000 & 1 & 0 & 0 & 0 & 1 \\
\boxed{8000} & 4000 & 8000 & 0 & 1 & 0 & 0 & 1 \\
6000 & 6000 & 3000 & 0 & 0 & 1 & 0 & 1 \\
\hline
-1 & -1 & -1 & 0 & 0 & 0 & 1 & 0
\end{array}\right].
\end{array}
$$

(Solution continues on the next page.)

Pivot on each indicated entry.

$$
\begin{array}{r}
-5R_2 + 8R_1 \to R_1 \\
\\
-3R_2 + 4R_3 \to R_3 \\
R_2 + 8000R_4 \to R_4
\end{array}
\left[\begin{array}{ccccccc|c}
x_1 & x_2 & x_3 & s_1 & s_2 & s_3 & z & \\
0 & \boxed{60{,}000} & 40{,}000 & 8 & -5 & 0 & 0 & 3 \\
8000 & 4000 & 8000 & 0 & 1 & 0 & 0 & 1 \\
0 & 12{,}000 & -12{,}000 & 0 & -3 & 4 & 0 & 1 \\
\hline
0 & -4000 & 0 & 0 & 1 & 1 & 8000 & 1
\end{array}\right]
$$

$$
\begin{array}{r}
\\
-R_1 + 15R_2 \to R_2 \\
-R_1 + 5R_3 \to R_3 \\
R_1 + 15R_4 \to R_4
\end{array}
\left[\begin{array}{ccccccc|c}
x_1 & x_2 & x_3 & s_1 & s_2 & s_3 & z & \\
0 & 60{,}000 & 40{,}000 & 8 & -5 & 0 & 0 & 3 \\
120{,}000 & 0 & 80{,}000 & -8 & 20 & 0 & 0 & 12 \\
0 & 0 & -100{,}000 & -8 & -10 & 20 & 0 & 2 \\
\hline
0 & 0 & 40{,}000 & 8 & 10 & 0 & 120{,}000 & 18
\end{array}\right]
$$

Create a 1 in the columns corresponding to x_1, x_2, s_3, and z.

$$
\begin{array}{r}
\frac{1}{60{,}000}R_1 \to R_1 \\
\frac{1}{120{,}000}R_2 \to R_2 \\
\frac{1}{20}R_3 \to R_3 \\
\frac{1}{120{,}000}R_4 \to R_4
\end{array}
\left[\begin{array}{ccccccc|c}
x_1 & x_2 & x_3 & s_1 & s_2 & s_3 & z & \\
0 & 1 & \frac{2}{3} & \frac{1}{7500} & -\frac{1}{12{,}000} & 0 & 0 & \frac{1}{20{,}000} \\
1 & 0 & \frac{2}{3} & -\frac{1}{15{,}000} & \frac{1}{6000} & 0 & 0 & \frac{1}{10{,}000} \\
0 & 0 & -5000 & -\frac{2}{5} & -\frac{1}{2} & 1 & 0 & \frac{1}{10} \\
\hline
0 & 0 & \frac{1}{3} & \frac{1}{15{,}000} & \frac{1}{12{,}000} & 0 & 1 & \frac{3}{20{,}000}
\end{array}\right]
$$

From this final tableau, we have

$$
x_1 = \frac{1}{10{,}000},\ x_2 = \frac{1}{20{,}000},\ x_3 = 0,\ y_1 = \frac{1}{15{,}000},\ y_2 = \frac{1}{12{,}000},\ y_3 = 0, \text{ and } z = \frac{3}{20{,}000}.
$$

Note that

$$g = \frac{1}{z} = \frac{20{,}000}{3} \approx 6666.67,$$

so the value of the game is \$6666.67. The optimum strategy for General Items is

$$p_1 = gy_1 = \frac{20{,}000}{3}\left(\frac{1}{15{,}000}\right) = \frac{4}{9},$$

$$p_2 = gy_2 = \frac{20{,}000}{3}\left(\frac{1}{12{,}000}\right) = \frac{5}{9},$$

$$p_3 = gy_3 = \frac{20{,}000}{3}(0) = 0.$$

That is, General Items should advertise in Atlanta with probability $\frac{4}{9}$, in Boston with probability $\frac{5}{9}$, and never in Cleveland.

The optimum strategy for Original Imitators is

$$q_1 = gx_1 = \frac{20{,}000}{3}\left(\frac{1}{10{,}000}\right) = \frac{2}{3},$$

$$q_2 = gx_2 = \frac{20{,}000}{3}\left(\frac{1}{20{,}000}\right) = \frac{1}{3},$$

$$q_3 = gx_3 = \frac{20{,}000}{3}(0) = 0.$$

That is, Original Imitators should advertise in Atlanta with probability $\frac{2}{3}$, in Boston with probability $\frac{1}{3}$, and never in Cleveland.

16. This exercise should be solved by graphing calculator or computer methods. The solution may vary slightly. The answer is that the manufacturer should emphasize modern cards with probability 0.088, old-fashioned cards with probability 0.418, and a mixture with probability 0.495, giving a value of \$78.87 for the game.

17. This exercise should be solved by graphing calculator or computer methods. The solution may vary slightly. The answer is that merchant A should locate in cities 1, 2, and 3 with probabilities $\frac{27}{101}$, $\frac{129}{202}$, and $\frac{19}{202}$, respectively; merchant B should locate in cities 1, 2, and 3 with probabilities $\frac{39}{101}$, $\frac{9}{101}$, and $\frac{53}{101}$, respectively. The value of the game is $\frac{885}{101} \approx 8.76$ percentage points.

18. (a) Row 3 dominates row 4. So, remove row 4 to obtain

$$\begin{bmatrix} 5 & 8 & 10 \\ 8 & 10 & 6 \\ 10 & 6 & 2 \end{bmatrix}.$$

(b) Using the matrix from part (a), the linear programming problem to be solved is:

Maximize: $z = x_1 + x_2 + x_3$

Subject to:
$$\begin{aligned} 5x_1 + 8x_2 + 10x_3 &\le 1 \\ 8x_1 + 10x_2 + 6x_3 &\le 1 \\ 10x_1 + 6x_2 + 2x_3 &\le 1 \end{aligned}$$

The initial tableau is

$$\left[\begin{array}{ccccccc|c} x_1 & x_2 & x_3 & s_1 & s_2 & s_3 & z & \\ 5 & 8 & 10 & 1 & 0 & 0 & 0 & 1 \\ 8 & 10 & 6 & 0 & 1 & 0 & 0 & 1 \\ \boxed{10} & 6 & 2 & 0 & 0 & 1 & 0 & 1 \\ \hline -1 & -1 & -1 & 0 & 0 & 0 & 1 & 0 \end{array}\right].$$

We arbitrarily choose the first column. The smallest ratio is formed by the 10 in row 3. We use this as the first pivot and arrive at the following matrix.

$$\begin{array}{l} -R_3 + 2R_1 \to R_1 \\ -4R_3 + 5R_2 \to R_2 \\ \\ R_3 + 10R_4 \to R_4 \end{array} \quad \begin{array}{c} \begin{array}{ccccccc} x_1 & x_2 & x_3 & s_1 & s_2 & s_3 & z \end{array} \\ \left[\begin{array}{ccccccc|c} 0 & 10 & 18 & 2 & 0 & -1 & 0 & 1 \\ 0 & 26 & \boxed{22} & 0 & 5 & -4 & 0 & 1 \\ 10 & 6 & 2 & 0 & 0 & 1 & 0 & 1 \\ \hline 0 & -4 & -8 & 0 & 0 & 1 & 10 & 1 \end{array}\right] \end{array}$$

The next pivot is the 22 in row 2, column 3.

$$\begin{array}{l} -9R_2 + 11R_1 \to R_1 \\ \\ -R_2 + 11R_3 \to R_3 \\ 4R_2 + 11R_4 \to R_4 \end{array} \quad \begin{array}{c} \begin{array}{ccccccc} x_1 & x_2 & x_3 & s_1 & s_2 & s_3 & z \end{array} \\ \left[\begin{array}{ccccccc|c} 0 & -124 & 0 & 22 & -45 & \boxed{25} & 0 & 2 \\ 0 & 26 & 22 & 0 & 5 & -4 & 0 & 1 \\ 110 & 40 & 0 & 0 & -5 & 15 & 0 & 10 \\ \hline 0 & 60 & 0 & 0 & 20 & -5 & 110 & 15 \end{array}\right] \end{array}$$

The next pivot is the 25 in row 1, column 6.

$$\begin{array}{l} \\ 4R_1 + 25R_2 \to R_2 \\ -3R_1 + 5R_3 \to R_3 \\ R_1 + 5R_4 \to R_4 \end{array} \quad \begin{array}{c} \begin{array}{ccccccc} x_1 & x_2 & x_3 & s_1 & s_2 & s_3 & z \end{array} \\ \left[\begin{array}{ccccccc|c} 0 & -124 & 0 & 22 & -45 & 25 & 0 & 2 \\ 0 & 154 & 550 & 88 & -55 & 0 & 0 & 33 \\ 550 & 572 & 0 & -66 & 110 & 0 & 0 & 44 \\ \hline 0 & 176 & 0 & 22 & 55 & 0 & 550 & 77 \end{array}\right] \end{array}$$

Create a 1 in the columns corresponding to x_1, x_3, s_3, and z.

$$\begin{array}{l} \frac{1}{25}R_1 \to R_1 \\ \frac{1}{550}R_2 \to R_2 \\ \frac{1}{550}R_3 \to R_3 \\ \frac{1}{550}R_4 \to R_4 \end{array} \quad \begin{array}{c} \begin{array}{ccccccc} x_1 & x_2 & x_3 & s_1 & s_2 & s_3 & z \end{array} \\ \left[\begin{array}{ccccccc|c} 0 & -\frac{124}{25} & 0 & \frac{22}{25} & -\frac{9}{5} & 1 & 0 & \frac{2}{25} \\ 0 & \frac{7}{25} & 1 & \frac{4}{25} & -\frac{1}{10} & 0 & 0 & \frac{3}{50} \\ 1 & \frac{26}{25} & 0 & -\frac{3}{25} & \frac{1}{5} & 0 & 0 & \frac{2}{25} \\ \hline 0 & \frac{8}{25} & 0 & \frac{1}{25} & \frac{1}{10} & 0 & 1 & \frac{7}{50} \end{array}\right] \end{array}$$

From the final tableau, we have

$$x_1 = \frac{2}{25}, x_2 = 0, x_3 = \frac{3}{50}, y_1 = \frac{1}{25}, y_2 = \frac{1}{10}, y_3 = 0, \text{ and } z = \frac{7}{50}.$$

Note that

$$g = \frac{1}{z} = \frac{50}{7}.$$

The optimum strategy for the hospital is

$$p_1 = gy_1 = \frac{50}{7}\left(\frac{1}{25}\right) = \frac{2}{7}$$

$$p_2 = gy_2 = \frac{50}{7}\left(\frac{1}{10}\right) = \frac{5}{7}$$

$$p_3 = gy_3 = \frac{50}{7}(0) = 0$$

$p_4 = 0$ (row 4 was removed).

That is, the hospital should assign one nurse with probability $\frac{2}{7}$ and two nurses with probability $\frac{5}{7}$. Never assign three or four nurses.

19. (a) $\begin{bmatrix} 17.3 & 11.5 \\ -4.4 & 20.6 \\ 5.2 & 17.0 \end{bmatrix}$

Because of negative entries, add 4.4 to all entries. The resulting payoff matrix is

$$\begin{bmatrix} 21.7 & 15.9 \\ 0 & 25 \\ 9.6 & 21.4 \end{bmatrix}.$$

The linear programming problem to be solved is

Maximize: $z = x_1 + x_2$
subject to: $21.7x_1 + 15.9x_2 \le 1$
$25x_2 \le 1$
$9.6x_1 + 21.4x_2 \le 1$
with $x_1 \ge 0, x_2 \ge 0.$

We will solve this problem using the simplex method. The initial tableau is

$$\begin{array}{c} \\ \\ \\ \\ \\ \end{array}\left[\begin{array}{cccccc|c} x_1 & x_2 & s_1 & s_2 & s_3 & z & \\ 21.7 & 15.9 & 1 & 0 & 0 & 0 & 1 \\ 0 & \boxed{25} & 0 & 1 & 0 & 0 & 1 \\ 9.6 & 21.4 & 0 & 0 & 1 & 0 & 1 \\ \hline -1 & -1 & 0 & 0 & 0 & 1 & 0 \end{array}\right].$$

We arbitrarily choose the second column. The smallest ratio is formed by the 25 in row 2. We make this the pivot and arrive at the following matrix.

$$\begin{array}{r} \\ -15.9R_2 + 25R_1 \to R_1 \\ \\ -21.4R_2 + 25R_3 \to R_3 \\ R_2 + 25R_4 \to R_4 \end{array} \left[\begin{array}{cccccc|c} x_1 & x_2 & s_1 & s_2 & s_3 & z & \\ 542.5 & 0 & 25 & -15.9 & 0 & 0 & 9.1 \\ 0 & 25 & 0 & 1 & 0 & 0 & 1 \\ \boxed{240} & 0 & 0 & -21.4 & 25 & 0 & 3.6 \\ \hline -25 & 0 & 0 & 1 & 0 & 25 & 1 \end{array}\right]$$

The next pivot is the 240 in row 3, column 1.

$$\begin{array}{r} \\ -542.5R_3 + 240R_1 \to R_1 \\ \\ \\ 5R_3 + 48R_4 \to R_4 \end{array} \left[\begin{array}{cccccc|c} x_1 & x_2 & s_1 & s_2 & s_3 & z & \\ 0 & 0 & 6000 & \boxed{7793.5} & -13{,}562.5 & 0 & 231 \\ 0 & 25 & 0 & 1 & 0 & 0 & 1 \\ 240 & 0 & 0 & -21.4 & 25 & 0 & 3.6 \\ \hline 0 & 0 & 0 & -59 & 125 & 1200 & 66 \end{array}\right]$$

The next pivot is the 7793.5 in row 1, column 4.

$$\begin{array}{r} \\ \\ -R_1 + 7793.5R_2 \to R_2 \\ 21.4R_1 + 7793.5R_3 \to R_3 \\ 59R_1 + 7793.5R_4 \to R_4 \end{array} \left[\begin{array}{cccccc|c} x_1 & x_2 & s_1 & s_2 & s_3 & z & \\ 0 & 0 & 6000 & 7793.5 & -13{,}562.5 & 0 & 231 \\ 0 & 194{,}837.5 & -6000 & 0 & 13{,}562.5 & 0 & 7562.5 \\ 1{,}870{,}440 & 0 & 128{,}400 & 0 & -95{,}400 & 0 & 33{,}000 \\ \hline 0 & 0 & 354{,}000 & 0 & 174{,}000 & 9{,}352{,}200 & 528{,}000 \end{array}\right]$$

This is the final tableau. From the bottom row, we find the z-value.

$$z = \frac{528{,}000}{9{,}352{,}200} = \frac{80}{1417}$$

Therefore,

$$g = \frac{1}{z} = \frac{1417}{80}.$$

The values of x_1 and x_2 are obtained by using the first two columns combined with the last column.

$$x_1 = \frac{33{,}000}{1{,}870{,}440} = \frac{25}{1417}, \; x_2 = \frac{7562.5}{194{,}837.5} = \frac{55}{1417}$$

The values of y_1, y_2, and y_3 are read from the bottom of the columns for the three slack variables after dividing the entries by 9,352,000.

$$y_1 = \frac{354{,}000}{9{,}352{,}200} = \frac{590}{15{,}587}, \; y_2 = 0, \; y_3 = \frac{174{,}000}{9{,}352{,}200} = \frac{290}{15{,}587}.$$

The optimum strategy for the fisherman is determined by finding the values of q_1, q_2, and q_3.

$$q_1 = gy_1 = \left(\frac{1417}{80}\right)\left(\frac{590}{15{,}587}\right) = \frac{59}{88} \approx 0.6705$$

$$q_2 = gy_2 = 0$$

$$q_3 = gy_3 = \left(\frac{1417}{80}\right)\left(\frac{290}{15{,}587}\right) = \frac{29}{88} \approx 0.3295$$

The fisherman should fish the inside banks with probability 0.6705 and fish a mixture of the inside and outside banks with probability 0.3295. They should never fish the outside banks exclusively.

The optimum strategy for the environment is determined by finding the values of p_1 and p_2.

$$p_1 = gx_1 = \left(\frac{1417}{80}\right)\left(\frac{25}{1417}\right) = \frac{5}{16} = 0.3125$$

$$p_3 = gx_2 = \left(\frac{1417}{80}\right)\left(\frac{55}{1417}\right) = \frac{11}{16} = 0.6875$$

There is a strong current with probability 0.3125 and no current with probability 0.6875.

Finally, the value of the game is found by subtracting from g the 4.4 that was added at the beginning, yielding

$$\frac{1417}{80} - 4.4 = 13.3125.$$

(b) Return to the original table and calculate the payoffs when fishing with the current has probability 0.25 and fishing with no current has probability 0.75.

$$\begin{aligned}
\text{Inside:} &\quad 0.25(17.3) + 0.75(11.5) = 12.95 \\
\text{Outside:} &\quad 0.25(-4.4) + 0.75(20.6) = 14.35 \\
\text{Mixture:} &\quad 0.25(5.2) + 0.75(17.0) = 14.05
\end{aligned}$$

The largest value is 14.35. The fishermen should fish the outside banks exclusively, with payoff 14.35.

20. Because of the negative entries, we will add 4 to all the entries, giving the matrix

$$\begin{bmatrix} 4 & 4 & 0 \\ 4 & 1 & 3 \\ 2 & 3 & 3 \end{bmatrix}.$$

The linear programming problem to be solved is:

Maximize $z = x_1 + x_2 + x_3$
Subject to:
$$\begin{aligned} 4x_1 + 4x_2 \phantom{{}+3x_3} &\le 1 \\ 4x_1 + x_2 + 3x_3 &\le 1 \\ 2x_1 + 3x_2 + 3x_3 &\le 1 \end{aligned}$$

with $x_1 \ge 0, x_2 \ge 0, x_3 \ge 0$.
The initial tableau is

$$\begin{array}{c} \\ \\ \\ \\ \\ \end{array}\left[\begin{array}{ccccccc|c} x_1 & x_2 & x_3 & s_1 & s_2 & s_3 & z & \\ \boxed{4} & 4 & 0 & 1 & 0 & 0 & 0 & 1 \\ 4 & 1 & 3 & 0 & 1 & 0 & 0 & 1 \\ 2 & 3 & 3 & 0 & 0 & 1 & 0 & 1 \\ \hline -1 & -1 & -1 & 0 & 0 & 0 & 1 & 0 \end{array}\right].$$

We arbitrarily choose the first column and use the 4 in row 1 as our pivot.

$$\begin{array}{r} \\ \\ -R_1+R_2 \to R_2 \\ -R_1+2R_3 \to R_3 \\ R_1+4R_4 \to R_4 \end{array}\left[\begin{array}{ccccccc|c} x_1 & x_2 & x_3 & s_1 & s_2 & s_3 & z & \\ 4 & 4 & 0 & 1 & 0 & 0 & 0 & 1 \\ 0 & -3 & \boxed{3} & -1 & 1 & 0 & 0 & 0 \\ 0 & 2 & 6 & -1 & 0 & 2 & 0 & 1 \\ \hline 0 & 0 & -4 & 1 & 0 & 0 & 4 & 1 \end{array}\right]$$

The next pivot is the 3 in row 2, column 3.

$$\begin{array}{r} \\ \\ \\ -2R_2+R_3 \to R_3 \\ 4R_2+3R_4 \to R_4 \end{array}\left[\begin{array}{ccccccc|c} x_1 & x_2 & x_3 & s_1 & s_2 & s_3 & z & \\ 4 & 4 & 0 & 1 & 0 & 0 & 0 & 1 \\ 0 & -3 & 3 & -1 & 1 & 0 & 0 & 0 \\ 0 & \boxed{8} & 0 & 1 & -2 & 2 & 0 & 1 \\ \hline 0 & -12 & 0 & -1 & 4 & 0 & 12 & 3 \end{array}\right]$$

The next pivot is the 8 in row 3, column 2.

$$\begin{array}{r} \\ -R_3+2R_1 \to R_1 \\ 8R_2+3R_3 \to R_2 \\ \\ 3R_3+2R_4 \to R_4 \end{array}\left[\begin{array}{ccccccc|c} x_1 & x_2 & x_3 & s_1 & s_2 & s_3 & z & \\ 8 & 0 & 0 & 1 & 2 & -2 & 0 & 1 \\ 0 & 0 & 24 & -5 & 2 & 6 & 0 & 3 \\ 0 & 8 & 0 & 1 & -2 & 2 & 0 & 1 \\ \hline 0 & 0 & 0 & 1 & 2 & 6 & 24 & 9 \end{array}\right]$$

Create a 1 in the columns corresponding to x_1, x_2, x_3, and z.

$$\begin{array}{r} \\ \frac{1}{8}R_1 \to R_1 \\ \frac{1}{24}R_2 \to R_2 \\ \frac{1}{8}R_3 \to R_3 \\ \frac{1}{24}R_4 \to R_4 \end{array}\left[\begin{array}{ccccccc|c} x_1 & x_2 & x_3 & s_1 & s_2 & s_3 & z & \\ 1 & 0 & 0 & \frac{1}{8} & \frac{1}{4} & -\frac{1}{4} & 0 & \frac{1}{8} \\ 0 & 0 & 1 & -\frac{5}{24} & \frac{1}{12} & \frac{1}{4} & 0 & \frac{1}{8} \\ 0 & 1 & 0 & \frac{1}{8} & -\frac{1}{4} & \frac{1}{4} & 0 & \frac{1}{8} \\ \hline 0 & 0 & 0 & \frac{1}{24} & \frac{1}{12} & \frac{1}{4} & 1 & \frac{3}{8} \end{array}\right]$$

From the final tableau, we have

$x_1 = \frac{1}{8}, x_2 = \frac{1}{8}, x_3 = \frac{1}{8}, y_1 = \frac{1}{24}, y_2 = \frac{1}{12},$

$y_3 = \frac{1}{4}$, and $z = \frac{3}{8}$.

Note that

$$g = \frac{1}{z} = \frac{8}{3}.$$

The visitor's optimum strategy is

$$p_1 = gy_1 = \frac{8}{3}\left(\frac{1}{24}\right) = \frac{1}{9}$$

$$p_2 = gy_2 = \frac{8}{3}\left(\frac{1}{12}\right) = \frac{2}{9}$$

$$p_3 = gy_3 = \frac{8}{3}\left(\frac{1}{4}\right) = \frac{2}{3}.$$

That is, the visitor should act appeasing with probability $\frac{1}{9}$, expect civility but don't fight for it with probability $\frac{2}{9}$, and expect civility and fight for it if it isn't given with probability $\frac{2}{3}$. The value of the game is $\frac{8}{3} - 4 = -\frac{4}{3}$.

21. $\begin{bmatrix} 50 & 0 \\ 10 & 40 \end{bmatrix}$

To find the student's optimum strategy,

$$\begin{aligned} &\text{Minimize} && w = x + y \\ &\text{subject to:} && 50x + 10y \geq 1 \\ &&& 40y \geq 1 \\ &\text{with} && x \geq 0, y \geq 0. \end{aligned}$$

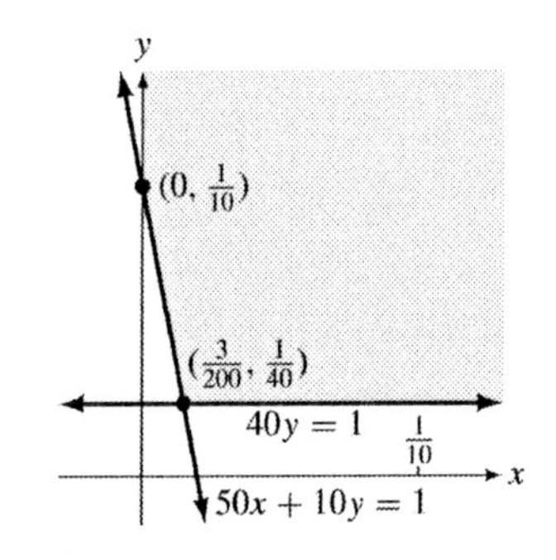

Corner Point	Value of $w = x + y$
$(0, \frac{1}{10})$	$0 + \frac{1}{10} = \frac{1}{10}$
$(\frac{3}{200}, \frac{1}{40})$	$\frac{3}{200} + \frac{1}{40} = \frac{1}{25}$

The minimum value is $w = \frac{1}{25}$ at $(\frac{3}{200}, \frac{1}{40})$. Thus, the value of the game is $g = \frac{1}{w} = 25$ points, and the optimum strategy for the student is

$$p_1 = gx = 25\left(\frac{3}{200}\right) = \frac{3}{8},$$

$$p_2 = gy = 25\left(\frac{1}{40}\right) = \frac{5}{8}.$$

That is, the student should choose the calculator with probability $\frac{3}{8}$ and the book with probability $\frac{5}{8}$.

22. **(a)** The payoff matrix is as follows.

		Kije			
		(3, 0)	(0, 3)	(2, 1)	(1, 2)
	(4, 0)	4	0	2	1
	(0, 4)	0	4	1	2
Blotto	(3, 1)	1	−1	3	0
	(1, 3)	−1	1	0	3
	(2, 2)	−2	−2	2	2

Note that the strategy $(3, 1)$ for Colonel Blotto means that he sends 3 regiments to the first post and 1 regiment to the second post; the strategy $(0, 3)$ for Captain Kije means that he sends 0 regiments to the first post and 3 regiments to the second post.

Row 1, column 1 of the payoff matrix means $(4, 0)$ for Blotto and $(3, 0)$ for Kije. Blotto sends more regiments to the first post, so he wins 1 point, plus 3 points for capturing Kije's 3 regiments. Neither leader sends any regiments to the second post, so no points are won there. The payoff here is $1 + 3 = 4$ points to Blotto.

Row 4, column 2 of the matrix means $(1, 3)$ for Blotto and $(0, 3)$ for Kije. Blotto earns a point for capturing the first post, but Kije sends no regiments there so there are no points for capturing regiments. Both leaders send 3 regiments to the second post, so there is a standoff and no additional points. The payoff here is 1 point to Blotto.

Row 5, column 1 of the matrix means $(2, 2)$ for Blotto and $(3, 0)$ for Kije. Kije earns 1 post-capturing point and 2 regiment-capturing points for the first post, while Blotto earns 1 post-capturing point for the second post. The net result is a payoff of 2 points to Kije, represented in the matrix as -2.

Continue in this manner to obtain all of the entries of the payoff matrix.

(b) Add 2 to each entry of the payoff matrix to obtain

$$\begin{bmatrix} 6 & 2 & 4 & 3 \\ 2 & 6 & 3 & 4 \\ 3 & 1 & 5 & 2 \\ 1 & 3 & 2 & 5 \\ 0 & 0 & 4 & 4 \end{bmatrix}.$$

The linear programming problem to be solved is:

$$\begin{array}{ll} \text{Maximize} & z = x_1 + x_2 + x_3 + x_4 \\ \text{subject to:} & 6x_1 + 2x_2 + 4x_3 + 3x_4 \le 1 \\ & 2x_1 + 6x_2 + 3x_3 + 4x_4 \le 1 \\ & 3x_1 + x_2 + 5x_3 + 2x_4 \le 1 \\ & x_1 + 3x_2 + 2x_3 + 5x_4 \le 1 \\ & 4x_3 + 4x_4 \le 1 \\ \text{with} & x_1 \ge 0, x_2 \ge 0, x_3 \ge 0, x_4 \ge 0. \end{array}$$

The initial tableau is

$$\begin{array}{cccccccccc|c} x_1 & x_2 & x_3 & x_4 & s_1 & s_2 & s_3 & s_4 & s_5 & z & \\ \boxed{6} & 2 & 4 & 3 & 1 & 0 & 0 & 0 & 0 & 0 & 1 \\ 2 & 6 & 3 & 4 & 0 & 1 & 0 & 0 & 0 & 0 & 1 \\ 3 & 1 & 5 & 2 & 0 & 0 & 1 & 0 & 0 & 0 & 1 \\ 1 & 3 & 2 & 5 & 0 & 0 & 0 & 1 & 0 & 0 & 1 \\ 0 & 0 & 4 & 4 & 0 & 0 & 0 & 0 & 1 & 0 & 1 \\ \hline -1 & -1 & -1 & -1 & 0 & 0 & 0 & 0 & 0 & 1 & 0 \end{array}.$$

Pivot on each indicated entry.

$$
\begin{array}{r}
\\
\\
-R_1+3R_2 \to R_2\\
-R_1+2R_3 \to R_3\\
-R_1+6R_4 \to R_4\\
\\
R_1+6R_6 \to R_6
\end{array}
\begin{array}{c}
\begin{array}{cccccccccc|c}
x_1 & x_2 & x_3 & x_4 & s_1 & s_2 & s_3 & s_4 & s_5 & z & \\
\end{array}\\
\left[\begin{array}{cccccccccc|c}
6 & 2 & 4 & 3 & 1 & 0 & 0 & 0 & 0 & 0 & 1\\
0 & \boxed{16} & 5 & 9 & -1 & 3 & 0 & 0 & 0 & 0 & 2\\
0 & 0 & 6 & 1 & -1 & 0 & 2 & 0 & 0 & 0 & 1\\
0 & 16 & 8 & 27 & -1 & 0 & 0 & 6 & 0 & 0 & 5\\
0 & 0 & 4 & 4 & 0 & 0 & 0 & 0 & 1 & 0 & 1\\
\hline
0 & -4 & -2 & -3 & 1 & 0 & 0 & 0 & 0 & 6 & 1
\end{array}\right]
\end{array}
$$

$$
\begin{array}{r}
\\
-R_2+8R_1 \to R_1\\
\\
\\
-R_2+R_4 \to R_4\\
\\
R_2+4R_6 \to R_6
\end{array}
\begin{array}{c}
\begin{array}{cccccccccc|c}
x_1 & x_2 & x_3 & x_4 & s_1 & s_2 & s_3 & s_4 & s_5 & z & \\
\end{array}\\
\left[\begin{array}{cccccccccc|c}
48 & 0 & 27 & 15 & 9 & -3 & 0 & 0 & 0 & 0 & 6\\
0 & 16 & 5 & 9 & -1 & 3 & 0 & 0 & 0 & 0 & 2\\
0 & 0 & \boxed{6} & 1 & -1 & 0 & 2 & 0 & 0 & 0 & 1\\
0 & 0 & 3 & 18 & 0 & -3 & 0 & 6 & 0 & 0 & 3\\
0 & 0 & 4 & 4 & 0 & 0 & 0 & 0 & 1 & 0 & 1\\
\hline
0 & 0 & -3 & -3 & 3 & 3 & 0 & 0 & 0 & 24 & 6
\end{array}\right]
\end{array}
$$

$$
\begin{array}{r}
\\
-9R_3+2R_1 \to R_1\\
-5R_3+6R_2 \to R_2\\
\\
-R_3+2R_4 \to R_4\\
-2R_3+3R_5 \to R_5\\
R_3+2R_6 \to R_6
\end{array}
\begin{array}{c}
\begin{array}{cccccccccc|c}
x_1 & x_2 & x_3 & x_4 & s_1 & s_2 & s_3 & s_4 & s_5 & z & \\
\end{array}\\
\left[\begin{array}{cccccccccc|c}
96 & 0 & 0 & 21 & 27 & -6 & -18 & 0 & 0 & 0 & 3\\
0 & 96 & 0 & 49 & -1 & 18 & -10 & 0 & 0 & 0 & 7\\
0 & 0 & 6 & 1 & -1 & 0 & 2 & 0 & 0 & 0 & 1\\
0 & 0 & 0 & 35 & 1 & -6 & -2 & 12 & 0 & 0 & 5\\
0 & 0 & 0 & \boxed{10} & 2 & 0 & -4 & 0 & 3 & 0 & 1\\
\hline
0 & 0 & 0 & -5 & 5 & 6 & 2 & 0 & 0 & 48 & 13
\end{array}\right]
\end{array}
$$

$$
\begin{array}{r}
\\
-21R_5+10R_1 \to R_1\\
-49R_5+10R_2 \to R_2\\
-R_5+10R_3 \to R_3\\
-7R_5+2R_4 \to R_4\\
\\
R_5+2R_6 \to R_6
\end{array}
\begin{array}{c}
\begin{array}{cccccccccc|c}
x_1 & x_2 & x_3 & x_4 & s_1 & s_2 & s_3 & s_4 & s_5 & z & \\
\end{array}\\
\left[\begin{array}{cccccccccc|c}
960 & 0 & 0 & 0 & 228 & -60 & -96 & 0 & -63 & 0 & 9\\
0 & 960 & 0 & 0 & -108 & 180 & 96 & 0 & -147 & 0 & 21\\
0 & 0 & 60 & 0 & -12 & 0 & 24 & 0 & -3 & 0 & 9\\
0 & 0 & 0 & 0 & -12 & -12 & 24 & 24 & -21 & 0 & 3\\
0 & 0 & 0 & 10 & 2 & 0 & -4 & 0 & 3 & 0 & 1\\
\hline
0 & 0 & 0 & 0 & 12 & 12 & 0 & 0 & 3 & 96 & 27
\end{array}\right]
\end{array}
$$

Create a 1 in the columns corresponding to $x_1, x_2, x_3, x_4, s_4,$ and z.

$$
\begin{array}{r}
\\
\frac{1}{960}R_1 \to R_1\\
\frac{1}{960}R_2 \to R_2\\
\frac{1}{60}R_3 \to R_3\\
\frac{1}{24}R_4 \to R_4\\
\frac{1}{10}R_5 \to R_5\\
\frac{1}{96}R_6 \to R_6
\end{array}
\begin{array}{c}
\begin{array}{cccccccccc|c}
x_1 & x_2 & x_3 & x_4 & s_1 & s_2 & s_3 & s_4 & s_5 & z & \\
\end{array}\\
\left[\begin{array}{cccccccccc|c}
1 & 0 & 0 & 0 & \frac{19}{80} & -\frac{1}{16} & -\frac{1}{10} & 0 & -\frac{21}{320} & 0 & \frac{3}{320}\\
0 & 1 & 0 & 0 & -\frac{9}{80} & \frac{3}{16} & \frac{1}{10} & 0 & -\frac{49}{320} & 0 & \frac{7}{320}\\
0 & 0 & 1 & 0 & -\frac{1}{5} & 0 & \frac{2}{5} & 0 & -\frac{1}{20} & 0 & \frac{3}{20}\\
0 & 0 & 0 & 0 & -\frac{1}{2} & -\frac{1}{2} & 1 & 1 & -\frac{7}{8} & 0 & \frac{1}{8}\\
0 & 0 & 0 & 1 & \frac{1}{5} & 0 & -\frac{2}{5} & 0 & \frac{3}{10} & 0 & \frac{1}{10}\\
\hline
0 & 0 & 0 & 0 & \frac{1}{8} & \frac{1}{8} & 0 & 0 & \frac{1}{32} & 1 & \frac{9}{32}
\end{array}\right]
\end{array}
$$

From this final tableau, we have

$$x_1 = \frac{3}{320},\ x_2 = \frac{7}{320},\ x_3 = \frac{3}{20},\ x_4 = \frac{1}{10},$$

$$y_1 = \frac{1}{8},\ y_2 = \frac{1}{8},\ y_3 = 0,\ y_4 = 0,\ y_5 = \frac{1}{32},\ \text{and } z = \frac{9}{32}.$$

Note that $g = \frac{1}{z} = \frac{32}{9}$. The optimum strategy for Colonel Blotto is

$$p_1 = gy_1 = \frac{32}{9}\left(\frac{1}{8}\right) = \frac{4}{9},\ p_2 = gy_2 = \frac{32}{9}\left(\frac{1}{8}\right) = \frac{4}{9},\ p_3 = gy_3 = \frac{32}{9}(0) = 0,$$
$$p_4 = gy_4 = \frac{32}{9}(0) = 0,\ p_5 = gy_5 = \frac{32}{9}\left(\frac{1}{32}\right) = \frac{1}{9}.$$

That is, Blotto uses strategies $(4, 0)$ and $(0, 4)$ with probability $\frac{4}{9}$ each, strategy $(2, 2)$ with probability $\frac{1}{9}$, and never sends 3 regiments to one post and 1 to the other.

The optimum strategy for Captain Kije is

$$q_1 = gx_1 = \frac{32}{9}\left(\frac{3}{320}\right) = \frac{1}{30},\ q = gx_2 = \frac{32}{9}\left(\frac{7}{320}\right) = \frac{7}{90},{}_2$$
$$q_3 = gx_3 = \frac{32}{9}\left(\frac{3}{20}\right) = \frac{8}{15},\ q_4 = gx_4 = \frac{32}{9}\left(\frac{1}{10}\right) = \frac{16}{45}.$$

That is, Kije uses strategy $(3, 0)$ with probability $\frac{1}{30}$, strategy $(0, 3)$ with probability $\frac{7}{90}$, strategy $(2, 1)$ with probability $\frac{8}{15}$, and strategy $(1, 2)$ with probability $\frac{16}{45}$.

The value of the game is

$$\frac{32}{9} - 2 = \frac{14}{9}.$$

(c) Let $B = \begin{bmatrix} q_1 \\ q_2 \\ q_3 \\ q_4 \end{bmatrix}$ be any strategy that Captain Kije could use, which means that it is a probability vector and $q_1 + q_2 + q_3 + q_4 = 1$. If Colonel Blotto uses the strategy $A = \begin{bmatrix} \frac{4}{9} & \frac{4}{9} & 0 & 0 & \frac{1}{9} \end{bmatrix}$ that was found in part (b), then

$$\begin{aligned}
AMB &= \begin{bmatrix} \frac{4}{9} & \frac{4}{9} & 0 & 0 & \frac{1}{9} \end{bmatrix} \begin{bmatrix} 4 & 0 & 2 & 1 \\ 0 & 4 & 1 & 2 \\ 1 & -1 & 3 & 0 \\ -1 & 1 & 0 & 3 \\ -2 & -2 & 2 & 2 \end{bmatrix} \begin{bmatrix} q_1 \\ q_2 \\ q_3 \\ q_4 \end{bmatrix} \\
&= \begin{bmatrix} \frac{14}{9} & \frac{14}{9} & \frac{14}{9} & \frac{14}{9} \end{bmatrix} \begin{bmatrix} q_1 \\ q_2 \\ q_3 \\ q_4 \end{bmatrix} \\
&= \left[\tfrac{14}{9}q_1 + \tfrac{14}{9}q_2 + \tfrac{14}{9}q_3 + \tfrac{14}{9}q_4\right] \\
&= \left[\tfrac{14}{9}(q_1 + q_2 + q_3 + q_4)\right] \\
&= \left[\tfrac{14}{9}(1)\right] \\
&= \left[\tfrac{14}{9}\right].
\end{aligned}$$

Therefore, the value of the game is $\frac{14}{9}$ regardless of what strategy Captain Kije uses.

23. $\begin{bmatrix} 63.2 & 100 & 94.1 \\ 81.2 & 0 & 89.3 \\ 89.5 & 100 & 44.0 \end{bmatrix}$

The linear programming problem to be solved is

$$\begin{array}{ll} \text{Maximize} & z = x_1 + x_2 + x_3 \\ \text{subject to:} & 63.2x_1 + 100x_2 + 94.1x_3 \leq 1 \\ & 81.2x_1 \qquad\qquad + 89.3x_3 \leq 1 \\ & 89.5x_1 + 100x_2 + 44.0x_3 \leq 1 \\ \text{with} & x_1 \geq 0, x_2 \geq 0, x_3 \geq 0. \end{array}$$

The initial tableau is

$$\begin{array}{c} \quad x_1 \quad x_2 \quad x_3 \quad s_1 \quad s_2 \quad s_3 \quad z \\ \left[\begin{array}{ccccccc|c} 63.2 & 100 & 94.1 & 1 & 0 & 0 & 0 & 1 \\ 81.2 & 0 & 89.3 & 0 & 1 & 0 & 0 & 1 \\ 89.5 & 100 & 44.0 & 0 & 0 & 1 & 0 & 1 \\ \hline -1 & -1 & -1 & 0 & 0 & 0 & 1 & 0 \end{array}\right] \end{array}$$

The final tableau is found using a calculator or computer program.

$$\begin{array}{c} x_1 \quad x_2 \quad x_3 \quad s_1 \quad s_2 \quad s_3 \quad z \\ \left[\begin{array}{ccccccc|c} 0 & 1 & 0 & 0.006888 & -0.008791 & 0.003112 & 0 & 0.001209 \\ 0 & 0 & 1 & 0.01265 & 0.004099 & -0.01265 & 0 & 0.004099 \\ 1 & 0 & 0 & -0.01392 & 0.007808 & 0.01392 & 0 & 0.007808 \\ \hline 0 & 0 & 0 & 0.005625 & 0.003115 & 0.004375 & 1 & 0.013115 \end{array}\right] \end{array}$$

The values of z and g are as follows.

$$z \approx 0.013115, \; g = \frac{1}{z} \approx 76.25$$

The values of x_1, x_2, and x_3 are read directly from the last column.

$$x_1 \approx 0.007808, \; x_2 \approx 0.001209, \; x_3 \approx 0.004099$$

The values of y_1, y_2, and y_3 are read from the bottom of the columns for the three slack variables.

$$y_1 \approx 0.005625, \; y_2 \approx 0.003115, \; y_3 \approx 0.004375.$$

The optimum strategy for the kicker is determined by finding the values of q_1, q_2, and q_3.

$$\begin{aligned} q_1 &= gy_1 \approx 76.25(0.005625) \approx 0.4289 \\ q_2 &= gy_2 \approx 76.25(0.003115) \approx 0.2375 \\ q_3 &= gy_3 \approx 76.25(0.004375) \approx 0.3336 \end{aligned}$$

The kicker should kick left with a probability of 0.4289, middle with a probability of 0.2375, and right with a probability of 0.3336.

The optimum strategy for the goalie is determined by finding the values of p_1, p_2, and p_3.

$$\begin{aligned} p_1 &= gx_1 \approx 76.25(0.007808) \approx 0.5953 \\ p_2 &= gx_2 \approx 76.25(0.001209) \approx 0.0922 \\ p_3 &= gx_3 \approx 76.25(0.004099) \approx 0.3125 \end{aligned}$$

The goalie should move left with a probability of 0.5953, middle with a probability of 0.0922, and right with a probability of 0.3125.

The payoff for the game is 76.25.

24. **(a)** For player A, choice 1 is to believe B when B says "ace," and choice 2 is to ask B to show his card when B says "ace." For player B, there are four choices. Choice 1 is to always tell the truth.

Choice 2 is to lie only if the card is a queen. Choice 3 is to lie only if the card is a king. Choice 4 is to lie if the card is a queen or king. These lead to the following payoff matrix:

$$\begin{array}{c} \\ \text{A} \end{array} \overset{\text{B}}{\begin{bmatrix} 0 & -\frac{2}{3} & -\frac{1}{3} & -1 \\ -\frac{1}{3} & 0 & \frac{1}{3} & \frac{2}{3} \end{bmatrix}}.$$

(b) Because of the negative entries, we will add 1 to all the entries, giving the matrix

$$\begin{bmatrix} 1 & \frac{1}{3} & \frac{2}{3} & 0 \\ \frac{2}{3} & 1 & \frac{4}{3} & \frac{5}{3} \end{bmatrix}.$$

The linear programming problem to be solved is:

$$\begin{aligned} &\text{Maximize} && z = x_1 + x_2 + x_3 + x_4 \\ &\text{subject to:} && x_1 + \frac{1}{3}x_2 + \frac{2}{3}x_3 \le 1 \\ & && \frac{2}{3}x_1 + x_2 + \frac{4}{3}x_3 + \frac{5}{3}x_4 \le 1 \\ &\text{with} && x_1 \ge 0, x_2 \ge 0, x_3 \ge 0, x_4 \ge 0. \end{aligned}$$

The initial tableau is

$$\begin{array}{c} \begin{array}{ccccccc} x_1 & x_2 & x_3 & x_4 & s_1 & s_2 & z \end{array} \\ \left[\begin{array}{ccccccc|c} \boxed{1} & \frac{1}{3} & \frac{2}{3} & 0 & 1 & 0 & 0 & 1 \\ \frac{2}{3} & 1 & \frac{4}{3} & \frac{5}{3} & 0 & 1 & 0 & 1 \\ \hline -1 & -1 & -1 & -1 & 0 & 0 & 1 & 0 \end{array}\right] \end{array}.$$

We arbitrarily choose the first column. The smallest ratio is formed by the 1 in row 1. We use this as the first pivot and arrive at the following matrix.

$$\begin{array}{r} \\ \\ -\frac{2}{3}\text{R}_1 + \text{R}_2 \rightarrow \text{R}_2 \\ \text{R}_1 + \text{R}_3 \rightarrow \text{R}_3 \end{array} \begin{array}{c} \begin{array}{ccccccc} x_1 & x_2 & x_3 & x_4 & s_1 & s_2 & z \end{array} \\ \left[\begin{array}{ccccccc|c} 1 & \frac{1}{3} & \frac{2}{3} & 0 & 1 & 0 & 0 & 1 \\ 0 & \frac{7}{9} & \frac{8}{9} & \boxed{\frac{5}{3}} & -\frac{2}{3} & 1 & 0 & \frac{1}{3} \\ \hline 0 & -\frac{2}{3} & -\frac{1}{3} & -1 & 1 & 0 & 1 & 1 \end{array}\right] \end{array}$$

The next pivot is the $\frac{5}{3}$ in row 2, column 4.

$$\begin{array}{r} \\ \\ \\ \text{R}_2 + \frac{5}{3}\text{R}_3 \rightarrow \text{R}_3 \end{array} \begin{array}{c} \begin{array}{ccccccc} x_1 & x_2 & x_3 & x_4 & s_1 & s_2 & z \end{array} \\ \left[\begin{array}{ccccccc|c} 1 & \frac{1}{3} & \frac{2}{3} & 0 & 1 & 0 & 0 & 1 \\ 0 & \boxed{\frac{7}{9}} & \frac{8}{9} & \frac{5}{3} & -\frac{2}{3} & 1 & 0 & \frac{1}{3} \\ \hline 0 & -\frac{1}{3} & \frac{1}{3} & 0 & 1 & 1 & \frac{5}{3} & 2 \end{array}\right] \end{array}$$

The next pivot is the $\frac{7}{9}$ in row 2, column 2.

$$\begin{array}{r} \\ -\text{R}_2 + \frac{7}{3}\text{R}_1 \rightarrow \text{R}_1 \\ \\ \text{R}_2 + \frac{7}{3}\text{R}_3 \rightarrow \text{R}_3 \end{array} \begin{array}{c} \begin{array}{ccccccc} x_1 & x_2 & x_3 & x_4 & s_1 & s_2 & z \end{array} \\ \left[\begin{array}{ccccccc|c} \frac{7}{3} & 0 & \frac{2}{3} & -\frac{5}{3} & 3 & -1 & 0 & 2 \\ 0 & \frac{7}{9} & \frac{8}{9} & \frac{5}{3} & -\frac{2}{3} & 1 & 0 & \frac{1}{3} \\ \hline 0 & 0 & \frac{5}{3} & \frac{5}{3} & \frac{5}{3} & \frac{10}{3} & \frac{35}{9} & 5 \end{array}\right] \end{array}$$

Dividing the bottom row by $\frac{35}{9}$ gives a z-value of $\frac{45}{35} = \frac{9}{7}$, so $g = \frac{1}{z} = \frac{7}{9}$. The values of y_1 and y_2 are read from the bottom of the columns for the two slack variables after dividing the bottom row by $\frac{35}{9}$: $y_1 = \frac{3}{7}, y_2 = \frac{6}{7}$. We find the values of p_1 and p_2 by multiplying these values by g:

$$p_1 = \frac{7}{9}\left(\frac{3}{7}\right) = \frac{1}{3},$$
$$p_2 = \frac{7}{9}\left(\frac{6}{7}\right) = \frac{2}{3}.$$

Next, we find the values of x_1, x_2, x_3, and x_4 by using the first four columns combined with the last column: $x_1 = \frac{6}{7}, x_2 = \frac{3}{7}, x_3 = 0, x_4 = 0$. We find the values of q_1, q_2, q_3, and q_4 by multiplying the values of x_1, x_2, x_3, and x_4 by g:

$$p_1 = \frac{7}{9}\left(\frac{6}{7}\right) = \frac{2}{3},$$
$$p_2 = \frac{7}{9}\left(\frac{3}{7}\right) = \frac{1}{3},$$
$$p_3 = 0, p_4 = 0.$$

Thus, player A should use strategy 1 with probability $\frac{1}{3}$ and strategy 2 with probability $\frac{2}{3}$. Player B should use strategy 1 with probability $\frac{2}{3}$, strategy 2 with probability $\frac{1}{3}$, and should never use strategies 3 and 4. The value of the game is $-\frac{2}{9}$.
Finally, the value of the game is found by subtracting from g the 1 that was added at the beginning, yielding $\frac{7}{9} - 1 = -\frac{2}{9}$.

25. **(a)** The payoff matrix is as follows.

	Rock	Scissors	Paper
Rock	0	1	−1
Scissors	−1	0	1
Paper	1	−1	0

Add 1 to each entry to obtain

$$\begin{bmatrix} 1 & 2 & 0 \\ 0 & 1 & 2 \\ 2 & 0 & 1 \end{bmatrix}.$$

The linear programming problem to be solved is:

$$\begin{array}{lrl} \text{Maximize} & z = x_1 + x_2 + x_3 & \\ \text{subject to:} & x_1 + 2x_2 \qquad\quad & \le 1 \\ & x_2 + 2x_3 & \le 1 \\ & 2x_1 \qquad\quad + \; x_3 & \le 1 \\ \text{with} & x_1 \ge 0, x_2 \ge 0, x_3 \ge 0. & \end{array}$$

The initial tableau is

$$\left[\begin{array}{ccccccc|c} x_1 & x_2 & x_3 & s_1 & s_2 & s_3 & z & \\ 1 & \boxed{2} & 0 & 1 & 0 & 0 & 0 & 1 \\ 0 & 1 & 2 & 0 & 1 & 0 & 0 & 1 \\ 2 & 0 & 1 & 0 & 0 & 1 & 0 & 1 \\ \hline -1 & -1 & -1 & 0 & 0 & 0 & 1 & 0 \end{array}\right].$$

Pivot on each indicated entry.

$$\begin{array}{l} \\ \\ -R_1 + 2R_2 \to R_2 \\ \\ R_1 + 2R_4 \to R_4 \end{array} \begin{array}{c} \begin{array}{ccccccc} x_1 & x_2 & x_3 & s_1 & s_2 & s_3 & z \end{array} \\ \left[\begin{array}{ccccccc|c} 1 & 2 & 0 & 1 & 0 & 0 & 0 & 1 \\ -1 & 0 & \boxed{4} & -1 & 2 & 0 & 0 & 1 \\ 2 & 0 & 1 & 0 & 0 & 1 & 0 & 1 \\ \hline -1 & 0 & -2 & 1 & 0 & 0 & 2 & 1 \end{array}\right] \end{array}$$

$$\begin{array}{l} \\ \\ \\ -R_2 + 4R_3 \to R_3 \\ R_2 + 2R_4 \to R_4 \end{array} \begin{array}{c} \begin{array}{ccccccc} x_1 & x_2 & x_3 & s_1 & s_2 & s_3 & z \end{array} \\ \left[\begin{array}{ccccccc|c} 1 & 2 & 0 & 1 & 0 & 0 & 0 & 1 \\ -1 & 0 & 4 & -1 & 2 & 0 & 0 & 1 \\ \boxed{9} & 0 & 0 & 1 & -2 & 4 & 0 & 3 \\ \hline -3 & 0 & 0 & 1 & 2 & 0 & 4 & 3 \end{array}\right] \end{array}$$

$$\begin{array}{l} \\ -R_3 + 9R_1 \to R_1 \\ R_3 + 9R_2 \to R_2 \\ \\ R_3 + 3R_4 \to R_4 \end{array} \begin{array}{c} \begin{array}{ccccccc} x_1 & x_2 & x_3 & s_1 & s_2 & s_3 & z \end{array} \\ \left[\begin{array}{ccccccc|c} 0 & 18 & 0 & 8 & 2 & -4 & 0 & 6 \\ 0 & 0 & 36 & -8 & 16 & 4 & 0 & 12 \\ 9 & 0 & 0 & 1 & -2 & 4 & 0 & 3 \\ \hline 0 & 0 & 0 & 4 & 4 & 4 & 12 & 12 \end{array}\right] \end{array}$$

Create a 1 in the columns corresponding to x_1, x_2, x_3, and z.

$$\begin{array}{l} \\ \frac{1}{18}R_1 \to R_1 \\ \frac{1}{36}R_2 \to R_2 \\ \frac{1}{9}R_3 \to R_3 \\ \frac{1}{12}R_4 \to R_4 \end{array} \begin{array}{c} \begin{array}{ccccccc} x_1 & x_2 & x_3 & s_1 & s_2 & s_3 & z \end{array} \\ \left[\begin{array}{ccccccc|c} 0 & 1 & 0 & \frac{4}{9} & \frac{1}{9} & -\frac{2}{9} & 0 & \frac{1}{3} \\ 0 & 0 & 1 & -\frac{2}{9} & \frac{4}{9} & \frac{1}{9} & 0 & \frac{1}{3} \\ 1 & 0 & 0 & \frac{1}{9} & -\frac{2}{9} & \frac{4}{9} & 0 & \frac{1}{3} \\ \hline 0 & 0 & 0 & \frac{1}{3} & \frac{1}{3} & \frac{1}{3} & 1 & 1 \end{array}\right] \end{array}$$

From this final tableau, we have

$$x_1 = \frac{1}{3}, x_2 = \frac{1}{3}, x_3 = \frac{1}{3}, y_1 = \frac{1}{3}, y_2 = \frac{1}{3}, y_3 = \frac{1}{3}, \text{ and } z = 1.$$

Note that $g = \frac{1}{z} = 1$. The optimum strategy for player A is

$$p_1 = gy_1 = 1\left(\frac{1}{3}\right) = \frac{1}{3}, p_2 = gy_2 = 1\left(\frac{1}{3}\right) = \frac{1}{3}, p_3 = gy_3 = 1\left(\frac{1}{3}\right) = \frac{1}{3}.$$

The optimum strategy for player B is

$$q_1 = gx_1 = 1\left(\frac{1}{3}\right) = \frac{1}{3}, q_2 = gx_2 = 1\left(\frac{1}{3}\right) = \frac{1}{3}, q_3 = gx_3 = 1\left(\frac{1}{3}\right) = \frac{1}{3}.$$

The value of the game is $1 - 1 = 0$.

(b) The game is symmetric in that neither player has an advantage, and each choice is as strong as every other choice.

Chapter 11 Review Exercises

For Exercises 3-8, use the following payoff matrix.

$$\begin{bmatrix} -3 & 5 & -6 & 2 \\ 0 & -1 & 9 & 5 \\ 2 & 6 & -4 & 3 \end{bmatrix}$$

3. The strategy $(1, 1)$ means that player A chooses row 1 and player B chooses column 1. A negative number represents a payoff from A to B. The entry at $(1, 1)$ is -3, indicating that the payoff is \$3 from A to B.

4. The strategy $(1, 4)$ means that player A chooses row 1 and player B chooses column 4. A positive number represents a payoff from B to A. Row 1 and column 4 lead to the number 2, which represents a payoff of \$2 from B to A.

5. The entry at $(2, 3)$ is 9. A positive number represents a payoff from B to A, indicating that the payoff is \$9 from B to A.

6. The strategy $(3, 4)$ means that player A chooses row 3 and player B chooses column 4. Row 3 and column 4 lead to the number 3, which represents a payoff of \$3 from B to A.

7. Row 3 dominates row 1 and column 1 dominates column 4.

8. Underline the smallest number in each row, and box the largest number in each column.

$$\begin{bmatrix} -2 & 5 & \underline{-6} & 3 \\ 0 & \underline{-1} & \boxed{7} & \boxed{5} \\ \boxed{2} & \boxed{6} & \underline{-4} & 4 \end{bmatrix}$$

There is no number that is both the smallest in its row and the largest in its column, so the game has no saddle point.

9. $\begin{bmatrix} -11 & 6 & 8 & 9 \\ -10 & -12 & 3 & 2 \end{bmatrix}$

Column 1 dominates both column 3 and column 4. Remove the dominated columns to obtain

$$\begin{bmatrix} -11 & 6 \\ -10 & -12 \end{bmatrix}.$$

10. $\begin{bmatrix} -1 & 9 & 0 \\ 4 & -10 & 6 \\ 8 & -6 & 7 \end{bmatrix}$

Row 3 dominates row 2, so remove row 2 to obtain

$$\begin{bmatrix} -1 & 9 & 0 \\ 8 & -6 & 7 \end{bmatrix}.$$

11. $\begin{bmatrix} -2 & 4 & 1 \\ 3 & 2 & 7 \\ -8 & 1 & 6 \\ 0 & 3 & 9 \end{bmatrix}$

Row 2 dominates row 3. Remove row 3 to obtain

$$\begin{bmatrix} -2 & 4 & 1 \\ 3 & 2 & 7 \\ 0 & 3 & 9 \end{bmatrix}.$$

Column 1 dominates column 3. Remove column 3 to obtain

$$\begin{bmatrix} -2 & 4 \\ 3 & 2 \\ 0 & 3 \end{bmatrix}.$$

12. $\begin{bmatrix} 3 & -1 & 4 \\ 0 & 4 & -1 \\ 1 & 2 & -3 \\ 0 & 0 & 2 \end{bmatrix}$

There are no dominated strategies.

13. $\begin{bmatrix} \boxed{5} & \underline{-4} \\ 3 & \boxed{\underline{-3}} \end{bmatrix}$

Underline the smallest number in each row and draw a box around the largest number in each column. The -3 at $(2, 2)$ is the smallest number in its row and the largest number in its column, so the saddle point is -3 at $(2, 2)$. The value of the game is -3.

14. $\begin{bmatrix} -4 & 0 & \underline{-5} & 2 \\ \boxed{6} & \boxed{9} & \boxed{8} & \boxed{\underline{4}} \end{bmatrix}$

Underline the smallest number in each row and draw a box around the largest number in each column. The 4 at $(2,4)$ is the smallest number in its row and the largest number in its column, so the saddle point is 4 at $(2,4)$. The value of the game is 4.

15. $\begin{bmatrix} \underline{-4} & -1 \\ 6 & \boxed{\underline{0}} \\ \boxed{8} & \underline{-3} \end{bmatrix}$

The 0 at $(2,2)$ is the smallest number in its row and the largest number in its column, so the saddle point is 0 at $(2,2)$. The value of the game is 0, so it is a fair game.

16. $\begin{bmatrix} -2 & 0 & \underline{-3} \\ \underline{-4} & 3 & -1 \\ \boxed{\underline{2}} & \boxed{6} & \boxed{4} \end{bmatrix}$

The 2 at $(3,1)$ is the smallest number in its row and the largest number in its column, so the saddle point is 2 at $(3,1)$. The value of the game is 2.

17. $\begin{bmatrix} -1 & \boxed{4} & \boxed{3} & \boxed{\underline{-4}} \\ \boxed{8} & 1 & 2 & \underline{-7} \end{bmatrix}$

The -4 at $(1,4)$ is the smallest number in its row and the largest number in its column, so the saddle point is -4 at $(1,4)$. The value of the game is -4.

18. $\begin{bmatrix} 2 & \underline{-9} \\ \boxed{7} & \underline{1} \\ 4 & \boxed{\underline{2}} \end{bmatrix}$

The 2 in row 3, column 2 is both the smallest number in its row and the largest number in its column. The saddle point is 2 at $(3,2)$, and the value of the game is 2.

19. $\begin{bmatrix} 1 & 0 \\ -2 & 3 \end{bmatrix}$

The optimum strategy for player A is

$$p_1 = \frac{3-(-2)}{1-(-2)-0+3} = \frac{5}{6},$$

$$p_2 = 1 - \frac{5}{6} = \frac{1}{6}.$$

The optimum strategy for player B is

$$q_1 = \frac{3-0}{1-(-2)-0+3} = \frac{3}{6} = \frac{1}{2},$$

$$q_2 = 1 - \frac{1}{2} = \frac{1}{2}.$$

The value of the game is

$$\frac{1(3)-0(-2)}{1-(-2)-0+3} = \frac{1}{2}.$$

20. $\begin{bmatrix} 2 & -3 \\ -3 & 5 \end{bmatrix}$

There is no saddle point, so the game is not strictly determined, and mixed strategies must be used.

For player A, the optimum strategy is

$$p_1 = \frac{5-(-3)}{2-(-3)-(-3)+5} = \frac{8}{13},$$

$$p_2 = 1 - p_1 = \frac{5}{13}.$$

For player B, the optimum strategy is

$$q_1 = \frac{5-(-3)}{2-(-3)-(-3)+5} = \frac{8}{13},$$

$$q_2 = 1 - q_1 = \frac{5}{13}.$$

The value of the game is

$$\frac{2(5)-(-3)(-3)}{2-(-3)-(-3)+5} = \frac{1}{13}.$$

21. $\begin{bmatrix} -3 & 5 \\ 1 & 0 \end{bmatrix}$

The optimum strategy for player A is

$$p_1 = \frac{0-1}{-3-1-5+0} = \frac{-1}{-9} = \frac{1}{9},$$

$$p_2 = 1 - \frac{1}{9} = \frac{8}{9}.$$

The optimum strategy for player B is

$$q_1 = \frac{0-5}{-3-1-5+0} = \frac{-5}{-9} = \frac{5}{9},$$

$$q_2 = 1 - \frac{5}{9} = \frac{4}{9}.$$

The value of the game is

$$\frac{-3(0)-5(1)}{-3-1-5+0} = \frac{-5}{-9} = \frac{5}{9}.$$

22. $\begin{bmatrix} 8 & -3 \\ -6 & 2 \end{bmatrix}$

There is no saddle point.
For player A, the optimum strategy is

$$p_1 = \frac{2-(-6)}{8-(-6)-(-3)+2} = \frac{8}{19},$$

$$p_2 = 1 - p_1 = \frac{11}{19}.$$

For player B, the optimum strategy is

$$q_1 = \frac{2-(-3)}{8-(-6)-(-3)+2} = \frac{5}{19},$$

$$q_2 = 1 - q_1 = \frac{14}{19}.$$

The value of the game is

$$\frac{8(2)-(-3)(-6)}{8-(-6)-(-3)+2} = -\frac{2}{19}.$$

23. $\begin{bmatrix} -4 & 8 & 0 \\ -2 & 9 & -3 \end{bmatrix}$

Column 1 dominates column 2. Remove column 2 to obtain

$$\begin{bmatrix} -4 & 0 \\ -2 & -3 \end{bmatrix}.$$

The optimum strategy for player A is

$$p_1 = \frac{-3-(-2)}{-4-(-2)-0+(-3)} = \frac{-1}{-5} = \frac{1}{5},$$

$$p_2 = 1 - \frac{1}{5} = \frac{4}{5}.$$

The optimum strategy for player B is

$$q_1 = \frac{-3-0}{-4-(-2)-0+(-3)} = \frac{-3}{-5} = \frac{3}{5},$$

$$q_2 = 0 \text{ (column 2 was removed)},$$

$$q_3 = 1 - \frac{3}{5} = \frac{2}{5}.$$

The value of the game is

$$\frac{-4(-3)-0(-2)}{-4-(-2)-0+(-3)} = \frac{12}{-5} = -\frac{12}{5}.$$

24. $\begin{bmatrix} 1 & 0 & 3 & -3 \\ 4 & -2 & 4 & -1 \end{bmatrix}$

Column 2 dominates columns 1 and 3, so remove columns 1 and 3 to obtain

$$\begin{bmatrix} 0 & -3 \\ -2 & -1 \end{bmatrix}.$$

For player A, the optimum strategy is

$$p_1 = \frac{-1-(-2)}{0-(-2)-(-3)+(-1)} = \frac{1}{4},$$

$$p_2 = 1 - p_1 = \frac{3}{4}.$$

For player B, the optimum strategy is

$$q_1 = 0 \text{ (column 1 was removed)},$$

$$q_2 = \frac{-1-(-3)}{0-(-2)-(-3)+(-1)} = \frac{1}{2},$$

$$q_3 = 0 \text{ (column 3 was removed)},$$

$$q_4 = 1 - (0 + \frac{1}{2} + 0) = \frac{1}{2}.$$

The value of the game is

$$\frac{0(-1)-(-3)(-2)}{0-(-2)-(-3)+(-1)} = \frac{-6}{4} = -\frac{3}{2}.$$

25. $\begin{bmatrix} 2 & -1 \\ -4 & 5 \\ -1 & -2 \end{bmatrix}$

Row 1 dominates row 3. Remove row 3 to obtain

$$\begin{bmatrix} 2 & -1 \\ -4 & 5 \end{bmatrix}.$$

The optimum strategy for player A is

$$p_1 = \frac{5-(-4)}{2-(-4)-(-1)+5} = \frac{9}{12} = \frac{3}{4},$$

$$p_2 = 1 - \frac{3}{4} = \frac{1}{4},$$

$$p_3 = 0 \text{ (row 3 was removed)}.$$

The optimum strategy for player B is

$$q_1 = \frac{5-(-1)}{2-(-4)-(-1)+5} = \frac{6}{12} = \frac{1}{2},$$

$$q_2 = 1 - \frac{1}{2} = \frac{1}{2}.$$

The value of the game is

$$\frac{2(5)-(-1)(-4)}{2-(-4)-(-1)+5} = \frac{6}{12} = \frac{1}{2}.$$

26. $\begin{bmatrix} 8 & -6 \\ 4 & -8 \\ -9 & 9 \end{bmatrix}$

Row 1 dominates row 2, so remove row 2 to obtain

$$\begin{bmatrix} 8 & -6 \\ -9 & 9 \end{bmatrix}.$$

For player A, the optimum strategy is

$$p_1 = \frac{9-(-9)}{8-(-9)-(-6)+9} = \frac{18}{32} = \frac{9}{16},$$

$$p_2 = 0 \text{ (row 2 was removed)},$$

$$p_3 = 1-(p_1+p_2) = \frac{7}{16}.$$

For player B, the optimum strategy is

$$q_1 = \frac{9-(-6)}{8-(-9)-(-6)+9} = \frac{15}{32},$$

$$q_2 = 1-q_1 = \frac{17}{32}.$$

The value of the game is

$$\frac{8(9)-(-6)(-9)}{8-(-9)-(-6)+9} = \frac{18}{32} = \frac{9}{16}.$$

27. $\begin{bmatrix} -4 & 2 \\ 3 & -5 \end{bmatrix}$

Get rid of the negative numbers by adding 5 to each entry to obtain

$$\begin{bmatrix} 1 & 7 \\ 8 & 0 \end{bmatrix}.$$

To find the optimum strategy for player A,

Minimize $w = x + y$
subject to: $x + 8y \geq 1$
$7x \geq 1$
with $x \geq 0, y \geq 0.$

Solve this linear programming problem by the graphical method. Sketch the feasible region.

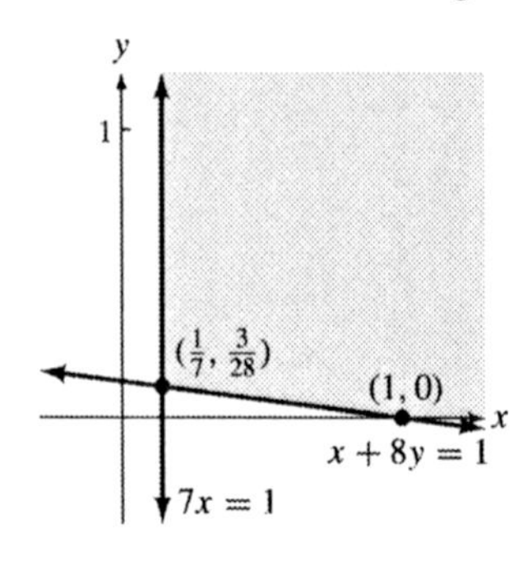

The region is unbounded, with corner points $(\frac{1}{7}, \frac{3}{28})$ and $(1, 0)$.

Corner Point	Value of $w = x + y$
$(\frac{1}{7}, \frac{3}{28})$	$\frac{1}{7} + \frac{3}{28} = \frac{1}{4}$
$(1, 0)$	$1 + 0 = 1$

The minimum value is $w = \frac{1}{4}$ at $(\frac{1}{7}, \frac{3}{28})$. Thus, $g = \frac{1}{w} = 4$, and the optimum strategy for A is

$$p_1 = gx = 4\left(\frac{1}{7}\right) = \frac{4}{7},$$

$$p_2 = gy = 4\left(\frac{3}{28}\right) = \frac{3}{7}.$$

To find the optimum strategy for player B,

Maximize $z = x + y$
subject to: $x + 7y \leq 1$
$8x \leq 1$
with $x \geq 0, y \geq 0.$

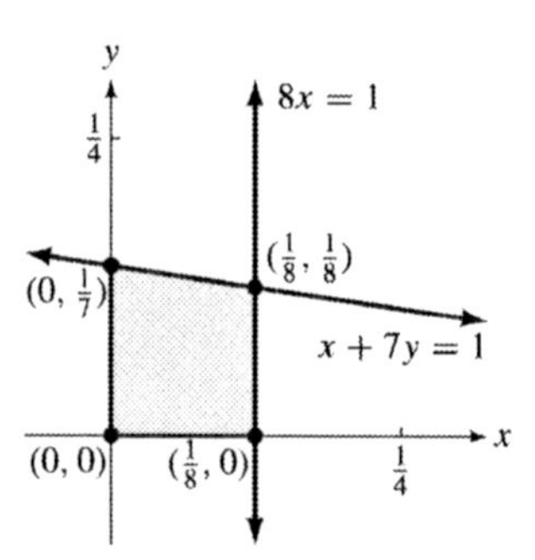

Corner Point	Value of $z = x + y$
$(0, \frac{1}{7})$	$0 + \frac{1}{7} = \frac{1}{7}$
$(\frac{1}{8}, \frac{1}{8})$	$\frac{1}{8} + \frac{1}{8} = \frac{1}{4}$
$(\frac{1}{8}, 0)$	$\frac{1}{8} + 0 = \frac{1}{8}$
$(0, 0)$	$0 + 0 = 0$

The maximum value is $z = \frac{1}{4}$ at $(\frac{1}{8}, \frac{1}{8})$. The optimum strategy for B is

$$q_1 = gx = 4\left(\frac{1}{8}\right) = \frac{1}{2},$$

$$q_2 = gy = 4\left(\frac{1}{8}\right) = \frac{1}{2}.$$

The value of the game is $4 - 5 = -1$.

28. $\begin{bmatrix} -2 & 2 \\ 3 & 1 \end{bmatrix}$

To guarantee that the value of the game is positive, we add 2 to all entries in the matrix to obtain

$$\begin{bmatrix} 0 & 4 \\ 5 & 3 \end{bmatrix}.$$

Let player A choose row 1 with probability p_1 and row 2 with probability p_2. Then

$$\begin{aligned} E_1 &= 5p_2 \\ \text{and} \quad E_2 &= 4p_1 + 3p_2. \end{aligned}$$

Let g represent the minimum of the expected gains, so that

$$\begin{aligned} E_1 &= 5p_2 \geq g \\ E_2 &= 4p_1 + 3p_2 \geq g. \end{aligned}$$

Dividing by g yields

$$5\left(\frac{p_2}{g}\right) \geq 1$$

$$4\left(\frac{p_1}{g}\right) + 3\left(\frac{p_2}{g}\right) \geq 1.$$

Let $x = \dfrac{p_1}{g}$ and $y = \dfrac{p_2}{g}$.

We have the following linear programming problem:

$$\begin{aligned} &\text{Minimize} && w = x + y \\ &\text{subject to:} && 5y \geq 1 \\ & && 4x + 3y \geq 1 \\ &\text{with} && x \geq 0, y \geq 0. \end{aligned}$$

Graph the feasible region.

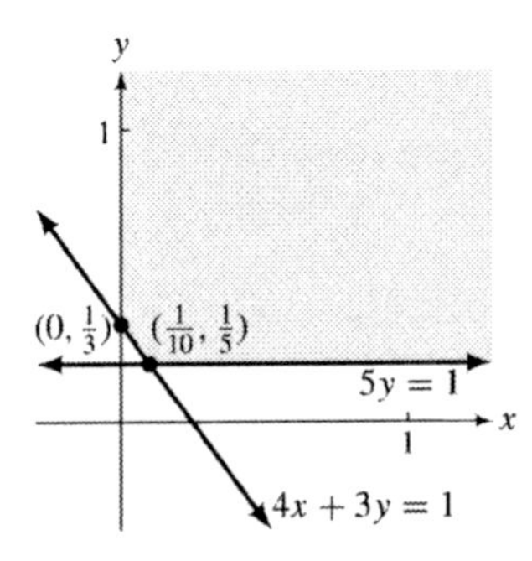

The corner points are $(0, \frac{1}{3})$ and $(\frac{1}{10}, \frac{1}{5})$. The minimum value of $w = x + y$ is $\frac{3}{10}$ at $(\frac{1}{10}, \frac{1}{5})$. Thus, the value of the game is $g = \frac{1}{w} = \frac{10}{3}$. To find the value of the original game we must subtract 2:

$$\frac{10}{3} - 2 = \frac{4}{3}.$$

The optimum strategy for A is

$$p_1 = gx = \frac{10}{3}\left(\frac{1}{10}\right) = \frac{1}{3},$$

$$p_2 = gy = \frac{10}{3}\left(\frac{1}{5}\right) = \frac{2}{3}.$$

Let player B choose column 1 with probability q_1 and column 2 with probability q_2. Then

$$\begin{aligned} E_1 &= 4q_2 \\ \text{and} \quad E_2 &= 5q_1 + 3q_2. \end{aligned}$$

Let g represent the maximum of the expected gains, so that

$$\begin{aligned} E_1 &= 4q_2 \leq g \\ E_2 &= 5q_1 + 3q_2 \leq g. \end{aligned}$$

Dividing by g yields

$$4\left(\frac{q_2}{g}\right) \leq 1$$

$$5\left(\frac{q_1}{g}\right) + 3\left(\frac{q_2}{g}\right) \leq 1.$$

Let $x = \dfrac{q_1}{g}$ and $y = \dfrac{q_2}{g}$.

We have the following linear programming problem:

$$\begin{aligned} &\text{Maximize} && z = x + y \\ &\text{subject to:} && 4y \leq 1 \\ & && 5x + 3y \leq 1 \\ &\text{with} && x \geq 0, y \geq 0. \end{aligned}$$

Graph the feasible region.

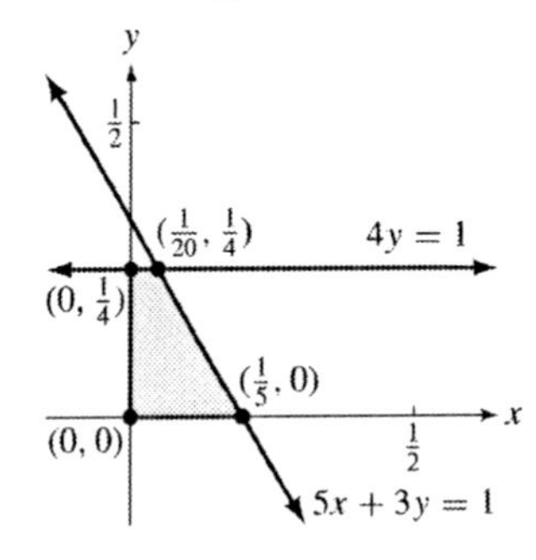

There are four corner points to consider: $(0, 0)$, $(0, \frac{1}{4})$, $(\frac{1}{20}, \frac{1}{4})$, and $(\frac{1}{5}, 0)$. The maximum value of $z = x + y$ is $\frac{3}{10}$ at $(\frac{1}{20}, \frac{1}{4})$. As before, the value of the game is $g = \frac{1}{z} = \frac{10}{3}$. The value of the original game again is $\frac{10}{3} - 2 = \frac{4}{3}$.

The optimum strategy for B is

$$q_1 = gx = \frac{10}{3}\left(\frac{1}{20}\right) = \frac{1}{6},$$

$$q_2 = gy = \frac{10}{3}\left(\frac{1}{4}\right) = \frac{5}{6}.$$

To summarize, player A should choose row 1 with probability $\frac{1}{3}$ and row 2 with probability $\frac{2}{3}$, while player B should choose column 1 with probability $\frac{1}{6}$ and column 2 with probability $\frac{5}{6}$. When these optimum strategies are used, the value of the game is $\frac{4}{3}$.

29. $\begin{bmatrix} 1 & 0 \\ -3 & 4 \end{bmatrix}$

Add 3 to each entry to obtain

$$\begin{bmatrix} 4 & 3 \\ 0 & 7 \end{bmatrix}.$$

To find the optimum strategy for player A,

$$\begin{aligned} &\text{Minimize} && w = x + y \\ &\text{subject to:} && 4x \geq 1 \\ & && 3x + 7y \geq 1 \\ &\text{with} && x \geq 0, y \geq 0. \end{aligned}$$

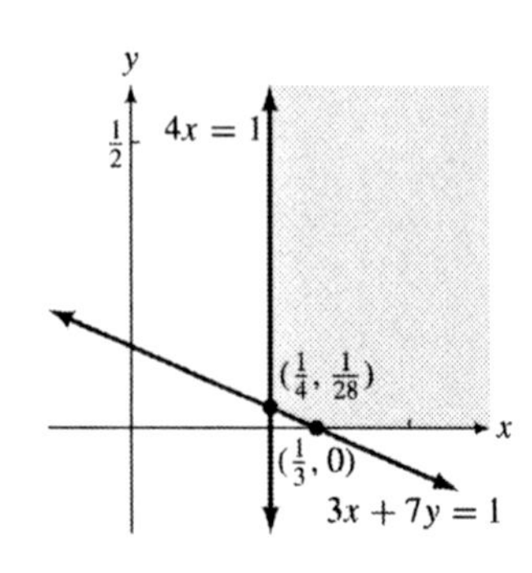

Corner Point	Value of $w = x + y$
$(\frac{1}{4}, \frac{1}{28})$	$\frac{1}{4} + \frac{1}{28} = \frac{2}{7}$
$(\frac{1}{3}, 0)$	$\frac{1}{3} + 0 = \frac{1}{3}$

The minimum value is $w = \frac{2}{7}$ at $(\frac{1}{4}, \frac{1}{28})$. Thus, $g = \frac{1}{w} = \frac{7}{2}$, and the optimum strategy for A is

$$p_1 = gx = \frac{7}{2}\left(\frac{1}{4}\right) = \frac{7}{8},$$

$$p_2 = gy = \frac{7}{2}\left(\frac{1}{28}\right) = \frac{1}{8}.$$

To find the optimum strategy for player B,

$$\begin{aligned} &\text{Maximize} && z = x + y \\ &\text{subject to:} && 4x + 3y \leq 1 \\ & && 7y \leq 1 \\ &\text{with} && x \geq 0, y \geq 0. \end{aligned}$$

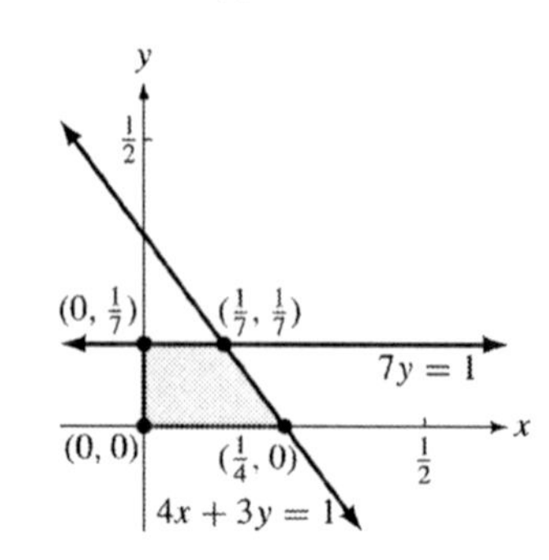

Corner Point	Value of $z = x + y$
$(0, \frac{1}{7})$	$0 + \frac{1}{7} = \frac{1}{7}$
$(\frac{1}{7}, \frac{1}{7})$	$\frac{1}{7} + \frac{1}{7} = \frac{2}{7}$
$(\frac{1}{4}, 0)$	$\frac{1}{4} + 0 = \frac{1}{4}$
$(0, 0)$	$0 + 0 = 0$

The maximum value is $z = \frac{2}{7}$ at $(\frac{1}{7}, \frac{1}{7})$. The optimum strategy for B is

$$q_1 = gx = \frac{7}{2}\left(\frac{1}{7}\right) = \frac{1}{2},$$

$$q_2 = gy = \frac{7}{2}\left(\frac{1}{7}\right) = \frac{1}{2}.$$

The value of the game is

$$\frac{7}{2} - 3 = \frac{1}{2}.$$

30. $\begin{bmatrix} 0 & -2 \\ -1 & 3 \end{bmatrix}$

To guarantee that the value of the game is positive, we add 2 to all entries in the matrix to obtain

$$\begin{bmatrix} 2 & 0 \\ 1 & 5 \end{bmatrix}.$$

Let player A choose row 1 with probability p_1 and row 2 with probability p_2. Then

$$E_1 = 2p_1 + p_2$$
and $$E_2 = 5p_2.$$

Let g represent the minimum of the expected gains, so that

$$\begin{aligned} E_1 &= 2p_1 + p_2 \geq g \\ E_2 &= 5p_2 \geq g. \end{aligned}$$

Dividing by g yields

$$2\left(\frac{p_1}{g}\right) + \left(\frac{p_2}{g}\right) \geq 1$$
$$5\left(\frac{p_2}{g}\right) \geq 1.$$

Let $x = \frac{p_1}{g}$ and $y = \frac{p_2}{g}$.

We have the following linear programming problem:

Minimize $w = x + y$
subject to: $2x + y \geq 1$
$5y \geq 1$
with $x \geq 0, y \geq 0$.

Graph the feasible region.

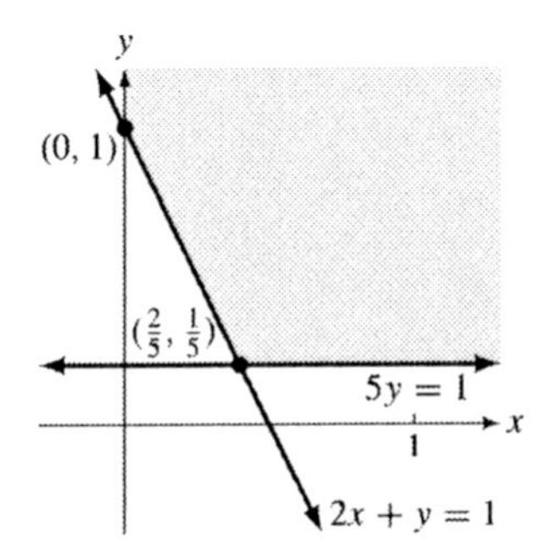

The corner points are $(0, 1)$ and $(\frac{2}{5}, \frac{1}{5})$. The minimum value of $w = x + y$ is $\frac{3}{5}$ at $(\frac{2}{5}, \frac{1}{5})$. Thus, the value of the game is $g = \frac{1}{w} = \frac{5}{3}$. To find the value of the original game, we must subtract 2:

$$\frac{5}{3} - 2 = -\frac{1}{3}.$$

The value of the original game is $-\frac{1}{3}$. The optimum strategy for A is

$$p_1 = gx = \frac{5}{3}\left(\frac{2}{5}\right) = \frac{2}{3},$$
$$p_2 = gy = \frac{5}{3}\left(\frac{1}{5}\right) = \frac{1}{3}.$$

Let player B choose column 1 with probability q_1 and column 2 with probability q_2. Then

$$E_1 = 2q_1$$
and $$E_2 = q_1 + 5q_2.$$

Let g represent the maximum of the expected gains, so that

$$E_1 = 2q_1 \leq g$$
$$E_2 = q_1 + 5q_2 \leq g.$$

Dividing by g yields

$$2\left(\frac{q_1}{g}\right) \leq 1$$
$$\frac{q_1}{g} + 5\left(\frac{q_2}{g}\right) \leq 1.$$

Let $x = \frac{q_1}{g}$ and $y = \frac{q_2}{g}$.

We have the following linear programming problem:

Maximize $z = x + y$
subject to: $2x \leq 1$
$x + 5y \leq 1$
with $x \geq 0, y \geq 0$.

Graph the feasible region.

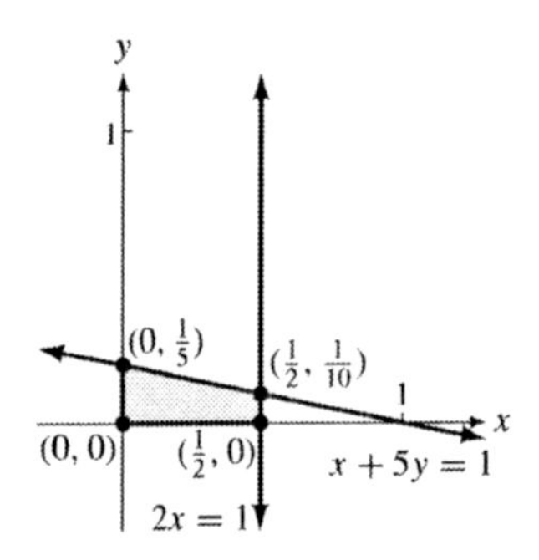

There are four corner points to consider: $(0, 0)$, $(0, \frac{1}{5})$, $(\frac{1}{2}, \frac{1}{10})$, and $(\frac{1}{2}, 0)$. The maximum of $z = x + y$ is $\frac{3}{5}$ at $(\frac{1}{2}, \frac{1}{10})$. As before, the value of the game is $g = \frac{1}{z} = \frac{5}{3}$. The value of the original game again is $\frac{5}{3} - 2 = -\frac{1}{3}$.

The optimum strategy for B is

$$q_1 = gx = \frac{5}{3}\left(\frac{1}{2}\right) = \frac{5}{6},$$
$$q_2 = gy = \frac{5}{3}\left(\frac{1}{10}\right) = \frac{1}{6}.$$

To summarize, player A should choose row 1 with probability $\frac{2}{3}$ and row 2 with probability $\frac{1}{3}$, while player B should choose column 1 with probability $\frac{5}{6}$ and column 2 with probability $\frac{1}{6}$. When these optimum strategies are used, the value of the game is $-\frac{1}{3}$.

31. $\begin{bmatrix} 2 & 1 & -1 \\ -3 & -2 & 0 \end{bmatrix}$

Add 3 to each entry to obtain

$$\begin{bmatrix} 5 & 4 & 2 \\ 0 & 1 & 3 \end{bmatrix}.$$

The linear programming problem to be solved is as follows.

$$\begin{array}{ll} \text{Maximize} & z = x_1 + x_2 + x_3 \\ \text{subject to:} & 5x_1 + 4x_2 + 2x_3 \le 1 \\ & x_2 + 3x_3 \le 1 \\ \text{with} & x_1 \ge 0, x_2 \ge 0, x_3 \ge 0. \end{array}$$

Use the simplex method to solve the problem. The initial tableau is

$$\begin{array}{c} \begin{matrix} x_1 & x_2 & x_3 & s_1 & s_2 & z \end{matrix} \\ \left[\begin{array}{cccccc|c} 5 & \boxed{4} & 2 & 1 & 0 & 0 & 1 \\ 0 & 1 & 3 & 0 & 1 & 0 & 1 \\ \hline -1 & -1 & -1 & 0 & 0 & 1 & 0 \end{array}\right] \end{array}.$$

Pivot on each indicated entry.

$$\begin{array}{r} \\ \\ \\ R_1 + 5R_3 \rightarrow R_3 \end{array} \begin{array}{c} \begin{matrix} x_1 & x_2 & x_3 & s_1 & s_2 & z \end{matrix} \\ \left[\begin{array}{cccccc|c} 5 & 4 & 2 & 1 & 0 & 0 & 1 \\ 0 & 1 & \boxed{3} & 0 & 1 & 0 & 1 \\ \hline 0 & -1 & -3 & 1 & 0 & 5 & 1 \end{array}\right] \end{array}$$

$$\begin{array}{r} \\ -2R_2 + 3R_1 \rightarrow R_1 \\ \\ R_2 + R_3 \rightarrow R_3 \end{array} \begin{array}{c} \begin{matrix} x_1 & x_2 & x_3 & s_1 & s_2 & z \end{matrix} \\ \left[\begin{array}{cccccc|c} 15 & 10 & 0 & 3 & -2 & 0 & 1 \\ 0 & 1 & 3 & 0 & 1 & 0 & 1 \\ \hline 0 & 0 & 0 & 1 & 1 & 5 & 2 \end{array}\right] \end{array}$$

Create a 1 in the columns corresponding to x_1, x_3, and z.

$$\begin{array}{r} \\ \frac{1}{15}R_1 \rightarrow R_1 \\ \frac{1}{3}R_2 \rightarrow R_2 \\ \frac{1}{5}R_3 \rightarrow R_3 \end{array} \begin{array}{c} \begin{matrix} x_1 & x_2 & x_3 & s_1 & s_2 & z \end{matrix} \\ \left[\begin{array}{cccccc|c} 1 & \frac{2}{3} & 0 & \frac{1}{5} & -\frac{2}{15} & 0 & \frac{1}{15} \\ 0 & \frac{1}{3} & 1 & 0 & \frac{1}{3} & 0 & \frac{1}{3} \\ \hline 0 & 0 & 0 & \frac{1}{5} & \frac{1}{5} & 1 & \frac{2}{5} \end{array}\right] \end{array}$$

From this final tableau, we have

$$x_1 = \frac{1}{15}, x_2 = 0, x_3 = \frac{1}{3},$$

$$y_1 = \frac{1}{5}, y_2 = \frac{1}{5}, \text{ and } z = \frac{2}{5}.$$

Note that $g = \frac{1}{z} = \frac{5}{2}$. The optimum strategy for player A is

$$p_1 = gy_1 = \frac{5}{2}\left(\frac{1}{5}\right) = \frac{1}{2},$$

$$p_2 = gy_2 = \frac{5}{2}\left(\frac{1}{5}\right) = \frac{1}{2}.$$

The optimum strategy for player B is

$$q_1 = gx_1 = \frac{5}{2}\left(\frac{1}{15}\right) = \frac{1}{6},$$

$$q_2 = gx_2 = \frac{5}{2}(0) = 0,$$

$$q_3 = gx_3 = \frac{5}{2}\left(\frac{1}{3}\right) = \frac{5}{6}.$$

The value of the game is

$$\frac{5}{2} - 3 = -\frac{1}{2}.$$

32. $\begin{bmatrix} 1 & -3 \\ -4 & 2 \\ -2 & 1 \end{bmatrix}$

Because of the negative entries, we will add 4 to all the entries. The resulting payoff matrix is

$$\begin{bmatrix} 5 & 1 \\ 0 & 6 \\ 2 & 5 \end{bmatrix}.$$

The linear programming problem to be solved is:

$$\begin{array}{ll} \text{Maximize} & z = x_1 + x_2 \\ \text{subject to:} & 5x_1 + x_2 \le 1 \\ & 6x_2 \le 1 \\ & 2x_1 + 5x_2 \le 1 \\ \text{with} & x_1 \ge 0, x_2 \ge 0. \end{array}$$

The initial tableau is

$$\begin{array}{c} \begin{matrix} x_1 & x_2 & s_1 & s_2 & s_3 & z \end{matrix} \\ \left[\begin{array}{cccccc|c} \boxed{5} & 1 & 1 & 0 & 0 & 0 & 1 \\ 0 & 6 & 0 & 1 & 0 & 0 & 1 \\ 2 & 5 & 0 & 0 & 1 & 0 & 1 \\ \hline -1 & -1 & 0 & 0 & 0 & 1 & 0 \end{array}\right] \end{array}.$$

We arbitrarily choose the first column. The smallest ratio is formed by the 5 in row 1. We use this entry as the first pivot and arrive at the following matrix.

$$\begin{array}{r} \\ \\ \\ -2R_1 + 5R_3 \rightarrow R_3 \\ R_1 + 5R_4 \rightarrow R_4 \end{array} \begin{array}{c} \begin{matrix} x_1 & x_2 & s_1 & s_2 & s_3 & z \end{matrix} \\ \left[\begin{array}{cccccc|c} 5 & 1 & 1 & 0 & 0 & 0 & 1 \\ 0 & 6 & 0 & 1 & 0 & 0 & 1 \\ 0 & \boxed{23} & -2 & 0 & 5 & 0 & 3 \\ \hline 0 & -4 & 1 & 0 & 0 & 5 & 1 \end{array}\right] \end{array}$$

The next pivot is the 23 in row 3, column 2.

$$\begin{array}{r} \\ -R_3 + 23R_1 \to R_1 \\ -6R_3 + 23R_2 \to R_2 \\ \\ 4R_3 + 23R_4 \to R_4 \end{array} \begin{array}{c} \begin{array}{cccccc} x_1 & x_2 & s_1 & s_2 & s_3 & z \end{array} \\ \left[\begin{array}{cccccc|c} 115 & 0 & 25 & 0 & -5 & 0 & 20 \\ 0 & 0 & 12 & 23 & -30 & 0 & 5 \\ 0 & 23 & -2 & 0 & 5 & 0 & 3 \\ \hline 0 & 0 & 15 & 0 & 20 & 115 & 35 \end{array}\right] \end{array}$$

Dividing the bottom row by 115 gives a z-value of $\frac{7}{23}$, so $g = \frac{1}{z} = \frac{23}{7}$. The values of y_1, y_2, and y_3 are read from the bottom of the columns for the slack variables after dividing the bottom row by 115:

$$y_1 = \frac{15}{115} = \frac{3}{23}, y_2 = 0, y_3 = \frac{20}{115} = \frac{4}{23}.$$

We find the values of p_1, p_2, and p_3 by multiplying the values of y_1, y_2, and y_3 by g:

$$p_1 = \frac{23}{7}\left(\frac{3}{23}\right) = \frac{3}{7},$$

$$p_2 = 0,$$

$$p_3 = \frac{23}{7}\left(\frac{4}{23}\right) = \frac{4}{7}.$$

Next, we find the values of x_1 and x_2 by using the first two columns combined with the last column:

$$x_1 = \frac{20}{115} = \frac{4}{23} \text{ and } x_2 = \frac{3}{23}.$$

We find the values of q_1 and q_2 by multiplying these by g:

$$q_1 = \frac{23}{7}\left(\frac{4}{23}\right) = \frac{4}{7}$$

$$q_2 = \frac{23}{7}\left(\frac{3}{23}\right) = \frac{3}{7}.$$

Finally, the value of the game is found by subtracting from g the 2 that was added at the beginning, yielding

$$\frac{23}{7} - 2 = \frac{9}{7}.$$

To summarize, the optimum strategy for player A is $p_1 = \frac{3}{7}, p_2 = 0$, and $p_3 = \frac{4}{7}$. The optimum strategy for player B is $q_1 = \frac{4}{7}$ and $q_2 = \frac{3}{7}$. When these strategies are used, the value of the game is $\frac{9}{7}$.

33. $\begin{bmatrix} -2 & 1 & 0 \\ 2 & 0 & -2 \\ 0 & -1 & 3 \end{bmatrix}$

Add 2 to each entry to obtain

$$\begin{bmatrix} 0 & 3 & 2 \\ 4 & 2 & 0 \\ 2 & 1 & 5 \end{bmatrix}.$$

The problem to be solved is as follows.

$$\begin{array}{ll} \text{Maximize} & z = x_1 + x_2 + x_3 \\ \text{subject to:} & \phantom{4x_1 + {}} 3x_2 + 2x_3 \le 1 \\ & 4x_1 + 2x_2 \phantom{{} + 5x_3} \le 1 \\ & 2x_1 + x_2 + 5x_3 \le 1 \\ \text{with} & x_1 \ge 0, x_2 \ge 0, x_3 \ge 0. \end{array}$$

The initial simplex tableau is

$$\begin{array}{c} \begin{array}{ccccccc} x_1 & x_2 & x_3 & s_1 & s_2 & s_3 & z \end{array} \\ \left[\begin{array}{ccccccc|c} 0 & 3 & 2 & 1 & 0 & 0 & 0 & 1 \\ \boxed{4} & 2 & 0 & 0 & 1 & 0 & 0 & 1 \\ 2 & 1 & 5 & 0 & 0 & 1 & 0 & 1 \\ \hline -1 & -1 & -1 & 0 & 0 & 0 & 1 & 0 \end{array}\right] \end{array}.$$

Pivot on each indicated entry.

$$\begin{array}{r} \\ \\ -R_2 + 2R_3 \to R_3 \\ R_2 + 4R_4 \to R_4 \end{array} \begin{array}{c} \begin{array}{ccccccc} x_1 & x_2 & x_3 & s_1 & s_2 & s_3 & z \end{array} \\ \left[\begin{array}{ccccccc|c} 0 & 3 & 2 & 1 & 0 & 0 & 0 & 1 \\ 4 & 2 & 0 & 0 & 1 & 0 & 0 & 1 \\ 0 & 0 & \boxed{10} & 0 & -1 & 2 & 0 & 1 \\ \hline 0 & -2 & -4 & 0 & 1 & 0 & 4 & 1 \end{array}\right] \end{array}$$

$$\begin{array}{r} -R_3 + 5R_1 \to R_1 \\ \\ \\ 2R_3 + 5R_4 \to R_4 \end{array} \begin{array}{c} \begin{array}{ccccccc} x_1 & x_2 & x_3 & s_1 & s_2 & s_3 & z \end{array} \\ \left[\begin{array}{ccccccc|c} 0 & \boxed{15} & 0 & 5 & 1 & -2 & 0 & 4 \\ 4 & 2 & 0 & 0 & 1 & 0 & 0 & 1 \\ 0 & 0 & 10 & 0 & -1 & 2 & 0 & 1 \\ \hline 0 & -10 & 0 & 0 & 3 & 4 & 20 & 7 \end{array}\right] \end{array}$$

$$\begin{array}{r} \\ -2R_1 + 15R_2 \to R_2 \\ \\ 2R_1 + 3R_4 \to R_4 \end{array} \begin{array}{c} \begin{array}{ccccccc} x_1 & x_2 & x_3 & s_1 & s_2 & s_3 & z \end{array} \\ \left[\begin{array}{ccccccc|c} 0 & 15 & 0 & 5 & 1 & -2 & 0 & 4 \\ 60 & 0 & 0 & -10 & 13 & 4 & 0 & 7 \\ 0 & 0 & 10 & 0 & -1 & 2 & 0 & 1 \\ \hline 0 & 0 & 0 & 10 & 11 & 8 & 60 & 29 \end{array}\right] \end{array}$$

Create a 1 in the columns corresponding to x_1, x_2, x_3, and z.

$$\begin{array}{r} \frac{1}{15}R_1 \to R_1 \\ \frac{1}{60}R_2 \to R_2 \\ \frac{1}{10}R_3 \to R_3 \\ \frac{1}{60}R_4 \to R_4 \end{array} \begin{array}{c} \begin{array}{ccccccc} x_1 & x_2 & x_3 & s_1 & s_2 & s_3 & z \end{array} \\ \left[\begin{array}{ccccccc|c} 0 & 1 & 0 & \frac{1}{3} & \frac{1}{15} & -\frac{2}{15} & 0 & \frac{4}{15} \\ 1 & 0 & 0 & -\frac{1}{6} & \frac{13}{60} & \frac{1}{15} & 0 & \frac{7}{60} \\ 0 & 0 & 1 & 0 & -\frac{1}{10} & \frac{1}{5} & 0 & \frac{1}{10} \\ \hline 0 & 0 & 0 & \frac{1}{6} & \frac{11}{60} & \frac{2}{15} & 1 & \frac{29}{60} \end{array}\right] \end{array}$$

From this final tableau, we have

$$x_1 = \frac{7}{60}, x_2 = \frac{4}{15}, x_3 = \frac{1}{10},$$

$$y_1 = \frac{1}{6}, y_2 = \frac{11}{60}, y_3 = \frac{2}{15}, \text{ and } z = \frac{29}{60}.$$

Note that $g = \frac{1}{z} = \frac{60}{29}$. The optimum strategy for player A is

$$p_1 = gy_1 = \frac{60}{29}\left(\frac{1}{6}\right) = \frac{10}{29},$$

$$p_2 = gy_2 = \frac{60}{29}\left(\frac{11}{60}\right) = \frac{11}{29},$$

$$p_3 = gy_3 = \frac{60}{29}\left(\frac{2}{15}\right) = \frac{8}{29}.$$

The optimum strategy for player B is

$$q_1 = gx_1 = \frac{60}{29}\left(\frac{7}{60}\right) = \frac{7}{29},$$

$$q_2 = gx_2 = \frac{60}{29}\left(\frac{4}{15}\right) = \frac{16}{29},$$

$$q_3 = gx_3 = \frac{60}{29}\left(\frac{1}{10}\right) = \frac{6}{29}.$$

The value of the game is

$$\frac{60}{29} - 2 = \frac{2}{29}.$$

34. $\begin{bmatrix} 2 & 1 & -1 \\ 0 & 1 & 2 \\ -1 & 2 & 0 \end{bmatrix}$

Because of the negative entries, we will add 1 to all the entries. The resulting payoff matrix is

$$\begin{bmatrix} 3 & 2 & 0 \\ 1 & 2 & 3 \\ 0 & 3 & 1 \end{bmatrix}.$$

The linear programming problem to be solved is:

Maximize $z = x_1 + x_2 + x_3$

subject to:

$$3x_1 + 2x_2 \leq 1$$
$$x_1 + 2x_2 + 3x_3 \leq 1$$
$$3x_2 + x_3 \leq 1$$

with $x_1 \geq 0, x_2 \geq 0, x_3 \geq 0.$

The initial tableau is

$$\begin{array}{c} \\ \\ \\ \\ \end{array}\left[\begin{array}{ccccccc|c} x_1 & x_2 & x_3 & s_1 & s_2 & s_3 & z & \\ \boxed{3} & 2 & 0 & 1 & 0 & 0 & 0 & 1 \\ 1 & 2 & 3 & 0 & 1 & 0 & 0 & 1 \\ 0 & 3 & 1 & 0 & 0 & 1 & 0 & 1 \\ \hline -1 & -1 & -1 & 0 & 0 & 0 & 1 & 0 \end{array}\right].$$

We arbitrarily choose the first column. The smallest ratio is formed by the 3 in row 1. We make this the first pivot and arrive at the following matrix.

$$\begin{array}{r} \\ \\ -R_1 + 3R_2 \to R_2 \\ \\ R_1 + 3R_4 \to R_4 \end{array}\left[\begin{array}{ccccccc|c} x_1 & x_2 & x_3 & s_1 & s_2 & s_3 & z & \\ 3 & 2 & 0 & 1 & 0 & 0 & 0 & 1 \\ 0 & 4 & \boxed{9} & -1 & 3 & 0 & 0 & 2 \\ 0 & 3 & 1 & 0 & 0 & 1 & 0 & 1 \\ \hline 0 & -1 & -3 & 1 & 0 & 0 & 3 & 1 \end{array}\right]$$

The next pivot is the 9 in row 2, column 3.

$$\begin{array}{r} \\ \\ \\ -R_2 + 9R_3 \to R_3 \\ R_2 + 3R_4 \to R_4 \end{array}\left[\begin{array}{ccccccc|c} x_1 & x_1 & x_3 & s_1 & s_2 & s_3 & z & \\ 3 & 2 & 0 & 1 & 0 & 0 & 0 & 1 \\ 0 & 4 & 9 & -1 & 3 & 0 & 0 & 2 \\ 0 & 23 & 0 & 1 & -3 & 9 & 0 & 7 \\ \hline 0 & 1 & 0 & 2 & 3 & 0 & 9 & 5 \end{array}\right]$$

Dividing the bottom row by 9 gives a z-value of $\frac{5}{9}$, so $g = \frac{1}{z} = \frac{9}{5}$. The values of y_1, y_2, and y_3 are read from the bottom of the columns for the three slack variables after dividing the bottom row by 9:

$$y_1 = \frac{2}{9}, y_2 = \frac{3}{9}, y_3 = 0.$$

We find the values of p_1, p_2, and p_3 by multiplying the values of y_1, y_2, and y_3 by g:

$$p_1 = \frac{9}{5}\left(\frac{2}{9}\right) = \frac{2}{5},$$

$$p_2 = \frac{9}{5}\left(\frac{3}{9}\right) = \frac{3}{5},$$

$$p_3 = 0.$$

Next, we find the values of x_1, x_2, and x_3 by using the first three columns combined with the last column:

$$x_1 = \frac{1}{3}, x_2 = 0, \ x_3 = \frac{2}{9}.$$

We find the values of q_1, q_2, and q_3 by multiplying these values by g:

$$q_1 = \frac{9}{5}\left(\frac{1}{3}\right) = \frac{3}{5},$$

$$q_2 = 0,$$

$$q_3 = \frac{9}{5}\left(\frac{2}{9}\right) = \frac{2}{5}.$$

Finally, the value of the game is found by subtracting from g the 1 that was added at the beginning, yielding

$$\frac{9}{5} - 1 = \frac{4}{5}.$$

To summarize, the optimum strategy for player A is

$p_1 = \frac{2}{5}, p_2 = \frac{3}{5}$, and $p_3 = 0$. The optimum strategy

for player B is $q_1 = \frac{3}{5}, q_2 = 0$, and $q_3 = \frac{2}{5}$. When these strategies are used, the value of the game is $\frac{4}{5}$.

36. If the chance of rain is 90% every day, carry an umbrella every day. For "player A," we will say strategy 1 is to carry an umbrella, and strategy 2 is to not carry an umbrella. For "player B," strategy 1 is that it rains, and strategy 2 is that it does not rain.

The payoff matrix is

$$\begin{bmatrix} 0 & -1 \\ -100 & 0 \end{bmatrix}.$$

$$\begin{aligned} p_1 &= \frac{a_{22} - a_{21}}{a_{11} - a_{21} - a_{12} + a_{22}} \\ &= \frac{0 - (-100)}{0 - (-100) - (-1) + 0} \\ p_1 &= \frac{100}{101} \end{aligned}$$

According to game theory, carry an umbrella with a probability of $\frac{100}{101}$.

In the first situation, there was no penalty for carrying an umbrella when there was no rain.

In Exercises 37-41, use the following payoff matrix.

		Management	
		Friendly	Hostile
Labor	Friendly	\$700	\$900
	Hostile	\$500	\$1100

37. Be hostile; then he has a chance at the \$1100 wage increase, which is the largest possible increase.

38. "Friendly" has a worst payoff of \$700 and "hostile" has a worst payoff of \$500, so the absolute worst payoff of \$500 can be avoided by labor being friendly. Therefore, a pessimist should choose the strategy of being friendly.

39. If there is a 0.4 chance that the company will be hostile, then there is a 0.6 chance that it will be friendly. Find the expected payoff for each strategy.

$$\begin{aligned} \text{Friendly:} \quad & \$700(0.6) + \$900(0.4) = \$780 \\ \text{Hostile:} \quad & \$500(0.6) + \$1100(0.4) = \$740 \end{aligned}$$

Therefore, he should be friendly. The expected payoff is \$780.

40. If there is a 0.6 chance that the new management will be hostile, then there is a 0.4 chance that it will be friendly. Find the expected payoff from each strategy.

$$\begin{aligned} \text{Friendly:} \quad & \$700(0.4) + \$900(0.6) = \$820 \\ \text{Hostile:} \quad & \$500(0.4) + \$1100(0.6) = \$860 \end{aligned}$$

Therefore, he should be hostile. The expected payoff is \$860.

41. The 700 at $(1, 1)$ is the smallest number in its row and the largest number in its column, so it is a saddle point, and the game is strictly determined. Labor and management should both always be friendly, and the value of the game is 700.

42.

		Economy	
		Inflationary	Stable
Stocks	Blue-Chip	2800	3200
	Growth	5000	−2000

The optimum strategy for Victor is

$$p_1 = \frac{-2000 - 5000}{2800 - 5000 - 3200 + (-2000)} = \frac{35}{37},$$

$$p_2 = 1 - \frac{35}{37} = \frac{2}{37}.$$

That is, Victor should invest in blue-chip stocks with probability $\frac{35}{37}$ and growth stocks with probability $\frac{2}{37}$.

The value of the game is

$$\begin{aligned} \frac{2800(-2000) - 5000(3200)}{2800 - 5000 - 3200 + (-2000)} &= \frac{-21{,}600{,}000}{-7400} \\ &\approx \$2918.92. \end{aligned}$$

43. $\begin{bmatrix} 2800 & 3200 \\ 5000 & -2000 \end{bmatrix}$

To guarantee that the value of the game is positive, we add 2000 to all entries in the matrix to obtain

$$\begin{bmatrix} 4800 & 5200 \\ 7000 & 0 \end{bmatrix}.$$

Let Victor choose row 1 with probability p_1 and row 2 with probability p_2. Then,

$$E_1 = 4800p_1 + 7000p_2$$
$$\text{and} \quad E_2 = 5200p_1.$$

Let g represent the minimum of the expected gains, so that

$$\begin{aligned} E_1 &= 4800p_1 + 7000p_2 \geq g \\ E_2 &= 5200p_1 \qquad\qquad\quad \geq g. \end{aligned}$$

Dividing by g yields

$$\begin{aligned} 4800\left(\frac{p_1}{g}\right) + 7000\left(\frac{p_2}{g}\right) &\geq 1 \\ 5200\left(\frac{p_1}{g}\right) \qquad\qquad\qquad &\geq 1. \end{aligned}$$

Let $x = \dfrac{p_1}{g}$ and $y = \dfrac{p_2}{g}$.

We have the following linear programming problem:

$$\begin{array}{ll} \text{Minimize} & w = x + y \\ \text{subject to:} & 4800x + 7000y \geq 1 \\ & 5200x \qquad\qquad \geq 1 \\ \text{with} & x \geq 0, y \geq 0. \end{array}$$

Graph the feasible region.

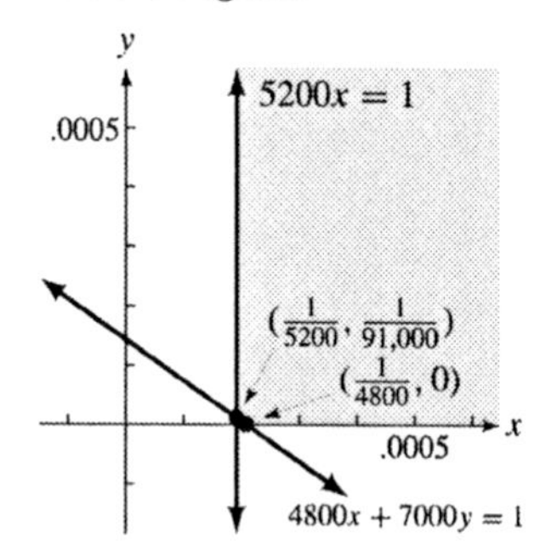

The corner points are $\left(\frac{1}{5200}, \frac{1}{91{,}000}\right)$ and $\left(\frac{1}{4800}, 0\right)$. The minimum value of $w = x + y$ is $\frac{37}{182{,}000}$ at $\left(\frac{1}{5200}, \frac{1}{91{,}000}\right)$. Thus, the value of the game is

$$g = \frac{1}{w} = \frac{182{,}000}{37} \approx 4918.92.$$

To find the value of the original game, we must subtract 2000:

$$4918.92 - 2000 = 2918.92.$$

The value of the original game is \$2918.92.

The optimum strategy for Victor is

$$p_1 = gx = \frac{182{,}000}{37}\left(\frac{1}{5200}\right) = \frac{35}{37},$$

$$p_2 = gy = \frac{182{,}000}{37}\left(\frac{1}{91{,}000}\right) = \frac{2}{37}.$$

Hector should invest in blue-chip stocks with probability $\frac{35}{37}$ and growth stocks with probability $\frac{2}{37}$.

44. $\begin{bmatrix} 2800 & 3200 \\ 5000 & -2000 \end{bmatrix}$

Add 2000 to each entry to obtain

$$\begin{bmatrix} 4800 & 5200 \\ 7000 & 0 \end{bmatrix}.$$

The linear programming problem to be solved is:

$$\begin{array}{ll} \text{Maximize} & z = x_1 + x_2 \\ \text{subject to:} & 4800x_1 + 5200x_2 \leq 1 \\ & 7000x_1 \qquad\qquad\quad \leq 1 \\ \text{with} & x_1 \geq 0, x_2 \geq 0. \end{array}$$

The initial tableau is as follows.

$$\begin{array}{c} \\ \\ \\ \end{array}\begin{array}{cccccc|c} x_1 & x_2 & s_1 & s_2 & z & & \\ 4800 & \boxed{5200} & 1 & 0 & 0 & & 1 \\ 7000 & 0 & 0 & 1 & 0 & & 1 \\ \hline -1 & -1 & 0 & 0 & 1 & & 0 \end{array}$$

Pivot on each indicated entry.

$$\begin{array}{r} \\ \\ \\ R_1 + 5200R_3 \to R_3 \end{array}\begin{array}{ccccc|c} x_1 & x_2 & s_1 & s_2 & z & \\ 4800 & 5200 & 1 & 0 & 0 & 1 \\ \boxed{7000} & 0 & 0 & 1 & 0 & 1 \\ \hline -400 & 0 & 1 & 0 & 5200 & 1 \end{array}$$

$$\begin{array}{r} \\ -24R_2 + 35R_1 \to R_1 \\ \\ 2R_2 + 35R_3 \to R_3 \end{array}\begin{array}{ccccc|c} x_1 & x_2 & s_1 & s_2 & z & \\ 0 & 182{,}000 & 35 & -24 & 0 & 11 \\ 7000 & 0 & 0 & 1 & 0 & 1 \\ \hline 0 & 0 & 35 & 2 & 182{,}000 & 37 \end{array}$$

Create a 1 in the columns corresponding to x_1, x_2, and z.

$$\begin{array}{r} \\ \frac{1}{182{,}000}R_1 \to R_1 \\ \frac{1}{7000}R_2 \to R_2 \\ \frac{1}{182{,}000}R_3 \to R_3 \end{array}\begin{array}{ccccc|c} x_1 & x_2 & s_1 & s_2 & z & \\ 0 & 1 & \frac{1}{5200} & -\frac{3}{22{,}750} & 0 & \frac{11}{182{,}000} \\ 1 & 0 & 0 & \frac{1}{7000} & 0 & \frac{1}{7000} \\ \hline 0 & 0 & \frac{1}{5200} & \frac{1}{91{,}000} & 1 & \frac{37}{182{,}000} \end{array}$$

From this final tableau, we have

$$x_1 = \frac{1}{7000}, x_2 = \frac{11}{182{,}000},$$

$$y_1 = \frac{1}{5200}, y_2 = \frac{1}{91{,}000}, \text{ and } z = \frac{37}{182{,}000}.$$

Note that $g = \frac{1}{z} = \frac{182{,}000}{37}$. The optimum strategy for Victor is

$$p_1 = gy_1 = \frac{182{,}000}{37}\left(\frac{1}{5200}\right) = \frac{35}{37},$$

$$p_2 = gy_2 = \frac{182{,}000}{37}\left(\frac{1}{91{,}000}\right) = \frac{2}{37}.$$

That is, he should invest in blue-chip stocks with probability $\frac{35}{37}$ and growth stocks with probability $\frac{2}{37}$.

The value of the game is

$$\frac{182{,}000}{37} - 2000 \approx \$2918.92.$$

For Exercises 45-49, use the following payoff matrix.

$$\begin{array}{ll} & \qquad\qquad\textit{Opponent} \\ & \begin{array}{ccc} \text{Favors} & \text{Wa- es} & \text{Opposes} \end{array} \\ \textit{Candidate}\ \begin{array}{l} \text{Favors} \\ \text{Wa- es} \\ \text{Opposes} \end{array} & \begin{bmatrix} 0 & 1200 & 4200 \\ -1000 & 0 & 600 \\ -5000 & -2000 & 0 \end{bmatrix} \end{array}$$

45. As an optimist, Martha would look at the best possible outcome from each strategy, and choose the best of them. If she favors the factory, she could gain 4200 votes; if she wa- es, she could gain 600 votes; and if she opposes the issue, she neither gains nor loses votes. The best of these options is to gain 4200 votes, so she should favor the factory.

46. As a pessimist, Martha would look at the worst possible outcome from each strategy, and choose the best of them. If she favors the factory, she neither gains nor loses votes; if she wa- es, she could lose 1000 votes; and if she opposes the issue, she could lose 5000 votes. The best of these options is to neither gain nor lose votes, so she should favor the factory.

47. If there is a 0.4 chance that Kevin will favor the plant, and 0.35 chance he will wa- e, then there is a 0.25 chance he will oppose it. Find the expected payoffs in votes under the three strategies.

$$\begin{aligned} \text{Favors:} &\quad 0(0.4) + 1200(0.35) + 4200(0.25) = 1470 \\ \text{Wa- es:} &\quad -1000(0.4) + 0(0.35) + 600(0.25) = -250 \\ \text{Opposes:} &\quad -5000(0.4) - 2000(0.35) + 0(0.25) = -2700 \end{aligned}$$

Martha should favor the new factory and expect a gain of 1470 votes.

48. If there is a 0 chance that Kevin will oppose the plant, and a 0.3 chance he will wa- e, then there is a 0.7 chance he will favor it. Find the expected payoffs in votes under the three strategies.

$$\begin{aligned} \text{Favors:} &\quad 0(0.7) + 1200(0.3) + 4200(0) = 360 \\ \text{Wa- es:} &\quad -1000(0.7) + 0(0.3) + 600(0) = -700 \\ \text{Opposes:} &\quad -5000(0.7) - 2000(0.3) + 0(0) = -4100 \end{aligned}$$

Martha should favor the new factory and expect a gain of 360 votes.

49. This game has a saddle point of 0 at $(1, 1)$. The value of the game is 0. The strategy $(1, 1)$ means that Martha favors the factory and her opponent also favors the factory. Therefore, each candidate should favor the factory.

For Exercises 50-52, use the following payoff matrix.

$$\begin{array}{ll} & \qquad\qquad\text{Rontovia} \\ & \begin{array}{cc} \text{Attack 1} & \text{Attack 2} \end{array} \\ \text{Ravogna}\ \begin{array}{l} \text{Defend 1} \\ \text{Defend 2} \end{array} & \begin{bmatrix} 4 & 1 \\ 3 & 4 \end{bmatrix} \end{array}$$

50.
$$\begin{aligned} p_1 &= \frac{a_{22} - a_{21}}{a_{11} - a_{21} - a_{12} + a_{22}} \\ &= \frac{4-3}{4-3-1+4} = \frac{1}{4} \\ p_2 &= \frac{a_{11} - a_{12}}{a_{11} - a_{21} - a_{12} + a_{22}} \\ &= \frac{4-1}{4} = \frac{3}{4} \\ q_1 &= \frac{a_{22} - a_{12}}{a_{11} - a_{21} - a_{12} + a_{22}} \\ &= \frac{4-1}{4} = \frac{3}{4} \\ q_2 &= \frac{a_{11} - a_{21}}{a_{11} - a_{21} - a_{12} + a_{22}} \\ &= \frac{4-3}{4} = \frac{1}{4} \end{aligned}$$

The value of the game is

$$\begin{aligned} \frac{a_{11}a_{22} - a_{12}a_{21}}{a_{11} - a_{21} - a_{12} + a_{22}} &= \frac{4(4) - 1(3)}{4} \\ &= \frac{13}{4}. \end{aligned}$$

Ravogna should defend installation #1 with probability $\frac{1}{4}$ and installation #2 with probability $\frac{3}{4}$. Rontovia should attack installation #1 with probability $\frac{3}{4}$ and installation #2 with probability $\frac{1}{4}$. The value of the game is $\frac{13}{4}$.

51. To find the optimum strategy for Ravogna,

$$\begin{array}{ll} \text{Minimize} & w = x + y \\ \text{subject to:} & 4x + 3y \geq 1 \\ & x + 4y \geq 1 \\ \text{with} & x \geq 0, y \geq 0. \end{array}$$

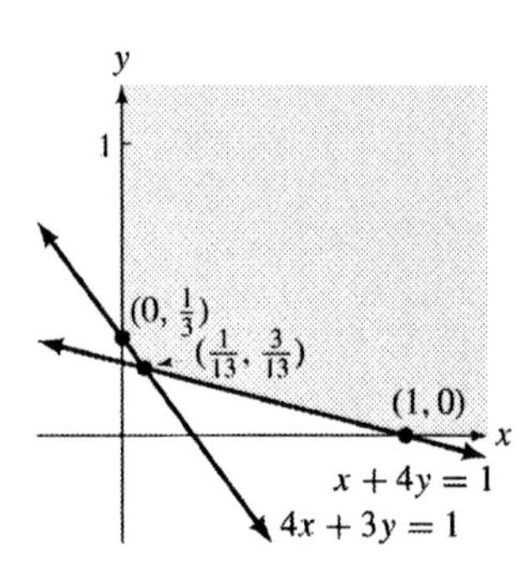

Corner Point	Value of $w = x + y$
$(0, \frac{1}{3})$	$0 + \frac{1}{3} = \frac{1}{3}$
$(\frac{1}{13}, \frac{3}{13})$	$\frac{1}{13} + \frac{3}{13} = \frac{4}{13}$
$(1, 0)$	$1 + 0 = 1$

The minimum value is $w = \frac{4}{13}$ at $(\frac{1}{13}, \frac{3}{13})$. Thus, $g = \frac{1}{w} = \frac{13}{4}$ is the value of the game. The optimum strategy for Ravogna is

$$p_1 = gx = \frac{13}{4}\left(\frac{1}{13}\right) = \frac{1}{4},$$

$$p_2 = gy = \frac{13}{4}\left(\frac{3}{13}\right) = \frac{3}{4}.$$

That is, Ravogna should defend installation #1 with probability $\frac{1}{4}$ and installation #2 with probability $\frac{3}{4}$.

To find the optimum strategy for Rontovia,

$$\begin{array}{ll} \text{Maximize} & z = x + y \\ \text{subject to:} & 4x + \ \ y \leq 1 \\ & 3x + 4y \leq 1 \\ \text{with} & x \geq 0, y \geq 0. \end{array}$$

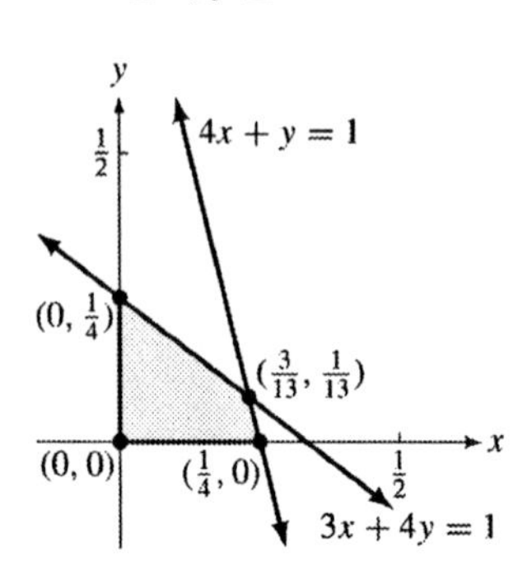

Corner Point	Value of $z = x + y$
$(0, \frac{1}{4})$	$0 + \frac{1}{4} = \frac{1}{4}$
$(\frac{3}{13}, \frac{1}{13})$	$\frac{3}{13} + \frac{1}{13} = \frac{4}{13}$
$(\frac{1}{4}, 0)$	$\frac{1}{4} + 0 = \frac{1}{4}$
$(0, 0)$	$0 + 0 = 0$

The maximum value is $z = \frac{4}{13}$ at $(\frac{3}{13}, \frac{1}{13})$. The optimum strategy for Rontovia is

$$q_1 = gx = \frac{13}{4}\left(\frac{3}{13}\right) = \frac{3}{4},$$

$$q_2 = gy = \frac{13}{4}\left(\frac{1}{13}\right) = \frac{1}{4}.$$

That is, Rontovia should attack installation #1 with probability $\frac{3}{4}$ and installation #2 with probability $\frac{1}{4}$.

52. The linear programming problem to be solved is:

$$\begin{array}{ll} \text{Maximize} & z = x_1 + x_2 \\ \text{subject to:} & 4x_1 + \ \ x_2 \leq 1 \\ & 3x_1 + 4x_2 \leq 1 \\ \text{with} & x_1 \geq 0, x_2 \geq 0. \end{array}$$

The initial tableau is

$$\begin{array}{c} \begin{matrix} x_1 & x_2 & s_1 & s_2 & z \end{matrix} \\ \left[\begin{array}{ccccc|c} \boxed{4} & 1 & 1 & 0 & 0 & 1 \\ 3 & 4 & 0 & 1 & 0 & 1 \\ \hline -1 & -1 & 0 & 0 & 1 & 0 \end{array}\right]. \end{array}$$

We arbitrarily choose the first column. The smallest ratio is formed by the 4 in row 1. We make this entry the first pivot and arrive at the following matrix.

$$\begin{array}{r} \\ \\ -3R_1 + 4R_2 \rightarrow R_2 \\ R_1 + 4R_3 \rightarrow R_3 \end{array} \begin{array}{c} \begin{matrix} x_1 & x_2 & s_1 & s_2 & z \end{matrix} \\ \left[\begin{array}{ccccc|c} 4 & 1 & 1 & 0 & 0 & 1 \\ 0 & \boxed{13} & -3 & 4 & 0 & 1 \\ \hline 0 & -3 & 1 & 0 & 4 & 1 \end{array}\right] \end{array}$$

The next pivot is the 13 in row 2, column 2.

$$\begin{array}{r} \\ -R_2 + 13R_1 \rightarrow R_1 \\ \\ 3R_2 + 13R_3 \rightarrow R_3 \end{array} \begin{array}{c} \begin{matrix} x_1 & x_2 & s_1 & s_2 & z \end{matrix} \\ \left[\begin{array}{ccccc|c} 52 & 0 & 16 & -4 & 0 & 12 \\ 0 & 13 & -3 & 4 & 0 & 1 \\ \hline 0 & 0 & 4 & 12 & 52 & 16 \end{array}\right] \end{array}$$

Dividing the bottom row by 52 gives a z-value of $\frac{16}{52} = \frac{4}{13}$, so $g = \frac{1}{z} = \frac{13}{4}$. The value of the game is $\frac{13}{4}$. The values of y_1 and y_2 are read from the bottom of the columns for the two slack variables after dividing the bottom row by 52:

$$y_1 = \frac{4}{52} = \frac{1}{13}, y_2 = \frac{12}{52} = \frac{3}{13}.$$

We find the values of p_1 and p_2 by multiplying the values of y_1 and y_2 by g:

$$p_1 = \frac{13}{4}\left(\frac{1}{13}\right) = \frac{1}{4},$$

$$p_2 = \frac{13}{4}\left(\frac{3}{13}\right) = \frac{3}{4}.$$

Next, we find the values of x_1 and x_2 by using the first two columns combined with the last column:

$$x_1 = \frac{12}{52} = \frac{3}{13}, x_2 = \frac{-1}{-13} = \frac{1}{13}.$$

We find the values of q_1 and q_2 by multiplying these values by g:

$$q_1 = \frac{13}{4}\left(\frac{3}{13}\right) = \frac{3}{4},$$

$$\text{and} \quad q_2 = \frac{13}{4}\left(\frac{1}{13}\right) = \frac{1}{4}.$$

Thus, Ravogna should defend installation #1 with probability $\frac{1}{4}$ and installation #2 with probability $\frac{3}{4}$. Rontovia should attack installation #1 with probability $\frac{3}{4}$ and installation #2 with probability $\frac{1}{4}$. The value of the game is $\frac{13}{4}$.

Extended Application: The Prisoner's Dilemma-Non-Zero-Sum Games in Economics

1. Since neither row dominates the other, Linda does not have a dominated strategy. Similarly, since neither column dominates the other, Mel does not have a dominated strategy. Linda and Mel should consider cooperating.

2. If they decide to cooperate, they will either both pick Chinese or both pick French, since disagreement leads to the worst payoff for each player. If they both pick Chinese, their combined degree of enjoyment is 6, whereas if they both pick French, their combined degree of enjoyment is 8. They maximize their combined enjoyment by both picking French.

3. Linda's expected payoff:

$$[0.8 \quad 0.2]\begin{bmatrix} 5 & 0 \\ 0 & 3 \end{bmatrix}\begin{bmatrix} 0.1 \\ 0.9 \end{bmatrix} = [4 \quad 0.6]\begin{bmatrix} 0.1 \\ 0.9 \end{bmatrix}$$
$$= [0.94]$$

Mel's expected payoff:

$$[0.8 \quad 0.2]\begin{bmatrix} 1 & 0 \\ 0 & 5 \end{bmatrix}\begin{bmatrix} 0.1 \\ 0.9 \end{bmatrix} = [0.8 \quad 1]\begin{bmatrix} 0.1 \\ 0.9 \end{bmatrix}$$
$$= [0.98]$$

Mel does better.

4. Let $[p_1 \quad p_2]$ represent Linda's strategy which maximizes her expected payoff. Then, her expected payoff is given by

$$E = [p_1 \quad p_2]\begin{bmatrix} 5 & 0 \\ 0 & 3 \end{bmatrix}\begin{bmatrix} 0.1 \\ 0.9 \end{bmatrix}$$
$$= [5p_1 \quad 3p_2]\begin{bmatrix} 0.1 \\ 0.9 \end{bmatrix}$$
$$= 0.5p_1 + 2.7p_2.$$

Substituting $1 - p_1$ for p_2, we find

$$E = 0.5p_1 + 2.7(1 - p_1) = -2.2p_1 + 2.7.$$

Since this is maximized when $p_1 = 0$, we have $p_2 = 1 - 0 = 1$. Thus, Linda should choose the strategy $[0, 1]$. That is, Linda should always choose French for an expected payoff of 2.7. If she does this, Mel might always choose French in order to maximize her enjoyment.

5. If Linda picks Chinese and Mel picks French, her degree of hapiness will be zero, however, Mel may not continue with his "always French" strategy since his degree of happiness would also be zero.

6. Since their combined enjoyment is 6 when choosing Chinese and 8 when choosing French, they may opt to make their decisions based on the following spinner. If the arrow of the spinner lands in the unshaded region, they will eat French. Otherwise, they will eat Chinese.

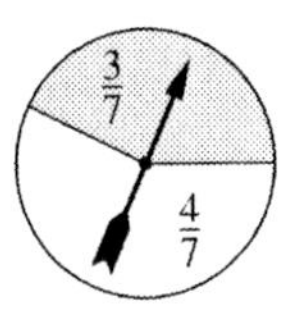